COUNSELING IN CATHOLIC LIFE
AND EDUCATION

THE MACMILLAN COMPANY
NEW YORK · CHICAGO
DALLAS · ATLANTA · SAN FRANCISCO
LONDON · MANILA
BRETT-MACMILLAN LTD.
TORONTO

Counseling
in Catholic Life and Education

By

CHARLES A. CURRAN
St. Charles College–Seminary
Columbus, Ohio

Preface by

EUGENE CARDINAL TISSERANT
Bishop of Ostia, Porto and Santa Rufina, Rome

Foreword by

MICHAEL J. READY
Bishop of Columbus

New York
THE MACMILLAN COMPANY

Nihil Obstat:

Paul J. Glenn, S.T.D., Ph.D.
Censor Deputatus

Imprimatur:

✛Michael J. Ready, D.D.
Bishop of Columbus

To His Excellency,

The Most Reverend Michael J. Ready, D.D.

PREFACE

Of all sciences, the study of man yet remains the most important. Other scientific advancement is ultimately meaningless unless it contributes in some way to human development, personal sanctity, and mutual understanding among individuals and nations. It is useless to mount the clouds with swift, great carriers, to span the earth with broad highways and vast bridges, and fill the land with gigantic factories and complex machinery for every material need and comfort, if men cannot be at peace with themselves and with each other. Material advances and conquests mean nothing, if man himself remains unimproved. Unless man can learn ways to control himself, it is useless to have gained control over all other things. Understanding nature without a corresponding understanding of man, is futile.

Even theology, guiding man with supernatural light and power and drawing as it does from the very fountainhead of Divine Wisdom, must yet borrow from the human sciences to aid and further its acceptance and effectiveness in leading men to the things of God. Consequently the Christian Apostle cannot be unmindful of science, especially of the psychological and sociological sciences. Herein lies the importance of studies such as Father Curran has made. The purpose of Father Curran's work is to help man conquer and control himself, to put the stamp of his reason on his own disordered actions with something of the same precision and integration that have enabled him to impress his reason on the material universe. If man could not do this in some way, then all would be hopeless pessimism and no human scientific advance would have any final meaning. But, among the many things the Catholic Church through her great scholars has given mankind, is an abiding confidence and assurance that man can, with God's help, overcome the disorder of his wounded nature in the saving Grace of Christ. This is the comforting message

vii

of St. Paul to the weak, confused, and fearful world of the first century and it remains at the heart of Christian optimism:

> For the law of the spirit of life, in Christ Jesus, hath delivered me from the law of sin and of death . . . for they that are according to the flesh, mind the things that are of the flesh; but they that are according to the spirit, mind the things that are of the spirit. For the wisdom of the flesh is death; but the wisdom of the spirit is life and peace.[1]

In this struggle against the disorder of his wounded nature man does not act against his reason or contrary to human knowledge. As St. Thomas especially so clearly unfolds, wherever possible he should harness all the facts of scientific research and understanding and bring them to the aid of his reason, which in turn will be supported by the might of the Grace of God. The Christian Apostle cannot neglect the power of science, especially those sciences which directly affect human conduct. He cannot smugly assume that he has no further need of psychological and sociological science; he cannot dismiss new developments in these sciences simply because they are new or even unusual. The Church has never acted thus. Even after thirteen centuries, saints like Thomas could willingly learn from Greek pagans like Aristotle. Today, in the work of the Apostolate, we too can learn from the research of science. If there are skills and techniques now available that show us how to enable groups and individuals to reach a more reasonable understanding of themselves and others, to gain control over their emotions and instincts so that in their daily actions, and social and community responsibilities, they are more able to see what they should do and follow it, then, thank God for such blessings in our time. ". . . The Church" as Pius XI told us, ". . . has no fear of the progress, even the most daring progress, of science, if only it be true science."[2] On the contrary, it welcomes those findings of psychological science which further growth in personal responsibility and reasonable maturity and freedom. Such findings make both for growth in personal sanctity and for the increasing assumption on the part of each man of those grave public obligations that being a citizen entails in these perilous social and political times. Whatever may have been the conditions of other

---

[1]Epistle of St. Paul to the Romans, Chapter 7, verse 23.
[2]Pope Pius XI: *The Catholic Priesthood*, Encyclical Letter, 1936, National Catholic Welfare Conference, Washington, D.C., pp. 40–41.

ages, the problems of our time necessitate the use of every available knowledge and skill which psychology and the social sciences can reveal about the actions and reactions of individuals and groups. The Apostolate must aim at creating a responsible citizenry, each of whom is a man of sound principles who can think reasonably even in the face of strong and compelling personal and mass emotion. To do this he must be aided to know and understand his own personality and the personalities of others. "In a people worthy of the name," says Pius XII, "the citizen feels within himself the consciousness of his personality, of his duties and rights and of his own freedom; and he joins to it a respect for the freedom and dignity of others."[3]

In the work of the Apostolate we cannot assume that the mere telling of men what they ought to do, is enough. This certainly is necessary, but knowledge alone is insufficient. Unless knowledge is given in such a way that it becomes active in the life of each man who hears it, teaching has been futile. Man is not only motivated by ideas but by what he feels in the dark and deep recesses of his emotional and instinctive being. We make a grave mistake if we treat man only as an intellect and overlook the sometimes blind and sometimes compelling contrary force of his emotional, physical and animal nature. A man may often know in principle, and in a general way, what he should do to live a responsible, upright Christian life. But in the immediate circumstances of his daily life, under the pressure of his own complex needs and the confusing demands of others, he still has the very difficult task of choosing the most reasonable personal and social means to carry out his obligations. In the Christian Apostolate we must meet the needs of the whole man. We must satisfy not only men's intellects by the teaching of the right theological and philosophical principles, but also men's wills by giving them help and opportunities to make responsible and right choices. These choices must enter into every action of their lives, at home, at work, in the parish, and in social activities, and in their duties as citizens of a city, a nation, and the world. We can do this only if we help develop in them the virtues of action, especially prudence and counsel. Through these virtues God's Grace will give forth fruit in the goodness of men's lives.

This is why St. Thomas, commenting on the text of St. Paul pre-

---

[3] Pope Pius XII: Christmas Message 1944. Cf. Atti e discorsi di Pio XII 1944, Roma, Instituto Missionario Pia Società S. Paolo 1945, p. 169.

viously quoted, says that the wisdom of the spirit, by which each
action of a man's life is judged in the light of his eternal destiny,
demands the development of the virtue of prudence. Prudence, which
is "recta ratio agibilium" presupposes in turn the right principles
of acting and involves three steps: 1) to counsel oneself rightly,
2) to judge rightly about the things which one's own counsel and that
of others reveals, and, 3) to act rightly in commanding oneself to
carry out what has been counseled. Consequently, says St. Thomas,
the prudence of the spirit should enable a man to counsel, judge,
and command himself in the light of the spiritual end of his life.
But, we notice that, unless a man has counseled himself wisely and
weighed well all the countless details that enter into his daily actions,
he will neither judge nor command himself prudently. The virtue
of counsel therefore plays an important part in those prudent judgments which make up the wisdom of the spirit and lead to the eternal
fruits of supernatural life and peace.[4]

Father Curran's book on counseling will therefore be a valuable
aid in the work of the Apostolate. Combining a thorough and accurate knowledge of modern psychological science with a sound
integration of Thomistic philosophy and theology, it offers ready at
hand for the work of Catholic Action a fund of very practical
information and skill. Father Curran makes two important distinctions which are most clarifying. First, he distinguishes between
guidance and counseling, showing that guidance is a kind of teaching
and spiritual direction in those things which the person to be counseled does not know. Counseling, on the other hand, is concerned
primarily with enabling a person to make the right choices and
actions to carry out in his personal daily life the things he knows
he should do. This distinction helps us to understand why merely
telling a person what to do does not of itself develop in him the
virtue of counsel which is a part of his own prudence. Father Curran
then distinguishes between the virtue of counsel, which resides in
the one counseled and enables him to act prudently, and the skill
of counseling, which must be possessed by the counselor. The counselor's purpose—differing from that of the teacher and guide—is
not so much to direct activity or give knowledge as it is to create an
opportunity where a person can develop the virtue of counsel in him-

[4]S. Thomae Aquinatis: In Omnes S. Pauli Apostoli Epistolas Commentaria, Libraria
Marietti, Taurini, Italia, 1922, pp. 107–108.

self and grow gradually able to control his confusing emotions and instincts so that he judges and acts in the light of the reasonable principles he knows. In this way, a man is responsive to the Gifts of the Holy Ghost, especially the Gift of Counsel.

As Father Curran unfolds the virtue of counsel and the skill of counseling with individuals and groups, we see revealed in all its subtlety the complex process by which the virtue of prudence is developed. Prudence is so personal that it is called "incommunicable," yet at the same time so basic that no right moral choice can be made without it. The virtues of counsel and prudence are essential if men are to be led not only to know their Christian responsibilities but to do them. For this reason all available psychological knowledge and techniques of counseling must be studied and mastered by the Christian Apostle. This is especially true in these times when social and political conditions demand of each Christian the maximum of personal responsibility and prudent action in the midst of world events which promote both mass emotion and personal turmoil and conflict. Consequently this book, *Counseling in Catholic Life and Education*, emphasizing as it does methods of fostering in each individual the development of the virtues of counsel and prudence, will have a significant and important role in the work of the Catholic Apostolate.

/s/ ✠EUGENE CARD. TISSERANT

Bp. of Ostia, Porto and Santa Rufina

Rome, November 30, 1951

FOREWORD

The practice of counseling has so recently and so rapidly affected society that it is widely considered the latest modern implement of educator, manager, supervisor, employer, psychologist, physician, clergyman, and even legal advisor. So many persons have turned counselor to meet the present-day demand for direction that startled common sense is justified in the suspicion that not all of them are qualified for their office.

A counselor has as great a need to understand the human person and to know how to offer sound assistance in anxieties and difficulties as a physician has to understand the human body and to know how to remedy its disorders. Lack of such knowledge removes the credentials from the hands of the counselor. Presence of this knowledge, with prudence in its application to human needs, makes the counselor a valuable and effective instrument for individual and social good.

Doctor Curran, who has devoted many priestly years to the study and practice of counseling, has the advantage of bringing his research and experience into the framework of sane philosophy and Christian truth. Doctor Curran is not interested in rootless theories. He does not promote clever utilitarian schemes of procedure. He joins ageless truth with modern scientific discovery in an attractive exposition of counseling, especially as applicable in Catholic life and education. This is a thorough study, but it is not dull or prosy. It is particularly valuable in the fact that it presents a wealth of practical suggestion as well as a clarifying explanation of human personality in action.

In this interesting and worthwhile study, Doctor Curran offers ample evidence of the truth once uttered by Tertullian: "Anima humana naturaliter Christiana"—the human soul by its nature is Christian. He shows that man normally tends to seek the Christian way of life and to find in it his natural as well as supernatural fulfillment.

Doctor Curran's study explains the work of conscience in the formation and application of Christian prudence. Indeed, the paragraphs on prudence offered here are distinctly timely and notably valuable. They constitute a penetrating discussion of a paramount virtue too little stressed or investigated by most modern philosophers and theologians.

For the learned but very fascinating work of Doctor Curran on *Counseling in Catholic Life and Education*, there is sure to be a wide and receptive circle of readers. Its effect should be one of incalculable benefit. It is a great joy to commend the devoted and learned author as well as his timely book to citizens seeking the sure guidance of Christian counseling.

✛MICHAEL J. READY
Bishop of Columbus

ACKNOWLEDGMENTS

The writer of this book wishes to express his appreciation first both to His Eminence, Eugene Cardinal Tisserant, for so signally distinguishing this work with a preface and to His Excellency, the Most Reverend Michael J. Ready, D.D., for graciously honoring it with a foreword. The writer also owes much to all who so willingly read the original manuscript and gave him the valuable aid of their comments and suggestions. He is especially grateful for particular kindnesses and considerations to the Right Reverend Paul J. Glenn, S.T.D., Ph.D., Rector of St. Charles Seminary, Columbus, Ohio; the Right Reverend Pietro Pavan, S.T.D., of the Universita pro Deo, Rome; the Very Reverend Michael J. Browne, O.P., of the Collegio Angelico, Rome, and now Sacri Palatii Apost. Magister; the Very Reverend Comerford O'Malley, C.M., S.T.D., President of DePaul University; the Very Reverend Felix Morlion, O.P., President of the Universita pro Deo, Rome; the Very Reverend T. Lincoln Bouscaren, S.J., Procurator General of the Society of Jesus, Rome; the Reverend John W. Stafford, Ph.D., of the Catholic University of America, Washington; the Reverend George Buchmann, J.C.D. and the Reverend Thomas A. Sabrey, S.T.D., of the Columbus Diocese; the Reverend Paul Philippe, O.P., the Reverend James M. Egan, O.P., of the Collegio Angelico, Rome; the Reverend Gerald Kelly, S.J., of St. Mary's College, Kansas; the Reverend Vincent V. Herr, S.J. and the Reverend Ralph J. Gallagher, S.J., of Loyola University of Chicago; the Reverend Fred J. Mann, C.Ss.R., of Denver, Colorado; the Reverend Pius Barth, O.F.M., of DePaul University and the Reverend Basil Heiser, O.F.M., of Carey, Ohio; the Reverend Mother Margaret M. Reilly, R.S.C.J., President of Barat College, Lake Forest, Illinois; and to Professors Jacques Maritain of Princeton University and Carl R. Rogers of the University of

Chicago. Here, particular mention should be made of the encouragement and help he received from the Very Reverend Robert E.
Brennan, O.P. The writer is also indebted to the publishers who
granted permission to reproduce material. Finally, he wishes to
acknowledge his sincere appreciation to all counselors and other
persons who permitted the use of their interview material and to
all who have, in times past, allowed him the inestimable privilege
of acting as their counselor.

CHARLES A. CURRAN

CONTENTS

PART II

THE PROCESS OF PERSONAL INTEGRATION THROUGH COUNSELING

Present Conflicts.—Past Causes.—New Self-Knowledge and Integration.

PART III

THE SKILL OF THE COUNSELOR

cepting Responses.—Shift of Focus.—The Counselor's Response Does Not Soften a Person's Difficulties.—Nor Emphasize Them.—Responses Should Further the Person's Self-Concentration.—Study of Actual Excerpts Can Improve Skill. *Some Causes of Resistance:* Failure to Reach Basic Attitudes.—Counselors Often Do Not Realize Their Mistakes.—Defensiveness of Counselor.—Some Alternate Counselor Responses. *A Successful Interview:* Structuring Statement.— Effects.—Lengthy Statements.—Realism.—Counselor Overstatement. —Self-Evaluation.—Reaching Causes of Conduct. *An Unsuccessful Interview:* Value of Typescript.—Conversational Responses.—Poor Structuring.—Returns to Questions.—Questions Produce Blocking.— Counselor Overenthusiasm.—Children More Openly Resistant. *Some Alternate Responses. Self-Concentration:* Interrupts Concentration.

Chapter   Page

dence: Teachableness.—Shrewdness.—Foresight, Circumspection,
and Caution.—Avoid Precipitation.—General Alertness.   *Counseling
Effectiveness and Intelligence.   Counseling and Other Virtues:*   Jus-
tice.—Courage and Moderation.—Humility.—Counseling Atmosphere
Aids Humility.—Humility is Truth.—Self-Knowledge and Hope.—
Not Infantilism.—Magnanimity.   *Counseling and Virtuous Living:*
Not Moral Science.—Individual Evaluation.—Counseling Aids This.—
Knowledge and Guidance Necessary.—Virtuous Living.   *Conclusion:*
Need for Prudence and Moral Virtue.—Commandments Tell What To
Do.—Personal Factors.—The Fruitful Development of the Individual
Personality.

CASE LIST

Description	Symbol	Excerpts Interview Number	Pages	Other References
Aviation Cadet	X	I	59, 99, 103, 114, 124–125	60, 126, 170– 171
		V	88–89, 112	
Aviation Cadet		IV	132–133	136–137
(Rogers & Muench)		V	133–134	
		VI	134	
		IX	134	
		X	134–135	
Billy	N	I	306	305–307
Buddy & Charles (Axline)		VI	311–312	
College Junior	Y	V	100	99, 168, 175, 248–249
Edna	R	II	223–225	226–228, 232–234, 240
Honor Student	K	III	67–68	69
Insurance Salesman (Snyder)		X	183–186	182
		XIV	187–190	
Jane (Madigan)		I	229–230, 232–233	231, 234
Joe	O	I	301–302	303–304
John	M	I	320	318–319, 321
Marjorie and Sally (Axline)			310–311	
Married Business Woman	Z	II	54–57, 144–146	58, 60, 142, 146, 148, 151, 170, 172,
		I	79	180–181, 188, 219–
		XI	149–150	221
Married Couple	U	I	109–111	
Married Woman	L	I	82–83	216–219
		III	83	
Miss H. S.—Success- ful graduate student	J	IX	95–97, 278–281	277, 282, 287
		X	283–286	

Case List

Description	Symbol	Excerpts		Other References
		Interview Number	Pages	
Mrs. A.	Q	I	235–236, 238–239	237, 240
Naval Ensign	S	I	252–253, 256–259	142, 251, 254–
		II	260, 267–268	255, 261–262,
		IV	272–273	266, 269–270, 276
		V	274–275, 349–350	
		VI	419–420	
Navy Nurse	T	I	126–131, 144	136, 171
Timmy (Axline)		VII	310	
Tom (Axline)		I	315–317	
		II	312–314	
Young College	W	I	58, 61–63, 80, 85–86	120
Woman, Miss W.		IX	119	
Young Man	V	II	81–82, 85	251, 417, 419
		I	104–106, 116	
		X	249–250, 417, 418, 420–421	

INTRODUCTION

WHY COUNSELING IS NECESSARY

Good counseling is important to all human relations because its purpose is to increase a person's self-understanding and reasonable self-control. In this book we will attempt to unfold the process by which people solve personal difficulties through counseling and various methods which aid in bringing this about. The final measure of good counseling is the degree to which it produces reasonable and successful daily action and, as a result, makes a person happier, more at peace with himself, and more able to grow in virtuous living. To accomplish this, the counselor's purpose and function must be precisely determined. *Counseling is, therefore, a definite relationship where, through the counselor's sensitive understanding and skillful responses, a person objectively surveys the past and present factors which enter into his personal confusions and conflicts and, at the same time, reorganizes his emotional reactions so that he not only chooses better ways to reach his reasonable goals, but has sufficient confidence, courage, and moderation to act on these choices.*

The purpose of this book will be to explain in detail the implications of this definition by: 1) an analysis of the changes the person himself undergoes in the process of counseling; 2) a delineation of the means which the counselors use to facilitate these changes; and, 3) a consideration of other functions which can prepare the way for counseling.

An adult or child may know in principle what he ought to do. Yet, he may be so overwhelmed and confused by the flood of conflicting urges, feelings, and goals in his own surroundings and immediate day-by-day activities, that he cannot see his way clearly to take the right path to the things he knows he should do. Often he chooses wrongly on the emotional impulse of the moment. Because of this, he needs the aid of a process by which, with God's help, he can integrate his uncontrolled instincts and emotions

1

so that they follow the insights of his reason. In this way he can formulate and carry out more consistently those reasonable daily actions that make a man of principle. In proportion, therefore, as a person can, with the aid of grace, control and direct his emotions by his reason and will, his actions will be in conformity with natural and supernatural laws.

Counseling, then, can be an important factor in helping both children and adults grow in reasonable understanding and responsible choices in their daily living and in the integration and coordination of their emotions so that they carry out these choices in their major life activities. This, in turn, will result in happier and more virtuous lives.

PROBLEMS OF MODERN LIVING

Even a brief consideration of some of the problems of our society will indicate why counseling is especially important now, and why, in addition to the emphasis on knowledge and more general educational techniques, we also need more skillful counseling methods.

The Family. In society generally, the family is threatened by the rising divorce rate.[1] One writer estimates that if the present rate of divorce continues, one out of every two marriages will have ended in divorce by 1965.[2] By contrast, in 1890, there were only six divorces for every one hundred marriages in the United States. In some counties, divorces now exceed marriages. While this problem may not be as great where both parties are Catholic, yet far too many Catholic marriages are ending in separation, divorce or the partners are living in states of unhappy conflict and tension.

The School. But we do not even need to go into later adult life to see evidences of the need for help with personal problems. In a survey of over a thousand parochial high school seniors (699)

---

[1]One American family broke up for every three—approximately—that were formed in 1945. More than 502,000 marriages ended in divorce courts in 1945, an all-time record representing a 25.5 per cent rise over the previous peak divorce year, 1944. The divorces were 31 per cent of the marriages, which totaled 1,618,331 in 1945, or about 8.7 per cent below the biggest year, 1942. Both marriage and divorce rates rise with prosperity, wartime or otherwise, and fall with depression. *Federal Security Agency Report.* Jan. 1946.

[2]Judge John A. Sbabaro: *Marriage Is On Trial*, New York, The Macmillan Company, 1947.

and college students (378) covering ten counties in the Diocese of Pittsburgh, Dr. Thomas J. Quigley reports that students want and need help

. . . to meet such personal problems and they are not getting it in high school. They are loath to discuss them with teachers, but quite willing to do so with a priest were one available in the school. There is some evidence that they would talk with teachers, if the teachers could display a greater interest in them. Apparently they expect parents, teachers, and priests to know they have problems, and to take the initial step toward any personal guidance. They hesitate to open the discussion but will gladly talk, at least to a priest, or their parents, if the subject is broached to them.[3]

A similar study made a survey of the guidance procedures of seven Catholic women's colleges. The Mooney Problem Check List was presented to 1,897 students. Of the 51,750 problems stated, 14,618 were indicated as serious. The greatest number of problems were listed in the areas of personal relationships and adjustment to college work. Sixty-three per cent of the students expressed a desire to talk with someone on the faculty. Forty-five per cent of that number indicated that they knew a person with whom they felt free to talk about these problems, while fify-two per cent indicated they did not. The person directing the guidance program was asked to list the areas in which she perceived the students' problems to be. These were then correlated with the students' lists and were found to vary greatly. In most instances there was a noticeable discrepancy between the directors' evaluation of the general areas of the students' problems and the students' lists. This might be interpreted to mean that in some cases at least guidance advisers may perhaps be unaware of the problems students actually have and may be directing their efforts to areas of only minor personal significance for their students.[4]

Industry. Other indications of this need can be drawn from industry. Roethlisberger and Dickson, after a thorough study of one large industrial plant, report that personal problems are

[3]Dr. Thomas J. Quigley: "Inquiry into the Religious Knowledge and Attitudes of Catholic High School Girls," Educational Office Report, Diocese of Pittsburgh, Pa., p. 23.

[4]Margaret Burke, R.S.C.J.: "An Evaluation of the Guidance Services in Seven Catholic Liberal Arts Colleges for Women," an unpublished doctoral dissertation from Loyola University, Chicago, 1951.

one of the three major factors to be considered in every worker problem.[5] Elton Mayo of Harvard confirms this same view.[6]

Medicine. The term "psychosomatic" medicine has been added to the physician's vocabulary because physicians are finding that patients need personal help in addition to medical and surgical treatment. The medical literature on this question is now abundant.[7] The patient's psychological state enters into the diagnosis of every major illness. Consequently, complete medical therapy generally involves offering the patient adequate counseling help.

Nursing. This is becoming a most important part of the training of nurses as well as doctors. A recent analysis of the future role of the nurse stresses the necessity for nurses to acquire counseling understanding and skill:

> There are many individual nurses who appreciate . . . how important is the kind of nursing care that seeks to alleviate anxiety and fear, to provide strong emotional support during the severe phases of sickness, and to help the patient during convalescence gradually to regain freedom from dependency. Such nurses see how potentially great are the implications, could they work particularly with prospective mothers and children before sickness and emotional problems develop.[8]

Religious Vocations. Even the decrease in religious vocations may be partially due to some of these same factors. Father Gerald Kelly, S.J., believes that

> . . . emotional maturity is required in the religious life no less than in marriage, and that immaturity explains many of the failures to make necessary adjustments to the demands of the religious life, just as it explains similar failures in marriage. If this is true and I have no doubt

[5]F. J. Roethlisberger and W. J. Dickson: *Management and the Worker*, Cambridge, Harvard University Press, 1939.

[6]Elton Mayo: *Human Problems of an Industrial Civilization*, Cambridge, Harvard University Press, 1945.

[7]Dr. Philip K. Arzt: "Psychosomatic Medicine in General Practice," *The Journal-Lancet*, Minneapolis, Vol. LXVIII, November, 1948. Dr. H. F. Dunbar: *Psychosomatic Diagnosis*, New York, Hoeber, 1943; *Emotions and Bodily Changes*, New York, Columbia University Press, 1938; *Mind and Body*, New York, Random House, 1947. L. J. Saul: "Physiological Effects of Emotional Tension," in J. McV. Hunt: *Personality and the Behavior Disorders*, New York, The Ronald Press Company, 1944. E. Weiss, and O. S. English: *Psychosomatic Medicine*, Philadelphia, W. B. Saunders Company, 1943. Helen L. Whitmer: *Teaching Psychotherapeutic Medicine; An Experimental Course for General Physicians*, New York, Commonwealth Fund, 1947. All Psychosomatic Medicine Monographs, *J. Psychosom. Med.*

[8]Esther Lucile Brown, Ph.D.: *Nursing for the Future*, New York, Russell Sage Foundation, 1948, pp. 82–84.

that it is then we can profitably avail ourselves of the psychologists' excellent studies on maturity in examining candidates for the religious life, and in guidance of other religious, and in the self-examination and self-reformation necessary for our own growth in perfection.[9]

Education. All this has led some serious-minded people to question whether our school program is entirely adequate. They point out that knowledge by itself is not a sufficient basis for virtue and character; it must be integrated and vivified in action. Bishop John F. Noll voices this objection:

We are hearing from every direction that products of Catholic schools and even of Catholic colleges are, on the whole, giving a very poor account of themselves, and even from casual observation, we know how true the charge is. To those who are bent on discovering the real explanation various opinions are volunteered. Some exonerate the school almost completely and throw the blame on the non-cooperative and even obstructionist home. Others charge that the character and the excessive amount of recreational life, as compared to former days, are chiefly responsible.

But those who, because really worried, are giving to the subject the most serious consideration believe that the basic cause is to be found (1) in the false assumption that religious instruction imparted in the school will of itself produce spirituality; and (2) in the neglect of the teacher to apply the catechetical lesson both to the child's own private conduct and to an apostolate in which he is in duty bound, even as you, to promote.

Religious education has too long been identified with religious instruction. If the assumption were correct the best informed Catholics would necessarily be the most spiritual men and women.[10]

Religious Conversion. Moreover, in the work of conversions, Bishop Sheen, who has had such remarkable success in bringing many souls into the Church, comments on the change of methods necessary to reach the needs of our generation:

Anyone seeking to bring God to souls ought to start with modern man as he is, not as he ought to be, and not as he was a century ago. Apologetics, or the science of presenting divine truth to unbelievers, is in some

---

[9]Gerald Kelly, S.J.: "Emotional Maturity," *Review for Religious*, Copyright 1947, by Gerald C. Ellis, Vol. VII, No. 1, p. 3.

[10]Most Reverend John F. Noll, D.D.: "What's Wrong With Our Schools," in *From a Friend to a Friend*, Huntington, Indiana, Our Sunday Visitor Press, 1944.

instances half a century behind the times; we are beating the dead dogs of rationalism and deism while ignoring the tragedies of the modern soul inside itself—cynical, morose and afraid. The modern soul is not going to God through order in nature, as he did a generation ago, but through his disordered self; he is looking for God not through a search for a cause of the cosmos, but through a yearning for redemption from his own frustration. It is one of the marvels of grace that God can start there, despite the fact that we too often feel that He must work on souls the way we start in our textbooks. God's grace can start anywhere, and with any condition of mind or heart. If the modern soul is frustrated, we will start with frustration.[11]

COUNSELING AND COUNSEL

Widespread Interest. This prevalence of personal problems has in consequence produced a widespread interest in counseling in a variety of people. Priests and seminary students are expressing the desire for increased knowledge of the intricacies of emotional conflicts and of ways of helping people with personal difficulties. Sisters and teachers in schools are anxious to reach the children in a more personal way, especially those who do not seem to fit in, are not making the most of the talents they have, or are in psychological and spiritual conflict. Psychologists, sociologists and social workers are finding counseling an increasingly important part of their professional service. Doctors and nurses, wanting to appreciate and treat the whole person as well as a particular illness, are seeking methods of understanding and helping people. Lawyers, overwhelmed now by marriage and family difficulties, are anxious to acquire some plan and program for their clients, to arrest the constant trek to the divorce court. Worker problems in factories are more and more brought to the industrial counselor. Furthermore, the rapid growth in specialized lay activities has produced an awareness of his responsibility to others on the part of the active Catholic layman. Parents are anxious to understand each other and their children and to avail themselves of whatever knowledge can help in making a more adequate home life. Besides this,

[11]Most Reverend Fulton J. Sheen, D.D.: *Techniques for Convert Makers*, New York, The Paulist Press, September 1949, originally from a Catholic Hour broadcast, National Broadcasting Company, 1949, sponsored by the National Council of Catholic Men and published as "The Love That Waits for You" by Our Sunday Visitor Press, Huntington, Indiana, 1949.

all of us want to understand ourselves and to penetrate more deeply into the motives of our actions so that we may better control our emotions and advance in sanctity through a more reasonable response to God's grace.

Specific Aim. Accordingly, the purpose of this book is the treatment of counseling and counsel, and, indirectly, prudence and the moral virtues. It does not, therefore, directly consider techniques of guidance and instruction. Counseling, as such, is primarily concerned with those methods and skills which facilitate self-directed choices through personal reorganization and in this way further the development of the virtue of counsel and ultimately of prudence. We are not treating here the more general field of knowledge and information that might be considered guidance. There is a growing present-day guidance literature both from secular and Catholic sources. We have always had available the many masterpieces of moral and spiritual guidance which the Church, through her theologians and saints, has given the world. There is still an additional need for more literature that applies these to modern Catholic life. But, while some consideration will be given to the relationship of counseling to both guidance and general education, the direct aim of this book is not to consider guidance. This discussion of counseling, then, presupposes adequate instruction and information and treats these questions only to explain more clearly some aspects of counsel or reasons for a particular kind of counselor method or statement.

Detailed Analysis. Recent research in counseling has resulted in a much more detailed analysis of the counseling process than was previously possible. The careful study of the contents of counseling interviews has been found to be one of the most valuable means of understanding the factors which enter into personal difficulties and of improving counseling skill. From this research that has been done on counseling, particularly during the war years, there is now available a large number of typescript and printed reports of actual interviews. In the illustrations used in this book, we have borrowed from this data. We have removed or changed, beyond all possible recognition all names, phrases, and circumstances that could in any way be identifying. When, for the sake of added readability, it was thought necessary to include some facts or circumstances, these are entirely fictitious. However, even when they are completely changed and disguised, such excerpts can still be very valuable and accurate in demonstrating the process of counsel as it actually takes place and the precise skill of the counselor as he responds to each statement.[12]

These excerpts therefore afford us an opportunity to enter into the actual interview with a thoroughness and vividness which heretofore would not have been possible. Such is the common humanity of us all and the similarity of our feelings and attitudes that the reader may often feel that his own reactions or those of someone he knows are being described by the person in the interview. This has been the experience of many who have read such printed material. This demonstrates, in a striking way, how much we really share in one another's intimate feelings and reactions. Recent research like this has revealed a much greater commonality and consistency than many of us may have realized, in the way we all react to various personal circumstances. Moreover, as we shall discuss in detail in this book, the process by which such personal difficulties are clarified or solved, also appears, from this same evidence, to be somewhat similar in each person and therefore to have more predictable factors than we may have thought. Previously this degree of similarity and consistency was not nearly so evident when we had to draw our conclusions only from the counselor's memory of what was said in the interview, or, at best, depend on the degree of accuracy of the counselor's notes.[13]

This kind of detailed interview material is primarily important for research. For successful counseling, the skilled counselor does not necessarily need notes or any other record of the interviews, since the effectiveness of counseling is determined mainly by the changes which take place in the person. But, since such research material is available to us, it will aid us to get a better grasp of the factors which enter into personal needs. Studying these excerpts carefully we can see, in a way that might be missed in the rapid flow of the interview itself, how emotional confusions and personal conflicts are affecting both the person's reasonable judgments and his actions. Moreover, without this knowledge, the reader

---

[12]See also Chapter XIV.

[13]Even when the counselor takes his own notes, it appears that he can remember only about one-third of the general content of an hour interview. See C. A. Curran: *Personality Factors in Counseling*, New York, Copyright 1945, by Grune and Stratton, pp. 4–7, for a résumé of research on the accuracy of interviewers' reports.

may not see why certain counselor actions or responses are important. This treatment is, of course, by no means exhaustive. The beginning counselor will want to read other literature on these points, especially in clinical psychology and allied fields.

THE PLAN OF THIS BOOK

Part One is mainly intended to supply a background for what follows. Chapter I considers the sources of personal problems, particularly in their relationship to the virtues of counsel and prudence. Chapter II gives a brief survey of recent developments in personality understanding and research, showing especially the trend in the direction of counseling skills which aid the person to acquire his own reasonable insights and make self-directed choices. These recent developments are a valuable addition to the traditional methods by which people can be enabled to solve personal difficulties and grow in virtue.

Part Two discusses the stages in the counseling process through which a person gains self-knowledge and integration. Chapter III examines the person's state of mind as he comes for counseling. In the remaining chapters of this section, however, we follow the steps of the counseling process by which people pass from a state of confusion and conflict to more successful and happier living. This growth is not so much in knowledge of what they should do. Generally, they had this knowledge before they came and it was one of the causes of their conflict. We see, rather, a slow change from discouragement, hostility, dependence, insecurity, and immoderate compensations to a more positive attitude about themselves and their ability to change. Simultaneously, as negations are expressed and thought through, they begin to see why they are failing. With this comes, sometimes at an almost imperceptible pace and sometimes suddenly, insights which relate problems to each other and to factors in the past or present environment. This relating process leads them finally to see fundamental causes that are at the basis of their difficulties. At the same time, there is an increase in the number of factors which indicate a growing courage and confidence in their ability to overcome difficulties and reach a more adequate solution.

At this stage new solutions begin to appear, are tried, and usually are found more successful, since a person now takes many more factors into consideration before he makes his decisions. These new solutions are, however, not always successful. The interview then offers a person the opportunity to re-examine the reasons for failure. In this way counseling helps him to happier and more virtuous living. The final stages of a successful counseling process, therefore, show a greater integration and coordination between the person's reasonable judgment and his emotional and physical urges. As a result, the person can make better choices and, when he acts on these choices, he finds he is more consistently able to reach what he is seeking.[14]

Part Three is devoted to the skill of the counselor. It was thought preferable here, to begin directly with the interview itself when the person had come to the counselor with at least some notion of the counselor's purpose and function. (Later, in Part Four, some more general considerations are presented about the counseling atmosphere and setting, and about various other ways people approach counseling.) Chapter IX, therefore, considers some steps in the beginning interviews which aid in establishing a counseling relationship.

Most of Part Three is however given over to making the prospective counselor aware of the different methods of responding to statements so that their deepest content may be objectively unfolded and understood. These awarenesses and skills, which appear to be essential to good counseling, are especially difficult to learn. They must, therefore, be studied carefully. For this purpose, particularly, excerpts of actual interviews are exceptionally valuable. This is perhaps the most important aspect of the whole counseling process.

Chapter X examines some of the more common statements which the counselor will meet in the earlier stages of the interview. Detailed excerpts are given of both successful and unsuccessful interviews. Through the repeated examination and study of these excerpts, it is hoped the reader will acquire something of the "feel" of a constructive counseling process and, at the same time, increase his ability to recognize faulty counselor responses.

---

[14]The contents of Parts I and II of this book might be used as a separate introductory course on the psychology of adjustment and thus be considered in the area of guidance. Chapter XVIII might also be added to this section if desired.

Chapters XI and XII include a number of situations which may arise in the later stages of counseling. Here the counselor is dealing less with emotional and conflicting statements than in the earlier stages, since the person has now begun to acquire new insights, is proposing new plans of action to himself, or re-examining these plans after he has acted on them. While a person's statements at the beginning stages usually have a predominantly negative and discouraged tone, in the later stages they are generally more positive and hopeful. The counselor, accordingly, must also learn to respond adequately to these more reasonable and constructive expressions.

While interviews with children follow the same general plan as those with adolescents or adults, there are some differences due to the age of the child and his normal inability to use words as freely as an adult. Consequently, in Chapter XIII, we have discussed some of the circumstances peculiar to counseling with children, particularly the use of play materials to help the child say what he feels and thinks.

Part Four is concerned with the more remote conditions and situations which promote counseling. These questions are taken up towards the end of the book because some of the points considered will probably be better understood after a detailed study of the interviews has revealed the specific purpose and aim of counseling. Chapter XIV treats some common elements which have been found to help or hinder the creation of a counseling atmosphere. This discussion considers aspects in both the counseling setting itself and the counselor's attitudes and background. Then, since people do not always face the need for counseling openly, a number of suggestions are included in Chapter XV which may help turn a vague personal relationship into a definite counseling one. Personal problems are also often presented in conjunction with the seeking of information or guidance. Counseling skill can, therefore, be used by people functioning in a variety of roles and positions. In Chapter XVI, we have made an examination of some of these functions in order to illustrate the part counseling can play in furthering their ultimate effectiveness.

People also commonly come to group instructions and discussions in the hope of getting, not only general information, but some aid with their personal difficulties. Consequently, group discussions, particularly around those topics that are apt to have personal implications, are also a valuable means of preparing the way and leading to group or individual counseling. For this reason, in Chapter XVII we have considered some skills in discussion that can encourage and facilitate counseling.

Finally, counseling and the virtue of counsel are part of the whole structure of the good life, particularly of the moral virtues. We have attempted to show, in the concluding chapter, how psychological adjustment is ultimately measured by the degree to which such adjustment reaches reality and produces that humility which, in St. Thomas, is "the reasonable pursuit of one's own excellence." This, then, and prudent living will, with God's grace, be the final measure of good counseling.

Illustrates Process and Methods. Not all counseling is, of course, as successful as the examples given in this book. Our aim here is to illustrate various aspects of the process and methods of counseling and we have, therefore, chosen our material accordingly. Much depends on the person's will as well as upon the counselor's skill. Additional factors, some hereditary and many environmental, probably account for significant differences. Methods of approach not mentioned here may also be necessary in certain instances. Much greater research on all these questions must take place before any conclusive answers can be given. We cannot anticipate, either, the movement of Divine Providence in a person's life so that it may be better for him "to bear those ills" he has, at least until a time of greater opportunity and grace presents itself when he may work them out. On the personal value of suffering, Sheed makes this comment:

Ordinary observation of life shows that suffering may work in two ways. First it may be good for the sufferer. We know that a man who has never known suffering is soft and undeveloped. His character lacks substance. Immaturity clings about him. And not only do we find that this minimum of suffering is apparently necessary for man's proper development. We also find that really great suffering, if it has been dominated, has the power of enriching the character of the man or woman who has suffered. Suffering, if it ruins some characters, enriches others. It is not necessarily an evil, but may be an immense factor for good. What it is to be depends, for every man, on the way he accepts it. It lies in him to dominate it or be dominated by it.[15]

[15]F. J. Sheed: *A Map of Life*, New York, Sheed and Ward, 1944, p. 102.

But counseling may help people accept and "dominate" their suffering in this sense. So, a counseling process, such as we have described here, does appear possible for many people and, when successful, can aid them to a more reasonable life adjustment.

Painstaking Skill. Counseling is a painstaking skill. It cannot be learned simply from a book. Having actual interviews as a counselor, preferably under supervision, is the best way to recognize mistakes and increase counseling effectiveness. Many have also found the undergoing of a series of interviews for their own personal problems has helped them in the appreciation and understanding of counseling skill. Here, we have attempted to develop a greater awareness of what is involved in the process of counsel and the skill that brings it about. This book is, therefore, for those who wish to be counselors and for those already doing counseling who feel the need to improve their methods. It is also for those who seek a greater understanding of the field of personal problems, counsel, prudence, and the moral virtues as well as counseling.

Not Exhaustive Treatment. The field of counseling has already become, in recent years, very extensive. It is, therefore, not possible to include all aspects of this development in this book. We have, however, attempted to present a consistent and practical treatment of counsel and counseling. But, we do not wish to suggest that this book is an exhaustive treatment of counseling or to imply the rejection of any methods that are effective in helping people with personal problems. On all questions treated here, much research and study has been done which we have not as such considered. There is a vast amount of work yet to be done. Particular methods are recommended in this book because they have been verified in the experience and research of many counselors and because they have proved to be practically effective in a wide variety of circumstances.

Thomistic Orientation. Moreover, without departing from the evidence of the data which the interviews themselves reveal, we have, in our theoretical considerations, attempted to join our findings with the broader conclusions of St. Thomas Aquinas in philosophy and theology. Our plan is to present the data of the interviews and to reason about this data; then, for the purpose of a wider integration, to coordinate the results of our investigation with the Thomistic synthesis. This is often possible because

Thomistic psychology is founded on the close observation of human action. This agreement is not, in any sense, a coincidence therefore, but comes from the very nature of Thomistic Realism and the consistency characteristic of truth. As often happens, St. Thomas had come to conclusions similar to those which modern research reveals, and he and others have already related these with the broader fields of philosophy and theology. Consequently, many of these concepts, such as the dignity of man and the necessity of personal freedom and responsibility, are at the heart of our civilization. But what, in addition, is especially significant for us in the modern development, is the skill of counseling and the refinement of methods which recent advances in psychology, particularly through the detailed study of counseling interviews, have uncovered for us. This in itself is a field so filled with implications as to challenge and stimulate the ingenuity of any investigator.

With the special emphasis that is being given to the study of St. Thomas in our time, fruitful new developments are taking place in many areas. Discussing this revival, Father Brennan says that:

First, we must have careful and intelligent expositions of the thought of the Angelic Doctor. . . . The second task is really the more important of the two and follows from the first. It is nothing less than a complete modernization of the thought of Aquinas. By this I mean that if we are to be true Thomists we must think and speak and write in terms of the problems of our age. . . . For these are the marks of a vital and personalistic philosophy: when it becomes the food and very sustenance of the mind; when it presents reasonable answers to our difficulties; when it fortifies us against the mistakes of the past; when it gives us an earnest of peace and harmonious living for the future. With a wisdom such as this we shall be protected against our own selfish inversions which would shut us off from communication with our own fellowmen. We shall realize, too, that neither the body of our philosophy, which is temporal and changing, nor its soul, which is eternal and immutable, can be neglected if we would have a complete vision of its truth.[16]

The problems of our age are particularly personal problems. The social turmoil of our time leaves in its wake an ever-increasing

---

[16]Robert E. Brennan, O.P.: "The Troubadour of Truth," from *Essays in Thomism*, edited by Robert E. Brennan, O.P., Copyright Sheed & Ward, Inc., New York, 1942, pp. 20–21.

number of shattered and disorganized lives. The general insecurity in which we all are now living heightens the personal insecurity of each of us. Men most commonly need help, therefore, not only in the orientation and integration of their ideas, but also in the orientation and integration of themselves. The intellectual disorder and social chaos which threaten us are accompanied by a widespread personal confusion and conflict. Not only is society itself disturbed, but many of its individual members are equally disturbed on the personal level of their own lives.

To meet this, then, it is necessary that we combine the intellectual integration of St. Thomas, his broad and deep understanding of the needs of the human person, with the skills and techniques which are so characteristic of the practical wisdom of our time. The spirit of our age is the spirit of research—of accurate, precise and detailed investigation. Its spirit is a practical spirit with a constant unfolding of new and more efficient ways of doing things. This combination of Thomism and modern skills is possible because a realistic philosophy will always be at home in the practical realism of honest and sincere observation. All that is necessary is to integrate them by interpreting them to each other. Whenever this can be done, the Thomist has gained some valuable practical tools in dealing with the individual, while the modern investigator has gained a broad integration which orders his findings into a harmonious place in the philosophical integration of our whole culture.

PART ONE

THE VIRTUE OF COUNSEL AND COUNSELING SKILL

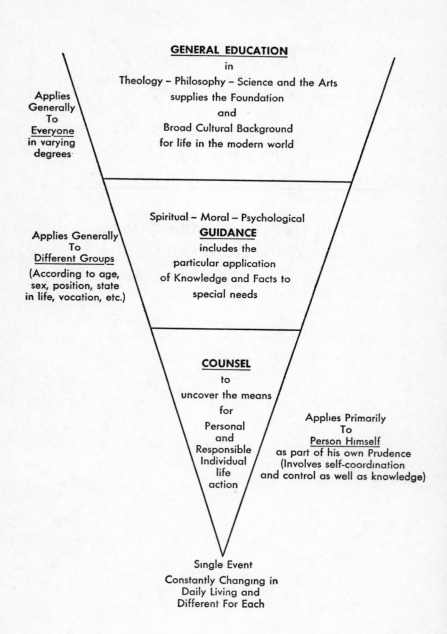

GENERAL EDUCATION

in

Theology – Philosophy – Science and the Arts

supplies the Foundation

and

Broad Cultural Background

for life in the modern world

Applies
Generally
To
Everyone
in varying
degrees

Spiritual – Moral – Psychological

GUIDANCE

includes the

particular application

of Knowledge and Facts to

special needs

Applies Generally
To
Different Groups

(According to age,
sex, position, state
in life, vocation, etc.)

COUNSEL

to

uncover the means

for

Personal
and
Responsible
Individual
life
action

Applies Primarily
To
Person Himself
as part of his own Prudence
(Involves self-coordination
and control as well as knowledge)

Single Event

Constantly Changing in
Daily Living and
Different For Each

18

CHAPTER I

COUNSEL AND PERSONAL
DIFFICULTIES

General and Particular Aspects. Personal difficulties usually
arise from two sources: either we lack sufficient knowledge to find a
solution or, knowing the general direction of the solution, we still
somehow are not taking the particular steps to reach our basic life
goals. Consequently, there is a general and a particular aspect
to every personal difficulty. We require norms and principles to
point us in the general direction of our ultimate goals and we
must have the capacity and ability to keep moving in the direction
of these goals in our day-by-day activities.

We have attempted to illustrate this in the diagram on p. 18.

We are all seeking permanent happiness. We want peace, certitude, security, and order. Yet, we live in the midst of constant
change which can leave us restless, uncertain, insecure, and disordered. We need to know in what ultimate direction to guide ourselves if we are to escape final disillusionment. All our actions
must, therefore, be centered on the permanent values of truth
and reality which Divine Revelation and human reason have given
us. This is the foundation upon which we can stand as we survey
the moving stream of changing events.

General Education. On the wide end of the triangle opening out
into universal principles which are permanent and certain is the
area of *General Education.* Founded on theology and philosophy,
this broad area also includes the field of the particular sciences
as they are related to laws and principles and the various arts
which form the cultural, social, and material world in which we
live. Without the foundation of a valid general education, a person's life will not be orientated to ultimate reality. Particular
choices based on special sciences or expediency may appear to work
for a time. But, if life is looked at as a whole and a man's purpose
is seen in its entirety then, without an adequate basis in ultimate

principles of living, particular choices must eventually prove short-sighted and ephemeral.

Guidance. As we move down the triangle, we consider the more immediate application of knowledge to each person according to his particular needs. While general education ordinarily applies to everyone, the second area usually applies to particular groups. Since we live in the contingent world we must be able, in a limited way, to find some security and achievement in the framework of a particular state of life with the aptitudes, skills, and vocation which God has given us. Consequently, we need also a detailed kind of knowledge and understanding of our own abilities and capacities, as well as of the responsibilities, privileges, and obligations of the different temporary or permanent situations in which we find ourselves. This kind of knowledge is more personal. Information on marriage, for example, has little meaning for children but grows increasingly important as the young adult approaches marriage. Many urgent personal problems can arise in courtship and marriage because of the lack of this special knowledge, which at other periods in life might be comparatively unimportant. In the same way, a more complete understanding of one's own psychological aptitudes and vocational abilities might better help a person to know what particular life achievements he could reasonably seek. To use another example: application of general moral principles to the questions of labor and management would enable one man to take a more intelligent and active part in his labor union, and another to have a better grasp of the responsibilities and rights of management. Moreover, for souls specially advanced in the spiritual life, more detailed and personal spiritual information and guidance is usually necessary.[1] These and similar ways of understanding are more applicable to immediate life problems than the knowledge acquired from general religious, scientific, and cultural education and training. Consequently, we might call this the field of spiritual, moral, psychological, or sociological *Guidance* to distinguish it from the more general area of education in theology, philosophy, and the other sciences and arts.

---

[1]See, for example, two recent discussions, R. Garrigou-Lagrange, O.P.: "Special Grace of the Spiritual Director," in *Cross and Crown*, Vol. II, No. 4, pp. 411–428, December, 1950; and also Pascal P. Parente, S.T.D.: *Spiritual Direction*, St. Meinrad, Indiana, The Abbey Press, 1950.

Counsel. In our daily lives there is still the final problem of the choice of ways to fulfill the tasks to which education and guidance direct us. This means coping with and controlling the personal disorder within us as our particular instincts and emotional impulses tend to reach for satisfactions not in conformity with the reasonable needs of our whole person, the rights of others, and the demands of reality. Daily living involves particular events which are unique for each individual and are always changing. Here, we are at the heart of the human personality where each individual person acquires, in a greater or lesser degree, the integration necessary to fulfill all the needs, obligations, and achievements of his life. The individual on his own personal responsibility must be able to carry out the principles and practical information he has received. He must have acquired individual integration both in his ability to cope with the disorder within himself, the unreasonable impulses of his emotions and instincts, and the disorder in the world, in other personalities and in reality itself. Knowledge must become activated in each individual's life as he copes with the single events in his daily actions. This is the function of *Counsel* as a part of each man's prudential judgment and action. We have put this at the point of the triangle.

Knowledge and Action. Consequently, when St. Thomas discusses the various virtues necessary for a good and happy life, he includes both the ultimate and the immediate aspects of human action. To be normally happy and virtuous, according to St. Thomas, we must not only know the reasonable goal of any particular action as it relates to the ultimate goal of our life, but our emotional and instinctive tendencies must be pointed in the direction of this goal, and we must choose from the various necessary intermediate actions those which actually lead us to the goal. In the Thomistic synthesis, the theological virtues of faith, hope, and charity give us the capacity to know and love God. The intellectual virtues of wisdom, knowledge, and understanding give the broad direction in principle to guide us to the right goals. But these virtues of themselves will not give us happiness and a good life. We must constantly take responsible, self-reliant action in the changing, material world. Consequently, we also must develop the virtues of *action*: prudence, and the moral virtues of fortitude, temperance, and justice.

While the other intellectual virtues give us norms, they remain speculative and abstract. Prudence, however, is the understanding of the immediate steps in our daily life to reach any desired goal. The other virtues of action are related to prudence. Fortitude, for example, may sometimes be demanded if we require courage to be persevering and patient in situations where our path towards a particularly difficult goal meets with discouragement and frustrations. In things comparatively easy, we may need temperance to restrain ourselves if our appetites tend to unreasonable excess. Justice may be involved, when there is any question of safeguarding the rights of our neighbor against our own exaggerated self-interest or protecting ourselves against the same abuses from our neighbor and the community. Religion, as a part of justice, will come into play in relating our actions to God.

We, therefore, need both to know the right way to live and to grow in the ability to understand and control our highly complex instinctive and emotional reactions. Then, in any particular choice, we need to survey all the immediate personal factors in our own past and present life so that we do all the minute acts which lead to the particular things we seek. Failure in even one small act can sometimes throw us off the path. In this sense, good action is similar to any other good work. An artist or craftsman must not only know what he wants but have instruments at hand and take the right steps to get it done. Knowledge of an art or craft will not of itself produce the completed work. So, in the work of virtue, a man acts with his whole person, not simply with his intellect. In addition to right understanding, he needs the proper instrumentation of his emotions and instincts, turning him towards the good work in place of making him hostile and resistant to it. At the same time, he needs the careful survey of all possible means at hand so that he takes the right steps to accomplish it.

Orientation and Integration. To make clear this division between guidance and education on the one hand and the peculiarly personal aspects of counsel, prudence, and moral virtue on the other, we have chosen the words *orientation* to indicate the former and *integration* to indicate the latter. Throughout this book, therefore, we use *orientation* in the sense of adequate guidance and education; and *integration* in the sense of the personal responsibility, reasonable coordination, control, and judgment about the unique, particular events in one's life which go with the virtues of counsel, prudence, and the moral order.

PROBLEMS OF ACTION

How Rather than What. Many difficulties of present-day living arise not so much because men do not know what they should do as because they are so emotionally disturbed they fail to do it. Their problems are in the realm of *how* rather than *what.* In our sense then, these problems involve a need for personal *integration* in addition to proper *orientation.* Mankind has always recognized that to know may be easier than to do, as Shakespeare's famous quotation indicates: "If to do were as easy as to know what were good to do, Chapels had been Churches and poor men's cottages, princes' palaces."[2] Catholic people, particularly those who are educated in Catholic schools and colleges, are often well informed. They are supplied not only with general information, but also with detailed knowledge of the rights, privileges, and responsibilities of different states in life. Special emphasis, for example, has been placed on the questions of labor and industry and more recently on matters of marriage and the family. In this way, many people know what to do. But, in singular contingencies—that is, in the particular, unique, and personal events of their own lives— they still may be failing to carry out what they know. With all the information that has been given them, they can be living in a state of unhappiness, guilt, and personal confusion because they lack virtue to act on what they know.

Emotional Confusion and Conflict. Personal problems then, while they may involve information and knowledge, are perhaps more often due to confusion about the right steps to take. This is usually accompanied by discouragement and a tendency to compensate by immoderate and unreasonable satisfaction in some other way. A man may drink excessively because he is not succeeding in his work or not getting along with his wife. He knows his drinking is wrong, and he has seen its sad consequences, but he does not see how to overcome his failure at work or at home. He relieves the pain of his failure by alcohol. A young woman may rush

2William Shakespeare: "The Merchant of Venice," Act I, Scene 2.

into marriage with an unsuitable partner, not because she could not recognize her partner's inadequacies, but because of her inability to find in her own family the love she needs. Problems of this sort call not so much for information as understanding. We cannot help these people simply by giving them more knowledge. They need, rather, a way to coordinate and control their disordered emotions, and, at the same time, to make more prudent choices in their immediate daily actions.

Emotions Can Resist Reason. A man's emotions are not under his control in the same swift, sure way that he moves his hand or foot. While they participate in reason because it belongs to their nature to obey reason[3] yet, continues St. Thomas, "they do not obey reason blindly. On the contrary they have their own proper movements, by which, at times they go against reason."[4] Our emotions must be managed, then, with methods similar to that "by which free men are ruled who have in some respects a will of their own."[5]

PRUDENCE AND COUNSEL

Personal difficulties usually come from the disorder of our emotions at war and in conflict with our reason. Either we guide our emotions or we are guided by them. The mass of details of life are apt at times to overwhelm us and leave us confused and disorganized. We need to reorganize ourselves. The core of this self-organization is prudence. But prudence is often popularly misunderstood. It is not simply caution, hesitancy in action, or mere passivity to avoid trouble; nor is it just a kind of inborn cleverness, as is sometimes supposed.[6] Prudence is the ability to act reasonably and it can be acquired. But, because of the individual character of each of our actions, prudence as such cannot be taught. Every action and event is different for each of us. We must face that action on our own responsibility. Prudence is, as St. Thomas points out,

[3]St. Thomas Aquinas: *Summa Theologica*, I–II, Q. 56, a. 4, translated by Fathers of the English Dominican Province, New York, Benziger Brothers, 1947. (Each time this translation is referred to, it will be indicated by the symbol (D). Reprinted from the *Summa Theologica* with the permission of Benziger Brothers, Inc., Publishers and Copyright owners.)
[4]*Ibid.*, reply obj. 3.
[5]*Ibid.*
[6]To many, the word "prudence," which comes from providence and therefore implies discretion and foresight, would probably even have some of the negative tones of "prude" which is apparently a contraction of it through French.

a very personal virtue. It consists in: 1) a survey of and inquiry into the best means and methods to reach our goals, 2) a choice of the means, and 3) action on the means.

The Survey and Inquiry of Counsel. The first prudent step, the survey and inquiry process, St. Thomas calls *counsel*. It is very important because of the almost infinite variety of possible conditions, circumstances, situations, and personalities, that can in one way or another affect our choice of various methods and means. St. Thomas says:

> Choice follows the judgment of reason in matters of action. There is much uncertainty because actions are concerned with contingent singulars which, by reason of their variability are uncertain. In things doubtful and uncertain, the reason does not pronounce judgment without previous inquiry. Therefore the reason must of necessity institute an inquiry before deciding on what is to be chosen; and this inquiry is called counsel.[7]

This uncertainty, from the very nature of the world of contingent singulars in which we live, is, according to Aquinas, one of the reasons we can conclude to man's basic freedom since,

> particular objects of activity are contingent and consequently the reason may judge in either way about them and is not determined to one side or the other. Hence the very fact that man is rational entails the possession of free will.[8]

Two Types of Goal-Seeking. St. Thomas in discussing counsel points out that it involves two types of goal-seeking. In one the goal is not impeded. Here, the person uses the survey evaluation of counsel to choose means which will lead him to what he wants since, in the large number of variables from which it is possible to choose, many will not bring him to the desired object or achievement. In the other type of goal-seeking, the path is blocked by obstacles which must be overcome, avoided, or circumvented. While difficulties may arise in the first situation, especially when the path to the goal is made complex by including a number of involved

----

[7]St. Thomas Aquinas: *Summa Theologica*, I–II, Q. 14, a. 1, in *Basic Writings of St. Thomas Aquinas*, Vol. II, translated by Anton Pegis, New York, Copyright 1945, by Random House. (Each time this translation is referred to, it will be indicated by the symbol (P).)

[8]St. Thomas, (P): I, Q. 83, a. 1.

stages, it is primarily in the second, obstacle-type, where personal conflicts most commonly occur.[9]

If, over a period of time, we find we are not reaching a solution to our problems we can grow increasingly discouraged and gradually lose self-confidence and hope. We may realize that we are compensating by going to excess in other ways. In addition to the courage and the ability to reorganize ourselves and set out again for our real goals, we must moderate these excesses. Popular psychology has made us aware of many of these compensation mechanisms, which go all the way from exaggerated forms of self-justification and rationalizations down to numerous kinds of inferiority complexes. When we are failing we need to resurvey the past and the present to discover other steps to our goals and, at the same time, reorganize ourselves so we can reach these goals.

COUNSELING

In this state of conflict and confusion, we generally need help. While we may be able to re-examine a problem alone and counsel ourselves, it is usually a longer process with greater disorder and personal suffering than if we had the aid of a good counselor. It is even possible to reach such a state that each attempt makes us further confused. By this time we may even have lost sight of what we are seeking. We may, therefore, sometimes need another person's assistance to objectify and clarify our conflicts. Such objective self-clarification we call *counseling*.

Giving Advice. A major difficulty here is that other people cannot help us merely by giving advice. Some may think they can, and they readily advise us. To many people, the word counseling always implies giving advice. They assume that when anyone needs help with personal problems he is seeking to be told what to do. A clue to this attitude is the phrase "If I were you . . ." with which the adviser often begins his statements. If the adviser were himself in the singular situation of the other person, and faced with these events, he would act in such a way. The retailing of how he

[9]"But fear incites to counsel more than hope does. Because hope is of good things, as being possible of attainment; whereas fear is of evil things, as being difficult to repel, so that fear regards the aspect of difficulty more than hope does. And it is in matters of difficulty, especially when we distrust ourselves, that we take counsel." *Ibid.*, St. Thomas, (D), I–II, Q. 44, a. 2, reply obj. 3. See also II–II, Q. 47, a. 8, reply obj. 1.

would act is considered counseling. Such counseling takes place everywhere—between friends at work, neighbors at home, school chums, and in similar relationships. No particular qualities are necessary to be a counselor of this type except perhaps that some-one seek our advice. In fact, many people act as counselors even when their advice is not sought. They feel themselves qualified to pass judgments on the actions of others, to correct them, and to offer suggestions about solving another's problems. This uninvited counseling is a common cause of quarrels, resentments, and general unhappiness wherever people live or work together. It may do some good but often it only produces the retaliation, "Mind your own business."

Satisfaction for Adviser. Two personal factors are involved here. The first is the satisfaction for the counselor when someone seeks advice. A person can feel somehow that he is stronger and more adequate if he appears to solve problems which baffle others. Some such feeling apparently prompts people to give advice even when it is not sought from them. People can even form the habit of advising others as an escape and compensation for the unsolved problems in their own lives. For some, every situation is an opportunity to tell others what to do. Such people become nuisances by concern-ing themselves with everyone's problems and faults. They give advice at every opportunity although that advice is seldom sought. It is this particular misuse of the role of counselor that is con-tained in many popular Scriptural sayings, such as, "Physician heal thyself," and "First cast the beam out of thine own eye."

Resistance. A second factor is a deep-rooted resistance on the part of the one counseled to being told what to do. The one advised seems often to resent the apparent superiority of someone giving a quick solution to personal problems with which he has been struggling for a long time. A basic feeling of human dignity and self-worth is offended. Most people, moreover, are anxious to appear in their best light before others. Any implication that they are unable to solve personal problems and are more or less inadequate is strongly resented and repelled. Consequently, even when one is in an advisory role, giving personal advice is still difficult. Nor does it always follow that the one giving advice is actually equipped and capable of right guidance. When the advice given is inaccurate and misleading, harm is done in proportion to the gravity of the problem and the degree of error of the guidance. Here, we have the "blind leading the blind."

Limitations of Advice.   Moreover, good advice does not of itself produce virtue. We have to *act* on that advice. It is comparatively easy to tell others what to do but much harder to carry out this advice when we ourselves are in the same personal conflict. If we are uninvolved we can be objective and unemotional. The solution to the problem can be clear and all the major factors evident. But, when we are personally involved, the force of our emotions can confuse and disrupt the calm objective judgment of our reason. In this state, to be directed and advised may only make us all the more resistant. If we know what we should do, we do not need more advice. We need help to objectify, understand, and control our emotions so that they no longer impede the judgment of reason. So, says St. Thomas, intellectual understanding and information are not enough

that a man may reason rightly about particular cases. For it happens sometimes that the universal principle, known by means of understanding or science, is destroyed in a particular case by a passion. Thus, to one who is swayed by concupiscence, when he is overcome thereby, the object of his desire seems good, although it is opposed to the universal judgment of his reason.

. . . Prudence not only helps us to be of good counsel, but also to judge and command well. This is not possible unless the impediment of the passions, destroying the judgment and the command of prudence, be removed.[10]

Our emotions can be so mixed up that even when people give us good advice we cannot accept it or even hear it. Our instinctive self-defense together with excessive self-justification or fear of rejection can cause us either not to admit our failure or to feel so discouraged and hopeless that we do not want to face it. People advising us may only make us defensively angry and all the more insecure and defeated.

Giving advice has great limitations, therefore, because it does not of itself take the place of counsel and prudence. While we have experiences in common with others who share in general the same life vocation, activities, and occupation, there is a point at which

10St. Thomas, (P): I–II, Q. 58, a. 4 and reply obj. 3.

the singular events of our life are unique. No one has experienced them before and no one will experience them again. These individuating aspects of each of us are the things that make us distinct, separate persons. At the same time, we have a common humanity and we live in a common material world. Principles and laws we usually learn from others. These make up the invaluable deposit of natural and supernatural knowledge which mankind has received and achieved through the ages. At any period in our life, too, we are part of particular groups and have in common, attitudes and abilities which we share with certain others. In this connection, also, the broad experience of those older and wiser than ourselves as well as the various aspects of moral, spiritual, psychological, and other forms of guidance can offer valuable information to cope with our own particular state and fulfill our special abilities. But, in the day-by-day experience of the flux of events as we meet them, our judgments must be our own. We alone undergo that singular experience and we, better than anyone else, if we think clearly, know all the factors which induce our own particular judgment. At the heart of our human dignity is the amazing capacity to guide and determine our own destiny by the choices we make in the singular events which make up our life experience. No one can do this for us. Like the virtues of courage and moderation that go with it and are founded on it, prudence is acquired only by action.

Counsel Is Necessary.   We often fail to carry out what we know, then, because we lack counsel, the first stage of prudent action. This will not be acquired merely by receiving more advice. By counsel we examine why we are failing; we survey our past and present. We may consult others if we need information, but we must integrate this information into new life plans. We then project ourselves into the future to see if these new plans might work. At the same time, we must reorganize our emotions so that they move us to successful achievement rather than to failure.

In this way counsel aids our will to more complete fulfillment by giving us a calm, over-all view of factors that contribute to successful action or previous failure. Simultaneously, there is a steady integration of various instinctive and emotional appetites around our reason so that they urge and aid us to do what we know we should do. St. Thomas, therefore, concludes, as choice is *intellect influenced by appetite*, thus pointing out that both concur in the act of choosing, so Damascene says that counsel is *appetite based on inquiry*, so as to show that counsel belongs, in a way, both to the will, on whose behalf and by whose impulsion the inquiry is made, and to the reason that pursues the inquiry.[11]

Counseling Aids Prudence. While prudence itself cannot be taught, its development through counsel can be greatly aided by the skill of a counselor. But, if it is to develop counsel and prudence, this skilled help does not of itself consist in giving advice or directing the person to solutions. In his discussion of counsel, St. Thomas points out that it takes for granted both facts and general knowledge of speculative and practical sciences since the purpose of counsel is directly related to immediate action. Its function is, therefore, highly personal. As he says, the things

which are taken for granted in the inquiry of counsel are any facts received through the senses and also any general statements known either through speculative or practical science. . . . Of such things counsel makes no inquiry but the term of inquiry is that which we are able to do at once.[12]

The counseling relationship as such, therefore, is for the purpose of integrating the knowledge of one's past and present in those circumstances and events that are so intimately related to a person, he alone can adequately know and control them. It is this function that is particularly the field of counsel as the first phase of a man's prudential judgment and action. To aid this is the main characteristic of counseling.

Self-Direction and Control. There can be no virtuous action without a person ultimately having self-direction and emotional self-control. We must be able both to judge and command ourselves well for the completion of a prudent act. Even if it were possible for one person to know and evaluate all the minute factors of another's life so that he could give him an accurate and detailed solution, this would not of itself produce a good life. As St. Thomas says,

When a man does a good deed, not of his own counsel, but moved by that of another, his operation is not yet quite perfect, as regards his rea-

11St. Thomas, (P): I–II, Q. 14, a. 1, reply obj. 1.
12St. Thomas, (D): I–II, Q. 14, a. 6.

son in directing him and his appetite in moving him. Therefore, if he do a good deed, he does not do well absolutely; and yet this is required in order that he may lead a good life.[13]

Consequently, some measure of counsel and prudence is required even in obedience. St. Thomas points out that obedience does not remove the necessity of counsel. So, in answer to the objection that to obey another would be a violation of a man's own counsel, he says,

God left man in the hand of his own counsel, not as though it were lawful to him to do whatever he will, but because, unlike irrational creatures, he is not compelled by natural necessity to do what he ought to do, but is left the free choice proceeding from his own counsel. And just as he has to proceed on his own counsel in doing other things, so too has he in the point of obeying his superiors. For Gregory says, "When we humbly give way to another's voice, we overcome ourselves in our own hearts."[14]

In this sense obedience is a demonstration of a high degree of self-control and personal integration where one can direct oneself to do what, in many cases, may be difficult. Such obedience to another, however, must be in matters that are fundamentally reasonable.[15]

Personal Responsibility. In developing counsel and prudence then, we especially need those skills which further responsibility, self-direction, and self-control in the individual coming for help. The problems of each person's life are so interwoven with many minute factors in his own past and present, a completely prudent judgment about them could hardly be made by anyone but himself. Methods which cause the counselor to take over and make decisions about another's personal problems appear to weaken rather than further a person's prudential judgment. In this case the prudence exercised is the counselor's. The other person may only be in a state of passive acquiescence. He may be no better off when he faces new problems alone.

Moreover, a person who is made passively acquiescent to some-

---

[13]St. Thomas, (P): I–II, Q. 57, a. 5, reply obj. 2.
[14]St. Thomas, (D): II–II, Q. 104, a. 1.
[15]*Ibid.*, a. 5, objections. See also Benedictus Henricus Merkelbach: *Summa Theologiae Moralis*, Paris, Desclee de Brouwer, 1935, Vol. I, p. 191.

one[16] may be as readily persuaded in another direction by someone else. This is particularly true in our time when the powers of
individual and mass persuasion often lead away from virtue and
reasonable life goals. Unless he has developed the capacity to make
his own prudent judgment, especially in personal problems, such
a person seems always to be looking for someone on whom to depend. Pope Pius XII has pointed out this danger of mass acquiescence as it affects the political and social order:

> The people and a shapeless multitude (or as it is called "the masses")
> are two distinct concepts. The people lives and moves by its own life
> energy: the masses are inert of themselves and can only be moved from
> outside. The people lives by the fullness of life in the men that compose
> it, each of whom—at his proper place and in his own way—is a person
> conscious *of his own responsibility* and *of his own views*. The masses,
> on the contrary, wait for the impulse from outside, an easy plaything in
> the hands of anyone who exploits their instincts and impressions, ready
> to follow, in turn, today this flag, tomorrow another. From the exuber-
> ant life of a true people, an abundant rich life is diffused in the state
> and all its organs, instilling into them, with a vigor that is always renew-
> ing itself, the consciousness of their own responsibility, the true instinct
> for the common good. . . . Hence follows clearly another conclusion: the
> masses as we have just defined them—are the capital enemy of true
> democracy and of its ideal of liberty and equality.[17]

Methods which foster dependency, therefore, even if they appear
temporarily successful, are opposed to the development of counsel,
prudence, and moral virtue. This coincides with the present psychological literature in the field of counseling. As we will discuss in the
next chapter, recent research is throwing new evidence on the importance of promoting a person's greater self-integration and his
ability to make responsible choices. These are essential to personal
adjustment and happiness.

Reason Illumined by Faith. According to St. Thomas, God's
help comes, not as a substitute for reason and the natural skills
with which science can supply us, but as a means of filling up the
inevitable gap between man's natural powers and the supernatural

---

[16]This kind of passive acquiescence is, of course, very different from reasonable and
responsible obedience which, for normal living, may often be necessary in a wide variety of
circumstances.

[17]Pope Pius XII: "Christmas Message, 1944," in *The Catholic Mind*, New York, Copyright February 1945, by The America Press, pp. 65–77.

possession of God which is essentially beyond man's nature.[18] The supernatural virtues do not work in any conflict with reason. So as Garrigou-Lagrange points out,

Acquired prudence is ignorant of the supernatural motives of action; infused prudence knows them. Proceeding not from reason alone, but from reason illumined by infused faith, it knows the infinite elevation of our supernatural last end, God seen face to face.[19]

But the infused supernatural virtues do not do away with the necessity of the acquired virtues:

The infused virtues give an intrinsic facility without always excluding the extrinsic obstacles . . . for this reason it is evident that the acquired virtue of temperance greatly facilitates the exercise of the infused virtue of the same name.[20]

This relationship of the infused and acquired virtues is illustrated by the following example:

How are the virtues exercised? They are exercised simultaneously in such a way that the acquired virtue is subordinated to the infused virtue as a favorable disposition. Thus, in another domain, the agility of a pianist's or a harpist's fingers, which is acquired by a repetition of acts, favors the exercise of the musical art that is in the artist's intellect and not in his fingers. If he completely loses the nimbleness of his fingers as a result of paralysis, he can no longer exercise his art because of an extrinsic obstacle. His art, however, remains in his practical intellect, as we see in the case of a musical genius who is stricken with paralysis. Normally there ought to be two subordinated functions that should be exercised together. The same holds true for the acquired virtue and for the infused virtue of the same name. In like manner the imagination is at the service of the intellect, and the memory at that of knowledge.[21]

The counseling process can, therefore, often be an aid to the removal of such extrinsic obstacles when these are due especially

---

[18]St. Thomas says, in his commentary in *The Trinity of Boethius* (Q. II, a. 3, ad. 5), that when the truths of human reason are dedicated to the life of faith, it is not adding water to wine but changing water into wine.

In this context it is interesting to recall St. Augustine's famous saying: "God orders us to do what we can, and to ask for the grace to accomplish what we cannot do by ourselves."

[19]Reginald Garrigou-Lagrange, O.P.: *The Three Ages of the Interior Life*, St. Louis, Copyright 1947, by B. Herder Book Co., p. 61.

[20]*Ibid.*, pp. 62–63.

[21]*Ibid.*, pp. 63–64.

to the disorder in a person's emotions and instincts and, what generally accompanies this, a confusion about the right steps to take in any series of actions.

Prayer. We should note here that since the attainment of man's complete fulfillment in God cannot be achieved by his natural powers alone, prayer and Divine aid are absolutely essential. Counseling, by itself, no matter how skillful, as we shall discuss elsewhere[22] may lead man to a temporary state of satisfaction and achievement, but it cannot bring him final and permanent happiness. God alone can do this. So, speaking of the necessity of prayer, Garrigou-Lagrange says,

> We could not insist too strongly on this point, for many beginners, unwittingly impregnated with practical naturalism, as the Pelagians and the Semi-Pelagians were, imagine that everything can be attained with will and energy, even without actual grace. Experience soon shows them the profound truth of Christ's words: "Without Me you can do nothing," and also that of St. Paul's statement: "It is God who worketh in you both to will and to accomplish." Therefore we must ask Him for the actual grace ever more faithfully to keep the commandments, especially the supreme precept of the love of God and of our neighbor.[23]

To achieve his ultimate fulfillment, therefore, a man needs to be aided not only by the natural movement of his reason towards order, integration, and achievement in particular life goals, but by a special movement of the Holy Spirit which enables him to reach God. As St. Thomas explains:

> Accordingly, in matters subject to human reason, and directed to man's connatural end, man can work through the judgment of his reason. If, however, even in these things man is aided by a special instigation from God, this will be out of God's superabundant goodness. Hence, according to the philosophers, not every one that had the acquired moral virtues had also the heroic or divine virtues. But in matters directed to the supernatural last end, to which man's reason moves him according as it is, in a manner and imperfectly, informed by the theological virtues, the motion of reason does not suffice, unless it receive in addition the instigation or motion of the Holy Ghost.[24]

22See Chapter VIII.
23Garrigou-Lagrange, *op. cit.*, p. 89.
24St. Thomas, (P): II–II, Q. 68, a. 2.

Human reason alone, even at its best, cannot entirely avoid error and confusion. So St. Thomas reassures us:

> Whether we consider human reason as perfected in its natural perfection, or as perfected by the theological virtues, it is unable under all circumstances to avoid folly and other like things. . . . God, however, to Whose knowledge and power all things are subject, by His motion safeguards us from all folly, ignorance, dullness of mind and hardness of heart, and the rest. Consequently, the gifts of the Holy Ghost, which make us amenable to His instigation, are said to be given as remedies to these defects.[25]

In the process of choosing the right means to his supernatural end, man will, therefore, be guided by the gifts of the Holy Ghost, especially Counsel. But, actions to which a man is guided by the gift of Counsel do not conflict with his reason but are a higher, more complete and integrated fulfillment of the reasonable goals peculiar to his individual personality and his life achievements. If the light of his own natural reason can bring him some measure of achievement and happiness then, in a much greater degree, these effects will be produced by the light of that Divine Reason of which human reason is the reflection. So St. Thomas says,

> A lower principle of movement is helped chiefly, and is perfected through being moved by a higher principle of movement. . . . Now it is evident that the rectitude of human reason is compared to the Divine Reason, as a lower motive principle to a higher: for the Eternal Reason is the supreme rule of all human rectitude. Consequently, prudence which denotes rectitude of reason, is chiefly perfected and helped through being moved and ruled by the Holy Ghost, and this belongs to the gift of Counsel. . . . Therefore the gift of Counsel corresponds to prudence, as helping and perfecting it.[26]

Garrigou-Lagrange adds,

> We must note that God sometimes moves us to act by deliberation according to the human mode, and at other times by special inspiration to act in a superior manner without deliberation on our part.[27]

[25]*Ibid.*, (P): II–II, Q. 68, a. 2.
[26]*Ibid.*, (D): II–II, Q. 52, a. 2.
[27]Garrigou-Lagrange, *op. cit.*, p. 91.

This action of the gift of Counsel, however, is in no way contrary to his reasonable nature and freedom:

> . . . it is proper to the rational creature to be moved through the research of reason to perform any particular action and this research is called counsel. Hence the Holy Ghost is said to move the rational creature by way of counsel, wherefore Counsel is reckoned among the gifts of the Holy Ghost. . . . The children of God are moved by the Holy Ghost according to their mode, without prejudice to their free will which is the faculty of will and reason. Accordingly the gift of Counsel is befitting the children of God insofar as the reason is instructed by the Holy Ghost about what we have to do.[28]

Immediate Life-Circumstances. The purpose of counseling, therefore, is to facilitate this research and deliberation of reason. Its aim is related to the immediate circumstances of a man's life. Even though he may know in general what he should do, the problems of a particular situation can be so wrapped up with intense emotion that, sometimes, even to try to work them out without help seems only to encourage precipitation and cause him to rush violently into a series of actions more unreasonable and sometimes even more tragic than before. People in such personal difficulties need a means by which they can bring to light the fundamental motives behind their confused and disordered urges so they can understand the hidden values and goals of their lives. Because they are failing to move towards these, they are in conflict.

Self-Knowledge. Counseling, then, can often be a valuable aid in achieving a greater degree of self-knowledge. Such self-knowledge, while it is essential to a better life, is not easily acquired. Spiritual writers have always pointed this out. So Tanquerey says:

> Self-knowledge is difficult to attain. Attracted as we are by outward things, we hardly care to enter into ourselves to scrutinize that unseen miniature world; we care even less, proud as we are, about discovering our faults.

Our interior acts are extremely complex. There is within us, as St. Paul says, the lower life of the flesh and the higher life of the spirit and often turbulent conflict ensues between them. In order to sift what proceeds from nature, what from grace, what is wilful, and what is not, a great deal of attention is required, a great deal of insight, of honesty, of

---

[28]St. Thomas, (D): II–II, Q. 52, a. 1, obj. 3.

courage, of perseverance. The light comes but gradually—a bit of knowledge leads to more, and this prepares the way for deeper insight.[29]

Counseling can further such self-knowledge by offering a person an objectifying and clarifying process which will help him uncover and reorganize the complex motives that make up any particular series of actions.

Prepare Person for Action. Moreover, in the process of performing any good action, a number of important steps are necessary. As Garrigou-Lagrange explains :

> From the moral point of view, one should descend in a thoughtful manner from reason, which determines the end to be attained, to the operations to be accomplished without neglecting the steps that intervene, that is, the memory of things past, intelligent attention to present circumstances, shrewdness in foreseeing obstacles that may arise, docility in following authorized advice. One must take time to deliberate before acting; "one should deliberate slowly and without haste," as Aristotle used to say. Afterward one must sometimes act with great promptness.[30]

Counseling can also be particularly helpful in the evaluation of these intervening steps—the memory of the past, attention to the present, and foresight of the future. It can be helpful, too, in producing a state of "teachableness" in which a person willingly seeks and absorbs necessary information he previously lacked. Before he can do this, he often needs an accepting and understanding experience of a different kind through which he can integrate his emotions so that he now has an appetite for what he knows he should do.[31]

By a process in which a person is able to talk freely to someone in whom he has confidence and who does not make him more resistant and emotional by trying to tell him what to do, he is often able for the first time to see previously hidden factors which enter into his problems. This broadens his outlook so that his choices are made in the light of more ultimate implications of his actions. If, at the same time, his appetites are directed towards these choices, he will then be able to carry them out in a happier, more productive, and virtuous way of life. On the achievement of

[29]A. Tanquerey: *The Spiritual Life*, Tournai, Belgium, Desclee, 1930, p. 225.
[30]Garrigou-Lagrange, *op. cit.*, p. 328.
[31]See Chapter XVIII, Counseling and Virtue.

this end, all the understanding and skill of the counselor is concentrated.

Counsel and counseling, then, begin with the immediate conflicts and confusions that impede everyday living. By helping a person to greater self-understanding and control of these, counsel helps him to his ultimate long-time and eternal life goals. Enabling a person to develop counsel will further his own prudence, courage, moderation, and reasonable consideration for others' rights. For this reason, the advances which have taken place in the field of counseling are important and valuable for Catholic living.

CHAPTER II

SOME IMPORTANT RECENT DEVELOPMENTS

Three Main Sources. There have been in recent years some significant developments in ways of aiding a person to acquire greater understanding of himself, his abilities, needs, and personal difficulties.[1] Three major sources may be considered responsible for the main contribution. The *first* centers around questions of learning, achievement, and adjustment in education. School problems often involve personal difficulties. And, since many student problems are also family problems, this may include both parents and children. On the later high school and college level, it may necessitate some aspects of vocational and marriage guidance. This has been the primary but not exclusive concern of educators and especially of psychologists. *Secondly,* due to the many cases of breakdown of family life, there has been a growing concern for ways of helping people in those personal difficulties which directly affect the family. This has been somewhat identified with the sociologists and the social workers, particularly those whose functions are identified in some way with community agencies and with divorce, separation, or juvenile courts. The *third,* results from the contributions of psychiatrists, physicians, and others primarily concerned with medical problems. These contributions mainly originated through their treatment of involved personality disorders. More recently they have been applying their knowledge and research to general medicine, particularly to psychosomatic problems.

Many Groups Contribute. In this study and research there has been no exclusive division. Each of the groups—medical, psychological, sociological, and social work—have borrowed freely from the learning, experience, and research of the others. Other groups, as well as many individuals are contributing to this growing knowledge. These various groups and individuals are, therefore, inter-

[1]See A. H. Brayfield: *Readings in Modern Methods of Counseling*, New York, Appleton-Century-Crofts, 1950, for a collection of significant articles on this development.

related in common projects. Each has adapted methods from the other and there is no clear distinction between the different contributions. Representatives of these groups often work together in a combined research project or service.

Knowledge and Experience. Two general trends are evident in this recent development. The first has been an attempt to acquire greater knowledge about all the factors that enter into personality growth and formation and, at the same time, to devise new ways of supplying this knowledge to others so that they may have a better understanding of themselves and the personal difficulties which they encounter. Such information may be broad and rather general as, for example, when the data is drawn from sociological statistics; or, it may be precise and directly applicable to the person himself as in psychological or vocational tests. The second trend has been an increase in study and research centering around methods of aiding people to think more objectively about themselves and, in the process, reorganize themselves so that they can now act on the information and understanding they have previously acquired. While the first trend is, therefore, directly aimed at the understanding of personality development as such and the offering of personal information, the second trend aims at discovering means to facilitate a person's assimilation and integration of the knowledge he has so that he can actually achieve a more mature, stable, and reasonable way of life. The first trend we have called *guidance*; the second, *counseling*.

GUIDANCE

As a result of the first trend, the main focus in helping people has been to acquaint them with pertinent information which, in some form, is applicable to themselves and their personal needs. This information is usually supplied by experts from various fields. This kind of information, therefore, varies greatly according to the knowledge, training, background, and point of view of the adviser as well as the different types of situations and problems for which the information is intended. This involves not only the uncovering of many general facts of which people might not previously have been aware, but also the special application of various known principles to their own particular state or circumstances.

Many Methods. There are many different ways of supplying this type of personal information. The number of people giving the information may vary all the way from eight or ten in a round-table discussion to one in an intimate personal talk. This information may be presented to a large audience of hundreds or to smaller groups, married or engaged couples, or one person. The kind of information given may be primarily religious, psychological, sociological, economic, legal, medical, or a combination of these. These programs may be sponsored by different organizations, such as, churches, schools, hospitals, Veterans' Administration programs, industries, diocesan chanceries, social agencies, or may be the result of individual initiative of variously trained people.

Various Experts. In the more general forms of mass education, the intention is to reach as wide an audience as possible. This includes special classes in schools, colleges, and public lectures. These classes and lectures involve experts who may discuss, for example, various phases of personal and family problems. In such a discussion on the family, a priest may give the spiritual and moral aspects of family life, a sociologist unfold its social implications, a lawyer discuss legal problems, a physician present the physical and medical questions, a psychologist or psychiatrist, the personal and emotional tones, and some other skilled person talk on budgeting and the other economic difficulties.

Round-Table. Another general education method is the public round-table. A round-table on the question of marriage, for example, may be made up of two married people, a young engaged couple, single persons and, perhaps, a lawyer, social worker, physician, or priest, depending on the length of time and number of people available.[2]

Team Approach. This same use of a number of experts may also be applied to each person or each couple. This can be seen in the case of veterans' problems, where it was not uncommon for a team of medical, psychological, sociological, economic, legal, and religious advisers to be available. This method of team advice is also being used in some diocesan chanceries in the United States.[3] When Catholic people apply to the chancery for permission for civil divorce or separation, their difficulties are discussed. If the problems

[2]Gretta Palmer: "Marriage Counsel from the Church," *Look*, July 1, 1948.
[3]In Chicago, Illinois, headed by Rt. Rev. Msgr. Edward M. Burke, J.C.D.

appear to be psychological, the couple is referred to a psychologist or a psychiatrist who is available; if there seem to be physical or medical difficulties, then a physician is at hand; where legal advice is necessary, the chancery can call on the immediate aid of a lawyer; and so on, thus attempting to supply adequate help for every type of difficulty.

Focus on Instructor. Since the emphasis here is on the giving of more complete information to individuals, either as part of a large audience or in a personal interview, the focus falls directly on the instructor. By training, background, and position, he is presumed to have the most knowledge of the topic under discussion. The instructor is, therefore, the central figure in the imparting of such information. The other person, either in an audience or sitting across from him at a desk, usually has a somewhat less active function. His role may be one mainly of giving attention to what is said and of posing questions to draw out more information, especially as this applies to his particular circumstances.

Diagnostic and Prescription Method. Sometimes, the one giving information may go further and attempt directly to form a person's judgment. This usually occurs more often in individual interviews than in groups. Here, the instructor not only supplies the person with whatever data he feels may be helpful, but he may also make precise judgments about how this applies and what the person himself should do. One might call this, to borrow terms from medicine, a diagnostic and prescription method. The person's psychological state and individual difficulties are analyzed and evaluated and a prescription is given. The type of prescription usually depends on the adviser's point of view, background, and spiritual and psychological concepts of personality. For this reason, any two experts may give different and even, in some cases, contradictory directions to an individual about the same problem. The prescription may be verbal or written. It is assumed that, if the person carries out this prescription adequately and co-operates with the adviser, his general state of well-being should be improved.

Some Difficulties Involved. In this latter approach, no distinction is made between the giving of information itself and the process of self-understanding and action that is necessary for personal reorientation. This has given rise to a number of difficulties. Information drawn from statistical studies, for example, while generally true, can be erroneous when applied to a particular individual. This occurs in the use even of the best and most accurate psychological tests. It is all the more likely to occur when the application depends, not on objective norms such as those of established test data, but on the diagnostic judgment of the person giving the advice. But, even if such judgments are valid in a particular case, the problem of the person's acceptance and assimilation yet remain. Simply to have planned an adequate solution to another's conduct does not of itself guarantee his ability or capacity to carry out that solution.

Guidance and Counseling. For these reasons, we feel that this first trend, which aims directly at giving people greater knowledge of various factors that enter into personality growth and development, should be classified under the heading of *guidance* to emphasize its primary function of supplying pertinent information. In this way, we can distinguish it from the second trend in recent research which involves the *process* itself of personal reorientation, by which a person is aided in acquiring new self-understanding and integration and better modes of action. This second trend can then be considering in the area of *counseling*.[4]

COUNSELING

Two Factors in This Development. Two factors played an important part in this increased understanding of the counseling process. First, through the contribution of many people—clinical psychologists, psychiatrists, social workers, and others—a method of helping people gradually developed which did not aim directly at supplying them with more personal information or diagnosing their problems and telling them what to do. Rather, the purpose was to offer them an experience where, through the understanding and skill of the counselor, they could think through their own problems and come to their own self-integrated solutions. The second factor which

---

[4]Throughout this book therefore, we use the word counseling in a more precise and limited way than is ordinarily understood by this term. The reader may, of course, prefer to consider counseling in a broader sense as also including suggestion, persuasion, guidance, instruction, and similar common ways of aiding people. Counseling, in the sense defined here, does not necessarily take the place of other procedures but rather is an added tool or means of furthering personal integration. Consequently, by this definition and treatment we do not mean to imply that other methods and procedures may not also be effective or necessary in particular cases.

paralleled this and aided its growth was the development of research skills centering especially around the exact transcription of interviews, and the devising of methods by which the content of these interviews could be analyzed and correlated.

Reasons for Development. This development came about for many reasons. The most obvious and important was the fact that guidance and advice were not always adequate. Educational programs and round-table discussions, while helpful, were often not enough. In fact, classes, lectures, and discussions sometimes only brought into sharper focus the personal difficulties of many individuals in the group. Often, too, when expert advice was given in individual interviews, it failed to aid people because more detailed information did not reach the basic causes of their problems. While a greater knowledge of religious, medical, legal, psychological, sociological, or economic factors was helpful in particular cases, there still remained a large number of people who either seemed to have sufficient knowledge of those fields or whose problems were not solved by this information.

In the formulation of this concept of counseling there was an increased awareness that direction and guidance, even when it is good advice, is often not helping the person, but only making him more dependent and unstable. Moreover, in those cases where some immediate change was noted, if one studied the process carefully, many persons were no better able to solve their problems afterwards. The relationship made them appear stronger so long as the psychologically more stable person was making decisions and guiding them. But, left to themselves, they were no stronger than before.

On the other hand, much of the resistance and hostility that one encountered in advice-giving, might be, not simply a question of bad will, but a strong, confused basic urge on the person's part to retain his independence and self-responsibility. Moreover, anyone dealing in human relations has been aware of that rather large class of people who are always seeking guidance and yet who never carry out the advice given. In fact, often when the advice would obviously be good for them, they do the exact opposite. On the contrary, it seems that a person must already be somewhat responsible to carry out directions.

This same difficulty was arising in psychological clinics and guidance centers. Thorough diagnostic tests were administered and the clinician made a painstaking effort to set out a new life plan and a more adequate program for a person. Still, in far too many instances, this program was completely rejected and the effort and skill of the clinician wasted.

Physicians had this problem for years in their personal relationship with patients. Even in matters of physical health and medication it was not always easy to get the patient to follow the advice of the physician. This problem became even more complex when personal difficulties and psychological confusions were growing more apparent as major factors in many illnesses. The physician found that these same patients, who would not follow his advice in matters of medicine, were even less willing to take advice and guidance about their personal lives.

Social workers, too, were meeting opposition when they attempted to direct their clients into more adequate ways of living. In other areas, there was also evidence of this same resistance of people against being advised in matters which affected the intimate details of their lives.

Dynamism in Human Personality. This brought a decrease in the emphasis on knowledge and advice. Many began to question the view that personality difficulties always involved a lack of knowledge. They questioned, too, the extreme environmentalist view that, for example, a person is actually incapable of overcoming an adverse environment such as a bad marriage or bad home surroundings. While not excluding the importance of knowledge, heredity, and environment, they began to think of the counseling process in relation to the dynamism in the human personality and the intrinsic power of self-change which they felt people had.

Freedom and Responsibility. An early evidence of this realization took place even among some of Sigmund Freud's first associates. Otto Rank, for example, gradually began to differ with Freud. Freud stressed the necessity of going into a person's past even to infancy—the so-called infantile fixation. The past, he held, determines the person's reaction to the present. Rank disagreed with this. For him, it was not simply the person's awareness of the way past experiences were determining his present reactions, but the person's realization, acceptance, and active taking possession of his own present experience. For Rank, the person was fixed on the past, not because he was absolutely determined that way, but because he feared the present and was unable to cope with it. This was the core, according to Rank, of personality maladjustment. The solution was to enable the person to meet the realities of the immediate present by uncovering and dispersing those fears of the present which caused him to cling to attitudes carried over from early childhood or infancy. The maladjusted person, said Rank, resisted change because his will was turned in the direction of negation. Resistance and refusal to follow advice, therefore, were not something directed against the counselor which should be broken down by the counselor; but were expressions of this negative will. The person's will could become positive only gradually, as the counselor left to him the task of making his own decisions in the interview. Rank's *will* differed from Freud's *wish* in that it was actually effective, not a passive element in a deterministic chain. For Rank, the will of the individual was itself a first cause of his adjustment; that is, the source of the cure was within the individual himself. The counselor was the means and the interview the occasion which the person used to reorganize himself. Rank, in discussing this question of will, said,

Free will belongs to the idea of guilt or sin as inevitably as day to night and even if there were none of the numerous proofs for the inner freedom of the conscious will, the fact of human consciousness of guilt alone would be sufficient to prove the freedom of the will as we understand it psychologically beyond a doubt. We say a man reacts *as if* he were guilty, but if he reacts so it is because he is guilty psychologically but feels himself *responsible*, consequently no psychoanalysis can relieve him of this guilt feeling by any reference to complexes however archaic.[5]

Rather than conceiving the maladjusted person as someone peculiar and abnormal, Rank maintained that everyone, to some degree, belonged to this class. A cardinal point for Rank was the distinction between *knowledge* and *experience*. The person was helped, said Rank, not by the psychological theory or interpretation of the counselor, but by the *actual experience* he underwent, in terms of *feeling* and *willing. He* must be the central figure—not the counselor. The counselor had to become a tool, the material which the person could use according to his needs.

[5]Otto Rank: *Truth and Reality*, New York, Copyright 1936, by Alfred A. Knopf, p. 62. (Italics mine.)

In Rank's opinion, it is this creative use of himself which the constructive counselor should permit, rather than the analysis of the problems of the person, which differentiated Rank's "dynamic therapy" from what he called "ideological therapy." The person, too, comes with an ideology, said Rank, which needs to be met, not with counter theory, but by the *reality of creative experience.* Whether or not the counselor functioned constructively depended in a large part on the kind of person he was, his ability to subordinate himself to the role of assistant and his capacity to meet the continually varying creative demands of the person in the interview.

Many Contribute to Counseling Skill. In addition to Rank, this general awareness was shared by many others. As a result, significant contributions began to appear which examined more carefully the process of personal re-orientation and the immediate factors which brought it about. New methods were developed for releasing and putting into constructive use the power within a person to solve his own problems. These contributions were made by people who represented a wide variety of points of view.[6] More recently this type of approach has become somewhat identified with Carl R. Rogers and those associated with him. Many other groups and individuals in psychology, psychiatry, social work, and allied fields have made important contributions to the unfolding of the counseling process and the refinement of counseling techniques. Rogers and his group, however, are especially noted for having devised detailed methods of analyzing counseling progress while, at the same time, introducing a more precise delineation of counseling skills than had been known before. Through the research of this group in combination with the findings of many others, aspects of successful counseling which were previously thought to be inextricably bound up with the counselor's peculiarly personal appeal, were unfolded and presented in an objective way that could be taught to others. Through the use of interview transcriptions particularly, these previously hidden personal skills of various successful counselors were found to have certain consistent characteristics that could be analyzed and demonstrated. In this way, the counseling process became more defined and organized. There were fewer

---

[6]See, for example, Robert Waelder, *et al*: "Areas of Agreement in Psychotherapy," *Am. J. Orthopsychiat.*, Vol. X, No. 4, p. 705, 1940.

random responses. As more and more counseling interviews were studied carefully it grew increasingly clear that each counselor statement—and even shades of meaning of individual words—was significant for the success or failure of an interview.

Various Names. This concept of counseling was given various descriptive terms. Some of its aspects were referred to as "non-directive." Unfortunately, this term has a negative tone and may give the impression that the counselor does nothing. For this reason, the word "non-directive" has been criticized. Other phrases have been used, such as "client-centered," to bring out that the focus is on the attitudes of the person coming for help, and not centered on what the counselor himself thinks or advises. The title "emergent counseling" suggests the way in which the person's clearer understanding and better choices slowly emerge from the counseling process. "Relationship therapy" emphasizes the importance of the relationship that is established between the counselor and the person coming for help.

Counseling, however, is more than any of these titles suggest. It is not a relationship of guidance, advice, or instruction, and in this sense the counselor is non-directive. He is non-directive, too, in that he does not direct the person to any set solution. He does not form any predetermined answers which he subtly suggests in his responses. Some people feel this is what the counselor actually does. We can see he does not do this when we examine many responses of the counselor. Subtleties and hidden suggestions are another form of determining the path the person takes in his solution. The counselor must be genuinely convinced that in the individual events of each life a person needs a kind of prudence which is "incommunicable." While the general principles and broad path of reasonable solution may be clear to many, the precise choice of means within the scope of the individual person coming for help is often known only to him. In this sense, the counselor makes no effort to determine his choice of particular, individual means. When a person can reason unemotionally, he himself can see and understand his powers and capacities for action. In this way, he will choose means of reaching particular goals that best accord with his increased self-understanding. The purpose of counseling is so to increase this self-understanding and emotional control that he can carry into action what he knows he should do. For this reason we feel that this concept of counseling may be described as *self-directive* and *self-integrative*.

The Counselor Furthers Self-Responsibility. If we assume that human nature is capable of change and can grow in self-understanding and responsibility, then the counselor's role as such is not one of advising and giving directions. Rather, he must acquire skills which will further the powers of growth for self-responsibility in the individual himself. In counseling, in contrast to guidance, the person's lack of knowledge is not the focus, but his inability to carry out what he knows. Actually, a person, even though he may lack professional training, is apt to know more than anyone else about his own personal problems, reactions, and attitudes if he can be given an opportunity to think them through calmly and unemotionally. This counseling process concentrated on developing a skill in counselors that would enable a person gradually to see himself more objectively and judge himself more reasonably. Consequently, a person is then often able to make more adequate choices of new ways to solve even very difficult personal, home, and environmental problems.

Precise Research into Counseling Process. The emphasis was, therefore, on the precision and sensitivity of the counselor's responses. Accurate reports of the counseling interviews had now great research value. Moreover, since the person's change in attitudes and self-knowledge was considered a main aspect of counseling success, it became significant to develop means of research into the process—as the person himself saw and expressed it—by which he passed from confusion and conflict to a greater state of happiness and self-responsibility. Consequently, research was carried out by which word-for-word transcriptions of interviews were studied carefully both to reveal the slow change in the person's attitudes and uncover means of increasing counseling skill.

Results of Recent Research. This research uncovered new insights about the nature of maladjustment and the powerful factors for self-responsibility, integration, happiness, and a more productive life within even a very mixed-up individual. In fact, the implication of these counseling results, combined with other similar developments, work against psychological concepts of personality determinism, and turn the attention of psychologists, psychiatrists, physicians, sociologists, social workers, and others to the powers of change and growth which lie within each human being. As Rogers in his 1947 presidential address to the American Psychological Association pointed out:

If we take the remaining proposition that the self, under proper conditions, is capable of reorganizing, to some extent, its own perceptual field, and of thus altering behavior, this too seems to raise disturbing questions, . . . We discover within the person, under certain conditions, a capacity for the restructuring and the reorganization of self, and consequently the reorganization of behavior, which has profound social implications. We see these observations, and the theoretical formulations which they inspire as a fruitful new approach for study and research in various fields of psychology.[7]

COUNSELING—AN AID TO PRUDENCE

We see in this development of counseling, an understanding of the counseling process similar to St. Thomas' conception of counsel and prudence. It provides the counselor with skills which further the person's own counsel and prudence. General knowledge and guidance, even when these are accurate, do not solve the uncertainty which is an essential part of the contingent world in which we live and act. Nor do they of themselves produce the responsible, prudent judgment necessary to virtue.

Personal Responsibility. In the counseling process, a person can pursue this necessary inquiry into the uncertain contingent singulars of his life. But the child or adult coming for help does not have his independence and responsible judgment taken over by the counselor. The person recognizes that the counselor's skill is essential and yet he himself remains the major factor in his own adjustment. The following statement, taken from an actual interview, indicates this effect:

. . . But this way you feel you're slowly working it out—you're not telling me, you're helping me, but I'm really figuring it out myself. I know *I'm* doing it.

As a person sees all the issues in a more integrated way, he is then gradually better able to carry out what he reasonably should do.

---

[7]Carl R. Rogers, in *The Am. Psychol.*, Vol. 2, No. 9, Sept., 1947.

PART TWO

THE PROCESS OF PERSONAL INTEGRATION
THROUGH COUNSELING

In Part One we have seen that the main purpose of counseling is to further personal integration through the development of counsel and prudence. We are now ready to consider how this takes place, as the counseling interviews reveal it. Part Two will discuss the stages through which a person gains self-knowledge and integration.

Present Conflicts. Obviously, before counseling can begin, people must be enabled to speak of their difficulties to someone. The need and significance of this is the topic of Chapter III. Chapter IV will consider some causes of a person's present conflicts. As a person talks about himself he reveals and begins to examine his personal difficulties. This usually uncovers some strong desires for goals that he is somehow not achieving. The means he chooses to reach these goals fail him or leave him only with a partial sense of fulfillment. He is in an emotional state where his positive desires are surrounded by negative, discouraged, and resentful feelings of failure and inadequacy.

Past Causes. As he examines these conflicts, a person often goes into the past, sometimes to very early childhood, to uncover experiences which still have great influence on his present attitudes. Consequently, in Chapter V of this section we will take up some of the faulty learning experiences of various home, school, and neighborhood situations as the interviews reveal them and attempt to show how such faulty learning is apparently one of the important causes of later childhood or adult difficulties.

The emotions themselves, however, can also be affected by past experiences. In Chapter VI we will discuss the peculiar way in which emotions may be aroused and then remain fixedly attached to a particular incident or incidents so that they are strongly affected whenever any experience similar to this original situation recurs in a person's life. People often discover that their present excessive emotions are due, not to the particular persons or experiences involved but to the way in which these situations contain some aspects of one of these earlier relationships around which they had a very deep emotional reaction that is still actively affecting them.

New Self-Knowledge and Integration. Simultaneous with his unfolding of past and present conflicts and confusions, a person's reasonable self-evaluation is also greatly activated through counseling. Chapter VII will show how counseling advances not only a person's self-knowledge but also his ability to learn more adequately the things he failed to learn or learned wrongly and at the same time to control his emotions so that he can act on what he now knows. Here the process is not so much that of acquiring new knowledge as of making better use of the knowledge he already possessed and of taking greater advantage of the learning situations which his present experiences afford. The final chapter of this section, Chapter VIII, will take up the process of judgment and action which, in the prudential function, come from a person's increased self-understanding and more integrated counsel. We will attempt to show how such judgments and actions, following upon the insightful survey and evaluation which the counseling process produces, result in happier, more productive and more virtuous living.

CHAPTER III

THE NEED TO TALK TO SOMEONE

New Understanding. Research on counseling interviews opened a new way of understanding the attitudes and needs of people when they are in personal conflict. Having a transcription of the actual interviews, detailed study was possible. In fact, going over the typescript afterwards often revealed significant words and phrases which the counselor did not catch during the interview. Interviews could be studied in this way many times and still uncover new tones and meanings. For this reason, at various places throughout this book we will reproduce at length some of these excerpts, reconstructed and disguised to remove identity but presented here in a form which is still sufficiently accurate for our purpose. Counselors and counselors-in-training have found the study and discussion of interviews one of the most effective ways of increasing their appreciation of the nature and degree of personal difficulties and of improving their counseling skill.

SOME CHARACTERISTICS OF INITIAL INTERVIEWS

Need to Unburden Self. As we studied the exact content of interviews, it became clearer why direction and advice are often not enough. A person who is deeply involved in personal problems may be in such a state of mind that any further pressure is like the straw that breaks the camel's back. He has usually been told what he should do, often many times, and it has not helped. The first thing such a person needs is an opportunity to unburden himself. To do this, he must be able to go to someone in whom he has confidence and whom he feels will understand and appreciate the weight of his problems and the degree of his own weakness. A person who comes for counseling is not seeking approval. On the contrary, the fact that he wants help indicates at least some confused desire to change. Often, this desire is strong and clearly expressed.

Illustration. We see this in these statements of a 40-year-old woman (Z),[1] mother of two children, who is involved in a serious infatuation with a man with whom she works. Soon after she and her husband were married, she realized that they were unsuited to each other but she still wished to make her marriage a success. During their twelve years of married life she had been unhappy but had accepted it for the sake of her own family and her children. Her husband always appeared cold and indifferent. He told her a number of times that he was sorry he ever married her. No serious difficulties occurred, however, until the war when—for patriotic reasons and since her mother had now come to live with them and could take care of the children—she again took up a particular type of work for which she had previously received special training. In her work she was closely associated with this one man particularly. It seemed to her that he had all the appealing qualities her husband lacked. He was also a Catholic, a widower about ten years older than she. Both had struggled against the attachment but were now, they felt, hopelessly involved. This is the second interview. She is speaking:[2]

P: But it—uh—it does good to talk it over with someone that can understand in an impartial way that uh—there's a lot of people that you couldn't say anything like that to—I know the person who told me to come to see you, he said after the first talk with you he was helped a lot.

C: It is a help to feel free like this to just talk things out with someone you know will understand.

P: That's right. I know when I came the last time . . . of course, I didn't—I didn't feel as free to say things as I do now. But—when you get those things off your mind, it relieves the strain a whole lot—but if you can't, it just keeps building up and building up like water behind a dam, and finally it's going to burst—and when it lets loose why, you just don't care what happens. (Pause)

State of Pressure. This feeling of intense pressure "like a dam about to burst" is typical. Unsolved conflicts like this, put a person in a state in which he feels he must do something. Yet, he cannot

---

[1] Designated by symbol (Z).

[2] P. is the symbol for Person; C., for Counselor. The one coming for counseling is variously called a counselee, a client, a patient, or some other designation. Throughout this book we will use the word "person." The counselor is also often referred to as the therapist.

see clearly what to do. This condition has many of the qualities of an actual physical pressure. For this reason, one of the great immediate reliefs is "to relieve the pressure" as people say, by talking to someone. This is the first helpful effect of counseling. A person can tell his problems to an understanding and uncritical listener. Such listeners are hard to find. Like these two people, many have no one among their friends and relatives to whom they can speak intimately. We noticed too that their freedom in talking to the counselor grew as the interviews progressed. They could not speak so freely when they first came. The counselor's manner made it easier to reveal themselves to him. As this woman's confusion and fears are poured out, the counselor cautiously responds to the basic feelings behind the release. In this way, there is a slow growth in self-understanding. As the person can talk about herself, she experiences a deep sense of relief, the emotions of insecurity and fear and the urge to escape her responsibilities are no longer so overpowering. She begins again to take courage and hope.

The interview continues (Z):

P: I know a lot of times he's said he wouldn't care if the whole mess were found out—the only thing was he didn't want to hurt his family. I've got people that I don't want to hurt either. I don't want to hurt anybody in that way. It looks like we're a victim of circumstances, (Pause) and we've got to work it out. (Pause) It's going to be hard to do though, after as far into it as we've gotten—it seems like you just can't break up over night what is force of habit.

C: You feel while there is a way out, it's not something that's going to happen immediately.

P: I feel confident there's a solution to this. (Pause)

Wavering Between Responsibility and Irresponsibility. Here, we have another typical attitude often found in opening interviews. There is a wavering between the person feeling herself a victim of some blind fate, "bad luck," "a victim of circumstances," etc., and the conscious facing and taking responsibility for her predicament. In one mood, she does not care what happens or who is hurt; in the other, she faces the grave harm that is, or will be, done to herself and others if she does not reach a reasonable solution. At the end of this statement, there is a note of encouragement—the focus is now on the responsible facing of the situation. Even after one interview, people often begin to feel greater courage and confidence that they can cope with their problems and find an answer.

The interview continues (Z):

C: Things are a little better for you, aren't they—I mean, you seem to be—

P: Yes, I have a better state of mind—I'm not so bitter or anything—before, I—if anybody'd say anything to me, I'd snap their head off —just jittery—and if anybody'd say anything to me, why, if I didn't like it, I'd tell them about it. I wouldn't be reasonable—I just couldn't see anything anyone else's way. Everything had to be done so that it would let me have time of my own. I didn't consider anybody else's feelings at all. I was just at a point where I was getting ready to blow up, and I had to get it off my mind, that's all.

C: Kind of relieved all that pressure—just to express yourself to someone.

P: You bet. (Pause)

Physical Tension. We notice, too, another factor that seems always to be associated with this emotional conflict state—the state of body tension which this woman describes as feeling "jittery"— which makes a person very irritable. This factor seems to give us a clue as to why physical disorders may accompany these conflicts. Persons like this will often complain of headaches, nasal swelling, severe stomach disorders, or skin eruptions. They may be stutterers or have facial tics. These and similar illnesses seem to be due, at least in part, to their state of hypertension.

We continue this excerpt as the counselor says (Z):

C: Yes, it's so—in a situation like this where we're free to speak— things become clearer in the process of talking them out as we go along.

P: Yes—it—uh—puts them in a different light—and I don't know— you can see things a little clearer. It's probably reasonable that whenever you've got everything all bunched up together, and you want to find the right solution, and yet you're always being pulled between two forces—one against the other. You can't seem to make head nor tail of it. . . . But this way, you feel you're slowly working it out— you're not telling me, you're helping me but I'm really figuring it out myself. I know I'm doing it.

C: Yes, it is your solution, isn't it? It isn't something in which someone can just tell you what to do. You know more about it than anyone else.

P: Uh-huh. That's right.

C: We can feel that we're doing it ourselves, slowly—better than someone just giving us orders—

P: Yes—someone driving you to it, you know—uh—well, you can't—uh—you can say that you will—when they tell you you have to do it—you have to do this and you have to do that—and it's all good and well, but, when you stop to figure out human nature, you just can't buck it that way—it's stronger than just to say so. (Pause) I know a lot of times there's been things that I wanted to do the worst way, but I knew that—well, human nature is just different from that—you can't buck it and get away with it. You want to do this, and you want to do that, and you know that—well—maybe it can be done, but you can't do it right then. You've got to take your time and work it out. If you jump in and do the job wrong—why, you've got to do it all over again. There's a right way and a wrong way. They say the right way is the easiest way, but sometimes it's kinda hard to find the right way. (Pause)

Narrowed Perception. The phrase "everything all bunched up together" gives us a further picture of this state. These people fulfill the old adage of "not being able to see the forest for the trees." Intense emotion, especially of insecurity, fear, and hostility, seems to narrow one's perception. A person tends, then, to focus on particulars, on minute details and to lose sight of the whole picture. In these states of narrowed perception his outlook gets more and more concentrated on himself. Like a person in panic, he does not consider any other factor but his own immediate self-protection. Being told what to do or pushed further by argument or persuasion is no help. A person can be so worked up that even good advice only threatens him. He may go in the opposite direction under such pressure, just to escape further conflict.

Confusion of Means. In this excerpt we have a demonstration of the difference St. Thomas makes between a person's intellectual understanding of the right goal of action, and his confusion about the intermediate steps as his conflicting appetites pull him in another direction. So, as this woman says, "You want to find the right solution and yet you're always being pulled between two forces—one against the other." "Jumping in and doing the job wrong" by precipitous and imprudent choices gets her nowhere. She realizes that the prudent way once found will be easier, but in this maze of confusion, it is painfully difficult to find this prudent path.

Need to Be Accepted and Understood. People in these states require a relationship in which they can feel their way slowly and cautiously until they gradually acquire a new set of attitudes. As their perceptions of themselves and others broaden, their understanding of their ultimate goals becomes clearer. Consequently, they also see their problems in a different light and begin to take more adequate steps for permanent solutions.

We will have occasion in other sections throughout the book to examine in detail what produces a successful series of interviews. Before such changes in self-understanding come about, more factors than simply being a good listener go into the process. Talking freely to someone about personal conflicts, while always helpful, does not by itself bring about any deep or significant changes. Successful counseling requires more skill than, as people sometimes think, merely being a patient and understanding friend.

This popular notion, however, does reveal one of the first necessities of counseling. A person needs to feel that someone accepts him and is willing to listen. In addition, most people need help in unfolding complex difficulties. Being listened to aids them temporarily. But this does not enable them to penetrate the basic attitudes which underlie their problems. Many people are in fact so tense, confused, self-conscious, and ashamed of these deeper personal conflicts, that it is very difficult for them to speak to anyone about them. This unfolds a prime necessity of any counselor's approach. For counseling to be possible, people need to feel that the counselor is sufficiently interested to listen to them and will not simply take over and try to solve their problems for them. Gradually, they grow aware that he is going to help them work out the problem themselves. The following excerpt from a first interview with a young college woman illustrates this (W):[3]

P: I've been afraid to come because I thought someone would just take me over and not give me a chance to help myself. They'll say do it this way and expect me to do it. (Pause)

C: You're fearful of just being told what to do and not being given any help to do it.

[3]Designated by symbol (W).

P: Yes—I know, in a way, what I want, I want some way so I can start to live differently.

Illustration. This need for someone to listen to difficulties and understand is even more evident when, in addition to a general state of personal confusion, the person is physically ill. The following is the beginning of an interview with an aviation cadet (X) :[4]

P: I'll tell you, until about a month ago, I felt as if my trouble was entirely physical. In fact, I guess it is a natural tendency to hope it is. I had severe headaches for about eight years, and for the past year and a half I'd say they'd become much worse, and I became extremely nervous and I was in the hospital for a month last winter, and they diagnosed it there as allergic rhinitis, and when I came here—I came here three months ago—I got a skin test out here and tested allergic to mold spores. They began giving me shots, but it didn't affect the headache in any way, so I went to see Dr. L., and after I had this test in the morning, I went back in the afternoon. In the course of the conversation, he maneuvered around very cleverly and asked me if anything had happened in my life which I would care to discuss. He said "Not since you've been here—I mean—maybe years ago." I asked him point blank if what I tested allergic to could have caused the trouble I mentioned. He said that—although it was possible, he did not think it probable in my case since I had it the year round. (Pause) I saw Captain A. at the field. He's one of the flight surgeons, and I went and talked to him about my trouble, and I found out I knew more about it than he did. I noticed when I was talking my headache got much worse and for about a week later I seemed to have just stayed that way, and became very nervous.

It is interesting to note the completely opposite reactions which the two physicians produced. Dr. L., an older, experienced and understanding man, even though he could offer no medical help, gave the cadet a feeling of acceptance and he could talk freely to him. As a result, he willingly came to see the counselor on the physician's recommendation.

The opposite effect was produced by the flight surgeon. He handled the interview in such a way that he produced violent resistance in the cadet, who left feeling he knew more about his

---

[4]Designated by symbol (X). This excerpt previously appeared in J. Mitchell and C. A. Curran: "A Method of Approach to Psychosomatic Problems in Allergy," *West Virginia Medical Journal*, Vol. 42, pp. 1–24, 1946.

trouble than the physician. Reading between the lines, we can see how the flight surgeon, having also made a thorough diagnosis and found no evident medical causes, probably conveyed a tone of both irritation and rejection to the cadet. Such a manner rather than helping the cadet only made him worse.

PROBLEMS NOT IMMEDIATELY EVIDENT

Some Reason for Coming. Usually, the more obvious personal difficulties are readily recognized. It is not hard, for example, to understand the infatuation problem of the forty-year-old business woman. The grave consequences are evident. Many problems, however, are not so clearly expressed or defined. People will come with only vague difficulties. They may not even talk about anything serious, so that the inexperienced counselor is apt to push them to give some reason for their coming. Studying the excerpts of many interviews, we grew to realize that every interview is significant no matter how trivial the content appears. Usually, if such an interview is handled skillfully, it will finally lead to the penetration of deeper problems and more fundamental attitudes. This is especially important in dealing with the problems of children. The counselor often does not clearly understand what is troubling the child and yet the child is greatly helped by the counselor's accepting and sensitive skill.[5]

Next to children, the most difficult group in counseling are young adults who often appear to have no definite problems. In adolescence, personal problems are not generally apparent. They may sometimes be noticed because of school failure or some similar occurrence, but if the adolescent is of average or superior intellectual ability, he may have no apparent school problem even though he is in deep personal turmoil. Adolescents have not yet faced adult adjustment problems such as those which occur in marriage. Consequently, there may be no definite focal point around which to explain their difficulties. What they feel is usually a vague inadequacy coupled with insecurity and fear that somehow they will be incapable of successful living. Extrinsic appearances sometimes help us. We usually detect those students who are withdrawn and

[5]See Chapter XIII.

excessively insecure. Many times, however, such extrinsic evidences are most misleading. Young men and women, who are socially accepted and prominent in school activities, may be carrying around deep personal confusions. Their external success does not give them any sense of real achievement. They may see this only as a compensation for their fundamental feelings of failure. Such people come to see a counselor on almost any pretext. They sometimes spend two or three interviews talking at random. The experience of many counselors is that this material has value, unimportant as it may appear. They feel that if the counselor does the right things, such interviews invariably lead to deeper and more significant awarenesses. It seems that a child or adult seldom, if ever, comes to a person whom he sees in the role of a counselor unless he has some basic problem, no matter how disguised this may be in his beginning statements.

School Problem Illustrated. Sometimes, poor school work, particularly on a college level, may be one of the first indications of personal turmoil. Ability that carried a student through high school is often not enough to get him through college without an opportunity to work out some of his personal problems. This is a different understanding of school failure than simply lack of knowledge, study, or initiative. We are slowly acquiring greater awareness of the complexities of the learning process. We know now that emotional states greatly affect learning.[6] It is one thing, for example, to read a report of a student's failure as a teacher or an instructor's class record shows it. It is another to hear that same person pour forth his own picture of his classroom inadequacy in a counseling relationship in which he feels he can speak freely. We see this in the following excerpt of a failing college student with high intelligence and aptitude ratings (W):

P: This morning, for instance, I didn't have any classes. I felt very clear and I decided that I would study some and pretty soon I became a little distracted and my mind started wandering and I couldn't

---

[6]As Mandel Sherman has shown, "The emotionality of an individual at the time he is learning a task has a definite influence upon his efficiency in the learning situation. His emotional balance or imbalance also has a definite effect upon his retention of material that he has learned and upon his ability to recall and put into use that which he may have learned well previously." "Emotional Disturbances and Reading Disability," in W. S. Gray: *Recent Trends in Reading,* Supplementary Educational Monographs, No. 49, Chicago, University of Chicago, 1939, p. 126.

concentrate very well—I spent about two-thirds of my time thinking
how to solve this problem and how I've been told, to get my mind
settled and get an interest in the subject. But when I work by myself
like that, I get butterflies like in my stomach.

Here, we have another expression of that physical hypertension
that so often accompanies personal conflict. One might predict that,
should this student's extremely tense state continue, some serious
physical disorder could result. Our physical and psychological systems react as a unit. We can stand only so much personal conflict
and confusion. When we are young our powers of resistance are
usually greater. Personal problems do not cause physical difficulties
at first, but, remaining a long time or hitting a crisis, they are apt
to back up and have destructive physical reactions. This is coming
to be known as the psychosomatic aspect of illness.

Advice Not Enough. The student's statement, "I've been told
to get my mind settled and get an interest in the subject," indicates
that others have told her what to do. She still does not know how.
When she tries to "interest" herself, she is unable to focus her attention. In the light of the release that follows, how meaningless
that advice is for a person like this. Yet, many people feel they
have completely solved their relationship to these problems by
some threatening reprimand. If we are dealing with a mature and
stable person, such a reprimanding statement may actually produce
results. Sometimes, too, as a variation of shock therapy, a violent
denunciation can, at least temporarily, cause the person to marshall
all his forces and change. The fact that these methods do temporarily work sometimes prompts people to use them consistently.
But most of the time such methods fail, as they certainly would
have failed with this young woman.

Reprimands. This strong rebuke method is common with child
problems. Again, it may sometimes work and its success can be
deceptive. If a child comes from a home that gives him acceptance,
understanding, and love, then a temporary rejection, reprimand, or
even the humiliation of physical chastisement will not seriously
hurt him. His general security and achievement will quickly offset
these. But these children are least apt to be conduct problems.
They are usually successful students, good in behavior and, therefore, seldom reprimanded. The disorganized home in which the

parents are cold, unaccepting, or quarrelsome, or the rigid home in which the children are sternly regimented because the parents want peace and quiet, are the places from which most conduct problems come. The child from such homes is usually the object of the strong reprimands. Even when he changes his conduct through fear, the treatment has more deeply intrenched his sense of insecurity and inadequacy.

Vague Fear and Confusion. We notice that the young woman student does not state any particular problem, but rather a general inability to stay at a task and keep her mind on it. This kind of expression is common in young people. In the twilight zone between childhood and adulthood, there is a wavering between fantasy and reality. This young woman does not yet have the security and confidence that she can live and succeed in the adult world. Her poor college class work and her failure to adjust socially with those around her, have overwhelmed her with a sense of personal inadequacy. She is fearfully concerned that she is unequipped for mature living. The interview continues (W):

P: Another thing I notice, when I'm talking to someone and I have to look right at them, it's quite a hard thing for me to do—I always try to look away and get out of it. Unless I make a conscious effort—it's very hard to talk to anyone. Whenever I feel discouraged the way I do now, I'm not very much at ease when I'm talking with someone. It's hard to get interested and concentrate on what they tell me. My mind just wanders—I can't express myself or argue logically either because I get self-conscious and—mixed up in what I'm saying—it's that way during a lecture, too, uh—I just dream away. It's easier than concentrating on what the professor is saying. When I can mix with people and talk to them I feel a lot better.

PERSON HELPED TO SPEAK FREELY

Counselor Aids This. We might smile at the young woman's statement, in this free-flowing excerpt, that she has a hard time talking with anyone. But, this is true. As we mentioned earlier, one of the first evidences of counseling skill is the way in which even withdrawn and taciturn people are enabled to express themselves and talk about very personal matters. Most of the time, when people do not speak freely we feel the fault lies with them, because they have never acquired facility in speaking. While this may be so, the counselor's skill can facilitate a person's ability to speak. This is one of the first differences apparent in a good counseling relationship. A person will sometimes say with great surprise, "You know, I have never been able to talk to anyone before like this." Because they experience such pleasure and relief, they may add, "This is really wonderful!"

Common Difficulty. While this difficulty in talking may be most common among adolescents, it is also not uncommon in adults. To be able to talk to someone is a simple but deep need of many people. From early childhood, they are unable to talk easily. They keep attitudes and feelings pent up in themselves. The more these emotions remain unreleased, the more their power to disturb increases. People carry this great burden primarily because they cannot talk freely about themselves. The few times they have tried to reveal themselves to someone, they received no understanding. Often, the feeling of rejection they experienced was so great that it made them fearful of ever again speaking intimately to anyone. A tragic aspect is that the person to whom they attempted to talk was probably unaware of what he did. He likely did not notice their confusion or appreciate the agony they were going through in the attempt to express themselves. This insensitivity may have caused him to dismiss them with a remark, an expression of impatience, or quickly to take over and give them long and detailed advice.

Large numbers of people in our society find it difficult to talk with others. This may be due to the increased isolation in which we live in large cities and the way in which we tend to wall ourselves from one another. Whatever the reasons, one of the most remarkable effects of a good counseling process is, at the same time, one of the simplest. It allows people, sometimes for the first time in their lives, to talk freely and relaxedly about themselves and, as they grow in confidence and security with the counselor, to pour forth many deep and hidden things that, as they will often say, "I have never told to another soul."

Be Oneself. Another aspect of talking freely to someone is the relief that comes from being accepted as we really are. Often we consider our problems unique, feeling they have happened only to us. When a person feels like this, to be allowed to share what he considers peculiar or unusual is a great relief. One understanding person seems to symbolize the whole of humanity. If a person can talk to someone, especially one who is in a respected and defined role, the feeling of peculiarity and the sense of isolation are noticeably decreased. This is one aspect of St. Paul's advice of "bearing one another's burdens." The sharing process lightens the weight of our problems.

The fact that others know our peculiar weaknesses and defects and still accept us, makes us feel less discouraged. It brings great self-confidence. The counselor's quiet and understanding acceptance must be real. It cannot be put on. The artificial reassurances that people often give in an attempt to cheer us, are superficial and lack deep understanding of our real problems. They not only do not help but oftentimes are deeply resented. By contrast, the true acceptance which a skillfully penetrating response conveys is never resented but is genuinely appreciated. It always encourages further expression.

Problems Not Unique.   The relief a person feels when he realizes that his problems are not unique is oftentimes dramatically indicated in group discussions of personal problems. After one has spoken freely about his peculiar reactions, another will blurt out, "Do you feel that way, too? Why, I thought nobody felt like that but me!" In more senses than one, ". . . the colonel's lady and Judy O'Grady are sisters under their skins."[7]

Lack of an Understanding Person.   The young college woman in the previous excerpt wants desperately to study and concentrate. She does not need to be lectured. The problem is that she cannot do what she wants. She is unable to concentrate, much as she tries. Yet, all through her twelve years of school, as she says elsewhere, no one paid any special attention to her. This misery inside herself, she bore alone. With all her confusions—because she was above average in intellectual ability—she could pass by doing below average work. In her pre-college work she was not, therefore, singled out as a school failure. Yet she was never really a part of the school; she was never understood. In her previous school career, there was no one skillful enough to detect her personal difficulties and offer her an understanding relationship. If this young woman had been less intellectually gifted she would unquestionably have been a school problem. In this confused state she would likely have failed.

[7]Rudyard Kipling: "The Ladies."

This failure could have caused her to become a conduct problem, subject to the reprimands and increased rejections which go with that designation. It is not hard to see how this might even have led to truancy and delinquency.

Some Awareness of Solution. Another interesting aspect of this excerpt is the student's vague awareness of what she ought to do. In the few instances that she has been able to "mix with people," she is happier. This point comes up repeatedly in a large number of cases studied. These people know what they should do in a greater degree than we generally think. In the rapid flow of a person's speech, the counselor could easily miss a phrase like this and remember only the general content of confusions and failures. But the fact that people do vaguely know what they should do and, in some small instances, have tried more successful solutions and found them happier, shows why counseling for them is more than simply giving information. Otherwise, they would continue to follow these happier activities, without any further blocking or confusion.

Needs Personal Integration. Assuming, though, that personal information and guidance were to be given this student, she is still the only one who can actually solve this internal turmoil. Adequate counseling must increase her capacity to cope with those contingent singulars. But it is not so much that she does not know what she should do to be happier. In some instances, she has known and done some things that made her happier. Her real difficulty is the instability inside herself. These strong impulsive urges to escape into unreality by daydreams make her unable to carry out any consistent activity. Counseling must aid her in developing her own prudent judgment by broadening her awareness of all the factors that enter into her confusions and, at the same time, increase her moral courage to continue to face her difficulties until she has worked them out.

As we go down through this interview, we see how the student's attitudes keep changing. This constant fighting with herself is a vivid demonstration of one phase of the battle of "flesh against the spirit and the spirit against the flesh," the instinctive urge to escape, at war with her reason. She wants to fulfill the responsibilities of reality. But because she cannot do what she should do, she is miserable. She keeps arguing with herself in a far more intense way than anyone could lecture to her; yet, that alone offers her no solution.

DIFFICULTIES OF EXPRESSION

Illustration. Not every person talks as freely as this young college woman. Since silence can be a real barrier, it might be valuable to parallel this with another excerpt, in which the person has greater difficulty in speaking. This excerpt is taken from the interviews of another young woman in college who works part time. As we notice her slow, hesitant speech, we might consider her incapable of college work and perhaps even of low intelligence. Actually, for two years she had been on the honor roll. Her marks, while still passing, were below the previous years. This was her original reason for coming to the counselor. She had also gone to a physician with a series of complaints that he diagnosed as psychosomatic. When he could get nothing from her in the way of a psychological case history he became very irritated. This probably increased her reticence in talking with the counselor. By the third interview, she has stated that she has a deep personal problem but has been unable to speak of it to anyone. The following excerpt is from the third interview (K) :[8]

C: You hardly know what to say.

P: No—(Pause)[9]

C: If you wish to speak of whatever is disturbing to you, perhaps it can be helpful.

P: It's been on my mind all day—I just don't know what—(Pause) I just get so, mm—I don't know—so disgusted.

C: You're pretty disgusted?

P: (Pause)

C: Would you care to speak a little more of just how you have been feeling?

P: I just get so—I don't know (Pause).

C: It isn't just too clear to me.

P: (Pause) Mmm—I just—I don't know—I just feel—I just get mad and disgusted with everything.

C: Pretty mad and disgusted with the way things are going.

P: Mmm, yes, (Pause). It's nothing that had to do with my work or anything like that.

---

[8]Designated by symbol (K).
[9]The pauses are approximately ten to fifteen seconds.

C: It is just your general attitude?

P: (Pause)

C: You can feel free to speak about that. Oftentimes, just speaking about things like that is worthwhile.

P: Mm—I don't know. I just feel as though everything has happened in the last six months or so.

C: The last six months have been pretty miserable . . .

P: (Pause)

C: That is, you don't know just what is the matter but today you feel kinda mad and disgusted with everything that has happened.

P: Yes, just everything—oh—I don't know—(Pause).

C: Everything that has happened is sorta piled up and you are pretty disgusted.

P: (Pause) Oh, I'll probably get over it sometime.

C: You'll probably get over it sometime, but you are pretty weary right now.

P: (Pause) I just don't know what to do. I mean, I don't know, know what there is I can do.

C: You're just pretty helpless, and don't know what to do about these things?

P: I know I have to do something pretty soon. I just can't even eat.

C: You feel you have to do something.

P: Yes, I mean the supervisor always stops and asks what I have eaten. I just can't eat. I'm not hungry. I just can't.

C: Kinda worries you when the supervisor stops you.

P: She doesn't like it, I know. She stopped me today.

C: You are quite fearful about what she thinks.

P: She probably is getting tired about all this stuff. I can't help it anyway—(Pause).

C: Yes, you feel she is getting kinda worried over it, and yet it isn't really your fault.

P: (Pause) I've been feeling so awful down and everything. I called home but it didn't help much.

C: You called home, but it didn't help much.

P: (Pause) I guess it did some.

C: It helped a little bit, but not too much.

P: (Pause)

Slow but Significant Process. This is a very difficult process for both the person and the counselor. We do not have even the beginning of the free flow of our previous excerpts and yet we are already at the third interview. If we examine this excerpt carefully, however, we notice that while the young woman is unable to express what she considers her deepest problem, she is able to get out her attitude of self-disgust, her feeling of misery, the sense of hopelessness, her inability to eat, the fear of the supervisor, and her confusions about home. Actually, this young woman had never been able to talk about herself that freely to anyone before. The value of release must be measured, therefore, not so much by the counselor's view of its effectiveness as by the attitude of the person talking. An extremely restrained and silent person, like this young woman, is beginning some deep personal revelations in this interview, even though the process seems as slow and painful as the proverbial "pulling teeth." Gradually, she was able to talk more about these same factors that, previously, she had never told to anyone. In the course of twelve interviews, she was able to unfold and think out an almost unbelievable life conflict. People who worked daily with her and even her most intimate friends never remotely imagined that she was in such difficulty.

Accepting Tone and Manner. In print, the counselor's responses in this interview may seem automatic repetition. His tone and manner, however, were kind and accepting so that, in the midst of the long pauses and with the normal variations of his voice, the responses did not sound nearly as mechanical as they appear. If there is a true tone of acceptance, repetition of this sort does not seem to be noticed by the other person. In these hesitant stages, the counselor's kind, understanding attitude seems the most important factor.

Not Push or Probe. The counselor did not try to push or probe but simply let the young woman know that he was receptive and considerate. He showed this acceptance as well by his quiet undisturbed manner as by his speech. The counselor was sincere in allotting the half-hour to this person. He had not fixed in his mind any requisite that she should speak freely or easily. This is most important. Otherwise, in our desire to secure free release, we are apt to show our resentment of the person's slowness. This resentment in turn will perhaps prevent any positive value coming out of the relationship. This is often missed by the beginning counselor. Unless the person coming for help can thoroughly be himself with all his disordered, hesitant and confused ways of expressing himself, he cannot feel he belongs in the interview. He will, like anyone in an uncomfortable situation, want to get it over as soon as possible and not want to return. The more difficulty he has in speaking and the more confusions he has to express, the more afraid he will be that he sounds foolish and appears ridiculous in the eyes of the counselor. This is true of everyone coming for help, from small children to old people. Consequently, essential to a good counseling interview is the counselor's ease and sincere acceptance of the other person, no matter how slow or disorganized this person's manner of expression may be. Anything else will hinder or destroy counseling. It will only increase the sense of failure, rejection, and confusion of the person whom the counselor was attempting to help.

PATIENCE AND SKILL

Personal Difficulties Common. As we examine these statements of people in personal difficulty, we see why patience and skill are necessary in dealing with them. The surprising thing is that these difficulties exist in a far greater number of the general population than most of us realize. These people are usually stable enough to carry on their daily work and fulfill major responsibilities. For the most part, we never know of these problems unless they come to us in a confidential and confiding way. Sometimes people can be near the breaking point without any apparent evidence. Even close friends have no idea of this. As we grow aware how common serious personal problems are and how often people may never have talked to anyone about them, we better appreciate what counseling can mean.

Be Prepared. The need for personal help is great in our society. When we realize that people whom we meet everywhere need this help, we grow more cautious and alert in the way we talk with others. This is particularly necessary when we are in positions which might afford them the occasion to seek our help. In personal matters, Catholic people are often more at ease with priests and religious than they are even with professionally trained lay people. Consequently, those who represent religion, as well as people in any kind of formal counseling positions, should be conscious of how others often want their help in personal difficulties. Even casual meetings, as we will discuss later, can be the first step in a significant counseling relationship.

Willingness to Allot Sufficient Time. When people do come to us for personal help, we must allow for the possibility of serious problems even though we have had no previous indications of this state. We must be willing to provide these people with a relationship over weeks or even months in which they can slowly integrate themselves. If they could solve their problems easily or could speak freely to everyone, it is unlikely they would need our help. In so far, then, as they come to us, we can be sure they are faced with difficulties which, for the moment at least, are too much for them. They need our aid not simply in telling them what to do but in allowing them to get their difficulties out so they can see all the factors more completely. In this way, they are in a better state to choose more reasonable solutions.

CHAPTER IV

EXAMINING PRESENT CONFLICTS

Problems and Negative Attitudes. As people talk about themselves in the beginning of counseling, they usually present a series of problems and conflicts in a somewhat disorganized and unrelated way. These expressions are accompanied by attitudes and emotions that are predominantly negative, hostile, and confused. In some areas at least, these people are not reaching what they really want. The fact that people have these negative emotions implies both an awareness of certain goals and an identification of themselves with these goals. Otherwise they would likely be indifferent rather than negative and would not come for counseling.

The Degree of Conflict. The intensity of these negative feelings seems to depend on the degree of failure, frustration, and inadequacy people feel. If the problems are minor or, though serious, are limited only to one area—for example, a work problem which does not involve any home conflicts or husband and wife disagreements— these negative feelings may not be too strong. Even in one interview, their tone may take a positive turn.

When, however, conflicts are more general and affect most major activities, people can be bitter and feel out of joint with everything and everyone around them. They do not see what steps to take to get out of this conflict. Everything they try leaves them in the same state. All doors seem closed. They feel greatly discouraged, approaching even to the point of hopelessness. Their general confusion may, in fact, be so great that they have temporarily lost sight of what they want. This is indicated in the following excerpt:

P: Sometimes I feel hazy. I mean I've always felt that way at times— just more or less like I was in a fog. I don't understand exactly what it is . . . It is the fogginess that bothers me more than anything else . . . Well, I mean, I feel there is not much I can do.

Confusions like this make a person fearful, anxious about himself, and depressed. Behind these confusions and conflicts, however, is the basic positive urge to think out his problems and take definite steps to solve them. If he did not have this urge, he would not be so affected by his failure. Not finding an answer, a person seems often to be both discouraged and threatened by an undefined feeling of approaching catastrophe. This is sometimes expressed in opening interviews, particularly when people have little sense of achievement in any life-activities. This may also help explain why people with serious personal problems seem generally to be so sensitive and fearful of advice or direction. Such advice may bring them to the verge of panic, since they already feel overwhelmed by their failures and confusions.

The Right Means. Somehow people with either minor or major personal problems appear to be unable to choose the right means to what they want. Significant achievements usually involve a complex series of steps extending over a long period of time. The person coming for counseling generally feels he is not reaching, or even moving towards, his desired goals because somehow he is not taking the right steps. As a result, he is caught between his desires to reach and possess various things he wants and the frustrations and disappointments which result when these desires are not realized.

INDEPENDENCE AND ACHIEVEMENT

Behind each of these frustrating and conflicting emotions is the strong urge towards reasonable, independent achievement. This urge increases as a person passes from infancy to adult life. In the small child, dependency, fear, insecurity, and frustration are obvious and understandable. The world is beyond him. It is a fearful unknown where he is a dwarf in the midst of giants. He must seek security in the loving acceptance and guidance of others, especially his parents. But at the same time, implanted in each child is a resistance to complete dependency and attachment. He wants some independent achievement. Even the very young child, as he learns to walk and talk, gets extreme delight in demonstrating what he can do. He has conquered two basic functional tasks which, until then, have been frustrations and barriers.

A child's early achievements, like walking and talking, reveal the intrinsic dynamism in each person. A man needs to assert himself by controlling his impulses and finding reasonable self-expression in his own actions and in things around him. If, as he continues through adolescence into adult life, he cannot grow in reasonable fulfillment, conflicts are set up. In proportion as he is unable to solve these conflicts, he becomes increasingly unhappy, fearful, and insecure. It gets harder for him to make the effort necessary to cope with his problems. A person usually gets more and more discouraged. In this state people sometimes grow more passive. They may again desire the reassurance and affection which childhood dependency brought them, and so seek these from parents or from new attachments. But they are still unhappy because passive dependency, for all its immediate security, blocks and stifles their fundamental urge to independent, reasonable choice and action.

This does not mean, of course, that the maturely independent man does not need or accept direction and guidance. On the contrary, he accepts such aid more readily than the emotionally insecure and dependent person. A reasonable person grasps the necessity of being helped by others in those areas in which he lacks sufficient information and understanding to direct himself. But he is cautious from whom he seeks such guidance and information. This is the exact opposite of the supine dependency of the emotionally unstable who seek guidance and direction as an escape from responsible choice and action.

POSITIVE AND NEGATIVE EMOTIONS

An Appetite for Something.   A person wants something and seeks to achieve it because it appears "good" to him. Any urge towards or appetite for a thing indicates that it is in some way pleasing and desirable. People often use the expression, "that's good!" in the sense that something is approved and worth seeking. Whenever anything is seen in this light, a person spontaneously begins to move to achieve it because he sees it as a means of happiness. Otherwise, the person will look at it objectively and not feel personally involved or attached to it. He will have, so to speak, no particular "appetite" for it. But whenever a person is pulled to possess a thing, it must have some special personal meaning and this meaning is, at that moment at least, in some way, connected with his desire for happiness. We use the word "appetite," then, in this general sense of an urge or movement towards anything that is seen as desirable.

Emotions Aroused.   Consequently, we create what might be called a perceptual field around a desired object. We move to obtain it, as we might towards any goal. Around this goal our emotions unfold. The urge towards something we want, we usually call "liking" or "loving" it, depending on the intensity of our feeling. Hatred or hostility are in a way the negative side of this urge because as we move towards something desired, we avoid or are hostile to any opposing contrary factors. This helps explain why, in opening interviews, we also find confused expressions of positive emotion, needs, and desires alternating with statements of hostility, resentment, and other negative emotions. Both reactions represent the seeking of desired goals. On the positive side, hope is stimulated as a person feels he can actually reach some desired object. Courage develops enthusiasm and self-confidence that he can attain his goals even though the path is presently blocked. Pleasure and satisfaction follow upon the achievement of anything desired. This satisfaction encourages a person to further achievement. Alternately, negative feelings of sadness and depression accompany the sense of loss if some desired thing is not obtained. This depression makes subsequent motivation more difficult. Apprehensions increase as factors arise which threaten to prevent some achievement. Fears and anxieties mount when a person is surrounded by these impeding situations and events. Anger often results when any of these threats is immediately present. Despair comes when someone feels completely unable to surmount these barriers or to avoid the threatening evil.

CONFLICTING EMOTIONS AND CHOICES

Emotional Turmoil.   Some or all of these different emotions are expressed in the beginning stages of counseling. Individuals coming for counseling are always in some degree of emotional turmoil. Their personality is, in this sense, a battleground for negative and positive feelings. They feel negative in proportion as they are faced with conflict and disorder. At the same time, there is a confused awareness of definite goals—certain things which they see as good and desirable and as the means of happiness. Their difficulty is that these desired goals are impeded by conflicting emotional and sense appetites so that many of their efforts end in failure.

Misled by Appearances.   Their choices, too, often mislead them. Objects and goals appeared good until they were achieved. Then they became a disappointment. Consequently, the plans of action these people set up usually never reach the main life goals they seek. They seem unable to choose the right means—at least to reach their ultimate goals. Their urge for some immediate good often takes them away from what they really want for more lasting happiness. Their will is disordered by conflicting appetites. What they choose under the appearance of good, sometimes disappoints and frustrates them when they have achieved it. Explaining this, St. Thomas points out:

The will is a rational appetite. Now every appetite is only of something good. The reason of this is that the appetite is nothing else than an inclination of a person desirous of a thing towards that thing. . . . . Consequently, in order that the will tend to anything, it is requisite, not that this be good in very truth, but that it be apprehended as good. Wherefore, the philosopher (Aristotle) says that the end is a good or an apparent good.[1]

A major factor in personal conflict and unhappiness is this fact: that a person can seek an apparent good which satisfies one or the other of his needs but which is actually contrary to the over-all reasonable good of his whole person. Problems arise because an individual's craving for particular personal, emotional, or sensual satisfactions are leading him away from the reasonable goals which he ultimately seeks. A man is, therefore, capable of a most complex self-deception. He can allow himself to be misled by particular urges to objects and goals which he knows will not really satisfy him nor ultimately be good for him.

This complexity of human motivation, while it is a comparatively new idea for modern man, is by no means new to the Christian tradition and spiritual life. As Rudolf Allers points out:

The thought that a human person might aim at ends not explicitly known or acknowledged by himself is therefore not altogether alien to the philosophy of the Fathers and their successors; and . . . is quite compatible with the fundamental ideas on the nature of the human mind that are to be found in the world of the great Christian thinkers.[2]

---

[1] St. Thomas Aquinas: *Summa Theologica*, I–II, Q. 8, a. 1, translated by Fathers of the English Dominican Province, New York, Benziger Brothers, 1947. Reprinted from the *Summa Theologica* with the permission of Benziger Brothers, Inc., Publishers and Copyright Owners.

[2] Rudolf Allers: *The New Psychologies*, London, Sheed & Ward, 1932, p. 74.

Hesitancy. Because this emotional turmoil which characterizes the initial stages of counseling may also be accompanied by a general state of failure and threat, a person may, in the beginning of the interview, be fearful the counselor will laugh at him or otherwise reject him. The person may not show this openly, but it is generally present. This fear has usually been increased by previous attempts at talking to someone and being made to feel ridiculous by the other person's reactions or comments. Such a person is likely to try the counselor with hesitant statements which are not too personal. The degree to which these statements flow through the counselor and are objectively responded to, will measure the person's increased sense of security. We will discuss the counselor's side of this in the section on the skill of the counselor.

Due to this fear and insecurity, it may take more than one interview before the deepest self-revelations are made. An example of this insecurity and fear might be the experience people have going up on a high diving board for the first time. They may jump off quickly but more often they stand for a time, to get used to the feeling of being up so high. A small disturbance can cause them quietly to climb back down the ladder. In a similar way, a person in the interview often feels surprised at being able to talk so freely about himself. This new experience, while satisfying, seems to have something of the fear and threat of the high diving board. It is an achievement to dive off the board but it is also threatening to be up so high. So, many people may be pleased at what they have been able to say about themselves and desire to go deeper. But they must be left to make the jump themselves, and in their own time. Any attempt to urge them quickly into their problems seems to cause them to turn away and avoid the plunge.

Given Security. This problem-stating aspect of the opening interviews must be so handled that the person in no way feels pressed either to state his deepest problems or to reach solutions about them. If he is put at ease, he will go slowly and cautiously into the unfolding process. In beginning interviews, people seem to sense that the greater their revelation of problems, the deeper they must go into themselves to reach solutions.

Discuss What He Wishes. For this reason, we can never be sure at what point the person may state his major difficulties. Sometimes, even after a number of interviews, he still may be holding back significant material. In some instances, he may complete a series of interviews without facing some basic problems. A year, or even a number of years later, the same person may return and immediately begin talking about things which he never mentioned in the previous series or mentioned only in passing. It is extremely important, then, that people be allowed to bring up whatever they wish. The counselor must guard against any display of irritation because a person does not immediately present what the counselor considers his "real" problems.

Self-Understanding Brings Confidence and Courage. The opportunity to be able to talk about deep feelings seems of itself to be a great aid in lessening the accompanying fear and insecurity. Once this disorganized and conflicting state of mental fog can be released to an understanding counselor, the person is more able to reach the sources of his difficulty. Getting these feelings out to someone who helps him examine and clarify them removes, among other things, the feeling of mystery and threat. He is no longer so afraid because he has a better understanding of himself. Apparently, the unknown and uncertain aspects of these confusions make them fearful. Once their sources are seen, the person can begin to do something about them. His confidence and courage gradually return. He takes heart again and starts to move towards what he wants.

We see this illustrated in the following statement from an interview later in the counseling series:[3]

P: Sometimes, I still feel kinda hazy—and, I mean, I just don't feel like myself. But now it's very easy to understand why. Of course, it doesn't worry me really too much because I know what it is. The thing isn't a mystery to me like it was before. Everything was so mysterious to me. I didn't know what was going on—what was happening to me . . .

While he is still somewhat disturbed, understanding his reactions has noticeably decreased the fear, anxiety, and discouragement surrounding them.

SOME EFFECTS OF CONFLICT

Unhappiness. These conflict states can be extremely painful and unhappy, especially when a person has struggled for a long time to

[3]See p. 72 for earlier statement by the same person.

work out a solution and not found one. People come for counseling to get some relief from this unhappiness. By themselves they can find no way out of these conflicting urges and needs. They are at cross-purposes with themselves. Consequently, opening interviews often contain deep statements of personal unhappiness, like the following (Z):

P: Well, sometimes, I just, I just, (sobbing) I just sit and hope that an understanding will come to me because I'm so tired of thinking and trying to know what's right and what isn't. I'm so miserable!

This married business woman has tried for so long to find an answer to her difficulties that she is now on the verge of complete discouragement.

Fatigue. In such a condition, a person is not only "tired of thinking," but also can be approaching physical exhaustion. The more recent views of fatigue define it as a psychological as well as a physical state. Bartley, for example, has pointed out that fatigue

arises out of conflict, either organic and physiological or that which is more directly and immediately motivational to start with. Irresolvable conflicts end in frustration. If the conflicts that happen to arise are not too suddenly imposed, or are not too great, the reactions themselves are something that develop more slowly. They constitute fatigue. . . . Fatigue is the desire to quit a given activity and turn to something else, arising out of the discomfort or impairment involved in pursuing the task, or in the relative failure in doing so for any reason; or it is the feeling of aversion toward instituting a given activity owing to the anticipated discomfort or relative inability in performing it.[4]

This helps us understand why a person in personal conflict is also apt to feel physically weary. He may not have enough energy even for the ordinary routine things that face him.

Fantasy Escapism. Sometimes conflict and confusion cause a person to turn in on himself and get farther away from the real world. A person's examination of these escape reactions often reveals that they are disguised forms of real qualities or achievements which he wants but has been unable to reach. Feeling he has failed to get these, he seeks substitute satisfactions. In late adolescence, for example, prolonging childhood daydreams can be one

[4]S. Howard Bartley: "Conflict, Frustration, and Fatigue," *Psychosom. Med.*, Vol. V, No. 2, April 1943, pp. 161–162.

means of escaping the hard realities of mature living. When young people feel surrounded by disorder and confusion they may seek some kind of peace and order in fantasy. Daydreams can offer them a simple and orderly substitute for reality. Because they can regulate these fantasies at will, this seems in some measure to compensate for the conflict and failure which they meet in the real world. It is not difficult to see how in some cases this attitude could, over a period of years, produce an extreme withdrawal so that people noticeably lose touch with reality.

In the following excerpt the young college woman expresses how much daydream fantasies meant to her as a compensation for failure. In the same context, she connects it up with another common escape reaction, that of scrupulosity (W):

P: In school, why, I would really feel rather blue and lonely and it was one thing I could always look forward to at night, before I went to sleep. I would dream my hours away there thinking about experiences that I would have. I used to worry about my belongings for fear they'd get dirty, especially my textbooks. I tried to keep them just like new and took a great pride in it because it meant so much to me—you might say I was scrupulous about them. I'd say these two kind of queer habits of mine just more or less carried me through grade school and high school. They were about all I lived for and I guess I used them to take the place of something more satisfying. I was very particular, too, about my room at home—everything had to be in exact order before I would get into bed. These things gave me a little bit of pleasure or happiness, but it didn't last.

Exaggerated Orderliness. Like daydreams, the tendency to have exact order in little things seems to be a means of making up for the general confusion which people sometimes experience. The real world affords them so few achievements that they are afraid of it. They compensate for this by seeking an excessive, artificial order in everything around them. They may make an established routine or the small details of a task so important that the slightest change exasperates or depresses them. Priests meet this problem in another form in confession and in spiritual guidance. The same tendency may also cause people to seek an exaggerated order in their conduct. Having no prudent judgment of particulars, they will accept only the most rigorous or safest moral solutions, even though such solutions may be impossible or highly impractical for them. But anything less makes them feel guilty.

Social Maladjustment. As these substitute satisfactions and fantasies add to his withdrawal from reality, a person may also feel isolated from others. Discouragement and failure seem to make it more difficult to join in group activities, as in the following (V):[5]

P: . . . If a person doesn't succeed in what they are doing, what they are motivated to, why they will, as I did, withdraw and that is the way I am. I got the thing pieced together and all of a sudden I got the thought, well, if I were motivated and kept on sticking my head up and get pushed down, why pretty soon a person is going to become so discouraged that they are not going to push themselves out and take another chance because they are just going to say, "What's the use?" I figured because of that and the family life and everything else, I just withdrew a little bit more each year until things had gotten to such a point that back here around Christmas time I started to wonder for fear I wasn't the only person that was alive. I must have gotten away from the present world that much that everything just kind of disappeared and I felt as if I were standing on a hill all alone and everything was gone and here I was all alone.

Behind this isolation is the positive need to take a part in social affairs. As he grows able to do this, he observes that his tendency to withdrawal and isolation begins to disappear. He sees how various factors from childhood "all linked together" to draw him "away from the group more than ever." He continues (V):

P: But the more I start going back in the group, the more these feelings seem silly to me. I know the other day I was thinking about something, I had my mind on something and I suddenly got the idea, "well, how in the world could I have gotten the idea that I was the only person existing. Here this person is every bit the same as I am." I don't see, I just couldn't account for it. I mean, I could account for it but the thing seemed so crazy that it didn't make any sense. So that is the way I think it is and I noticed, too, when I look at things objectively I take a whole different attitude on many people's lives. I see things as all linked together to build one construction and the other things pointing to it. I was also thinking that all through grade school whenever there would be a party, or a football team being gotten up, or anything like that I would always be the one to shy

[5]Designated by symbol (V).

away from it. Probably because I wasn't any good at the stuff; but had I had a real motive for it, I imagine I could have gone out with the group but because everything went against me I just withdrew. And one thing that used to make it hard for me was along about the fourth grade I had to wear braces on my teeth and somehow that just drew me away from the group more than ever and it seemed as though I was just isolated from them like as if I were a Japanese or something and the rest of them were American. That sort of distinguished me from them and I never did get back into things quite right after that I don't think. (Pause) So it was a lot of things altogether. (Pause)[6]

Seek Quick Solution. Another common reaction to unsolved personal problems is the blind urge to escape into some other activity almost as if one were in a state of panic. Marriage, for example, can sometimes unfortunately be seen in such a light when it offers a chance to get away from an unhappy home, a difficult job, or school failure, particularly for the girl. This is possibly a meaning in the phrase "run off and get married." This escape urge seems also to be the mood of many people who want a divorce. Problems pile up and a husband or wife sees no solution but "to call it off"— to get away from it. This woman (L),[7] for example, has an intense conflict with her in-laws who are in her house. She appears convinced divorce is the only solution.

P: His parents live with us. We do things they don't like and they do things we don't like—I mean—I'm just not satisfied there. But my husband can't afford to, you know, have another home because he just built that and paid so much for it—I don't know I'm just about ready to call it a day. That's how I feel.

C: Really feel almost at a breaking point right now. It is extremely

---

[6]This point is important in alcoholism. In a study of a thousand alcoholics, it was found that poor social adjustment was a major factor: "This picture of poor social participation or almost no social participation is particularly significant as it describes the educational and marital condition since these both antedate the period of excessive and compulsive drinking. Both education and marriage occur long before 35 years of age; yet alcoholism before 30 is rare, generally appearing between 35 and 50. Of the arrested group here considered, for example, about 3 per cent were under 25, less than 10 per cent under 30. The overwhelming majority were undersocialized in at least these two respects before becoming inebriates. Their inebriety probably made the situation worse." Sheldon D. Bacon, Ph.D.: "The Alcoholic: A Study in the Interplay of Individual and Social Factors," Lectures at the Forum-Conference, Ohio State University, January 1945, p. 13.

[7]Designated by symbol (L).

difficult for you to have them there—it causes a lot of strain and dissension as far as you're concerned.

P: That's right.

But three interviews later her perception of the marriage has changed. She sees now it was not her husband but his relatives and some of her own attitudes. As a result, things are better.

P: . . . I really hadn't thought any more about going on with the divorce. I'll just kind of wait and see how things turn out before I rush into anything like that.

C: It seems now better to proceed a little cautiously and to go slowly and to wait and see how things will turn out.

Not Real Solution. A year later, the woman informed the counselor that her marriage was fine. Incidentally, a previously bad skin condition, which had also cleared up during the interviews, had not recurred, suggesting a strong psychological component. Having an opportunity to examine and clarify her problems and negative feelings, she was able to make a reasonable judgment and work out a satisfactory solution. Her real desires were not to end the marriage, as she at first thought, but to find some relief from the constant tension created in the home by the in-laws. With this solved, the marriage was preserved.

POSITIVE ASPECTS OF CONFLICT

Some Positive Will. In these deep conflict states, the person's intense unhappiness continues to move him to find some better solution. Although he may appear completely discouraged and hopeless, this positive urge is still sufficiently powerful so that it brings him to the counselor. Coming to the interview indicates at least a confused desire to change. Consequently, the counselor can depend on this positive force. It will grow increasingly stronger as conflicts and confusions begin to clear up.

Confused Awarenesses. There are other obscure but significant motives which underlie a person's unhappiness and conflict. As we saw earlier, even negative, resistant emotions indicate some awareness of a desired goal. These negative feelings are directed either towards contrary factors or towards barriers that impede the person's reaching what he wants. At the time he expresses these negations a person may not see this clearly. But the intensity of these negations is a disguised reflection of how much he wants the positive goals to which these negative feelings are in some way attached. This is an important point and helps us understand why a "self-directive" method can actually be effective in the area of personal problems. The counselor, in these matters, does not need to supply motivation. On the contrary, direct persuasion may sometimes block a person from deeper penetration into his problems by making him fearful, insecure, or even hostile. The counselor can rely on the person's desire for happiness and reasonable achievement, and on the movement and gifts of the Holy Spirit. As we shall discuss later, if the counselor happens also to function in other capacities in relation to this person, as, for example, a teacher in the classroom, or a doctor or lawyer, he will, of course, sometimes give direct motivation and encouragement. But this is distinct from his role as counselor and takes place at another time or in a different setting. Moreover, if the counselor is not careful, these other roles can sometimes increase a person's resistance to him as a counselor.

The fact that people come for counseling, that they are unhappy and have expressed these negative feelings, indicates, therefore, without their needing to say it, a number of temporarily submerged but important positive attitudes. Their urge to reasonable self-understanding and action, their desire to change and achieve a happier state, shows some confused awareness of the basic life goals they really want but are not reaching. If they did not have some definite purposes and goals and some desire for these, they would be in no conflict. This kind of indifference to basic life goals is only evident in severe mental disorder, when a person has lost contact with the real world. Such people do not seek help.

Hidden Ideals.   We see evidence of the submerged positive self-understanding in another characteristic of opening interviews: the expression of resentment towards themselves.[8] These expressions of self-disgust and self-rejection often reveal people's awarenesses of what they ought and want to be. Feelings of inferiority to others generally imply ideals they have for themselves. In the following

---

8Actually this kind of self-disgust seems to come from a person's exaggerated notion of himself. Consequently, true self-acceptance goes in the direction of a more genuine humility.

excerpt we notice that this young man, in expressing inferiority and self-rejection, also brings out some disorganized positive statements of what he desires to be (V):

P: I got a letter from a friend the other day. He is about my same age and I guess he is about tops in his position. I mean, he seems to be accomplishing all sorts of things in doing best in his school work and getting along and taking part in social activities. I just sorta wonder what he must have inside him that's different and pushes him on that way. When I compare myself with him why I just feel very inferior to him. After that, when I'd meet others, I'd get cold and gruff. Once in a while though, I'd hit a streak and feel pretty good and get interested in sports and things—but I'd feel depressed when I'd be alone for a time.

Even this brief statement of his inferiority brought with it the desire to be more sociable. Obvious as these needs may be, a person may not see them so clearly until he has expressed them to some‐ one. His previous feeling would be only one of vague inferiority. The positive desires behind this inferiority would not be apparent to him until he had talked about his feelings in this way.

Barrier to Independent Responsibility. Hostility can also be directed against any factors that impede the path of desired goals. When a person talks about his negative feelings towards others, he usually reveals certain things which these people symbolize. This is often due to the part they played in his earlier life, particularly if he was in some way so dependent on them that he absorbed their way of looking at things. As a person grows in independent self-determination, however, he may find that many of the things these people represented are inadequate for his personal happiness. At the same time, he may resent the way such people still desire to assert their control and possession. We see this in the comments of the young college woman (W):

P: I've been raised by uh—a very Victorian type of person—my grand-mother is—and uh—she's, I have a battle within myself in regard to her. . . . She's very possessive of me because, of course, I'm the only thing she has. But she also has those very, very Victorian ideas about life, which you just don't expect—people just don't do that. And since I've been away we've just clashed on so many silly things. You just can't imagine . . . she has such a—oh, how can I explain it—such a perverted idea about things that go on. For instance, if I go out with anyone, and if I don't tell her exactly where we went and what we did, then she'll walk around with a suspicious air, and I know what she's thinking and she'll pick me, and pick me all day . . .

REASONABLE EMOTIONAL CONTROL

Opposing Motivation.   In the excerpts from beginning interviews cited here, we observe how people are swaying between positive and negative urges. A person coming for counseling wants happiness but is confused about particular steps and various intermediate stages along the path. He is moving towards some things or away from them, depending on whether he sees an object as desirable or as a threat and impediment to a desired goal. He is in a state both of "volition" and "nolition" as St. Thomas calls it. *His difficulty is that many of those individual actions which would lead to his ultimate long-term goals are not seen in a desirable or positive light.* On the contrary, they may seem most undesirable and a person's first reaction is to avoid or resist them. *Alternately, particular persons, places, or things which actually lead away from his real goals, present themselves to him in a way that makes them appeal very strongly.* Conflicts come because of these two opposing motivations. St. Thomas explains it this way:

. . . the sensitive appetite has something of its own, by virtue whereof it can resist the commands of reason. For the sensitive appetite is naturally moved, not only by the estimative power in other animals, and in man by the cogitative power which the universal reason guides, but also by the imagination and sense. Whence it is that we experience that the irascible and concupiscible powers do resist reason, inasmuch as we sense or imagine something pleasant, which reason forbids, or unpleasant, which reason commands.[9]

Pleasant and Unpleasant Aspects.   Every personal problem is a complex interweaving of these pleasant and unpleasant aspects. Because of a person's state of conflict and unhappiness, the unpleasant negative aspects are talked about and examined first. However, the more positive and reasonable phases of a situation gradually begin to come forward, as the negative tones are thought

[9]St. Thomas, (D): I, Q. 81, a. 3, reply obj. 2.

through and clarified. Often, just speaking of these negative feelings in the interview removes some of their disturbing power. As a result, even by the end of the first interview, a person may be much more positively disposed to reconsider and re-evaluate the various factors that, until now, have caused him to fix so negatively on some person, place, or thing.

Recall and Reflection on Emotions. We notice here that the "expressing" or "releasing" of these negative emotions in a counseling interview is actually the memory or "reminiscence" of these emotional experiences and not simply the emotions themselves. People are in the interview to work out a reasonable and happy solution to their problems. The first stage is to get these negations out so they can examine and clarify them with the counselor's objective assistance. This relationship is, therefore, calm and unemotional. An important part of the counselor's skill, as we shall see, is to keep it that way. Consequently, even when the person is discussing his negative attitudes towards himself or others, he is doing it in a fundamentally unemotional way. His reason is at work examining, comparing, and relating these emotions to their more basic causes. This kind of counseling process is a demonstration of St. Thomas' statement that human memory not only recognizes and reproduces past events but, in combination with the cogitative power of reason, can trace down individual past experiences and relate them to their causes and purposes. Expressing these negative feelings about a person, place, or thing in an objective counseling relationship, is one of the first stages in acquiring a new understanding of these various hostilities and the important positive motivations which underlie them.[10]

Clarification of Emotions. Once these resistant emotions are sufficiently unfolded, a person begins to have a more reasonable view of himself and these conflicting situations. This results in a more positive and balanced judgment of the people and events that were previously so resented. Counseling does not necessarily remove the emotions surrounding a particular person, place, or thing. It changes the direction of the emotions. For example, a person may still be angry but his anger is now directed at some obstacle in the

---

[10] ". . . man has not only memory, as other animals have in the sudden recollection of the past; but also reminiscence by syllogistically, as it were, seeking for a recollection of the past by the application of individual intentions." St. Thomas, (D): I, Q. 78, a. 4.

path of a reasonable goal. Such emotions, rightly directed, supply added impetus towards achieving desired goals.

Clarification Process Illustrated. In the following excerpts the aviation cadet, in thinking out his own values, finds himself differing with his uncle's way of life (X):[11]

P: I don't know just how that ties in, but I've got to learn not to be so tense. I've got to learn not to be so particular. I just happened to realize that in the last few days. My uncle always prides himself on being very thorough but I really think at least for the present generation he is wrong in being so thorough, because while it might have worked out a hundred years ago, nevertheless, today things are different, and you're expected to be faster and quicker. So, one thing I can do is to be less sensitive to little things and not be quite so tense about everything I do. I think that together with controlling myself when I'm in the mood for being so nervous and upset will set me quite a ways on the road to being more normal and healthy.

C: Two important factors now are to relieve much of the tension from unimportant details—to relax in what you do—and to restrain your feelings so as not to be too nervous or too upset.

This young man is slowly disentangling his life goals from those of his uncle. In the beginning of counseling he felt strongly resentful towards his uncle. But as he acquires the ability to make his own judgments and gain satisfactions from responsible achievements his hostility and resentment towards his uncle decrease. He continues:

P: At times I feel if I were just an average guy like most fellows I wouldn't let things bother me too much. I would just go out in a sensible way and look at my own life and just consider problems as something that could be settled. People don't hold unkind thoughts toward their parents or anyone else at home. They just try to look at it in a Christian way and go about their own business. My uncle wasn't always this way. He used to be good towards us. I suppose it's probably because he isn't better himself that things don't go better with him and the rest of the family. But there is not really anything I can do about it and the big thing is to try to get out and forget it all. I don't know, if I'd just look upon it as being an ordinary problem the same as anyone else has and what I must do, and should do, is to work hard at my assignment at the base and then I could probably settle it quickly.

[11]In an earlier interview, the cadet told of his uncle's living in his home.

He can now reject what the uncle does but still accept and respect his uncle as a person. Later in the interview series, he realizes that the tendency to blame his uncle was a way of avoiding the responsibility for guiding his own life. In this evaluation we notice he does not change his view that his home life was unhappy. Recognizing this unhappiness, however, he is able at the same time to accept the people in the home. Now, it is no longer a question of reforming his uncle but of making his own judgments and carrying out his own life plan:

P: And along with that idea I have kind of gotten away from the idea of blaming my uncle for everything because while I do think the home life is terrible, a lot of times I like to use that as an escape though because I know it has affected me, but at the same time I know that a lot of this stuff is my own fault and it is only going to be through me that it will be ironed out. And even though I'm talking about my uncle and while it may be true, nevertheless, I should put some of those ideas away and get wise to what I should do and start doing it.

Not Complete Unrestraint. This is significant evidence that there is no absolute compulsion in the direction of these disordered emotional and sense appetites, as some psychologists and psychiatrists have thought. As these people can talk about these urges and examine them objectively, they also begin again to have some control over them. We notice in the excerpts from later interviews that the compelling force of these disordered urges grows less intense as people broaden their outlook so as to keep before them their individual, reasonable goals and a more complete view of their main life purposes. Consequently, the person moves gradually towards greater emotional maturity and stability. The solution to personal problems is, therefore, not in the direction of complete emotional release and unrestraint. On the contrary, a person has a fundamental drive to control and order his emotional urges. His happiness is in a measure determined by the degree to which he can do this. Such reasonable self-control and integration are, therefore, possible and are the ideal normality that he naturally seeks. As St. Thomas puts it:

. . . from the fact that the irascible and concupiscible resist reason in something, we must not conclude that they do not obey.[12]

12St. Thomas, (D): I, Q. 81, a. 3.

Rather, as he points out in the same context,

> in man the sensitive appetite is naturally moved by this particular reason. But this same particular reason is naturally guided and moved according to the universal reason: wherefore in syllogistic matters particular conclusions are drawn from universal propositions. Therefore, it is clear that the universal reason directs the sensitive appetite, which is divided into concupiscible and irascible; and this appetite obeys it. But because to draw particular conclusions from universal principles is not the work of the intellect, as such, but of the reason: hence it is that the irascible and concupiscible are said to obey reason rather than to obey the intellect. Anyone can experience this in himself.[13]

St. Thomas explains that this conflict is due originally to the effects of original sin. While man's reasonable nature was not intrinsically affected, he is now in a much less integrated state. To achieve any reasonable integration in an action, he must struggle against ignorance, unrestrained self-will, discouragement, and various excessive compensations.[14] It is still possible, however, for him to reach a reasonable solution to his problems, particularly if he has God's special help. He is not in any state of complete frustration but has the capacity for reasonable control of his actions.

Positive Urges Organized.   We have seen also that the content of opening interviews is not entirely negative. The fact that the person is unhappy and has come for help on his own responsibility indicates a fundamentally positive will. This positive will, however, has, for the most part, been indefinite and confused. Before he came for counseling, a person's positive will may have been vaguely indicated in a number of ways. He may have gone to relatives or friends for help and found that even those who were sympathetic did not understand, and perhaps made him resistant and irritated by their advice and direction. He may have sought other kinds of distraction in activity, amusements, or hobbies but found these to be, at best, temporary alleviations. He had no way to tackle his problems directly. His attempts to solve them were sporadic, disorganized, and inconsistent.

Disorganization Becomes Threat.   The very disorganized state of a person's problems can itself become a threat to him. These prob-

13*Ibid.*, a. 3.
14St. Thomas, (D): I–II, Q. 85, a. 3.

lems can be on his mind all the time and be a constant worry because they are not seen clearly. Rather, they form a vague, unfocused, but threatening background that colors all his actions; even those that may bring him some measure of achievement and pleasure. We see this in the following excerpt:

P: I have had quite a lot to worry about, but it's been over a period of years—I mean which may have something to do with this. I don't know—maybe so. Maybe you can tell me, I don't know. But, I had a very unfortunate thing happen to me right after I finished school about ten or eleven years ago, and it's been a constant source of worry to me all the time. It's been something that I haven't been able to talk with anyone, you know, I mean it's something that I can't discuss with anyone, but uh (Nervous laugh) maybe uh (Pause) if you think that it might help me to uh—well, if it might help me to tell you about it—I'll tell you what it is. (She tells what is preying on her mind.) Well, it's been an awful worry to me. I mean it just preys on my mind all the time. I mean worrying about it. And all these things just put together, just about drive me crazy, and uh—it just keeps me in kind of a whirl all the time. It bothers me all the time. It's on my mind all the time. It's the hardest thing in the world for me to tell him because I don't know how he would react, you see, I've just—I've just harbored this thing so long, you know, and even my family doesn't know—the true circumstances under which it happened. It just happened, and I didn't want to discuss it, and I didn't discuss it, and I just tried to—I just kept it to myself because I didn't want to discuss it.

This disorganized awareness of problems often involves, as in this case, a particular situation that a person has never been able to speak to anyone about. Through counseling, the person can now begin to face and work out his problems directly. Instead of these worries and conflicts "preying on his mind" and being a constant source of disturbance, a person now has a means by which, one by one, they can be uncovered and examined calmly and objectively. The interview becomes a focal point around which he can center his attack. Through it he can channel his positive urges and harness all his desire to solve his difficulties. Previously, the person was spreading himself in many directions to escape or compensate for his feelings of failure and inadequacy. None of these was effective in solving his problems or in giving him any measure of contentment. On the contrary, they usually were leading him all the farther into confusion and unhappiness. Through counseling, he strengthens his positive urges by focusing them much as a diffuse light becomes powerful when it is concentrated.

Growth of Positive Attitudes. As the interviews proceed, we notice how these favorable, positive attitudes towards himself and others grow more pronounced while negative and hostile ones decrease. People make statements about feeling better, having more courage to face their problems, and greater hope of finding a solution. The fact that they have come for counseling and have begun openly to face their difficulties brings them much satisfaction. This satisfaction increases with every further achievement. These positive feelings do not of themselves indicate greater self-understanding, but they are generally the first stage away from discouragement and hopelessness. A person can again feel there is some chance for him to reach a better state of self-integration.

Growth in Self-Acceptance. Before he came for counseling, the person has been groping more or less unsuccessfully with personal issues. He is dissatisfied with himself.[15] He may even feel worthless and incapable of meeting the conflicts of life and attempting any meaningful achievements. Successful living seems to be beyond his power. He does not understand why he cannot be as others and have the normal achievements which he wants and which others seem to get without too great difficulty. In the process of the interviews, there is an unfolding of the reasons behind these blockings and inadequacies. Through them the positive feelings gradually become self-understanding. This self-understanding is a major part of the changes which the counseling process introduces into a person's life.

Counseling Activates Self-Knowledge. So, although his opening statements are predominantly negative because the person is upset and confused, yet they also contain evidence of positive urges and disorganized self-knowledge. Such a person usually knows more about himself than people may credit him. The difficulty is that he cannot see himself clearly enough to use this knowledge. Coun-

[15]Raimy shows this self-disgust factor as characteristic of opening interviews in his negative self-reference category. In successful interviews, by the middle of the counseling process there are ambivalent attitudes towards self and finally, at the end of counseling, expressions of satisfactions and self-acceptance. (Victor C. Raimy: The Self-Concept as a Factor in Counseling and Personality Organization, Ph.D. thesis, Ohio State University, Columbus, Ohio, 1943.)

seling as such then does not give knowledge in the sense that the counselor gives the person new information. The counseling process, however, often enables a person to seek and acquire added information both from his own more alert observation and from others. But these are effects of the interviews themselves and not a part of counseling. The main consequence of counseling is that it aids a person to use his knowledge in such a way that it becomes integrated self-understanding. Through more adequate use of what he already knows, he is then in a position to make better choices, within the means that are available to him, to reach desired goals.

CHAPTER V

EXPLORING CHILDHOOD INFLUENCES

In the state in which a person comes for counseling, he ordinarily is aware only of a series of conflicting urges and feelings that somehow are preventing him from doing what he should. He may recognize in himself a number of characteristics different from those around him. He may feel inferior, see that he is not achieving all that he might, fear that his marriage is failing, or in some other way be conscious of a lack of certain necessary virtue or accomplishment. Generally, he does not connect any of his present problems with the past or even with any other factors in the present.

Sources of Conflict. As people talk about themselves, however, and with the counselor's aid begin to examine the underlying motives and causes of their conflicts, their self-examinations usually carry them gradually into the past. As these new awarenesses dawn on them, they are often surprised to discover how the past can still be affecting their judgments and attitudes. But many personal conflicts which show themselves in later life seem rooted in a person's earlier experiences, particularly those of childhood. The home, school, and other early influences are sources of stability and strength, provided the values they represent are permanently effective. But when any of these values is unsound, it can cause disturbance.

At the time these disturbances take place, the child is apparently at least partially aware of them. As the years go by, the actual situations are often forgotten but the disturbing and confusing attitudes or emotions they engendered seem to retain their power to influence his judgments and reactions. They therefore continue to produce increased conflict through the years. As the child grows into adult life, he must face reality and assume responsibilities. Somewhere in a person's process of development, the needs for responsible, self-determined decisions assert themselves. Because these attitudes and emotions do not meet the demands of a person's present life, they generate further insecurities and fears. Then these conflicting values begin to take their toll and produce the kind of unhappiness that is characteristic of the opening interview.

Consequently, as people examine themselves in counseling, they often grow aware that many of their present ways of judging persons and situations are unsound because, 1) they seem never to have learned a valid scale of values for their present living, or 2) somehow, even when their values are basically reasonable, their emotional reactions are disordered and in conflict with these values. Both of these conditions are usually present in varying degrees and, during the process of counsel, the person gradually disentangles and separates them.

In the present chapter, therefore, we will consider some excerpts from counseling interviews in which childhood influences seem to have set up inadequate life values and attitudes. In the following chapter we will attempt to show how emotions can themselves be so affected by past experiences that they cause confusions and disturbances in a person's present reactions.

THE HOME

The home is the first place in the child's experience from which values are acquired. Later, his relationship is gradually extended to the neighborhood and then to the school. These factors can sometimes reinforce and sometimes offset the home influence. The home directly teaches the child many values. The child acquires others by imitation. The home in particular—among other early childhood influences—may create an atmosphere that is not conducive to adequate learning. As a consequence, adults in interviews often discover that they have never really acquired a workable personal scale of values. We see this indicated in the following excerpt of a college graduate student (J):[1]

C3: This, what reality is, in a sense, or what are the norms which represent reality—in relationship to yourself—that's confusing, isn't it? And you're just unsure whether it's ever been figured out entirely.
P4: Yes, I don't know that, but I know that all people, in order to have some kind of working relationship, must have something worked out, I mean personally, they have their own scale figured out as to what

[1]Designated by symbol (J).

it is, and they go by that. And right now, I don't think I have such a personal scale. I think that having seen clearly what two factors were at work here and then, uh, uncovering the one, and discarding it, here I am with a new one, but I still don't have a scale to measure it or other things.

C4: It's a new way of evaluating yourself, and therefore it needs a great deal more delineation.

P5: Uh huh. This is the first time that I've felt free to do that.

C5: It's your first real acceptance of a positive worthwhile self in a—shall we say—a fundamentally realistic sense.

P6: Uh huh. (Pause)

In this case, from this woman's early memories, the tones of the home were critical and unaccepting. As a result she seemed never able to accept herself as a real person who had worth and meaning. This produced a sense of artificiality in everything she did and left her without the power of objective self-appraisal and judgment. This kind of awareness of the inadequacy of early learning due to a lack of understanding, acceptance, and approval is comparatively common in counseling.

Early Learning Motivation. Personal understanding, acceptance, and approval seem to be basic to any valid learning process. When such positive recognition is not given, particularly to a small child, he loses many of his urges to learn. He also ceases to have the self-confidence necessary for the responsible coping with problems that are within his capacity to solve. From his earliest memories, a child apparently needs to be conscious of receiving affection and approval from adults and particularly from one or both his parents when he successfully completes any task. Such success and approval build up his ability and courage to meet similar situations when they arise again. Otherwise, he may tend to withdraw and not attempt a task that brings no apparent reward in approval and affection. When these approval and affection experiences are noticeably absent from his early life, a person may never acquire an adequate scale of personal values. Values and ways of acting, if they are acquired at all from these early influences, may often be only passively accepted or imitated and not actively learned and integrated into a person's life plan. In addition, a person's reaction is apt to be one of resistance and defense which seems to leave him with a deep feeling that he has somehow been hurt and shunted in his normal personality development. This is indicated as the graduate student continues (J):

P11: Another thing, this is the one time when I have really got everything out that was in myself and when nobody did anything about it—like at home, you know, when I would have been criticized—I mean it was just accepted.

C11: That is, this is kind of a second revealing of yourself and at first somehow in the home it was attacked and criticized. Now having been done again is—it has been accepted and so it is very positive.

P12: And I suppose that's why I uh, have played so many roles and been so artificial, because uh, I suppose in a way I was hurt very deeply at home. I was sort of determined that, well, if it happens once, shame on you, but if it happens twice, shame on me, and I wasn't going to be caught again I suppose. (Pause) Because, uh, I mean, their—their statements and so on, they weren't uh—I mean if they were objectively true, it would have been all right, but they weren't. I mean, you could have accepted it if it were a real situation, but when you realize that, that it was wrong, well then, you just don't want to take any chances on its happening again.

C12: That is, sort of feeling basically that they were wrong in it, you didn't want to leave yourself open for them to do that to you again.

P13: Yes, and I suppose that probably happens to a lot of people. And I don't suppose—if it hadn't been for this—I know I would never have changed. I mean, I suppose it is very unusual for it to have broken and come out again.

C13: Kind of a second birth, which wouldn't—would not have been possible, in your view, except through this relationship—that is, through a relationship of this kind.[2]

Reasonable Recognition of Worth. Consequently, it is often necessary for parents and others, especially those in some supervisory or superior role, to make statements which recognize real achievements and give genuine approval. Reasonable recognition of the opinions, judgments, and achievements of children and adults does not seem to contribute to any excessive pride or superiority complex. Rather, this gives them the feeling of adequacy and security they need to continue to make responsible choices in their lives.

Moral Virtue. The motivation must be such, however, that it gets its main value from the reality itself and not merely from the

[2]See Chapter XII for a more detailed discussion of the excerpt.

accompanying affection and approval. Otherwise it will not be permanently effective. The young child's motivation seems more focused on receiving affection and approval and less centered on the value of the independent achievement of the task. As he grows older, however, his concern is more with the integrated achievement of the goal itself and the satisfaction this brings and he is less interested in the approval and affection reward that may still go with it. Both factors seem to be always present in most motivation, but independent self-appraisal seems the more important for mature and adequate adult living.

In some ways, since the small child in his immediate short-term goals and actions tends to excess in his enthusiasms and lack of restraint, his major moral virtue might be said to be temperance. As the child grows older, reasonable insight gives him the capacity to plan and aim at achieving longer-term goals. To reach these he must begin to acquire that patience and perseverance which are necessary to cope with temporary frustration and failure. He must also recognize limits that go with both his rights and his duties towards the rights of others. In this sense, then, the more important virtues for older children might be said to be fortitude and justice.

Dominating Personalities. In addition to lack of understanding, acceptance, and approval, another factor people often uncover in counseling is the way in which the dominance of one individual in their home or early environment produced an insecurity in judgment and a lack of self-confidence. Some homes center around one person, whose attitudes everyone else reflects. When such an influential person is especially dominating, he or she may take over the home and determine its value. This may seriously impede the child's growth in responsibility. When all judgments in the home are made by adults, the developing child gains no confidence in his own ability to make decisions. The mother, father, sometimes a grandparent or even an older brother or sister, may so absorb a child's life that he never acquires a sense of his own identity or conviction of his power of judgment. When these people are "always right," and "always know best," the child feels he must consult them before he decides anything. He is insecure when he does not have their support and direction. This insecurity may cause him great unhappiness even in early childhood. It comes to a head, however, especially in adolescence, when he is forced to begin to set up his own life patterns and acquire his own convictions.

Indecision Illustrated. In the following excerpt the aviation cadet indicates this inability to make decisions (X):

P: You wouldn't have two opposing forces and I think that works out pretty well because I know lots of times I tried to do things in lab period—when a person is on their own and they have to follow the instructions and carry them out themselves, I've found I had—it's just like pulling teeth to try to think anything through, and that makes me think I've got a pretty weak will and not—I know there really isn't any such thing actually, but I mean I'm more or less led by the strongest urge that I have rather than by what I know is right. For instance, I get a conflict inside myself and I decide that I've not got much spunk—I figured out what I should do—I should go out and get interested in something and make some friends. I realize that I'm doing wrong in not being more sociable and that I can develop myself the way I should be. . . . And I just drift from side to side in making a decision—really it's not anything within me that makes a decision—it's just drifting with the strongest force you might say.

At this stage the aviation cadet feels pressed to make some decisions about himself. Yet he is not sure what to decide since he now has no way of consulting the home. We saw in the excerpts in the previous chapter that, as he thought through his instability, he realized that many of his ideas were directly influenced by his uncle. Now, he was gradually discovering that his uncle's views were not always the views of other people. If he sought advice from others he found himself caught between what his uncle told him and what others expressed. In the midst of this, he could make no secure judgment. Elsewhere he describes his feeling as similar to that of climbing up a stair in an amusement park fun-house and noticing a ball rolling down a track in the same direction he was climbing. So, he said he did not know whether he was going up or down and could not trust his own judgments.

Dependency. When a parent has made all the decisions, the child or young adult may later need to depend on companions for guidance. He often cannot make his own way without the support and reassurance of his friends. The following excerpt is taken from a young woman, a college junior (Y).[3] Previously she had been very dependent on her mother. Being away from home she was now guided

---

[3]Designated by symbol (Y).

by three older girls. These girls made up her schedule. She went to them for advice on every class assignment. As the interviews proceeded, she came to recognize that she was as capable as these girls. As she grew confident in her abilities, she began to understand the reason for the intense hostility which she often felt both towards her mother and these girls, even though she was dependent on them. She saw that this hostility was the confused result of her desire to make her own independent judgments. The following excerpt gives one of the first steps towards this independence (Y):

P: You know, I did a remarkable thing today and I just feel wonderful about it. You know what I did? I actually went over and made out my schedule for the next quarter and handed it in, got it approved without even consulting my board of directors. This is the first time I ever did anything like that. Ever since I have been up at —— I have always had to consult Mary, Betty, and Sue about everything I took. This time I just made up my mind I was going to do it myself and I did it. You ought to have seen the look on their faces. I went to H.'s and they were sitting there having cokes and I said, "Well, I got my schedule all set and approved"—You could've knocked them over with a feather! Then, I kind of breezily like said, "I'm going to take French this quarter too. I thought I'd like French better than Spanish." At that their faces really fell because just the day before they all insisted that I should take Spanish because I would like it much better than French. So you see I am really a new person. I really surprised myself with that one!

Reasonable Self-Confidence. In this instance, the girl's mother was very conscious of not wanting her to become "proud and vain." Consequently, from this girl's earliest memories, her mother belittled any of her achievements or abilities. This brings up the point of the degree to which many adults seem focused on keeping a child from "thinking too much of himself." Perhaps too, more than is commonly realized, the mass effects of industrialism has made people feel much less personally secure and adequate than in previous non-industrial societies. Whatever the reasons may be, interviews like these often reveal that, for many people, the process towards mature virtue is not in the direction of curbing any excess of personal pride but rather in overcoming their lack of a reasonable self-esteem. Somehow their past environment seems to have left them with insufficient confidence and courage to make those decisions necessary for responsible virtue.

Progress Away from Inferiority. In the case of these three people, the reasonable evaluation which counseling facilitated made them realize that they had more worth, ability, and capacity for responsible decisions than they had credited to themselves. Consequently, the growth in humility for them was away from this unreasonable inferiority which St. Thomas calls pusillanimity or infantilism. Interestingly, he points out that it would be gravely wrong to be responsible for this kind of infantilism if it prevents achievements, and impedes the reasonable fulfillment of abilities which God has given.[4] He comments elsewhere[5] that parents themselves can cause this infantilism. They do this particularly by not allowing a child normal opportunities for the various independent choices that are within his capacity as he grows into maturity. This same responsibility for inferiority complexes would also appear to apply to teachers in schools and others, who, in a confused desire to keep children "humble and obedient," do not give them a chance to develop courage and confidence in themselves.

This does not mean any questioning of the value of genuine humility which involves a reasonable pursuit of personal excellence nor of the importance of that responsible obedience which is essential to any civilized and mature living. Sometimes, however, while the intention no doubt was to achieve[6] these, the motivation offered and the means used seem to have produced only an immaturity and insecurity of judgment. Such a sense of personal inadequacy is the exact opposite of that reasonable humility which is necessary for a courageous and at the same time temperate and just way of life.

Responsible Religious Virtue. This has implications for the religious and spiritual growth of the child into adult life. Religious values accepted passively as part of the conditioning of the home and school atmosphere would not of themselves be adequate for stable and mature Catholic living in adult life. Somewhere in the

---

[4]St. Thomas Aquinas: *Summa Theologica*, II–II, Q. 133, a. 1. Translated by Fathers of the English Dominican Province, New York. Benziger Brothers, 1947. Reprinted from the *Summa Theologica* with the permission of Benziger Brothers, Inc., Publishers and Copyright Owners.

[5]Commentary on St. Paul's Epistles Ad Col., C. 3, v. 21, Eph, C. 6, v. 4.

[6]What Pope Pius XII has said to teachers about the children in their care, applies as well to parents: "Give them also a knowledge of their own personality and thus of the greater treasures of freedom; train their minds to sound criticism, but at the same time imbue them with a sense of Christian humility, of just submission to the laws and the duty of mutual dependence among men." Pope Pius XII: "Papal Guidance for Teachers," *Catholic Action*, Vol. XXXI, No. 10, October 1949, p. 18.

process of maturing, the young Catholic must integrate and activate all the religious and the moral values which Catholicity represents to him. Only if they are part of his active life plan, consciously accepted and determined by himself, can they really become effective in promoting his growth in sanctity. The passive acceptance of religious values might account for many of the collapses in adult life of those children from religious homes and Catholic school background. These values evidently were never actively integrated into their lives. Consequently, when grave issues faced these people, they were not capable of responsible, self-reliant judgments about their religion. Instead, they were as easily made dependent on some other influence which led them in the opposite direction.

Even among those young people who have decided on the religious life, there often remain personal problems and home attachments which, if not clarified, may lessen the spiritual value of their later dedication. In the religious life itself there may be a need, not only of religious instruction or guidance in the principles of the spiritual life, but also of a counseling process which would enable religious to understand more clearly their own inadequacies and confused or conflicting tendencies. As Father Gerald Kelly has pointed out:

> It is not inconceivable that young men and women might enter religion without having accomplished any real separation from the parental apron strings. It is possible, too, that this exaggerated dependence on parents might spoil an otherwise promising vocation, or that ingrained dependence will be merely transferred to a kindly superior, confessor, or spiritual director. In fact, even for those who are not unduly dependent, the religious life of its very nature contains certain dangers to proper growth in maturity. This type of life calls for much more dependence than is normally had in adult life; if this is pressed too far it can readily change childlikeness into childishness. It is a wise superior or director or other person in authority who encourages a salutary self-confidence and wholesome spirit of initiative in his subordinates.[7]

Parental Conflicts. Quarrels between the parents is another influence on both the child's security and his confidence in his parents' word. If the parents agree, a child can find at least temporary security in what they tell him. Even a dominating parent is giving a

---

[7]Gerald Kelly, S.J.: "Emotional Maturity," *Review for Religious*, Copyright 1947, by Gerald C. Ellis, Vol. VII, No. 1.

child some guidance. But confusion arises when parents themselves are in conflict and openly argue in front of the children. We see this in the following statement by the aviation cadet (X):

P: Each of our parents seemed to try to turn the children against the other. Now my mother's mother, my grandmother, lived there from time to time, and she seemed very put out, because she was not permitted to have an active hand in running the house, and in raising the children, and she very openly stated to anyone that happened to be around, that she didn't understand why she didn't have an active hand. She did everything she could to turn us against my father. As I said before, I don't think it was intentional, they did what they thought was right, but it's just a lack of knowledge as to how to properly raise children, and just what part each should play in raising the children. My mother, I think, was inclined to permit her mother to think for her without reasoning things out for herself, and I think she was weak in that respect. And uh, the fact that each parent talked about the other, and tried to outdo the other. One would tell us we could do a certain thing, and when the other found out we were permitted to do it, we were told we couldn't and it was just a great deal of uncertainty, not knowing what to do. We couldn't believe our parents.

Such a conflict deeply affects a child. He seeks support from both parents in forming his ideals and determining his values. If the parents disagree, the child is inevitably caught between the two. He cannot be sure they will do what they say and he cannot trust them. To be forced to choose one against the other increases the child's misery and inadequacy.

Any serious parental quarrels can bring on this conflict. It is most striking, however, in the case of divorce or permanent separation. The following is typical of statements made by many adults who were children of divorced or separated parents:

My parents' divorce, even though it came before I was old enough to understand, brought grief and bewilderment and fear that lay over all the years of my childhood and adolescence. From the time I met my father, I felt an instinctive desire to know him. I learned to watch every car and search for him everywhere. But there was an unreasoning fear mingled with the hope . . .

Throughout my teens I was lonely. . . . I treasured pictures of my parents together taken in the years before their separation, and tried to reconstruct their home. I wanted to remember that there was a time, even though I could not recall it, when we had had a home together.[8]

Parental Rejection. Sometimes the rejection of a parent can be so overwhelming that it becomes one of the central motives of a person's life, as in the following excerpt:

P: And when I was thirteen, I went to learn my trade. My father who was a farmer told me I never would be a farmer—"you're sick all the time, so I'll give you a trade," and he did. And the lady where I was working—my boss' wife—I was yellow and a kinda sickly boy—so she put me in the hospital. I was in the hospital for about two weeks— . . . and it was just like somebody told me something when I saw my mother—black eyes, good-looking woman—and just like, it seemed at that minute, I had in my mind that when I grew up, she would always be my enemy—and she was. That's the reason I moved to this part of the country.

If one child is preferred by the parents, the neglected child can suffer serious emotional handicaps. Children are usually preferred because of physical appearance, superior intellectual abilities, or because they resemble one or the other parent. Rejection may come to the less gifted child if he is constantly compared to a brighter brother or sister. We see this in the following excerpt. This young man had just finished high school without getting a diploma while his brother, a year younger, had graduated with honors. From early childhood, he suffered by comparison with his brother. His insecurity is now so great that after a few days he had to leave his first job in a state of nausea, vomiting, and nervousness. In this excerpt from the first interview he is talking about another job (V):

P: It's sort of funny, you don't know which one to take. (Pause)
C: At one time you're secure in going ahead and at another time you're insecure and fearful, you don't know which way to go.
P: (Pause) I think all those fears that I've built up,—I know they have a basis, but I mean, just doing something about them. It's funny, this fear—when you know the thing to do. Of course, for some people it might be just like doing anything for them. Knowing all these things, in one sense, and knowing how to fight against them are two different things.

---

[8]Anonymous: "My Father Is a Stranger," *Woman's Digest*, November, 1948.

C. You've got them kind of catalogued now but still don't know what to do about them. This is what is hard.

P: It's a hard task—when you've been going to school all your life and now all of a sudden there's no school any more. You haven't got but three or four hours in the day during high school and that pattern is kind of hard to get out of—it never struck me quite that way before. Well, my mother seems to understand but my father doesn't you know, it doesn't quite strike him that same pitch. If I could find a job I would like, and I could be happy in . . . I do want to work, it's not that, if I could find something I could be happy doing. If I could adjust myself in a job, you know, like anybody else. I'd like to work and get some things ahead, you know, clothes especially and save money. And then, my father's so much against me. He was so much against me even trying to graduate from high school after two years in the sophomore year, while Jeff got through in less than a year. The day I got my diploma—it wasn't really a diploma, just a kind of certificate, they call it—he didn't even look at it, didn't even congratulate me or anything and it just kind of hurts being around that all the time, you know. Just little things that are said like, oh, he just kind of throws things up all the time. I thought if I could just get away from it, being around that all the time,—maybe I take things too much to heart, more than most people take them, and I think that's true. I think things, little things, hurt me more than the really big ones. You know, I've reached the point now I don't know what to do or where to go or what I'm going to do next.

C: As you think about it, it isn't that you wouldn't want to work, it's the home situation that bothers you now. (P: Uh, huh.) You feel if you could just get away, that perhaps you're too sensitive to it.

Insecurity. The feeling that his father has no interest in what he does and is always pointing out his faults leaves the young man fearful and insecure. He has no confidence in himself since, judging from his father's attitudes, he has no ability. Anything he did seemed meaningless because it was so inferior to his brother's achievements. While this young man is obviously not as gifted as Jeff, he is capable of an ordinary job and a normal family life. His father would probably have been amazed if he knew how devastating his constant preference of Jeff was. Yet, such preferences often happen without the parents' being consciously aware of the extent of damage which is done to the neglected child.

This excerpt continues (V):

P: Maybe I'm just too sensitive, because I know that they're good to me. There's nothing I really *am* wanting.

C: There are a lot of very positive things in the home, aren't there?

P: That's right, I like it, I like things around me at home, you know. I've always been teased, I guess since that time, you know I tried to leave home. And it's just things like that. I realize I've been tied to my mother's apron strings and not free like most people are, simply because of those things that happened back when I was little. It was something that I was never encouraged to overcome, you know, it is really there because I can do things as well as the next person can but it's just that awful feeling that goes back so far.

C: They always keep bringing that up.

P: Uh, huh. I don't know. I can take it, of course, I can sit there and laugh it off as well as the next person can, I mean it's just a joke to them but sometimes it kind of hurts me. Of course, I realize perfectly well that I'm not like Jeff. I can't do things like Jeff can. I'm not the kind of a person that can just pick up stakes and move around like he can. I just can't do that, I never have been able to. They realize it, but I can't see why they should rub it in. People are different the world over, I mean, not all people are alike and just because I'm so totally different from Jeff, why should it be so much rubbed into me?

C: It's more that you feel that when you get the chance to see it clearly you can cope with this tendency to want to be home. You also understand how it did come about from the past and see why you're different from Jeff.

P: Uh, huh. (Pause)

Compensation. We notice already a more positive tone in his appreciation of his home. He also indicates a not uncommon type of compensation that can occur in a home. If one parent prefers one child, another child may be supported by the other parent. In this case, a successful, aggressive father favored the brighter, more achieving son. The mother, partly through sympathy and more probably because of her own needs, increased the other son's insecurity by encouraging him to be dependent on her. Often because a successful husband may have little time or inclination to give his wife the affection and attention she needs the wife may find these in the children, or, what is probable in this case, in the child the father rejects. But this kind of concern for the child has more self-love in it than many parents realize. To compensate for her husband's lack of affection, a mother may prolong her maternal satisfaction by keeping the child excessively dependent and infantile. We notice that this young man's attachment to his mother has not helped him grow in mature self-confidence. It has only served to increase his personal insecurity and fear. By contrast, the younger boy seems to have no such excessive attachment and has much greater self-reliance.

THE NEIGHBORHOOD

Influence of Associates. Each person is a complex combination, not only of the attitudes of his home, but of many people with whom he associated. A person is often unaware of the sources of many of his particular values. The school and companions can also be great influences. If the child is able to be a part of a group, he has many attitudes moderated by his companions. Association with other children give the child an opportunity to face and judge many home values. This may begin even before he goes to school. Slowly he realizes that his father and mother are not always right and what is done in his home may not be what other people do or what they should do. He begins in this way to form attitudes which are his own.

Neighborhood Characteristics. It is not difficult to see how the general tone of a particular group, neighborhood, culture, or type of employment, contains common attitudes toward life. These attitudes penetrate each of the children. They are passed from one to the other, not only by the home, but by their association with one another. Each confirms the views of the whole group. This would explain why neighborhoods have certain characteristics and tendencies which show up consistently.

Shaw demonstrated that the same neighborhoods, in Chicago, tended each year to produce the same proportion of juvenile problems. The neighborhoods also had the same variations in both truancy and adult crime:

A second major finding is that rates of truancy, delinquency, and adult crime tend to vary inversely in proportion to the distance from the center of the city. In general the nearer to the center of the city a given locality is, the higher will be its rates of delinquency and crime. . . . Another striking finding in this study is the marked similarity in the distribution of truants, juvenile delinquents, and adult criminals in the city. Those communities which show the highest rates of juvenile delinquency also show, as a rule, the highest rates of truancy and adult crimes.[9]

While living in a delinquent area would not of itself cause delinquency in an individual, yet a child who is unfortunate enough to be raised in one of these areas has many more factors to work against than one raised in a suburban home. The neighborhood influence is strong enough to be a major factor of difference in the general degree of delinquency, truancy, and crime which are reported each year. If neighborhoods are so influential in delinquency, they likely also are a strong force in a child's life in other less observable ways.

Double Culture. One conflict that is sometimes uncovered in interviews is the situation of a first generation American child of foreign parents. Such children are often raised in a community whose inhabitants are largely from the same section of Europe. They absorb both the old country attitudes and the peculiar adaptations which the first generation children have made to the American culture in which they are now living. Yet, these adaptations are colored by their foreign background. They differ from those of a group of American children whose forefathers had been in this country for some generations.

The first generation child must sometimes face some almost diametrically opposed goals and values in the same life situation. In his home and neighborhood, the child is used to certain customs and traditions. As he begins to mix outside his community, he may find himself in conflict. He may recognize that people look on him differently. This often serves to increase his self-consciousness and insecurity. He has one set of values, judgments, and purposes from the home. When he goes out among his companions, he has to acquire another set in order to be accepted by them. He may be confused by these conflicting loyalties. In living this double life, a child may feel guilty when he returns to the home. This guilt is not clearly understood or analyzed, but it can produce a deep feeling of worthlessness. Even as an adult, he may feel he belongs nowhere—neither to America nor to the country from whence his parents came.

One young man working out this problem only came to realize that he was really an American after he had an opportunity to be

[9]Clifford R. Shaw: *Delinquency Areas,* The University of Chicago Press, Chicago, 1929, pp. 202–3.

stationed in his parents' native country during the war. He experienced great happiness in knowing that, though he could speak their language, he was not like these European people. He was never sure before that he belonged in America.

Consequences in Marriage. In marriage adjustments particularly, divergent family and social backgrounds may be a major cause of conflict. One of these is the contrasting characteristics sometimes resulting from the farm and the city. While these differences are decreasing, they still may be a contributing cause to serious marital misunderstanding. In the following excerpt a young couple, after three years of marriage, are on the verge of separation. They have no children. The woman feels the husband does not love her because, in her judgment, he is cold and unemotional. She finds his family are the same. He, in turn, cannot understand her reaction. She is speaking (U) :[10]

(W—wife; H—husband; C—counselor)

W: (Speaks in a rapid, fiery tone) His people—I consider them almost without emotions—they are very unemotional. I don't consider any of his family to have normal emotions, and our family is just the opposite . . .

H: (Speaks in a slow, calm, and somewhat halting manner) But I never doubted that my mother loved me. I have several brothers and sisters —all of us are in comparatively good health. I don't think there is any major difference between us. Well, I have one or two I like better than the others. But there has never been any family fights or family arguments. We don't get around to visit each other very often. We're spread out all over the country. I think my wife feels because we don't get around to visiting each other that we don't care anything about each other.

C. As you think about it, that is the major difference in the way you judge . . .

W: (Interrupts) I don't think he loves me because he never shows it. I try to take that into consideration from his background . . .

H: We are slow to show any emotions. We are slow to become angry. I never get mad at the time it comes up. After I leave the situation I think of something I should have said, and it makes me mad I didn't say it. But I just don't get mad at the time.

[10]Designated by symbol (U). In this instance the husband and wife came together for the first interview and then, as is customary, it was left up to them whether they would continue to come for joint counseling or come separately. They decided to come for separate interviews. (L) is the subsequent series of excerpts of the wife.

C: In other words, your whole life was rather on a placid basis where you were sure of affection . . . and your wife's was the exact opposite.

Difference of Values.   Conflicts like this can happen because of the difference of men and women's values. Men tend to value the large, seemingly important goals; women, the smaller symbols of affection and consideration. In this case, this difference is increased because the man came from a quiet, unemotional home and the wife from a warm, affectionate one. Both judge their relationship by what they knew in their parents' home.

This difference may never have been clear to these two people before. One person can draw wrong conclusions from another's actions because he never understands how the other feels. A husband may assume that his wife always reacts as he does. Because of this, he may never grasp that, in some instances, she has been deeply hurt or rejected. As in this case, a man's inability to understand a woman's need for reassurance and affection is often a cause of marital conflict. Many quarrels are the effect of this basic rejection which the woman feels. The husband often does not understand this. He may consider expressions of affection unmanly and therefore unnatural. He expects the woman to see how faithful and responsible he is in what he considers the important side of their marriage. The woman, on the other hand, cannot easily be persuaded that expressions of affection, regard, and appreciation in little things are unimportant. They are often the only reward she seeks in return for what she does. This is demonstrated as the interview continues:

W: He never does anything just on the spur of the moment. He never gets a thrill out of anything . . .
C: That bothers you—that calm sort of manner. You would like him to get a little more alarmed.
W: Occasionally—I think it's only normal.
C: You'd like some expression of emotion sometime.
W: I think he should try to change.
H: Even to the point of being unnatural.
W: Yes, I do think so.
H: ,I've tried to for two and a half years.
C: You've tried to change but can't.
H: If I spent half of our income on gambling (Cites other things he could do)—if I did these things, she would have reason to think I didn't love her.

W: He never tells me he loves me.
H: When was the last time you told me you loved me.
W: I stopped! (Emphatic)
C: You just stopped being affectionate too.
W: Before we were married he didn't act like that.
C: There is a difference since you've been married.
W: He never even puts his arm around me.
C: It seems to hinge around that expression of affection.
W: He says its unnatural—he said it wouldn't be natural.
H: Flattery and compliments never were natural for me. I don't say that there's anything wrong in doing it. I say it isn't natural. She judges me by the only criteria that she has.

Growth in Mutual Understanding.   As these differences are talked out in the unemotional atmosphere of the interview, people grow to know and understand each other better. By themselves, without the counselor's help, such an exchange could have ended in a violent quarrel. This way two people can begin, perhaps for the first time, to see each other objectively with all the differences which their opposite backgrounds and attitudes produce.

THE SCHOOL

Influential Personalities.   Paralleling the neighborhood and the home, another important factor is the school. One or a few individuals may also symbolize the school's influence. Sometimes different influential personalities stand out at each stage of school progress. Attitudes developed in the school can be opposed to the home and the neighborhood. In the study of delinquency, Healy and Bronner[11] found that the desire to appear in the good light of even one adult was a major factor of difference between the group of delinquents and a group of non-delinquents from the same families. If, in a noticeably delinquent neighborhood, the child can yet remain a non-delinquent by the influence of one person, it seems likely that he would acquire many other values through the same kind of influences. In measuring the effectiveness of the school, the home, and the neighborhood, a major factor seems to be the degree to which influential persons are represented in these different groups.

11Wm. Healy and A. Bronner: *New Light on Delinquency and Its Treatment,* New Haven, Yale University Press, 1936.

School in Conflict with Home.   Sometimes in his desire to profit from his education, the child must undergo conflict. The brighter child, for example, may want to improve his speech. As his speech becomes different from that of his companions he may experience isolation and rejection. This can be particularly strong in a foreign neighborhood or in homes of lower social status. Sometimes parents may resent the "airs" which they feel the child is "putting on." The choice of other educational goals may clash with the values of the neighborhood, his companions, and his home. These choices demand a mature measuring of home and neighborhood against the reality which the school represents.

Illustration.   This type of conflict with the home does not always discourage a child. It can spur him on with strong ambition. Intense resentment against criticism may add to a person's determination to succeed just to show his parents how wrong they were. The following excerpt demonstrates this (X):

P: (Pause) I've often had persons tell me that I was very ambitious, and I've just been thinking these last few days—I've been, uh—I got partly through college by working and attending mostly night classes. I don't think I did it because I was ambitious. I'm just like the person who sometimes goes out and gets drunk—just for revenge. I really think I started studying to show them that I could be something. Either that, or else I felt I wanted to master something—to be sure of something. I guess I felt as though I would have more confidence if I completed a certain course and had that knowledge. And I guess, to a great extent, that was so. If a person has a reservoir of knowledge, he feels more free than he would be if he didn't have that training.

C: There's an achievement value in your studies and also a sense of satisfaction in disproving all that belittling.

P: I suppose that is it (Pause) but I think it—it started out as revenge although it, uh, the same as a person who loses his job, and goes out and gets drunk. He feels "Well, I'll show them." He's not hurting anyone else but himself. In this case, it so happened that what I did was of benefit instead of harm. But, I just thought of that angle the last two or three days.

C: The motive was perhaps the same. It's just that you chose a positive thing rather than something like drinking.

Unfortunately, this kind of "revenge" motivation often takes its toll by leaving the person in a disturbed and unhappy state. While his success proved this man's ability and vindicated him against the criticism of his family, it still left him without any sense of real achievement. It had not given him stability or security.

THE CHURCH

Teaching the child his religious obligations can cause him to follow the values of the school and Church. In the first grade, even, differences can appear when, for example, the child starts to question the parents' absence from Sunday Mass. He may also begin to examine other actions of the parents which do not agree with what he is taught in school. With the support of the school and especially of the Church and the Sacraments, he often acquires the maturity and stability to make his own judgments and follow steadfastly his spiritual goals in the face of parental indifference or even some opposition.

On the other hand, if a child is strongly attached to someone in the home or neighborhood who does not support these values, he may be in a state of deep conflict. Such religious conflicts may be more common than we realize. The school may appear to be giving a child religious knowledge and understanding. Actually, much of this information may never become real motivation because persons to whom he is strongly attached differ with these ideals. The child may superficially accept the instructions and practices to fit in with the school program but never integrate them into his own conduct.

Co-operation Necessary—Church, School, Home. Consequently, the degree to which Catholicity is activated in the child's life cannot be measured simply by the information he receives in the school or even by the way he acts in church as long as the school is supervising his actions. We must consider also how those persons who have the strongest influence on the child support his religious goals by their own good example and actions.

This might be a clue to why some mixed marriages turn out well for Catholic children and many do not. Likely, if the most wholesome influence in the home is the Catholic, it will represent basically Catholic values. The children will absorb these. On the other hand, if the most appealing parent is the non-Catholic, even when the Catholic partner may be practicing his religion, the main influence on the child may be that of the non-Catholic. In either case, such differences between parents on so vital a matter as religion cannot but cause some conflict in the child.

Parent May Symbolize Religion.   Often, hostility to religion can result because of the light in which religion is presented. Adults may still retain a strong feeling of resistance to religion without knowing why. They have carried over this hostility from some experiences in childhood. In the following excerpt, as the aviation cadet talks about this feeling in the interview, he sees the causes more clearly (X):

P: Well, I—this is another thing I want to talk about—ever since I was a kid I've had a hard time going to church and now, as I talk about it, I think I know why. My mother is very religious. I think she brings that in everything—religion is in everything. I think it turned all of us against it. I know I'm wrong about it, but a person more or less judges, arrives at a decision based on his own personal experiences. Even though he realizes everyone isn't the same, why, sometimes it's pretty hard to convince oneself. Now she seemed to think that because she went to church everything she did was right, whether it was or not. I think that was partly due to the fact, I mean partially accounted for her ignoring others' ideas and opinions. And, uh, if something would happen which we didn't want to happen, she'd say, "Well, that happened because you didn't go to church." Now I think that's a bad thing to do and I tried to convince her. But just gradually as we grew up we got away from it. I mentioned that to bring out the idea again that they tried to force religion on us—force us to do it without reasoning and by their own actions turned us against something that really was good.

C: Yes, religion had been in your home a symbol of your mother's always being right and like a number of other things, you turned against it in your reaction against her, in a way.

P: (Pause) And, uh, I think too, she seemed to take into her confidence persons at the church and evidently she would mention things about us and before they would even meet us, they would be turned against us. We could tell by their expression. When we were introduced or met them they just seemed to say "Well, you're the one she's been talking about." And it seemed to be that they were right when they agreed with her, and if a person didn't agree with her, they were wrong. This is to a great extent the way everyone feels—if a person agrees with one, why he is right, if he doesn't, he's wrong,—but that isn't always the case.

C: The added factor too was that the church people who became sort of intimate with her began by resenting you without even having met you.

Even though this cadet recognizes his feeling is unreasonable and that he should not judge religion by the actions of a few people, yet he and the other children have all been affected by the mother's unfortunate tones. Now, in adult life he is just beginning to separate religion itself from the extremely hostile childhood emotions which were attached to it. This same conflict can be produced in the school or elsewhere by the imprudent actions of anyone who symbolizes religion. While this type of unreasonable hostility is most commonly formed in childhood, it can also be produced in adults, particularly if they are already in a somewhat emotional state from other causes. These people may quickly be turned against religion because of the actions of only one representative.

The growing process of self-determination, too, can sometimes cause young people to rebel against their religion, not for what it is in itself, but as a symbol of the home. They may, for example, rush heedlessly into an invalid marriage on the urge to "live my own life." The tragedy of these choices is that they are hurried escapes under the guise of taking personal responsibility. They are not the kind of responsible integrated thinking that a counseling process would have produced. These same situations thought out calmly and slowly in interviews could have resulted in the ability to distinguish the religious values from the tones of personal dominance and conflict which the home may have. Unfortunately, when these distinctions are not made, they can result in the emotionally disturbed person making a total rejection of the home and everything it represents. In particular instances, when the home is Catholic, such confused persons can, for reasons often not clear to themselves, stop going to Mass and participating in Catholic activities. The unanalyzed motive for this may often be only the confused, vague desire to be on their own and to be independent of anything which symbolized the unreasonable dominance of the home.

CHILD AND ADULT VALUES

Conflicts can result when the child is denied the normal growth experience which the other children around him enjoy. We notice this in the following excerpt from the young man whose brother was preferred by his father (V):

P: Well, it seems this way, as I look back on it, I really didn't know it at the time. To answer the question truthfully I really didn't know at the time I was doing something to escape. I didn't realize that till about the last year. I would go to bed at night and dream about being a hero in my dreams. I know I was pretty unhappy and ignored by the rest of the kids—I used to want a baseball glove so much and I guess I didn't stress it enough because my father didn't seem to think much about it. I never got it. I guess he thought I'd get hurt.

This is a significant point. Adults are often unaware that a child may have involved reasons for wanting some particular thing. This boy felt isolated from his companions. Getting a baseball glove would have helped him to feel a part of his group. By contrast, his father did not know his world. Could he have understood the child's real reasons, he no doubt would have preferred him to be playing baseball in place of his daydream compensations.

This same conflict may be symbolized in clothes. Even in early school years boys and girls can be made miserable because the parents fail to realize that their clothing is not suited to the standards of the group. A boy who is overly protected by his mother and given too many new clothes may feel too dressed up. Alternately, another may be sensitive because he is dressed poorly. The parents, too, can quickly dismiss a child's request because they do not grasp why he wants a particular kind of clothing. Yet, this can sometimes be a desperate effort on his part to feel he belongs to the group and to bid for the group's acceptance.

Often, the motive in the parents' refusal is simply an economical one. They do not look beyond that. One of the most disturbing kinds of economy is often practiced by making children wear clothes after they do not fit. This conflict can leave permanent scars, particularly if it takes place around the highly sensitive period of early adolescence. Girls in early adolescence are often forced "to wear clothes out." In this blossoming period, when a young girl is apt to be markedly self-conscious, a skirt or sweater that is too tight can become a symbol of extreme conflict. In such a situation, one young girl went through this period in a constant state of agony. Later, as an adult, she felt that much of her extreme self-consciousness, which was now a serious personal handicap, was due to this kind of experience. Describing it in an interview she said, "They might as well have asked me to go down the street naked I felt so miserable." The parents, of course, would never have dreamed of putting the child through this torture if they had understood, and she herself was unable to express it to them. Yet, because their values were simply to save money by having her use all her clothes they completely missed the complexity of the problem as the girl reacted to it.

This conflict of values between the adult and the child takes place because the adult misses many things essential to the child's world. A baseball glove, a new dress, sweater, or similar object can represent an important means of social acceptance. For a child to be denied these may sometimes seem to bar him from a world in which he needs to feel he belongs. With no normal outlet the child may turn to his fantasy world to make up for these denied achievements. The child seldom, if ever, speaks to anyone about this world.

Real Need Behind the Symbol.   The problem here is not what the object is, in itself, but what it means to the child. If he can feel that the parents or other adults, even in their refusal, understand and accept him and, at least in some way, appreciate why he wants the object, much of its symbolic attraction seems to disappear. By discussing the problem in an accepting and understanding relationship, the child can get beyond the symbol to the deeper need of achievement and acceptance which he feels. Once these deeper needs have come into the open, both parents and child can begin to think out constructive ways of fulfilling them.

Punishment.   This same difference of values between the adult and the child often shows itself in the choice of punishment. The adult may consider that the punishment involves only a slight embarrassment or minor inconvenience and penalty. Yet, for a particular child, already in a state of confusion, such a demand may stir up an emotional volcano. The adult may never realize the hurt engendered in the child. This is one of the greatest difficulties in dealing with children. Unless one is sensitive to the child's feelings we cannot tell when the punishment or reprimand may be far in excess of the misdemeanor. Because each child's reactions are his own, there is no common rule. It seems likely that when a child strongly resists a comparatively small punishment, the child has deeper reasons. These he may reveal to an understanding person, especially if this person is not involved in the enforcement of discipline, at least in this instance. This is one of the ways in which a skilled counselor can uncover hidden motives and confusions behind even small disobediences or infractions of rules. Once these basic conflicts are revealed to a sympathetic person, the child usually undertakes the punishment or neglected task with surprising willingness. If, on the other hand, such disturbances are not expressed and thought out, they may result in greater resentment. The individual infraction or penalty assumes added importance because of what it symbolizes to the child.

PAST INFLUENCES PRESENT

In this discussion of childhood influences, we have mentioned only a few of the factors which may be important in an individual's background. There may, of course, also be other past influences coming from some earlier phase of adult life. We have, however, emphasized childhood experiences because they are most commonly mentioned and are usually the most fundamental. These illustrations, taken from adult interviews as they review their childhood, demonstrate how particular environments and the attitudes they produce can carry over and affect adults' present lives. Somehow either the values presented or the emotional tones which were set up around them, prove inadequate for mature living.

How Not to Learn. Mowrer describes some of the effects of this type of inadequate learning experience by saying that it produces a person "who has *learned how not to learn.*" As he explains,

By this I mean that through his resistances, which are acquired on the basis of problem-solving, he becomes capable of staving off the emotional changes which are normally produced during the course of socialization.[12]

Another way of putting this would be to say that the inadequacies of early learning experiences seem to produce a state of "unteachableness" which involves both an inability and an unwillingness to learn from later situations. The result is an absence of docility—in the sense of teachableness—which, rightly understood, should be

[12]O. H. Mowrer: "Implications of a Two-Factor Learning Theory," *The Psychological Service Center Journal*, Vol. II, June, 1950, p. 121.

a part of a person's prudential judgment and action.[13] Consequently, the reaction patterns which a person has developed from these earlier experiences seem to impede his learning much of what he could learn from many later situations. The effects of a person's having "learned how not to learn" can assume a wide variety of forms. But the realization of this tendency is common during counseling. In the following excerpt from Miss W. the young college woman (W), towards the end of a counseling series, we have an illustration of one form that it can sometimes take:

P: Well, I just now or very recently discovered that a lot of times I uh, read things into situations which aren't there, and really make up a whole situation, and then I got to—and then I thought about at home—my grandfather almost any time anything is discussed—like a person, a relative or a neighbor—it's usually about some person or maybe it's some international affair—after everyone has said what they want to say, then he'll start. And he always begins by saying "Now I imagine it's this way . . ." and he'll go on and he'll put everything that comes to his mind into this thing. And he actually hasn't read it or done anything else, I mean, he has just known what he's heard from the conversation, generally at the table. And he just makes up the whole thing in his own mind and at that time without even thinking about it, he just comes out with whatever is in his mind.

C: That is, you see a connection between your own tendency to make a sort of imaginative unfolding of a situation which is not the reality and then act on that, and your grandfather's tendency to take a few phrases someone says about something and build up a whole imaginary unfolding of it and then draw his conclusions from that kind of an imaginary picture.

P: Yes, I suppose I may have got that from him, although it's more obvious in him, because I don't start off by saying I imagine, I probably use some other word, like I feel or I think or uh—but even so it's imaginary. So it's just the same, regardless of how you term it.

C: It's more obvious in him, but you're pretty conscious now that it's the same thing in you, in perhaps a little more subtle form.

We notice here that this young woman was not just unwilling to learn from her experiences. Rather she had acquired a way of immediately falsifying an experience to the point where she could make her own personalized but unrealistic interpretation of it. Since,

13See p. 181 and Chapter XVII.

as she later clarified, she always read her own life patterns into every situation and interpreted each experience according to these fixed patterns, she was in a position where she could learn very little. This tendency to imaginative falsification which she had had for years removed from her the possibility of sharing in the reality of many experiences.

Stereotyped Reactions. When a person is in this negative state of having learned how not to learn, he seems to make little conscious effort to grasp the complexity of any real experience he undergoes. This seems to produce, as we shall discuss in the next chapter, a simple (in the sense of uncomplicated) view of any situation. Consequently, any judgments or actions which such a person is forced to perform, he makes on these uncomplicated and therefore basically inadequate views. This may also help explain, as we shall see, the "stereotyped reactions" which appear to be so characteristic of many people with personal problems. These unsound judgments and the actions following from them do not solve their difficulties but, on the contrary, leave them in an almost continual state of conflict and confusion. Yet somehow, without counseling, they seem often unable to get a different view of themselves or their surroundings.

Combination of Influences. Cameron[14] uses the phrase "biosocial matrix" to designate the various biological and social factors from which a person thus acquires the intricate combination of values and attitudes that go to make up his present acting self. To this might also be added the psychological and spiritual influences which affect him. We might then speak of a bio-social-psycho-spiritual matrix. Out of these experiences, a person builds up "adjustive techniques" to use Cameron's phrase, that is, ways of meeting the various life situations he encounters. These apparently stay with him all through life, unless, by some conscious process such as counseling, he is able to re-examine these background factors and establish new ways of meeting and coping with his daily experiences.

Counseling Re-evaluation. Counseling then gives a person an opportunity to resurvey these values and attitudes and, in the process, make up for these childhood deficiences. In so far as the childhood experiences of many people do produce adequate adult attitudes and values, we can say that one of the results of counseling

14N. Cameron: *The Psychology of the Behavior Disorders*, Boston, Houghton-Mifflin, 1947.

is to enable people to re-live their childhood. Through the penetrating analysis of counseling, they can arrive at something of the same approach to their present adolescent or adult life that another person would have who had received all these values and positive emotional tones from his childhood. This may account for statements about a *new birth* or new personality which often occur in the later stages of counseling. We saw one expression of this in the excerpts of the graduate student at the beginning of the chapter.[15]

Orientation in Addition to Integration. During this phase of counseling re-evaluation especially, it is often necessary for a person to seek ways of reaching not only personal integration but also an even more fundamental life re-orientation. This can lead him beyond the area of counsel proper to questions which involve ultimate life values. It is at this stage particularly that informational and instructive functions may also be requested, either from the counselor himself or from others. Such people, for example, are commonly moved to make a deep and intense personal re-evaluation of their religious beliefs and practices. We will see examples of this under the section on the skill of the counselor.

That such self-reorganizing effects can take place through counseling is very encouraging. It makes it possible for people who have had inadequate childhoods, to be able to achieve a successful and stable adult life and to hand on these mature attitudes to their own children or to all who come under their influence in whatever positions they may occupy.

[15]See also pp. 96 ff.

CHAPTER VI

UNCOVERING SOURCES OF EMOTION

In the early stages of counseling, there are invariably strong emotional disturbances. These disturbances may or may not be accompanied by the lack of values, self-worth, and judgment which we discussed in the previous chapter. People, through counseling, often become conscious that excessive emotional reactions to particular persons and situations are major contributing factors to many of their personal confusions and conflicts. Such emotional reactions, however, and the physical components that may be associated with them, while they too have their origin in the past, follow a pattern differing in some ways from that of the influences we have just considered.

EMOTIONAL CONDITIONING

Certain modern developments, particularly in the study of emotional conditioning, give us a clue to the intensity and subtlety of these reactions. While many of these experiments have been conducted with animals, one can see parallel states in human beings which demonstrate the degree to which man's own animal nature oftentimes affects his psychological reactions. Through the study of counseling interviews increased evidence is appearing which demonstrates that man can control and even change much of this type of conditioning after he has gained insight into its causes and begun to make more integrated choices.

Illustration. These studies on conditioning were begun by the experiments of Pavlov with dogs. In one of the early experiments, Pavlov combined the bringing of food to a hungry dog with the beating of a metronome. The effect was to cause the saliva in the dog's mouth to flow freely. After a period of time he no longer presented the food to the dog. The beating of the metronome alone was enough to produce the flowing of the saliva. By consistently relating two objects which are naturally unrelated, the metronome and the food, the reaction which is naturally associated with one experience, the flowing of saliva as the food is sensed, came to be associated with the other, the sound of the metronome.[1]

Word Lists. The results of these studies of Pavlov and others on conditioning have been helpful in understanding some types of human reaction. Human emotional tones, while they appear in more complex forms than these simple experiments, often seem to follow the same general pattern. Certain emotions may have been earlier associated with a particular incident or a series of incidents. These emotions become attached not only to the incident but also to many surrounding circumstances. When any one of these circumstances is reproduced the person can feel strongly favorable or unfavorable without at the moment knowing why. His reaction is merely the reproduction of his positive or negative feeling towards the earlier incident, with which the present experience was once associated. This can be true of even so minor a circumstance as the sound of a word. This is one of the reasons why various word lists have been devised as aids to personal understanding. A word like candy, for example, will generally produce an immediate positive reaction. When asked to analyze this reaction most people will relate experiences when they enjoyed candy. A phrase like "chocolate cherry candy," however, will divide a group into positive and negative sections. The negative group will recite a series of previous incidents usually associated with the nausea of once eating too many of these candies. Some may be negative because, as they analyze it, they are focused on the sense of touch and anything "sticky" disturbs them. A word like "lobster" is particularly interesting because the positive or negative reaction often depends on which sense a person's imagery is centered upon. The negative reaction will often be associated with *seeing* the lobster in its wild state, particularly with its pincers. The positive tone is often due to *tasting* the lobster as a prepared delicacy. Such feelings will usually immediately recall an early experience when a person was pinched by a lobster or crayfish or, alternately, enjoyed for the first time a delicious lobster dinner. When these people had the favorable or unfavorable reaction to the word, however, they were not, at the moment, conscious of this chain of connected circumstances. As one author expresses it:

[1] Ivan Petrovich Pavlov: *Conditioned Reflex*, Translated and edited by G. V. Anrep, London, Oxford University Press, Humphrey Milford, 1928.

We know that such conditioning can take place in early infancy, even before the age of verbalization. It may persist for a lifetime, the individual remaining unaware of the source of his emotional reaction. These conditioned responses are peculiar in that they may be established in one trial and they apparently are not easily extinguished. Furthermore—and this is of great interest for us—they show a good deal of irradiation; that is, the same emotional response may be evoked by a stimulus which only resembles the original conditioning stimulus.[2]

WHOLE PERSON INVOLVED

Unit Reaction. Similar kinds of reaction, in more complex forms, can enter into many difficulties. The person knows that somehow his reaction to another person, situation, or place is exaggerated and unreasonable, yet he does not know why. As he talks about himself in the free-flowing manner that a skilled interview produces, various incidents come up. These at first appear unconnected. As the person continues to examine them, however, these incidents gradually become related—often around some earlier experiences not clearly remembered before.

Illustration. We see an indication of this in the following account given by the aviation cadet (X):

P: I can hear a door bell and someone walk heavily and all sorts of things like that. I seem to be constantly on a tension. I become very nervous. I've gone over a week without eating. I couldn't touch anything, that was last winter when it was positively the worst, and although the weather was bad down there, it was very damp, and one of the things which I tested very allergic to is damp weather—at least three months ago when I was tested at the army base. Dr. L. said he had never heard of a case where dampness caused such a violent reaction. I think maybe that this physical trouble more or less set off a nervous condition and resulted in the extreme nervousness and this would explain the fact that I couldn't eat and I'd throw up and a couple days I could hardly talk last winter, I was so nervous. It seems logical to me, so I've been trying to analyze the condition. I can tie up a lot of things that happened in my environment with present day occurrences. In other words, although the condition has actually disappeared, things currently remind me of it, and the reaction seems to be just as it would be had the condition remained present.

[2]A. H. Maslow and Bela Mittlemann: *Principles of Abnormal Psychology*, New York, Copyright 1941, by Harper Brothers, pp. 88–89.

C: I'd like you to feel free to speak of yourself. I think the freer you are in this relationship, the more good may possibly come of it.

P: Well, I realize that. Dr. L.—I think—was rather hesitant at first, because he didn't know how I would react, but I was in a way relieved when he told me that there might be some psychological things there. Although I guess a state of mind sometimes is pretty hard to change. Well, anyway, it goes back to home life—I guess many cases do. Uh—my parents never got along. I'm the oldest of six children—three brothers and two sisters. Well, it's hard to find a logical beginning, I guess, but the—I always say this, I uh—I really hated to go home when I left work—I hated to go home because I just didn't know what to expect. It was always arguing, and constant disagreements.

Inter-relationship. This cadet moves quickly from physical complaints and symptoms to a vague awareness of psychological causation and then to a statement about his home. This demonstrates how the spiritual, psychological, and physical factors in man are combined to make up one unit experience. This kind of quick transition from one topic to another happens often in counseling. Sometimes the realization of a relationship between two factors comes so suddenly the person is surprised and cannot understand why he had never seen the connection before. This cadet, until now, had always hoped that some medical diagnosis and treatment would solve his difficulties. While he was also aware of these personal problems, he did not consciously connect them with his physical state.

Psychological Causes. Once he accepts the possibility of some psychological causation he sees how his present reactions are in some way determined by earlier experiences. As he says: "Although the condition has actually disappeared, things currently remind me of it and the reaction seems to be just the same as it would be had the condition remained present." Here, he gives an important clue. In these situations the past seems to be significant only as its effects carry over into the present. Although these effects are hidden, they can still be sources of confusion and disturbance. In this case, as he works out the problem later, his position in the army has some aspects similar to the domination he experienced from his parents at home. When he was young he was forced to do what his parents said, no matter how unreasonable. The few times he "talked back" he was punished very severely. His resentment smouldered and he left home as soon as he was old enough to make his own way. When he was drafted, the army reproduced some aspects of the old home atmosphere from which he had escaped. Consequently, even minor army discipline filled him with hostility. Since he could not openly resist, it backed up and apparently produced states of extreme physical tension and illness. Yet, while he knew his strong reaction to the army was not justified, he did not know the cause.

Heightened Sense Reaction.   Another interesting factor in this excerpt is the way this man's psychological conflicts are associated with an extreme reaction to sound. This kind of heightened sensitivity, together with the physical disorders he describes, is often expressed in opening interviews. Frequently, too, even after one interview, people say that these complaints have decreased.

Focus on Body.   The cadet's earlier tendency to feel that his difficulties were entirely physical, illustrates how physical symptoms may sometimes be unconscious escapes from facing more personal causes. Many people feel that if the difficulty is in their body, they are somehow relieved of any responsibility for it. As soon as this cadet faces the possibility of some psychological causes, he comes up rapidly with statements about his home life.

Physical Symptoms.   This type of complex reaction seems, therefore, to cause emotional confusions as well as physical effects which take various forms. This helps us to understand why certain people break out in a skin rash when some situations face them, others have asthma or get intense stomach disorders, and the like. This does not mean that there are no medical causes of these illnesses, but that often some peculiar conditioning also enters into the reaction.

Illustration.   In the following statements by a navy nurse, we learn that abdominal pains reappeared when she returned home after a three years' absence. She had had a thorough physical examination and there was no evidence of an organic difficulty. Earlier, through counseling, she had acquired some understanding of the causes of this physical reaction. Yet, this by itself was not sufficient to prevent its recurrence when she returned to the same home atmosphere. We notice in the following excerpts how physical reactions and psychological needs fuse together (T) :[3]

P: I was trying to think back—my Mother used to ask me if I had stomach pains. I didn't even know about them. She would keep ask-

[3]Designated by symbol (T).

ing me if I felt all right. I suppose I found out it was a nice way to get out of things because she would always seem so anxious for me to feel all right. She would even excuse me from doing things during that time. I just thought it would be a good thing to be sick. It solved a lot of problems, fights with my brother. I could go, "Oh, Mother," and she would come running and then scold him for hurting me.

C: You connect it up with a pattern of defense and affection because your mother made so much of it.

P: Yes, she used to bundle me up and make sure I felt all right. I remember the first time I had a thing as bad as this—so violent. It was just before I went to the hospital to go in training. I suppose leaving home caused it. This was the first time. I couldn't keep anything on my stomach either. The pain lasted for four or five days at that time.

Affection-Security Symbol. The mother's affectionate concern became gradually identified with the daughter's physical reaction. Just before she went into training, the confused threat of separation and loneliness made the physical reaction all the stronger. Returning home after her navy experience brought back the personal conflicts that were part of her reasons for going into the navy. These problems centered around the excessive protectiveness and fears with which the mother and father had surrounded the girl. They did everything for her and encouraged her to be dependent on them. They quietly resisted any of her urges to assume mature responsibility. The mother was an especially fearful person who had put many vague fears into the girl's mind during her childhood. In the previous series of interviews, the girl worked out how her parents had opposed her entering training and only reluctantly gave their consent. Gaining their consent was, she felt, the first independent step of her life. Other members of the family also tended to control her. This motivated her to join the navy soon after finishing training. Now, as these problems recurred upon her return home, the physical symptoms also reappeared. But, since the mother had died while she was in the navy, the affection need now became attached to the father (T):

C: It's sort of dawned on you that going back home did introduce a lot of unsolved problems.

P: You know those pains—I haven't figured out whether it is a fixed habit that came on when I was right back in the old surroundings although there is a difference.

C: You are not just sure whether it was the conditioning of the surroundings.

P: Or if there is something there to bring it back. I had to laugh, the
first thing I thought of was having Dad come after me—the old pattern. I didn't think it out. I was trying to think back through and see
if there were any problems that could cause some confusion but so
much has gone on recently. (Pause) I knew before I came back that
I should think it out but I didn't take the time. After I worked this
out in interviews before, I could just think over problems that were
disturbing me. All during the navy I wasn't bothered seriously with
these pains at all.

C: The spontaneous seeking of your father again makes you feel that
perhaps there are a lot of things which, if you had thought them out
as you usually do, might have prevented this reaction.

The reason why, in cases like this, one particular physical reaction
takes place rather than another is not clear. Why, for example, was
it intense abdominal pain in this case, rather than some other physiological symptoms such as those described by the aviation cadet
(X)? In this case it seems to have something to do with earlier experiences. The nurse mentions that her mother always inquired if
she had these pains. This may have been enough to create the focus
on that particular illness. Gradually, a confused need of affection and
security is simultaneously associated with the illness. To be ill for
this girl meant getting special affection and consideration in preference to her brother.

Returns Years Later.   After the mother's death, the father continued that symbolization so that, even as a mature woman with
nursing and war experience, her first urge was to call her father. She
is surprised at this because she had not felt this urge for years. Later,
in this same interview, the nurse gives a clearer understanding of
why the conditioning situation returned (T):

P: (Pause)It is funny, I mean, before when I was a kid and I would
have these pains it never bothered me in doing what I wanted to do.
I could always go to school. I liked school and I never missed it because of them or if I were going to a basketball game.

C: As you think about it, if you really had something you wanted to
do, it didn't bother you.

P: I suppose after a time because there was such a conditioned reflex
then it did interrupt things that I really wanted to do. It began to

take over. Then I suppose my father, in a sense, while it wasn't done exactly the same, would symbolize what mother had done. (Pause) I mean, while he actually didn't bundle me in bed, he would see that I had everything that I wanted.

C: The two views sort of fused together as an affection and security symbol.

P: Uh huh. (Pause) Those needs for affection and security must be awfully strong.

C: You are rather struck by how deep they really are.

P: Coming home would be like slipping back into a routine. There wasn't much pressure. I wasn't even in any hurry to go home, knowing that things would be all right. I would kind of give the high-sign and the people at home would take care of me. You know I noticed in the navy even when things were pretty hot I would not have the least trouble because it was in such a situation that I did really think it out. And thinking it out, I wouldn't be confused.

C: It is an insight that when things are pressing you have the least difficulty. It is when there are these sorts of vague states of dependency that these other reactions appear to come back.

P: It is like getting on a train, you know you can't get there any faster than it takes you and you know when you get on where you are going. In going home, I thought I will get what I want—no hurry about doing anything.

C: Sort of relaxing into a passivity and let them take over in a sense.

P: Uh huh, but it wouldn't necessarily have to be that way now. It seems the expedient thing to do is let things ride for a while. Now that I know it and can see it, that would be a pressure because I would accept the responsibility to work out my own decisions.

C: Having seen it clearly, what you want now is to be doing things yourself even though you might conform to the same pattern as in the past.

P: Yes, that would make all the difference in the world.

C: Not so much what you do but the way in which it flows through you.

P: Yes, things would look the same but I would know within myself this is the situation which seems to be necessary here and now. But simply because I see it that way—I have a responsibility in it. Even while they are doing most of the work, I would realize it is what I want; it is going to a goal I want and I am very responsible. I would take an active part in it and that would be a big difference.

C: It is the way the thing goes through you which determines whether you are actively integrating yourself with it.

P: Yes, very much so. I probably have been very passive these weeks in these things.

C: You are conscious of this passivity.

P: Yes, I can see why. Things are changed and I am just feeling my way but still I wouldn't have to be passive about the whole thing.

Passivity. The nurse now identifies her state of passivity with the return of these reactions. After the series of interviews which preceded her going into the navy she understood why these pains took place. That awareness enabled her to control them. As long as she was in the navy, acting independently, she had confidence and assurance in her judgment and there was no return of the physical pain. As soon as she returned home, she stopped making the judgments and evaluations which had been so characteristic of the last three or four years. The return home brought the earlier passivity and the ready, easy dependence on her father and family. This, in turn, was connected in her mind with the return of the conditioned pain. It seems that whenever this person became passive and gave in to states of dependency the conditioning took over. As she said, she can either "get on a train" and let others guide her life or direct herself and make her own judgments.

Responsibility and Achievement. Later in the same interview, the nurse realizes that as long as she is in the home she can let this childish passivity take over. She contrasts this feeling with the achieving, active period of the previous summer when, upon leaving the navy, she had been very successful in a combined teaching and research project. This experience she considered the most significant of her life (T):

P: I mean, I know you can learn something from every situation. I am becoming aware of it but not really as much as I should be. There again the pattern of passivity is so strong—it is even stronger after ten or fifteen years—it is right there to step in whenever I am off guard.

C: It is getting clearer that you are almost always on the verge of passivity if you're not careful.

P: Although, what I have done this summer means more than anything else. It's really been the period of the biggest achievement in my life.

C: You see it as a really great achievement for you.

P: Even more than those years in the navy and I don't consider them a total loss by any means . . .

C: All that is part of a new life which is meaningful for you.

P: Yes, I can better appreciate it after this past summer.

C: Last summer is a focal point around which you can survey things more clearly.

This demonstrates how the satisfying states of mature adults are those in which they are making their own judgments and achievements. This nurse is now conscious that her choice lies between her passive childish acceptance of the home values and her mature determining and judging issues for herself. When her judgments agree with the home, there is yet an important difference between making them herself on her own responsibility or passively letting the home determine them for her. The abdominal pains were clues which, as she traced down their origin, led her to this deepest self-understanding. It was not the home itself that brought them on but the mood of passive dependency. Through the years, the abdominal pains had become associated with this mood, due probably to the mother's original emphasis. Now she understood how they disappeared and her own personal happiness increased in proportion as she thought through and took direct responsibility for her decisions and actions.

PSYCHOSOMATIC UNITY

The previous excerpts illustrate the complex inter-relationships between physical, emotional, intellectual, and voluntary factors in man. That spiritual and emotional conflicts could disorder even physical functions, as described by the aviation cadet and the nurse, may appear surprising. Many people are prone to think of the body as a fixed organic structure only remotely connected with man's spiritual powers. Such a split conception of man seeks organic causes for every physical illness. From the evidence of what we now refer to as psychosomatic medicine, however, as we see indicated here, many illnesses include personal problems of an emotional, intellectual, and spiritual nature. When a person can bring these more fundamental psychological factors out into the open and think them through, the physical symptoms often become much less disturbing and even disappear.

This demonstrates the basic unity of the human person and reaffirms the Aristotelian-Thomistic awareness that the "psyche" or soul is the first principle of operation of the body. So, as St. Thomas maintained, "the whole corporeal nature is subject to the psyche and is related to it as its matter and instrument."[4]

GENERAL LIFE SITUATIONS

In addition to past emotional experiences affecting certain physical reactions, their influence is also evident in other personal areas. They are commonly found in problems of marriage adjustment, work satisfaction, school achievement, and similar situations. There may not be any associated physical illness.

Slower Process. The awareness of past conditioning is not always as immediate as in the previous excerpts. Sometimes a slower process through a series of interviews is necessary before relationships between present confusions and past experiences are uncovered. In the following excerpt another aviation cadet, after a long period of training, is still unable to solo:[5]

P: I was more eager to go up that second time, but something went wrong. It's disgusting—not pathetic—it's disgusting. I was determined to make a good flight. I thought I would, I knew I could make a good flight, but I didn't. When I was little and living with dad, I used to do things wrong when dad had told me to do them right, and was whipped for it. Dad was always sure when we did things wrong that we did it on purpose. I was always afraid of dad. I never knew him very well until recently. I've always analyzed him coldly, and I've never talked to him unless I had to. Dad was always right and I was always wrong—so he said.

C: You've always been afraid of your dad for the way he's treated you.

P: Yes, this just popped into my mind. One time dad wanted me to build a coal-bin, and he told me just exactly how I should do it. He went away, and I did it some other way. When he got home, he whipped me terribly. I was petrified by him.[6]

The cadet continues talking about his father, telling how as a child he had been beaten repeatedly by the father.

---

[4]St. Thomas Aquinas: *Summa Theologica*, I, Q. 78, a. 1, translated by Fathers of the English Dominican Province, New York, Benziger Brothers, 1947. Reprinted from the *Summa Theologica* with the permission of Benziger Brothers, Inc., Publishers and Copyright Owners.

[5]Not to be confused with (X), p. 59.

[6]This excerpt and the following ones from this case are taken from G. A. Muench and C. R. Rogers: "Counseling of Emotional Blocking in an Aviator," *J. Abnorm. and Soc. Psych.*, Vol. 41, April 1946, pp. 207–15. By permission of the *Journal* and the American Psychological Association.

P: When times got better, he became more generous and easy going. He did as much as he could for us.

C: Sometimes you hated your father, and sometimes you liked him.

P: I liked him, and hated him violently. (Pause) It's funny how I started on this. I wonder how it ties in though. (pause)

Surprise Statements. This is an example of how, in the free flow of the interview, a person will bring up something and then be surprised at what he said. The cadet found himself talking about his father in relation to his problem of flying. He did not know why the thought of his father came up and at the time saw no connection between the two. In the next interview he mentions it again:

P: You know after the last interview I wondered what made me tell you the things I did. Could it be possible that the instructor is a symbol of my father? Is that hatred coming back to blot my memory? Could that possibly be significant?

C: You wonder if perhaps the instructor might be a symbol of your father.

P: Yes, he was telling me what to do just like Dad always did. I fully intended to carry out the instructor's instructions; I couldn't not want to do them. Maybe I forgot because I thought of Dad and wanted to forget.

Later in the interview he compares his experiences with his father and his reaction to following instructions, but he is still not certain of this connection:

P: All the way to the airport I was wondering about that. Many times Dad told me to do things I didn't want to do, and I did them although I hated to do them. Maybe that's why I wasn't following directions; I disliked to follow orders.

C: You wonder if you didn't follow orders because of that deep-rooted hatred of following your fathers orders.

P: I may have felt I didn't like to carry out orders but it wasn't conscious.

He then explores the possibility that he fails to follow instructions because he does not want to follow them.

P: That's right. Again today I did something wrong. Today the instructor told me to make 90° turns and I only carried out one all the time knowing I should have carried out more than that. I hate to think I didn't want to, but I guess I didn't want to because I was in a position to make a neat rectangular field turn.

In the early part of the sixth interview he summarizes the conclusions he has reached. He seems to be reacting to his instructor as he formerly did to his father. But, he is still not sure:

P: On the basis of what we've done thus far the instructor may have been considered in the role of my father and as he was telling me what to do I probably didn't want to because I thought of him as my father—but I don't know—I'm not sure.
C: You wonder but you're not sure if you considered the instructor as your father.

Buried Resentment.   In the seventh interview the cadet sees that he disliked the instructor from the beginning and has been repressing this resentment exactly as he used to repress his resentment towards his father. In the subseqent interview he expresses the intense feelings about his father's treatment that he has kept pent up for years. He sees for the first time how deeply his father's actions have affected him. By the ninth interview the relationship is getting clearer:

P: Could it be that I still hated father, and it acted up in my flying?
C: You wonder if perhaps your hatred for your father is tied up with your flying difficulty.
P: Perhaps the instructor's role showing me what to do—laying down the law, his tone, his attitude may have struck that note somehow, because I hated him.
C: You hated the instructor.
P: That's right, and thinking it was my father. Here he was giving me something that had to be done. Oh, yes, and another thing. When I was young I always was bawled out for something I didn't do. The instructor said on our last flight, "Why didn't you do it?" I gave him the same answer I always gave my father, "I don't know."

In the tenth interview he lines it up:

P: He's always impressed gliding turns on me as a part of the instructions—his verbal instructions. Now as I think about it I was plainly not carrying out those instructions, you might say deliberately disobeying. I remember saying something like that in another interview, but I couldn't understand why. I never gave the instructor a good rational excuse, I must not have wanted to. That's queer. I might not have wanted to. I made no effort to follow his instructions even when he was telling me.

C: You didn't follow his instructions up in the air even when he was telling you.

P: It seems that way. If you could apply that to other maneuvers it might be. I really want to fly though. Maybe that's why I haven't done so well—a dislike to follow directions. Gee, that's pretty well tangled up. Let me try and draw a parallel there. My instructor is to my father as my instructor's directions are to my father's directions. Even though I thought I wanted to, I really didn't want to.

C: You feel there's a parallel to your father's and instructor's directions.

P: I wanted to fly badly. That may be the block. That's probably the answer to the question. I guess I didn't have it formulated before I came here today, but I sure do now.

C: You feel that may be the center of your problem.

P: That's right. Flying is grand. By George, why did I have to get an instructor that reminded me of father? If I got an easy instructor all the way through would it have been easier? There's a good possibility I would have been the best in the group.

Past and Present Relationship. During a period of high emotional tension, when the cadet was trying to solo, the sound of the instructor's voice, similar to that of his stern father, was enough to bring forward reaction states acquired in early childhood. Yet, before counseling, the pilot did not recognize the relationship between the two and had even forgotten his intense resentment of his father. He had first to bring to the surface the strong hidden bitterness which still remained from his father's treatment of him. Then he began to see the relationship of these states to his blocking at the instructor's directions. It was not an accident, therefore, that in the free release of an early interview he mentioned his father even though at that time he thought it completely out of context. The counselor himself could not have guessed the highly complex relationship between the two until the cadet expressed it. The process of talking freely in a skillful accepting atmosphere often brings up problems of which the person was not previously conscious. As he thinks along with the counselor, the relationship of these problems to his present difficulties unfolds itself.

Cause and Effect. This is another important point evident in counseling. When we speak freely our whole person seems to affect the content of our release. We find ourselves talking about things which, if we were planning a strictly logical speech, we would never bring up. Yet, in the process of this free-flowing release, there is a far deeper cause-and-effect relationship than we realized. This further demonstrates the Aristotelian-Thomistic concept of the unity of the human person.

Conscious Control Possible. Moreover, reactions and motives have compulsive and confusing power in proportion as they are hidden and unknown. Once they are brought into conscious awareness and understanding, they are usually far less mysterious and distorting. As one writer states:

> All human beings want the same things. The trouble is that there are many possible paths to these ultimate goals. When we are presented with a choice of paths, we frequently choose foolishly because of poor attitudes toward the world, usually acquired in unfortunate experiences in childhood and usually carried about unconsciously. It is because of this unconsciousness that we behave foolishly. An unconscious desire is independent of logic and intelligence, and thus the first task of deeper psychotherapy is to make the unconscious conscious. Once it is conscious, our intelligence, our past experience, our sense of humor, our logic may be brought to bear upon solving the problem of how we may achieve what we want most, i.e., happiness, love, self-respect.[7]

Previous conditioning seems especially to cause basic instinctive reactions to take over when reason should normally be in control. A person may feel strongly urged, for example, to escape or to seek security in some person or situation, without clearly knowing why. This is counteracted by thinking out the causes of these reactions and consciously connecting up past states with present issues. In this way, as connections become known, the reactions lose much of their force. Moreover, they are not so feared because they are understood. It is much less confusing for the cadet to know that he is reacting to the instructor's voice in the same way he reacted to his father. It is less discouraging for the nurse (T) to know that returning home brings with it a mood of passivity, even after a long

---

[7]A. H. Maslow and Bela Mittlemann: *Principles of Abnormal Psychology*, New York, Copyright 1941, by Harper Brothers, pp. 11–12.

period of responsible achievement. The conscious, reasonable analysis of why we react as we do to certain situations brings security through the understanding of the connection between past and present factors. It is also a positive, responsible assertion of a person's reason over the conditioning that has been controlling him.

This ability, through skilled counseling, to uncover emotional and physical reactions fixed deeply in the past and to reorganize them according to reason, demonstrates how much even man's elemental reactions are subject to his cogitative process.[8] We see this especially illustrated in counseling as the person is able to trace these present disturbing reactions to their origin in his past. Having discovered and related them, he is able to lessen the force with which they have previously influenced his judgments and actions.

Not all personal difficulties are caused, of course, by such hidden reactions. Often they may be due to an inadequate survey of present factors. But these reactions, to some degree at least, generally enter into those conflicts that are at all serious. Consequently, adequate self-knowledge usually involves an awareness of subtle instinctive and emotional urges as well as of our more immediately conscious motivation. These are often in conflict with the reasonable goals of particular actions. But the fact that the sources of these reactions are not consciously known or understood, makes their effects so disturbing. For this reason, too, such motivation is most difficult to uncover without help. Skillful counseling can be a great aid in objectifying and clarifying such hidden and confusing urges. Once these urges are brought to the conscious awareness, reasonable understanding and reorganization is possible.

[8]See St. Thomas, (D): I, Q. 78, a. 4.

CHAPTER VII

ACQUIRING SELF–UNDERSTANDING AND INTEGRATION

A person's earlier history is important in counseling, therefore, mainly because past influences are in some way affecting his present conflicts. As a result of multiple factors in both his past and present way of life, he is, as we have seen demonstrated in the excerpts, in an almost continual state of confusion. This confusion has more of an intellectual than an emotional connotation. So, in the beginning of counseling, as people talk about the conflicts and emotional turmoil they feel, they also express their inability to understand why they act the way they do. They lack both self-knowledge and self-integration.

INSIGHT

Practical Integration of Knowledge. Insight, therefore, involves both an increase in self-understanding and the ability to act on the knowledge one has acquired. In the counseling process, when insights become significant, it is not simply that people acquire new knowledge of themselves and others. Counseling may make them realize their lack of certain information and, as a result, they set out to get it. But, this is not the most significant effect of insight. The possession of knowledge does not of itself imply the ability to act on that knowledge. There must also be the practical integration of knowledge within the here and now of each one's life. It is this latter aspect to which the term insight is especially applied. As we examined the interviews, we noticed that, in this insight stage, the person either takes the knowledge he already had or new knowledge which he has acquired and filters it through himself so that it becomes an integrated part of his whole plan of action. His perceptions are now impregnated with this knowledge. This integrating and dynamic aspect of insight is its main function in counseling.

138

Concrete Issues. Ideally, a man should be able to maintain his reasonable judgments through any series of personal, concrete experiences. But it is very difficult to keep this consistency. As unreasonable actions mount, they produce a state of dissatisfaction, unrest, and unhappiness. A person needs counseling in proportion as he is failing to apply reasonable principles to his individual actions. Insight enables him to judge objectively the particular concrete issues in which he is involved. As the person, through the responses of the counselor, is able to penetrate his emotions and discover the basic issues and values motivating his conduct he can begin to plan more realistic solutions. The counseling process, therefore, helps a person to be reasonable about concrete issues that were previously emotionally confused. His judgments are now made in relation to principles of conduct which he already knew but somehow, without counseling, was not applying to these individual situations.

Objective Judgment. Insight, then, includes both impersonal knowledge and the singular, concrete event which is highly personal. Insight brings these two together and enables a man to act in a personal issue with the same objective judgment and integration he would have were he judging the conduct of someone else. This gives us a clue to why the counselor, even though he does not offer advice or information in the counseling interview, is an essential part of the objectifying and impersonalizing process which produces insight. The counselor's responses mirror a person's problems for him and enable him to survey them with the same impersonal perception that he might have of the problems of someone far removed. The counseling interview, then, has much in it similar to the surveying of oneself in a mirror. A person can slowly change himself as he sees, with increasingly less distortion, how he has been acting, and why. The reasonable judgments he holds up to himself are the models to which he gradually conforms as he sees himself more clearly. This change is not immediate nor easy. But he is stimulated and encouraged as his actions better fulfill these reasonable norms. He grows more satisfied with what he sees as he surveys himself in the interview. This explains the increase in expressions of satisfaction, hope, and courage which begin to show themselves. These positive expressions accompany new insights and resultant choices which more completely fulfill what a person wants to be.

REACHING REALITY

Self-Deception. Basic to his confusion about other factors is a person's own state of self-deception. People in need of counseling seem unable to see themselves as they are. The objective and impersonal relationship with the counselor gives them a more accurate view. What a person discovers about himself through these insights is not always pleasing or favorable. Often, he must face and admit for the first time a rather ugly image of himself. Yet, even this is better than the previous self-deception. As people grow in knowledge of themselves, they discover that although they may not have all the exaggerated accomplishments of their fantasy pictures, they still have more abilities than they have used. This dawning awareness produces greater courage and self-assurance as the reality which they see in counseling proves to be true in the real world of action.

Reality Brings Security. Any aspect of reality seems more fearful and threatening when we do not understand it than when we can look at it squarely and objectively and begin to plan about it. In this sense, the acceptance of facts is fundamental to the development of the virtue of counsel, as St. Thomas remarks. Somehow, when the facts of any situation are not seen clearly, there arises a state of threat. In the beginning of counseling, people seem generally afraid or at least insecure. It is difficult to understand why reality should threaten them but it seems to be connected with their confusions. As they come to see themselves and others more objectively, they grow less insecure. Persons, places, and things which they had previously resisted or considered in a very negative light, assume more positive tones. Alternately, situations that provided defenses or escapes lose their attraction.

Comparison With Visual Process. One way of understanding this is to compare it to the visual process. There are two aspects of vision, peripheral and central. This difference is based on the distribution of the cones and rods in the eye. Peripheral vision includes all broad, general perceptions which are only vaguely recognized. Central vision is the precise and clear delineation of objects. Peripheral vision produces an instinctively protective reaction. This reaction, for example, enables us to avoid threatening objects, such as approaching cars. It is constantly alerting us, particularly in situations when we must act instantaneously. Peripheral vision, too, because it is diffuse and blurred, is unsatisfying. We want to get objects in our central vision so that we can see their exact proportions. Central vision frees us from the insecurity and threat of the peripheral field. It is also more satisfying to have an accurate and sure knowledge of things as they are.

Intellectual insight seems to work in a somewhat similar manner. It effects a clarity and security similar to that of central vision. In the early interviews, problems are distorted. People do not lack solutions but these solutions are only vaguely and confusedly seen. As insights grow and the causes of their difficulties become precise and clear, people gain confidence and have fewer urges to quick defense.

Like a person surveying a room and growing aware of the precise form and proportion of objects that were at first blurred, so, through the consistent surveying of the various personal issues and feelings which enter into the past, present, and future, the person in the counseling interview gradually gets a more complete knowledge of himself and his world. By repeatedly going over various aspects and feelings of situations, he becomes more familiar with them. This familiarity, as in learning anything, aids him in gaining new understanding. He gradually associates his reactions with similar attitudes he observes in others. He no longer feels unique. What was before vague and diffuse, becomes more sharply defined. As he sees himself and his world in a more ordered and accurate way, he gains confidence and he can begin to act more independently and successfully.

Distortion Due to Emotional State.   This distortion, which persons in the beginning stages of counseling experience, is associated with their state of emotional tension. Emotions seem attached to particulars. As we grow emotional, we focus on precise issues and it grows more difficult to see the whole of a question and to be able to relate particulars together. Emotions produce a narrowed perception of isolated incidents and details. These particular aspects at first usually appear to be unconnected. The insightful view of reason reveals a broadening and integrating understanding of all the issues as they are related to one another. The more a person is involved in conflicting emotions, the more his judgment is apt to be formed only on a limited survey. This narrowing of the perceptual field, then, seems to be a major factor in the way conflicting emotions disorganize a person. This disorganization can take place even when a person knows that the path down which his emotions are leading him will not bring him to an adequate and reasonable solution. He can still keep fixed on some immediately satisfying aspect and allow this to motivate him to act contrary to his reasonable understanding.

Tension and Defensiveness. This distorted view and its accompanying emotions can put a person in such a state of tension that any remark which ordinarily would not be disturbing can cause him to feel threatened. In this state, he may get an almost animal satisfaction in unreasonable and even violent defensiveness. We noticed this characteristic in the excerpt of statements by the married business woman (Z),[1] whose personal problems make her very irritable. She describes herself as being ready "to snap everyone's head off." Later in the interviews, this woman discussing one such incident, remembers other factors—the twinkle in the man's eye when he made the remark and his obvious sincerity. She then realizes that the remark was not an attack but a joke which contained a sincere comment. In this way, insight broadened her awareness of the incidents and of her own tendency to defense. But as long as a person is in a highly emotional state, he is often unable to acquire this broad view. He is apt to judge and act on isolated details without admitting to himself that this is an incomplete picture.

In the same way, the naval ensign, in a quarrel with his fiancee, reacts with intense anger to a passing phrase she used. Later, as his emotions quiet down, he realizes that the particular incident was not enough to have caused this intense reaction. But, at the moment, his perceptions were so narrowed, he could not see this. As he thought it out, he grew to see for the first time, how excessively jealous he was.

SEEING THE TOTAL PICTURE

We have commented before how hidden motivation often affects our actions. The motive for this man's reaction to his fiancee was actually buried in his past. This is one of the most striking features of insight. What appears to be an isolated incident will, when thoroughly analyzed in a series of interviews, be the means of unfolding a large and complex panorama of motivation. When the per-

[1]Pp. 55–57.

son first brings up these various incidents and reactions, they appear to have no connection with one another. But, as he examines them and unfolds the motives behind them, they all begin to fit together to become parts of a composite picture. Such a picture usually reveals fundamental life needs which the person has either not been achieving or achieving only in a partial way. Before counseling, he was often totally unaware of these needs.

Simple Solutions. As we studied the typescript of interviews in which people described highly emotional reactions, we noticed that these reactions seemed generally to be associated with a tendency to seek and act on the simplest and most immediate perception of any situation. This appears to be one of the main sources of precipitation in human conduct. If we do not make a conscious effort to survey all the issues, we seem spontaneously to follow the simplest and most immediate solution to any problem. We resist complexity and must force ourselves to face it, probably because it takes greater effort to work out something complex. Simple solutions are much easier. This tendency toward simplicity seems to be a characteristic found generally in nature. So, Lillie has pointed out that, "Unguided natural processes tend automatically toward simplicity and uniformity rather than toward complexity and diversity."[2]

Unfolding Complex Factors. But, in many instances, the simple solution is misleading.[3] Consequently, as long as a person does not examine his motivation, he continues to be misled by his uncomplicated view. In this sense, his emotions move him along the path of least resistance. This may explain why, as we noticed before, emotional conflicts and the influences of past reactions are often associated with a person's state of passivity. This changes as the person begins to think out these reactions. Emotions become less confusing as their sources are revealed through active analysis. At the same time, the influences of the past, even as they affect a person's physical state, are less compelling when a person has surveyed and related all the factors influencing these reactions.

---

[2]Ralph S. Lillie: *General Biology and Philosophy of Organism*, Chicago, Copyright 1945, by The University of Chicago, p. 85.

[3]This tendency towards simple solutions is, in another form, found to be one of the main sources of prejudice. See G. W. Allport and B. M. Kramer: "Some Roots of Prejudice," *J. Abnorm. & Social Psychol.*, Vol. 41, July, 1946, pp. 229–239. Also Judy F. Rosenblith: "A Replication of Some Roots of Prejudice," Vol. 44, October 1949, pp. 470–490.

We see this in the following insightful statements by the nurse, whom we previously discussed (T):

P: I am trying to line it up in my mind under points. The old pattern for affection, easily giving into passivity, but the basis of all was selfishness.

C: As you turn in on yourself, the need for affection and passivity go together.

P: I feel okay now. In fact, I don't even have any pain now. I knew better but I see it was simply because I didn't think it out. Knowing it, but if you don't work it out, it doesn't apply.

C: Just to know isn't enough, there must be a constant working with yourself.

P: Whenever there is a new experience, although it might have been learned before, it must be actively learned in each situation.

C: It must be integrated in each new experience. Sort of woven in, so to speak.

FRUSTRATION

Illustration. This tendency towards simple, immediate action based on a narrow and inadequate survey of all the factors, is commonly found in opening interviews. Because this is a false view of the situation, it invariably produces frustration. This is illustrated in the following excerpt of the married business woman who is involved with a man in her office (Z). This excerpt is taken from the second interview:

P: Well, this set-up I was telling you about when we talked the other day—John was working with me in the office yesterday. He said he just had to talk to me. He said he hadn't told me before—but he was going to marry this woman—you know the one I told you he was going with. I told him I didn't think he should . . . I didn't know whether I was telling him right or not. (Pause)

C: You feel it would be a bad thing for him to marry her.

P: Well, the way I figured it, I thought it would, because it would ruin his life, and he's more a daydreamer—he builds a lot of dreams around things, but uh—I don't know—he wouldn't be happy with her I know that. He admitted that he wouldn't but he said he would be out of this city, and away from everything . . . He broods quite a bit. He gets these melancholy spells, you know, and he just wants to tear loose. He can't hold himself anymore—and he says he just thinks he's going to go crazy. Well, I've done that myself. A lot of times I've had that difficulty to hang on. I'm in pretty bad health anyway—that doesn't help matters any. Sometimes I just want to take what I have and not worry what comes afterwards.

C: You do tend to take just what you have—not to think about the consequences, eh?

P: That's it. Sometimes they're pretty serious (Pause) but I don't know—I've—I've been awful low this last year—several times I just wanted to give up the ghost. You feel so miserable, and then you know how circumstances are too, and you can't better them anyway. And I've doctored and doctored, and still it won't do any good. (Short pause) But I suppose I might just as well make up my mind to keep on battling it though. It's kinda hard to do that sometimes though. (Pause)

C: It isn't easy, is it?

P: But, uh . . . I don't know . . . Everything's bad, my health, my nerves.

C: Yes, you feel things are pretty black sometimes, don't you?

P: That's right. (Short pause) Well, it looks like there's no outlook—nothing to look forward to. The same things over and over. I've told John several times, I've said "Keep your chin up, and keep battling. I've wanted to quit lots of times myself but—" He gets discouraged and he's going to do this and do that. My husband—he travels quite a bit you see and so we're sure he doesn't know anything about our affair and once John got pretty much down in the dumps and he talked about going to my husband and telling him I was going to ask for a divorce but then he started thinking and thinking and he said he couldn't do that. And another time he was at an office party and my husband was there too and he said he could hardly stand seeing my husband and I together. He went out on the veranda and he said he stood there a long time wondering whether to just come in and come up to us both and tell my husband just the way the situation really was. He said he stood there for about an hour—everything imaginable running through his mind—even the idea of just going in there and shouting the whole story at the top of his voice. He finally just went to the cloak room and got his coat and walked home without even saying goodbye to anyone. That's one thing—I wouldn't want to be the cause of anything like that. You hear people say about affairs like this, "All you have to do is just call it off,"—but I know that—if I could do it without hurting anybody, but as sure as I do with him, he's going to do something drastic and that *would* be terrible!

C: That's putting it mildly, isn't it?

P: That's right. It's got me right in the middle. I know things are not

just the way I would like to have them at home but—well, I guess all
in all it's just what I call a mess.

C: Yes, it's just pretty bad for both of you.

The series of simple, immediate activities here proposed will not
bring any final solution because they are focused on the narrow
relationship of the man and herself. John's urge to rush into marriage
is a confused desire to end it some way. The same motivation is behind his thought of wanting her to secure a divorce. Both people are
miserable, yet they apparently see no way out of the intense infatuation that has gripped them.

Stereotype Reactions.   When people in conflicts of this sort cannot arrive at any adequate solution, they often tend over a period
of time to give up their efforts to change. They begin to follow their
urges blindly with a lessening regard for the consequences. The
normally motivated individual faced with a problem keeps examining his motives and actions and trying different solutions until he
is successful. But people in a prolonged state of frustration seem no
longer to vary their conduct. Their reactions grow stereotyped and
fixed. They appear to lose sight of their original goals. As a result,
they gradually become less affected by the actual or possible consequences of their actions. We notice this suggested in the woman's
phrase, "Sometimes I just want to take what I have and not worry
what comes afterwards." In this state, people may rush into some
escape or aggression reaction that has tragic results. In a recent
study of these frustration states, Maier points out that,

Frustration–induced responses seem to be an end in themselves. They
are not influenced by consequences except in so far as the consequences
may alter the state of frustration, whereas motivated responses are a
means to an end. . . . Frustration–instigated responses are either non-
constructive or destructive in nature whereas motivated responses are
constructive.[4]

This fixity of reaction in the face of continual failure to overcome
an obstacle seems to be largely instinctive. Maier sights the same
type of behavior in animals when they are faced with a problem they
cannot solve. Punishing the animal for its failure makes no change in
its behavior.

[4]Norman R. F. Maier: *Frustration*, p. 160. Reprinted by permission. Copyright, 1949,
McGraw-Hill Book Company, Inc., New York.

After a short while in the insoluble problem situation and with pressure applied to force behavior, the animal develops a response to the situation that has no adaptive value in the sense that it is adequate to the situation or in the sense that it is superior to any number of other possible responses. Nevertheless, the appearance of the behavior is associated with a decline in resistance to jumping. Thus an animal that is forced to respond in the insoluble problem situation may always choose the card on its right, despite the fact that this choice is punished on half the trials. This type of response is not selected by the method with which the reward and punishment are used. At the same time it is not a mere random response but is consistently expressed and so must be considered as a response to the situation.[5]

Becomes Blind Defense. In a somewhat similar way, when a person ceases to think out his actions, his estimative animal reactions seem to take over in the face of his recurring failures. His actions are then apparently less due to any conscious motive than to a kind of blind defensiveness. They have more of the quality of instinctive reactions to what appear to him to be threatening situations. This state of threat, as we discussed previously, seems generally to accompany intense personal conflict.

This might help to explain why these people, without counseling, may remain for years in the same difficulties. While these conflict situations may afford some temporary satisfactions, they ultimately produce unhappiness.[6] Yet, such people often seem to be making no effort to change. Left to themselves, their perceptions are so frozen on simple, isolated aspects of their situation and their reactions so stereotyped, they may never make any further adaptations in their behavior. They continue in their unhappy state unless extrinsic causes eventually bring a change.[7]

[5] *Ibid.*, p. 27.

[6] Dollard and Miller, in discussing Maier's experiments, point out that the rats are rewarded on every trial, at least by escaping from the punishing air blast. So the person, too, gets some satisfaction in his stereotyped solution but this satisfaction is of a temporary and inadequate nature. J. Dollard and N. Miller: *Personality and Psychotherapy*, New York, Copyright 1950, by McGraw-Hill, p. 47.

[7] Johnson speaks of the IFD process, that is, the creating of an *ideal* that is unrealistic and beyond what the person himself can really accomplish. This, in turn, results in *frustration* because the ideal is not realized. The effect of this failure and frustration is a state of *demoralization*. This may carry through a person's entire life unless by some process, like that of counseling, he reconsiders his scale of success and realizes that his success must be measured on a more realistic basis. Only in this way will he recognize that he is failing much less than he had previously thought. Wendell Johnson: "The Semantics of Maladjustment," in L. A. Pennington and I. A. Berg, ed., *An Introduction to Clinical Psychology*, New York, The Ronald Press, 1948.

BROADENING AWARENESS

Remove Threat.   The first step in a person's choosing and acting in the direction of his real goals is to free himself from these fixed reactions by changing his focus from threat and failure. For this reason counseling is especially helpful, since it does not threaten a person further by appearing to force him to a solution. It relies on his own submerged but positive desires for reasonable conduct. At the same time, it offers him a relationship in which he can receive acceptance and understanding. In this way, the person's reasonable analysis counteracts his instinctive failure reaction. The interview, as we discussed earlier, becomes the focal point around which he can center his vague and disorganized urges for a more adequate solution. Even the choice of coming for counseling is itself a strong positive expression and a break in his fixed conduct pattern. In this one significant movement, he has taken a big step away from negation and failure. As he broadens his perceptions of his situation, he also becomes more aware of what he actually wants. By this re-examination of motives, the stereotyped reactions are replaced by constructive actions which are means to his goals.

Even the first counseling interview will usually give some evidence of this broadening awareness. For example, there is a slight indication of this in the married business woman's statements immediately following the excerpt just given (Z). She uses the phrases, "I've got people I don't want to hurt either," hinting that other factors besides the interest of herself and John are weighing on her mind.[8] Already, she has taken a quick glance at these other factors as her outlook has broadened momentarily. Obviously, she knows her obligations and responsibilities to her husband and family. But, until now this knowledge has been of no real value in motivating a different type of conduct.

Effects of Insight.   Ten interviews later, this woman has an entirely different view and she is not seeing the man any more. He, having also come for counseling, obtained a transfer to another department. As it often happens, her attitude towards others has changed, especially towards her husband. Her husband, in turn, no doubt in response to this, is more considerate of her. Still feeling the loss of the other man, she is yet happier in her choices:

8See p. 55.

P: . . . When John and I were together it just sorta pushed everything into the background. (Pause) . . . My husband's taking a better attitude too than he had been. He's been a little more considerate and affectionate, and with him showing that attitude, why maybe I can just pick up where I left off. Maybe my attitude towards him in the past hasn't been the way it should be . . .

C: You feel in a way that it just depends upon you whether you could find life adequate with your husband now.

P: Well, I think I could, because things are much different than they were at home. But you just can't turn aside and say, "Well, I'm going back to where I was"—even though I—if I really wanted to—I couldn't do that. It's hard to give John up after all the good times we've had and the things that we've done, but when you stop and think of what could have happened, why you see things different. (Long pause) . . . but I know even now, just by not seeing John, I'm better physically and spiritually too.

C: Things do seem better physically and spiritually for you.

P: Yes, the way it was before I wasn't really happy, it was just a state of conflict and misery and fear of being found out and thinking of the kids and all—no, it really wasn't happy, even when it seemed most enjoyable.

C: Yes, that is seeing things very clearly now and when you see all sides of it, it is not happy.

P: No, it isn't. There's no happiness in it. You're always under a constant strain. (Pause) I'll lose a lot in a worldly way but I'll gain too.

C: While you would lose in a worldly sense you would also gain . . .

P: I would gain more than I would lose, spiritually. (Pause) You can't get mixed up in things like that, but what you lose. If you go along with it every day for awhile and then you stop to think how big the thing really is, and what it could mean, (Pause) . . . I hope John goes back to his home town now. He lives in the East. It would help us to each live our own lives—not to feel responsible to each other.

C: You'd like him now to live his separate life and you'd like to live yours with your husband.

P: That's right.

C: You'd like to feel that you weren't responsible to him when you go with your husband, and he's not responsible to you when he takes someone out . . .

P: But, I do feel that I have an obligation to my husband rather than to John, because after all when you stop to think of it—some of the things my husband has done for me and here I have been just using my work as an excuse and going places with John, when I should have been with my husband, I shouldn't feel too good about it. I've made up my mind to quit work too—I should never have started again. I can see that now.

While there is still some concern about the man's attachment to her, her real life goals are now before her. She has found her direction again. She is happier in adhering to her marriage and family responsibilities. She has these clearly in front of her; the steps she is taking are leading her to them; and her appetites, while still in some disorder, are turned towards her reasonable duties. She not only *knows* but *feels* that this is the right way for her. A letter three years later confirmed this. Her marriage is more secure than it ever was before. It was indirectly learned that the man had left that city and also remarried by this time.

No Additional Knowledge.   As we examine these statements, we find no indication of new knowledge. Everything the woman says here she knew at the beginning of counseling. The change is in her own focus on what she knew. In the earlier stages, her awarenesses of her husband and family were apparently completely separate from her immediate satisfactions with John. It was like looking at two seemingly unconnected pictures. When she was with John she saw only that relationship and its pleasure. As she says, "When John and I were together, it just sorta pushed everything into the background." The rights of her husband and family and the consequences of her actions to them and herself are blurred, indistinct background that she does not look at. From this focus, her relationship with John is colored in a pleasing and attractive light which gives it a strong appeal. The disturbing background is so vague that it does not change this appeal. Like any other distorted and confused image, as we saw, these background factors appear more as a personal threat, which causes her to avoid looking at them.

Picture in Focus.   The result of counseling was to light up this background and bring it distinctly before her. Her perception broadens and deepens to include the whole picture. Her husband and family are all part of her relationship with John. She cannot look at this relationship without at the same time seeing them. This changes the entire tone of the picture. As she unfolds the different things her husband and family mean to her, the blurred and disturbing background now becomes precise and clear. To look at it is no longer threatening. Bathed in this new light, the relationship with John changes its color. Its pleasure is much less when it is seen in the light of its grave consequences. Its misery and unhappiness appear. So, the counselor's response, "When you see all sides of it, it is not happy," is accepted because it exactly expresses the way the woman now feels. She has begun to acquire an appetite for those things which she always knew she should be doing. Her sensitive urges are more disposed to follow her reasoned, long-time goals than to be led to an immediate but ultimately unhappy fulfillment with John. This switch in motivation is not easy. She will lose the appealing satisfactions of being with him. But she can offset that by the conscious awareness of how much she will gain in the better relationship with her husband and family and in the spiritual tranquility which meeting her obligations brings her. So, she can say, "I'll lose a lot in a worldly way but I'll gain too. . . . I would gain more than I would lose, spiritually." This is not simply an isolated resolve. It expresses her integrated view of all the factors involved.

Actions Follow Organized View. Being able to keep all aspects of her personal situation before her—the background of her family responsibilities as well as the foreground of her pleasure with John— she can plan her actions according to this more organized view. Before, the blurred background of family responsibilities was not distinct enough to counteract the strong immediate appeal of John. Now, while there is no direct change in John's power to attract her, she is no longer focused on him alone. With the complete picture of her total personal and spiritual relationships constantly present before her, his attraction is outweighed by the less sensitive and emotional but more ultimately powerful appeal of right reason.

THE PERCEPTION OF RELATIONSHIPS

Isolated Aspects Integrated. One of the most significant aspects of insight, then, is the way it facilitates a person's power of seeing relationships between various aspects of his problems. Before counseling, he sees his problems as isolated and unconnected. He acts on a series of simple perceptions. These miss many complex factors that make up the complete picture. Consequently, even when these actions bring immediate satisfactions, they leave him in the same conflicts. Counseling enables him to relate his problems together, trace them to their sources and reorganize them in the order of their real importance. At the end of this insight process this woman has, as one person described it, a map to aid her in understanding how she came to be in such a conflict state and to indicate her way out. The counseling process enables a person to get a new and more integrated view of himself and his situation. His fixed and narrow perceptions broaden and integrate. In this way, the major contribution of counseling as such is not to give her new knowledge but rather to provide her with a technically skillful opportunity for personal reorganization and reintegration.

Research in Vision.   Some recent research in vision provides interesting parallels in the organizing and integrating process of insight through counseling, and the process by which a person is able to see and reproduce a composite series of objects more accurately. While the problems of human conduct are far more complex, yet certain similarities exist. They help demonstrate how the unthreatening and accepting atmosphere of a counseling interview reproduces in its own way the conditions most conducive to organized and integrated seeing. The ability to organize and integrate all the complex features of a painting or of a landscape demands a structured experience that is in many ways like the counseling experience.

Perception Often Lacks Unity.   The tendency towards simplicity, which Lillie observed to be characteristic of all nature, also affects a person's approach to the problem of seeing. This is demonstrated in a technique of perception recently developed by Hoyt Sherman and others. Most adults without training do not have the ability to see a complex picture or scene as an integrated whole.[9] If a group of untrained people are observing the same scene, as a general rule, each will see isolated features and lose the total perception. If, for example, a picture is flashed on a screen, some will only see the objects that are in one corner. The middle and the other side will be blurred. Other observers will see objects on the opposite side or the center and the alternate sides will be confused. Few will agree even about the general contours of what they saw. None will agree on exact details. Each person is usually in for a great surprise when the scene is again flashed on the screen and he can compare his original impression with what he actually saw. Before anyone can learn to

[9]Interestingly, most small children have this ability. It is lost some time in childhood.

reproduce a scene accurately he must acquire the ability to see all its features in the integrated and organized way.

Hoyt Sherman points out that:

. . . the degree to which one succeeds in getting unity in his drawing significantly depends upon the degree to which he succeeds in getting unity in his seeing. Teaching students to draw with satisfactory pictorial organization is to a major degree a process of teaching them to see with perceptual unity—that is, to see all points in a motif with relation to a focal point. The artist needs to be able to see the whole field at which he is looking and to see it in such a way as to place the parts in the whole through referral of the parts to a focal point.[10]

Similar to Insight Process.   The artist has a perceptual problem similar to that of a person wishing to solve personal problems. Both are faced with particular factors that must be integrated. If the untrained artist follows his first perception, he will not get an adequate picture of the whole but will only reproduce some disorganized aspects. In this same way, one who is confused about personal problems must relate his difficulties to the source of conflict. In the beginning of counseling, the person is fixed on a series of isolated perceptions. His actions based on these views do not bring him to his goal. He is not reaching what he really wants because he does not see all the factors in a unified and coordinated manner. He can keep acting on these inadequate perceptions for years, and be continually in conflict because he can reach no satisfactory answer. As we saw, this may result in a fixed frustration type of reaction which produces a goalless, stereotyped conduct. It is especially in situations like this that counseling interviews can be very helpful. As in art perception, a person needs the repeated experience of looking at himself in the counseling process, before he can acquire an integrated view of himself and his world.

Requires Concentrated Effort.   This ability to see in perceptual unity can only be attained through constant effort. It takes concentrated attention to unify perceptions and bring together all the objects in a scene. Passivity here, as in other human actions, leads to a narrowed perception, which oversimplifies the complexity of the observed landscape. So Sherman points out:

[10]Hoyt L. Sherman: *Drawing by Seeing*, New York, Copyright 1947, by Hinds, Hayden & Elredge, p. 2.

If a student is passive and inattentive when looking at a motif, he will not see it with perceptual unity. There needs to be as much of "reaching out and seizing" the image as of "receiving" it. In the beginning, students need practice in establishing this aggressive frame of mind.[11]

Growth in Unity. This concentrated attention brings the slow growth in unity and integration as the objects relate themselves little by little to each other. This may explain why the repeated expression and analysis of the same personal problems in the counseling process gradually bring the person a more integrated view of himself and his problems.

Sherman also points out that,

Teaching people to see with perceptual unity is as much an unlearning process as it is a learning one. Most objects in our adult environment have become familiar through many associations. Rather than being seen for themselves, these objects serve merely as symbols for still other things with which our minds become occupied. We are no longer attentive to the optical forms of things in their optical background. Training students so that they can become attentive to visual qualities and relationships is a matter of breaking these crusts of conventional reaction and introducing a fresh approach to the seeing act.[12]

Changing Emotional Tone. We have already discussed the earlier influences and the conditioning process by which personal reactions become fixed and certain experiences receive exaggerated emotional tones. This was characteristic of the opening interviews in which people had certain fixed attitudes which determined their reaction to other persons, things, or situations. As they gradually achieved insight, they began to view these same experiences in an entirely different light and emotional tone. So, the young aviator, unable to solo, had first to perceive the broad factors in his tension and irritation that caused him to tighten up in the plane. These included the sound of the instructor's voice and that of his father which, in turn, symbolized a harsh and stern critic of whom he was very much afraid. He grew to realize that these hidden factors were behind what appeared to be a simple problem of desiring to solo. He had then to unlearn the deep relationship between the sound of

[11]*Ibid.*, p. 9.
[12]*Loc. cit.*

a harsh voice and all the long buried attitudes within him. He had to acquire the same "fresh approach to the seeing act" as the artist.

Seeing What Is. If the artist follows his first impulse he is apt only to see "one side of the picture" and to deceive himself by attaching to it a symbolic meaning which it does not actually have. He must make an active effort to bring about an integrated seeing of the picture as a whole. Part of this process involves disentangling the reality from built-up associations which deceive him. So, too, the same self-deception results unless a person makes a conscious effort to reach out and grasp all the integrated factors that enter into his personal situation. Otherwise he will focus on an immediate good which, while temporarily satisfying, is at variance with his real purpose. When he follows this particularized view, he finds himself restless and bitter as his reason passes judgment on these actions. The problem here is not that he did not know in what general directions his actions should go. He is off on a detour which leaves him increasingly farther away from his reasonable norms. Each time people get lost in these emotional by-paths, they condemn themselves.

Relates Intermediate Areas. Insight in counseling lights up the intermediate areas between the reasonable norms of conduct which people know and the immediate acts necessary to fulfill these norms. The old saying of the forest and the trees seems to fit. A man looking up through the trees can see, off in the distance, the mountain peak which is his ultimate destination. Down in the underbrush he cannot find his way in the step-by-step path necessary to reach the mountain peak. He finds himself lost in the shadows which the trees create and he travels in the proverbial circles. Time after time he may look up at the mountain peak and think he is getting closer. Later, he realizes that he is no closer than before, as the path brings him back where he started. Applying the example, the immediate emotional urges which offer temporary pleasure appear to lead to happiness and peace of mind. Actually, once the temporary satisfactions have been fulfilled, they leave the person no closer to his goal than before. He, too, like the traveler in the forest, feels discouraged, confused, and frustrated. With all his effort he has made no progress. This kind of discouragement seems to be characteristic of many when they come for counseling. They know in a general way the kind of life plan they want for themselves. Yet, they may be acting on some momentary opposite motive. Even when they try new paths, they find themselves led in the same emotional circles.

What insight does, then, is reverse the process of the old saying. People can now see both trees and forest in an integrated view. To find his way, the explorer often climbs a tree and surveys all the extension of the forest—its valleys, hills, underbrush, and tall trees. The explorer needs to see what lies ahead to prepare himself to meet the change in contour and nature of the obstacles. He designates certain landmarks that he can keep before him when he goes again into the underbrush. Similarly, the interviews are the means of this integrating outlook and planning. The person can set up a particular destination for himself. As he goes again into the confusion of daily living, he holds this immediate goal in front of him. Having reached that he can look for further goals. In this way he is going steadily in the direction of the ultimate plan of conduct which he always wanted for himself but could not reach. The contrast, after a number of interviews, in increased positive emotion and confidence is also much like the encouragement which the traveler feels as he finds himself getting nearer his destination, after having wandered for a long time in circles.

THE REASONING PROCESS OF COUNSEL

Relation of Means to End. Consequently, like the explorer's survey of the steps to his destination, the integrated understanding which counseling brings does not concern the ends or goals of conduct, but the complex intermediate means by which these reasonable goals are reached. It is this integration of means which is the particular function of the survey process which constitutes the virtue of counsel. Life goals themselves are presupposed in counsel. It is the purpose of a valid education to supply these goals by enabling a person to reach the right intellectual conclusions and to have a knowledge of all facts essential to right living. This understanding of principles and facts, while taken for granted in counseling, is necessary before any totally integrated view of reality would be possible for a person. But, such things are extrinsic to counsel. The person either comes to the counseling process with such orientation or he must acquire it in an educational or guidance relationship outside of counsel. "Of such things," says St. Thomas, "counsel makes no inquiry."[13] The insights that result from counseling are concerned with the elaborate series of steps necessary to reach these various goals, and the complex interweaving of positive and negative emotions, in proportion as the person is or is not approaching or achieving such aims.

This reasoning process of counsel, since it is directly related to action in the immediate concrete world in which a person lives, is the reverse of the reasoning process which relates things to law, principle, and ultimate causes. So,

> . . . the term of inquiry in counsel is that which we are able to do at once. For just as the end is considered in the light of a principle, so the means are considered in the light of a conclusion. Wherefore, that which presents itself to be done first holds the position of an ultimate conclusion where the inquiry comes to an end.[14]

Acts From Integrated View.   Consequently, before a person can move with any security, even towards the first stage of his goal, he must have worked out an integrated perception of the whole field of action pertaining to that goal. The person must see that each one of a series of actions leads him to his reasonable goals. Only then can he proceed even to the first act with any certainty of success and achievement.

Precipitation.   When a person fails to see all the intermediate steps in the light of his ultimate goal he tends towards precipitation and imprudence. He will be motivated, not by any positive awareness of his ultimate purpose, but by the immediate, pleasant or unpleasant attraction of the first action itself. If, for various reasons, some of the intermediate steps necessary to his goal strike him as unpleasant he will avoid them and be led down a conflicting and frustrating by-path.

Constant Struggle Against Disorder.   Moreover, even when a person has reached a reasonable solution, consistent effort is necessary to maintain this reasoned view. Otherwise he may find himself again moved by some elemental emotional urge in conflict with reason. Because man lives in a world of contingencies, in the midst of dis-

---

[13]St. Thomas Aquinas: *Summa Theologica*, I–II, Q. 14, a. 6, translated by Fathers of the English Dominican Province, New York, Benziger Brothers, 1947. Reprinted from the *Summa Theologica* with the permission of Benziger Brothers, Inc., Publishers and Copyright Owners.

[14]St. Thomas, (D): I–II, Q. 14, a. 6.

order outside and within himself, the effort towards integration is a constant task. A man is actually in the flux of movement all the time. He must constantly be coping with this movement and bringing order into it. This tendency towards disorder and disintegration in man seems also to be part of a similar tendency in all nature. As Lillie points out,

> Unless counteracted by directive action the casual or random element in nature tends to increase. If things are left to chance, not only does organization of any high degree of complexity fail to develop, but what organization there is tends to lapse or disappear. Hence in those cases, such as living organisms, where the existence and activity of the system depend on a special and complex organization, it appears necessary to assume the continued operation of a stable directive influence or factor which pervades the whole system and excludes or compensates casual factors whenever these conflict with the special vital requirements.[15]

Integrative Factor Necessary. In nature, an active counterprocess is necessary to preserve any complex type of reaction. This is applicable also to human nature. Human choices that are made in the light of reasonable insights are, as we have seen, a powerful active counterprocess. Such insightful choices can bring about personality integration. To maintain this integration, reasoned analysis is necessary in the evaluation of each action so that the various appetites may be disposed towards the over-all good of the whole person. Otherwise, they follow their natural tendencies towards the immediate good which attracts them. So, as we saw in the example earlier in this book on page 55, if a person allows himself to focus only on incidents which make a situation appear to be an attack, all his appetites will react in defense. He must, by reasoned analysis, uncover other factors to change this defensiveness. Alternately, if, as in the case of the married business woman (Z), an immediate situation, such as the infatuation with an attractive man, is seen in the light of the particular satisfactions it offers, the person's appetites will be strongly moved by this simple perception. Only when she has consistently alerted herself to all the complex factors which make her whole relation with the man a dishonest one, is she able to turn her intense desires away from him and in the direction of her husband and family.

15Lillie, *op. cit.*, p. 176.

From the point of view of biological research, Lillie makes the same observation:

> In our experiences of natural processes, *the presence of an integrative and directive factor,* having control over an extensive field of activity, *is most readily observed in voluntary action carried out in pursuit of a* purpose. Here "psychic aim" becomes dominant and determines the special direction of what happens in the physical field. Obviously, voluntary action is not independent of physical factors but is carried out in intimate conjunction with them; the normally acting neuromuscular system is a physical system having definite and constant properties without which the action would not be possible. The significant factor, however, is that the precise form which this action takes is dependent not only on this physical organization but also on the motivation and aim in the conscious mind of the agent. In some unknown manner the psychic aim determines that events take a special and definite course, rather than one of many others which are possible in the physical sense; there is a selection out of a wide range of possibilities.[16]

The power of "voluntary action carried out in pursuit of a purpose," which Lillie describes, is particularly evident in the insight that comes from counseling. We have observed the process of insight integrating the field of the factors which enter into the life experiences of a person and seen how, as this integration and broader understanding take place, new and more adequate choices are possible.

Affects Whole Person.   This self-integration extends not only to restoring harmony between the various conflicting emotional and instinctive appetites but also to the whole physical person. This is perhaps best demonstrated in the psychosomatic effects which the medical use of counseling is uncovering. When skin conditions clear up, fatigue and tension are released, serious gastro-intestinal disorders are lessened, or asthmatic conditions improve, we are dealing with effects which go beyond intellectual knowledge and reach into physical functioning and co-ordination. This seems to be explained only if we assume that what takes place in the counseling process involves the whole human being and not simply the knowing or even the willing function alone.

Beyond the Material and Physical.   But this personal integration is brought about, especially, through the functions of knowing and

16*Ibid.,* p. 181 (Italics mine).

willing, of insightful, self-directed choices. As we have studied the problems of personality confusions and conflicts, we have seen the intense drive of the person revealing itself in wanting to know why he is acting the way he is. As the understanding of the causes and relationships of his various motives become clearer to him, he is able to make self-initiated changes in both his outlook and conduct. Many of the basic needs which these persons reveal—like security, love, independence, and happiness—cannot of themselves be measured or reduced to any quantified terms. Yet it is these non-quantified needs which, more than anything else, seem to be the basis of the fundamental adjustment or maladjustment of the individual. But because we are dealing with an integrated human being, failure to fulfill these needs seems to have a noticeable effect on many physical functions.

This basic unity of the person explains why the fulfillment of the needs for order, integration, reasonable self-esteem, independence, security, and the like may be far more successful aids in curing the total illness of a person than attempts to treat the particular organic difficulties, which are only the physical effects of disordered emotions and unfulfilled spiritual needs. Actually, if these basic needs are fulfilled, the person seems much more able to bear and cope with the effects of a particular organic disease or physical illness.

Long-Time View. Moreover, choices which result from counseling flow from a broader, insightful view of life goals and purposes. They include also the foregoing of an immediate satisfaction for one that is more enduring and permanent, even though it may be delayed and achieved only after a prolonged effort of self-control. So, as Rogers says:

In counseling, insight generally involves a choice between goals which give immediate and temporary satisfaction, and those which offer delayed, but more permanent, satisfactions. In this respect, the type of "creative will" which acts upon the situation is no different from the choice exercised by the child who decides to forgo the immediate ice-cream cone in order to save his nickels for the prized roller skates. He chooses the course which gives him the greater satisfaction, even though that satisfaction is delayed. Thus, Barbara gains immediate satisfaction out of self-approbation as she condemns other young people for being frivolous, undignified, and social. She has the satisfaction of considering herself much more nearly perfect than they. When able to face the choice freely, however, without defensiveness, she definitely prefers the satisfactions which will come from being one of the group and engaging in social activities. She makes this choice in spite of her recognition that the first steps in this process of socialization will be difficult and painful and that the rewards will be delayed. Or, in the case of Mr. Bryan, the client sees clearly enough the satisfactions of escaping life and responsibility through his neurotic symptoms. Yet, after considerable uncertainty, he chooses the course of adult development, not for its immediate, but for its long-time satisfactions.[17]

Ultimate Fulfillment Only in Eternal Reality. This awareness that insight tends to move through the "difficult and painful . . . . not for its immediate, but for its long-time satisfactions" might be carried to ultimate conclusions. The analysis of the counseling process demonstrates that increased insight and a broader understanding of his personal values, aims, and purposes enable a person to direct himself towards, and eventually to reach, more ultimate goals that are more permanently satisfying. But no transient, material thing can, upon analysis, produce the permanent security, peace, and lasting happiness that each one seeks. The fear of loss is the other side of every human possession and security. This kind of evaluation should logically lead a person to seek a final and ultimate Good, which will be a permanent source of happiness. God, of course, must have supplied the means of supernatural help to enable man to fulfill his striving for an ultimate and permanent possession of all that is both true and good. We know from the science of Theology that God does supply these means through actual and sanctifying grace. So, as Garrigou-Lagrange says,

It follows that man in his every deliberate act should live not only in a reasonable but in a supernatural way, since everything he does should be ordered at least virtually to his last supernatural end, the goal of his journey. . . . We ought to live as reasonable beings and also children of God redeemed by His only Son. We must not only submit our passions to reason but subordinate reason itself to faith, to the spirit of faith, and subject all our natural activity to the life of grace and charity, in fidelity to the Holy Ghost.[18]

[17]Carl R. Rogers: *Counseling and Psychotherapy*, Boston, Copyright 1942, by Houghton Mifflin Co., p. 210.

[18]Garrigou-Lagrange, O.P.: *The Love of God*, St. Louis, Copyright 1947, by B. Herder Book Co., pp. 299–300.

Human motivation has as its final goal, then, an ultimate and permanent good, which can be possessed without the fear of loss and the threat of disintegration. Particular goals can be stages along the way. But none of these particular goals is really capable of totally satisfying man, or of stilling this intense pursuit of a greater good and more permanent security that lies at the center of the unrest which penetrates man's being.

The process of insight through counseling is a means by which a person relates the minute details of his life to his reasonable goals. It cannot in any way take the place of ultimate goals or supply, of itself, the means of man's final fulfillment. To revert to our analogy of the traveler, insight aids him to direct himself rightly in the intermediate stages of his journey through the complex underbrush of daily living. If he looks, he can see, in the distance, "a mountain in which God is well pleased to dwell,"[19] which is his real destination and by which he can measure the progress of his journey.

[19]Psalm 57.

CHAPTER VIII

ADJUSTING TO REALITY

Self-Knowledge and Integration. Successful counseling brings an increase both in self-knowledge and self-integration. Taken together, these enable people to arrive at a more realistic way of living. As we have seen, the interviews aid a person to relate his problems with past and present factors. Through these insights the deepest kind of self-understanding comes about. Almost like the parts of a jigsaw puzzle, various aspects of his problems begin to fit together, forming patterns and designs. At the end of this insight process, he knows how he came to have these confused and disorganized attitudes and he can plan more adequate solutions. Accompanying this there is a steady increase in self-integration, so that the person can actually carry out the solutions he plans without being impeded by his disordered appetites. A person begins to feel positively about the things he knows and sees he should do. The counseling process not only reveals in detail the right steps to his reasoned goals, but disposes his various appetites so that they impel him in this direction rather than lead him down confusing and frustrating bypaths.

Results. The effect of this development in both self-knowledge and integration is to bring people a greater degree of self-approval, security, peace, achievement, and happiness. It also brings them closer to reality. Whereas previously they were out of joint with reality, they now can plan and act in it with greater confidence. Their will to responsible and reasonable achievement is actually verified in their daily living. They are, consequently, in a better state of personal adjustment.

SOME DETERMINANTS OF SUCCESS

Responsibility for Changing Self. Even when the counselor is skilled, not every counseling series is successful. Elsewhere we have spoken of the urge to independent and responsible achievement, which is characteristic of even a very small child.[1] This power of self-determination is also fundamental to the changes which take place in counseling. A person gets out of counseling what he puts into it. In proportion as a person has a positive will and desire to change, interviews can aid him to reach a better and happier state. But some positive desire for change and at least some implied need for help, seem basic to the counseling process. Success in counseling is dependent upon the person either coming to the interview on his own responsibility, or, at some time during the series, actually facing and taking some responsibility for changing himself. The degree to which he accepts such responsibility and need for changing himself seems to determine in a large measure the degree of adjustment which he achieves through counseling. While there are some methods which, as we will discuss later, can sometimes make it easier for people to come for counseling, there seems to be no skill that will enable persons to face themselves when they are fundamentally unwilling.

Self-Examination Readiness.   For various reasons a person is ready to look at himself at one period in his life although he was unwilling to undergo such an examination previously. Certain personal crises often appear to promote a desire and need for counseling. As we have seen, the increasing unhappiness of a person's present life is one of the most effective causes. Misery and conflict are themselves strong pressures in the direction of a new way of living. An important point, too, is the degree of actual grace a person receives. Whatever the reasons are, however, at one time a person may be willing and ready for counseling and at another he may not be.

Counselor's Ability.   The counselor's ability is also a major factor here. Often a person has the will to change, but the counselor's bad responses frustrate this positive will. This kind of counseling, instead of helping a person, only makes him further resistant and negative.

Positive Will Essential.   Consequently, the counseling process can encourage and develop a person's positive will even when it is covered over with many negations and hostilities. It cannot, however, create a positive will. There seems to be a point at which any

[1]See pp. 73–74.

man can turn in on himself and so freeze his perceptions and isolate his attitudes that he has no positive will to change. He simply negates. In this negative state there is a kind of incrustation and withdrawal from reality. Defense reactions are built up by nourishing hurts, rejections, and failures, and by fantasy methods of escape. As people grow in such personal confusions they think more and more of themselves and less of the real world of persons and things beyond themselves. Experienced counselors, therefore, even at the end of the first interview, still may not be sure that the person wanted the interview and will actually return. Sometimes, too, a person lightly touches on what appears to the counselor to be a grave problem and does not return to it again in that interview and may not in subsequent interviews. Such problems can, of course, be solved through counseling and yet not be mentioned, particularly if they are in some way connected with other solutions the person worked out in the interviews.

Power to be Negative. This power of the person to be negative, to resist change, even to a happier state, to withdraw from reality and plunge more deeply into himself, is at the heart of human freedom. In this we have penerated into a deep metaphysical and theological question which involves the problem of evil itself. Evil is basically nothing, in the sense that it is an absence. For this reason, St. Thomas and others define it as the absence of good. It is the lack of a unified integration. A man, by the very nature of being able to will, can will away from things. By willing to negate, he wills in the direction of nothing. In this path of negation a person wills something, usually, but it is in such adverse relation to what he could have willed, and what was best for him, that it moves him farther away from his real goals.

We have seen that a strong degree of negativism is characteristic of opening interviews. When a person begins to talk about himself, the content contains various negative emotion factors that we have previously described. The statements of problems are highly colored by this resistant, negative attitude. But, hidden beneath are sufficient positive urges to bring him for counseling.

CHANGES IN ATTITUDES TOWARDS SELF

Self-Rejection. This negativism in opening interviews often shows itself most powerfully by the way in which it is turned against the person himself. This is expressed by intense feelings of self-rejection and disgust. These, too, may be combined with unreasonable and excessive feelings of guilt. Such guilt, when analyzed, is another form of self-rejection. As a person's views of himself and his environment become more integrated, he also has a more positive attitude towards himself and a greater degree of self-acceptance. This, in turn, gives him a more objective judgment of what he has done in proportion to what he should have done. Consequently, his feelings of guilt are often less intense. He then may not feel so responsible for every failure as he brings into consideration other factors that may lessen or even remove his responsibility in some instances. He is no longer harrassing himself with intense negative attacks and feelings of worthlessness. He can encourage himself by positive acceptance of his own worth and achievement.

Rebellion Against Limitations. In this sense many personality problems contain a basic rebellion against a person's limitations. The process of counseling, on the other hand, involves the direct acceptance of self and one's limited capacities. The person begins to move towards goals within that sphere without any excessive self-condemnation or inferiority feelings for what is beyond him. This movement is away from the extreme of pride and pusillanimity in the direction of the reasonable self-worth of humility.

Destructive Self-Criticism. This self-rejection or disgust, however disguised it may be from the counselor, seems generally to be present in serious personal problems. This is another reason why, as we have seen, direct advice is often so intensely resisted by people who do not give any extrinsic appearance of personal conflict. They know, in a confused way, what they should do and are already criticizing themselves more sharply than the counselor would ever dare. But this self-criticism is a negative attack on themselves. It must be aided by the counselor's sensitive responses to become positive self-understanding and acceptance. The counselor's skill takes into account this power of negation. He does not throw at a person a choice for which the person is not ready. We have discussed how any suggestion of change, even when a person may have positive desire for it, may so threaten and disturb him at that moment that he pulls away and avoids it. Rather, the counseling process allows the person to begin slowly to unfold himself. He gets a growing satisfaction of release and joy at facing reality, which is great enough to offset the pain and resistance he feels about looking at himself and seeing the necessity of change. If this positive satisfaction of facing his problems and getting things out in the open is not allowed a person, and insights are given him before he has brought them up in the interview, the will to negate may quickly take over, and the person backs away and avoids the issue. Accompanying this power of negation, instinctive feelings of defense and threat seem to be aroused. But, if a person experiences the satisfying and stimulating feelings of accepting reality and being honest with himself, he can stand the pain which this self-investigation may bring.

Deep Satisfaction From Facing Self. The positive urge a person has to face himself in an interview is deep and meaningful for him. This may be missed by the counselor, because he does not know the unique circumstances of the person's life which make some apparently small thing very hard for him to talk about. Yet, when he is able to express it, the person gets extreme satisfaction at having the courage to bring this up in the interview and get it out of himself. People often explain this with a statement like, "That was really hard to talk about but I feel much better now that I've gotten it out of my system."

Growth in Courage. The counseling process, therefore, produces a renewed sense of courage to face the present and cope with it. The skillful acceptance of the counselor encourages the person's feelings of assurance and self-worth. As long as a person feels worthless, he lacks confidence in his ability to reach a reasonable solution. This may cause him to be excessively dependent on the judgment of others. He will also be continually subject to the recurrent conditionings of earlier attitudes. He needs the courage to begin to take responsibility for himself and face the present.

Consequently, in the later stages of a successful series of interviews, we note the more frequent appearance of statements indicating that the person is now facing his problems and working out better solutions. The person accepts responsibility for his difficulties and begins to make more reasonable decisions about them. In dependent people there is also a noticeable increase in statements of independence. This is in contrast to the tendencies to escape responsibility, to depend on others, and to seek everyone's advice, which are so often characteristic of these same people in the beginning stages of counseling.

Small Self-Initiated Actions. At first a person usually builds up confidence in his own ability by a series of small, self-initiated actions. In themselves these actions may appear insignificant and yet have deep implications for a new way of life. For example, in the instance of the college girl who was so dependent on her mother and her friends (Y),[2] we see the indication of a new life pattern in her choice to wear a particular hat. She had received it as a gift the previous Christmas but had never been able to wear it because, the first time she put it on, her mother laughed at it and called it "silly." In three interviews she saw that she was too affected by many of her mother's attitudes. The evening after the third interview, while she was home for spring vacation, she got out the hat again and the next morning put it on. She went downstairs expecting more ridicule, but nothing was said. While riding on the bus, one of her friends remarked what an attractive hat it was and how well it looked on her. At first glance this seems a trivial incident. But, put in the framework of her new self-awarenesses, the incident acquires greater significance. Her action was motivated by insights which she had recently gained into her excessive dependency on her mother's opinions. In this light, the courage to wear the hat and the satisfaction of being complimented had important implications. As she re-examined the experience, in her next interview, she realized that it had given her a greater sense of conviction about her own judgment. She now knew that even small self-directed choices were more meaningful and happier than her previous dependency. This in turn stimulated her to more important responsible actions.

THE MEANING OF ADJUSTMENT

Gradual Unfolding of What Is. These effects come about because counseling produces a gradual unfolding of the person's understanding of what is. As we have seen, the beginning states of maladjustment, as they are revealed by the content of opening interviews, give a picture of the person and his environment that is out

[2]P. 100.

of focus, disorganized, and inadequate. His contact with reality, even the reality of himself, is warped and distorted. For this reason, his judgments and actions do not produce success and fulfillment. In fact, his contact with reality may be so unstable that he has no consistent views or judgments and fluctuates around a series of attitudes. His state of maladjustment is proportionate to the degree that his understanding of himself and his environment is at variance with reality.

Realism. Considered in this way, psychological adjustment as such does not depend on social norms or on adaptation to environment. The process of adjustment is determined by the way a person's judgments and actions more adequately reach reality. Consequently, the evidence of successful counseling interviews offers an additional demonstration of the validity of a realistic philosophy of personality. The rightness of practical judgment, St. Thomas says, consists in this, "that one apprehend a thing as it is in itself."[3] The degree to which contingent singulars are reached in each situation and appropriate judgments and actions devised to meet them is the measure of good personal adjustment.

Consistency. Because of this ability to penetrate reality in himself and other things a person, through counseling, can realize, measure, and understand his degree of maladjustment and become gradually aware of what he really is and what he can do. He also has the power of entering into the reality of his environment and understanding it better. As a result, he is less disturbed by changing moods.

Conforming to Reality. Adjustment, as the interviews reveal it, then, is not simply conformity to the group as is often popularly supposed. It is, rather, a greater delving into the reality of oneself and other things and the conformity, first, of one's knowledge, and then, of one's actions to the reality discovered. Adjustment means the fitting of oneself to what *is*—whether this is what others do or not. In this sense, social conformity and approval would not of themselves denote adjustment. But, because adjustment conforms to that which is, it may often be shared by many people as a social

[3]St. Thomas Aquinas: *Summa Theologica*, II–II, Q. 51, a. 3, reply obj. 1, translated by Fathers of the English Dominican Province, New York, Benziger Brothers, 1947. Reprinted from the *Summa Theologica* with the permission of Benziger Brothers, Inc., Publisher and Copyright Owners.

norm. Reasonable men, over a period of time, can usually come to certain basic agreements which reach reality. Many of the customs and traditions which are accepted in Christian and democratic society are norms of psychological adjustment. They are norms, however, not simply because a particular group arbitrarily sets them up and approves them, but because they are basically reasonable. This would explain why the reasonable analysis of the counseling interviews usually leads the person away from socially unapproved conduct to a more accepted type of action. Such socially approved action is often the more reasonable and better course for the person to take in his own life. The person accepts this ordinary way of acting, however, not simply because most people act like this, but because he sees it as the reasonable way of life.

Not Necessarily Environmental Change. Moreover, successful adjustment does not necessarily involve a radical change of environment, as was sometimes thought. The evidence which counseling reveals about a person's ability to make a more realistic reorganization of himself often makes environmental changes unnecessary. There may, however, still be need of such changes in some cases. But, even here, the person can usually see this and bring it about himself. Time after time we see people, at the end of a successful series of interviews, able to go back to the same environment and live adequately and happily there. The married business woman (Z)[4] whom we quoted earlier, gave no indication that there was any definite reform in her husband. He is the same person. As she gets a different view of her marriage and can treat him differently, he in turn responds to that treatment. Fortunately, no one made any attempts to get her to change her environment or to encourage her to leave her husband and marry the other man who seemed to be more suited to her. This, of course, is in sharp contrast with the easy solutions of a quick divorce and of marrying the other person that are so often given for such difficulties.

New View of Environment. That environmental change is not always necessary is demonstrated also in the case of the aviation cadet (X) which we have been quoting. A determined and successful uncle has completely absorbed his earlier life. He discovers that many of his uncle's attitudes are not valid for his present life. With all the hostility and confusion which this conflict has produced in

[4]Pp. 148–151.

him he can, as he thinks it out, arrive at his own life plan and yet accept his uncle, respect him, and appreciate what he has done for him. At the same time, he knows that he can no longer passively accept the uncle's values as a substitute for thinking out his own judgments. He says, towards the end of counseling, that he feels sure he could return to his home without losing what he gained from the interviews. In the same way, the nurse (T) recognized how the home symbolized states of passivity and brought on the concomitant physiological conditioning. Having thought that out, she did not feel any necessity to leave home. But, while she could live in the home and accept many of the home's values, she realized that she must determine and accept those values on her own independent responsibility. She could no longer be happy simply by absorbing them from others as she had in early childhood.

Social Consequences of Adjustment. The realistic evaluation which counseling facilitates also helps re-establish normal relations between people. This is one of the reasons why counseling often enables a person to live happily in a previously unhappy relationship. An individual becomes able to distinguish between the actions of others and the tensions and misunderstandings which may have been attached to these actions. Human relationships can become complex because each person reacts to the attitudes of those around him. If a person in an emotional state misinterprets some remark or action of another this, in turn, may cause the other person to become defensive and more readily misinterpret him. This starts a series of vicious circles which increases as the misunderstandings grow. A succession of such incidents may arouse emotions on both sides to the point that even small remarks and completely unrelated actions become symbols of personal difference and rejection. This is popularly described as making "mountains out of molehills." Incidents and remarks small in themselves and unrelated can, as emotional tension rises, be consistently misinterpreted until they pile up to be huge barriers between people. Actions and reactions only serve to increase this emotional turmoil and confusion.

Adjustment to reality reverses this popular saying. Mountains become molehills again as the person quietly surveys the motives and issues which entered into a situation or a series of remarks. When a person is able to objectify the incidents and see other explanations and factors, the large emotional barriers, which seemed at first so great, slowly begin to shrink as broader understanding and deeper penetration of underlying causes come about. As these issues can be looked at reasonably, the person can reach their reality. Knowing what the issues really are and estimating with more accuracy the motives and causes behind both his own and the other person's reactions, he is able to plan and act in a happier and more successful way.

Moreover, as a person's insight enables him to penetrate the real meaning of these past situations and remarks, he grows more positive and understanding in his actions with regard to others. This causes other persons with whom he regularly comes in contact to feel accepted by him so that they are less defensive and emotional themselves. In intimate relationships such as those which exist between husband and wife, any positive change on the part of the one will often be quickly reflected in the attitudes of the other. We saw in a previous excerpt that as the wife grew more understanding and appreciative of the husband, she observed his increased consideration and affection toward her (Z).[5]

Illustration. We have attempted to show in the diagram on page 173, this difference in personal relationships that exists between actions resulting from the narrow perceptions of emotional states and those solutions flowing from the broad perceptions of reality.

First Plan Follows Narrow View. This diagram illustrates the process of adjustment of a senior high school girl, a recent transfer from another school. She was already insecure and defensive when she came to the new school (A). Because of this she interpreted some of the remarks of her classmates as a personal affront (B). This caused her to fear further hurt by them (C). These factors taken together resulted in the choice of a plan of conduct (D) wherein she withdrew herself from her classmates and made little effort to be friendly. Since she was focused on these three factors, A, B, C, she chose a consistent plan of action, D, related to them. This action met with a different interpretation on the part of her classmates, who assumed her to be superior and snobbish. This increased their unwillingness to be friendly towards her, which only fixed more firmly the new student's desire to avoid them.

Broadening Outlook. This state soon became very unhappy for

[5]Pp. 148–151.

TRIANGLE I shows the

**NARROWED
EMOTIONAL PERCEPTION**

due to insecurity already present on entering a new school situation.

TRIANGLE II shows the

**BROADENED SURVEY
AND UNDERSTANDING**

of other factors as a result of counseling interviews.

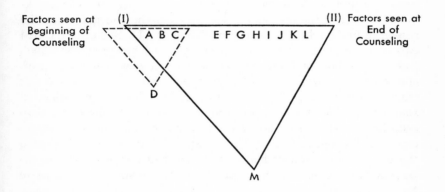

Factors seen at Beginning of Counseling   (I)   A B C   E F G H I J K L   (II) Factors seen at End of Counseling   D   M

D—PLAN OF CONDUCT:

Avoid others in order not to be hurt by rejection

EFFECT of these actions: Unhappiness and Sense of Inadequacy

M—PLAN OF CONDUCT:

Responsibility on self to make friends
Expected too much acceptance

EFFECT of these actions: Increased Happiness and Personal Adequacy

the new student. This and her noticeable decline in grades finally caused her to seek counseling. During four interviews she rethought the problems of her social rejection and unhappiness. She realized for the first time how insecure (E) and defensive (F) she was when she entered the new school. Seeing this, she began to recognize that different interpretations (G) could have been made of each of the small incidents which she had built up to make her feel so rejected. As she went back over the memory of those first days, she realized that her insecurity made her seek more acceptance and consideration than any new student would normally receive (H). As she gained these insights, it became clearer that the reactions of the other students were not a rejection of her. She concluded that any new student would be likely to undergo a similar experience (I). Looking at herself in the interviews, she saw that she had not taken the responsibility for being friendly or fitting in (J). She even recalled two or three statements in which she extolled her previous school. But, as she thought it out, she knew that the new school was preferable in many ways (K). She put this together and saw that her plan of conduct was one which would cause her to be thought a snob and not apt to win friends in any group (L). She resolved to drop her patterns of withdrawal and her demands for excessive acceptance. She began to take direct responsibility for breaking down the wrong impression of herself that she had created (M). An interview later, after a week of acting on this plan, she was able to relate that her first judgments of her new classmates were wrong, that they were willing to accept her, and that she was rapidly feeling part of her new group and beginning to acquire personal friendships with two or three. She was soon doing as well scholastically in the new school as she had in the previous school. In six months, her teachers considered her one of the student leaders. She expressed herself to the counselor as being happier than she had ever been before.

Second Plan More Adequate. Looking at one series of factors—A, B, and C on the chart—choice D followed, although it produced unhappiness and a state of inadequacy. On the other hand, as causes of the unhappiness and inadequacy were examined objectively and past memories re-surveyed, factors E, F, G, H, I, J, K, and L are brought into focus for the first time. A new personal responsibility for facing the school problem was accepted, and a new plan—M—

was devised, which, when acted on, produced greater happiness and a sense of acceptance and self-worth.

Fundamental Changes in Minor Acts. This situation of school adjustment affords a simple demonstration of how counseling, by unfolding more real factors than a person had previously seen, changes his actions to produce greater success and happiness. Even here these changes, while superficially only affecting this girl's school adjustment, actually involved fundamental attitudes that will permanently influence her later life.

This illustration, like that of the young woman's decision to wear her Christmas hat, shows another significant aspect of these first steps in meeting reality. Particular actions which result from counseling, especially with adolescents and children, may not in themselves appear to be dramatic changes. But, seen from the view of the possible later harm that was prevented by these changes and the future good this person's new responsible plan of action will achieve, such new choices can have major permanent consequences. The new plan of life which this girl devised for a better high school adjustment, could perhaps be a main factor in making her later adult life successful. The tendency towards suspicion and misinterpretation which produced her unhappiness in school could, if unchecked, seriously vitiate her relationship with her husband in marriage or, assuming she was called to a religious life, make community living difficult and even impossible for her. Preventive, constructive changes of this sort are seldom generally appreciated because it requires a degree of expert knowledge to understand what might otherwise have happened. Yet, the ultimate effects of this kind of counseling with adolescents or children can extend even further than the more apparent and dramatic results achieved with adults in some personal crisis, such as that revealed in the excerpts of marriage counseling.

Choices and actions, then, come either from the narrowed perception of a situation when we act unreasonably or they can follow the broadened, insightful view in which many more factors are seen and analyzed. As a person is able to take other factors into consideration, he is equipped to plan a more realistic solution. When emotional reactions are not thought out, they usually come from a partial view of reality. They seldom meet the real problems. Consequently, they generally only cause more unhappiness and failure.

To plan solutions satisfactorily, a person must see all the issues in a clear, integrated way so that his choices meet each issue squarely without the distortion of emotional bias. Even if the situation still arouses strong emotions, the choices that result are then guided by the calm survey of his reason.

Peace and Security in Reality. In this way, a successful counseling process gives evidence of the power of the individual person to reach what *is*, and to find peace and security in proportion as his actions and understanding are penetrated by and anchored in things as they are. The person arrives at his newly determined actions by a deeper penetration of himself and other reality, combined with a new power to conform his actions to his greater awareness of what is. It is through this process of reaching and conforming to reality that a person acquires greater happiness, peace, and security. This power of penetrating reality is within himself and not something which the counselor gives him. The experience of the interviews enables him to unfold many aspects of himself and things around him which he had neither been able to see clearly nor evaluate before. As this unfolding takes place, the person has the power within himself to make objective judgments. When he acts on them, these judgments prove more adequate in the livable world. His reasonable analysis, once he is able to bring all the factors into focus and to survey and evaluate them, is a means by which he reaches reality in a greater degree than he previously could.

REASONABLE JUDGMENT AND ACTION

Guilt. This deeper penetration of what is and the acting upon it, which is so characteristic of the later stages of successful counseling and of normal adjustment, also introduces with it, as we have seen, a greater state of self-approval. Accompanying this is a gradual cessation of those feelings of guilt which are usually indicated in the earlier stages of counseling. More or less intense states of guilt have generally been considered a part of personal maladjustment. The explanations and solutions proposed around this question of guilt, however, have been more controverted. For example, as we saw earlier, Rank broke with Freud on just this point.[6] For Rank, guilt and a feeling of responsibility went together. Successful ther-

6See pp. 45 ff.

apy, then, consisted in the creative use of this confused sense of responsibility, which is indicated in a person's expressions of self-condemnation and guilt. The study of interviews gives added confirmation to this Rankian view that the person's sense of guilt also involves some capacity for responsibility and some ability to change himself. By skillfully enabling him to turn his attacks away from himself into a positive urge to cope with reality, counseling gradually brings about a decrease in self-rejection. In so far as such a person's actions steadily grow more in conformity with reason, they produce less feelings of guilt.

Conscience. Rightly understood, this reasonable, insightful pressure on our acting self which produces either guilt or self-approval can be called conscience. It may be defined as the judgment of reason passed upon our acting self. When our actions conform to what our reasoned judgment holds up, so that they fulfill all the factors which related insights reveal, our reasoning self can approve. The result is growth in self-esteem and acceptance. This produces the state of self-approval so characteristic of the closing counseling interviews, when the person is consistently more satisfied with himself and his actions.

Conscience as such, then, is an act by which the knowledge that a person has, is applied to a particular situation. So, St. Thomas says,

> Conscience, according to the very nature of the word, implies the relation of knowledge to something: for conscience may be resolved into *cum alio scientia*, i.e., knowledge applied to an individual case. But the application of knowledge to something, is done by some act. Wherefore from this explanation of the name it is clear that conscience is an act . . .[7]

The same objective power which enables a person to analyze and evaluate himself in the counseling process we call conscience when this judgment is made of things that are morally right or wrong. As Glenn explains,

> Conscience is the intellectual consciousness or reasoned awareness of right or wrong in a situation here and now to be judged. . . . It is the same cold reason with which we work out a problem in mathematics,— only, to be entitled to the name *conscience*, it must be engaged upon

[7]St. Thomas, (D): I, Q. 79, a. 13.

issues of right and wrong, good and bad, and not upon mathematical quantities. The judgment of conscience is always a *reasoned* judgment.[8]

Counseling Furthers Reasonableness.   Counseling can aid in this process because, as the person mirrors himself and slowly sees all the factors that enter into a given series of actions, he grows more able to work out in detail the immediate means to carry out a reasonable solution. This seems to be the basic difference before and after counseling. Before counseling the individual may and usually does consider himself guilty of an unreasonable series of actions. Sometimes, this feeling of guilt is excessive, but often it is objectively reasonable. While he recognizes the wrongness of his actions, he is glued to immediate needs which are desirable and attractive. He feels himself unable to do without the things which fulfill these needs. Through counseling, he is able to see that, while these immediate needs are pleasurable, they are ultimately unhappy and dissatisfying. Moreover, he can now relate other factors which, in his focus on these immediate pleasures, he previously avoided considering. As he begins to act on these new insights, he finds that they bring him a greater permanent happiness and self-approval. This in turn further stimulates him to follow out his reasonable judgments.

Degree of Responsibility.   But, unless a person makes a conscious effort to reach out and grasp all the integrated factors that enter into a situation, he may find himself led quickly by a particular emotion to seek an immediate good which, while temporarily satisfying, is at variance with the integration of the whole good which he is seeking. It will, therefore, lead him away from his real purpose. He is responsible for having failed to make the integrated effort since he had the basic ability of such integration. Consequently, it is not entirely an excuse for the person swept along by his emotions to say he could not help it. In many instances he actually could have controlled these impulses, provided he took the necessary means of impersonalizing his relationship to the situation, particularly through the aid of a skilled counselor. He would then be more able to objectify and see all the factors which enter into his practical choices. As long as he fails to do this, he may be quickly conditioned by emotional tones such as hostility, threat, or anger which particular persons, places, or things have for him. These emotions may be

[8]Paul J. Glenn: *Psychology*, St. Louis, Copyright B. Herder Book Co., 1936, p. 294.

so strong that, unless he makes an intense effort to prevent it, he will
find himself swept along into a path of conduct which is unreasonable and in the long run solves nothing. He is still capable of broadening his perceptions by reasonable analysis so that he can combat
this tendency to immediate reactions and precipitant judgments. He
can slowly learn to take solutions which include much greater integration of the various factors which enter into his problem. We
see this taking place as we compare the early interview excerpts in
which these attitudes become related together and form themselves
into integrated, unified solutions. These, in turn, give a realistic and
accurate evaluation of the complex aspects of the personal problems
presented.

It is difficult to know where responsibility lies in cases of this sort.
Objectively, we can consider any unreasonable act morally wrong.
We cannot, however, always make the person performing that act
completely responsible since, in particular instances, his responsibility may be diminished either from lack of knowledge, which could
be considered invincible (that is, which he had no opportunity or
obligation to acquire) or by the degree to which his emotions made
him incapable of acting reasonably at that time. As Moore points
out:

Not only ignorance but also emotional conditions affect human responsibility. Whenever one is in such a violent emotional state that he
does not see clearly what he is doing or is driven to act impulsively and
without reflection, responsibility is diminished and perhaps to such an
extent that it is taken away entirely and the individual is not guilty of
doing what is itself a wrong and criminal act. Fear is the emotion which
most often clouds consciousness and diminishes guilt. It must be borne
in mind, however, that merely being threatened with consequences, no
matter how serious, does not in itself do away with responsibility . . .
What one does, however, under the influence of momentary excitement
may or may not be a fully responsible act. All depends upon whether
or not one clearly knows what he is doing and what it entails, and does
or does not do it in the light of a clear and adequate insight. The whole
problem of legal responsibility for crime is theoretically simple, and all
the difficulty arises in demonstrating in a court procedure the presence
or absence of the clear and adequate insight.[9]

[9]Dom Vernor Moore: *Principles of Ethics*, Philadelphia, Copyright 1937, by J. B. Lippincott Co., pp. 34–35. See also Patrick O'Brien, C.M.: *Emotions and Morals*, New York,
Grune & Stratton, 1950, for a detailed discussion of this question.

Threefold Function of Conscience. In these emotional states, however, the counseling process can help a person conform to the norms of his conscience by enabling him to see and plan more reasonable individual actions. But counseling as such cannot change a person's conscious judgment and guilt about the past. In his discussion of conscience, St. Thomas makes an important distinction:

> . . . conscience is said to witness, to bind, or incite, and also to accuse, torment, or rebuke. And all these follow the application of knowledge or science to what we do: which application is made in three ways. One way in so far as we recognize that we *have done* or *not done* something: "Thy conscience knoweth that thou hast often spoken evil of others" and according to this, conscience is said to witness. In another way, so far as through the conscience we judge that something *should* be done or not done; and in this sense, conscience is said to incite or to bind. In the third way, so far as by conscience we judge that *something done is well done or ill done,* and in this sense conscience is said to excuse, accuse, or torment. Now, it is clear that all these things follow the actual application of knowledge to what we do.[10]

This threefold distinction makes clear the limits of counseling and the virtue of counsel. A person's conscience can witness and retain evidence of past unreasonable conduct as well as give approval or disapproval to the present actions and serve as a guide to the future. While counseling and counsel involve the consideration of the past, they are primarily to aid in more adequate solutions to one's present and future conduct. There is no way in which counseling can change the past. Facts, past or present, are presumed in the process of counsel.[11] Consequently, no counseling procedure, however thorough in reorganizing the personality and improving conduct, can ever erase what has been. The past remains an incontestable fact. Its wrong actions must be cast on the mercy of God. To avoid facing the wrongness of past actions by simply trying to blot them out of one's memory would be the exact opposite of facing and adjusting to what is. Such an attempt seems ultimately only to cause greater disturbance. Actually, as we have seen in the interviews, it is by taking responsibility for his past actions, evil as well as good, that a person is able to face the present and begin to cope with it. So, in the case of the married business woman (Z),[12] if she had continued

---

10St. Thomas, (D): I, Q. 79, a. 13. (Italics mine.)
11P. 30.
12Pp. 55–56.

to rationalize that she and John were the victims of circumstance or of some blind fate, she would never have taken steps to think out and ultimately solve her problems.

Wrongness of Past Actions Remains. Successful counseling can, therefore, prevent a person's greater accumulation of guilt and self-condemnation by turning disorder and confusion into positive insight and more reasonable action. It may also diminish a person's sense of guilt, when it is simply excessive self-rejection. But it cannot remove the actuality and the conscious memory of the wrongness of past actions. Conscience still remains to accuse a person each time he thinks of something he should have done which was either "not done" or not "well done." The approval of conscience for present actions, which now conform to one's reasoned judgments, cannot change the past.

The Sacrament of Penance. We have, in this important threefold distinction of St. Thomas, a clarification of how counseling, although it can be an important aid in the growth of virtue, can in no sense be a substitute for the Sacrament of Penance. In sacramental confession, the person faces and recognizes his guilt and confesses his sins to God in an orderly and objective way, with faith in and the assurance of Divine forgiveness and redemption through the merits of Christ. So, even though the person must actively cooperate by sincere sorrow and resolve to change, this grace comes from the sacrament itself. The priest, in giving absolution, acts with Divine power and authority. The person does not *forgive* himself but *receives* forgiveness from God through the sacrament.

Docility to Reality. While counseling cannot remove guilt of past wrong actions, it can however activate a person to more conscientious present and future conduct. This can happen in many instances, even without any special instruction or guidance. As Glenn says,

> When a person has passed the stage of infancy he comes to understand (not reflexly at first, but directly) that there is an order in things, an order that must be conserved and not upset . . . . Education or instruction helps the child to come readily to the realization of good to be done and evil to be avoided, but the realization is, after all, a *reasoned* realization, and, in a normal person, would be ultimately reached even in the absence of any instruction bearing directly upon the point. In every situation where obvious moral issues are involved even a child of seven will make a reasoned judgment about the course of duty,

whether he actually follows that course or its opposite. What is true of the child is more manifestly true of the adult. Now, the judgment of reason that something *here and now to be decided upon* is *good* and *to be done* (or at least *permitted*) or *evil* and *to be avoided*, is called *conscience*.[13]

One reason for this is that reality is itself an effective teacher. Counseling enables persons to become docile in the sense of teachable. It does this, as we have seen, by relaxing them from the state of threat and resistance which previously prevented their acceptance of the teaching and guidance of others. But, even without this, counseling enables people to learn from experience, putting them more in touch with reality itself. People, through counseling, grow to realize that happiness and peace are often found where they previously least suspected. Sometimes a person will say he is beginning to live for the first time. His life until now had been so cluttered up with various escapes and confusions that reality had no real meaning for him. It was not possible for him to learn by experience. Contact with reality usually meant frustration and discouragement. This so crystallized his reaction that he gained little from experience. In fact, as we saw, such frustrated reaction can become so stereotyped that it grows indifferent to consequences.

As a result of counseling, people begin to look at reality in a new light. Even small incidents can be filled with meaning for them. As they re-examine experiences in the interviews they learn many things which these same experiences never revealed to them before. Consequently, they often find that their real means to greater happiness and peace do not consist in dramatic and exaggerated achievement, but in simple commonplace actions and responsibilities which they previously had overlooked or even despised. In this sense, they are docile to reality because they are in a state of insightful penetration in which they are teachable. They now can learn from the experiences which reality affords them.

Illustration.   We see this illustrated in another case of marriage infidelity, in which the counselor is a psychologist acting in a university clinic and does not represent any religious or moral solutions. Yet, the conclusions reached actually lead the person to a better moral life as he acquires an integrated view of all the factors in-

13Glenn, *op. cit.*, p. 295.

volved. Having acted on this more realistic view, he is happier and gains a zest for living a responsible married life.

In the first interview, an insurance salesman of about thirty talked about his indifference to his wife and their marriage and his extramarital affairs. By the tenth interview, however, he has achieved a sense of responsibility towards the marriage. He is beginning to act on this new awareness which in turn causes his relationship with his wife to improve:[14]

P75: Yes, and my relations with Marie have been more amiable and I feel so much better in the marital sense with Marie.

C75: And so things seem to be going better as a consequence.

P76: Yeh. Now why, I'm not sure. I think there's a little more interest on her part, but I think part of it—or most of it—is in myself. At least it's been a happy two weeks. And then, too, I'm going away again, and that helps, because coming home is always such a happy occasion.

C76: There's been some change in Marie and some of these other things, but you feel that most of the change has come about in you.

P77: It's been that, I think. I've been in a more pleasant frame of mind. I've been under a good deal of pressure at work with deadlines and so on, but they haven't been crowding in on me so much as they do sometimes. It just seems that I'm generally happier.

C77: Despite the continuing pressure from work and so on, *you* seem to be happier and, as a consequence, the relationships at home are happier.

P78: But I don't want to take the credit for it. It may be physiological, but I think it's psychological. I just have a better feeling. Maybe it's tied up with the determination to cut out these other affairs, but there is a growing tendency on my part not to be explosive when I'm feeling unpleasant. There's been times in the past when my resistance to explosiveness has been very low. Lately my resistance has been high. I think it's partly due to Marie. I came home last night and dinner was waiting for me. I felt like a king, and I made it plain to her that I enjoyed it so very much.

C78: With a change on your part and a change on Marie's part, things seem to be going very well.

Less Tense and Irritable. We notice this follows a pattern similar to the excerpts previously quoted. This man is now becoming

---

[14]The excerpts of this case are taken from William U. Snyder: *Casebook of Non-directive Counseling,* Copyright 1947, by Wm. U. Snyder, New York, Houghton Mifflin Co., pp. 243-262.

conscious that he is "feeling better," that he is not so "explosive," that he has a more positive outlook. He is getting along better with his wife, due mostly to the change in himself. Even the pressure in his work does not "crowd" him so much. He indicates that he is determined to break off his extra-marital affairs. He has already taken steps to do this. The following excerpt is continued from the same interview. The counselor is responding to a previous statement:

C80: It seemed almost as a plateau period while you were trying to decide which way you really wanted to go, is that it?

P81: That's right, and the situation seemingly would make me have qualms. But it didn't, and I expect it didn't really because I decided once and for all that that would be the last time; it was as if I had determined to go forward and put a stop to that sort of thing. And it seemed not a difficult thing to do, but a natural thing I wanted to do.

C81: It was more that you wanted to put a stop to it rather than that it was something you should do.

P82: That's a shrewd reflection, and I'm getting more and more the conviction that we haven't wasted our time here. And for reasons that I can't put my finger on, it should be simpler for me to avoid these things because of my growing feeling of responsibility to Marie. I demand things of her, and yet I haven't given in turn. I am beginning to feel more and more obligated to her. And so I don't with such coolness step outside of my obligation and visit other women as I once did. And I've said before that she hasn't made me particularly dependent upon her. I'm not so sure now. Maybe, if she was gone, I would realize how dependent I was on her.

C82: You have demanded things of Marie, but haven't demanded things of yourself which would make her happy in return. I gather that you now feel that you want to *give* to Marie, not as an obligation, but because you seem to be generally happier when you do.

P83: That's pretty much it. That's a good statement. It's more of a positive thing now than a negative one.

C83: And at the same time, I gather that you are beginning to wonder if you are as non-dependent on Marie as you once thought.

P84: It's very easy for me to say that I'm not dependent on Marie. But I'm suspicious of final statements. If I should be separated from her, I feel now that I should appreciate her so very much. You see, I haven't been looking for love at all in our marriage relationship, and I haven't been looking for it in my relationships outside the marriage situation. All I've been doing there is philandering. The relationships outside of marriage are temporary, if you can call them such.

Increase in Integration and Self-Criticism. The breaking off his relationship with the other women was not as hard as he thought because, having reasoned out his responsibility to Marie, he now began to *feel* as well as to know it was the right thing. His appetites are no longer so strongly disordered but are turned in the direction of his reasonable obligations.

He is aware that the interviews, by bringing out and high-lighting his responsibility to his wife, have aided him in this decision. His attitude towards his wife is becoming much more positive, as he surveys all that she means to him. We observe his deep accusation against himself as a selfish philanderer in the last part of this excerpt. Earlier we commented on this phase of self-criticism. He now accepts this judgment of his previous actions. But, had the counselor in the beginning said this to him, we can surmise from the statement in the next excerpt, the intense resistance it would have created. Here, we have a completely reorganized view of marriage. For the first time he understands something of what his marriage should really mean.

Broadening Awareness Aided by Counseling. As we have observed repeatedly, in the later interviews of a counseling series, there is evident the characteristic broadening awareness of the responsibilities involved. These factors were known but not considered in the earlier plan of action. Moral obligations are no longer seen as burdens but in the positive light of something the person himself wants to do. The realization of how much happier and peaceful he is, confirms him in his new plan of conduct. It is very satisfying to do the reasonable thing.

Later in the interview, the husband expresses his awareness of the part the counseling process played in his more integrated and happier view. He is surprised at how much easier it has been for him with this aid than he had expected:

C94: So you definitely feel that, as far as your relationships with Marie are concerned, they have improved one hundred per cent for a period of time now.

P95: That's right. Oh, Marie is still not the cook perfect, or the housekeeper perfect, but my admonishings have been gentle, if any.

C95: You feel that, although there may not have been too great a change on Marie's part in certain things, that your attitudes in regard to those things have changed.

P96: I believe they have, and yet, frankly, it hasn't been at the expense of much consciousness on my part. Does that happen? I just don't know.

C96: That is, you wonder if a change can come about without your being conscious of trying to make that change.

P97: That's right. I just don't want to be naive and say that this change has to be due to what we have done at this table. But I *know* that it is the *greatest* cause for the change. There may be other factors, like my work, a change in Marie, and so on, that help to make me more agreeable, too. I'm not perfect or a new person, but my temperament has been of fewer moods, and less apartness. The changes have been perfectly obvious to Marie, too, and she tells me so.

C97: You feel that the same personality pattern is by and large there, but that there seems to be greater control and more integrated functioning.

P98: That says it very well. Yep, that's it. The same personality with greater control and more integrated functioning.

C98: And you feel that this new integration can provide a basis for continuing happy marital relationships, is that it?

P99: That's it exactly. And the role that you played did it. If you had said to me to quit browbeating my wife, or to stop this, or to stop that, it would have been a useless attempt. I think that technique would have completely failed. Instead *I've* brought these things out time and again, time and again. The fruits of these discussions are that I'm better, and that the cure has been effortless on my part. I'm not perfect or anything, but I've been so much better, and it's noticeable to others, especially Marie.

In this excerpt we have an interesting delineation of the contrast between a self-directed integration process and the resistance which directions and advice would undoubtedly have encountered. Because of the counselor's skill, this process of change seemed so effortless that the person was hardly conscious of it. Yet, when we look at the change itself, we have a complete reorganization of life activities. His marriage is on a secure footing for the first time.

It must be noted, however, that this man came for counseling on his own urging. He had, therefore, submerged but positive reasons to stop his philandering and live a more responsible married life, even though he was not immediately conscious of them. Without counseling they would probably have produced only confused guilt feelings and spasmodic efforts to change. The interviews focused this positive urge and gave it the power to bring about new self-awareness and reasonable integration in both his feelings and his conduct.

More Permanent and Stable Life Plan. Four interviews after this (the fourteenth) his new life pattern has become stable and secure and is very satisfying:

C114: Well, how have things been going since we were together the last time?

P114: Well, I really have nothing new to add. There is nothing serious on my mind. There are no new fresh worries. Everything is going along in good shape; in fact, I'm in a frivolous mind this morning. Maybe I'll let you take the lead. (Laughs) But the pattern I discussed last time is still pretty constant, and I think even more stable and more clear to me.

C115: So things have been going along at a pretty even keel.

P115: Yes, at a very even keel. In other words, as I said last week, I felt at least that I had arrived at a point of departure, both from the standpoint of what I thought and the conduct that I was evidencing.

C116: Things are pretty clear both from a thought standpoint and from the behavior standpoint.

P116: Yes, I want to throw one more thing into that. It hasn't come to pass yet, but I'm thinking of doing some work in addition to my own work. I am preparing to drive myself professionally more than is required. Call it sublimation if you will. It is an effort to supplant some of my other interests by interests in more constructive channels. That has already begun by my working on a book either for myself or for my boss.

C117: You feel that it might help to develop interests in things like work since it would help to take up the slack that is left by leaving out these other interests that you've had in the past.

P117: That's the theory. At least there's more of an interest in pursuing those things than there ever was in the past. I think, among other things that have transpired here, you have through your subtle processes stimulated my conscience gland. (Laughs) Before I was a free agent. But now it's pleasant to think that before I wasn't immoral, but certainly amoral, and now I feel that I would like to be a moral person. There is overall a sort of healthy resolve on my part. I think it's healthy to walk in the paths of righteousness without being dramatic about it, simply because I can find life more worth living.

C118: Before, you used to consider this business in sort of a negative way, that is, here are certain things which society says we shouldn't do. Now I gather you feel that it's more a positive sort of thing. That you want to do the right things, not because they are necessarily right *per se*, but because they lead to your own greater happiness and make life generally more worth living.

P118: That's a good reflection. I used to think that life would be drab without these other things. But things are *not* worse now, but so much happier.

C119: Your attempts to play the game according to the rules has made the game more interesting.

P114 is typical of the last stages of counseling, when a person is probably only going to come for one or two more interviews.

This man's actions have now been brought to coincide with what he knew he should do. His conduct was obviously immoral before but he was unwilling to face it. His insightful plans have been verified in more reasonable action. This has produced a feeling of stability and evenness in his life.

In place of escape activity he has greater interest in his work and in new achievement. He knows from experience, now, that a responsible, moral life is actually happier and more satisfying. Counseling has brought him an overall "healthy resolve" to continue to live according to more reasonable norms. Previously, he could not have believed that the commonplace family responsibilities could be anything but drab. But, having followed the insights that counseling revealed to him, he is surprised and pleased to find out how much happier he is. Contrary to his earlier expectations, this new way of life is far more stimulating and interesting than the old one. Others could not tell him this; he had to learn it from reality itself. Through counseling he was able for the first time to penetrate and to evaluate the real meaning of his marriage. Having acted on this awareness, he has a stabler, more peaceful, and happier existence.[15] This reveals a completely reorganized series of per-

---

[15]The reader may find it of interest to compare these statements with those of the married business woman (Z) given on pp. 149–150 to see how, when counselors have approximately the same degree of skill, the process of insight and new choices is often very similar even though the people involved are in completely different circumstances. Considering that marriage infidelity, of the sort these two cases indicate, is considered one of the most difficult of all marriage problems to reconcile, we see the widespread implications of this counseling skill as an aid to the prevention of separation and divorce. See, John L. Thomas, S.J.: "The Urban Impact on Catholic Families," *The Am. Cath. Soc. Rev.*, X, 4, December, 1949, pp. 258–67, in which adultery, irresponsibility, and drink are indicated as the three highest factors in marriage breakup. All three usually contain significant psychological aspects.

ceptions. What was before an attractive and stimulating adventure in clandestine romance has no longer any meaning. What was previously considered drab, puritanical, and restrictive, is now a healthy, normal way of living according to the rules.

Reasonable Fulfillment. Centuries ago Tertullian spoke of the "anima naturaliter Christiana" to indicate that the Christian way of life is the one naturally most satisfying. Reason, then, if it is aided to be objective by freeing itself from the strong emotional and instinctive impulses and confused and narrowed perceptions, can reach reasonable solutions. These reasonable solutions are productive of an intrinsic sense of decency, self-approval, and achievement in living.

As the interview continues, this man analyzes his original self-centered motivation that led to illicit affairs:

P119: That's right. I'd like to add one more thought, and that's this. You have noticed from time to time that a great deal of my drive, my sadness and my joys, have centered about the complex idea of how to get myself liked. We talked a little about this earlier. I still feel that, as I watch my meanders at the insurance company, especially with girls, that much of *that* I feel in the same sense of the social necessity that I have always felt. I am an extremely personal person, and you have noticed that yourself. Therefore, despite my original motives which are honorable, when I find girls responding to me, that very fact opens up the possibility of more intimate relations. If I didn't need these responses to needle my ego, I might save myself a good deal of trouble. It comes back to the fact that I'm a personal sort of person, and I like to respond warmly to others, and I like their response in return.

C120: You feel that the need to be socially accepted tends to lead to these other kinds of relationships.

P120: Those lead to the involvements which brought me here. If there was a little more introvertiveness on my part—where I could be more self-contained—I would be so much less prone to trouble. I have a way, in spite of myself, of relationships being either hot or cold. Therefore, the thought occurs to me to pursue it beyond the superficial stage. If I wasn't impelled to do that, I would stay out of the trouble I've had in the past.

C121: You like people, and want to be liked in return.

P121: I like people, perhaps because I want to be liked. The things I want are direct. On my last birthday, I got lots of cigars and cards from the kids, and I feel that that's evidence of the warmth of feeling I try to give others. I like them, but that also forms a nucleus for a step to go farther.

C122: You feel that your warmth of feeling toward others brings with it the possibility of potential involvement.

Before, his need for personal acceptance overcame all restraints. Now, he recognizes that he must control this urge since it "forms the nucleus for a step to go farther." His personal kindness tends to excess. With this insight goes a desire for more self-restraint. He can see how this urge, unless controlled, could lead him again into the kind of involvement which was unhappy, disloyal, and at variance with the responsible married life he genuinely wants to live.

Although more complex and far-reaching, this awareness and the change in actions which it produced, is similar to the changed outlook shown in the previous diagram of the high school girl. As we see, this man's insights also gave him a different view of his previous actions. His new plan includes increased self-restraint even in normal feminine relationships, a growing sense of responsibility to his wife, a desire for real love in marriage, and the channeling of his interests into constructive work. This is in marked contrast to the selfish inconsideration and philandering of his previous way of living. When he carries out these resolves, he finds he has gained in peace of mind, emotional stability, greater enthusiasm for his work, self-control, and much finer and more satisfying relationship with his wife. The overall result is an effective desire to lead a moral, responsible life.

PARTICULAR PURPOSE OF COUNSELING

Ending of Interviews. Counseling is not a permanent relationship but one which serves a particular purpose. The person himself is the best judge when the counseling interviews have served this purpose. He generally shows this by indicating that he is happier and more satisfied with himself. As problems clear up, better decisions are made and acted upon. He finds fewer things to talk about in the interviews. About this time he begins to suggest that he likely need not come many more times. We saw one suggestion of this in the previous excerpts.

The closing of an interview series may have various meanings. Much depends on the depth, intensity, and quality of the problems discussed. If the problems are minor, the person may return later for interviews at a deeper level. If, on the other hand, the problems involve basic reorientation, the interviews may have life-time consequences. Sometimes the interviews lead a person to realize that he lacks sufficent knowledge. This may occur, for example, in a question of a vocational choice, such as a religious vocation or some profession. At the same time, the person may feel he does not have the information or understanding at hand to make any further personal decision. In these cases, interviews may be renewed again after the information has been acquired and the person wishes to think out and judge what he has learned.

Renewing Counseling. Interviews may be renewed when a new series of problems arises in a person's life. This is particularly true of younger people as they pass from one stage of development to another. For example, a young man, having worked out certain adolescent confusions, may return in a year or two to discuss vocational choices. Later still he may wish counseling to help him decide if he should marry a particular girl or perhaps help him in his choice of a religious vocation. If he marries, he may come again for interviews at some point early in his marriage when misunderstandings and difficulties are arising. In this case he may bring his wife so that the two may work their problems out together. At other times, a person may feel the need for counseling because of confusions at work, the choice of a different kind of employment, or complex personal relationships in business, professional, or factory life. At the death of one of his children or his wife, a person may again be faced with new adjustments for which he uses the counseling interview. His own grave illness, injury, or accident, might necessitate counseling. These needs would be characteristic of any normal individual as he passes into different life stages and activities. At any of these steps, a counseling series could aid him in reorganizing his attitudes, goals, and purposes. The counseling process is a practical tool which a person may use whenever personal problems are so complex that he cannot see them clearly enough to puzzle them out himself.

Obviously there is no point at which life is entirely free of difficulties and complex personal choices so that the process of counsel continues throughout life. Here we see the wisdom of the traditional spiritual practice of the *particular examen* each day, by which people evaluate the motives and the other factors that go into the actions of that day. If it were possible, therefore, counseling would often be an efficient means of solving even ordinary difficulties, or planning the daily activities which a person must undergo. But such opportunities for consistent counseling would not ordinarily be within the scope of most people. For this reason, then, we speak of counseling only at periods of special difficulties where a person would be likely to come to someone for help. Were counseling available, however, it would seem advantageous to use it, even in minor situations, in so far as this would help a person to understand all the issues more quickly and plan more adequately than he could without counseling. In a quotation previously given from St. Thomas[16] we saw that counsel is involved in working out a valid plan of action for new ventures as well as reorganizing oneself after repeated failure. Counseling could therefore be valuable also in the planning stages of any complex activity even before a person attempts to do it.

Permanent Effects. Generally speaking, however, the effects of an interview series seem lasting. They appear to bring such fundamental changes in an individual that he continues to be able to solve even difficult problems on his own. In this sense, the counseling process often produces a remarkable permanent growth in the virtue of counsel. Such a virtue, being a "habitus" in the Thomistic sense, remains after the counseling interviews are over. The person has acquired a consistent ability to make the necessary survey of the past, present, and future and the other steps which enter into a prudent judgment. It is not uncommon for people to express this a number of years after counseling. They are conscious of their capacity to be objective about themselves and others, to see problems broadly, and appreciate many more factors which enter into their decisions. This "habitus" of prudent judgment causes them to be less frustrated and confused in even complex personal situations.[17] Consequently, there is little likelihood of their necessarily needing counseling interviews again except for some major crises in their lives. Even here, as we have discussed, the interview series is usually shorter. A person tends to be more objective about himself and

16See pp. 24–25.
17See pp. 409–410.

sometimes even in one interview can reach a clear, secure, and accurate judgment even about difficult questions.

IMPLICATIONS

Counseling, of course, does not always produce such completely integrating effects. But, in a surprising number of cases, as a result of successful counseling, people appear to retain their positive, optimistic outlook in place of their previous negation and depression. Their philosophy is now fundamentally realistic. Adjustment for them involves moving out to reality and coping with it. They move away from self-deception. Their insights and actions are more in line with being, with what is. As a consequence, their major life activities are consistently more achieving and happy. This happiness is, as one wrote some years after counseling, "not a mountaintop type of thing but a constant sense of well-being and purposefulness."

Optimistic View of Human Nature. One significant implication of this process of adjustment to reality through counseling is that it confirms both an optimistic and a non-deterministic view of human nature. If man's positive will does bring about personal change and a movement away from negation and resistance, and this is observable in a process of counseling, then a theory of pessimistic determinism is untenable. Otto Rank maintains there is a contradiction in Freud's position on this point:

In psychoanalysis we find both aspects but not harmoniously united, rather they stand side by side as one of the numerous unreconciled contradictions. As therapy, analysis is optimistic, believes as it were in the good in men and in some kind of capacity for and possibility of salvation. In theory it is pessimistic; man has no will and no creative power, is driven by the id and repressed by the superego authorities, is so unfree and still guilty. Here lies before us so transparent a contradiction that one can only wonder how it was possible and must again recognize therein a psychological problem so fundamental that it leads far beyond a critique of psychoanalysis.[18]

Consequently, if man can be helped to a better and happier life, it can only be because he has within himself some power and capac-

[18]Otto Rank: *Truth and Reality*, New York, Copyright 1936, by Alfred A. Knopf, pp. 61–62.

ity for change which he can activate. In this sense, any process of therapy that does not imply some power to change in man will be contradicted by the success of its own method. A method of therapy is meaningless unless there is some possibility of change.

Adjustment to Ultimate Reality. This movement of a man's positive will in the line of being, which counseling facilitates, rather than his withdrawal into negativism, is also essential to any relationship with God. Negative will impedes the development of what he would reasonably achieve. It produces discouragement, failure, and frustration. On the other hand, the slow movement of positive will, which the counseling process reveals, produces a steady growth in the direction of reasonable achievement and successful fulfillment. This positive will also makes possible the further special help of God to the soul, since, as St. Thomas says, some positive will is necessary for this:

Now for a thing to be amenable to the motion of a certain mover, the first condition required is that it be a non-resistant subject of that mover, because resistance of the movable subject to the mover hinders the movement.[19]

Adjustment to reality would, therefore, imply ultimate reality as well. While an individual counseling process itself may not involve such adjustment, these implications seem involved in the nature of the adjustment process as counseling itself reveals it. People can come for counseling for the solutions of immediate problems which may change with changing circumstances. In this sense, as St. Thomas says, *"Counsel is concerned not with things ultimately certain but only certain for a time and in particular circumstances."*[20] When these change, the solution worked out may again prove inadequate.

But, in the counseling process, if the movement of insight involves a greater awareness of what *is* and a person's gradual adjusting to the reality of himself and his environment, then it also involves his continued deeper penetration of reality. Insight is, as we have seen, the seeking of the long-time, permanent goals in preference to the more immediate, transient ones. For this urge to reality and happiness to be permanently and completely fulfilled, man must be able

19St. Thomas, (D): II–II, Q. 19, a. 9.
20*Ibid.*

to rise above the limitations of the partial reality or participated beings of himself and the world in which he lives. If the degree of man's own reality is limited and finite, as it obviously is, then he cannot of himself reach the Ultimate Being and permanent, enduring fulfillment he seeks. Final frustration would, therefore, be inevitable. But man, if he sincerely seeks it, will be aided by the special action and gifts of the Source of all Being, God Himself. In this way it is possible for him to reach complete fulfillment in the ultimate goodness and being of God, Who, as St. Thomas says, "alone fills the capacity of the will."[21] Man's final adjustment to reality, then, can be said to include not only the natural virtues which he acquires by his own reason, but also the supernatural virtues and the gifts by which he is especially enabled to reach God. In this sense, moral theology may be defined as, "the movement of a reasonable creature into God."[22] The total fulfillment of man's positive will demands an ultimate condition in which his positive will to reality is "overwhelmed by the Sovereign Good clearly seen."[23]

[21]*Ibid.* I–II, Q. 4, a. 4.
[22]St. Thomas, (D): II, titulum.
[23]Reginald Garrigou-Lagrange, O.P.: "Eternal Youth," *Cross and Crown,* Vol. II, No. 1 (1950), pp. 17–23.

PART THREE

THE SKILL OF THE COUNSELOR

In this present section, Part III, we will discuss the counselor's skill in the interview itself when a person comes seeking counseling. In Chapter IX we will explore some of the means by which counselors aid a person to understand what his own and the counselor's functions are. Chapter X will go more deeply into the analysis of the types of responses which both indicate the counselor's acceptance of the person and understanding of his difficulties and at the same time enable the person to penetrate into the more basic causes of his conflicts. Chapter XI will consider some particular demands that may be made on the counselor as the counseling process begins to increase a person's self-insight and control. Chapter XII will discuss factors associated with the closing stages of counseling and with subsequent counseling series. Chapter XII ends with a summary of some of the important types of counselor responses and also with some suggestions that may help the reader evaluate his own counseling attitudes. Since interviews with children may make some additional demands on the counselor's skill, the closing chapter of this section will take up some particular considerations peculiar to child-counseling.

PART THREE

THE SKILL OF THE COUNSELOR

CHAPTER IX

ESTABLISHING THE COUNSELING RELATIONSHIP

Accepting and Understanding Atmosphere. While, thus far, we have considered mainly the various stages in the counseling process as the interviews reveal them, we have also commented when some important phase of the counselor's function was demonstrated. We have not, however, treated these counselor skills directly. But by now the reader has, no doubt, become aware of the importance of the person's feeling that he is accepted and understood by the counselor and, at the same time, that he is going to be helped to work out his own solutions on his own responsibility. These two factors appear to be essential to the process of counseling. Somehow, a person does not generally unfold and think out complex personal problems except in an atmosphere of acceptance. But if this acceptance is such that it makes him dependent on the counselor for solutions and decisions, it will not further his own self-initiated judgments and actions. An important part of the skill of a good counselor, then, is his ability to promote responsible and reasonable evaluation and action by establishing a climate of acceptance and understanding which, at the same time, does not foster dependency.

GENERAL PURPOSE OF COUNSELING SKILL

Strengthening Positive Will. When a person comes for counseling, as have seen, he is in a state where his positive will towards reality is more or less impeded, depending on the degree of disorder of his appetites. This state has produced frustration and confusion in proportion to the seriousness of the conflicts. The constructive power of a person's will to reasonable achievement is in a sense bound up by these conflicts and frustrations. Malice in the will, as St. Thomas explains it, involves a kind of willing nothingness (malum), in the sense that a person can keep willing less in the direction of an integrated reality, away from what is. The first important effect of the counselor's skill is to release the personal dynamics contained in the positive will with which the person came for help, so that it may begin to produce more reasonable self-evaluation and constructive action.

Skilled counseling gives a person a means of channeling and focusing his positive will. Previously, the person's will may have been expended in fighting or criticizing himself, attacking others when they misinterpreted or misunderstood how he felt, or escaping direct responsibility by depending on others' judgments. The counselor enables this negation to turn into constructive channels. Put simply, one aspect of counseling skill is to stay out of the way of a person's negations and not let them be deflected against the counselor. By doing this the counselor allows a person's positive will to reality, which is the other side of his conflict state, to begin to show itself and to center its power on constructive action rather than being shunted off in destructive and conflicting reactions against himself and the counselor or in supine attachment to the counselor. A person's positive will is, therefore, directed toward the clarification of himself and his difficulties.

Meeting Reality. Moreover, since counseling is also a social situation, a person undergoes a constantly dynamic contact with reality itself. The interview, then, not only prepares the person for reality by giving him an opportunity for deeper self-understanding, but it is the real world. It, therefore, brings with it the actual fulfillment of his positive will to reach reality. This helps explain the steady growth in the integration of all his appetites, which successful counseling brings about. Solutions are not planned abstractly or in fantasy as they might have been before. Problems, having been faced and thought through in the social relationship of the interview, are already more in touch with what is. Each objective clarification of the counselor is filtered through the person's calm reason as he re-examines what is stated back to him. Plans then determined upon have been measured, to some degree, by reality in that each aspect of the solution has been looked at objectively and impersonally through the mirroring response of the counselor. Consequently, these plans are much less apt to be precipitous and emotional. It is not difficult to see why these plans are generally more successful than previous ones.

FACTORS AFFECTING COUNSELING

Attitudes from Previous Experiences. People often come to the counselor with definite attitudes that may either hinder or aid the establishment of a counseling relationship. These attitudes have been determined by their previous experiences. Small, and apparently insignificant things, can set off a series of previously fixed reactions so that the person can become strongly resistant to or, alternately, excessively dependent on the counselor almost from the first. Such reactions can seriously impede the success of all subsequent relationships. The most deceptive part of this is that the incidents or situations which can create this unfavorable atmosphere are, taken by themselves, often so minor that they can be readily overlooked. Yet, these small, almost unnoticed, elements may have minimized or even prevented good counseling.

While a person may want counseling and realize that he has a need for it, he may still be insecure about the kind of counseling he is going to receive. Sometimes he will search for months or even years before he meets someone whom, as he says, he "felt free to talk with" or who "was the kind of person I felt I could tell this to." This was demonstrated in some of the statements given in previous excerpts, where individuals with serious personal problems could find no one with whom they were free to speak. The unfortunate part of this is that, among the people such an individual has met, there no doubt were a number who could have helped him. But the first impression each of these made on him blocked, before it got started, any possibility of his bringing personal problems to them. Yet, these people were probably unaware that they had created such resistance.

Personal Factors. Since such complex reactions can sometimes be attached to even simple incidents or remarks, small and apparently unimportant factors can sometimes play a significant part in determining a counseling atmosphere. But because many of these factors are highly personal, we cannot anticipate them all. Part of the counselor's skill, as we shall see, is to be constantly alert to any unfavorable emotional tones a person may attach to what he said or did. These often vary as a person's feelings change. The counselor must learn to respond to these feelings in such a way that it enables a person to express, clarify, and understand the causes of these reactions.

Common Factors. In the experience of counselors, however, a number of common factors have come to light which can aid in establishing counseling. Unless these are consciously observed, they may be overlooked. If they are neglected, the results may sometimes be seriously affected and yet the counselor himself may not realize this has happened. They are, of course, not equally important. But, taken together, these common factors make for the beginning of a good counseling relationship.

SOME BEGINNING STEPS[1]

Most Favorable Beginning. A counseling interview seems to begin best when a person telephones, writes a letter, or visits the counselor and says directly that he wants and needs the counselor's help with some personal difficulties. He is ready to face his problems and he knows, at least in general, that the counselor is someone especially equipped to help him do this. When such a person comes for the first interview, he is usually relieved when the counselor makes him aware that counseling offers him an understanding and skillful relationship where he himself can think out better solutions.

Such a beginning of counseling often takes place, especially after a counselor becomes known. When a number of people have been helped, they readily and generously tell others. As they describe the relationship, they fix in the other person's mind what this kind of counseling involves. Consequently, it is not necessary for the counselor to describe the counseling relationship to these people. They grow to understand it as they experience it in the first half-hour or hour interview. At the end, they see clearly what their role is. By this time, too, they have already sufficently realized the value of the interview so that they want to return. They know its purpose and understand how they should use it.

1. Describing the Relationship. At other times, however, the person may not clearly know what the counseling interview is and how he is to act in it. Some counselors have felt that it is helpful

[1]See also C. A. Curran: "Structuring the Counseling Relationship," *J. Abnorm. and Social Psychol.*, Vol. 39, pp. 189–216 (1944); published also in *Readings in Modern Methods of Counseling* edited by A. H. Brayfield, New York, Appleton-Century-Crofts, 1950. In C. A. Curran: *Personality Factors in Counseling*, New York, Copyright 1945, by Grune & Stratton, the author discusses this question in Chapter II. This book also gives detailed research and discussion of the process of counseling therapy in one recorded case of twenty interviews.

if the counselor's response explains the relationship that is to exist between them. This has been called a "structuring" statement. He may say,

Oftentimes people need someone they can talk freely to, in a situation where they can work out solutions to their problems. Somehow we often find that thinking things through together with someone seems to be a better and more efficient way of reaching solutions to many personal difficulties.[2]

Sometimes a person may express confusion about using the counselor's time. A simple statement of the counselor's willingness to spend the time with him can aid this. The counselor may say,

I realize you feel a little self-conscious about using my time but I am glad to spend the time with you.

Or he may say,

I've had experience with others in similar situations and I know that talking things out this way has been very helpful to them and I'm very willing to help you in the best way I can.

We notice that the counselor does not promise the person anything or try to persuade him that the interviews are going to help him. He simply states that others have been helped by the same process and leaves it up to the person to decide whether he wishes to use it for himself. The counselor must be careful not to try to "sell" the interviews. If he is not cautious, he can throw the focus on himself and take the sense of responsibility away from the person by assuring him he will get help. The counselor cannot give such assurance because he cannot predict such help. The person will get out of the interviews what he puts into them. If he takes the responsibility and makes the personal effort necessary to reach deep insights, new and better choices can be the result. But, he is free not to do this.

[2]This involves a question that is difficult to put into words. Actually, as Rogers points out, "structuring," descriptive phrases of this sort are far less effective than the counselor's fundamental attitude of thinking and feeling with the person towards the person's own self-unfolding and integration. Consequently, the more thoroughly willing the counselor is to accept and penetrate the person's attitudes with him, the less necessary any such descriptive statements are. Some counselors feel that such statements even impede progress. See Carl Rogers: *Client-Centered Therapy*, New York, Copyright 1951, by Houghton Mifflin, pp. 19–64. See also E. H. Porter: *An Introduction to Therapeutic Counseling*, Boston, Houghton Mifflin, Copyright 1950, by E. H. Porter, pp. 87–122.

He may choose here and now the present, unhappy state in preference to the struggle required for significant changes. The counselor can help in this process if people are willing, but he cannot force them to change. Left to their own decisions, some may decide not to continue a counseling relationship because they fear the changes it may bring. If their attitudes are accepted, however, and the relationship kept open, they may find it possible to return at some future time.

2. *Limiting Structuring Statements.* If they are to be made at all, usually one or two such "structuring" statements about the kind of relationship that exists between the counselor and the person, are sufficient. Sometimes at the beginning of the second interview, a restatement of the relationship may be considered necessary to establish clearly in a person's mind what the counselor's role is. Anything more than this is apt to be a confused effort on a person's part to get the counselor to take responsibility from him through the ruse of having the counselor repeat his explanation a number of times.

3. *Responding to Dependency.* When these confused expressions of dependency do occur they can also be used constructively. If the counselor sensitively responds to the person's desire to depend on him, it can be the first stage of an illuminating analysis which reveals this tendency to the person, sometimes for the first time. After a person recognizes that his dependency on others has always been a basic part of his life plan, he can begin to work out a different mode of acting and one that will eventually make him happier.

4. *Assuring Confidence.* Where there might be any doubt in a person's mind that the counseling information will be kept confidential, the counselor may wish to clarify this with a statement like:

Of course, whatever you say here will be confidential and no use will be made of it without your permission.

5. *Adhering to Time Set.* The length of the individual interview often depends on circumstances. Experience in counseling shows, however, that a definite time should be set at the beginning of the interview and adhered to. This may be fifteen minutes, a half hour, or an hour, depending on the availability of both the counselor and the person. But some time limit is important. Life is filled with limitations and restraints. Maturity implies conforming to these limits.

The interview is, in a sense, a microcosm of typical experience. One can often notice that people who cannot face the responsibilities of life tend, either to come early and want to see the counselor immediately, or to come late and expect him to carry the interview for the whole stipulated time. Generally speaking, unless it is obviously offensive, it seems better to adhere to the time arranged—beginning at that time even when the person comes early and when the person is late, ending at the time set even though the interview is proportionately shorter. In this small but significant way, the objective limits of the real world are made an important part of the interview.

6. Maximum Time for One Interview. Much discussion has taken place around the question of whether there is any special significance to the length of an interview. Practically, there has been a general consent that an hour seems long enough at any one time. A good counseling interview is a powerful experience. An hour somehow seems sufficient for such an experience. Some may feel that they can extend it two or three hours, but the general practice of counselors has been to limit the time to not more than an hour for any one session. In particular instances where it is necessary to see a person a number of times in one day, it seems better to have some kind of intermission. Having interviews in the morning, afternoon, and again in the evening, or even simply walking out of the room for a five minute break seems to help. It temporarily changes the person's extreme focus on himself and his problems that is characteristic of the counseling session.

This, though, is considered by most experienced counselors to be an exceptional situation. Generally, one interview a week or at the most, two interviews a week, of an hour or even a half-hour's duration seems the more ordinary procedure. A valuable aid in deciding how many interviews to have is to leave it up to the person himself to determine how often he wants to come. Where there exists a good counseling relationship people usually make a very sensible judgment. But if the counselor does not have time for more than one interview a week, he should honestly say so. Otherwise, the person will sense his unrest and tension and recognize that he should not have come so often. In this as in other things the counselor's attitudes are almost always felt by the other person and can seldom, if ever, be successfully disguised.

7. Announcing Remaining Time. There seems also to be some
value in announcing the time remaining, five or ten minutes before
the end of the interview. It is a polite and easy method of informing
the person of the approaching end of the interview. Some maintain
that it also acts as a stimulant for the facing of particular problems
or the reaching of insights that have been put off during the earlier
part of the interview. This is a matter for further research. The
study of interview typescripts sometimes indicates noticeable insights in the last few minutes, after the time has been announced.
It is open to question, however, whether that same material would
not have been brought up even if the time had not been announced.
But, distinct from this, the announcing of remaining time is justified simply on the grounds of preparing the person for the end of
the interview. This prevents an abrupt closing of the interview,
which may leave the person with a feeling of hanging in mid-air and
of not being able to say all he intended.

At the end of a person's statement the counselor can openly look
at his clock or watch and say,

Yes, we have about five minutes or so left in our time.

This never seems to offend. On the contrary, it brings relief because
the person can then prepare for the end of the interview by saying
what remains in his mind to say. When the counselor ends the interview with

Well, our time is up.

or something similar, the person is prepared for such an ending and
is already relaxedly expecting it.

8. Setting Time for Next Interview. A significant point, too,
especially in the beginning interviews, is the counselor's setting up
of a time for the next interview. Unless the counselor has acquired
a habit of it, this obvious point is sometimes overlooked in the
confusion of ending an interview. If it is overlooked the person is
not sure if and when he is to return. This can be serious for people
who are already insecure and fearful that others do not accept them.
Sometimes the counselor may have forgotten to take down a person's
address or telephone number (and sometimes even his name). If
the person then fails to telephone the counselor, counseling has been

broken off through the apparently slight oversight of failing to arrange a next appointment. A definite time for the next interview creates a feeling of stability. The interview ends on the tone of establishing and preserving a bond between the counselor and the person. Otherwise the person is apt to have only a confused idea about whether or not he is to return. He may express this with a phrase like, "I'll drop in and see you again sometime."[3]

9. *Define Relationship.* The setting up of the next interview can also be an occasion for a clearly defined expression of the relationship, if this appears necessary. The counselor may say,

> Oftentimes it's helpful to talk these problems over with another person as you have now and I am certainly very willing to spend the time with you. So, if you wish, I would be glad to see you again, perhaps in a few days or next week.

The counselor should then relax and quietly wait to see the reaction. Often the person's acceptance will be a spontaneous, "I would like that," or "I would like to come again." Sometimes it may produce a conflict and the person may say,

> Why, I just don't know. I don't know whether I need to come back or not. I don't know whether these problems are that serious or not—whether it will do any good to talk about them.

The counselor can respond to this doubt as he would to any basic attitude. He may say,

[3]The results of recent research seem to indicate that, in particular instances, when an interview took place without the person having had any time to prepare the content, significant material was uncovered which the person was not conscious of or did not think he would speak about. The results were surprising in some instances. Some of the persons who underwent the experience of having such unannounced interviews said that, compared to the interviews that they had when they knew in advance they were coming at a definite time, the unannounced interviews were more spontaneous and, they felt, sometimes reached more fundamental awarenesses. In the announced interviews they tended to rehearse beforehand what they were going to say, and part of the content of the interview was simply a reproduction of that rehearsed material rather than a spontaneous thinking process. This is, of course, a field for continued research. The present practice with most counselors, however, is to announce the time of the next interview, since it is usually the most practical method. An important factor in the success of these unannounced interviews was that there was no threat in having an interview when these people had not expected it. They had agreed to such a procedure and were completely willing to undergo it. Otherwise, such attempts—without their willing cooperation—would appear to be forcing an interview, and would likely produce resistance and blocking. Such unannounced interviews would only seem possible when the counseling relationship is well established and understood.

You're not sure if there's any value in this or if the problems are serious enough to warrant your coming again.

This will often enable the person to say, sometimes hesitantly, that he wants to return. If he does, a definite time should be set. Writing it down while the person is in the room may help to show that a formal relationship has been established. If, on the other hand, he is not sure, then, the counselor can say,

Well, if you wish to come next week or sometime later, I'd like you to feel free to call me. I'd be glad to spend the time with you.

This leaves the relationship open. Whenever the person so decides, he can re-establish it.[4]

10. Responses Should Fit Into Context. The various counselor statements illustrated here are, of course, taken out of their normal context in the flow of the interview itself. This may appear to give them a coldness and even a formalism which they do not actually have in good counseling.[5] These counselor statements must be made in response to a stated or implied need on the person's part for some clarification of the relationship.[6] As a person gains an understanding of the limits of the interviews, particularly in the matter of time, and also as he grows aware that the counselor will help but will not take the responsibility for solving his difficulties, the way is cleared for him to express and focus his own positive will on solving these difficulties. When this is combined with the other factors in the counselor's skill, it can be the beginning of a dynamic counseling process.

[4]Subsequent chapters will give a detailed discussion of this type of response. The person's cautious insecurity can only be appreciated if we realize that such personal problems have sometimes never been discussed with anyone. See also p. 77.

[5]When people *hear* a response with its relaxed and warming tones as it was (or should be) *spoken* by the counselor, they often comment how differently the response sounded from the way they thought it would, simply from having *read* it on a printed page.

[6]Sometimes, because of particular circumstances, additional clarifying statements may be necessary. The case in marriage counseling cited on pages 183–190 illustrates the function of such clarifying statements. In an earlier interview, the person relates some physical details of his marriage relationship. Details like these may sometimes be given in a medical or clinical setting similar to the one in which this case occurred, because of the person's mistaken notion—due possibly to the popular influence of Freudian theories—that he is supposed to give this kind of information. Since detailed physical information is not necessary for marriage counseling—although it may sometimes be an aid to a physician giving medical guidance—the counselor could have clarified this point with a simple structuring statement. This might have aided the person to cut through immediately to more basic problems. Similar situations can occur in other counselor settings, as, for example, counseling in industry when minute job details may be given on the same misconception that such details are in themselves important in counseling.

CHAPTER X

INITIATING COUNSELING DYNAMICS

The major contribution of the counselor, however, is his consistently penetrating responses during the flow of the interview. As the person uncovers his feelings, or deeper attitudes, or gains new self-awareness, the counselor must follow his statements carefully and accurately project them back or "reflect" them in his responses. These responses should hold up before a person an objective view of his feelings and attitudes towards himself and others. This enables him slowly to piece these attitudes together and get a more integrated and deeper understanding of himself. As we have seen, this broadening self-perception leads him finally to more positive and more successful life choices.

Since the counselor's role is one of mirroring the attitudes and feelings which at that moment are contained in the person's expressions, he functions best when he reflects the person's attitudes most exactly. *He should not speak too rapidly.* His voice and manner should be *calm* and *sincere.* The person will recognize that the counselor is choosing his words carefully, but this is not disturbing. If anything, it helps the relationship. In this connection, a typescript can be misleading since those responses which appear "wooden" and flat when read, may actually have *sounded* warm and accepting.

Such a skill is not easily learned. Good counselor responses have a deceptive simplicity when we see them in an excerpt from a successful interview. Usually we must try such counseling ourselves before we recognize how difficult it is to make consistently clarifying responses that do not block or impede a person's self-investigation.

CONVERSATIONAL RESPONSES

One of the main difficulties for the beginning counselor is the great difference between various counseling responses and the kind of statements he is accustomed to make in his ordinary relations with people. Responses made in everyday conversation fall into a number of categories. When people state facts and draw a conclusion from these facts, we might agree or disagree with the facts, the conclusion, or both. We might consider the statement untrue because the facts are inaccurate. We might judge it illogical because the conclusion drawn does not follow from the facts. We might continue the reasoning by filling it out with our own ideas. We might disagree and challenge a particular point. This disagreement could be cautious and hesitant or it could be abrupt and even vehement. These different types of responses would be aimed primarily at the *factual* and *intellectual* content of what was said.

Another common type of response is one that mainly intends *to give acceptance*. It may be a noncommital agreement such as nodding one's head. It might go further and commit a person to the same logical position by saying, "I agree with you." With more enthusiasm one might say, "I completely agree with you! That's exactly the way I think and I have always held the same view!" These kinds of responses are not so much concerned with ideas as with conveying a sense of *agreement* with and *approval* of the other person.

Twofold Need. The problem here is that the person speaking has a twofold need. He apparently wants understanding and agreement with his ideas. But often his deepest need is to be accepted by the other person. Unfortunately, any disagreement with ideas may also appear to be personal rejection. Consequently, it is difficult for people to disagree without giving the impression of rejecting each other and of a lack of sympathy and understanding. This seems to be the main reason why many discussions end in arguments and personal hurt. This subtle transition from discussion to offense seems to hinge on the confusion between intellectual disagreement and personal rejection. For this reason any statement of intellectual disagreement runs the risk of carrying with it the sting of personal rejection, by implying a lack of understanding and appreciation of the other person.

This difference between the intellectual content and the personal need contained in statements is very common and yet is seldom recognized. People may agree or disagree with each other, not on the ideas expressed, but because of the accepting or hostile emotional tone they contain. If we observe a discussion carefully, we can notice consistent opposition between certain people on any series of ideas. We may notice, too, that some people usually group together. This is often due to their resistance to someone holding the other position or to their feeling of being accepted by the group which represents the opposition. They may actually have little real conviction about the ideas. We will discuss this point in detail in Chapter XVII.

COUNSELING RESPONSES

Agreement Not Always Helpful. In the area of personal difficulties, however, a counselor does not necessarily help people by agreeing with them, because they may not agree with themselves. A person's ultimate realistic attitude about himself is not always the one he expresses. If the counselor puts himself behind the attitude first expressed, he crystallizes that attitude. If later, the other person wishes to express an opposite view, he cannot, without feeling that he is now disagreeing with the counselor. This delicate balance, between the changing statements of the person coming for help, as he expresses different views of himself and his problems, and the necessity of the counselor remaining uninvolved, is one of the things that makes the counseling process so difficult. If the counselor takes a definite stand on one view, he may force the person to accept that view and work on it. But the counselor has no way of knowing this will be the final attitude which the person has towards himself or that it is his deepest and most significant insight. In order to be productive of increasing insight and deeper understanding on the part of the one coming for help, the counseling relationship must keep flowing. It cannot fix or freeze the person on any set attitude, until he himself has reached that conviction and has proved it to himself by adequate new choices in the world of reality.

Acceptance. The counselor, therefore, while not agreeing or disagreeing with the logic or intellectual content of the statement, must learn to give a tone of *acceptance* and *understanding* of the person's problem. This is no easy matter and the skill involved is one that can only be learned through concentration and effort.

The simplest forms of this skill are the elemental responses, which give acceptance without any commitment. Such responses are "uh, huh" and/or the nodding of the head as well as slow statements of

"Ye-e-e-s-s-s." These responses have a slight tone of questioning, which keeps the responsibility on the other person and encourages him to speak on. The person can get the feeling that he is flowing through the counselor and being accepted by him. Yet, there is, at the same time, no crystallizing attitude of agreement and no effort to take over and give the person a solution to his problems.

Another variation of this neutral accepting response is a simple re-statement of what the person said, in somewhat different words. If is it brief, such an "echoing" response at least gives the person a feeling that he is being listened to and accepted. But if the counselor's responses consistently go no deeper than this mere repetition of the same content, they will eventually be resisted.

A further development of this kind of acceptance is in the form of a question in which the counselor asks the person to explain the problem. The counselor may say,

Would you care to express that a little more?

or,

It is not just too clear to me, could you explain it further?

Such questions offer no agreement or disagreement with the position the person has taken, yet they convey an interested concern in the details of the person's problem.

These kinds of statements are not difficult. For this reason, they are usually the first thing a person learns about a self-directive or self-integrating counseling skill. But, while there is some value in these neutral accepting statements, they are not generally the responses that bring about deep insights. To understand this, we must go a step further in the analysis of types of counselor responses.

On this point, however, it is surprising how successful an interview, or even a counseling series, can sometimes be when only these kinds of simple acceptance responses are used. This was found to be true, in some instances, by counselors who had little or no training in this skill but who had heard or read about it, attempted to use it and were amazed at their success the first time. These simple responses, however, did not always prove so consistently effective in their later counseling. One explanation for this success, though, may be that these counselors had a deep respect for the integrity of the persons they were counseling and they somehow were able to convey this, especially through the genuine "warmth" of their expressions. Another possible explanation is that people who listen to others and accept them may actually be comparatively rare in our aggressively active society. A person's having found someone who would listen and understand therefore—in place of quickly taking over and giving advice or admonition—may of itself have been the main factor in the person's being able to talk out and think through his difficulties.

Penetration[1] *into Basic Attitude or Recognition of Feeling.* A far more significant class of counselor responses, however, are those which are variously called recognition or responding to feeling, emotional tone, or basic attitude. These are among the most important counselor responses. There is a difference between the verbal form a person's emotional release may take—for example, the series of incidents he may recite to illustrate how he feels—and the basic emotional attitude at the heart of this release. Personalities and facts brought up in the flow of a person's speech may, taken by themselves, appear to be separate and unconnected. Yet, as we examine them carefully we find, like spokes around a hub, that they are joined together because the person feels they indicate or demonstrate an emotion-charged attitude. The counselor's response, therefore, must go beneath the factual level and the verbal form of a person's expression. This is a distinction not readily understood. A skilled response involves a sensitivity to the underlying tone of such a statement. Such a response must penetrate the attitude or feeling which motivates the situations or actions the person has described. Sometimes the phrase, "You feel . . ." followed by the underlying emotion may hit this. This phrase, however, may become a habit and be used so much that it causes irritation.[2] A better response catches the attitude or emotion directly. For example, "You are angry because . . ." or "You are hostile to . . ." may do it.

----

[1]The word "penetration" used here may imply the interpreting or reading something into a response not actually contained in the person's expression. The word "reflection" however, which might be used instead, suggests only the flat re-stating or echoing what was said. What we mean here is somewhere between these two. Some counselors use the word "implementation" to suggest the whole process by which the counselor becomes a tool for the person's self-clarification and reorganization.

[2]See footnote, p. 230.

This class of responses is also sometimes called the "recognition" of basic feelings or attitudes. This implies that a person's recognition of these in himself through the counselor's response is something different from the feelings or attitudes themselves. To put it another way, *it is one thing for a person to feel and act on a strong emotion and another to recognize this feeling and understand why it is motivating his action.* When a person understands even one such emotional motive, he has gained in self-insight.

Just as the basic feelings are the hub within a series of incidents, so a person's various attitudes and goals are usually in some way incorporated in, or motivating the expression of these feelings and incidents. There is, apparently, a distinction between the feeling a person has which he recognizes through the counselor's response and his further statement of the basic attitude or reason why he has such a feeling. The counselor's response must also penetrate and reflect this—often at the same time. We have therefore grouped these two kinds of responses because, as a general rule, the statement of a feeling brings with it an almost immediate unfolding of the attitudes and reasons which seem to be causing the feeling. A person can move then from the recognition of his feelings to an examination of some of these attitudes and goals.

Conflicting Motive Patterns. This often reveals an even more fundamental series of motive-patterns or life-plans which the counselor must reflect. These are more basic than either the feelings or attitudes and somehow occur in one form or another in almost every situation the person finds himself. The person may put in such words as "always," "usually," "generally" which may give the counselor a clue to these more consistent motive-patterns. Conflicts have resulted because, without the person's clearly understanding it, such motive-patterns are somehow impeding the achievement of desired goals or threatening the loss of some goals already possessed.

Integrating Responses. As various counselor responses unfold these underlying feelings, attitudes, or fundamental motive-patterns, the person steadily grows able to piece together the different ways in which his emotions and conflicting motives are moving him. He begins slowly to relate these to past and present factors in his life and to bring in other persons, attitudes, or problems which now appear to be more and more linked together. As we mentioned in our earlier discussion of insight, this aspect of self-knowledge has some similarity to the process of seeing a picture or landscape in an integrated way or solving a jig-saw puzzle. First, there is a consistent and concentrated examination of each motive and a survey of the forming patterns. Then, gradually, the person sees how one action fits into another to make different patterns. Like solving a puzzle, the first stages are the most difficult. As the general outlines of motive-patterns are recognized and understood, it is easier to fit them together.

Whenever two or more factors are related together in a statement, the counselor makes an *integrating response*. Here, he not only reflects the feelings expressed, but he precisely states whatever factors the person has disclosed which appear to relate these feelings to one another or to more fundamental causes.

The counselor's warm, calm, but sincerely accurate reflection of the basic motives behind a series of disturbing incidents which a person has related together, enables him to see himself objectively in action. This revelation is not simply a reproduction of his actions but a penetration into the feelings and attitudes that are behind these actions. The person, lost in the recitation and emotion of the incidents themselves, cannot see this clearly without the counselor's skilled help. As a result of this, there is then a gradual recognition of the inadequacies of many of the means which the person has been employing, as well as a greater understanding and appreciation of many factors in himself and others in his life situation.

Self-Reorganizing Responses. The counselor's recognition and integration of these kinds of self-accepting and re-evaluation statements will usually be followed by the person's proposing and considering various new plans of action. These he hopes will better fit the person he now knows himself to be and more adequately reach his desired goals or fulfill a particular purpose. Accompanying this he will report on the results of some of these new plans when he acted on them, in order to examine their degree of success or failure. Such statements will call for *self-reorganizing responses*. These ordinarily come with frequency only in the later stages of the counseling process as a person is able to evaluate and accept himself more objectively and at the same time to set about a slow, steady, but generally more effective process of self-reorganization. In this chapter we are more immediately concerned with responses which commonly occur in the beginning stages of counseling and enable the counseling process to gain momentum. In the subsequent chapters of this section, we will discuss in greater detail these later integrating and self-reorganization responses.

DIFFERENT TYPES OF RESPONSES ILLUSTRATED

To illustrate the difference between penetrating and integrating responses and those which merely stay at the level of factual content, we can consider the following: A woman speaks of difficulties with her in-laws living in the home (L). She explains these difficulties in detail. She is irritated by the mother-in-law's interference when she has visitors. She relates how the mother-in-law takes over the kitchen and tells her how to cook, how she continually comments that the house needs cleaning, that the wife does not know how to iron clothes, does not dress well, nor prepare her husband's shirts as she should. If we analyze this series of statements we notice that they all flow from a basic feeling and attitude. It is a resentment of the mother-in-law for taking over the wife's role. This is behind the recitation of the incidents. Each incident illustrates the wife's resistance and resentment of the mother-in-law's tendency to absorb what the wife feels is her position.

Agreement. A person might respond to this statement in a number of ways. He might, for example, agree by citing a similar irritation, and perhaps give details of some other difficulties he has encountered. If he did this the discussion might go further into the problems of cooking, ironing, or mothers-in-law. It would, consequently, stay on the same level as it began.

Disagreement. The counselor might disagree and defend the mother-in-law with some excuse, such as, "Well, she is old and you shouldn't pay any attention to her," or "Well, after all, she had the boy before you did and you should be able to put up with and understand those things." Here, too, the response remains on the plane of the incidents recited. In this disagreement, the wife might feel a personal rejection. One could guess that she might respond with further insistence on her grievance, especially if she felt it strongly. She might even begin to show some resentment toward the other person for taking the mother-in-law's part and would therefore only have been made more negative.

Noncommital. A counselor might avoid this by a noncommital "Yes," or nodding his head, or he might ask,

Would you care to talk a little more about those difficulties?

This would give acceptance but it would not unfold any deeper attitude.

Responses to Basic Attitude. A more significant response would reach the core of the feelings at the center of the resentment. It would uncover and hold up to the person the emotion and basic attitude which have made these incidents so disturbing to her. The mother-in-law is resented because she takes over the wife's role and is critical of her. The feeling is resentment and the basic attitude motivating this resentment is the mother-in-law's dominance and criticism. The counselor must be alert to catch this as she talks. When she stops, he responds quietly,

You resent your mother-in-law for taking over and being critical of everything you do in the house.

Such a response will invariably be accepted. It will often even elicit an enthusiastic, "Yes, that's it exactly," or "That's right!" or "That's just the way I feel!" From the person's tone it would seem evident that she had released something significant and that she had been helped by the way it flowed through and was understood by the counselor.

Simple agreement with another or even a neutral accepting or "echoing" response seldom produces so strong an affirmation of being completely understood. Alternately, if the listener disagrees, not only is the person apt to feel he was not understood but he may show increased resistance and irritation. An upset person will often only keep insisting on his point adding still more details and incidents and perhaps ending with an implied or open expression of resentment towards the listener.

A most important point to be noted here, however, is that these counselor responses are not interpretations or intuitions of what is behind what a person says. They are responses to feelings and attitudes actually contained in the statements themselves at the moment the person makes them. As we will see, resistance seems almost always to follow the counselor's attempt to read into a person's expression any basic patterns or motives which he may actually have, but which he has not as yet expressed in any way. This is especially a difficulty for counselors with a tendency to "diagnose" or read behind a person's stated reactions or motives. These are delicate and subtle distinctions which are hard for the beginning counselor to understand or catch consistently in his responses. We will, therefore, have occasion to discuss them in greater detail in this and subsequent chapters.

Once a feeling or attitude, contained in the person's expression, has come to the surface through both the person's statement and the counselor's response, it is subject to the person's reasonable evaluation. This often leads to the eventual unfolding of a complex interweaving of basic life-patterns and goals which in some way conflict with one another. This woman was so upset by her home situation that she had already applied for a divorce. Yet, during the process of three interviews, as she gradually analyzed her feelings about her mother-in-law, she began to see that she resented anyone who attempted to "take her over." She recalled, as examples, the parking lot man on the previous day telling her how to park her car, her husband's earlier instructions on how to drive, and other such incidents which, as she thought about them, she realized should not have caused her to react as strongly as she did. Later, these incidents and her reactions to her mother-in-law somehow seemed to be connected with an intense resentment of her older sister who, from her earliest memories, had also "taken her over." At this point she expressed being vividly aware, in a way she had never realized before, how many little mannerisms of her mother-in-law were similar to those of her older sister. In addition she also realized that she was actually much more tolerant towards a number of other women of about her mother-in-law's age even when they did almost the same things. Here, too, her perception of her husband, previously so focused on his taking his mother's part in all their quarrels, slowly broadened and she could state that most of the differences with her husband were probably more attributable to the confusing home situation than to any particular quality which she disliked in him.

As each of these developing awarenesses are brought forward and incorporated in a series of incidents and details, the counselor must reach into the core or hub and pull out the feelings, attitudes, goals, motive-patterns and related awarenesses which the person has expressed.

DEMONSTRATION FROM COUNSELING INTERVIEW

To demonstrate particularly how the counselor's responses penetrate a person's feelings and attitudes, let us look again at the excerpt given on page 144 (Z). The counselor's first response in this excerpt is:

You feel it would be a bad thing for him to marry her.

The simple acceptance in this response enables the woman to go more deeply into her feelings about the man with whom she is involved. By the end of this release she has also made some significant statements about herself, ending with, "Sometimes I just want to take what I have and not worry what comes afterwards."

Two Sides to Any Conflict. This is one side of her conflict. The other side is the desire to reach a more reasonable solution, and not merely to escape. The counselor responds to this first attitude with, "You tend to take what you have, not to think about the consequences."

Her satisfaction at being understood is shown by the person's immediate agreement in the phrase "That's it!" This in turn allows her to face the danger of such consequences in the statement, "Sometimes they're pretty serious." She now looks at a number of incidents which show how serious the consequences could actually be. Her negative attitude is already giving way to a slight positive tone towards the end, "But I suppose I might just as well make up my mind to keep on battling it, though." Then, she expresses the difficulty this positive attitude involves, with, "It's kind of hard to do that, though."

The counselor, in a short but incisive response, conveys a genuine acceptance of her difficulties in the phrase, "It isn't easy, is it?" This permits the person to go further into her conflicts with "Everything's bad . . . my health, my nerves."

The counselor makes no attempt to turn the person's attention away from her troubles. He sincerely accepts the gravity of the situation in the response, "Things are pretty black sometimes." Again there is an enthusiastic, "That's right."

Feeling that her difficulties are appreciated by the counselor, she then recites incidents which demonstrate these difficulties. We see how serious the situation is for her. She is able to express the fears she has of what may happen. We notice the simple, quick but understanding response of the counselor, "That's putting it mildly, isn't it?"

Counselor Responses Need Not Be Long. These counselor statements demonstrate that good responses do not have to be long or ponderous. Short, precise responses can aid a person to talk freely and further the flow of his ideas. Through such penetration of motives, growth in self-understanding is facilitated. Sometimes easy conversational responses, such as the counselor used here, are very effective. Because of their brevity, however, one should not overlook the skillful analysis that went into their formulation in the rapid flow of the person's release. The counselor had to follow carefully every word in order to reach the person's basic feelings and attitudes. Then, in simple, concise statements, he delicately uncovers some of these fundamental tones behind the related incidents.

Some Typical Factors. A number of elements in this short excerpt are typical of the kind of confused statements a person makes at the beginning of an interview series. Yet, even in this excerpt, we notice that the first part is more negative and resistant than the last. In the beginning, the counselor could have created an argument by almost any suggestion. Counselor suggestions might also have blocked the woman's expression of her fears about the man's threat of demanding her divorce. She would probably have felt that the counselor was not only rejecting her ideas, but was failing in sympathy and adequate understanding of the difficult position she was in. This, in turn, could have pushed her into further argument with the counselor.

Effect of Accepting Responses. When the counselor accepts her basic feelings and attitudes, however, the person is able to unfold deeper fears and confusions. Yet, by the end of the release she begins to take courage and to suggest to herself that she must "keep on battling it, though." This statement is more effective coming from the person herself, after she has looked at her difficulties, than if the counselor had given her this advice.

This positive attitude grows so that by the end of the next long response she is thinking about breaking off the relationship with the man. But, for people to tell her simply to put an end to it shows, in her opinion, that they do not appreciate how complex the problem is. We can see that if the counselor had argued, he would probably have been put in the category with those people who say, "All you have to do is just call it off." This woman would likely not have listened and only have felt that the counselor, too, had no appreciation of the serious complexities involved.

Shift of Focus. Besides the change from negative attitudes to more positive ones, there is another change evident in this excerpt that is typical of many opening interviews. In the beginning the woman is not talking about herself but about the man. Interviews often begin with statements about the problems of other people. Sometimes a person will even say that he is not coming for himself but to help someone else. Such a person only gradually looks at himself and admits a need for help with his own problems. This transition can happen so easily and smoothly in a skillful interview that we may not notice it. If, however, the counselor had failed to respond accurately to the deep feeling of this person, the hour interview might never have gotten beyond the discussion of whether the man should marry this other woman. This further demonstrates what is meant by the surface content of a response in contrast to the deeper attitudes or emotional tones which lie behind the verbal expression. The counselor, in responding to these deeper feelings and not discussing the question of the marriage, enables the woman to go rapidly into the relationship of the man with herself. By the next response, she is no longer talking about the marriage. She is now thinking out his attitudes and her fear of what he might do if she breaks with him. She then dwells on her own tendencies to rush into a solution without considering the consequences. She sees how such a solution would be invalid in this case and probably have serious consequences.

The Counselor's Response Does Not Soften a Person's Difficulties. We may wonder why the counselor responds the way he does, instead of attempting to soften the person's difficulties or talk her out of them. The next counselor response, for example, simply summarizes her recitation of the difficulties and suffering she and the man are going through: "It's just pretty bad for both of you." There is not even a slight suggestion of considering the situation to be any better than the woman herself has indicated. It has been found that an effective aid in promoting positive growth is the person's realization of the unhappiness of his present situation. If the counselor tries to persuade him that his problems are not so great, the person is apt to feel that the counselor does not understand. This will prevent him from revealing any deeper feelings. He may become either hostile or silent. To lessen a person's concentration on the unhappy aspects of his present situation is often to destroy his most effective motivation, since it may be necessary for a person to become sharply aware of this unhappiness in order to make the effort to change. As he gets "fed up" with the effects of his present life, a person is often more strongly urged to a different way of living.

Nor Emphasize Them.   On the other hand, it seems unwise that the counselor should place greater emphasis on the person's difficulties than he himself feels. This, too, may cause a person to feel he is not understood. It might make him reply with a more positive statement such as, "Well, things aren't quite that bad." This would not be his real feeling, but simply an expression of resistance to the counselor.

Responses Should Further the Person's Self-Concentration.   There seems to be a significant difference between a statement that comes from the depth of a person's growing awareness and conviction, and one that is made in response to the counselor's suggestions. When a person answers that things could be worse, simply because the counselor overstated how bad they are, or when he states that things are better because he does not want to disappoint the counselor, he is not speaking from personal insight. His attention is centered on the counselor. A good response never takes the person's attention away from himself. Rather, it keeps the focus directly on the state the person feels himself to be in at that moment. This is one of the reasons why he can unfold and understand his feelings in a way that is not possible in a conversation or when he simply mulls his problems over in his own mind. The enthusiastic statements of "That's it!" and "That's right!" are not only indicative of this woman's feeling of being accepted and understood, but they also produce more intense concentration on the causes of her present unhappiness. This brings out other reasons and motives not clear to her at the beginning of the interview.

Study of Actual Excerpts Can Improve Skill.   This phase of counselor sensitivity can be improved by continued study of detailed excerpts and by experience in counseling. One may compare counseling to the skill of mastering the piano. Fingering out the theme of a particular classic is not difficult. Anyone can recognize the notes. So, it is not hard to give elemental acceptance to people's statements in an interview. With a little more effort, one can also learn to recognize common negations people express, such as, hostility, confusion, fear; and certain positive attitudes like being hopeful and feeling encouraged. But, the skill of counseling is subject to the same progressive advancement as the skill of the pianist. The musician must gain a high sensitivity to reproduce all the subtleties and complexities of a composition. So, counselors may vary in skill from the simple, elemental reproduction of one feeling or attitude to delicate and sensitive kinds of responses which contain nearly all the intricate combinations of feelings and insights of a particular statement.

One should realize, too, that the short incisive responses in the previous excerpts are themselves skillful just as the trained perfection of the concert pianist is demonstrated even when he fingers out a simple melody. This comparison can be carried further. As an amateur pianist disturbs and irritates because he does not reach the exact tone, so the beginning counselor is apt to disturb with inexact responses. The smoothness of the interview, and the feeling of peace and ease it gives the person, is determined largely by the precision and clarity with which the counselor reaches basic attitudes and feelings. This cannot be seen so clearly in successful series of interviews because, like an accomplished pianist, a skillful counselor's responses appear effortless. But, if it were possible to reproduce the same interviews with a less skilled counselor, we might be surprised and even startled at the difference.

SOME CAUSES OF RESISTANCE

Failure to Reach Basic Attitudes. When the counselor fails to reach a fundamental feeling or attitude, resistance and even open differences may occur. We see this in the following excerpt from an interview with a sixteen-year-old girl who is involved in delinquency (R) :[3]

[3]Designated by symbol (R).

Second interview: Edna came in apparently very angry and indignant at being kept waiting.

P1: This is *my last Tuesday!* (Pause)

C1: Why didn't you come on time?

P2: How could I? I didn't get out of school early enough. I walked clear out here.

C2: Why did you walk? Why didn't you ride the streetcar?

P3: That would take away from my pay.

(She said she got $2.50 a week from her mother and she bought her clothes with it.)

(Because the other interviewing rooms were filled, the interview took place in the children's room. There were only small chairs in the room and I asked her to see if she could get two big ones. She couldn't find any and she didn't like sitting on the small ones.)

P3: Boy! My mother is sure going to tell that Miss H. when she sees her. This is my last Tuesday. I'm not coming here any more. I miss school and miss my tests. Miss H. doesn't care. I'll get my mother and she'll get a doctor and take him down to that Juvenile Center. She'll pay the doctor fifteen dollars a trip and he'll tell them down there there's nothing wrong. My mother says there's nothing wrong with me and there's no sense in making me come out here every Tuesday. What do those crazy people think I am? They made my brother come out here too, when there was nothing wrong with him. I walk clear out here and wait all this time.

(Edna's speech was very stormy. She said a few more things in this vein, repeating the phrase "my mother said" a number of times.)

C3: Now look, Edna, you were to be here at 9:30. You didn't come and I had to take care of these other children. That is why you had to wait. That wasn't my fault, was it?

P4: No, it wasn't your fault, but I don't see why I have to come out here at all. It's all that Miss H. She's the one who makes me miss my school and fail. They made my brother fail. They don't care. I couldn't get here earlier. I had to see the teacher and she was late. I promised to do something for her.

C4: But you promised me last Tuesday you would come here at 9:30 and I was waiting for you. You promised me first.

P5: Well, I forgot to tell the teacher yesterday I had to come here, so I had to see her this morning. It took me an hour to get excused. I had to go down to the office.

C5: Well, whose fault was that that you forgot? Was it mine?

P6: No, I guess it was mine all right. (With some resentment) But I'll tell you one thing, I don't like walking clear out here every Tuesday.

Someone stole my galoshes at school and my feet are wet now. Some boy, I'll bet.

C6: Why do you say a boy?

P7: Well some boy was caught stealing other things at school. Anyway I've got a job beginning next Tuesday working after school taking care of a cash register. (She looked up at me expecting me to show surprise.)

C7: That's fine.

This is an interesting excerpt because the counselor already had some understanding of the theory and skill of a self-directive counseling process. The counselor—a woman with previous counseling experience in another setting—said afterwards that she sincerely thought she was applying this skill. Until she saw the stenographic shorthand notes, however, she did not realize how far off her responses were.

Counselors Often Do Not Realize Their Mistakes. This illustrates an important point. Because counseling is so personal a relationship, many counselors do not realize their mistakes. It is only after some concentrated study—particularly of excerpts from successful interviews—that a person grows aware of ways to improve his own counseling. The result is, that what counselors *think* they do in a counseling interview and what they *actually do* are oftentimes surprisingly different. But until they have acquired this disturbing and even humiliating awareness about themselves, they may not be open to any further understanding or training in counseling skill. In fact, sincere people are sometimes apt to dismiss the idea with a casual, "There's nothing new in that. I have always been doing it that way." They may and generally do, in fact, believe this. Yet, were they to have a skilled observer at one of their interviews or were a record to be made of it so that such a skilled person might go over it afterwards, these people might be surprised at what they said and at the opportunities for constructive growth which were missed because of their responses. This was the reaction of the counselor as she discussed the content of this particular interview in conference with a number of counselors.

Defensiveness of Counselor. Throughout this excerpt, the counselor seems excessively anxious to justify her own position. Probably this is due to the tone of attack and rejection in the girl's opening phrase. This kind of statement, with an implied personal sting in it, is one of the most difficult to handle—especially if it begins the interview. All of us want to feel we are successful. This may cause us to look for some reassurance that the time we are spending with a person is, at least, appreciated. But if, as this girl does, a person openly rejects our efforts, it sometimes taxes a counselor's skill not to become defensive and even hostile himself. In this case, the counselor unfortunately gives in to her urge and attacks back with, "Why didn't you come on time?"

Instead of becoming aroused and threatened by the girl's statement, the counselor could have quietly accepted the girl's feeling of resistance. The counselor might have said,

> You don't want to come again and you are not going to come.

She might have even gone a little deeper with a shorter but more incisive phrase,

> You're just fed up, aren't you?

Both these responses would have cut into the girl's negative feelings and given her a chance to express them. This, she very likely would have done in the next statement, probably at some length. Instead, a series of attacks and counter-attacks follow. In place of her second attacking response, the counselor might have said,

> It was a pretty long walk for you, wasn't it?

This would give the girl a feeling that her difficulty and effort in coming were understood. Such a response would no doubt have been more effective than the direct criticism, and might have enabled the girl to admit that she could have taken the streetcar if she had not wished to be late.

The counselor also interprets the girl's next long statement as a personal attack on herself. In an effort to gain the girl's acceptance, the counselor then pleads her own case. In explaining this afterwards, the counselor said that until she went over this excerpt, she had not realized how much her sympathy and liking for the girl were confusedly motivating her to excessive seeking of the girl's acceptance. She reached this self-awareness only as she tried to explain to the counseling group the reason for making this response. This also illustrates another point that is quite common. We are not always conscious of our own needs in a counseling interview. But, even though we do not recognize them, these needs will crop out and affect our responses.[4] Consequently, growth in counseling skill often necessitates a corresponding growth in the counselor's self-understanding.

In place of her self-defense, the counselor might have said,

You and your mother are pretty angry about the whole business and you're going to do something about it.

This would have allowed Edna to drain off more hostility and look at it and perhaps to realize at the end that, since it was a court case, there were limits to what she and her mother could do.

The counselor might have responded,

You are kind of mad at being kept waiting.

This might have allowed Edna to examine her anger and enabled her to face the fact that it was her own fault.

The counselor's effort to plead her own case contains this positive factor, however: it shows that she is interested in keeping Edna's good will. Edna seems to recognize this in her next response, as she now directs her hostility towards Miss H. By this time, the counselor herself has become so personally involved, though, that she does not see this. She still identifies Edna's statements with a rejection of herself. Interestingly, when the counselor saw this response she said that no one could have convinced her she would ever have used such a personal tone towards someone she was counseling. Such recognitions are, of course, very humiliating for the counselor and yet they provide an extremely powerful impetus for the improvement of counseling skill. Sometimes it is only when a person is clearly ashamed of his responses that he is willing to make the difficult and tedious effort necessary to acquire greater skill.

Some Alternate Counselor Responses. The counselor might have responded,

You really blame Miss H. for the whole thing

or,

You feel Miss H. just wants you to fail

4See pp. 332–338.

in this way giving Edna a chance to unfold more of her negative
attitudes about Miss H. Such unfolding will often improve the relationship of the two people because positive values and meanings
underlie these negations.[5] Edna's statements here are only one side
of her attitudes. The other side is a constructive, reasonable one.
The counselor, however, having started on this track of personal
defense, continues it. In the next excerpt, both Edna and the counselor keep up their defenses. Instead, the counselor might have
synthesized the content with,

A number of things came up that made you late.

This sort of response, while not reaching any feeling, would give
acceptance and understanding and in addition would probably remove from Edna any further need to continue talking about that
aspect of the situation. Forced to face the obvious fact that she herself was responsible for her own coming late, Edna admits it. This
kind of forced admittance, however, has little constructive value.
This is shown by Edna's next statements, which indicate continued
defense and hostility.

Instead of seeking information about the incident concerning the
galoshes, the counselor might have said,

You don't like having to walk clear out here every Tuesday.

In the final response the counselor seems so pleased because the
interview is taking an apparently small positive turn, that she gives
quick reassurance. Actually, considering the degree of hostility and
unreality thus far, it is unlikely that there is anything really positive
in the statement. Although the counselor had contact with her for
some time after this, Edna never again mentioned the job. It probably never materialized, and may even have been concocted on the
spur of the moment to get some recognition. Statements made in
this way are quite different from the constructive plans which emerge
in a good counseling interview. Such statements of plans are never
made until people have some objective grounds for making them.
This is one of the reasons why their plans so often do work out
in contrast to their previous failures. They are not simply attempting
to get the counselor's approval. Their plans flow from real self-
knowledge.

[5]Pp. 72–73.

A SUCCESSFUL INTERVIEW

We cannot, of course, repeat an interview but we can reproduce parallel interviews of persons with similar problems and background. By contrast, the following excerpt from an interview with a delinquent girl of about the same age and environment as Edna, shows the insights achieved through another counselor.[6]

CASE OF JANE—AGE 16, FIRST INTERVIEW: Jane brought two photographs with her which she showed to the Psychologist who introduced us and when the latter left she said she wanted me to see them too. I commented that they were fine pictures. She explained that they were of her brother and sister and she placed them out of sight and "settled back" as if to ask what was to come next.

C1: Perhaps you wonder why you were sent for this morning.

P1: Yeah, I'm to come over to talk with you for an interview. What do you want to know?

C2: Well, this is to be a different kind of interview. It will be about what you want to tell me rather than anything that I would ask you. In other words, it will be an hour which you can use to talk about your problems—things that bother you—uh—how you feel about things—things that you may be worried about.

P2: (slight pause.) I don't know where to begin from.

C3: It's hard to know where to begin.

P3: (laughs) I don't know where to start. Uh, would you like to hear how I got in trouble?—or what's bothering me now? (Nervous giggle) That's right you just said I could talk about anything that was bothering me. Uh,—I ran away from home—four days—the reason why is that I got pretty disgusted where I lived—I got into trouble with girls at the Court. They gave me another chance. I knew I wouldn't be good so I moved into the Center with two social workers. My sister moved in too. I got fed up. (She tells about the bother of signing in and out where she was going, with whom and how long she intended to be gone—whenever she went out.) And then my boy friend—a boy I went to school with—we got a crazy idea—to get married. Well, that was before I had a chance to think it over. Then I realized that it would be crazy. He wouldn't be here long, and I knew he couldn't take me across on the boat with him—uhh—but what's really bothering me is—I want to go home and make something of myself. I want to get back into school. (Words lost—tells that she was expelled from school, but they'd take her back now.) I got expelled when I got into trouble.

[6]Virginia E. Madigan: "An Illustration of Non-directive Psychotherapy," *J. Clin. Psychol.*, Vol. 1, No. 1, January, 1945, pp. 36–52.

C4: It's been rather tough-going, running away from home, living at the Center, getting into trouble and then being expelled from school.

P4: You said it! My aunt—my sister really has faith in me. Everybody *there* does. The psychiatrist there wants to work with me, the medical social worker, the Juvenile Court. Really what I want is to get back home and make something of myself. I've got diabetes—can't work very hard—but I want to get a good job, get back in school and work afterwards. My sister works. I could work after school, I could buy myself the "extras" and save her money. If I could go home to —— —— well, they'd understand me and they want to help me.

C5: You feel that the people there are really more understanding of you. You'd have more of a chance back there.

P5: (Agrees. Talks on that even the school principal who expelled her likes her, testified for her at Court.) If I get back home—oh—it all depends on the Court and what they say here. If I get back to —— I'm not going to have anything to do with my old friends. You know those old friends weren't really friends. They knew what I was doing but they didn't put me back on the right track—they weren't friends. They let me go on—.

C6: You feel that even your friends let you down.

P6: Not "even my friends" they weren't friends at all. You know my sister and brother had it even more hard than I, but they got a year in college even. (She goes on talking very rapidly about the good jobs her sister and brother have had and that it should really be easier for her than it was for them.)

C7: You feel that they made something of themselves and that you can do the same.[7]

Structuring Statement. We notice that the counselor begins immediately with a statement which accepts the obvious feeling the girl has. The girl naturally wonders why she has been called to this stranger's office. Jane's response indicates that her previous experience in interviews always involved answering questions and giving information about herself. The counselor, recognizing this, makes a "structuring" statement which defines simply and precisely that this

---

[7]If the reader wishes, he might cover the counselor's response with his hand or a blotter and make his own responses. He might also do this with the other excerpts reproduced at various places throughout the book. It is a good way to practice this skill. See pages 330 ff. The reader will observe that the counselor here begins nearly every response with, "You feel . . ." At first sight one might be surprised that Jane does not resist this. One reason probably is that this phrase in actual speech is more of an elision and therefore is much less noticeable and irritating than its bold position in print might indicate. The counselor, however, might better have avoided such repeated use of this phrase and penetrated more directly into the basic attitudes expressed.

is a different relationship. It tells also how long the interview will be and that the girl can talk about whichever of her problems she wishes, not only in a factual way, but by unfolding her feelings, too. In this way the girl has now clearly before her an initial awareness of what the interview is to be and what her function is. Jane's response indicates a general willingness. But it reveals some confusion about what she is to do. The counselor here shows skill by not going into further explanation, as she might have done. A less alert counselor could have started to offer reasons why this type of interview would be better for Jane than the others that she had undergone. This could have quickly led the counselor into the position of having to answer a series of dependency information questions from Jane. The counselor does not do this but simply accepts Jane's difficulty in starting to talk. This further relaxes Jane. She can now digest the original structuring statement. After a certain hesitancy, she goes directly into her problems without any prompting or encouragement from the counselor.

Effects.   Some readers may be surprised at the apparent suddenness with which Jane unfolds herself in this long release. This, however, is not unusual when an opening interview is handled skillfully. Even though Jane did not come of her own volition, she is obviously in personal difficulty and has deep feelings about it. Given a chance to express her problems and feelings in a clearly defined but accepting and understanding atmosphere, she readily takes advantage of it. Such a girl could have been as defensive and hostile as Edna, had the wrong responses been used. She, however, soon sees the counseling relationship in a positive light. Her will to achieve reasonable self-understanding is then strong enough to cause her to begin to unfold herself to the counselor.

Lengthy Statements.   A long release like this is difficult for the counselor. He may not be able to keep in his mind everything that was said. It is also hard for him to know what attitudes and feelings ought to be recognized. In this case, the counselor accepts the girl's problems by summarizing some of them. Another response might have been a more general survey such as,

You thought of getting married as a way out but you saw that would be foolish—you really want to go back to your own school and make something of yourself there.

A number of other responses could have been made. The reader might wish to try some himself. Jane's reply indicates the common reaction to a good counselor statement. She goes further into her positive, constructive evaluation. Interestingly, Jane repeats her desire to go home and make something of herself. The counselor, as we notice, did not include this in her previous response. It is often observed that if the counselor misses or does not sufficiently unfold a deep desire or basic awareness, the person himself tends to repeat this, either in his next statement or in some other part of the interview. Somehow, until his feelings and insights have not only been expressed, but have been adequately projected back by the counselor, the person appears to have a sense of incompleteness. He seems to need to restate such things until they are finally objectified in the counselor's response. The counselor catches this in her next response.

Realism. Jane then explores the possibility of her returning home. But she also expresses the realistic limitation that it depends on the court. This cautious realism is in contrast to the fantasy negativism of Edna. What Jane says in this calm evaluation is very different from Edna's (R) grandiose plans about her mother, the doctor, and her new job.

Counselor Overstatement. In the last part of her statement, Jane faces some factors in her past environment that she will have to cope with if she returns there. In response the counselor makes an overstatement. For our purpose, this is fortunate because it reveals how even the slightest counselor misstatement will be picked up. When an interview goes along smoothly, we may not always realize the counselor's skill. Such a slip as this, while not seriously endangering the interview, since the counselor quickly recovers, does show how delicate this process is. After resisting the counselor's overstatement, Jane continues her self-revelation. The interview gets back on the track with the counselor's accurate response.

The following excerpt continues the interview:[8]

P7: Yes. I've done a lot of talking but never did what I said. That's why the Judge and everybody—well, I'm here to see if I really did mean what I said (words lost—but she talks vaguely about a diabetic coma she had which made it necessary for her to be in —— Hospital

[8]*Ibid.*

—she launched into another vague account of a serious illness—pneumonia—her sister had—). All the time she was delirious she talked about me—she was so worried about me. She got sick worrying about me, you see. It was my fault.

C8: You feel that you had something to do with her sickness.

P8: That's right.

C9: That it was sort of your fault.

P9: Yes—I caused my brother a lot of worry too. They've been too good to me to cause them trouble. I want to show them I can make something of myself. I want to prove it to myself too. I ought to, too.

C10: You feel that you owe it to them as well as to yourself to make good.

P10: (crying) Not only to them—but to my aunt and uncle too. (Tells that she disgraced them.) The neighbors all talk about them, about me—they say, "Look at what you raised." It wasn't their fault. They did a lot for me. I just didn't think before I did those things.

C11: You feel that it wasn't really fair for the neighbors to blame your aunt and uncle for what you did when it was your fault. You didn't think first.

P11: Yes, I don't pity myself. I can't have my father and mother back. All I have is my brother and sister. I've got to do something for them. Why—you know (tells about the many sacrifices her sister has made to buy her things and try to make her happy). When she only earned $11 a week, she spent half of it on me. I've lost so much school work —for illness—two years. Maybe if I went to night school too, I could make some of it up. I live with my aunt now, I could study there. My sister moved out of the Center too. She wants me to go back to school. So does my aunt. I want to, too. I want to make up what I've lost and graduate.

C12: It's awfully important to you then that you catch up on what you missed at school and then get ahead.

Self-Evaluation. The value of the previous counselor response ("You feel that they made something of themselves and that you can do the same ") can be seen in the result which it produces. For this girl to admit, in the short space of six responses that, "I have done a lot of talking but never did what I said" may appear unusual. Someone might even say that this is simply a stratagem to make a good impression. But this kind of candid evaluation can often occur in good counseling. The counselor's response in C8, "You feel that you had something to do with her sickness," taken by itself, would be a direct attack. Yet, since it is a response to the person's self-accusation, it is accepted. The counselor now projects the tone of responsibility which P7 contained. Jane accepts the responsibility and goes more deeply into what she has done and how she wishes to make amends. The counselor makes no effort to turn off this statement, but recognizes it. Jane's crying shows the feeling that has been reached. Here, her broadening self-examination has not only resulted in a re-enforcement of her positive resolutions but it has also produced an expression of a desire to change. The counselor again responds to the aspect of Jane's personal responsibility. (The counselor might simply have accepted the crying by stating "You feel all this very deeply, don't you?") Jane continues her evaluation of her situation and makes a further re-enforcement of her resolve. The counselor's response reflects only the positive attitude about returning to school.[9]

Reaching Causes of Conduct. Such rapid insights and resolutions coming in the brief interval of the first half-hour of an interview would not of themselves have the constructive force of the same judgments if they were made after a longer series of more penetrating interviews. Yet they do indicate a positive affirmation on the part of this girl to face the limits of reality, to recognize her own responsibility for what happened to her and to make an attempt at a better school and home adjustment. Her statement that she is dependent on the decision of the court and not on her own whims demonstrates a definite objectivity. Her recognition of what she has lost, without at the same time pitying herself excessively or dwelling unduly on her misfortunes, shows the beginnings of a genuine and honest realism. These kinds of careful, restrictive statements are not generally found in the fantasy resolutions that such delinquent girls may make in an emotional mood of repentance. Comparing the excerpts given here with the previous statements by Edna, we can see a significant difference in approximately the same amount of counseling time. Where Edna never got beyond argument and disagreement with the counselor, this girl penetrated into some of the causes of her conduct. She also was beginning to see new and more reasonable ways of acting.

[9]The reader might want to form a number of responses which catch more adequately all the tones Jane has expressed in this last statement.

AN UNSUCCESSFUL INTERVIEW

Value of Typescript. The next excerpt is included to give the reader an opportunity to try his hand at correcting the counselor's responses. This often helps a person to recognize the difference between a superficial content response—which parrots back what was said or asks a question which has nothing to do with the flow of the interview—and a penetrating response, which reaches the heart of the attitudes that lie behind a series of incidents. In this sense poor counseling excerpts can be valuable for counselor training, since we do not so readily notice mistakes in more skillful interviews. But even in successful interviews, most responses can be improved after a person has had time to study the typescript carefully. This is another reason why careful study of interview excerpts can be helpful in improving counseling skill. A counselor cannot change an interview once it has taken place, but he can, by concentrated study, grow alert to his mistakes and improve his subsequent counseling. The counselor in the following excerpt has had some training in counseling. He begins the interview with some attempts to reach basic attitudes; but, he does not consistently succeed.

This interview is with a mother whose daughter, age 7, has a speech difficulty for which there were probably psychological causative factors. This is the first interview (Q).[10]

C1: You haven't lived here long, have you?
P1: No, we haven't.
C2: How long has it been?
P2: About three months ago. We were staying in an apartment but now fortunately we have rented a house of our own and there's a chance that we may be able to buy it. (Pause) R. has been doing better in school the last few days. The teacher says she's getting along better and doing things that she wouldn't do before. She still won't do a lot of things though that they want her to. (Long pause. Mrs. A. looks blankly at the counselor.)
C3: You probably are wondering just why you are here and just what we are planning to do. Since R. is really your problem and since you know her a lot better than we do, we feel that perhaps we can help her get rid of some of the things that may be causing her speech blocking. You and I will try to work out some of your problems in

[10]Designated by the symbol (Q).

your relations with R. (Long pause. Mrs. A still looking quizzically at the counselor.)

C4: Would you care to explain a little more your relationship with R. and something maybe about yourself?

P4: Well, I think I've told the woman that we talked to before about everything that I know.

C5: Yes, well, she didn't talk to me very much so I don't know too much about that . . .

P5: Well, I, I don't know what to say except the medical examination seemed to indicate that there was no handicap in R.'s speech. We always thought that it was physical but they said they couldn't find anything. They said something about its being a psychological problem; that she just had bad speech habits and so they recommended then that we come over here. (Pause) R. didn't speak at all like I suppose other children would and we've noticed for a long time that she wasn't able to speak as well as other children her age.

C6: Her being unable to speak like other children worried you.

P6: Well, we were disturbed, not exactly worried. I have been sick a lot and my sister who was living with us took care of R. (Pause)

C7: What's your husband's attitude? Is he at all concerned about R.?

P7: My husband hasn't seemed to bother about it one way or the other. He's concerned about her health and all that but he doesn't seem to be concerned about her education or her speech as such. He doesn't seem to spend much time with her although he has lately taken some interest in her. My husband does seem to be a little more interested now.

C8: What did he think about bringing the child here?

P8: He didn't seem to have any objections.

C9: And now you feel R. is doing better in school.

P9: Well, that's what her teacher says. They seem to want me to come there and talk sometimes. I just don't know why they want me to come. But it seems to be a good school and R. seems to like the second grade—that's the one she's in now. It's a good school I believe.

C10: Yes, I have heard that it has a good reputation. (Pause)

C11: How did R. take your leaving her to come here?

P11: Oh, she seemed to take it all right. She always likes to stay home and she seems to be more at ease there than anywhere else. She has a lot of dolls that she plays with and she likes to be at home. Some women I know do not want to leave their children or if they leave they make up all kinds of things but I have never done that. I just told R. that I was coming here and that we were going to talk about her speech and she didn't say anything at all. I don't like to lie to her.

Conversational Responses. The counselor began the interview with two conversational statements which were not seriously concerned with getting information. Such conversational statements at the beginning of an interview can often throw it off the track. Every person has had many experiences where he answered questions of an interviewer. If the counselor starts asking conversational questions in this way, the person may immediately feel that this is to be a question-and-answer relationship. This seems to have happened here. Consequently, if we follow this excerpt through the various statements and responses that are given, we notice that the interview never got beyond information. This illustrates how a person can quickly attach a previously conditioned reaction to a few phrases. Because Mrs. A., like everyone else, has answered questions in an interview many times before, she apparently accepted this as the same kind of relationship. She seemed to be already settled into a mood of being silently cooperative by waiting for further questions. The responsibility for the interview was now definitely on the counselor. This perception would have to be changed by some penetrating responses on the part of the counselor. But, since this did not take place, the interview produced only factual content.

Poor Structuring. The counselor's third statement was an attempt to "structure" the relationship. If we contrast this with the one made in the previous interview,[11] we notice that here the counselor unfortunately went too far in insisting that R. *is* Mrs. A.'s problem. This and the two conversational questions which preceded it, instead of being accepted by Mrs. A., seemed to cause some slight confusion and resistance, as shown by the long pause and blank stare. The counselor then made a noncommital inquiry and Mrs. A. openly expressed some resistance to any further explanation. In the next statement we notice the counselor was a little defensive. Here, he could have made a structuring response indicating that this was to be a relationship of feelings and emotions as well as problems. This was done in the previous excerpt.[12] The counselor, however, kept the interview on a surface level by asking for more information.

Returns to Questions. In his next response the counselor attempted to reach the feelings behind the incident recited: "Her

[11]P. 229, C2.
[12]*Op. cit.*

being unable to speak like other children worried you." Apparently, the counselor went too far in his use of the word "worried." Mrs. A. was probably correcting the counselor in her answer that they were "disturbed, not exactly worried." But, even though it was an overstatement, the counselor's response at least turned the interview in the direction of basic feelings. He might have continued this in the next response. Instead, he asked for more facts. This only misled and misdirected the interview and carried it further away from the penetration of any deep feelings. The interview continued on this question-and-answer basis until the end of the excerpt. The counselor had had some previous training in the informational type of interview and, as will generally happen, when he lost touch with the feeling tone of Mrs. A.'s statements, he reverted to informational questioning. The interview continues:

C12: You are very honest with her.

P12: Yes, I always have been. (Long pause.)

C13: You didn't feel that R. got much help in the school she was in before.

P13: No, I don't think that she did. They had a lot of things to do but she took little part in them. She seemed never to be interested in anything else but her dolls at home and she always wanted to get back home to play with them. About the only thing that she likes besides playing with her dolls is when I read stories to her or something like that. Otherwise she, well, she didn't take any interest in school at all but they thought they would put her in the second grade here because they thought it would help her.

C14: Does she play with the dolls all the time or does she put the dolls away when you read to her?

P14: Oh, she does both sometimes but I, I think now she likes to hear the stories better and she does talk some now.

C15: She's talking more now than she did before.

P15: Yes, more than before.

C16: Do you know of anything that might account for that?

P16: Well, I suppose maybe she had to have some way of saying what she wanted and I guess maybe that's part of it.

C17: How did you feel when she didn't talk before, did it bother you?

P17: Well, no, it didn't bother me. I naturally tried to get her to speak as much as I could. Now she has a lot of signs that she can use.

C18: She seems to want to use signs rather than use words.

P18: Yes and then my sister didn't bother much about her so that was part of it too.

C19: Your sister wasn't really interested in her as you were.

P19: About as interested as I, but sometimes she couldn't make out her signs and she would come to me to find out what she meant.

C20: What do you think about the attention angle, do you think she does this to get attention?

P20: N-n-no, I don't think so. Maybe she did it some but I don't think so. I suppose maybe until she was about four or so I didn't pay much attention and then some of my friends started commenting about her not speaking very well and that made me conscious of it and I suppose I began to sort of want to force her to speak. I would always talk with her much more and sometimes I think this may have had more to do with her difficulties than I realized at the time.

C21: You feel your focusing on it at that time may have caused some of her difficulty.

P21: Well, I don't know that, that's just one of the things that occurred to me.

C22: Well, I think that's quite significant and that's a worthwhile observation on your part and that's really the sort of thing we hoped would come out of our talk. You see, if there's no physical cause here then the problem must be psychological and so we naturally are trying to find out what the difficulty is and what's the cause of it.

P22: Well, you know, she knows a lot of words, that is she understands a lot of words but she just doesn't want to speak or at least try very hard.

C23: How do you explain that?

P23: Well, I can tell that she understands and I make her say the word or repeat the word to me although she doesn't say it very plainly.

C24: You've really tried to help her quite a bit, sort of forcing her to use words that you know she knows and things like that? (Throughout this the counselor had the feeling that Mrs. A. was somewhat confused at the discussion and did not quite know what to make of the interview thus far.)

Questions Produce Blocking. Instead of giving positive recognition to Mrs. A.'s honesty with the child, the counselor continued his conversational manner in his first response to Mrs. A.'s previous statement. The counselor again tried to put the interview on a deeper level and apparently made a stab in the dark (C13) hoping perhaps to get some response from Mrs. A. While Mrs. A.'s next statement was primarily factual, she did express the positive factor of a change in R. The counselor unfortunately missed this. This series of staccato questions and answers was obviously getting nowhere.

Counselor Overenthusiasm. In his response to Mrs. A.'s statement in C21, the counselor accurately recognized, for the first time, Mrs. A.'s attitude. Significantly, this produced a further positive affirmation by Mrs. A. This positive turn seemed to take the counselor off balance. He got suddenly enthusiastic and even persuasive. Apparently he was so relieved at this quick positive turn that his enthusiasm escaped him before he could control it. Unfortunately, Mrs. A. reverted to the factual level and the counselor was again thrown back into his informational questioning. Had the counselor responded to her statement with even a neutrally accepting response like, "She doesn't really use the words she knows," he probably would have obtained much more information than he received from his direct question. But, to the counselor's dismay, as his note indicates, after this question, the interview was back again in the confused state where Mrs. A. was staring blankly at the counselor.

Children More Openly Resistant. Resistance of this sort is often less open with adults than with children. Children generally do not feel bound by any unnecessary politeness. Consequently, when they disagree with a counselor's response, they are apt to state their resistance very abruptly. We notice this childlike characteristic can still be seen in 16-year-old Edna (R). Adults, however, may feel constrained to be more proper. Their negation and resistance may not be so apparent until we examine the content of their response. When adults say, "Perhaps you are right," or "It may be," or even, "I will think over what you say," or, "We'll try it out," they do not always mean this. These may be polite phrases to cover over their resistance and disagreement. If we study their later interview statements, or observe their actions after the interview is over, we often find evidence of this resistance and negation. Sometimes such people may begin the next interview with a statement like, "We tried what you said and it didn't work," or, "I thought over what you told me but I don't believe it applies to me." Out of politeness, they waited until the next interview to express this disagreement openly. Children and even adolescents will not usually do this. For this reason, resistance and negation are often more apparent in child or adolescent interviews.

SOME ALTERNATE RESPONSES

By his directing and questioning manner the counselor produced this resistance as well as kept the interview on a superficial conversational level. Consequently, the person did not even begin to make any penetrating analysis of herself or her problems. Contrasting this with excerpts of similar length where the counselor's responses reached underlying emotional tones, we can see how much deeper and more intense the person's self-evaluation was. Here, the interview was not reaching any depth because the counselor was determining the content by questions which had little relationship to the feelings or motivations of Mrs. A. For example, instead of the response, "What's your husband's attitude? Is he at all concerned about R.?" —which had nothing to do with the previous statement—it would be interesting to know what might have happened if the counselor had responded to her general feeling of disturbance and confusion about the child and about her own illness. He might have said,

Your own illness and trying to do everything you could for the child and not being able to help her, made it very difficult for you.

This would have permitted Mrs. A. to go into her feeling of confusion and discouragement over the child, which also was flooding over into her general discouragement. This might possibly have uncovered a state of conflict between Mrs. A. and her husband which could have been a significant factor in the child's difficulties.

Unfortunately, we cannot know this because the counselor's unconnected and somewhat prying question about her husband led the woman to a superficial discussion of her husband's attitude. Even here, had the counselor been sensitive to the veiled feeling of resentment because the husband was not taking more interest, some release on the part of Mrs. A. might have taken place. The counselor might have said, for example,

Until lately, your husband really didn't give the child any time and only took care of his physical needs.

This would have given Mrs. A. an opportunity to express her possible resistance and objection to the husband's attitude. Instead, by the end of this excerpt, neither the counselor nor Mrs. A. quite knew what the point of the interview was, thus far.

SELF–CONCENTRATION

A major aspect of good counseling skill, therefore, is the way it keeps a person concentrated on his own self-perception. He is focused on himself, but in a way that is unemotional and entirely different from a withdrawn or daydream kind of self-concentration. In the counseling relationship, this self-evaluation is objectified. It becomes like an unfolding panorama of varying views of the same object. Each different attitude and incident can be looked at over and over again as a person talks and his feelings and insights are penetrated and reflected by the counselor. With each new insight, there is an increase in detailed understanding and depth of self-perception. The counselor's response to a basic attitude or feeling allows a person to see it clearly and reasonably and yet does not disturb or interrupt his deep penetration of himself. Rather, the counselor's response heightens a person's attention on the analysis and synthesis of his problems.

Interrupts Concentration.   But, if the counselor asks questions, argues, rebukes, or advises, he is substituting a different perception, like throwing a different slide on a screen. The counselor now becomes a *person,* advising, questioning, or reprimanding. In this way, his own personality is projected into the interview and this interrupts the concentration of the one coming for help. The counselor's interjection of himself into the flow of the interview forces the person to make an abrupt change in his concentration on his own problems. He now has to turn his attention to what the counselor is advising. He must then analyze what is said, agree or disagree with it. This process, in a sense, splits him across two worlds of perception: his own which he feels intensely and is trying to get understood and accepted by the counselor; and the counselor's perception, judgment, advice, or direction, which must be analyzed, digested and either accepted or rejected. This would seem to be almost like the experience of trying to look at two slides at the same time. We can imagine, for example, the disturbance that would result if, when a person is concentrated on one slide and just beginning to fathom its details, the projector were suddenly to show another slide. Even though the slides were different views of the same landscape, it would be very disturbing to be forced to switch rapidly back and forth from an absorption in the details of one to a quick analysis of the other.

In a somewhat similar way, questions or responses which direct attention to the counselor project themselves into a person's free-flowing release and block a person's further penetration of his own problems. The degree to which the person is allowed, then, unencumbered by the counselor, to penetrate deeper and deeper into his own hidden motives and confused reasons for acting the way he does, is, consequently, one of the important factors in the solving of personal problems.

This might also give us a clue to why a person is often irritated and made resistant by counselor responses which do not reach his basic feelings or attitudes. He may sense that, instead of helping him, they are interruptions which actually impede the concentration necessary to see his problems clearly. He resists such distraction and shows it in his increased tension and irritability towards the counselor. Such counselor statements or questions may also create in the other person a feeling of rejection and of being misunderstood, a fear of ridicule, and the general state of threat. To this may be added a person's feeling that the counselor is making himself superior by such an approach. Some or all of these things could account for the disturbed and resisting reactions which are often evident whenever the counselor attempts, even in a small way, to take over or center the attention on himself.

CHAPTER XI

LATER COUNSELING PHASES

As the counseling process gains momentum, the superficial logic with which people explain their actions to themselves and others and the feelings associated with these actions are not, in themselves, too important. A more important thing is to enable these people to understand the basic motives or life-patterns which consistently motivate their actions in any particular situation or relationship. It is usually because of these fundamental factors that they are unhappy and in conflict. The initial explanations they give, and the emotions they talk about, are the means by which they get to know themselves better as they think these explanations and feelings through. This deepening self-understanding is the core from which the constructive results of the counseling process develop.

FIVE PHASES OF COUNSELING

Since each interview is different, there is no way of knowing exactly what kinds of statements will occur or in what order. There are no final clues to the path an interview will take. Fortunately, however, we have come to recognize certain general trends which are common to a large number of interviews. In this sense, the counseling process is not as haphazard as is sometimes thought. This observed consistency is a great aid to the improvement of counseling skill. While there will always be wide individual variations in the personal circumstances discussed, the general process of emotional clarification and growth in self-understanding is often suprisingly similar. For this reason, studying the counseling process in detailed interview excerpts and painstakingly practicing counselor responses to these excerpts will greatly improve counseling skill. The counselor will find these same general characteristics recurring many times in his own interviews. We have, therefore, included some of these in the present chapter. We have divided them into five general phases but these are not distinct stages since they fuse into one another as the counseling progresses.

I. PROBLEM-STATING

In the first phase, the problem-stating or unfolding stage of the counseling process, the person is negative towards himself and his problems. These negations must be drained off before he can look at the basic values and goals behind his negations. For this reason this is also sometimes called the "release" or "ventilating" stage. The early interviews may consist entirely of negative statements or they may include some examination of basic values, depending on how deeply in conflict the person is or how free he feels to talk with the counselor. This negation aspect is often synonymous with self-deception. The superficial explanations these people have been giving themselves do not ordinarily come from real self-knowledge. They are usually artificial and unreal. In this conflict state, the person is unhappy because he is not adequately reaching reality. The other side of this conflict is a positive urge to reality, happiness, and achievement. It is this urge which brought him to the counselor and which the counselor's skill must preserve and further.

II. ANALYSIS

As the person talks about his hostilities, conflicts, and confusions, he begins to be loosened from his rigid state of negation. The counselor's warm, calm, impersonal restatement of the person's basic feelings has a freeing value. Once he can look at these feelings objectively, as the counselor reflects them, they become something outside himself that he can analyze and think about less emotionally. When such evaluation is not apparent in the interview itself, it often occurs between interviews. The interview has brought many things to the person's conscious awareness which he did not see before and, at the same time, has drained off some of his negative emotions. Consequently, when he leaves the interview, he can look at these previously hidden values and motives in a more positive light. This more positive self-examination phase is the *analysis* stage.[1]

---

[1]This use of the word "analysis" may suggest to some the restricted meaning it has in psychoanalysis. We mean it to be understood in its common usage.

III. SYNTHESIS

As he pursues this analyzing process over a period of time, he gets a more integrated view of many factors that underlie his conflicts. It is out of this second contemplation of his more fundamental personal values that the deep, insightful understanding of himself comes about. Gradually, as he gets these basic purposes and values out, he sees how they are related to the past and present issues and how they form clues to reasonable goals that he has not been reaching. Through the projecting skill of the counselor, he can actually think about himself in a way which his conflicting emotions had previously prevented. Seeing his problems more clearly, he can reason about them instead of being so emotional and fixed in his reactions. He begins then to relate his problems and acquire from his past and present state an integrated understanding of how they came about. This is the *synthesis* stage.

IV. PLANNING AND V. RE-EVALUATION

As the first phase—the negative phase—fuses into the statement of positive goals and values and deeper self-understanding, so these second and third phases flow over into the planning of more adequate solutions. This fourth phase is, then, inter-related with the fifth, where a person re-evaluates, sometimes with some emotion, the experiences which occurred when these new solutions were acted on. These are *planning* and *re-evaluation* stages.

Consequently, while none of these phases is distinct, there is a greater emphasis on negative emotion, release statements at first, but towards the end, the emphasis is on reasoned evaluation, planning, and finally, action. What seems to bring an end to the interview series is that a person's positive will no longer needs to be directed towards clarifying his negative emotions or even to reasoning about problems or planning solutions. He is now actually flowing into reality and gaining increased satisfaction from reasonable adjustment and achievement there. He has reached a positive state which people sometimes express by saying, "I don't see any more problems right now that I need to work out." This may, of course, not be a person's deepest level, but it is as deep as he wishes to go at that time.

SOME COMMON ATTITUDES AND FEELINGS

Negative Attitudes. People bring out many feelings and attitudes as they think out their problems in an interview. To all these, the counselor must learn to respond sensitively and accurately.[2] In opening interviews, as we have seen, expressions of "feeling confused" often occur. In this state, the person does not clearly know what is wrong and sees no way out. Statements of fear and insecurity generally accompany this state. Hostility attitudes are common. A person may be angry with himself, other people, or situations which in some way are connected with his conflict state. There will also be expressions of unhappiness. These may be associated with urges to escape. People may also feel that others, upon whom they depend for love and acceptance, are not responding. They may express feeling rejected. Often there will be guilt and self-criticism for acting in unreasonable and unsatisfactory ways. Statements containing these kinds of feelings can be found in most early interviews as people struggle through the fog and disorder which are characteristic of personal problems. The counselor should reflect them precisely without either lessening or exaggerating their tone.

Positive Tones. Somewhere in the interview process, however, as the counselor's responses penetrate and unfold these feelings of confusion, hostility, rejection, and the like, some positive statement of needs, such as love, acceptance, achievement, security, peace, and happiness, will begin to appear. A person may express unfulfilled or partially fulfilled goals. After dwelling on his difficulties, he may see a brighter side and give himself credit for this more positive pic-

---

[2]The reader may wish to go again over the excerpts in Part Two to review how, in the early stages of counseling, these various conflicting emotions are expressed. He may want especially to study the way the counselor responded.

The following attitude classification of Reid and Snyder may also prove helpful:

Lack of Confidence	Worry	Ambition	Certainty
Insecurity	Loneliness	Antagonism	Escape
Self-defense	Affection	Longing	Skepticism
Guilt*	Confidence	Self-pity	Envy
Obligation	Joyful	Surprise	Humor
Doubt	Hopeful	Interest	Not Classifiable

*An example of the synonyms classified together under a single heading, ("Guilt") would be: guilt, self-accusation, apology, apologetic, self-blame, self-reproach, shame, ashamed, self-disapproval, self-criticism. Dorothy K. Reid and William U. Snyder: "Experiment on 'Recognition of Feeling' in Non-Directive Psychotherapy," *Journal of Clinical Psychology*, Vol. III, No. 2, 128–135, April, 1947.

ture. He may recite certain achievements he has already reached, some relationships where he is loved or accepted, and some things in which he does find real security.

One indication of the seriousness of the person's problems is the absence of these positive expressions. When positive attitudes come out towards the middle of the first interview, generally the person's situation is not too serious. The interview series will not be of long duration since such problems are usually not deep. But, if the early interviews are primarily negative, it seems to indicate that the problems are serious and one may expect a much longer interview process.

Since it is generally characteristic of counseling, this process from negative emotion to positive emotion and insight statements can be a help to the beginning counselor. Even in the first interview there are generally some statements of self-worth. A person will express some confidence that he could do some of the things in which he has been failing. There is, also, usually some evidence of hope and a desire to be different. There may be some self-acceptance and a recognition of qualities that he has not really developed. This may bring an urge for greater achievement. The counselor may miss these because, at first, they may be surrounded by negative attitudes. Later in the interview, they may gradually become separate so that they are made in distinct statements. By the end of the same interview, there may be a number of positive emotion and insight statements that do not contain any negative emotion.

Respond to Both Positive and Negative Tones. Without in any way neglecting or minimizing the predominant negative tones, the counselor's responses should also reflect these positive attitudes. This is particularly important in the early stages when a person is apt to be discouraged and depressed. The counselor's recognition and clarification of these small positive statements are the toe-holds that enable a person to continue the struggle to reach insightful self-understanding. Small successes and achievements often become more significant when seen at the end of the counseling process, than we might have thought when they were first stated. The girl who is extremely insecure and distrustful of her own judgments, for example, expressed some slight positive security and enthusiasm that perhaps she could pick her own clothes (Y).[3] In an interview or so,

---

[3]Discussed also on p. 168.

this enabled her to wear a hat that her mother, who was excessively critical of her, had said did not suit her. As we saw, by the next interview she reported that she wore the hat, that it suited her, and that other people liked it on her. These are very small steps indeed, yet, as we trace them, we notice that the positive attitude—that she could pick her own clothes—ends in the achievement of being able to wear a hat of her own choosing and security in that choice. In this, she has made a small but significant movement towards self-esteem and confidence in her personal judgments. This brings, among other things, a later independence from her companions' excessive domination of her. Had these first expressions of positive attitudes been missed, they might not have been productive of her later self-confidence and achievement.

Fuse Together. In the actual interview, these negative and positive phases are not always clearly distinguished. This is one reason why an interview demands so much of the counselor's concentrated attention. A person's statement may contain some negative aspects, some values, or even, sometimes, the relation of these values to fundamental life goals and new solutions. Counseling is facilitated by the degree to which the counselor catches and projects these factors. The most progress seems to result when the counselor is able to reflect all these varying aspects. To do this, in the rapid flow of the interview itself, demands a highly sensitive and alert skill. We see this illustrated in this excerpt from a later interview with a young man we have previously quoted (V):

P: There's something that's been bothering me that I'd like to talk about. It's rather weak on my part to have it bother me—nevertheless it does though. There's this queer fact of a kind of feeling of isolation from everybody else, and that seems to bother me—at times —not as much as it used to, but it still does. And—I don't know— at times, I feel as if I'm very stupid to entertain such ideas, but nevertheless the thing does come to me—and I thought I might bring it up. There's the thought that somehow feeling, maybe it's possible that I'm isolated from everyone else, and I'm—ah—possibly, just in another world all by myself, and that the rest of them just don't count. That thing—that thought used to terrify me awful when it first used to come to me, but now it doesn't bother me very much, and yet, I sorta —going around sorta acting with that thought in view. I don't really give in to it any more—because, I realize just naturally a person shouldn't get to have such a thought. I feel that God after all put everyone in this world and it seems as if He somehow put into everyone's nature the ability to feel natural and adjust himself, so I can't see why above all things I should have such a thought as that.— (Pause)—And especially when I have to adjust to some problem I've got to face or meet, when that thought comes to me at that time, that somehow I think that there isn't anyone else and there's just no world or anything, that thought just seems to disgust me to think that I even will think about it at times. And I don't know, one thing about that idea, when it comes to me at times, I realize there's no basis for such a thought like that. But since it does get me at times, I thought I might bring it up. (Pause) I have the thought that—I remember when I was younger—I think it was somewhere when I was about five or eight years old, I—used to get the queer thought that the rest of the world was catering to me.—That I was someone of great importance. It never used to worry me, but I kinda took it as being natural.—So that this idea isn't altogether new to me—I mean as far as seeing I'm a little something different from the rest of the group— sorta realizing I'm different from the rest of the group. It has come before. (Pause)

Before reading the counselor's response made in an actual interview, the reader might go over this excerpt for both the negative and positive tones. In this complex statement of past confusion and discouragement, one might easily miss, for example, the constructive significance of the short phrases, "Now, it doesn't bother me very much" and "I don't really give in to it anymore." He might also miss the urge to face these past isolation tendencies, which seem to be the person's main motive for bringing them up now. Unless the counselor is alert, he may be confused by this rapid flow of words and give more weight to the problem than the person now feels. The counselor's response, without being too long, must balance these self-rejecting and self-accepting factors.

The reader may now wish to compare his response with the following one which was immediately given by the counselor:

C: You feel that somewhere in childhood, five or so, you have always had that thought that the whole world to some degree catered to you, and now as you look at it in your own judgment, you see that it's really a very foolish thought, and you really feel that the way to solve it is to get out and be with others, and then it seems ridiculous.

The counselor's "the way to solve it is to get out and be with others" is not an overstatement in this case, since he is drawing from what the person said in his previous statement. It might, however, just as well have been omitted.

Problem Stating. Accompanying these negative and positive attitudes, there is, as we know, the statement of problems. We would expect this, since the person who comes for counseling naturally feels the responsibility of explaining his difficulties. It is significant to note, however, that the problem-stating content is generally in proportion to the counselor's skill. Many people have many more problems to express than they are given an opportunity for, in most unskilled relationships. The tendency of untrained people is to take over and give advice. Unless the counselor is consciously self-restrained, the person does not have a chance to express all the problems he intended. Usually, because of the insecurity a person feels when he comes to the opening interview, he does not quickly go into the deepest expression of his difficulties. Rather, he cautiously begins with more superficial and less serious problems.[4] A person at first is hesitant and careful. Consequently, problems stated first in the opening interview are often not the most significant. A person is not sure of the counselor and is not going to commit himself too freely. But, if the counselor is skillful, the person grows rapidly secure and feels increasingly free to express his difficulties as the interview progresses.

Counselor Misstatement. The insecurity of a person coming for help is often so great that even routine statements of the counselor are enough to disturb and threaten him. We see this happening in the following excerpt from a beginning interview. A naval ensign (S)[5] was accompanied to the first interview by a fellow officer who knew the counselor. His fiancee, a nurse who was functioning as part of a counseling research project, had previously talked over the nature of the research with him. She felt that a number of personal problems were seriously affecting their relationship. The ensign is discussing at this time his need for a religion. Actually, he had begun taking instructions in the Catholic religion sometime before, from a Navy Chaplain, but had dropped them because he felt he could not live up to the duties and obligations of Catholicism. This excerpt

4See pp. 85–87.
5Designated by symbol (S).

is taken from the early part of the interview; the ensign has been talking about his interest in religion (S):

C1: Would you care to speak of the reasons why you feel religion would be of value to you?

P2: Well, one thing, I guess I'll be taking it up on my own accord. I always thought about religion, but never went in for it before. I always felt very strongly towards it, but never had a chance to develop it. I mean I never went in for it, but when I was in combat I felt the need of it and now I'll have plenty of time to study.

C2: Yes, while your background has not been any too religious even though you thought about things religious, it was the combat experience that really brought you a real religious need.

P3: Yes, I believe it was. (Pause)

F: (Fellow Officer) He always thought about it before.

P3: Yes, I always thought about it, but never felt I needed any help. Felt I could get along by myself. As a child I would go to church sometimes.

C3: That is, as a child you did go to church.[6] (Long pause)

C3: Would you care to speak a little more of yourself?

P4: It would be a little embarrassing right now.

F: Maybe I should have waited outside.

C4: Suit yourself. I mean, don't feel that you have to speak of anything you don't want to. I was just more or less proposing a general topic of discussion rather than any particular question.

P5: You mean something of my illness or something.

C5: Well, I don't know anything of that. You can speak of that if you wish. I was thinking more in terms of the needs that you feel you have. That is, you speak of feeling more or less that you could get along without religion up until more recently, and it has been your combat experience that has made you feel the need of something more, and I was sort of clarifying that change that you spoke of as having taken place in yourself.

P6: Perhaps being away from home so much—no one to see me—I get rather lonesome at times, and then I've known a lot of boys that have gone to church. Of course, I didn't go to church when I went overseas. We seldom had church on the ships I was on. I don't know—religion seems to make things a little closer to me, seems to make me feel more relaxed. I have often felt the need. I think it is something I've missed.

C6: Yes, you think that prayer and the realization of a sort of relaxing

---

[6]This is a poor response and may account for some of the resistance.

influence that it has—all those things—and especially your experiences abroad seem to build up to a real need for religion.

Skilled Recovery. The relationship seemed to be beginning smoothly enough until (P4) the ensign became threatened and embarrassed by what appeared to be a routine question of the counselor. His friend, knowing what was behind the ensign's reaction, was also embarrassed and felt out of place. The counselor, aware now that he had unwittingly got into something deep, relaxed the situation by responding to the person's resistance and indicating that he was simply proposing a general topic. Not only the words, but also the counselor's quiet, sincere, relaxed tone were important here. Any defensiveness in a situation like this would only have produced more defense from the other person.[7] The ensign then stated the source of his embarrassment—referring to his earlier battle fatigue for which he had been temporarily hospitalized. While—as it was later explained—this had only kept him out of combat for a short time, he was obviously still self-conscious and sensitive about it. The counselor's response put the interview back on a solid basis. The ensign was sufficiently at ease to respond to the original statement concerning his need of religion.

This quick exchange is filled with subtle feelings. We see a routine response completely misinterpreted. The counselor was intending simply to structure the relationship as one where the person could talk freely about himself. But this met with resistance which might have led to open hostility and anger, had not the counselor handled it so easily and sincerely. This illustrates the degree to which problem-stating must be left to the person himself and not forced on him. In this case, the counselor did not know at this time of the ensign's previous experience. But, even if he had, we can see it would have been unwise for him to suggest it until the ensign had himself mentioned it.

Insight Readiness. Generally, a person must bring up personal material before the counselor can respond to it without creating resistance. The counselor's probing usually makes him resist further. The counselor must also be careful not to put overtones into his responses which suggest further information he may have, but which the person has not revealed in the interview. Most people seem to

[7] P. 171.

be threatened by the counselor's uncovering material which they are not, at that moment, ready to face or discuss. Left to themselves, though, these people will usually bring up these problems. They will bring them up, however, at a time when they are psychologically ready and willing to face them. Since it depends on the degree of a person's positive will, he himself knows when this is. In the free, relaxed, unthreatening atmosphere of the interview, he can talk sincerely and objectively about himself. He is then apt to be far more critical and demanding of himself than any adviser could be. Yet these demands will be more constructive and significant and produce more adequate changes than "just being told what to do."[8]

This is one of the reasons why guidance should be kept distinct from counseling. In counseling, we assume the person has adequate information from other instructional and informational relationships. But, even where the counselor feels this may not be so, it seems better to wait for the person to make some indication of this and then propose the possibility of providing further information in another relationship. This opportunity almost always comes if the counselor is skillfully patient. The person generally will state that he probably does not know enough about a certain point to make an adequate judgment. When people do not say this, they usually *know* what they should do, otherwise they would not be in such conflict. But to push this at them before they are emotionally ready to face it, only defeats the purpose of counseling.

FORKING RESPONSES

A person may begin an interview with one solution in mind. But, as he talks, other factors come out. He may state what his difficulties are and what information he needs. But if this were the real solution, there would likely be no need for him to come for counseling. Gradually, he realizes he has been working on this solution for some time and it has not proved successful. He begins to suspect that the answers are elsewhere. The counselor must be alert to this transition, by which a person begins to face a broadening understanding of himself. It often is revealed in an expression like, "Well, of course, there are other things too that probably enter in here." As a person mentions other factors, the counselor's response should reflect the per-

[8]See pp. 185–186.

son's movement away from a focus on one particular kind of problem or solution. So, the counselor may respond,

It isn't just this one thing—there are other factors that make up the total picture of your problems.

This helps the person to know he can talk about these other aspects if he wishes. We call this a "forking" response because it does not channel the person in the direction of any one problem but lets him take up whatever he considers important at that moment. In a single statement, a student may say that he thinks the reasons for his class failure are due to a particular professor, difficulties at home, and irritations that upset him in a part-time job. The counselor cannot tell which of these is really significant. He should respond equally to all three and let the person decide which he will discuss further. He might respond,

It seems to you that your difficulties come from the professor, and then from your home, and also from your work.

The dawning realization that other factors enter into a problem generally takes place in the beginning interviews. For a person to understand that he can talk about all these different factors seems to aid in the speed and thoroughness with which he thinks through all his problems and their inter-relationships. As long as the person feels that the interview is limited to a particular kind of discussion, he is not free to bring up all his problems. If he feels, for example, that he must talk exclusively about study problems to the school counselor, or physical symptoms to the nurse or doctor, or religious questions to the priest or nun, he is often not able, in an interview with any one of these persons, to bring in all the factors which affect him. The things he might say to a doctor would be different, for example, from what he might say to a priest. But all these factors really go together as a unit series of reactions to make one picture of himself. A person is often not able to solve his religious difficulties unless he is also free to state the way in which they affect him in his general activities. On the other hand, when he goes to the doctor he needs understanding and appreciation of his spiritual values, since they can play a significant part in his physical health and general psychological well-being. Consequently, whatever his position, the counselor's response must enable a person to feel he can explore all the aspects of his problems, and that he is not limited to one particular area of examination and evaluation.

Illustration. We see this illustrated in the following excerpt which is a continuation from the first interview with the naval ensign (S):

C7: Would you care to explain a little more your feelings about religion being helpful?

P8: I don't know just what you mean—feelings about religion being helpful. You mean in those fears?

C8: Yes; that is, your seeing religion as a possible help for those disturbances.

P9: Well, I went through so much, it is kinda hard to talk about it.

C9: You find it kinda hard to talk about it?

P10: Yes, it is kinda hard (Pause). But I do feel that religion could help me (Pause). Those boys who had it seemed to get along a lot better. You could see it helped them. What little I've gotten so far has helped me too.

C10: You pretty definitely are convinced of the value of religion to you in your own difficulty, and you have actually seen it work in others. It has brought you a certain sense of value just in what you have so far (Pause). Oftentimes, if you feel free to talk it can be quite helpful. I'd like you to feel free to talk about yourself, if you wish (Pause). You seem to feel convinced that religion will offer a means of solution.

P11: Yes, I really do.

C11: Yes, I think it is good to feel very free in a relationship of this sort, and I think the insight you do have as to religion offering a real solution is very worthwhile, but I think too, it is very good that you can feel free to talk about yourself.

P12: I have an insight into my problems; I know what can be done and all that. I think religion can be of real help to me. I think I have always felt that to a certain extent, and I want to know more about it.

C12: It is fairly clear that the religious interest has always been there. It is just that these problems have brought it clearcut before your mind, even though it was always there.

P13: I believe that is right (Pause). I guess it comes when you are away from home, and then I felt that was when the religion would help me. I wish I could have had this before I went across. It would have helped.

Having previously stepped unwittingly into deep water, the counselor is more cautious. We notice that his carefully worded question is also a slight "structuring" statement, since it includes the possibility of the ensign expressing his feelings as well as his reason for needing religion. But, in P8, we notice that the ensign, still sensitive about his combat fatigue "illness," interpreted the counselor's question as a probing one and again shows slight resistance. The counselor in C8 includes the idea that he might want to discuss how religion and these disturbances tie up. We see the forking point in the counselor's response. As we look at it now, we can say that this forking response might better have been avoided here since it only promoted more resistance.

The ensign was still too insecure to accept this response. The counselor in C9 responded directly to his feeling of resistance and this relaxed him and he continued with his discussion. C10 was the first instance where the counselor was clearly attempting to establish the relationship as a counseling one. He encouraged the person to talk freely about himself. Until now, if we examine the counselor's previous inquiry statements, he had always tied it up with the ensign's need for religion. This response, as we see, was a little broader.

Having made that structuring statement, however, he then responded to P10. This is an interesting counselor response. We saw previously how he was quickly alerted to the ensign's deeper problems when his routine inquiry brought so strong a reaction. Then, when he responded to the ensign's question about his fears, he was resisted again. Now, clearly aware that the ensign needs to talk about these personal problems, whatever they are, or he would not keep bringing them up, the counselor sandwiches a structuring statement in between a content response.

In these circumstances the value of this approach allows a threatened person, such as the ensign, to take either side of that response. If he feels any further need to talk about his personal problems, the counselor has now made it clear that this relationship will accept and understand that.

In C11, the counselor further clarified the double relationship that may be possible with him. We notice that although P12 begins with resistance, by P13 the ensign has hit a little deeper level in his explanation of his need of religion. The interview continues:

C13: If you could have had the religious point of view, it would have been quite helpful for you before.

P14: Yes, I am quite sure it would have. All these things which I should have known, I was never instructed that way. I just missed that, and then before that I never felt the need.

C14: Those were things you did not feel the need of before, and you regret you didn't have them before.

P15: I regretted it very much, but I do not feel too deeply responsible because those things should have been brought before me when I was growing up.

C15: You feel some responsibility, but also a feeling that you did not have those things when you should have had them (Pause).

P16: This I don't doubt now—that through religion I have a different outlook on life—that is not entirely the solution. If it were entirely the solution I would have had a better attitude immediately.

C16: It is very clear that, while it has been helpful to have this new understanding, it hasn't solved everything.

P17: No, it hasn't solved everything. It is very clear in my mind that something in my life is missing.

C17: There is something there that is not the way you want it.

P18: That is right. I have seen a great deal of this type of thing in the Navy. I have seen what it can do to people, and I guess I have a fear of its happening to me.

C18: The associations that you have had have built up another fear.

P19: Yes, the associations have bothered me greatly.

C19: You seem to feel that what has happened to others may take place in you.

P20: Yes, and it is very difficult to take those thoughts out and to relieve some of the pressures, and, as I said before, religion may help me not only in that, but to make a better life, to give me a better outlook on life, to be of more good to society and to have a basic interest. I believe up to this time I have had nothing to believe.

C20: You want something to tie up to. You have never really had that before. You want religion as an aid to clear up some of those ideas, and you feel that it will give you some purpose in life and some value to what you do.

P21: That's right, and I have seen from a child what broken homes mean to people, how they disturb people, etc., and I have made up my mind that I will not have such a home. Having religion can be a help in this and in stabilizing the home.

C21: You are being very honest, and you see pretty deeply in your life the effects of a broken home and you don't want that to happen to your home. You are convinced that religion would be a real aid in stabilizing your own home.

P22: Yes, that is very true (Pause).

C22: There are a lot of motivations for religion not only in the immediate trouble you are having, but in giving you a purpose in life and in stabilizing your own home life.

Cautiously suggested through this excerpt were the personal confusions with which, in addition to religion, the ensign felt perhaps the counselor might be able to help him. These personal problems, though, are only hesitantly and vaguely stated.

We notice the care with which the counselor responded. He did not push but he let the ensign develop his own ideas slowly and easily. This enabled the officer to say frankly that he had disturbing thoughts; that he was sure something was missing in his life; that while the lack of religion was a great factor, there were other things missing, too. He felt that religion would give him a different outlook on life. He was convinced that the insecurity and unhappiness of many homes were due in no small way to the lack of religion.

Here we see the effects of the counselor's skillful handling. This demonstrates a situation that is very common. People in an emotional state seem unable to discuss anything without tension. They also invariably interpret in a personal way something that is said. Since the first stage of their emotional state is negativism, this interpretation will almost always show itself in resistance or open difference. They may soon become abrupt in their manner, insistent, and sometimes even offensive. Yet this really has nothing to do with the topic under discussion but actually is caused by their fundamental conflicts which, while not openly faced in the relationship, still prevent them from calmly discussing anything else.

But, since the counselor did not let the situation become a personal difference, the ensign can now make an open statement of his problems. The counselor in C16 makes a sharp forking response and the ensign accepts it. The counselor then makes a further forking response as the ensign hesitantly but definitely begins to go more deeply into his personal feelings.

Realizing now that he is on firmer ground, the counselor continues to respond clearly and exactly to the ensign's conflicts. While this part of the interview continues around the ensign's need for religion, it is now on a more personal level.

By the beginning of the next interview, however, the ensign, who has come alone this time, has accepted a definite counseling relationship. Interestingly, there is an immediate broadening out of insights. They are no longer centered on the need for religion but are directly related to his state of confusion, especially about his anger and irritation towards his fiancee and his reading of popular psychology books which only added to his "mixed-up" feelings.

Interview II. (Person comes alone.):

P29: I got here this afternoon without much trouble.

C29: That's fine.

P30: It wasn't really difficult at all—I was off duty at 2:20.

C30: You found you could make it all right.

P31: Yes (Pause). Well, I really don't know how to tell you how I'm getting along. I don't know whether there is much change or not. I have been reading some.

C31: I didn't hear what you said.

P32: I said I have been reading.

C32: Uh, huh . . . (Noise outside prevented the counselor from hearing distinctly.)

P33: I still have my fears, especially about our marrying—I have such resentment towards her. I don't manifest my anger to any degree except when I'm tired, but I still have it—I don't know why. I never have been able to find out exactly why from the beginning.

C33: You don't know whether things are better or not. Things seem a little better. The fears are still there about marrying this girl and your resentment.

P34: Sometimes I feel disgusted with everything. I mean, I've always felt that way at times—just more or less like I was in a rut. I don't understand it.

C34: You have always felt that disgust sometimes, but you notice it now particularly and you don't just know what it is.

P35: That's true. And I don't know exactly what your point of view on myself is. I don't want to feel that I'm imposing on you—I just don't know what your reaction was—the idea of my coming here like this.

C35: You're not just sure what your role would be in relation to me. You're not just sure what you should talk about.

P36: Yes, that's true. Somebody gave me a book on psychology and I read it. But I believe that only made matters worse.

C36: You feel it didn't really help you to read that psychology book. You believe it just mixed you up more.

P37: Yes, I believe it just mixed me up a little more.

Responses Aid Independence. The reader might wish to compare the counselor's handling of the opening conversation with that on pages 238 and 239. Here, we notice, the responsibility is always left with the ensign. The counselor asks no conversational questions. This interview begins on an interesting forking situation. The ensign first mentions his reading. Because there was some noise, the counselor missed some of the first statements. The counselor's statement that he did not hear was safer than to have guessed at a response. The ensign goes immediately into a more detailed discussion of his personal problems. Then, he expresses his insecurity about talking of these. He wants to talk about them and feels he can in this relationship but he still needs some reassurance.

The counselor does not give that reassurance, however, but clearly responds to his insecurity. Then, when that is accepted, the counselor responds to the insight in P36 and the interview is off on a deeper level. Such a response is more effective than the sought for reassurance. As he explains later, one of the ensign's problems is his dependency on others and his tendency to be excessively affected by what they say. In fact, he is hostile and resistant to a number of people including his fiancee because he wants to be able to work things out himself. Had the counselor given reassurance, the interview might have started on a dependency relationship, which probably would have made the ensign eventually oppose the counselor as he did these other people. This verifies St. Thomas's comment about people fearing to be dependent on others. As we shall see, the counselor later has an opportunity to make a forking statement which sets up a religious instruction as well as a counseling relationship for the ensign. As we know, he had previously begun to take instructions elsewhere but did not continue them. Possibly this same thing might have happened here had he not first been able to speak of and clarify these personal conflicts.[9]

[9]This raises the interesting question of the degree to which a state of unhappiness moves people to seek Catholicism, not simply out of a sense of duty towards God, but also as a source of personal happiness and security. One writer comments: "In the stories of some converts, we find that the sense of duty towards God is more apparent, while in others there is more consciousness of happiness accruing to the convert himself. We do not intend to stress or exaggerate this opposition. Catholic theology will never acknowledge a conversion as true, if the sense of duty towards God is entirely lacking; on the other hand, no convert expects to find only unhappiness, misery, or disappointment in the Church. Catholic morals have their principles in something between pure eudaimonism and the categorical imperative of duty, and we must have towards God a love which at the same time is a love of friendship and a utilitarian love in the highest sense. Therefore, to become a Catholic is at the same

WEIGHING BOTH SIDES

Another common situation occurs when a person brings out a series of factors and balances them on the two sides of the scale of his judgment. As he lines them up, he is not sure which one he should choose. It seems more effective for the counselor to make no attempt to weight the scale in one direction or the other but calmly to respond to both sides of the conflict. He may say,

You don't know what to do—which way to go

or

You don't know which side has the most value.

In this way, he keeps the conflict state in the exact proportion that the person feels it. The conflict will slowly be resolved in one direction as the person sees more clearly which is the more reasonable path for him.

Generally, if the counselor attempts to persuade him to one side, the person will become threatened and may defensively revert to the other side. Since these conflicts are about highly personal issues, the person almost always knows more about them than the counselor. But, since the person is often emotionally tense at this stage, his positive urge may not be too strong and he can quickly revert to his negativism.

Sometimes a person's judgment is weighed in the balance against the judgment of another whom he respects. This is especially common in children and adolescents where the growth in self-judgment

---

time a sacred duty towards God and a real happiness to the convert. Yet, in one's conscious thinking, one of these two may dominate and become more apparent. We have, then, two different, but not absolutely opposed, kinds of conversion. St. Paul, who after seeing Christ's glory only asked, 'Lord, what do You want me to do?' can be called an example of the first. The Dutch convert, A. J. D. van Oosten, who after his conversion wrote a brochure entitled 'The Joys of the Convert' may be called an example of the other.

"This new classification intersects the other we have already enumerated. Truth, sanctity, and beauty can be viewed as something to which it is a man's duty to conform, but they are at the same time something very good to a man. To someone like St. Augustine, who was acutely unhappy in his sins and who was really desiring sanctity, or to a man who is troubled with questions on the meaning of life, Catholic sanctity by grace and Catholic truth are a glorious answer to difficulties. On the other hand, Cardinal Newman's sermon on 'The Parting of Friends,' his last sermon as an Anglican, clearly indicates that the truth meant to him a very stern call of duty." C. F. Pauwels, O.P.: "Theological Problems of Conversion," *The Thomist*, Vol. XI, No. 4, October 1948, pp. 420–421. See also the statement of Bishop F. J. Sheen, Introduction, pp. 5–6.

is a new and often strange experience. The child's slow awareness that he may be right and the adult upon whom he has depended may be wrong, is something which he at first finds difficult to accept. In adult life, too, such conflicts often take place. The counselor will find it better to respond cautiously. In a counseling interview no attempt is made to weight the judgment—on the assumption that the person himself knows his responsibilities and obligations and will weigh them if he is allowed to do so calmly and reasonably with the aid of the counselor's skill.

In his first confused expression, a person may appear to be going against established authority or the rights of others. But, as the person's own reason is increasingly able to bring its light on all the factors in the situation, he will gradually see the reasonable necessity of authority and whatever other individual rights are involved. The reasonable norms on which ethical standards, regulations, and supervision are set up in any particular situation or institution will themselves be known and understood by any reasonable person. Consequently, if the person in the interview slowly becomes more reasonable, by learning to understand and control his emotions, he, too, can finally accept these regulations and restrictions. When further information or explanation appears necessary, especially if the matter is highly personal and the person is emotionally tense, it seems preferable, as we will discuss later, to set up a separate relationship before or after the counseling interview.[10]

Responsibility Difficult. The process by which the person struggles to face the responsibility of thinking out his problems and making independent decisions about them is often hard and laborious. The change is usually from an attitude of insecurity and defensiveness, and even the tendency to depend on other people's judgments, to a conviction that a person must solve these problems himself. This is no easy transition. The counselor's responses need to recognize and clarify this struggle. The responses should unfold the person's conflicting expressions of a desire to make independent judgments and act on his own and, at the same time, of the fear and insecurity which may have caused him to be defensive or to lean on others for decisions. By doing this, the counselor gives the person a genuine feeling of being understood and accepted.

[10]See p. 365.

But the counselor must be careful in his choice of words in these beginning states of responsibility. Since, at this stage, these people may be easily threatened, a counselor's overstatement of feelings can be harmful. Besides this, in those cases where a person's insecurity causes him to want to depend on others, he often seeks to lean on the counselor. This, we will see,[11] may result in open or subtle attempts to get the counselor to give advice or pass his opinion on some personal question. The counselor avoids this because he knows it will only encourage further dependency. He must, however, not be too quick or abrupt in turning the responsibility back on the person. If he is not on guard, the counselor may find himself feeling slightly threatened by the person's tendency to depend on him. This may cause his response to be sharp and even rejecting. Such abruptness can seriously hurt the developing relationship. The resultant resistance and emotional tension may only cause the person, either not to come back for a subsequent interview, or to be all the more determined to get the counselor to advise him and give him answers to his personal problems.

If the counselor is responsive to the struggle for independence and the difficulty a person feels in facing personal issues, the person will gradually grow more secure. Slowly he gains confidence that he can reach solutions which will be his own and at the same time be a better plan of life for him.

[11]Pp. 346–347.

CHAPTER XII

THE FINAL STAGES OF COUNSELING

Gradually, as a person pours forth incidents and problems, he begins to see relationships between them. Like the other positive attitudes, this insight into relationships is less common in the early interviews, although it may sometimes occur. In some instances, even after a comparatively short negative release, insights begin to appear before the end of the first interview. But, generally, when this takes place, as we have seen, the problems are not deep and are solved in that same interview or in a few subsequent interviews. This may also happen when there was a previous series of interviews.

INTEGRATING RESPONSES

Broadening Self-Awareness. Slowly the person begins to discard old and inadequate patterns of judgment and action for newer and more penetrating views of himself and his goals. The counselor must be alert to reproduce these shifting tones. Often, in these integrating stages, a person speaks at some length about himself, connecting and reorganizing a whole series of experiences. The counselor's responses should synthesize and coordinate these. Sometimes, the counselor must simplify and clarify extremely involved statements. These responses are particularly difficult. But it is these responses which most help the person acquire a greater self-understanding and move him towards more positive attitudes.

This progress may be almost imperceptible in the first interviews. Yet, this snail-like broadening of self-awareness finally brings to the person a wider and more reasonable understanding of his problems and a more adequate and all-inclusive kind of solution. We have seen this demonstrated elsewhere when we studied the relationship of insight and choice.[1]

[1] The reader may wish to study again the excerpts given in Chapters VII and VIII to see how the counselor's responses aided this process. The excerpts given there also demonstrate many of the things pointed out here.

This phase of relating problems usually proceeds from an examination of previous solutions. The person recognizes either the inadequacy of these solutions or, at least, that some further plans are needed. The more clearly a person can see himself in each response, the more rapid is his growth in self-understanding. In this way, insight is objective self-understanding which the person acquires through the counselor. But it is a self-understanding that is a true reflection of the person himself, and not the result of the counselor's diagnostic judgment. For this reason, it does not threaten the person and push him too rapidly towards insights which he is not yet ready to accept. As the person brings his attitudes to light and sees them clearly through the counselor's responses, he is able to accept them. In the light of this acceptance, he can plan new ways of acting. What we discussed with regard to information,[2] is also applicable to insights. Awarenesses which a person might have resisted in an interview or two before, had the counselor attempted to force them on him, he now absorbs more readily and integrates into his conduct when he faces them himself. Somehow, once a person has spoken of feelings and attitudes in an interview, he seems ready and able to examine them objectively and do something about them.

Exact Insight Reflection.   For this reason, as we said earlier, it seems that *the counselor's responses should not go beyond the feeling, attitude, or insight expressed.* If the counselor's statement includes something the person has not expressed, then resistance almost always follows. In a smooth-flowing interview this resistance may be slight and will dissolve with the next good response. But a number of such resistances coming together can seriously impede the counseling process. This can sometimes happen even in the later stages of counseling, particularly when the interview is positive and the counselor is over-anxious for more progress. Sometimes, too, the counselor, especially if he has been trained in psychological diagnosis, may find himself anticipating the person's conclusions. His statements may be diagnostically correct, yet the person is not ready for them and consequently may balk.

Illustration.   In the following smooth excerpt, continuing from the second interview with the ensign, there is only one slight overstatement of feeling. Yet we see the ensign buckle. It taxes the

[2]Pp. 253–254.

counselor's skill to get the interview back on an even keel. The counselor is responding to a previous statement (S):

C1: The thing that bothers you most and makes you feel irritated and angry inside is that feeling you often have of being too dependent on your fiancee. At other times, you don't feel that at all. There is, too, a kind of confusion—of things being up and down.

P2: And I try not to let the thing bother me. It doesn't bother me unless I am very tired now. Otherwise I go along and it doesn't bother me. Or this irritation that sometimes goes with it. And I just can't help wondering what may be the outcome after we are married.

C2: There are times, when you sort of control it and not let it bother you. But at other times you feel there is not much you can do.

P3: That's right. Well, I mean, I feel there's not much I can do. I mean, I think about it, but I don't feel like doing anything. I start wondering if there is anything I can do—I really don't know what you mean. How did you mean that?

C3: When this irritation at feeling you may be too dependent on her does come over you, you begin to wonder. It makes you wonder whether after marriage it will get worse or not.

P4: Yes—naturally at times it does bother me a great deal. (Pause)

C4: You feel quite conscious of that.

P5: Yes, I guess that's the thing that bothers me more than anything else, wondering just what might come of it. I remember I read an article one time, I think it was a psychiatrist or somebody writing in a magazine and it told about—ah—feelings like that and said if they went too far they could break up a marriage and destroy a person's love for another person. It seemed to say that there wasn't much you could do about it. I don't like to feel that our marriage can't be as normal as other people's. I think if two people have a lot in common and like each other's company and seem to get along well together, there's nothing too greatly wrong with their relationship and I think it could produce a happy marriage when you really love someone. It's hard to bring out. But that article keeps sticking in my mind. When you read something like that that seems to be so personal, it's hard to get it out of your mind.

C5: This feeling of being so dependent on her and yet being so irritated by it was—you became even more conscious of this when you read that article and the threat that if it went too far it might break up your marriage sticks in your mind now. You don't really feel that, and you feel there is something you can do about it even though the article acts as a threat over you.

P6: Yes, that's right, it still bothers me. (Pause)

We notice that the counselor's second response (C2) contains a double statement—a response to the man's positive feeling that he can control this reaction and, at the same time, a response to the negative side. When he reflects the negative aspect, however, the phrase, "You feel there is not much you can do" suggests a tone of hopelessness. But, if we examine carefully the man's previous statement, he does not express hopelessness but rather an insecurity about the outcome. He is "wondering what may be the outcome after we are married." In the man's next statement, he is trying to square his feeling with what the counselor has just said, "Well, I mean, I feel there is not much I can do."

Then, he realizes that it is not what he felt so he tries it again and says, "I think about it but I don't feel like doing anything." He makes another try, "I start wondering if there is anything I can do." Finally, he realizes that was not the feeling he had. He reverses himself and makes a confused, resistant statement, "I really don't know what you mean. How did you mean that?"

Here is an intriguing point. The initial acceptance in the phrase, "That's right" is due, apparently, to the general flow of the interview. The man has become so used to the smoothness with which the counselor's responses always fit his attitudes and feelings that he is expecting an easy, flowing response here, too. Then, as he begins to react to the response, he grows aware that somehow it is not what he felt. He tries to restate it so that it does fit, finds he cannot and ends questioning what the counselor meant. This kind of confused and resistant reaction often follows a counselor's overstatement or misinterpretation. The person may begin to agree, with a phrase like, "Yes, I see what you mean." Then, there will be a pause followed by a disagreement, often beginning with "but . . ." This second expression may contain either a series of conditions which change the response, an open difference with the counselor, or even a statement directly contradicting him.

Calm Restatement of Correct Feeling. What can the counselor do when such a thing happens? In this case, we notice the counselor recognizes his overstatement and the person's resistance. He calmly repeats the negative tone with a more exact feeling. It is not discouragement and hopelessness as in the earlier response, but wonderment: "It makes you wonder whether after marriage it will get worse or not."

With a slight hesitancy, the man accepts it. A second successful counselor response puts the interview back on its easy, flowing track. The ensign then goes on to explain how his insecurity on this point was increased by reading an article. This was in the back of his mind when he made his original statement (P2).

When the Statement Is Forgotten. Sometimes the counselor cannot remember the mistake he made. He is not always able to pick it up so precisely as this counselor did. If he cannot remember, it is better to say so:

I'm sorry I guess I missed that. Would you care to speak a little more about it—the way you really felt?

This accepts the person's reaction of not being understood and, at the same time, may allow the counselor another chance to examine what the basic attitude was. The counselor may say,

Perhaps I missed what you meant. It isn't too clear to me.

And the person may restate or simply continue the unfolding of his deeper feelings. In one of these ways, the person can accept the counselor's statement that he made a mistake and the interview is re-established on an understanding basis. Whenever the counselor finds himself mixed up, the best procedure seems to be to express his confusion to the person, and together they usually can work out the difficulty.

Danger of Defense. One danger in such situations is the spontaneous reaction the counselor may have to defend his response. If he is not on guard, he may find himself trying to persuade the person to accept his response. In the previous excerpt, the counselor might have made a statement like,

Well, you spoke about that irritation and dependency urge that just comes over you and in that sense you just feel sort of discouraged and hopeless, don't you?

This self-justification gets farther away from the real feeling; which was not discouragement, but "wondering" what might come after marriage. Such a counselor explanation would probably only produce resistance, which would begin to show itself both in the person's response and in the increased tension of his manner. But, even if the person accepted this, the counselor has put a feeling of discouragement into the situation when it had not actually been expressed by the person. The counselor, in directing him to feelings which his statements did not contain, is impeding the person's recognition of his real feelings and attitudes.

Complicated Insight Statements. As the interviews progress, and the person's insightful understanding of himself deepens, a broad panorama of past and present factors may be interwoven in a complicated way. The counselor's response is most effective when it sharply restates the related insights and new choices but distills out the person's complex recitation of circumstances. In this way, a person hears back a precise delineation of his new self-understanding. At this stage, when the person is putting together new and often very significant self-realizations, the counselor—in the few seconds allotted to him for a response—must be extremely alert and sensitive, to catch all the feelings and attitudes expressed.

Summarizing Response. When the person has expressed a comparatively long series of insights, some counselors see value in a summarizing response which ties these insights together, as in the counselor's fifth response in the previous excerpt (C5). There seems to be a definite value in such a counselor synthesis, even though these insights have been previously stated by the person. But the counselor must be careful that such responses do not become so long and involved that they impede the flow of the interview. Present research and understanding of this point indicates that it is better to keep counselor responses comparatively short—even at the risk of missing some insights and feelings. Responses that are too long and cumbersome may delay rather than further insights. Such summarizing responses are usually not made by beginning counselors. They demand a high degree of concentration and focused attention. When made by a skillful counselor, they seem to have definite value. If they are too long, however, they may slow the progress of the interview by distracting the person's attention and delaying his further penetration into himself.

PLANNING NEW SOLUTIONS

Somewhere in the interviews, the counselor will recognize the person's suggestion of new plans and solutions. These statements usually indicate the forming of a different life-pattern and will finally result in significant choices. They follow invariably upon a series of related insights. As these new plans are proposed, the counselor accepts and restates them.

Weighing Plans. Often, a person's statement will also contain some reasons or values that he sees in certain projects or actions. There is usually a weighing of various plans of action, and a period of indecision, about which to follow. The counselor, as in other kinds of indecision, makes no effort to throw any weight in one direction or the other, but carefully responds to the value that the person himself sees in the various actions he has in mind. In this kind of foresight and planning, the person himself knows his own life and environment better than anyone else. He knows, too, his capacities here and now to carry out particular actions. He is himself able to think out the best immediate choice, when the counselor's responses aid him to think objectively. The counselor can be most helpful in these highly significant stages of planning if he sincerely reflects the pro's and con's of the different paths which a person is proposing for himself.

NEW CHOICES

The planning of new solutions leads to new choices as the person begins to act on his plans. The person may try different plans and come back to evaluate the successes of each of them over a period of interviews. Gradually, he will form a conviction about which of the plans is the most fruitful and will best succeed. It is especially important, here, for him to have a relaxed and secure feeling that he can take his time and measure each new step carefully and calmly before and after he takes it. By now he knows that the purpose of counseling is to enable him to objectify and analyze the results of the different steps he is taking, and judge for himself the path that is best for him.

Positive Feelings and Attitudes. Usually these new choices are productive of enthusiasm and increased positive feelings of hope and courage, as well as of growing self-esteem and confidence. It is important that the counselor recognize both the successes reported as a result of new planning and the growing enthusiasm and positive emotions expressed with them. Just as looking at the bad side produced the conviction of wanting to change so, when changes have been made it is very helpful for a person to see their good effects. Looking at the success and greater happiness, security, and peace these changes bring, is important in fixing the person's conviction of the values of this new way of life. This also increases his enthusiasm and gives him the courage necessary to jump the hurdles that yet remain. "Nothing succeeds like success" is the old adage. This is illustrated in the rapid progress many make after a few successful choices. The thrill that comes to a person from being able to do even small things that he never thought he could, is a powerful stimulation to further development.

Illustration. The pleasure and satisfaction which people express in these stages should be mirrored to them, so that they can take a reasonable self-esteem from the image they see of themselves. The counselor's responses, therefore, while not exaggerating an optimistic tone or enthusiastic feeling, should accurately hold up the positive values and real achievements which the person's statements contain. The reader can study how the counselor does this in the following excerpt from the fourth interview with the ensign(S):

P1: Yes. (Pause) I can readily say—easily say—that things are much better than the first time I saw you, and I can say, too, that the talks with you have meant a great deal. I can see now that these talks have made the difference, because everything else has been the same.

C1: Fairly clear to you that the events seem to go together and it is the talks that have brought about so much help for you and such a change?

P2: Yes, because all of these things that I had on my mind that were whirling and whirling around that I told you on my first visit—mostly on the second visit—they don't bother me. There were so many of them that I don't remember what they were now. A great many of them have lifted and they have uncovered this original confusion about my fiancee and I believe as soon as I overcome that, I will be completely straightened up.

C2: It is definite that it has helped you a great deal to talk freely in this relationship. You hope now that it can bring about, too, the further clearing up of that one last thing and then things will be pretty well for you.

P3: Yes. (Pause) I don't know where they are going to send me. It may be to M——, and I really don't want to go clear down there. (Pause) However, I do have a week lay-over which is authorized to me and I am hoping I can get situated somewhere in the vicinity so that I might continue on with the talks and as soon as that is over I should be completely fixed up. I really hope that I can continue coming here. The way it stands now I presume I will be able to come once more this week. The way things have been coming along I have hopes that it will be through soon. (Pause)

C3: The likelihood now of your being sent away does interfere somewhat.

P4: Yes. (Pause)

C4: Pretty high hopes that most of these things will be cleared up now soon?

P5: Yes, it is a relief to know that you have—that you can turn to someone to talk to and it's a little disturbing to be suddenly taken away from these talks that we have been having which sort of put down those things inside of me. I feel that if I can get around here somewhere and I can continue talking with you that I will have a much better chance of getting everything completely straightened up.

C5: Pretty good statement of it,[3] isn't it, that because of such a quick removal from the talks here—you are a little fearful. If you could be given duty around close and the talks could continue, it would be much better.

P6: Yes, I think it would. (Pause) I don't believe there is too much, other than that, which has been bothering me lately. (Pause) Just seems to be narrowed down to a couple of things.

C6: Just a few things remain which bother you. Everything else is pretty well cleared up, isn't it?

P7: Yes, the angry feeling which I felt toward that one officer especially is still there but—sometimes it is stronger than other times, but not nearly like it was and I believe that relieving my mind is helping me in that respect—is taking away that bitter feeling, and also as I said the last time, I notice it more when I get fatigued.

C7: It is fairly clear to you that the irritation is the effect of both being tired and then those other confusions.

ENDING COUNSELING

Looking at his positive achievements, in the later stages of the interviews, a person can see a growing consistency in his ability to act more reasonably and to live on a happier and more achieving

---

[3]This counselor tends sometimes to use this commending phrase to begin a response, particularly one that shows insight. While this does not seriously affect the relationship at this stage, the counselor might better have omitted this type of mild approval.

basis. This makes it possible for him to begin to think of terminating counseling. Realizing his competence in working out his own solutions and acting on them, he becomes aware that the significant service which the counselor rendered him is no longer essential. The person will begin to propose an ending of the interviews. At first this may be accompanied by expressions of insecurity and hesitancy, as was indicated in the previous excerpt. The counselor responds to the possibility of ending the interviews and the person can think it out as he did other plans. The person can then decide to end the interviews if he feels he no longer needs them. Usually a person will express the desire to be able to return if new problems and needs arise. The counselor accepts this situation and leaves the relationship open; should the person ever wish to return, he may do so.

Expressions of Gratitude. In this process, too, the person will generally speak, sometimes at length, of how much the counseling relationship has meant to him. These positive attitudes should also be precisely reflected by the counselor. We see this illustrated in the following excerpt from the fifth interview with the ensign(S):

P1: Yes, I do not know exactly whether to say pleased but I feel more like living, more like doing things. I'm beginning to do a lot of things now I've always wanted to do. As a matter of fact I've always had a great love for fishing. Ever since I have been a kid I wanted to go out fishing and I wanted to have my own rod. Last week end I went home, and I went out and took my little brothers; and I saw a nice rod and just bought it, and I got what I wanted. Kids get a kick out of doing things like that . . . I bought the kids candy and ice cream and I get quite a kick out of that. Sorta doing things for other people a little bit.

C1: Yes, it's quite satisfying to have always wanted a good rod and to go out and actually achieve that, and then the happiness you brought the kids, too, makes you happy. (Pause)

P2: Yes . . . We're making definite plans for our marriage now. We both really want that now. I don't know where I'm going to be sent. I know where I will go from here, but I will only be there a short while. I'm really beginning to live now. Before, I don't believe I knew how. Before, I always thought about—well, as far as pleasure was concerned—drinking and things like that. I stopped drinking entirely. And those things that I did think about don't seem to have much of a hold anymore—I mean they don't seem to mean much. I'd like to get out and take part in sports and other activities. (Pause) I'm really beginning to plan a lot of things I want to do.

C2: You're seeing things differently now and you're beginning to do and plan things for yourself and for others too—things that you've always wanted to do.

P3: Yes—(Pause) I still hold that officer and then my family—more or less—a grudge—I don't believe I shall ever get over it. It's just there and although I'm good to my family—parents—there were so many things missing. I don't want to forget that, because I want to provide my children with those things.

C3: Even though you are good to your family—there is still a feeling of hostility which you question whether you'll ever get over. You want your children to have what you missed. The officer fits into that too for what he did.

P4: Yes. (Pause) I can really say—that—that you are responsible for this great change in me.—I cannot think how else it could have happened. And I shall be thankful to you the rest of my life.

C4: It's fairly evident to you that there is a connection between these thoughts . . . and fears about marriage and irritations clearing up, and the interviews here.

P5: Yes, that's true—I'm sure of it. As I talked these things over I could see each time that I was getting better—things were clearing up and the fears weren't nearly so strong. My girl and I got along much better. I didn't fly off like before. There's nothing else to account for the change but these interviews.

C5: It's apparent to you that these were not just casual contacts—but they did have great meaning and significance for you each time.

P6: Yes, I'm sure of it. (Pause)

C6: I think that's a very good statement of it—there is a great deal in this sort of thing—it's very obvious that the effects would indicate that.

P7: Yes. I should say so. (Pause)

C7: Feel very deeply grateful for all this, don't you?

P8: Yes, I do and I would like to do something for you.

C8: (Pause) You do want to express your gratitude in some way.

This positive self-understanding and action is in sharp contrast to the ensign's confused and disorganized statements when he first came to see the counselor. We can see that he will leave the interviews knowing that he wants to live a responsible married life, that he needs religion to aid him in this, and that he can have confidence in his ability to meet new situations as they arise.

Degree of Effectiveness. This counseling series ended after two more interviews. One might wonder if, in a short series of seven interviews, insights deep enough to have a permanent effect on a person's life could be achieved. Some assume that a much longer series of interviews is necessary for basic and significant life-changes. In this particular case, it was possible to follow the progress of the naval officer over a period of five years. The ensign returned after a year to report his coming marriage and his completion of instructions. A survey made five years later confirmed their marriage adjustment. At this time, too, the ensign, a civilian again, referred gratefully to the counseling. From his own report and that of his wife and two other people whom he freely included in his letter of reply, there seems no reason to doubt the permanent effectiveness of the insights he had achieved. This corresponds to the more recent experience of counselors, that deep and penetrating self-understanding and permanent new life-choices can be arrived at in a much shorter counseling process than had previously been thought possible.

Length of Interview Series. As we have seen, the length of any interview series will be determined by the depth and complexity of the person's problems and the degree of his confusion.[4] There seems to be no other rule. Sometimes what a person came for is reached in one interview. At the end, he may say relaxedly,

You know, I see that clearly now and I know what I am going to do and I don't think I need to talk to you any more about it.

Determined by Person. This may happen in the second, sixth, tenth interview, or longer. The person himself is the best judge when the particular problems for which he came are solved and when he no longer needs counseling to think reasonably about them. When he clearly understands that it is up to him, a person is generally very conscientious about not using the counselor's time beyond what is required. Toward the end of an interview series, statements often occur in which the person is putting pressure on himself. He may say that he has been coming about long enough, or, that he only wants to come a few more times because he recognizes how kind the counselor has been and how valuable his time is. Such a relationship as this is the exact opposite of the self-centered, dependent type, where the person becomes a nuisance and irritation to the

[4]See pp. 187–188, 190.

counselor by his inconsideration, his refusal to adhere to set appointments, and his continued interference and interruption of the counselor's other work. This seldom occurs in the counseling relationship as we have described it. The counselor can feel confident that, when a person's problems are clear to him and he feels able to carry out reasonable solutions, he will inform the counselor. The person himself seems to know best when, at least for the time being, he no longer needs to come for interviews.

As new problems arise or new situations create different problems, a person may come again to the counselor and re-establish a series of interviews. Often, the second and third series are shorter than the first. But, they may be longer and more intense because the person is now ready to face deeper problems, which he had avoided or did not have in the first interview series. Even here, the second and third series seem generally to go more smoothly and produce insights more rapidly than the beginning series.

SUBSEQUENT COUNSELING

Deeper Self-Penetration.   A later interview series may enter much more thoroughly into basic personal life-patterns than an earlier series. While the earlier counseling may have been about some particular persons or situations, the subsequent series can begin immediately to consider a fundamental personal reorganization. The following excerpt, for example, is taken from a third counseling series. The first series, begun when this young woman (Miss H. S.) was a high school senior, was focused on some adolescent adjustment problems, the solution to which resulted in a decision to go to college even though this involved great effort and sacrifice. The second series took place around more serious adult adjustment problems as she finished college, particularly the question of an immediate marriage which was possible for her but which she decided against. While she touched on various aspects of herself in these two series, especially her feelings of inferiority and inadequacy and her fear that, if others really knew her, they would reject her, her main consideration was directed towards problems extrinsic, so to speak, to herself.

But in this excerpt from the ninth interview, Miss H. S., now a graduate student, is in the midst of an intense and thorough personal re-evaluation. In the previous eight interviews of this series she had unfolded and clarified for herself that, while college and graduate work were satisfying achievements, they still left her feeling that she had no value as a person. This was the same worthless feeling which she had had almost as long as she could remember. She was able to trace the origin of this to some of her earliest childhood experiences when, for a very short period only, she remembered herself as being accepted and loved. Then, with the coming of a younger sister and a switch in family circumstances, she became definitely a burden, particularly to her mother. From here on, in her home life, she could only remember veiled criticism and rejection coupled with adolescent antagonism from the younger sister because she was physically more attractive and more socially acceptable than her younger sister. The mother, too, seemed to foster this antagonism because she preferred the younger sister.

In this interview she has come finally to accept herself as a person of worth and meaning and she now finds that she must establish a whole new personal plan of life (J):

P1: But now as I no longer see myself as a failure—I mean, I basically feel that, that I'm worthwhile and, and that I can do well in a lot of things—seeing that on one side and no longer feeling worthless—I still have yet to uh, see things in true perspective. I mean, uh,—I can see that the thing is not on this side of the card, but is on the other side of the card, but I still don't know exactly what's on that side.

C1: You've got more unfolding to do on this, shall we say, completed self-awareness, now, having clearly accepted yourself in this worthwhile way.

P2: But, I don't know exactly how to do that. Uh, you have to have an objective measure, I think. And yet I suppose that it's always going to be somewhat subjective because it's always yourself. But it has to somehow equate reality and it's just knowing what the perspective is.

C2: Somehow, the real situation which will measure it, will have to filter through you and depend, in a sense, on your understanding and interpretation of that reality.

P3: But not altogether, I don't think. I don't know exactly—I don't know whether other people have tried to work this out before or not, but I don't know, uh, how you measure—how you really know what you are in relation to other people—that's not exactly a norm, but it's—it's something, because you live with other people and uh—I just don't know.

C3: This, what reality is, in a sense, or what the norms which represent reality, in relationship to yourself—that's confusing, isn't it? And you're just unsure whether it's ever been figured out entirely.

P4: Yes, I don't know that, but I know that all people, in order to have some kind of working relationship must have something worked out, I mean, personally they have their own scale figured out as to what it is, and they go by that. And right now, I don't think I have such a personal scale. I think that having seen clearly what two factors were at work here and then, uh, uncovering the one, and discarding it, here I am with a new one, but I still don't have a scale to measure it or other things.

Inadequate View of Self. Some readers may perhaps wonder why a young woman, a successful graduate student, should still have had so intense a questioning of her self-worth. Recent experience in counseling, however, is uncovering the significant fact that large numbers of people who are apparently successful, get much less meaning from their lives than others might think. Why this is so, is one of the unexplored realms of personality. But somehow it seems that many people, due possibly to circumstances going back to the very earliest years of their lives, as we discussed earlier, seem to have acquired a faulty view of themselves—what might be called an erroneous "self-percept"—from which all their attitudes towards themselves and others seem to have their origin. If this self-percept, as in this case, causes the person to feel he is worthless and inadequate, then all subsequent life activities, no matter how successful, seem never entirely to be able to eradicate this self-rejection. As the years go by, this sense of worthlessness and rejection may recede from the person's conscious awareness and yet it seems to continue to cause an elusive and almost indescribable feeling of discontent, unrest, and unhappiness.

As this excerpt continues, we notice that, for this young woman, the re-acceptance of herself has many of the qualities of a new birth. Unfortunately, the printed page cannot reproduce the gentle, hushed tones of her voice. It seemed to the counselor not unlike a woman's first wonderment at having a child.[5] Throughout this excerpt she is speaking slowly, almost meditatively but with intense feeling. The interview continues (J):

[5]See Carl R. Rogers: *Client Centered Therapy*, New York, Copyright 1951, by Houghton Mifflin, p. 129, for a further discussion of this "newborn" feeling.

C4: It's a new way of evaluating yourself, and therefore it needs a great deal more delineation.

P5: Uh-huh. This is the first time I've felt free to do that.

C5: It's your first real acceptance of a positive worthwhile self in a, shall we say, a fundamentally realistic sense.

P6: Uh-huh. (Pause)

C6: Quite pleased at all that, aren't you?

P7: Yes, and it's deep. I think I'm going to cry again. I mean, it's like a, a new baby. You're afraid its skin or something is fragile. (Sobbing softly.[6] Pause)

C7: It's a very delicate bringing something into being in yourself that you sort of see you have produced? (The counselor, in turn, speaks very slowly and quietly.)

P8: And forcing it to come out this way is the only way to do it.

C8: It's one of the final stages of getting it born.

P9: Yes.

C9: That is, there is a real meaning in saying that and saying it in this way. That's something very significant.

P10: Yes. Because it's uh—it no longer remains uh, there no longer remains any possibility of its being something unreal, because it's something recognized in reality that is actually taking place, like a project. Whereas if you just think about it—you'd never be sure and you really can never take anything—any growth or anything positive from it.

C10: This is bringing it into being in a very real sense for yourself and that having been done, you can draw sustenance from it and achievement from it. Somehow or the other, without having done that, it wouldn't be a source of further growth.

P11: No. Another thing, this is the one time when I have really got everything out that was in myself and when nobody did anything about it—like at home, you know, when I would have been criticized —I mean, it was just accepted.

C11: That is, this is kind of a second revealing of yourself and at first, somehow in the home it was attacked and criticized. Now having been done again—it has been accepted and so it is very positive.

P12: And I suppose that's why I uh, have played so many roles and been so artificial, because, uh, I suppose in a way I was hurt very deeply at home. I was sort of determined that, well, if it happens once, shame on you but if it happens twice, shame on me, and I wasn't going to be caught again I suppose. (Pause) Because, uh, I mean,

[6]Soft crying of this sort, particularly with women, seems often to be associated with deep insights. This crying has apparently no tones of sadness but rather signifies both relief and vivid awareness.

their—their statements and so on, they weren't uh—I mean if they were objectively true, it would have been all right, but they weren't. I mean, you could have accepted it if it was a real situation, but when you realize that, that it was wrong, well then, you just don't want to take any chances on its happening again.

C12: That is, sort of feeling basically that they were wrong in it, you didn't want to leave yourself open for them to do that to you again.

P13: Yes, and I suppose that probably happens to a lot of people. And I don't suppose—if it hadn't been for this I know I would never have changed. I mean, I suppose it is very unusual for it to have broken and come out again.

C13: Kind of a second birth which would not have been possible, in your view, except through this relationship—that is, through a relationship of this kind.

P14: I'm sure of that. And now—now just in some remote way, I can see that in Cameron[7]—in the way all the different types of behavior that he describes, by saying that they originate in the bio-social matrix of a person's life, uh, he doesn't have any mechanistic views of them —he sees them as adjustive techniques of some situation or the other. The wild forms that they can take! But they're understandable. And you can see how people uh, go off into them. Because they never have a chance. I think some original situation sets something up and they never have a chance to break it. (Pause) The things just keep building up and then—there's some kind of a culminating point and it might be neurosis or psychosis even.

C14: You can see, in Cameron particularly, how fixed adjustive methods can become—and you can see in the ordinary course how they would just remain that way.

P15: Uh-huh. This is kind of getting off of working things out, but it just fits in. I mean, I think that this is a step in the—in a way to understanding it—from that point of view, this is sort of a microcosmic experience of its working out.

THE COUNSELOR'S ATTITUDE AND MANNER

Implications for Counselor. In this excerpt, in addition to its revelation of the deeper self-realization that a later counseling series may unfold, there are some further implications for the counselor's skill particularly as seen through the eyes of the person undergoing the counseling process. In P10, for example, we see how the interview and the counselor fuse together to become reality—social reality

[7]N. Cameron: *The Psychology of Behavior Disorders*, Houghton Mifflin, New York, 1951.

certainly but still something basically objective and real. It is this
kind of relationship that allows this person to become, for the first
time, a "real" person in the truest sense. Artificialities are no longer
necessary as defenses and escapes. As the person's and the counselor's
reasoning selves come together and share a common world, it seems
to enable a person, in a way never before possible, to accept the
fact that his own reasoning capacity has truly reached reality. He
can feel that he has genuinely extended himself out beyond the
self-deception of previous artificial life patterns, to something lasting and permanent. While this "new" self originated in the person's
reasoning, it somehow, through counseling, is endowed with meaning
and purpose beyond and, in a sense, independent of the person who
produced it.

The Counselor's Honesty and Accuracy. P11 and P12 reveal the
curative power that this combined self- and counselor-acceptance
brings. In this process somehow are destroyed all the false values that
others had effected in her first groping for life meanings and purposes. Now she can begin to look at herself in the calm, naked light
of her own and the counselor's understanding and, stripped of all
her protective artificialities, still find herself a person of far greater
real worth than she had ever before thought possible.

These statements reveal, too, how essential to this kind of self-
fulfillment are the counselor's attitudes and responses which are
genuinely accepting but, at the same time, thoroughly accurate and
honest. A person, striving so desperately to overcome artificialities
of lifetime duration, can only succeed when the sincerity and honesty
of the counselor equals his own sincerity and honesty. If the counselor's attitudes are in any way false or artificial themselves, they
cannot possibly share in or aid such unsparing self-honesty. But
because the person, through a combination of those various things
which go to make up a good counseling atmosphere, somehow knows
that the counselor's acceptance is genuinely reasonable, real, and
fair, his own acceptance of himself can be equally reasonable and
fair. As a result, for this young woman, the wounds of past social
and affectionate relationships seem on the way to being permanently
healed.

In the next interview her re-evaluation goes beyond her relationship to herself and others and penetrates clear through to her
relationship with God (J):

P1: I was thinking—as a result of that last interview it was almost like a rebirth again. As I thought about it during the week I realized that the same thing I had felt before in relation to all other people, I felt also in relation to God. I don't think I really basically could feel ah, a real wholesome relationship, I mean that God could really love me. But as a result of that interview and now from this talk here, I really see that very clearly now.

C1: That is, somehow this week it came to you that God could possibly love you. Never before have you really felt that within yourself.[8]

P2: Well, ah, I can go along so long and pray and then all of a sudden I'm back again to the very beginning and I feel as though I've never had anything in a spiritual way. And I think that's the reason, because I just can't feel that it can be so. (Cries softly. Pause)

C2: This whole sense of sort of total failure in regard to God even though you can go for a while with some feeling of prayer and Divine acceptance—this final total failure that comes seems to be all bound up with all these other previous feelings of worthlessness.

P3: Yes and ah, I think I had the sort of false impression, I mean even though I know I have received so much, I just have to almost cut it off to be as though I didn't because somehow I just can't accept the fact that that could be so.

C3: Even though you are in a sense objectively aware of many gifts from God, and many real aids from God, yet in a basic sense you somehow can't accept that objective awareness.

P4: And I know in the last interview one of the things I said, one of the awarenesses that I had, was that the next time that I had interviews I wanted to have them somehow around spiritual values and this sort of fits in with that.

C4: Having worked these things out with regard to others and yourself it seems that going right along with that the next thing was to work it out with regard to God.

P5: (Pause) That was just a very sharp perception to see that so clearly.

C5: It was actually a very deep insight.

P6: I can see but I can't understand that God is not what I think He is.

As the interview continues, she draws a striking parallel between the unsparing realism which the counselor represents to her and that same relationship with God (J):

[8]This is a counselor over-statement. The person is not exactly saying this.

C6: There's a distinction between your seeing, your awareness, in a sense, and your real absorbing of that awareness, your real penetration or assimilation of it.

P7: (Pause) And something like the way I can't look at you very well, (Laughs) I can't look at God.

C7: Somehow there's a relation between the two some way.

P8: Maybe the connection is to what I said before that you were the first person that I couldn't fool.

C8: The sort of clarity of things or the reality seems to be the common bond. God is in this same world of someone that you cannot fool so there's almost a hiding in a way.

P9: And in that way, ah, just like a baby again, because for so long I have lived in a world where I knew that I was all covered up, so to speak, sort of insulated from everyone for so long (Pause) so there just aren't any experiences, you're just not able—I'm thinking of new skin or something again—when the skin has been burned you can't put it near real bright lights or something.

C9: Somehow or the other this skin has been hurt or burned or yourself, if you will—you're almost afraid now that you can't stand a clear light. (Pause)

P10: I don't know what that goes back to, I don't think I've had a tragic life or anything of that sort. I don't know why but I guess I'm really afraid if I expose myself to God that I never could recover if anything happened. (Crying softly)

C10: It's a tremendous feeling somehow that you have to keep covered —that being just yourself totally in front of God would be devastating. (Pause)

P11: (Nods slowly. Pause)

As the interview continues she explains that she was always aware how this artificiality, so characteristic of her relationship to everyone, was also affecting her relationship to God. Yet until she had cleared away all these other sources of worthlessness and defense she was not able to face herself with such a thorough and ultimate evaluation (J):

P12: This is awfully hard to talk about. (Pause)

C12: Right now you are conscious of a kind of blocking or at least a difficulty.

P13: Well, I've always felt that in relation to this. And I think that's maybe one reason why I never, why I would never actually face it before. Well, probably not the only reason because I did have other areas to work out. (Pause)

C13: The difficulty isn't new and you're conscious of its being a major factor in the delay of this although there were other things in a way probably that you had to clear up first.

P14: Uh, huh. (Long pause) It's funny, in some ways I want to laugh but not because it's humorous or not because it's light. I don't know exactly why. (Pause)

C14: It's a kind of an urge to laugh but in a way it seems sort of out of context with your awareness of the seriousness of the thing itself. It's not at all laughable even though there is that urge.

P15: Yes, I guess I'm just glad to be able to face these things now. But, I'm afraid to talk about them too—because they are so meaningful that I don't want any of that artificiality (Pause) which I am so capable of to spoil them. (She speaks very slowly, seemingly having difficulty controlling her voice.)

C15: You are very careful and cautious about this thing now, aren't you? It's so fine a thing for you that you want to deal with it in the most honest and sincere way you can and not in any way to spoil it by what you feel is your tendency to artificiality.

P16: Yes, and the reason that is so is because—I don't know where I started to be artificial—but I'm aware of always having been able to "grin" and sort of by that being able to make everyone—I don't know —(Pause) to think that I was a happy, simple sort of little girl or something. (Pause) But the reason that has meaning here is because being able to be that way, at school especially, with the Sisters (Pause) when I was first beginning to learn about prayer and things like that (Pause) I never could be sure that anything religious wasn't as artificial as I was. (Sobbing)

C16: Somehow as this thing unfolds in your expression of it, prayer and your own artificiality are hitched together.

P17: (Long pause) And the thing is so awful because I think the things I did as a child were so right, I mean, it was true again—that was the right thing but it was because of all the deceptiveness and artificiality, I could have no certitude that it was true and then as I grew older (Pause) as I wanted to throw that artificiality off, you see the thing to do was to throw off too so much of what I saw was in a religious way artificial for me. The thing that makes it so striking an awareness for me is seeing somebody like N. and G. who have such a deep conviction about those same things. And it's reality and it's truth for them and I never could have been sure of that and I'm not really sure of it. I'm beginning to be but so much of it I'm not sure of.

C17: That is, somehow, what you really were as a child in a sense seems very real to you, yet, there seems to be all this covering over of it and there is such an artificiality there now that you never have been able entirely to accept that reality. You see this, shall we say, childlike prayerfulness in others—the reality of it—their genuine sense of the real in their religious actions, brings that contrast very sharply to you.

P18: Yes, and I've been surprised at myself especially this last year at really how cynical in a way I am about religious things and I can see how people would easily give up their faith, would easily, ah, lose all the richness of it because of that. In my personal life there was truth and the purest truth and yet the worst deception wedded so closely together that I could never separate them. (Pause)

C18: It's an increasingly sharper penetration of your own possible cynicism, isn't it, in that because, in your own life, truth and artificiality were so closely lined up, you could see how you could reject what you really see as deep fundamental truth in the confusion of rejecting all the artificiality that became somehow or the other associated with it.

Respect for Person's Integrity. Seeing through the eyes of this person undergoing counseling, the almost awesome honesty and integrity which the counseling relationship represents, the reader can perhaps understand better than through any other description how crucially important is the counselor's restraint of his own urges to control, possess, or in any way to misinterpret reality to anyone coming to him for counseling. The counselor's whole personal attitude and manner, as well as his responses, must be suffused with a genuine respect for the integrity of the person. He must have a sense of the sacredness and inviolability of human personality at its deepest and most intimate level. This is what gives meaning and purpose to the careful way in which he responds only to what the other person has actually shared freely with him. It is neither persuasion nor dominance nor cajoling because the counselor is convinced that, in matters so intensely personal, only when he aids a person to increase his own reasonableness can his counseling ultimately result in any truly prudential choice and action. Such a counselor attitude respects, in its most real sense, the basic "incommunicability" of prudence and all moral virtue founded upon such prudence.

In these excerpts, we see how a person's constructive responsibility steadily develops as she grows encouraged "to be herself" in the best meaning of this phrase and finds acceptance and understanding of that self in the unsparing realism of the counseling interview. Through this she can make a positive growth in increased "being" herself. This brings her not only an honest and sincere facing herself in the light of her own reasonable judgment but also gives her confidence that others knowing her as she really is, can accept and love her too. But most of all, God Himself now becomes, for the first time, a real and loving Being and not a fearsome image from which she must hide in her artificiality. Here then is true love of self which, previously side-tracked by confused and disordered life-reactions, now gives birth to a much greater justice and love in her honesty, respect, and regard for others and in her final facing of herself and God. In this way all the counselor's concern and skill are bent upon furthering the person's true and reasonable pursuit of his own excellence. Such genuine humility keeps constantly moving further away from exaggerated self-importance or excessive self-rejection and all other forms of self-deception, into a true being oneself. The final goal of such self-being need not be limited to one's natural capacity alone, fine as this reasonable self can be, but can, with God's help, find ultimate realization in the total actuality of complete Being to which all real self-fulfillment and achievement tend.

SUMMARY

The following schema may be of help in summarizing some of the kinds of statements which occur in counseling, most of which we have discussed in this section on the counselor's skill. But, as we have seen in the excerpts from actual interviews, such statements never appear in so orderly a fashion. They are always intricately interwoven in a complex web of personal—and often disturbing and painful—circumstance.

Unless this has become clear from what has already been said, the mere memorization of categories like this may obstruct rather than improve the counselor's effectiveness. Such categories may only produce mechanical responses which lack a genuinely deep personal understanding and acceptance and consequently contain no real warmth. These seem seldom if ever to result in penetrating self-clarifications.

COUNSELOR RESPONSES
to the person's statements of

(SELF-KNOWLEDGE)

Basic Feelings

> towards self and others contained in a series of facts or personal incidents

Attitudes or Goals

> incorporated in or motivating these basic feelings

Fundamental Motive Patterns

> which relate these feelings and attitudes to other similar life-situations

Broadening Awareness

> of the extent of problems and self-involvement

Conflict

> when one goal is impeded by another goal or some fundamental life-pattern

Relation

> between past and present factors or between various present factors, persons, emotions, attitudes, or problems

Integration

> which fit together a series of motives, feelings, and life-patterns

Satisfaction

> with some aspects of his present mode of acting, some particular achievement, or the facing of a problem, seeing a relationship, getting a new view of self or similar positive, encouraging, or hopeful expressions

Inadequacy

> of previous or present methods to reach desired personal goals

(SELF-REORGANIZATION)

Acquiring and Accepting

> new views and attitudes towards self, others, and various life-situations

Changes in Fundamental Motive-Patterns
>   as a result of new self-understanding

Balancing and Weighing
>   alternate new ways of coping more effectively
>   with personal conflicts and disorders in the
>   way of desired goals

Choice
>   of some new plans of action

Success in Action
>   as a result of new plans

Failure in Action
>   as a result of new plans

Re-evaluation
>   of why plans succeeded or failed

Changes in Plans
>   to improve performance and increase success

Decision to End Counseling
>   at least for a time

TEST OF COUNSELOR ATTITUDES

Since the counselor's attitudes are also most significant in successful counseling, we have included here a brief project which may aid the beginning counselor to become aware of his attitudes. Below are included two excerpts—one from an interview of a young woman and the other, of a young man—accompanied by a check-list of some possible attitudes and feelings a reader might have as he reads these excerpts. The counselor's responses are omitted. After reading each of the excerpts, the reader may wish 1) to check those attitudes and feelings which he himself experienced during the reading; 2) to fill in, on a separate piece of paper, the responses he would make to each statement if he were the counselor.

I. Mother-daughter Relationship

P1: Well, I've been upset over my mother. You see, ah, well I'll have to explain this first. My mother married my father when she was about eighteen and she was only nineteen when I was born. Then later they got a divorce and my grandparents raised me and my two brothers. So my mother really seems like an older sister in a way—my grandmother's always been like my mother. But now that I've grown up, my mother seems to want to do everything for me and control my life even though I'm twenty-three years old. This upsets me all the time. I'm terribly upset now. It's the same old thing. Do you want me to tell you what happened? (C. nods head slowly.) All right. Well, see, mother let the car run out of gas. She had to leave it there all night. Then when she went there in a cab she couldn't get it started and she had to have it hauled to a garage. So, in the meantime she promised a neighbor she'd help her move and she borrowed M's car last night and did that and she didn't get quite finished and she was bound and determined that she had to do it again today so she called up everybody. It wasn't for herself at all—just for this woman. I was so mad I told her well, she had certainly done as much as she ever would have needed to do for that woman. No, she just had to do it. So, I didn't do anything to help her. It's the same thing with everything. Mother is so overly generous. I mean, she never considers herself at all and I have to refuse offers of her to help me out all the time, to come up and pick me up, or to do this and she does anything, you know, but she never thinks of herself so I got to thinking about it today and I've been feeling awfully bad about it. I know I wouldn't have any more obligation than she did. Oh, she got the car going but there was no sense in it but still since she did it, I should have helped her. Then my grandmother said, "Well, Nora does anything for anybody and no one will help her." Then I felt pretty low. Then we had a little difficulty with granddad and I got kind of tired of it. That's about all there is. But, as I say, you know, I haven't thought anything out because this has been on my mind. (Pause)

P2: It's like with this work at the Club. I've taken the responsibility of doing it and I was perfectly willing and I wanted to do it. Well, they wanted to do it too. Grandma likes something different. She wants something to give a little interest I guess to her life. And mother's doing it to help me. I mean, she'll type. I told them I didn't want them to. I would have gotten it done. I told them I didn't want them to do it. I think she worked on it yesterday. I took the responsibility. Then afterwards I got to thinking of when she wanted to help that woman and I wouldn't help her, so I felt pretty bad about it. But this is just one of any number of cases. It's just the way she is. I don't know what to do about it.

P3: That's right. And then she'll do all the work if I'm not around she's so anxious to get everything done. I mean, she feels responsible to take care of the house even though she works all day and my grand-mother's well able to take care of it. My grandparents could easily afford to get help and they would—if she wouldn't do so much. I don't care. I don't pay any attention to it. It's not my responsibility but I kind of think I should help her out. I feel that I should so she doesn't have so much to do. It's just this same old question. I mean, I decide in my mind that I should do a certain thing and then after I do it I'm not quite sure. Just like it was today. I thought, well, if she wants to go out there and play around helping her move, it's all right. Then I began feeling sorry for her after I saw her out there because I didn't help her.

As I read this, was I

—— 1. thinking about this girl's mother and what someone should tell her
—— 2. irritated with the mother's excessive urge to help others
—— 3. experiencing with the girl her confusion about her mother
—— 4. thinking about what I would do if I were in this girl's place
—— 5. experiencing with the girl her resistance to her mother
—— 6. thinking about someone who has a similar kind of mother or grandmother situation
—— 7. irritated with the girl in not being more able to take her own responsibility
—— 8. experiencing with the girl her guilt sometimes about her attitudes towards her mother
—— 9. irritated with the girl for not being more decisive
—— 10. experiencing the girl's conflict in resisting the mother
—— 11. urged to encourage the girl not to pay any attention to her mother's attitudes
—— 12. feeling sorry for the girl's mother
—— 13. thinking of the girl's mother as being like myself
—— 14. thinking of the girl's mother as being like my own mother
—— 15. thinking of a similar situation that I know
—— 16. thinking of some ways in which the girl's situation applies to myself
—— 17. urged to encourage the girl to live her own life

(The reader may now wish to write in his responses to I.)

II. Chemistry Graduate Student

P1: I don't really know what's behind this but my hands have been bothering me quite a bit for quite some time and it has a lot of practical difficulties, like in Chem lab, they're really awfully sore, especially if they're cracked very badly, I can just put my hand any place and it burns. Often acid or something has fallen on the table and hasn't been washed off or even when I just uncork a bottle of acid, why the fumes from it make my hands burn and it's really a kind of handicap in my work. I don't think it decreases my efficiency that much but actually I think I would get along a lot better if I didn't have it and I would like to try to work it out and see if I can't get rid of it.

P2: Yes, there would. It seems that at Christmas time I was working more in the lab and even though I used the gloves my hands were swollen and they stuck to the gloves and they would sweat, you know, because of the rubber—no air got to them and that didn't seem to help any. They seemed to be just as bad. It seems that they swell immediately now. It's a kind of a bother to bother with gloves all the time so I didn't use any yesterday because they weren't too bad but now today they are all swollen again about twice their size and they're itching pretty badly. I have some coal tar and it is helping them but when they're blistered it doesn't seem to do much for them. The doctor I'm going to—he's a skin specialist—said that there are probably psychological factors in it. So, I'd like to try to figure out what they are and why.

P3: I think that if I would know what factors actually seem to have bearing on it, I might be able too—I can't avoid water all the time, I have to wash, but still I might be able to cut it down somewhat. It does seem that alcohol and water bother them a lot. Sometimes for awhile I even wore gloves when I took a bath because they were so bad.

P4: And it seems that once they get like that, ah, anything after that is a constant cause of irritation and particularly in lab, we have to wash everything off—it's kind of a dirty place, even though you keep washing stuff your equipment never stays clean. If you wash it one day, you think you've got it all clean and all you have to do is rinse it off but the next day you have to wash it all over again. There's only the cold water and the cold seems to bother them too and so it just seems like there isn't any chance for them to heal once they get started. I mentioned that acid and so forth does bother them and then they not only burn but crack more. In this cold weather I notice that after I come in from outside my hands are awfully sore just from the cold. It seems to, I don't know exactly what it does, it doesn't seem to dry them out so much but it just seems to hurt.

As I read this, was I

—— 18. sorry for the man
—— 19. thinking of the possible physical causes of his illness
—— 20. admiring his courage in continuing to work
—— 21. experiencing the way his hands must impede his efficiency
—— 22. recalling a similar kind of illness or injury
—— 23. wondering about the doctor's suggestion of psychological causes
—— 24. feeling this man's urge to get the psychological factors worked out
—— 25. thinking how alcohol and water would hurt his hands
—— 26. recognizing with him the way alcohol, water, and soap affect his hands
—— 27. thinking how my hands are affected by similar chemicals or the cold
—— 28. thinking of some remedy I might recommend

(The reader may now wish to write his responses to II.)

COMMENTS

Attitudes 3, 5, 8, and 10 seem the ones which have most consistently resulted in responses similar to those actually given in the interview. Since these excerpts were both parts of successful counseling series, these responses were apparently of definite assistance to the two persons in the unfolding and thinking through of their difficulties. The counselors' responses can therefore, to some degree at least, be used as models.

Attitudes 1, 4, 11, 13, and 17 seem often to be associated with the kinds of responses which would tend to give advice. In a person who has been struggling with this problem as long as this girl, superficial advice might only result in making her resistant. Attitudes 2 and 11 might cause the counselor to reveal a tone of hostility to the girl's mother. Since the girl herself is somewhat confused in her own attitude toward her mother, such hostility might readily have pushed her to strong defense of her mother and repeated protestations that the counselor did not understand and even a feeling of greater guilt because she had given the wrong impression of her mother to the counselor. Attitudes 7, 9, 12, 13, and 17 on the other hand, might easily have led the counselor to indicate a tone of rejection to the girl and leave her feeling that the counselor did not genuinely appreciate her difficult position. Attitudes 6, 14, 15, and 16 might possibly indicate a counselor's own personal involvement in a situation similar to this. If what a person says suggests something in the counselor's own life, he must be alert lest this "blind spot" cause him to lose some of his objectivity. If this happens, the counselor may find himself momentarily as disturbed as the person.

In the excerpt from the chemistry graduate student, attitudes 21, 24, and 26 seem most commonly to accompany responses similar to those actually made in the successful interview. Attitudes 18 and 20 might readily be behind a counselor's strong urge to express reassurance, pity, or praise. While such statements might not seriously hinder counseling, they might create some resentment and they would have added nothing to the counseling process as such. In an excerpt like this, however, the most tempting aspect is the way it appeals to a counselor's urge to ask questions, diagnose, or propose suggestions. Attitudes 19, 22, 23 25, and 28 might readily result in this. Attitudes 22 and 27 could suggest the personal involvement of the counselor and this too might motivate him to suggest remedies or share factual experiences. The following are the responses which were actually given in the two interview excerpts:

(*Mother-daughter Relationship—Counselor Responses*)

C1: The immediate thing with your mother is the one thing now you're focused on and it hinges around her extreme consideration for others —sort of giving herself or doing everything for others and your resistance to that. Yet, when you did resist it, now as you think it over you feel, in a way, guilty that you didn't help her because she is so generous in offering herself to you and everyone else. So, you're in a kind of conflict now. You felt urged to resist her because you didn't see too much point in what she was doing and having resisted her, you feel guilty now for having done that.

C2: The fact that she is so willing to do things for others and for you is really the cause of a lot of conflict in you, isn't it? You don't quite want to go along with all that and yet when you don't go along with it, then you feel guilty because of so many things she's done for you.

C3: The problem hinges around deciding a pattern of conduct different from hers, doesn't it? When you decide that, because you don't agree with what she's doing, you find yourself feeling guilty because she still does it anyway. Then you realize that she's sort of excessively burdened without your help. It's hard for you to know which side to take in those situations when they arise.

(*Chemistry Graduate Student—Counselor Responses*)

C1: It's actually a barrier in a way to your efficiency and there would be a real advantage in clearing it up some way.

C2: Your work and the doctor's comment develop all the more pressure on your part to get the thing cleared up somewhat—at least to get the psychological side worked out if you can.

C3: Pretty evident that alcohol and water and soap particularly seem to have a rather obvious reaction.

C4: Lab and the fact that you have to keep cleaning things adds to it plus the cold weather too—all go together.

The reader may find it helpful to prepare such a list of the attitudes he has as he reads the various other excerpts given in this book and also even to make such a list before or after a particular counseling interview of his own. A number of beginning counselors have found that their attitudes do creep into their responses; that when, for example, they checked off "advising" types of attitudes, they ended up giving advice in the interview itself. On the other hand, as their awareness of their own attitudes increased, they found that making a concentrated effort to respond to the attitudes and emotions the person himself has just expressed, was also a great aid in restraining their own urges to advise, question, be irritated, and the like. In the actual interview itself a main part of the counselor's skill seems to be his complete loss of focus on himself and his own feelings and attitudes. He centers all his reasoning on understanding, restating, and integrating the person's release and clarifications. This, in turn, seems to give the deepest kind of "real" acceptance to the person as well as facilitate his increase in self-knowledge and self-reorganization.

CHAPTER XIII

ADDITIONAL SKILLS WITH CHILDREN

Generally speaking, there seems to be comparatively little difference between the interview process with children and that of adolescents or adults. Often, even a small child talks freely and the interview follows the paths we have described. The same skills in responses are necessary and, if properly used, favorable results can follow.

SOME CHARACTERISTICS OF CHILDREN

Dependency. There are, however, some things characteristic of children. Dependency is normal for a child. The younger he is, the more fearful and insecure he is. He naturally seeks answers from others, particularly from parents and other adults whom he respects. In counseling we cannot expect the same growth in independence in children that we look for in adults. But counseling can aid children to work through problems, and begin to face responsibilities which are part of their particular period of development. Like adults, children, too, have confusions and conflicts. Their problems are simpler and usually not so deeply imbedded. Consequently, a child can generally see through them more rapidly than adults and reach solutions more quickly.

Sensitivity. Sometimes the way in which even a very small child solves what appears to be a grave problem, is amazing. The beginning counselor is often surprised at the shrewd observation and understanding of children, when they talk freely in an unthreatening atmosphere where they can express their real judgments of people and situations. Because we live in an adult world we may fail to recognize the sharpness of the child's reactions and the intensity of his feelings. We do not always appreciate how he is affected by the emotional tones around him. Actually a child seems to be most sensitive to conflicts and disturbances of any sort.

Need Acceptance and Understanding. The child especially is a barometer of the feelings in the home. If the atmosphere of the home is one of love, acceptance, and understanding, the child will feel secure. But, if there are tensions and hostilities, even though these are apparently hidden by parents who never display their feelings in front of the child, they are sensed by the child and he is disturbed. His own need for affection is so great, he seems to recognize the slightest barriers in the flow of love to him and to others in the home. Even the very small child knows what is going on and feels these tensions and hostilities. He often cannot express them. His inability to express himself, however, is not the same as a lack of feeling. If the emotions in the home give him security, peace, and love, the child has a good chance of developing a mature and stable character. If they produce fear and conflict, the child will suffer from this psychological and spiritual malnutrition. This inadequacy, like the lack of proper food, will eventually affect his approach to the problems of life.

Not Take Complete Responsibility. Since his natural state is one of dependency, the child cannot take responsibility in the same manner as an adult. Many problems which he will be expected to face later in life, he can reasonably leave to others for the present. The adults in his world, particularly his parents, have most of the responsibilities for the major difficulties of his life. His own horizon of responsibility is, therefore, more limited than it will be later. In fact, one of the problems peculiar to adolescence seems to be the growing awareness of how much larger the responsible world is for the adult than for the child. Consequently, we cannot expect the child in the interview to react to responsibilities as an adult. His problems must be understood in relation to the responsibilities normally due him.

Excessive Responsibility Injurious. If too much adult responsibility is placed on the child, he may never have an opportunity to grow in normal self-reliance and security. All work and no play makes Jack not only a dull boy but an insecure one. If he is too quickly shouldered with adult problems and worries, he loses the spontaneous and carefree attitudes necessary to children of his age. He is not allowed to live in a world that is comparatively relaxed and reassuring. Children have many fears which adults do not have If, in addition, a child has too many adult problems thrust upon him, he may be overwhelmed by the tribulations of life. Such adult threats are dangerous for a small child. Consequently, the child usually rebels against such excessive responsibility. In this, he is acting more reasonably than if he were to seek a responsibility for which, in his present state of life, he is not equipped. Such overburdened childhoods often produce an unstable adult life.

IMPORTANCE OF PARENTS

Co-operation of Parents. The child, then, while he is capable of reasonable judgment in proportion to his age and abilities, is, at the same time, directly and immediately dependent on his family and particularly on his parents. Child counseling must, therefore, be carried on in close co-operation with them. This preservation of the common family bond seems best accomplished by the careful structuring of the counseling relationship so that at no point is the responsibility for the child taken from the parents. Parents must not be given the impression that the counselor is, in any sense, going to try to solve the child's problems without them. This is important even in the telephone conversation or casual contact which begins counseling. Parents should be aware that the child's outlook and actions have the best chances of improvement when the parents themselves also come for interviews and think through their side of the situation and their responsibility for the child's condition.

Parental Conflicts. One way parents may escape their own inadequacies and failures is to blame the child. This is usually not done openly. But, if one studies carefully their statements in an interview, they often reveal a tendency to avoid responsibility for what the child has done. This seems to be a particularly difficult problem in our society. People often marry without completely accepting the responsibilities of family life. Consequently they do not understand the things that are necessary to give children a stable and happy life. Parents are sometimes unwilling to face the fact that their actions and attitudes are often the cause of the child's misconduct. They may accept this only after they themselves have undergone a counseling process. As they begin to think things out together, they gradually become aware that their unrecognized resentment of the child, because he interfered with their adult activities or their preference for one of the other children in the family, may have strongly influenced the child's reactions. The parents too sometimes need help with their own problems before they can acquire insights into why the child is acting as he is.

THE CHILD INTERVIEW

Brought by Parent. The small child ordinarily does not come to the interview by himself but is brought by the parents. They, and his teachers, are generally the ones who first recognize his problems. Left to himself, a child usually will not face any difficulties or come to anyone for help. This is largely because he does not know where he can obtain help or how to go about expressing his problems to anyone. An exception to this occurs when primary school teachers are skilled in counseling small children. Here it is not unusual for children to bring up and work out problems on their own. Generally, however, the parents, sometimes through the intermediary of the school, bring the child to the counselor. Without the co-operation of the parents, the counseling relationship is definitely impeded. Even though counseling can sometimes be successful without the parents' direct co-operation, it probably would have produced greater growth for the child had the parents themselves, either individually or together, also come for counseling.

Adult Interest. The child's feeling that an adult is taking an interest in him and accepting him, is itself a powerful aid in the child's change of conduct. We saw elsewhere, in the discussion of delinquency, how, in the study of pairs of children with the same general background, the main difference in the non-delinquent was the fact that some adult had shown an interest in him. The sincere interest and concern of an adult are of great value to the child. Even without any attempt at skill or method, the willingness of an adult to listen and understand is often powerfully effective in bringing about changes in a child's attitudes. This sense of acceptance between the child and the adult is one of the strongest effects of the counseling relationship.

Reassurance. In the same way, too, the willingness of the parents to come for interviews and to think out their relationship to the child is often a strong reassurance. The child grows aware that his parents are really concerned about him, that they want to understand him better. This adds to his appreciation of them and to his realization that they do love him or they would not be making these efforts to find out what is the matter. This, too, like the listening process of the counselor, can be a powerful element in the child's change of conduct.[1]

Importance of Play Materials.   Because of his inability to express himself, as well as his feelings of strangeness, a child is generally unable to talk as freely as an adult in an interview. For this reason, play materials are an important aid in child counseling. Play is the natural world for the child and toys are an ordinary medium of expression. He can usually speak more easily with the help of toys. Besides this, the child often uses play with the toys to speak for him.

Counselor Responses.   In general, the counselor responds to the child's feelings and attitudes as he would to an adult. He must, of course, use language that is within the range of the particular child's understanding. He must learn, too, to grasp quickly the child's mode of saying things through his facial expressions, body mannerism, postures, and the manner in which he plays with the toys. The responses should be short, relaxed, and natural. Children are quick to catch artificiality and they resent it. Children also resist being "talked down to." The counselor, of course, must avoid "baby talk" or any kind of affectation. The child responds readily to quiet, sincere speech that reflects his feelings and attitudes in a simple, clear, unaffected way.

FEARS

Illustration.   Since fears form a great part of the insecurity of a small child, they are often the center of many of the child's early problems. Children may have fears of the world, because it contains so many new things they do not know. Often they are afraid of being rejected, left alone, or even "annihilated." They are afraid of their own weakness and inability to meet all the difficulties which face them. A small child may only be able to reach these fears and cope with them in his play world and in terms of his familiar toys. We see this demonstrated in the following interview.

---

[1]Counseling with people in old age seems also to have some of the characteristics of child counseling. The acceptance and understanding, both of the counselor and of the other adults in the family circle, are of major importance. Like children, too, old people often make noticeable changes in conduct without any expressed insights or explanations.

Joe is a six-year-old boy who is not adjusting to school. As the mother gave his background, it became evident there were many other problems in addition to the school problem. The excerpt which follows is from an interview with the mother and father (O) :[2]

MOTHER: . . . I know he has a lot of emotional problems. He always makes statements like, "I'm going to run away." I haven't taken them seriously, but he did run away, and so—but he shouldn't, I mean a child that age, shouldn't brood on such a thing and what happens to you after you die. He's an only child. He uh—has never had a play-mate his age . . . I think another thing—if he ever had a chance to excel, it might give him a little more confidence . . . Now, I think such things as the bedwetting and so on are probably an outgrowth of these other problems—nightmares and things like that. He dreams of a prowler standing up on some kind of wheels and coming at him . . . The other day he said, "Oh, dear, I wish I wouldn't have to go back to school," and I said, "Why?" and he said, "Because I'm so afraid of people."

FATHER: I wonder about his getting in fights with these children his own age in school. They pick on him simply because he doesn't defend himself at all. He just cries . . . I was just wondering whether uh—when we find out it's a case of his not wanting to fight back and they continue to pile abuse on him, why, if we shouldn't uh—shouldn't develop some method to make him fight back for his own self-protection. Every day he comes home from school crying.

Excerpts from play interviews with Joe:

One of the problems which the mother discussed was nightmares. In the interviews, Joe pretends he is in nightmare land in which the toys are nightmares and the people are nightmares. In a series of interviews he gets rid of all the nightmares except one, which is a magic nightmare. Although this nightmare keeps coming back to life, he successfully imprisons him at the end of the interview. The following is from the seventh interview:

JOE: This nightmare plane is definitely exploded. There's one more nightmare plane. The nightmare plane is knocking things over. Bang! Bang! . . . The father gets up and chases the nightmare plane. . . . Zoom! Crash! The nightmare plane exploded. Now, the nightmare doctor is walking down the street, and he don't see the river, and he

---

[2]Designated by symbol (O).

goes and walks right into the river. And the water goes up and up and over him until the nightmare doctor is drowned.

C: Now, the nightmares are gone. The nightmare plane exploded and the nightmare doctor just went in the river.

J: No, here's one more nightmare. He knows some magic that will keep him getting back to life. He can't die.

C: There is still another nightmare.

J: The baby can't get him dead. They wish they could. He hides behind here. They want to get him dead.

C: They are trying very hard to get rid of that last nightmare, but they haven't done it yet.

J: The tree falls on the nightmare man. It kills him.

C: The magic nightmare man is now killed.

J: Now, we will start putting things up.

C: Now, you can start building up again, since the nightmares are all gone.

J: Just as they get things together again, the nightmare jumps up. People don't know what to do to keep him dead. (Joe builds a jail out of blocks and puts the nightmare man in it.)

C: They are all trying to keep the nightmare man in jail with blocks all around him so he won't get out.

J: Yeah, they are putting the blocks on top too.

In the next interview, he is a giant—a giant who is "not afraid of anything." It is not hard to see why the mother reported that, as far as she knew, he had not had any nightmares now for two weeks. When the interviews end after three more sessions, the mother reports:

We're very happy about his other problems. He's done beautifully. . . . There's quite a change. . . . I don't think we have any problem any more. I think he's quite normal. I'm very happy. His school work has greatly improved. His teacher says that he plays with the other children now. He doesn't come home crying any more.

Play Is the Child's Language.   This excerpt may appear unusual to some adults who have lost touch with early childhood. Such expressions of children seem strange only because, as adults, we are no longer aware of the child's way of saying things. But, to anyone at all familiar with a young child's manner of expression and communication, it is apparent that Joe has used the toys and the play fantasy surrounding them to objectify and get out of himself these fearsome nightmare images.

When an adult talks he can aid his expression by a free and varied use of analogy. He may say that he is "in a rut" and "afraid of a crackup." The little child has not yet acquired such use of language. But he may have the same feelings. If so, he might draw a deep ditch. In fact, he might keep making it deeper to communicate to the counselor how much "in a rut" he really felt he was. Or, to show his fear of a "crack-up" he might take two planes or two tanks or anything available and crack them up repeatedly (but not break them). In the same way, too, as an adult will only cautiously reveal his fears or deep problems, so a little child might spend some time drawing his ditch deeper and deeper, before he would communicate to the counselor that he was down at the bottom of it. The counselor can no more push him to this statement before he is ready to make it or show it by drawing himself there, than he can push an adult to admit his deep state of discouragement until he has expressed it himself. The little child, too, undergoes the same process of being insecure in the interview and of gradually acquiring security through the counselor's warm, accepting, and understanding responses.

Seen in this light, then, Joe, by putting the nightmare man in jail and surrounding him with blocks, is equivalently saying that he probably is beginning to get control of the fears which have previously bothered him so much. In the next interview, when he identifies himself with the giant who "isn't afraid of anything," he is saying in this context that now he feels he has these fears in hand and he does not think they will bother him any more. If we can judge by actions, the mother's report would seem to verify this.

Objectify Fears. In this way, with the counselor's help, the child is able to look at his fears by turning them into more familiar objects of his play and story world. Seen and expressed through the toys and play, the fears somehow lose their paralyzing effect. They become a part of the real world as he is gradually able to live with them and control them. This excerpt is typical of many interviews which produce noticeable changes in a child without his being able to give any detailed explanation of why he has changed. Unquestionably such interviews give the child a strong feeling of assurance and security because he recognizes that the counselor accepts and understands. By being enabled to get his fears out before an adult, in play symbols, and to objectify them through an adult's response, the child can then cope with them on a more realistic and less terrifying basis.

As we previously discussed, in relation to adults, one of the qualities which gives fear its power over the small child appears to be his inability to look at it squarely. This is similar to the reaction of seeing an object with peripheral vision.[3] As long as a thing remains confusedly on the periphery of the child's outlook, it constantly threatens and scares him. Somehow, if he can get it directly in front of him, he can measure it for what it is. When he can do this through the language of his toys, such fears often seem to lose their disturbing force. In this particular excerpt, Joe gives no clear explanation of why he is able to control this fear after the nightmare man is dead. But the parents' report and the change of his conduct show that, somehow, he does understand himself and his world better. The nightmare fear is no longer a source of insecurity and confusion.

REJECTION

Illustration. In addition to fears, the small child, through the symbolism of play material, can express deep feelings of rejection or acceptance. For example, another first grader who feels himself completely isolated from his group, plays with airplanes and has all the American soldiers destroyed by one enemy plane. By reason of talk about war, he already recognizes an enemy as someone who is not wanted, and who may even be hated. Gradually, he identifies himself with the pilot of the enemy plane. As in the case of Joe's nightmares, so for this child, the activities of the enemy plane express basic feelings. Some of these are not difficult to interpret. In his playing the enemy pilot, we have a vivid expression of a young child's feeling of group rejection. He feels his companions are against him; so he becomes an enemy who attacks them, and whom they fear and hate.

In the process of counseling play, the child acquires an ever increasing feeling of belonging to others and of being accepted by them. At the same time that he begins to participate with other children in games in the school yard and in other activities, his play

[3]Pp. 140–141.

in the interview changes. He is no longer an enemy pilot, but has joined the American forces and is now part of the American army. In this way, he communicates his new feelings of belonging to his group.

Not Wanted. The parents, meanwhile, in thinking out their side of the problem together, gradually faced the fact that, having been married only a year at the time, they had resented his coming. The father, especially, admitted a confused hostility to the child because, at first, he took so much of the young mother's time and attention. The father felt somewhat neglected. Yet, neither he nor his wife had clearly seen these feelings before. Having thought them through in a series of interviews, they were both better able to accept their real relationship to each other and the child. This, too, of course—as well as the play interviews—was an important factor in the child's improvement.

Other Child in the Family. The following is typical of the kind of reaction that often takes place when a three-and-one-half-year-old wakes up one morning and realizes that his world has been shattered by the introduction of a little stranger, who now is the center of attention and has robbed him of his position in the home. In addition to some minor hostile actions against the baby, when the mother's back was turned, Billy had, since the baby's arrival, developed a number of physical irregularities, including vomiting, which the pediatrician diagnosed as psychogenic. If not rectified, this physical condition could become serious. The following situation took place during the first counseling session with Billy.

For some time after the interview began, Billy played indifferently with the toys, saying nothing. Gradually, he included the counselor in his play, by demonstrating his ability to fly planes and maneuver the various mobile toys. Some conversation accompanied this play. There was then some molding, fingering, and patting of loose clay, and a comparatively long period during this process when he said nothing to the counselor. There was, however, a growing sense of community between the two, indicated by the various looks and warming smiles which Billy was beginning to give the counselor from time to time. In such ways, a little child indicates, sometimes far more effectively than an adult can with words, how much the counselor's acceptance, attention, and understanding mean to him. Then, suddenly, with a pause and look, not unlike that which an adult might make when he was ready to present a really serious problem, Billy looked up and said (N) :[4]

BILLY: A big black hole.

C: You would like to have a big black hole.

B: Yeah! A big black hole. (He is speaking rapidly and making gestures to show how big.)

C: You would like to have a great big *deep* black hole.

B: Yeah! A great big deep black hole, a great big deep black hole, a great big deep black hole (Repeated very fast. Pause. Billy then went through a series of scooping out gestures to show how deep the hole would have to be. There was another pause, then Billy resumed.)

B: Get the baby.

C: You would like to have the baby now.

B: Yeah! (He gave the counselor a long look as if not quite sure he could confide this secret to him. Then, suddenly and rapidly he speaks.) The baby in the big black hole, the baby in the big black hole, the baby in the big black hole. (Billy ran and got an imaginary cover, put it over the hole and then jumped gleefully up and down on the spot, singing, "the baby in the big black hole!")

An adult in the same situation, whose peace of mind and domestic tranquility had been shattered by a series of misunderstandings and rejections, might talk about a separation or a divorce or he might even say that he never wanted to see the other person again. Billy, having something of the same intense feelings, explained them in the strongest way he knew. The parents, who lived in a new section of the city, mentioned that just previous to this interview Billy had been out with his father to watch the men dig a sewer. This had suggested to him a way of expressing how deeply he felt about the baby's disrupting his world.

Attention on Baby. The parents in their interview were, about that time, growing aware of how much more attention and consideration they were giving the baby than they were giving Billy. They were beginning to realize that Billy was not entirely wrong in his feeling that they had somewhat neglected him in favor of the younger and more attractive child.

In the same way as it happens with an adult, once Billy was able to get his feeling out in an understanding relationship and express it in an objective way, so that it could be reflected back calmly and im-

[4]Designated by symbol (N).

personally to his dawning understanding, the feeling seemed to lose its hold over him. Just as the adult gets so much help from "being able to tell someone about it," so the little child seems to get the same positive lift when he can communicate his feelings through the toys and play. As the parents recognized their attitudes and began to change them so Billy's reaction, too, became more positive. In a comparatively short time, the vomiting ceased and his manner toward his baby sister improved.

THE COUNSELING SETTING

The Room. To achieve these kinds of results, the play room and material do not have to be elaborate. Ideally, a playroom should be simple and natural. It should allow the child ordinary freedom of action. If paints are used, he should have some freedom to smear. An aid to this is to surround an ordinary room with plaster board screens three or four feet high. This protects the wall. If the child should happen to splatter paint or make finger marks, the counselor does not need to be cautioning him continually. The temporary walls can be folded up and put aside after the play session. If necessary, the floor, too, can be covered with canvas or some other material that can be rolled up.

The Materials. Ordinary materials are used, such as dolls, guns, soldiers, a house with furniture and rooms which can be organized and arranged. Certain toys aid special needs. A bottle of water with a nipple, for example, allows the child to be a baby if he wishes. If the situation permits it, materials with which he can make noise, such as guns, whistles, and some sort of pounding toys may be included. Finger paints are also helpful as a means of symbolic language. Clay material is valuable. It should be soft enough so that the child can mold it into images and forms. If possible there should be a sandbox for small children. A small puppet stage is also an asset. The child can get behind it and put on a show with the puppets or, as often happens, forgetting the puppets, he can give a monologue about himself and his feelings.

It would be misleading, however, to give the impression that child counseling could only be successful in such a setting as this. We have found play interviews successful even in a well-kept and well-furnished parlor. Here, extreme limits had to be placed on the child. He could make no noise and had to be very careful with the toys. Even within such limits counseling can be effective. Interviews can also be carried on in an ordinary classroom with only a few toys, dolls, or clay.

Limits on the Child's Actions. Limits, of course, are as essential to child interviews as they are to interviews with adults. However, except in the matter of time and some similar factors, adults are usually governed by more or less normally accepted social manners. These limits are self-imposed by the adult and the counselor seldom has to invoke them. Most adults, too, even in matters of speech, conform their words and phrases to standards which they judge would be proper and acceptable to the counselor. This may vary somewhat according to the counselor's role. They may speak a little differently to a physician, for example, than they might to a priest. In general, however, there are only minor variations in the manner of expression, and it is rare that the adult says or does anything for which the counselor might have to call forth restrictions.[5]

With children, though, particularly those who are very young or who are more anti-social, direct limits may sometimes need to be invoked. While children, too, are generally governed by social amenities, they are less affected by them. The clue to child interviews, therefore, is freedom within limits. There are the normal restrictions against destroying property, or attacking the person of the counselor. The permanent furniture of the room, telephone, lights, windows, and similar objects are considered "out of bounds," in the child's play expression. Within such normal limits, the child should be free to choose his own play materials and to play and talk about whatever he wishes in the same way as the adult determines what he discusses.

Twilight Zones. Within these normal limits, however, are a number of twilight zones that may or may not arise. Bixler points out,

Wherever possible it seems desirable to use well-defined limits. Both the child and therapist can achieve greater comfort when confronted with concrete demarcation between acceptable and unacceptable behavior. Such limits are easier to distinguish and are less apt to lead to insecurity on the part of the therapist . . . No matter how hard one may try, it is unlikely that he can remove all relative limits. If for no other

[5]This, of course, would be increasingly less applicable as we enter into the more extreme types of adult disorder, particularly those demanding institutional care.

reason, the therapist will see many of his "rigid" limits melt before the uncanny ability of the maladjusted child. With consummate ease he manages to place himself squarely on the line of demarcation between acceptable and unacceptable behavior. To what extent the therapist may go in setting rigid limits will be determined in part by his own comfort with intangible limits.[6]

Invoking Limits. Acceptance and understanding are as essential to the flow of a child's interview as they are in adult counseling. The main considerations here, therefore, are not only what the child wants to do, but the degree to which his conduct disturbs the counselor's feeling of ease and relaxed "at oneness" with him. Assuming such limits are not excessively rigid, they can be as effective in counseling as limits in matters of injury to furniture or the deliberate breaking of toys. Limits, as Bixler points out, cannot always be determined beforehand. The counselor must often make his judgment from the individual circumstances. He should then state the limit. Such limits, when calmly and firmly imposed, do not involve any rejection of the child. "Under these conditions it is quite possible to feel acceptance of the child and his attitudes while rejecting a phase of his behavior."[7] It is important, too, whenever possible, to reflect the child's attitude or underlying emotion, so that he may have a chance to understand the urge that makes him want to break the limit. Such reflection is generally sufficient to cause the child to desist. When, for example, through the counselor's accepting and clarifying statement, he sees the motive for his anger, he very often is no longer urged to hurl the toy he is holding in his hand but quietly puts it down and continues his play.

If, however, the child does violate the limits, then the interview should end immediately. The child should know that the violation of a stated restriction is the cause of the ending of the interview. At the same time he should be made aware that he can renew the interview again at the next appointment. Bixler's comment on this is,

The therapist may find that the more precise his limits and the more quickly they are invoked, the easier it is for him to use them therapeutically.[8]

[6]Ray H. Bixler: "Limits Are Therapy," *J. of Consult. Psychol.*, Vol. 13, No. 1, February 1949, p. 3. Reproduced with the permission of the *Journal* and of the American Psychological Association.

[7]*Ibid.*, p. 4.

[8]*Ibid.*, p. 11.

Limits Are Reality. Such limits, like those of the real world in which he lives, are very valuable in enabling the child to meet reality and adjust to it. Having recognized such limits and conformed himself to them, he has moved a step further in his struggle to attain a better way of life.

Illustrations. In the following excerpt, the child recognizes how the counselor's skill in reflecting his attitudes towards her restriction makes the interview much more than playing with toys.

TIMMY (picking up a handful of sand and looking at the counselor with a twinkle in his eye): Right square in your hair this'll come.
C: You'd like to throw it at me just because—? (Counselor stops deliberately to see if he will finish the sentence. He does.)
T: Because *you* won't let us come back.
C: Because I can't let you come back, you'd like to throw it at me.
T: (smiles, and sifts the sand gently through his fingers, kneels down in the sand table beside the counselor, and says in a voice of gentle wonder): How do you always know why I do what I do?
C: You think I understand you pretty well.
T: You really do. You must be magic.[9]

The young child senses the delicate way his feelings and attitudes flow through the counselor. Somehow he becomes more aware of himself through her. To see his motives so clearly amazes the child. As the counselor reflects his feelings back to him, he understands why he wanted to throw the sand. Once the feeling is brought out in the open, the attack motive ceases. The child's tension and irritation are gone. He is filled with the sense of acceptance, through the counselor's sensitive understanding of his attitudes.

The child sometimes symbolizes his hostility by rebelling against one of the limits. The counselor should insist on the demands of reality and, at the same time, give acceptance and understanding of the child's hostility. We see how this is done in the following excerpt of an interview with a group of children, where one child deliberately uses a forbidden object to express hostility:

(M keeps lifting receiver of real telephone, casting glances at counselor.)
C: You want to see what you can do, but we are to use the play phone only.

---

[9]Virginia Axline: *Play Therapy*, Boston, Copyright 1947, by Houghton Mifflin Co., p. 260. (The symbol C. for Counselor has been substituted for Therapist for all excerpts taken from this book.)

(M begins to dial phone and continues to look at C.)

S: Marjorie, quit doing that.

M: Let me dial it like this.

C: You don't like to be bossed. You want to have your own way.

M: Let me do it just once.

C: You want to see just how far you can go.

M: Just once more and then I'll quit. (When she begins to dial, C goes over to phone where Marjorie has both hands on it, and is pleading for "just one more.")

C: You don't want to see someone get the best of you.

M: (Angrily) Just once more. (Clings to phone.)

C: It makes you mad at me, but you are to use the toy phone to play with.

M: (Loudly) Let me do it just once!

C: You don't like it when someone says you can't do something, and then you beg them until they let you.

M: Just once more; no one answers.

C: You can get mad at me, but play with the little phone.

S: Marjorie, get away from there.

M: Just once more. (At this point S brings over a tube of glue and asks counselor to open it. M watches her, then walks over to toy phone, picks it up but immediately puts it down.)

S: Is it O.K. if I paste two pieces of wood together?

C: You always want people to tell you what you can do.

M: Sally, you dumb ape. (Kicks block on floor.)

C: Makes you still a little mad because you couldn't use the phone.

M: Sally, come and tell me where you got the hammer.

S: No.

M: Why not? (S ignores her and tries to put glue on wood.) This old gooey stuff. It won't stick.

M: I'm glad.[10]

The counselor insists on limits and, at the same time, clarifies the child's feeling. This dissolves negative emotions more effectively than a reprimand or punishment. In the following excerpt the child has begun to throw blocks:

C: You're not afraid, Buddy, but those big blocks might hurt someone. Use these smaller ones.

BUDDY: Okay. (He hurls the smaller ones up against the ceiling and they bounce all around the room. Charles, who wears glasses, looks a bit fearful.)

[10]This excerpt is taken from material collected by Virginia M. Axline. Reproduced with her permission.

CHARLES: Now you be careful, Buddy.

BUDDY: I ain't a-scared. (He hurls a handful of blocks skyward.)

C: Buddy, you might break Charles' glasses. Please don't throw any more.

BUDDY: I ain't a-scared.

C: We know you're not scared. That isn't the point. It might hurt someone in here.

BUDDY: I ain't a-scared. (But not throwing any.)

CHARLES (yelling at Buddy): Well, do you want to *hurt* somebody?

BUDDY: (yelling back) No! I don't want to hurt somebody.

CHARLES (screaming at Buddy): Well, then.

BUDDY: (screaming back) Well, yourself. (He tries to take Charles' blocks. They have a tussle. Both boys are now standing up in the sand table. Charles gets the best of Buddy, who sits down, grabs up the celluloid bulldog and a block and hammers the dog.) I'll kill you, Charles. This is you, see? I'm beating you up.

C: When you can't hit Charles, it helps to pound up the toy.

BUDDY: (throwing a handful of sand wildly) I'm mad! I'm mad! I'm mad!

C: You *are* real mad.

BUDDY: (Laughing) Nope. All over now.

C: You got over it in a hurry.[11]

The limits placed on his actions arouse Buddy's resentment to a climax of "I'm mad! I'm mad!" Yet, when the counselor holds up this feeling to him, the child relaxes.

Sudden Insights. A child's insights often take place quickly and produce immediate change in his actions. Such new understanding of himself or others may pop right out in the middle of a play experience. In the following excerpt Tom is playing with a puppet:

T: (holding up the boy puppet.) This is Ronny the bad boy. Boy! is he bad. He is now at home in bed. His *father* is downstairs. He wants him to get up. Ronny's father is always bossing him around. (Laughs) But he doesn't get very far as you shall see. (T's voice changes completely.)

FATHER: (Ugly tone of voice) Ronny. Get out of bed.

R: (sleepily) Don't want to.

F: You hear me. You get out of bed or I'll—

R: Or you'll what?

F: I'll come up there and I'll make you.

R: Don't brag so.

11Axline: *op. cit.*, p. 252.

F: You get ready and go to school.

R: I don't want to go to school. I don't like school. Besides—I—I—I—
I got a stomach ache.

F: A stomach ache? You *are* a liar. And you're dumb. You don't learn
a thing in school.

R: Why don't I?

F: 'Cause you're dumb. You're the dumbest white boy I ever knew.

R: I am not dumb. I'll show you. I'll—I'll—I'll—Well, I'll—(F.
spanks R.)

R. Ow! Ow! Oh, you mean, mean man.

Later:

F: What is your name?

R: Ronny.

F: Ronny what?

R: Ronny Gooseberry.

F: Are you a smart alec?

R: Am I a smart alec? I just hate myself for being a smart alec.

F: Listen you.

R: Listen *you*.

F: Why I'll murder you.

R: Oh yeah! Well we'll see about that. (F. and R. fight. R. beats up F.
who begs for mercy.)

F: I'll send my son after you. (R. disappears, then comes up again, this
time as the son.)[12]

Ronny's admittance "Am I a smart alec? I just hate myself for
being a smart alec" is a deep statement of Tom's attitude towards
himself. This kind of reflective, objective awareness if it is clarified
by the counselor often produces striking changes in the child. As with
adults, the child's seeing himself objectively in a very distasteful light
is the first step in the direction of a different plan of conduct.

What is deceptive and surprising about children is that they may
not need a long interview process to arrive at this. The awareness
can come suddenly, and with it a new mode of action spontaneously
develops. Probably because a child's memory of past experiences is
less involved and his reactions are closer to the surface, insights come
more rapidly than with adults. Sometimes the change is immediate.
These quick changes of insight and conduct illustrate one of the
most fascinating aspects of child interviews. With adults we expect
a slow process of change and a very hesitant acceptance of new

[12]*Ibid.*, pp. 34–36.

insights and new attitudes. But children are more mobile and free in the interview experience. Somehow, once they start to face a situation, they face it completely and without reserve. Consequently, we may be a little startled at the rapid change when these objective insights have been reached. Despite this, these changes are often permanent and produce lasting effects, as the parents verify over a period of weeks or months.

Recognition of Dramatic Roles. While the child identifies himself with the play and finds it a means of expressing his own attitudes and feelings, he never seems to lose the awareness that it is play. No matter how intensely involved the child may become in his play, he somehow keeps before himself the contrast of reality with play. This is often indicated in interviews where the child will distinguish between what he can do in play and what he would do in the real world. We see an example of this in the following excerpt:

Tom: . . . This would be fun, too. (Picks up the puppet) I could make up plenty of funny plays about the fixes I get in. Just my autobiography would bring tears to their eyes.

C: You think your life is sad.

T: Well, I mean it is certainly full of something. I'm always in trouble. (T. puts puppet on his hand.) Now see here. I'll *murder* you if you don't do as I say. See? (Voice is completely changed—low, deep, threatening.)

C: He feels like murdering someone.

T: I do, too, sometimes. Only of course (laughs) I don't. Respect for the law and all that, you know. But tell you what. Next time I come I'll put on a play. Episode One. My life and troubles.

C: All right. Next time you come you present your life and troubles.[13]

The child uses particular words and phrases, in his dramatic roles, for strong effects. He is not concerned with actual meanings or even logical sequences. Language is used to express feelings more than ideas. He may use phrases as "kill" and "murder" as he does in this play, without giving them any of the tones an adult would understand and feel. Whether he mentions it or not, the child seems quite aware of the dramatic situations and, like any good actor, is making the best of his lines and getting as deep an emotional tone into them as he can. He knows, however, that he is in a play experience. In

[13]*Op. cit.,* p. 33.

addition, he has the calm, objective responses of the counselor to enable him to see his feelings and to understand them in that aspect of himself which the play is unfolding. If, however, the counselor is unsure of this and feels more at ease if he has clearly defined the *play* aspect, he may wish to make such a structuring statement.

Compromise. Like the adult, the child does not always see his problems clearly at the opening of the interview. He may not be willing to admit that he has any problems. There is the same tendency to avoid facing the seriousness of the situation. Children also often say that they only came because someone else sent them. We have seen how adults do not always face the responsibility of their problems in an opening interview. We can see this same avoidance of responsibility in play interviews. But, the openness of the child makes the avoidance more obvious. The child may state that he has no problems and, in the same breath, express his need to tell his difficulties to some accepting person, as in the following interview:

FIRST CONTACT. Tom came into the room, wearing his hat and coat, and sat down at the table. He had a little tin whistle in his hand and twisted the mouthpiece off and on as he sat there. His expression was very serious. He avoided the counselor's eyes.

TOM: Well, here I am. I just came because . . . out of curiosity, you know. I couldn't understand what Mother was talking about. She said that you would help me with my problems, but I don't have any problems.

C: You don't think you have any problems, but your curiosity made you look into this.

T: Oh, yeah! I'm curious. Always stickin' my nose in everything. Thought I'd come and see.

C: You would like to see what counseling is like.

T: Counseling. That's the word I couldn't remember. Yeah, only I haven't any problems. (Pause) Except that . . . well . . . a . . . my dad . . . *step*-dad, really . . . I can't stand him and he can't stand me, and when he's home and when I'm home there's trouble, trouble, trouble. I make too much noise. I'm in the way. I put my feet up on things. We can't stand each other. The only time I can bear to be around the house is when he is gone.

C: You and your father don't get along well together.

T: My *step*-father.

C: Your *step*-father.

T: But I don't have any problems.

C: Even though you and your step-father don't get along, you don't feel that that is any problem.

T: Nope. And all the kids pick on me. They don't like me. (Pause) I can't think of anything to say. Mother said I was to talk about my problems, but I don't have any problems.

C: Let's forget what your mother said to talk about. Just talk about anything you want to bring up. Or don't talk at all, if you'd rather not.

T: Like that flag episode last week? You want to hear about that? They all ganged up on me. 'Cause I said "I spit on the flag." And I said, "Heil Hitler." They all ganged up on me. But I really didn't spit on the flag. I just did it to get their goats. Believe me, I did, too.

C: You wanted to get their goats and you certainly did. To say something shocking like that got their attention right away.

T: I don't know why I did it, though. I really wouldn't spit on the flag. I'm a good American. I have too much respect for the flag to spit on it. But that's what I did. They ganged up on me and beat me up. I was outnumbered.

C: You can't understand why you sometimes do things like that.

T: Not because I got beat up, either. I just—But I haven't got any problems.

C: You don't like to admit that you have problems.

T: That's about the size of it. I really have more than my share of problems. My step-dad. And our substitute teacher. Gosh, she's mean. And nobody likes me. I don't know why. I don't think there's a person alive who doesn't have problems.

C: You really believe that everybody has problems, then, and that you are really no different from anyone else.

T: Only I'll admit that I've got problems. Some people won't admit it.

C: You're ready to start by admitting that you've got problems.

T: My life is no picnic.

C: You're not very happy.

T: Would anybody ever know what I say? My Mother or anybody? Are you writing what I say down?

C: I'm making some notes; but no one will ever be told what you say during this time.[14]

T: (with deep sigh) You know this is a mighty peculiar situation. Are you writing this down?

C: Some of it. Just for my own information.

---

[14]The counselor obviously meant this in reference to school authorities, playmates, and the child's immediate situation. She evidently did not feel it was necessary at this time to explain to the child that she might want to use these notes later in a disguised form.

T: Yeah. (Long pause)

T: Teachers don't care what happens. No one cares what happens to a guy, and here it is after school and you're not even my teacher and I don't bother you. I don't get in your hair. And yet————(shrugs shoulders)

C: You didn't think other people cared enough about what happens to a guy and yet . . . [15]

This process of facing the need for help, which comes about much more slowly with adults, takes place quickly here. It is none the less very well handled. The transition from a compromise state to the open facing of himself with, "I really have more than my share of problems," comes so suddenly the counselor's contribution to it could easily be missed. The same transition which took place in two or three minutes in this excerpt might take a whole interview or more with an adult. But the steps are the same: from a stage of insecurity and unwillingness to talk about himself and his problems, to a feeling of acceptance and security with the counselor, and then complete freedom in admitting that he needs the counselor's help.

Note-taking. This excerpt also illustrates the way the counselor deals with questions of note-taking. The child is quietly told that the material is confidential and the notes are for the counselor's own information. Having made this statement, or implied such a relationship, the counselor must stand by it. A grave hurt could come to the child if the material, which he expects to be kept secret, is revealed to his parents or to school authorities. The counselor must genuinely feel that his role is to help the child work out his own problems in his own way and not one where he must investigate the child's attitudes and report them.

Confidences. This is particularly important in matters that involve school discipline. The authority and regulations of the school, like any other limits of reality, must be maintained. Any place where a large number of people are together, must have regulations to protect the common rights and freedom of everyone. The child knows and understands this. When he finds it difficult to conform to these limits, he needs the aid of an understanding person to enable him to see why he cannot adjust. Neither the counselor nor the child

[15]Axline: *op. cit.*, pp. 30–32.

are attempting to change the limits of reality. They are, however, trying sincerely to work out together the confusions and conflicts which make it difficult for the child to conform. While he is going over his confusions and hostilities with the counselor, he needs the security and protection of a confidential relationship in which what he says is a genuinely privileged communication. The counselor must be careful not to let any statements or attitudes enter into any other contacts with the child which the child might feel were drawn from counseling information. This is not easy. It is best done if the counselor openly faces with the child the fact that he has other roles, such as, teacher, disciplinarian or some other form of authority. The child must realize that even though he will keep this particular information secret, he may be forced to act in these other roles according to information which is publicly known to him. If this is presented openly the child can understand these different roles, and the necessity the counselor may have of enforcing discipline in such an official role. By this open method the child is given the opportunity to make his choice of counseling in the face of these other counselor functions. The child may decide that the other roles are so threatening to him that he cannot talk freely to the counselor. He may either seek someone else or decide to speak no further of the personal things which are bothering him. He should be free to do this without in any way incurring the counselor's resentment. The counselor's relaxed acceptance of the child's resistance seems the best way to enable him to begin to unfold himself. If he decides to continue to talk, there has been no misunderstanding.

Attachment to Mother. With small children, the attachment to the mother is sometimes so great that a certain amount of understanding and skill may be necessary before a counseling relationship can be set up. In the following case it took nearly a half-hour before the beginning of a play interview was possible (M) :[16]

The mother came in with John, age five. John is very resentful and hostile to his younger sister, age three. His behavior has reached the state where the parents do not know "what to do with him." He is holding very tightly to his mother's hand. Two counselors meet the mother and John in the waiting room. There are a few pleasantries and then one counselor says:

[16]Designated by symbol (M).

C: Mrs. Jones, I'd like to see you, if you wish, in this room.
C2: Johnnie, would you care to come in this room with me? (Then C2 walks into the room.)

In the following diagrams we have indicated the positions and gradual process by which Johnnie comes to accept the counseling interview:

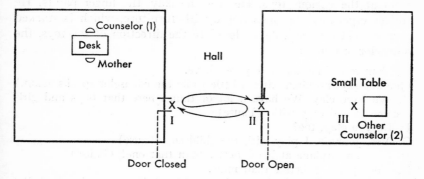

The first counselor and the mother enter the counseling room and the door is closed. As soon as the door is closed, Johnnie stands just outside in the position *I*. He begins to cry; the sobs come alternately loud and soft. This continues intermittently for about ten minutes. The mother, seated before the one counselor inside the closed door, must determine whether or not she is going to open the door. This constitutes the opening content of her interview. Because she is already somewhat aware of her tendency to over-protection, we are at the heart of the problem for the mother. If the mother can allow Johnnie to remain outside the door and face the situation on his own, she has begun to see him as a distinct person and not someone she must always make dependent on her.

Counselor (2) walks into the room and sits down at the small table on which there is a pile of clay. He says nothing but begins to finger the clay and maneuver it. He makes different objects with it, now and then looking in Johnnie's direction. After about ten minutes, Johnnie walks slowly over towards the open door of the office. He watches what Counselor (2) is doing. The counselor does not immediately respond to this. He lets some time go by and then quietly:

C: You're kind of watching what's going on in here.

JOHNNIE: No! (Emphatically) He turns back and runs over to the closed door again crying even louder than before.

Soon he returns and stands in the open doorway, still watching the counselor. He has stopped crying. About fifteen minutes of the half-hour interview has already passed. He begins to look around the room at the various toys. He sees the clay, the finger paints. He notices especially the open house with furniture, which is stacked over against the wall. As he looks in the direction of the toys, the counselor responds:

C: Your're looking at the toys we have.

(Johnnie says nothing. After a little while the counselor speaks again.)

C: We have clay. We have a lot of things here that boys and girls come in and play with. (Pause)

J: Do you play, too?

C: Yes, Johnnie, I play with the children. (Pause)

J: I got an airplane at home better than that one! (Pause)

C: Your plane is better than mine.

J: That old stuff! I don't like that stuff! (Referring to the clay) Bet I can make something better than you can! What ya making?

C: You're sure you can make a better airplane than this one.

J: Sure I can! Wantta see me?

C: You'd like me to see you make an airplane.

J: Sure, I can make a plane!

By this time Johnnie has walked slowly over and started to take up the clay, and an interview relationship has begun.

With many small children the beginning of a counseling relationship in which, like Johnnie, they freely leave the mother's protection and come to accept a relationship with the counselor, is sometimes a difficult process. Yet this, too, is somewhat similar to the opening interview with adults. First, Johnnie moves from a dependency in which he is pleading for the mother's sympathy by crying at the door, to compromise by standing in the doorway of the counseling-play room. Finally, he begins active participation in the play. This is not unlike the way a dependent, insecure adult compromises in his approach to the counselor, and then gradually begins to take the independent steps of talking about his problems in the interview.[17] Allen, commenting on a small girl's use of a doll, points out,

17P. 340.

The doll which at the beginning was a protection and a mask, and thus the means of avoiding her real self, was utilized by child and therapist as an aid for the child to come more into the open when she could begin to be herself.

Beginning where the child actually is and dealing directly and immediately with his feelings, rather than with his problem behavior and its causes, give an immediate impetus and meaning to the therapeutic process. The child is taken for what he is, and is not squeezed into any theoretical scheme nor cajoled into giving up any particular "secrets" or content. Whatever form the child's feelings may take, angry or fearful, happy, or sad, aggressive or placating, talkative or silent, "co-operative" or "unco-operative," they engage the therapist's immediate interest because these are the indicators of a troubled child floundering around to find a way of adapting himself to the world in which he lives. The child is accepted as having, within himself, the potentiality for achieving a new inner balance as he is helped to find value in a living relationship. Thus the therapist enters at once into a significant relationship with the child and becomes a growth-inducing influence throughout the steps that follow.[18]

By the end of the first half-hour, this child had accepted the counseling-play world as his own and begun to participate in it. Once a child has accepted the relationship in this way he soon begins to project himself, his feelings, and his problems into the counselor's world. Toys and other play materials are used as aids to communication with the counselor. Through this objective play and the counselor's responses, the child can begin to think objectively about the real world in which he lives. In such counseling interviews, the child is reached on the level most familiar to him. The child may have difficulty in carrying on any sustained and consistent conversation but—he can play. Here, he is at his best. Unhindered by the blocking of adult speech, he can let himself flow into his play and reach acceptance, understanding, and self-knowledge as he sees himself in the play and in the counselor's calm, penetrating responses.

[18]F. H. Allen, M.D.: *Psychotherapy With Children*, New York, Copyright 1942, by Norton & Co., pp. 120–121.

PART FOUR

THE APPROACH TO COUNSELING

In our previous discussion of the counseling process and skill in Parts II and III we were concerned principally with the actual counseling interview itself. This still leaves unexplained a number of broader questions. One such question might be raised about those circumstances and conditions which may aid or discourage a person's coming for counseling. We also ought to consider what can be done when people with personal difficulties do not directly request help from the counselor, either because they do not know he can help them or because they are not ready to face their need. In this section on the approach to counseling, therefore, we will treat, first, how some aspects of the counseling atmosphere and the counselor's own personality and needs may promote or impede counseling. We will then take up, in the following chapters, the way in which certain other roles or positions may sometimes prepare the way for counseling or operate in conjunction with it.

CHAPTER XIV

PREREQUISITES FOR A COUNSELING
ATMOSPHERE

THE PLACE

Privacy. Before people can begin counseling, certain qualities are necessary in the counseling setting itself. One of the first requirements is a private and quiet place. This obvious point is sometimes overlooked. In his anxiety to help others, the potential counselor may fail to realize that the place he has chosen is not suitable for relaxed conversation. For a satisfactory counseling atmosphere, it is not necessary that the room be well-furnished. It may be very plain. It does not matter either, if there is a desk or a formal office. Ideal conditions are not always possible. Successful counseling has taken place in a classroom, an ordinary parlor, or even in some rather neglected place. The most important thing is for the person to be at ease in coming there; to feel that he is wanted and that he can speak normally without too much fear of being overheard.

Security in Speaking Freely. Quiet and privacy are basic to any feeling of freedom. From personal experience we know how tense and even irritating a situation can become if it is noisy or if our privacy is constantly interrupted. This, of course, applies especially in counseling. Unless the room has doors that can be closed and walls that are in some measure soundproof, both the counselor and the person will feel tense and restrained. Such insecurity is generally fatal to counseling. These factors have to be considered in the light of the reticence that is characteristic of any discussion of personal problems. Any further difficulty or interference may be too much and the counseling does not take place.

Not Secret. The place set aside for counseling should, however, be sufficiently open and obvious so that there can be no misunderstandings or adverse comments. This is not only to protect the reputation of the counselor and the person; it affects the counseling itself. If the two people feel ill at ease because of comments, the relationship, even when it achieves some good, is apt only to produce guilt feelings. Usually these feelings will outweigh the good coming from the interviews and cause the relationship to break up.

It is, therefore, essential that counseling be seen as an open, objective, and basically sound relationship. It should not have any tones of secrecy or removal. Even though the rights of privacy and personal confidence need to be preserved, yet it can be generally known what the relationship is and why the person is coming. Others, especially those who are superiors or associates, should have at least some general understanding of the need for such a counseling function. Otherwise, misunderstandings and confusions may arise which can result in personal hurt to the counselor or the person. It would appear better not to attempt counseling under such circumstances. One of the sufferings which a trained counselor may have to undergo in certain situations is the realization of the pressing need for counseling, evident in a number of the children and adults who come to him and yet, at the same time, be faced with a lack of understanding of this need on the part of his own associates. The counselor, in so far as he can, may have to inaugurate a patient process of education in the purpose and need of counsel and counseling before his counseling function is recognized and understood, or, sometimes, is even possible.

Helps Define Relationship.   A definite place for the counseling interviews gives a formal tone to the relationship. This helps define in a person's mind that counseling is a special kind of relationship— distinct from others at which both the counselor and the person may perhaps talk together. The person then has no difficulty in keeping counseling separate from the various other contacts he may have with the counselor. Casual meetings, while valuable in beginning a counseling relationship, as we will see, ordinarily do not seem to accomplish much until they have been channeled into a more formal setting. Security, permanence, and freedom from interruptions, are not usually possible in these chance circumstances. They can best be achieved in a place set up for private conferences.

Importance of First Impression.   Because people coming for counseling are often insecure and self-conscious, it is important that everything be done to make them feel at ease. This extends even to the manner in which the receptionist answers their telephone call or receives them at the door. These small things, so small that they are sometimes completely neglected, often influence the security a person feels when he actually begins a counseling interview. In one counseling center, for example, there was an observable difference when a hired secretary was absent for a month. Trained counselors then took turns answering the telephone and meeting people as they came into the waiting room. Their manner, compared with that of the office girl, was so different in skilled acceptance, that it was apparently the cause of increase in the number of people who returned for interviews. No other change had taken place which could account for it.

This seems strange only if we are focusing on the later aspects of counseling, without realizing that the initial experience is often the one that seems to fix in a person's mind what the relationship is going to be. The telephone conversation or the waiting room atmosphere can sometimes become symbolic of the whole experience. If it is friendly, accepting, and gives a tone of understanding and welcome, then the person begins the interview with pleasant expectancy and relaxed security. On the other hand, if the tone is irritating or rejecting, this will add to the degree of insecurity which the person already feels.

Everyone concerned should, therefore, be at least sufficiently understanding so that he does not lessen or destroy the positive feelings which brought the person to see the counselor. People answering the telephone, opening the door, or at the desk in the waiting room are all key persons in the success or failure of counseling. These positions are usually considered somewhat unimportant and may be given to people who are not sensitive to personal relations. Such people may sometimes impede counseling.

THE COUNSELOR'S POSITION

Confidences. Everyone assumes that the material of a counseling interview will be kept private and personal. This not only requires that certain safeguards be present in the choice of the place for the counseling interview, but it also places special demands on the counselor himself. Once it becomes known that a counselor violates confidences even in a small way, his effectiveness will be seriously impaired. This must be particularly emphasized in interviews with children. When adults express confidences people generally consider them seriously and do not readily violate them. They are not always so conscientiously aware of their obligations to children. But, as we discussed in the previous chapter, the confidences of children are equally important. A child who feels he has been betrayed in a confidential relationship with an adult may be deeply hurt and may even become bitter as he broods over it. Consequently, if, for any reason, the counselor intends to use the information children give him, he should state this openly to the child before the interview begins. If the counselor does not make this clear, then the child has a right to assume a state of confidence for private revelations.[1]

Positions Involving Authority. Some positions which people have may seem in some way to be in conflict with and impede their functioning as counselors. It is generally thought that positions directly involving authority may prevent the confidences necessary to counseling. The Code of Canon Law considers a similar conflict of roles in relation to the Sacrament of Penance when it advises that superiors and masters of novices are not generally to be confessors to their subjects unless the subject freely and sincerely seeks it. For this to be habitual, there must be a grave cause.[2] Spiritual directors in seminaries seldom have anything to do with discipline or recommending students in faculty meetings. These and similar norms and customs have come about because of the difficulties that may arise when a person has to carry out a position of authority and, at the same time, function in a highly personal relationship.

Self-Control and Caution. Consequently, for a person to occupy a disciplinary, supervisory, or superior role and, at the same time, be a counselor, demands self-control and caution. In this case, the counselor should explain that he has this other position. If the counselor is the principal of the school, for example, he has obligations to enforce discipline and carry out school regulations. Any child who comes to him for counseling should be aware that this

---

[1]This presumes a knowledge of what constitutes confidential material and how it may ethically be used. For a detailed treatment of this question see Robert E. Regan: *Professional Secrecy in the Light of Moral Principles: With an Application to Several Important Professions*, Washington, D.C.: The Augustinian Press, 1943; also "Moral Principles Governing Professional Secrecy with an Inquiry into Some of the More Important Professional Secrets," Studies in Sacred Theology, No. 60, 1941, The Catholic University of America, Washington, D.C.

[2]H. Noldin, S.J.:*Summa Theologicae Moralis*, New York, Copyright 1935, by Frederick Pustet, C.N. 518, Vol. III, Nos. 2, 3, pp. 355–356.

new relationship will not change the principal's attitude in other matters. In adult life, too, conflicts may arise between acting as a counselor and certain other positions. If these other roles are understood, and the child or adult still chooses this particular person for counselor, then counseling would seem to be possible. There should be no pretense on the counselor's part, however, and he should make clear his other functions and obligations.

Interview Report. Sometimes, for the purpose of research, or to study more carefully his counseling, or for some other reason, the counselor may want some form of interview record. He may, for example, want a stenographer to take notes. This can be done openly. Experience in research has shown that where there is a just cause for it, people recognize its validity and generally give consent. If it is to be used publicly, people naturally want all identifying material removed. If a stenographer or note-taker comes into the room, he should sit in an inconspicuous position becoming "part of the furniture." Children and adults pay little attention to such a third person once a reasonable explanation of his presence has been given. In instances when the counselor himself is taking notes, people will sometimes ask to look at the notes.

From the experience reported by psychological clinics and counseling centers,[3] there seems to be no difficulty in obtaining recordings of interviews when the clinician gives the reasons why he wants to preserve the recording, and can assure the person that all identifying statements will be removed. It is customary in such research to tell the person that if there is any material he does not want recorded, the counselor will turn off the machine. In a few instances, when he wishes to speak of material he would rather not have reproduced, the person simply says he wishes the machine turned off.

But, as we have pointed out elsewhere, such records or notes of interviews are not necessary for counseling success. The changes in the person himself are the principal determinants of whether he has been helped by the interviews. Consequently, we wish to caution here against the indiscriminate recording of interview material. While people may not generally refuse this when it occurs in a strictly professional research atmosphere, as Porter indicates, they

[3]E. H. Porter, Jr.: *An Introduction to Therapeutic Counseling,* New York, Houghton Mifflin Co., 1950, Copyright by E. H. Porter, Jr., 1950, pp. 167–8.

would likely object and even strongly resent such suggestion of recording in many other situations.

Preserve Personal Dignity. The personal dignity of the one coming for help as well as his rights to privacy and secrecy must be preserved. This increases the person's respect both for the counselor and the integrity of the relationship. People grow more confident and secure in such a relationship and are apt to go much deeper into personal problems and difficulties. They are reassured by the honesty and sincerity of the counselor and his realistic acceptance of them as persons.

If a person does not feel that he is in a position to preserve the integrity of personal interviews, or, knowing himself, he is aware that he tends to speak too readily of what others say to him, he should refer private and personal interviews to someone else. This is a position in which one can do great harm. It is possible to so destroy a person's trust in others that he never readily confides in anyone again.

IMPROVEMENT OF COUNSELOR'S SKILL

In the prerequisites for a counseling atmosphere, while both the counseling setting and the counselor's position have certain significant implications, yet by far the most important aspect is the counselor's own willingness to concentrate on the improvement of his counseling skill. Setting and position are ultimately meaningless if the person in the counselor's role remains insensitive to the major tones and attitudes which appear to constitute constructive counseling. Nothing, therefore, contributes so much to the ease with which people can approach counseling as the counselor's own increasing awareness of ways to improve his responses.

Practicing Responses. In the writer's experience, many counselors, as we have already mentioned a number of times, have improved their skill by the study of interview material such as we have produced throughout this book; by practicing responses to that material and comparing these to the responses that were actually made. As the repeated playing of the same piece on the piano somehow improves a person's ability in playing not only that selection but all other selections, so the repeated study and examination of even one small excerpt of a successful interview seems to bring with it an increase in the counselor's sensitivity in his own counseling with others.

Use of Available Material. Our frequent use of interview excerpts for illustration and study in this book might, in a sense, be misleading. It might give the reader the impression that he cannot improve his own counseling without such a record of his interviews. In addition to the fact that such recordings may be offensive in certain settings and therefore defeat the purpose of counseling, just a detailed report of one's own interview would seem, of itself, to be of no particular value in improving one's counseling. As in the acquisition of any other skill, there seems to be no substitute for effort and perseverance in the development of a good counselor. A student of piano, for example, if he is alert to even the elements of music, can recognize many mistakes as soon as they are made. If he is not so alert, unless he has the advantage of a skilled musician to listen to his playing and suggest improvements, the student is still probably not going to improve much by merely listening to his own records. In any event, neither his own awareness of mistakes nor some more expert person's pointing out mistakes to him, will of themselves improve his playing. At best, they are a first stage. He still must undergo the hard process of correcting these mistakes. This can often be done, and perhaps is most commonly done, by the continued playing of two or three familiar pieces that he has played already many times before. So, in some similar way, it seems less important to emphasize the necessity of an abundance of actual interview material, either one's own or someone else's, and more important to emphasize the thorough and repeated use of the many interview excerpts that are now available.

Excerpts Aid Skill. For this reason, even the comparatively limited number of actual excerpts which are given in this book can be valuable aids in improving the counselor's skill, if he is willing to undergo the tedious effort of repeatedly practicing his own responses to the person's statements. He can do this at varying intervals with the same excerpt, as we have mentioned, by covering the counselor's actual response as it was made in the interview or writing out the person's statements without the counselor's responses and filling in his own responses to these statements. Then he can compare the different responses he makes with those made in the actual counseling. If he does this a number of times, he may grow more and more aware, that, as his ability to penetrate basic attitudes, feelings, and insights increases, his responses will generally become more like those made in the successful interview. Assuming that the successful counseling response reproduced in the printed excerpt would generally be a more adequate one than that of the beginning counselor, he has the advantage of being able to compare his own responses with those which successfully implemented the person's greater adjustment and happiness. In fact, experience in this process of increasing their counseling skill has caused some counselors to feel that it was a much more difficult thing to make an adequate response when faced with a typescript of an interview than in the actual interview itself. In one instance, for example, one counselor repeatedly made poorer responses in a practice session with one of his own interviews than he had previously made in the interview itself. On the other hand, those whose responses with the practice typescript seemed most adequately to correspond to the person's stated awareness experienced an increased sense of improvement and ease in their ability to respond in their own actual counseling experiences. After a person has spent some time on such a detailed study and practice of responses, he should therefore be more aware of all the factors that go into understanding, clarifying, and self-reorganizing counseling. This in turn will be the most constructive thing he can do to create an improved counseling atmosphere and further the growth in responsible and adequate living of those who may come to him.

THE COUNSELOR'S PERSONAL QUALITIES

Knowledge and Stability. The counselor's background, personality, and his own psychological needs and weaknesses can also affect the success of counseling. Certainly, a counselor should be a mature and responsible person. The requirements necessary for the acquisition of counseling skill would demand this. In addition to his understanding of counseling, he ought to have a broad knowledge of the general characteristics that go into personal problems. This would usually be considered to include the fundamentals of such subjects as psychology, sociology, social case work, philosophy, and theology. Above all, the counselor should be sincerely desirous of helping people to help themselves. All his skill and energy should be turned in this direction. He should have an objective and realistic purpose and not use his counseling role as a disguise for some type of personal escape or compensation. These requirements would seem most commonly, but not always, to be found in people already occupying religious, professional, educational and similar positions of responsibility, those from whom someone would ordinarily think of getting personal help. Sometimes, however, a person not in such a position may actually function well as a counselor and, alternately, one who is in a recognized counseling role may do very poorly.

Seek Help if Necessary. The counselor should be conscious of his own limitations. He should be willing to accept help from other skilled people, particularly from psychologists, psychiatrists, physicians, sociologists, and social workers. Very fruitful and mutually advantageous relationships can exist between the counselor and these professions. Whenever, for example, there is even a remote question of serious physical or personality disorder, a psychiatrist, physician, and psychologist should be consulted. The counselor, too, may require the aid of a priest since, as we have seen, personal issues often involve religious questions or lead to a greater awareness of religious need.

Tendency to Dominate. An awareness of the counselor's own personality blind spots is very important to him. He should know his own tendencies. If he is a person with a need to dominate and one who, in a confused way, seeks to have people dependent on him, he may find it hard to be consistent in a counseling role. This is, of course, a tendency in everyone, apparently because it enhances our own sense of security to feel that we are able to guide and direct others. Consequently, it is easy to deceive oneself into thinking that, by creating a strong personal attraction between a person coming for help and ourselves, we are actually promoting a wholesome psychological and spiritual relationship. Actually, this goes against the experience of counselors, who find that a dependency relationship only increases the person's feeling of inadequacy and loss of personal integrity. While it may temporarily afford some strength and support, in the long run the person is all the more insecure when the relationship is removed. Spiritually, too, this is apt to be a kind of false friendship. Often, as Tanquerey points out,

. . . it is but a sort of masked egotism, since one loves the other because of the pleasure he finds in his company. Undoubtedly, he is ready to be of service to him, but this again in view of the pleasure he experiences in drawing the other closer to himself.[4]

Importance of Objective Methods. To avoid this kind of unwise psychological and spiritual attachment, the counselor should be on the lookout for his own weakness in that direction. He must check the methods by which he establishes a relationship, so that it is not based simply on personal appeal. Counseling must be an objective relationship in which a person can work out his own personal problems with the aid of the counselor, but without any feeling of being possessed, or any final need to depend on the counselor. The acquiring of counseling skill aids in avoiding unwise and unfruitful relationships. As long as counseling is aimed at the increased integration of the individual person, and is not in any way used for the purpose of fulfilling the needs of the counselor, it will be helpful. But, if counseling is used as a disguise for the counselor's personal needs, it generally leads to a relationship that is both psychologically and spiritually unproductive if not harmful.

The great spiritual writers and directors have always been aware of the need to be carefully objective with people who come to them for personal spiritual aid. This applies equally to all forms of counseling. They did not deny the deep feelings of gratitude which people whom they helped had toward them, and they accepted a wholesome kind of affection.[5] But yet, they were aware that such relationships could lead to excessive dependencies and an increased feeling of inadequacy and instability on the part of the person coming for help.[6] As Garrigou-Lagrange explains, speaking of the spiritual director,

---

[4]A. Tanquerey: *The Spiritual Life*, Tournai, Belgium, Desclee & Co., 1930, p. 288.

[5]St. Francis De Sales: *Introduction to a Devout Life*, Part 1, C. IV, Ross, New York, Benziger Brothers, 1926.

[6]Pere LeClerq comments that, "The spiritual director does not work for himself but for Christ and for his fellow men. He must renounce that very tempting joy of making others to his own image, of putting on them his own imprint and of prolonging and perpetuating in them his own personality. His ideal must be to enable those whom he guides to be able more and more by themselves to follow in the light of Christ and under the movements of the Holy Spirit. In reality this ideal cannot be absolutely attained for even the most holy have some need of submitting their conduct to the judgment of another but the director must always keep before him that his ultimate goal ought to be for him to be no longer needed. . . . Certain spiritual authors have tended to identify as much as possible the spiritual director as a true superior and to attribute to him an authority properly so called in virtue of which he decides even the minute details of a choice of a state in life: the submission to a director

His charity ought to be disinterested and to incline him, not to draw hearts to himself but to lead them to God. On this point, Tauler is exacting and says that certain directors who draw souls to themselves are like hunting dogs that eat the hare instead of bringing it back to their master. Whereupon the hunter whips them soundly.[7]

Excessive Reassurance. Another tendency that may further dependency or in some other way disturb counseling, is the counselor's desire to "mother" or reassure the person. There is naturally a feeling of pity and sympathy for those who are in personal distress. Understandably, then, the counselor may feel urged to give reassurance and encouragement to one who appears in need. Experience in counseling shows that such reassurance, while not without value, is less effective than the kind of calm, quiet acceptance that enables a person to gain intrinsic confidence in himself. Reassurance from someone else is artificial. As we have seen elsewhere, psychologically disturbed people often tend to have strong feelings of self-rejection. Before new and constructive choices are possible, such persons need to change this attitude to a more positive acceptance of themselves, and the vocation, aptitudes, abilities, appearance, and general state of life that God has given them. The counselor's reassurance, instead of leading these people to responsibility and self-esteem, often makes them all the more anxious to please him. This can restrict their freedom to speak of weaknesses and inadequacies because they fear the loss of his acceptance. Sometimes, too, they grow to resent their dependency since they vaguely recognize that it is impeding their responsible self-development. These attitudes can block the re-examination of motives and weaknesses. But without such painful facing of one's inadequacies there can be no integrated insight and significant self-understanding.

---

becomes then an obligation of obedience strictly speaking. Pere de Guibert has justly remarked that this conception has no foundation in tradition and ecclesiastical teaching. That differing from superiors properly speaking the director is not appointed by God but chosen freely by each so that a person does not practice towards a director the same obedience that one would to a true superior." Translated from Georges LeClerq: *La Conscience du Chrétien:* Aubier, Editions Montaigne, Paris, 1946, pp. 248–249. See also *Rivista di Vita Spirituale,* Anno V, No. 3, Roma 1951, for detailed discussion by a number of spiritual writers of the relationship of obedience to spiritual direction. They generally agree that it is not one of obedience, strictly speaking. However, in spiritual direction, it is important to remember that the person accepts the spiritual director's guidance not simply on human faith and confidence, as would be true of most other guidance, but as an act of supernatural faith.

[7] R. Garrigou-Lagrange, O.P.: *The Three Ages of the Interior Life,* Vol. I, St. Louis, Copyright 1947, by B. Herder Book Co., p. 262.

Sincere Concern. This is not to say that the counselor is cold and indifferent. His manner should indicate that he is making a sincere, careful, and reasonable effort to aid the person in the best way he knows. If the counselor is genuinely desirous of helping others grow in self-integration and independence, he can honestly say this when a dependent person raises a question about the counselor's somewhat restrained manner. The person will soon recognize the objectivity and sincerity of the counselor. He will become aware, too, of his own tendencies to want to depend on others and to seek affection and support rather than face his problems and solve them.

Need for Success. Sometimes the counselor's own need for success will cause him to seek some statement from a person that he is being helped or is feeling better. This kind of elicited reassurance will only hurt the counseling relationship. If a person actually is not feeling better or if he is at that moment much worse, he will be blocked in expressing this. The counselor's obvious attitude of wanting him to feel better and improve will make it difficult for a person to face deeper issues. Before he can see these issues and gain insight into them, he must be free to talk about them. While he is working out these problems he may even feel more miserable and unsuccessful. If his problems, even though serious, are in the general class of ordinary difficulties, these negative attitudes are usually transient in the process of counseling. As we saw, negative emotion in the first part of an interview generally turns into some positive expression towards the end of that same interview or in subsequent interviews, if the counseling has been skillful. The counselor must be convinced of this and be perfectly willing to let people advance at their own speed. When they reach a more reasonable solution, they will express positive feelings of success because they actually have them. These will not be artificial statements of improvement made just to please the counselor.

Impatience. Impatience is another urge against which the counselor must be on guard. The urge to see immediate results is often combined with the desire to feel that we have achieved these ourselves. This may cause a counselor to want to push the person to a more immediate choice of solutions. He may feel that he is not reaching conclusions quickly enough, that he is taking too long to come to the decisions the counselor thinks he should make. If the counselor has this attitude, he will find it creeping into his responses.

The person himself will feel the counselor's impatience. It will make it all the harder for him to be relaxed and at ease in the relationship.

Such an attitude of impatience or of "pushing" a person to insights and choices will only make him grow more resistant and increase his confused feelings. This rise in emotion may become directed against the counselor himself and will endanger the success of the counseling. It will make it more difficult for the person to see the reasonable choices he should make because, as we have seen, any kind of emotional pressure tends to increase the urge to self-defense and narrow a person's perceptions. This is at variance with the broad, over-all view of reasonable insight. Such insight, as we know, seems best achieved in a counseling relationship that is quiet, relaxed, and peaceful and, at the same time, gives a person the feeling that he is truly accepted and understood. Consequently, any impatience or irritation on the counselor's part seems generally to block and impede successful counseling.

Check Egotism. Put in another form, it could be said that the counselor must keep in check his own egotism. This urge to feel superior and to think that, because people are coming for help with personal problems, they are in some way subject or inferior, can be a serious spiritual disorder as well as an impediment to counseling. The counselor must always be conscious of the work of grace in the soul and of the capacity for reasonable self-responsibility that each individual has. It is important for him to recognize his limited function in another's spiritual and psychological development. As Dom Chautard has pointed out,

Now for a man, in his practical conduct, to go about his active works as if Jesus were not his one and only life-principle, is what Cardinal Mermillod has called the HERESY OF GOOD WORKS. He uses this expression *to stigmatize the apostle who so far forgets himself as to overlook his secondary and subordinate role, and look only to his own personal activity and talents as a basis for apostolic success.* Is this not, in practice, a denial of a great part of the Tract on Grace?[8]

In this secondary and subordinate role, the counselor must spend himself for others in such a way that God's grace and their own reasonable insights may be productive of a more adequate psychological and spiritual integration and a happier life.

[8]Dom Jean-Baptiste Chautard, O.C.S.O.: *The Soul of the Apostolate,* translated by J. A. Moran, S.M., Techny, Illinois, Mission Press, S.V.D., 1941, pp. 12–13.

Counselor's Personal Conflicts. The counselor should be aware that his own personal conflicts and hostilities may affect his attitude towards the person coming for help. In the same way, personal confusion can often cause a teacher or speaker to be impatient and irritable or to reprimand and condemn excessively. If this happens and the counseling relationship becomes jeopardized, it appears wiser for the counselor to recognize this and call it off. Any attempt to force counseling after a strong personal rejection seems generally to add to the bad effects that have been produced.

Personal Change in the Counselor. We saw previously[9] how the counselor, in examining his failures, often discovers attitudes and needs in himself that he had never before realized. Since these are affecting his counseling, he must make some changes in himself as well as some improvement in his skill. When the counselor recognizes that certain of his personal tendencies are impediments to the psychological and spiritual growth of people whom he desires to help, it is an added motivation for him to strive for more objective kinds of responses. Moreover, as the counselor sees the effects which good counseling can produce in helping people grow in psychological and spiritual integration and tranquility, he finds it easier to curb these personal tendencies and needs.

Counselors often express this as they become aware of their need for greater counseling skill. The following comment is typical:

In my own life there was a real revelation as to what I had sometimes been doing with people—using my personal authority on them because I expected them to defer to my personality and to my answers. I saw that many of the failures I have had in handling delinquents, with people who were having marriage difficulties and so forth, came from my aggressive attitude and my impatience because they could not take my solutions . . . . As I began to check on and improve my approach, I saw people gain in self-understanding. I grew to trust peoples' choices in things that concerned their own personal lives, after they had these new insights.

The fruits of good counseling are themselves one of the greatest means of encouraging the counselor to continue his efforts to improve himself and his counseling skill.

[9]Pp. 225–226.

CHAPTER XV

DISGUISED EXPRESSIONS OF COUNSELING NEED

Until now, we have been mainly concerned with the various phases of the counseling relationship which can occur after the person has somehow acquired a general idea of counseling and seeks such personal aid. But not all people who need counseling face their difficulties so clearly and directly. Some may not even know what counseling is. Consequently, in this chapter we will discuss some of the other methods of approach that people sometimes use. In these situations, the desire for counseling is not expressed openly, but only vaguely and confusedly suggested. It is important for the counselor to be able to recognize this disguised approach so that these people's confused need may be channeled into a definitely structured counseling relationship.

COMPROMISES

Straddling the Issue. When people are in personal conflict they often tend to compromise. This is illustrated by the reaction of an insecure child in school when he is asked to address the class. His respect for the teacher moves him to leave his seat and come to the front of the room. The teacher tells him he must turn and face the students. He turns and attempts to face them but is afraid of their laughter or rejection. An interesting compromise may result. The child will often turn sideways in an effort to address both the teacher and the students. But he is accomplishing neither. He is not directly addressing the students and he is not facing the teacher. He has tried to meet the pressure from both teacher and class by turning sideways. This, like every straddling of issues, achieves neither purpose. In something of the same way, people sometimes compromise when they are faced with personal problems. We saw some evidences of this in our discussion of interviews with children and how the counselor enabled this to become a constructive relationship.[1] This same compromise reaction is often true of adults, although it takes a more complex form.

Types of Compromise. Some adults do not directly accept a need for counseling but feel merely a vague identity with the counselor. They may see him as someone who is understanding and kind and whom they would like to know better. Their approach may begin with a friendly chat or even an invitation to dinner. If a person symbolizes someone who could help them, if he is a priest, doctor, a professional psychologist or psychiatrist who is known as such, or is in some similar position, people may invite him to their home, promote such activities as a golf match, bridge game, and the like in the confused hope that this social relationship will provide an opportunity to talk about their personal problems. If the counselor is a teacher, a person may stop after class to raise some question about a class matter. With children, the relationship may begin with the typical walking back and forth to school with the teacher, staying after school to help clean the room, etc. These are often confused forms of identification with the counselor without any request for counseling.

Counselor Must Recognize These. It is important, then, that the counselor be alert to the compromise nature of many such invitations and encounters. He must be aware that these people may really want counseling, but that, like the child unable to face the class, they are not quite ready to face the pressure of an interview. They do the next best thing. They try to identify themselves with someone who seems to be sympathetic and understanding but they do not involve themselves in a counseling relationship with him. They may be fearful of his rejection and lack of interest. They may not be sure that he has the time to spend with them or the inclination to help them. They are usually also uncertain how he will receive their personal disclosures.

CHANNELING COMPROMISE

Can Be Constructive. Such compromises can be an index to significant personal material and the beginning of a deep relationship. But the compromise situation itself rarely offers the kind of privacy and generally relaxed, constructive tone which promotes

[1] See p. 320.

counseling. Consequently, the counselor must first channel the confused urge for help in the direction of a more positive and secure
relationship.

Illustration. This type of disguised approach to counseling often
occurs, and usually follows a somewhat predictable pattern. The
process of channeling such an approach into a counseling relationship is illustrated in the following example. A young woman student
in a psychology class approaches the instructor after class with this
inquiry:

> In that case you gave of the lady who felt she had never been loved
> as a child—who was having such a difficult time, because of her fear of
> losing her husband so she, ah—needed illness to be sure her husband
> loved her by the care he gave her, what, what would you think of this—
> what would you think of ah, well, let's see, let's say a young person,
> say it was a young man, or even a young woman, who just ah, seemed
> to be feeling that, that she wasn't getting along at home do you think
> she'd eventually end up with something like that?

Compromise Self-reference. Underlying this question is the undefined fear that, somehow, not feeling accepted at home may lead
to an unsuccessful marriage. Questions like this often occur when
personal material is used in lectures, class material, writing, and
sermons. People identify themselves with the material and illustrations. Examples of marriage difficulties, personal problems, childhood fears or conflicts, etc., will usually touch some individuals and
they apply them directly to themselves. We see this in the question
the young woman raised.

We notice, too, that she hesitates in her disguise, first making it
a young man. Sometimes persons will change the sex and the ages
in their questions and still be referring to themselves. They may
recite details of the problems of a friend or relative and ask, "What
do you think of this? What would be the explanation of his conduct?" Or, they may mention that they have read a particular book
or article and they wonder what the counselor thinks of it. The
person can be referring to himself in each of these inquiries. But
these are compromise references. He is not yet directly facing his
personal need. Rather, this is an effort to appear not to be including
himself, and yet get some personal help.

Counselor Responses. Such a question must be carefully handled by the counselor if it is to be channeled into a constructive counseling relationship. He may, for example, ask the person to speak a little more about it, as in the following:

You're interested in the relationship of this same problem with, say a young person, a young woman perhaps, and you wonder if it would apply. (Pause) Would you care to express that a little more?

This may not be necessary. Often a response which simply accepts and rephrases the person's interest will bring out a further statement. Sometimes, it will enable the person to say immediately:

Well, it's a personal problem.

A person may say,

Well, it's someone whom I know very well and when you brought that case up, I immediately thought of it because I am concerned about this person.

Other statements similar to this may indicate that the problem is serious and, in some way, personal. Usually, as the counselor responds to a person's interest, he will begin to give more details of his problem. The recitation of such details may make him somewhat self-conscious and he may end by saying,

Well, I suppose I shouldn't be taking up your time now. It just interested me and I thought I'd bring it up but—I just was thinking about it when you mentioned those things.

This kind of self-consciousness can destroy a relationship just as it begins to become personal. The counselor must make the person aware that he is interested in seeing him again and talking more about this question with him. He may say,

Yes, that's an important point that you raise and—as you say—it has a real personal meaning for you. Both of us, I suppose, are a little pushed for time right here.

He may continue,

It's a little late now and I do have another appointment but I wonder if we might talk more about that. I have an office where I oftentimes see people, students or others, who want to talk over material and I would be very glad to talk more with you about it. (Pause) I could possibly see you sometime tomorrow. (Or whatever time the counselor has free.) Would you—would you wish to do that?

Definite Appointment. The counselor must, consequently, have in mind what times he has available for appointments of this sort. One experienced in counseling will look at his appointment schedule before he goes to a class, lecture, or any other social function where he may possibly encounter these disguised expressions of personal need. If the person accepts an appointment, as people often do, a precise time and definite relationship are now set up. Otherwise, the person may say he will telephone sometime or "drop around" to see the counselor. This remains vague and is the same compromise state as before. But when a definite appointment is offered, he is presented with a new situation. He has a clear choice either of facing his counseling need or avoiding it. The degree of personal conflict which brought him to such a compromise state is often sufficient to cause him to want to discuss the matter further. But the counselor can block this positive urge if he goes too far and attempts to persuade a person that his problem is personal and that he ought to come for counseling. This usually seems only to cause resistance and defense.

Avoids Overinterpretations. In the above illustrations, the counselor does not persuade. He simply channels the student's interest into a more private and definite relationship. The counselor's statements do not go beyond what the student expresses.[2] The counselor does not say that people come for personal problems. The student avoided saying it was a personal problem, so the counselor leaves it as a student-instructor relationship. The counselor does, however, recognize the personal involvement of the student in the question and that it is something rather serious. This helps make the student aware that here is an understanding person and someone who probably would accept a discussion of personal problems. The result may be such an answer as this:

Well—let's see, tomorrow—well, I guess, yes, I guess I could come tomorrow. I, yes, I believe—that—all right—two o'clock you say, all right, yes. Where is it? (The place being given, the student continues.) Yes, well, I'll be over there then around two.

[2] See pp. 232 ff. for examples of resistance when the counselor overinterprets responses.

Such hesitancy is generally evident because the person is suddenly faced with a changed relationship which he had not foreseen in his original inquiry. The counselor can set up the time by saying,

Yes, well, we can talk, say for a half hour and call it off around two-thirty.

If he wishes it to be an hour, he can say that. If he does not have much time, he can say,

I won't be able to see you for too long, but we can talk for fifteen minutes or so anyway.

He may say,

I feel more at ease in discussing questions like that in a place where we can sit quietly and where it will be private.

In this way, a definite counseling appointment has been established. This can be the beginning of a constructive series of interviews.

In this illustration we can see how a confused, compromise need for help has become definite and precise. The person now knows that he is going to see the counselor the next day or week, for a definite time, when he can talk in detail about the particular personal question which he brought up. Surprisingly, such people often begin the interview itself with a direct statement of personal problems. They may not mention, or mention only in passing, their original inquiry. This demonstrates the compromise nature of such inquiries. However, people do not always accept the offer of an interview. Sometimes this is because they do not consider the problem serious enough to take the counselor's time or because they are not as yet ready to face it directly. They may delay and then call the counselor. In any event, they now know one understanding person to whom they might eventually be able to speak about their difficulties.

SOME COMMON COMPROMISE SITUATIONS

This channeling process can take place during a conversation at a dinner, a meeting in a home, a friendly discussion on a train, a social gathering, a card party, or any similar affair where people happen to mention some kind of personal difficulty or question.

These situations can readily arise for priests, religious, doctors, lawyers, social workers, nurses, or anyone else from whom people think of getting this kind of help. Because these people's desire for help is not at first clear even to themselves, they generally begin with indefinite statements similar to those of the young woman in the illustration. But, when clarified and channeled by the counselor, such vague statements can be the beginning of constructive counseling.

A further advantage of this channeling process is that it helps to solve the disorder that seems inherent in the unpredictable way people often present personal problems. With what is sometimes irritating regularity, people may choose the latest time in the evening when one is ready to leave, the most confusing period of the day, the time at night when one's retirement hour is already overdue, and similar situations, to begin to suggest what may be an involved personal problem. Channeling of this type can give sufficient acceptance and understanding so that the person does not feel rejected and at the same time provide a more suitable time for the actual counseling. The counselor will then be apt to do a better piece of work and the person will probably ultimately feel much less guilty about using the counselor's time than he would, for example, if he ended in keeping him up half the night hearing about his difficulties.

Hidden Needs.   Counselors must be aware, therefore, that hidden behind a minor problem or a simple question there are often issues of major importance to the person's life. But, such situations require a deeper counseling relationship, which the counselor must first establish. A young woman, for example, who dropped out of college to work in an office comes to a counselor for a friendship visit. In a short time she is talking about her unhappiness in the office. Skillfully handled, this leads to a series of counseling interviews, which results not only in the girl's returning to college, but also in her seeing that her basic need and desire has always been for the religious life. Previously, however, she had never been able to face this. Courtship problems, too, can themselves be symptoms of deeper conflicts. An engaged person may be vaguely aware that his or her choice was unwise, yet, without counseling, has not the clear vision or courage to do anything about it. Sometimes, disagreements between a young couple about moral issues have very deep causes. A conflict over contraception can be the means of uncovering hidden fears and insecurities. In one particular case, a young woman had witnessed the death of her mother in childbirth, and so had an intense fear of having children which she had not clearly seen or understood before. This was brought out and clarified by counseling interviews. Without counseling, one could have predicted grave difficulties or even break-up for this marriage. Courtship and engagement difficulties, which may appear very small in themselves, may also reveal a religious vocation which previously was not clearly seen. These are only a sampling of the wide variety of ways in which these disguised counseling needs are at first expressed.

When, therefore, a child or an adult asks a question or seeks any additional personal information or assistance, it is difficult to determine if instruction is his primary need or if his seeking of information is the first vague, compromise stage in his approach to counseling. Consequently, anyone who is known as a counselor or is in any position in which people might come to him for counseling, must recognize the indications of a possible deeper need in such inquiries. He should give people a chance to talk about these personal issues and, as the deeper need is uncovered, gradually structure a counseling relationship with them. If, in these situations of disguised personal need, counseling is not made available, these people have lost a valuable opportunity to face and reorganize their lives in a way that may never occur again.

Compromises During the Interview. Even after they have come for a counseling interview, some people, especially those with a background of insecurity and dependency, may not at first accept the responsibility for changing their conduct. Such people may also compromise by attempting to get the counselor to give them information, advice, or direction of some sort. If they can do this, they have succeeded in throwing the responsibility for solving their difficulties on the counselor. Often, a person's tendency to escape responsibility by turning counseling into an information-giving interview, and the counselor's natural urge to take over and express his own ideas, go together and take the interview off the track. What might have been a successful counseling relationship becomes simply another experience in confused compromising. Once again the person has failed to think out the real causes of his difficulties and take responsible action about them.

Counselor Avoids Taking Responsibility. For these reasons, when people present themselves in any way that might imply a need for personal help, it seems better for the counselor to leave the responsibility of explaining and clarifying his problems with the person himself. When this is done, one is often surprised at the amount of knowledge a person has. He may ultimately understand his problems and their solutions more adequately than the counselor would likely have been able to instruct him in them. Sometimes, even a person's specific information is accurate and detailed.

Besides, if a person's difficulties are due mainly to his disordered emotions and instincts, which prevent the carrying out in daily action of what he knows he should do, simply giving him further information will not help. When the counselor imparts information the person has, the interview cannot be considered successful. It may even have made him resentful because it did not allow him a chance to talk out and think through his problems, or it may only have further confirmed his urge to avoid making his own responsible judgments. In any case, he has not been provided with an opportunity for any constructive personal integration.

CHAPTER XVI

INFORMATIONAL ROLES THAT MAY
FACILITATE COUNSELING

A further important point to be considered when people ask questions, however, is that they may genuinely seek information, not simply as a disguised approach to counseling or a compromise avoidance of facing responsibility, but because it is actually necessary. The one to whom they come for such information is usually determined by the particular type of knowledge they are seeking. They may come, for example, to a priest for religious instruction or moral guidance, to a teacher for some additional explanation of the class matter, to a doctor for medical knowledge, to a lawyer for legal advice, to a psychologist for test information to aid in self-understanding or vocational choices, to a sociologist for marriage guidance, and to representatives of various other functions which in some way offer personal help. Any of these informational situations may also involve counseling.

COUNSELING AND INFORMATION

Two Ways. This combination of counseling and information can occur in two ways. During the process of counseling, a person may become aware that he requires further information in order to make an adequate judgment. Alternately, a person may come directly for such information and, in explaining his need, suggest various personal factors, the solution of which may call for counseling.

Preserve Distinct Relationships. If both counseling and some form of informational interview are necessary, the person should be aware when the focus in on the instructor and when, in turn, the focus is on him in the counseling relationship. In a counseling interview, the person coming for help has the direct responsibility for the relationship and for whatever insights he receives from it. The counselor mirrors, objectifies, and clarifies the person's thinking as he talks about himself. In an informational interview, however, the relationship is centered around the instruction. It is the instructor's responsibility to organize and explain the facts and principles involved.

The one who is doing the counseling may prefer to let someone else give necessary information or instruction, either because he is not equipped or because he foresees that such an informational relationship will interfere with counseling. But, if he has decided to accept an informational role also, his seeing of the person at distinct times may lessen the danger of confusing the two functions. One time can be exclusively for counseling, when the responsibility is kept on the person coming for help. The counselor here adheres strictly to a counseling role. The other meetings can be formally defined as some form of information or objective instruction, which the person has sought from the counselor because of his particular position. Here, the focus will be on the instructor. The personal implications of this information can then be clarified and thought through in the counseling interviews. Using the first half-hour for the one, a short intermission, and the second half-hour for the other may work if the instructor is sufficiently skilled in counseling that he does not let the two relationships overlap and interfere with each other.

INFORMATION DURING COUNSELING

Forking Response. When, during counseling, a person expresses a need for further information, the counselor can often clarify the two relationships with a "forking" response. He then suggests the informational relationship in addition to counseling.

Illustration. We see this illustrated in the following excerpt from the fifth interview with the ensign, who having worked out some major personal problems, expresses his desire for more religious knowledge (S) :[1]

P11: Yes, I want to learn more about the religion now at least—my girl says you are pretty well informed on religious matters too. I have a number of questions I'd like to ask you because I know I can talk to you now.
C11: Yes—you are much more at ease with me now and you'd like to get some religious information from me.

[1]Discussed in detail in Chapter XI.

P12: Yeah—these other things are much clearer now for me and I want to go ahead and get married now and I would also like now to know more about the religion angle and my girl suggested—and I thought it was a good idea—that maybe you'd answer some of my questions about the religion.

C12: As the personal things are clearer for you, the religious information need is now the thing you want and you wonder if I could supply you with that too.

P13: Yeah. I realize it's a little different than this stuff we've been talking about—there's just a lot of things about religion I don't know and if you would—I'd appreciate whatever information you'd give me.

C13: Yes. It's a little different relationship than your thinking out personal things where the spotlight, so to speak, was on you and you wonder if I would say, take over and give you whatever religious information I have.

P14: Yes, if you would, I'd appreciate it. Of course I understand that on the personal stuff, I got to decide that myself and you've been a real help in doing that. These religious talks would be different, I see that.

C14: Yes, I think we can certainly set it up that way if you wish. We might continue these personal discussions if you feel the need of them further. Or, we might spend an hour on religious discussion where I would be in the role more or less of teacher. This would be an entirely different relationship and I think it is good for us to see that. Or, another possibility would be for you to take your religious instruction from some priest—I could recommend someone to you. And we could keep the relationship with me just as it is, for you to use for your own personal needs—possibly a half hour or so for personal discussion.

P15: Yes, I see what you mean.

C15: We could set it for a half-hour religious discussion and a half-hour personal talk, if you wish—more or less separating the two. (Pause) But I leave that up to you. (Pause) Well, our time is about up. (Pause) Suppose we leave it ride until the next interview and we can work it out together then. I can see you again Tuesday, same time, if that's suitable.

P16: (Rising and preparing to leave). Yes, that's fine. Well, I'll see you then Tuesday. Probably I won't need any more of these personal talks after that. Things are much better now and I'm very grateful to you.

Such "forking" opportunities may sometimes occur even as early as the end of the first interview. When such a clarification of roles is made, the person can still have the use of the counseling interview if he wishes and also receive the information he needs.

Propose Informational Relationship. A "forking" situation, such as the one illustrated here, may not always take place, however, or, when it does, the counselor may have missed it. In place of this, the counselor can sometimes propose the possibility of an informational relationship as he and the person are going to the door, after the interview is over. But, unless the situation is handled carefully, this may disturb or even prevent the possibility of counseling.

Danger of Compromise. It is, therefore, definitely better if the counselor is alert to these informational needs when they actually appear in the person's statements. The instructional relationship is more secure when it is an evident response to a person's stated need. In this way, if he wishes, a person can retain both the counseling and instructional functions as long as he feels they are necessary. But the counselor must always be careful that he does not merely encourage compromise. This seems best achieved when the counseling relationship is held tightly for itself and the other relationships are clearly distinguished from it. Counselors who have acquired the "feel" of a sound counseling process are apt to be more accurate than those of less experience in determining when the seeking of information is realistic and genuine and when it is a compromise disguise.

COUNSELING NEED IN INFORMATIONAL INTERVIEW

Equally as common as the development of an informational need during counseling is the opposite situation, in which people come directly for information and in the process suggest a more complex personal involvement which necessitates counseling. While this approach may also have some of the tones of the type of disguise we discussed in the last chapter, it differs from this in that there is a valid need for the information sought. The counseling relationship in this case does not, therefore, replace the instruction, but accompanies it and aids its assimilation and integration. Where the seeking of information is a disguise, a person usually has no real interest in the answers that might be given to his questions, or, he already knows those answers. Here, however, the information has an actual constructive value for the person and may, in fact, be the occasion that moves him to a more direct facing of his personal needs.

Impediments to Acceptance.   Moreover, personal factors can also impede the acceptance of information, even when it is needed. According to one recent study, any personal information seems most readily accepted when, 1) an emotionally relaxed atmosphere has been created for both the person and the instructor; 2) when the person has acquired positive attitudes about himself and his problems; 3) when the person is ready to act on the information; 4) when the information is directly related to the person's needs and, 5) when the information fits in with the person's picture of himself and his problems.[2] Information, therefore, that a person would reject at one time might be acceptable if presented at a later period, when his attitudes have become more positive and his self-understanding has increased. Consequently, unless people have gained adequate insight into their more pressing personal problems, they may be in no suitable psychological state to accept or integrate any type of personal instruction. For this reason, counseling is often a necesary adjunct to such instruction.

Personal Implications.   The information most apt to promote some expression of counseling need is generally that which most directly affects the person in his immediate life and calls for a fundamental change in his outlook, his plan of conduct, his friends, his work, or some other intimate factors. This can occur in a variety of ways, some of which can be anticipated and others which are so subtle that the instructor could not have suspected them until he recognized the emotional tone of the other person's reaction. It is, therefore, important for the instructor to be aware of some of the signs that may indicate such personal involvement.

The Instructor's Tone.   Whenever information is emotionally disturbing a person may be urged to resist not only the information itself, but also the one responsible for giving him that information. Consequently, such a discussion should be kept particularly free of tones which might be interpreted as the instructor's will to dominate or force his own opinion. The instructor may find it helpful to speak impersonally using phrases like, "The school regulations require . . ."; "The Church teaches . . ."; "The test results reveal . . ."; "The application of the law in this case is . . ."; and similar statements, whenever possible, so as to avoid any suggestion that might make the

[2]R. B. Kamm and C. G. Wrenn: "Client Acceptance of Self-Information in Counseling," *Educational and Psychological Measurement*, Vol. X, No. 1, Spring 1950, pp. 32–42.

information appear to be merely the instructor's personal view. In this way, the instructor can often prevent a condition from arising in which resistance to the information he is giving has been also turned against himself.

Part of Reality.   Such norms, regulations, unflattering test information, etc. should, therefore, be presented as part of the reality of a person's life. They should not imply any personal attitude of the instructor. When, for example, the Church, following Christ's words, has determined that a consummated sacramental marriage is dissolved only by death, this is part of the spiritual world in which every Catholic must live; or, if test results show a person is apparently not capable of achieving certain professional goals he must face these limits in himself and his abilities. If the instructor himself remains uninvolved he is in a good position to inaugurate counseling around the person's problem of conformity to these limits.

Instructor Remains Objective.   The instructor, moreover, must be on his guard against becoming affronted and offended if the other person wants to discuss or even argue about a regulation or a disturbing piece of information. Objection and argument, or at least some resistance and discussion, are often the means of negative release—which anyone in a serious conflict may need before he can see the limits of reality clearly. Allowing the person to express his feelings openly, and responding to them, is often the first stage of a constructive counseling process. If, instead of turning the situation into a personal difference, the instructor clarifies the feelings which the person has against the information offered, he will more readily aid understanding and acceptance. But, if he attempts to force acceptance by strong personal persuasion or insistence, he may only increase and crystallize the person's hostility. It will be directed now, not only against the painful limits which the regulation or other information places on him, but also against the instructor. Such hostility often causes people to break off the relationship. They have not only rejected the information, but they have been denied the opportunity of a counseling process that might have aided them to see its reasonableness and objective validity and adjust their lives accordingly.

SOME TYPICAL SITUATIONS

Since there is a wide variety of such informational situations which may lead to counseling, we cannot anticipate them all. However, there are a number which have some elements that are peculiar to them. In discussing these in some detail, we will illustrate factors which are also likely to occur under many other circumstances.

INDIVIDUAL OR GROUP INSTRUCTION

One situation that may call for counseling can arise in certain types of individual or group instruction and discussion. This is particularly common when the implications of the topic discussed demand some degree of maturity, independence, and emotional stability before they can be accepted and assimilated. This may sometimes occur, for example, in the religious instruction that is given to persons interested in Catholicity. In some of these cases, there may be personal confusions which the instruction alone does not reach. Because of these unexpressed difficulties, people may not be able to continue their religious study. Sometimes, a person's strong home ties are a major impediment to his becoming a Catholic. A mother or father may be both a powerful influence and great personal need for the person coming for instructions. At the same time, the parent may have deep prejudices against Catholicity. This same opposition can come from a husband or wife. In addition, then, to their conviction of the truth of the religion, persons in such situations would also need to develop a responsible independence to enable them to take the steps necessary to enter the Church. Sometimes, with young adults, it is their first serious difference with their parents. The ability to take this step involves a personal integration and depth of self-understanding which instruction by itself would not include. An integrated counseling process would often be helpful in giving such people the adequate assurance and conviction they need. If the instructor has acquired counseling skill or can readily refer them to such a counselor, he can give these people an opportunity for the clarification of personal problems as well as instructions. In this way, they can take better advantage of the information they are receiving.

PSYCHOLOGICAL OR SOCIOLOGICAL DATA

A situation similar to this often confronts psychologists, sociologists, vocational counselors, and others who are in any way involved in the interpretation of personal data. The administering and interpreting of psychological tests, the citing of sociological studies, and other functions which give people objective knowledge about themselves and their abilities, or indicate their chances of success in a particular field, profession, occupation, vocation, and the like, may not only give them more knowledge, but may also stimulate them to face and think out some personal problems. To further discussion of this sort some have found it helpful to give the person an approximation of the degree of accuracy of the test or other data used. In presenting test data, for example, the informant might say,

This test, of course, is not infallible but has about eight out of ten chances of being right.

Often, in the subsequent discussion far more significant personal material is disclosed than the tests or general statistics could reveal. Such discussion can be the start of a series of counseling interviews.[3]

SCHOOL ADJUSTMENT AND LEARNING

Study Difficulties. Classroom failure or some other difficulties in school or college adjustment may also promote a counseling relationship in combination with some form of tutoring.[4] Since

[3]Ray H. Bixler and Virginia H. Bixler: "Test Interpretation in Vocational Counseling," in *Readings in Modern Methods of Counseling,* edited by Arthur H. Brayfield: Appleton-Century-Crofts, New York, 1950, pp. 184–192, published also in *Educational and Psychological Measurement,* 1946, *6*, 145–155. Copyright 1946 by G. Frederick Kuder. Edward S. Bordin and Ray H. Bixler: "Test Selection: A Process of Counseling," *Educational and Psychological Measurement,* VI, 1946, pp. 361–373. A. W. Combs: "Nondirective Techniques and Vocational Counseling," *Occupations,* Vol. 25, February 1947, pp. 261–267. B. J. Covner: "Nondirective Interviewing Techniques in Vocational Counseling," *J. Consulting Psychology,* Vol. 11, 1947, pp. 70–73. R. B. Kamm and C. G. Wrenn: "Client Acceptance of Self Information in Counseling," *Educational and Psychological Measurement,* Vol. X, No. 1, Spring 1950, pp. 32–42. G. A. Muench: "An Evaluation of Nondirective Psychotherapy by Means of the Rorschach and Other Tests," *Applied Psychology Monograph,* No. 13, 1947. Julius Seeman: "Client Reactions to Vocational Counseling," *J. of Consulting Psychology,* Vol. 13, No. 2, April 1949, pp. 95–104.

[4]See, Mary Jane Mulvey: "A Tutoring-Counseling Relationship Between Teacher and Pupil for Removal of Emotional Blocks to Learning" (Master's Thesis, Ohio State University, Columbus, Ohio, 1948) for an interesting discussion of this type of school function with delinquent adolescent girls. Each found the tutoring relationship totally acceptable as a place to discuss and think through personal problems. The findings of this study were synopsized in an article: Mary Jane M. Ivancic: "A Way to Ease Emotional Blocks to Learning," *Understanding the Child,* Vol. XVIII, No. 2, April 1949, p. 45.

See also, Virginia Axline: *Play Therapy:* New York, Copyright 1947, by Houghton Mifflin, Chapter 16, pp. 141–159; and illustration, pp. 172–176 (this book).

emotional disturbances generally affect school work, classroom problems may provide the simplest way through which to reach these underlying personal conflicts.

Reading. In reading problems, Gates found the following background factors significant:

1. Apparent indifference of teachers or parents to the child's welfare, often resulting in feelings of insecurity and neglect.

2. Apparent hostility of teacher and parents—suggested by scoldings, prediction of failure, etc.

3. Apparent anxiety of teacher and parents—shown by constant inquiry, supervision, or excitement.

4. Overprotection of child by parents—helping the youngster so much that he learns to do little for himself.

5. Apparent conflict in the purpose or desire between parents or between parents and teacher.

6. Conflicting desires of pupil due to sibling rivalry or rivalry with other children.

7. Persisting emotional tensions resulting from the embarrassment or ridicule attending failure in oral reading, recitation, and tests.[5]

These same characteristics would most likely be true of many other learning difficulties. Moreover, since reading disability is one of the common causes of college failure, these factors can occur, too, on a college level. Here, especially, reading inadequacy is usually combined with faulty study habits, in the correction of which the student may also need help.

Conduct. In behavior problems, a considerate attempt at understanding the student would probably be more effective than constant reprimand or punishment, which seems to accomplish little. As English and Pearson point out:

parents and teachers often feel that this child is lacking in character, that he has no sense of responsibility, and is incapable of self-discipline, and as a result, they use every measure they can think of to get him to discipline himself to take responsibility. They often deal with the

---

[5]Arthur I. Gates: "The Role of Personality Maladjustment in Reading Disability," *Journal of Genetic Psychology*, Vol. LIX, September, 1941, pp. 77–83. See also: R. H. Bixler: "Treatment of a Reading Problem Through Non-Directive Play Therapy," *Journal of Consulting Psychology*, 1945, pp. 105–118.

latter in a curious way. Because the child has no sense of responsibility they take on all of the responsibility for him . . . they forget that a sense of responsibility comes from taking one's own responsibility and that the best discipline comes from practical reality.[6]

Not An Artificial Relationship. A tutoring relationship should be established around a definite school problem. If it is just a blind, the child or adult will recognize this. He may grow suspicious and reject the relationship altogether. In the process of discussing the school problem, however, the tutor-counselor should be delicately responsive to any personal expressions which the student makes.

Double Need. The tutor should not become so focused on the tutoring process that he misses the student's desire to talk about himself. These statements will, at first, only be made in a vague and hesitant manner. If the tutor-counselor is not alert, he will miss them. But, once the student understands that he can talk about himself, he may readily begin to unfold personal conflicts. His release should be accepted and his basic feelings recognized in the counseling responses. Somewhere, the tutor-counselor will have a chance to hold up the person's twofold need to him with a response like,

You feel in a way that you need both help with your study habits and reading and at the same time a chance to talk about these personal problems.

Such a response gives the person an opportunity to see his personal need and accept it. The counselor can then clearly structure the relationship so that part of the time is spent in tutoring and part in counseling. The tutor-counselor must be careful, however, not to let the two criss-cross and interfere with each other.

Even when the school problem is not clearly defined, if the tutor-counselor assumes a counseling attitude, he often enables the discussion to reach a personal level almost immediately. The student himself may realize that his real problems are connected with his personal confusion.[7] He may already be convinced that if he can clear these up, the school difficulty will take care of itself.

Tutoring in combination with counseling can often be effective in those circumstances in which students are too self-conscious to face

---

[6] O. S. English and H. J. G. Pearson: *Emotional Problems of Living,* New York, W. W. Norton and Company, Inc., 1945, p. 297.
[7] Excerpt, pp. 61–62.

their need for personal help directly. They may also be too fearful of the ridicule of other students to come openly for counseling. This would generally be more common in high school and grade school than in college. When the counselor is in the role of tutor he provides the student with an acceptable reason for coming to see him. Neither his parents, friends, nor fellow students misunderstand his need for help in his school work, especially if he is failing. He is not threatened since he can freely explain to others why he is coming. On the other hand, the relationship is not false because, even when the entire time is spent in personal counseling, the student himself has accepted this function as basic to clearing up his school difficulties. There is, consequently, no artificiality about calling it tutoring. But it is a more comprehensive and thorough kind than is usually done under the heading of such a function and its results will be proportionately more effective.

In this way, the child or adolescent is not embarrassed and yet is offered an opportunity, if he wishes, to think out his problems. With the help of such a counseling-skilled tutor, he can often reach basic insights that will not only aid in his school progress but affect his whole life adjustment.

MEDICAL SETTING

Psychosomatic Illness.   Since personal problems are often important in illness, counseling may sometimes be a significant factor in the patient's recovery. Consequently, in addition to giving medical information and medication, the doctor or nurse is often in a good position to prepare the way for, or to inaugurate, counseling. While the factors previously discussed, also apply here, there are some additional aspects peculiar to a medical setting.

Hospitalization.   Physicians have expressed the opinion that hospitalization, or some form of illness which keeps the person in bed or at least in the house, often seems to promote the kind of self-examination which moves a person to seek counseling. In particular instances it seems apparent that if the person were not confined to a sick-bed he would have been too taken up with his immediate activities and daily concerns to have faced personal issues. Yet, when a person skilled in counseling was available, the illness proved to be a fortunate occasion for a significant re-orientation of his life.

This has widespread implications for psychosomatic and spiritual problems, and for a counseling service carried on by religious, doctors, nurses, and others connected with the care of the sick.

For this reason, we will report briefly on a detailed research project in which counseling and medical care were combined.[8]

RESEARCH REPORT

Patient's Unfolding of His Personal Problems. The acquisition of counseling skill seems to be a valuable aid in enabling a patient to unfold and delineate personal problems without either being self-conscious or seeking excessive reassurance and support. Generally, it can be assumed that the patient will feel that he has the responsibility to explain his illness. In this research project the physician or other person taking the initial history, rather than quickly taking over the responsibility with a series of questions, responded to the feelings or emotions which the patient expressed—on the assumption that psychologically disturbed patients, whether they indicate it or not, are really in need of someone with whom to speak freely. Interestingly, this procedure, in many cases, produced even more complete and accurate medical information than, in the physicians' judgments, would probably have been achieved in responses to their routine diagnostic questions. Yet, no effort was made to focus the patient's statements on physical symptoms.

Twofold Role. A questionnaire prepared in such a way that it supplied much pertinent information was found helpful. This was the basis of a separate diagnostic relationship in which the physician, in conjunction with his physical examination, could require through verbal questioning, whatever further information he deemed necessary. Using this method, the physician could structure his double role as both counselor and physician. He could carry out a thorough and consistent medical diagnosis and, at the same time, offer the patient an hour, a half-hour, or even fifteen minutes of constructive self-evaluation in a counseling interview. This was done by clarifying

[8]J. Mitchell and C. A. Curran: "A Method of Approach to Psychosomatic Problems in Allergy," *West Virginia Medical Journal*, Vol. XLII, No. 11, pp. 1–24, December, 1950. C. A. Curran: "Nondirective Counseling in Allergic Complaints," *J. of Abnorm. and Social Psychol.*, Vol. 43, No. 4, pp. 442–451, October 1948. J. Mitchell, C. A. Curran, W. F. Mitchell, Iola Sivon, and Ruth Myers: "Personality Factors in 'Allergic' Disorders," *J. Allergy*, Vol. 18, pp. 337–340, 1947. J. Mitchell, C. A. Curran, and Ruth Myers: "Some Psychosomatic Aspects of Allergic Diseases," *Psychosom. Med.*, Vol. IX, pp. 184–191, 1947.

to the patient that many physical ills have psychological difficulties as part of their cause, and that the best kind of case history is a personal one that continues each time the patient comes. In this way the case history interview became also a relationship in which the patient could think through with the physician the experiences of the days between treatments, and evaluate objectively the emotional factors and conflicts which might have entered into his physical reactions.

Significant Results. Not all patients, of course, responded to counseling; either because their illness had few psychosomatic factors or because they were not ready to face themselves in an interview. But, of those who did respond, a significant number were helped by counseling. As they gained insights into certain attitudes and reactions, they grew increasingly conscious of the constructive part the interviews were playing in their recovery. Some saw clearly that personal problems and confusions were the major cause of their particular illness and, as they gained insight into these problems and were better able to cope with them, their physical state improved. After three years' research and application of this technique in a medical clinic, it was found that

This new point of view has had a noticeable effect on our ability to diagnose many cases which heretofore were always unsolvable frustrations. We have been able to help a considerable number who, had they come previously, would have been eventually turned away with little or no improvement, or may even have been made worse by the use of physical treatment or nonspecific injections which would have tended only to fix the neurosis more deeply, and to build up additional resistance to any suggestion that the symptoms could possibly arise as the result of emotional disturbances.[9]

The counseling medical history is, at the same time, comparatively free of those difficulties which have arisen with the use of some other methods. Another approach to psychosomatic diagnosis—for example, the use of sodium amytal or pentothal narcosynthesis—seems quite often to create intense emotional disturbance in the patient when he learns what he has said. The same information can be obtained by counseling skill, without having these bad effects on

[9]Op. cit., J. Mitchell and C. A. Curran: "A Method of Approach to Psychosomatic Problems in Allergy," p. 7.

the patient. Moreover, the use of sodium amytal seems also to require a skillful interviewing process.[10]

Others Aiding Physician. Recent psychological and medical research is revealing so widespread an unfolding of personal problems in illness that it seems probable the physician himself will need to enlist the help of others to meet this aspect. The acquiring of some counseling skill seems a practical way by which nurses in hospitals and private practice and medical social workers can also be of a valuable aid to the physician in this field.

In the experience of nurses who have acquired this skill, it seems best to block the patient's release of personal problems during those times when other medical care or nursing service is given. It is not uncommon for patients to begin to talk about themselves while the nurse is giving them a bath or some similar care. Some have found it preferable to channel such release into a definite interview at a set time later in the day. The nurse may say,

Yes, it's a very great problem for you, isn't it? Suppose we don't talk about it now and this afternoon at, say 2:00 o'clock to 2:30, we can set the time aside and just discuss that together.

The nurse may also find it helpful to make a brief statement of the relationship that may exist between personal problems and certain illnesses which the person has. She may then say,

Doctors and nurses are now being trained in skills to help people think out such difficulties. I have had such training and I would be glad to set aside some time, and we might think them through together.[11]

Patients are often relieved when such clarifying statements are made. It is sometimes their first opportunity to face problems that they may never have been able to express to anyone before. Because the very nature of illness, particularly hospitalization, seems to be one of the natural stages for a re-evaluation of one's life, it is especially important to have some counseling-skilled person available.

In the same way, too, social workers in the hospital, or as home

[10]J. H. Mitchell, S. Cohen, and C. A. Curran: *International Correspondence of Allergy,* IX and X, 1947; H. S. Ripley and S. Wolf: "The Intravenous Use of Sodium Amytal in Psychosomatic Disorders," *Psychosom. Med.,* Vol. 19, pp. 260–267, 1947.

[11]These statements must, of course, fit into the context of the person's release and may need to be accompanied by other structuring responses. In such situations the counselor must avoid any tones which might appear abrupt or curt.

visitors, can also be an aid in the psychosomatic components of illness. Since the problem is so widespread and the need so great, more research is necessary to know the degree to which other skilled people may be of counseling assistance to the physician and specialist in facilitating and clarifying problems which are affecting a person's health. Moreover, because of the extreme significance which spiritual problems and needs have for this whole psychosomatic question, priests and religious, in addition to their other important functions in the care of souls, can be of especially valuable service here. In matters of a spiritual or personal nature, people often will confide in them far more readily than in anyone else.[12]

USE OF AUTHORITY

It is evident, too, in some instances that certain children or adolescents, absorbed in their own activities, would not have come to see the counselor unless the parents, school, court, or some other authoritative source, demanded it. Yet, such counseling has sometimes been remarkably successful. The pressure of the law, either civil or ecclesiastical, may also have a similar effect on adults. Like hospitalization, the realization of certain consequences of law may be the occasion for the facing of issues which a person might otherwise have put off. Often, this forces him to the recognition of limits to his conduct and of the necessity for readjusting himself to conform to these limits. This kind of situation is often met by lawyers, social workers, and others associated especially with divorce and juvenile courts. Officials in ecclesiastical marriage courts particularly may also often be in a similar position to inaugurate counseling.

Clarifying Resentment. When such pressures are applied, however, a person usually comes to the first interview with some hostile and resentful feelings. But, skillfully handled, these feelings, like any other negative emotions, can often be dispersed in the process of the first interview. As a result, the child or adult may be willing to return for more interviews on his own. If he has gained sufficient satisfaction from the first interview—especially in feeling he could talk freely and be understood—he sometimes welcomes the renewing of such an accepting and helpful relationship, even though he was actually somewhat forced into the initial interview.

---

[12]For religious who are especially dedicated to works of mercy, this is a special opportunity to practice "counseling the doubtful" in conjunction with their corporal work.

Generally speaking, such situations as these place special demands on the skill of the counselor. Otherwise the dependency, insecurity, or hostility which persuasion, disciplinary or legal order can produce, may block the establishment of a counseling relationship. Further study could profitably be made on these points and similar referral questions to discover more adequate ways of making counseling available to those who seem unable to face the responsibility of such a relationship entirely on their own.

EMERGENCY SITUATIONS

Another instance in which the question of some procedure in addition to counseling might arise is in what might be called an emergency situation. This may occur when, due usually to a highly emotional state, a person seems to be on the verge of an action that, in the counselor's judgment, is very unreasonable. Some counselors may feel that, in such a case, a cautious counseling process should be abandoned in favor of some direct persuasion, or encouragement, or other means to urge the person to a more reasonable solution, or, alternately, others may decide that they cannot continue a counseling relationship with a person in the event of such a contingency.[13] Bixler's comment that there should be a "concrete demarcation between acceptable and unacceptable behavior"[14] with reference to the invoking of limits in child counseling, seems also to apply to counseling with adults. The counselor must make his own judgment on the conditions under which he can adequately function as a counselor and the limits he feels it necessary to invoke. Here, too, much research remains to be done in order to discover the most constructive uses of limits and restrictions. At the conclusion of his article Bixler points out:

limits may be of greater therapeutic value than our current interest implies . . . It may be that the use of limits on behavior is equally as important as acceptance of the attitudes which provoke behavior.[15]

[13]We are not referring here to a seriously disordered mental condition but only to a temporary state of tension or confusion of a psychologically normal person. Obviously, where there is any question of a person's harming himself or others special safeguards should be provided. This is generally best achieved by placement in a hospital ward or institution especially equipped to care for such emergencies.

[14]Ray H. Bixler: "Limits Are Therapy," *J. of Consult. Psychol.*, Vol. 13, No. 1, February 1949, p. 3.

[15]*Ibid.* p. 11.

Affected by Counselor's Skill. A number of factors may be involved, however. One is that the more successful the counselor is in establishing the counseling process and enabling a person to unfold and think out his problems, the less often these emergency situations seem to arise.

Release and Clarification Often Bring Reasonableness. A second factor is that people do not always intend to do what they say. That is, in many instances the most effective deterrent of an unreasonable action is to allow a person to "get it off his chest" as the popular saying has it. Even though at this stage a person may appear to be convinced that he is going to commit the action, often, after he has been able to speak freely and relaxedly about it, he is much less anxious to carry it out. The more accurate the counselor's responses are in penetrating his deep feelings, and thus stimulating the person's reasonable evaluation, the more this seems to be true. We saw this in discussing such situations with children.[16] It seems also to apply to adults. The most effective preventative measures are often the kind of responses that help the person see himself objectively. He is then more able to see the same unreasonableness in his proposed conduct that the counselor himself sees in it.

A further point here is that skillful counseling as such never involves agreement with or approval of what a person is doing or plans to do. In a counseling relationship that is properly structured, both the person and the counselor are very aware of this. It is only when the counselor miscues and uses inaccurate or badly phrased responses that he becomes in any way involved.

If, however, the counselor thinks that he may have given the impression of agreement and approval of some action or plan that seems unreasonable and therefore unacceptable to him, he can state this openly to the person. If, in addition, the counselor has reason to think that the person may not know the serious medical, legal, spiritual, or other consequences of the action he is planning, the counselor can suggest a separate guidance session at the end of the counseling period where such consequences might be explained and discussed. He should, however, be particularly alert to the factors we have previously considered in this chapter particularly those on pages 351–354 and 362–363. Even when—as is often the case—

16P. 310.

the person already may have had this information and understanding, such a guidance session may help the counselor be at ease in the counseling relationship since he can now be more secure in the conviction that he did what, at the time, he thought he ought to have done.[17]

Another factor is that in everyday relationships one of the motives for advising, directing, encouraging, persuading, or reprimanding someone is the relief another gets from feeling that he at least "*did something.*" If we know the details of such a situation, however, we sometimes discover that such attempts at prevention did not actually succeed. It is a matter of common experience that such methods do not always deter a person from an unreasonable action but can even, sometimes, catapult him into it.

Avoid Panic. Consequently, in situations of this sort it is of extreme importance that the counselor keep himself carefully in control and not allow himself to be panic-stricken. He may find from experience that, when he is calm enough and skillful enough to allow the person the opportunity to unfold and evaluate objectively all the consequences of the proposed unreasonable action, he may have accomplished more than might have been achieved by any other method. This is a question that depends finally on the counselor himself, his degree of skill, and whatever other obligations he may feel are involved.

A Separate Relationship. If some intervention appears advisable, it often seems preferable to separate this clearly from the counseling process itself, for reasons we have already discussed.[18] In such situations, calling on someone else to assume this other function would perhaps be the best way to preserve intact the counseling relationship. In this event, the person still has the counseling interview to aid him to assimilate what he was told. Should the person actually carry out the unreasonable action, he still has some recurrence to the counseling relationship to think out its consequences and reorganize himself. If the counselor himself assumes any of these other roles, he may remove all possibility of the person's recurring to him to discuss what he did. A person may then feel that the counselor will only reject him, or he may be so self-conscious of what he did that he is unable to face the counselor again.

[17]See also Moore's comment on page 179.
[18]Pp. 348–349.

INSTITUTIONAL PLACEMENT

Certain extrinsic situations, too, may produce counseling or bring the need in greater focus. We saw how, in a medical setting, hospitalization or confinement may encourage it. Institutional placement may in some instances also be an aid to counseling. The experience of three counselors in an institution for delinquent girls, for example, led them to conclude that the discipline, order, and routine of the institution itself actually aided in the acceptance of the counseling interview. A number of girls reached significant insights about themselves, which the counselors felt would not have been possible outside the institution.[19]

PERSUASION

As we have seen, the counselor himself makes no effort to persuade or argue a child or adult into counseling. Persuasion is, of course, an important part of many other functions and, if rightly directed, can sometimes be effective in guidance and education. But, the degree to which such persuasion by others would encourage people to come for counseling who might not otherwise do so, has not been clearly established. Perhaps certain types of persuasion, such as telling a person how much help another received from similar interviews, could be more effectively utilized in the stages preceding counseling. This area demands greater investigation and research. In individual instances it seems quite evident that some people come for counseling because others have persuaded them and assured them how much good they will get from it. The interview itself must be skillfully handled from that point on in order to enable the person to grow in self-responsibility and new life-choices. Yet, it is possible that, in the insecure and disorganized state some people were before they came for counseling, they might not even have made contact with the counselor, had not someone else directed or encouraged them to it.

[19]See also Mary Jane Mulvey: "A Tutoring-Counseling Relationship Between Teacher and Pupil for Removal of Emotional Blocks to Learning," Master's Thesis, Ohio State University, Columbus, Ohio, 1948. (This study was conducted in one of the schools of the Sisters of the Good Shepherd.)

CHAPTER XVII

GROUP DISCUSSION AND GROUP COUNSELING

Group Counseling. Ordinarily, when people come for counseling, they do so individually. An exception to this may occur in the counseling of a husband and wife, when both lives are so interrelated they need to think their problems out together. Sometimes business partnerships and similar close cooperational activities may promote joint counseling, at least about the problems these people have in common. More rare are those situations in which larger groups of five, ten, or more desire a common counseling experience. This may be centered around difficulties peculiar to an entire group, such as occurred during the war in the case of the amputees, or takes place now with alcoholics. Group counseling may also be used for temporary adjustment problems as, for example, in industry, for the purpose of clearing up personnel conflicts that may arise from time to time within various departments. When such common problems do exist and the group desires it, group counseling can take place and often be very successful.

Special Methods. Group counseling sometimes assumes special forms, as in Moreno's[1] psychodrama, in which people re-enact before each other and the counselor, the feelings and impulses that were behind a particular situation. Another type consists of a definitely structured group experience with comparatively few limits, as in the methods of Slavson and, in another form, of Fritz Redl, particularly in his work with delinquent and under-privileged children.[2]

Can Follow Counseling Process. Successful group counseling may also result from a process similar to that of individual counseling, which we have previously described. But, because of the rapid inter-

[1] J. L. Moreno: *Group Therapy*, New York, Beacon House, 1945.
[2] Fritz Redl: "Diagnostic Group Work," *Am. J. Ortho.*, Vol. 14, pp. 53–68, 1944. S. R. Slavson: *Introduction to Group Therapy*, New York, Commonwealth Fund, 1943. See also: Nicholas Hobbs: "Group-Centered Psychotherapy" and Thomas Gordon: "Group-Centered Leadership and Administration" in C. R. Rogers: *Client-Centered Therapy*, Boston, Copyright 1951, by Houghton Mifflin Co.

play of expression and emotion, such group counseling makes special demands on the skill of the counselor. Consequently, the more alert a counselor is to the feelings and attitudes expressed in individual interviews, the more successful he is apt to be in this same type of group counseling.

GROUP DISCUSSION

Group counseling as such, however, is much less common than a more general approach which begins with group discussion. Discussion skills can often facilitate clearer thinking and acting in the group, especially about common problems. They can also readily turn a discussion into group counseling when it is necessary, and, if individual counseling is needed, prepare the way for a personal interview. To achieve these results, however, some special skills are necessary on the part of the discussion leader.

Purpose of Discussion. In discussion, the concern is not with personal problems as such, but with the orientation of ideas in each individual who makes up the group. Discussion is constantly taking place whenever groups wish to exchange ideas or to clarify and deepen their understanding of something they have been studying. It goes on continually in the classroom whenever a student either asks a question or wishes to express his idea about some point that has been explained. It is the central activity in the vast promotion of study clubs which have come to have so important a part in community, parish, and diocesan life. It usually accompanies the meetings of any society or organization. Discussion extends to almost any religious group, as, for example, a convert inquiry class. It is a significant part of labor and industrial gatherings, and of such particular interests as pre-marital and marital conferences.

The Leader's Special Function. The discussion leader as such is not an instructor or lecturer. If he is a teacher in a classroom, he should clearly distinguish his instructional role from that of discussion leader. If he is participating in a study group, unless he has been called in as an expert to lecture on a particular topic, he should not use the time to present his own ideas and experiences. The discussion leader's role and purpose are directly related to the discussion itself. His chief function is to promote a free exchange of the group's views. They are presumed to have sufficient knowledge and information either from some objective classroom text and the instructor's explanations and clarifications; or from pamphlets, notes, or from a previous series of lectures, if it is a general study group. The point in discussion is to produce an atmosphere in which ideas come alive in each member of the group and through which, on his own responsibility, each will begin to act on his new convictions. Understanding and conviction which lead to action in the circle of each one's life is the purpose of a discussion group. All the leader's activities are determined by this purpose.

VARIOUS USES OF DISCUSSION

In Industrial and Social Organizations. Discussion skills seem particularly important now in various industrial and social relationships because of the peculiarly isolated and regimented lives that many people are forced to live. Modern society, due probably to the widespread development of mass production methods and the growth of large cities, tends of its very nature to rob an individual of that sense of personal identity and meaning which he normally had in older, less regimented, and more individualistic times. But, the natural spontaneity and freedom of human nature often seems to revolt against such mass organization. The basic need of each personality to express itself seems fundamental to peace and happiness. A person wants to make at least some decisions about the means to be used to reach certain goals and other details of group activity or organizational projects.

Frustration Reactions. When this opportunity is not supplied, emotional conflicts and confusions increase. They are apt to express themselves in personal resentments and disorganized emotional reactions. Summarizing the studies made on each individual's need to participate in some of the decisions of a group and to have some personal part in organizational projects, Allport says,

. . . What the industrial psychologist has discovered is that when the work-situation in which the individual finds himself realistically engages the status-seeking motive, when the individual is busily engaged in using his talents, understanding his work, and having pleasant social relations with foreman and fellow-worker, then he is, as the saying goes, "identified" with his job. He likes his work; he is absorbed in it; he is productive. In short, in McGregor's terms he is industrially *active*; that is to say, he is participant.

When, on the other hand, the situation is such that the status-motive has no chance of gearing itself into the external cycles of events, when the individual goes through motions that he does not find meaningful, when he does not really participate, then comes rebellion against authority, complaints, griping, gossip, rumor, scapegoating, disaffection of all sorts. The job-satisfaction is low. In McGregor's terms under such circumstances the individual is not active; he is industrially *reactive*.

In the armed forces, in federal employment, in school systems, the same principle holds. Ordinarily those at the top find that they have sufficient comprehension, sufficient responsibility, and sufficient personal status. *They* are not the ones who gripe and gossip. It is the lower-downs who indulge in tendency-wit against the brass hats, who complain, who go AWOL, become inert, or gang up against a scapegoat. When in actual combat, all the energies and training, all the personal responsibility of which a soldier is capable, are called upon, then egos are engaged for all they are worth. Men are active; they have no time to be reactive; nor have they reason to be.

Accepting this analysis as correct the problem before us is whether the immense amount of reactivity shown in business offices and factories, in federal bureaus, in schools, can be reduced, as it is when men at the front are using all their talents and are participating to the full in life-and-death combat.

We are learning some of the conditions in which reactivity does decline. Friendly, unaffected social relations are the most indispensable condition. Patronizing hand-outs and wage-incentive systems alone do not succeed. Opportunities for consultation on personal problems are, somewhat surprisingly, found to be important. And as members of this Society have shown, group decision, open discussion, and the retraining of leaders in accordance with democratic standards yield remarkable results. One of Lewin's discoveries in this connection is especially revealing. People who dislike a certain food are resistant to pressure put upon them in a form of persuasion and request; but when the individual himself as a member of a group votes, after discussion, to alter his food-habits, his eagerness to reach this goal is independent of his personal like or dislike. In other words, a person ceases to be reactive and contrary in respect to a desirable course of conduct only when he himself has had a hand in declaring that course of conduct to be desirable.

Such findings add up to the simple proposition that people must have a hand in saving themselves; they cannot and will not be saved from the outside.[3]

[3]Gordon W. Allport: "The Psychology of Participation," address given at the annual meeting of the Society for the Psychological Study of Social Issues at Columbia University, September 16, 1944, published in *Psychological Review*, Vol. 53, May 1945, pp. 122, 123.

When, therefore, a person is deprived of his sense of individual participation and responsibility, it seems to destroy his enthusiasm and consistency in carrying out any joint project. But, if the same activity is presented with the aid of a group discussion skill in such a way that each individual can personally identify himself with it, penetrate its reasonableness and see it as a part of his own goals, then he seems to have more enthusiastic, consistent, and happier relationship to it. Discussion skills can, for this reason, be especially valuable in promoting positive and productive attitudes among groups in various cooperative enterprises.

Important to Education. Discussion is essential to education. A classroom that is entirely teacher-centered and allows little or no opportunity for the student to express, clarify, and integrate his ideas and difficulties, is very poor education indeed. The teacher is a necessary but secondary agent in the educative process. The student is the primary agent and, unless his interests and personal responsibility are stimulated so that he actively considers and absorbs the matter that is presented to him, no true education has taken place. As Maritain has pointed out, interpreting the thought of St. Thomas,

All this boils down to the fact that the mind's natural activity on the part of the learner and the intellectual guidance on the part of the teacher are both dynamic factors in education, but that the principal agent in education, the primary dynamic factor or propelling force, is the internal vital principle in the one to be educated; the educator or teacher is only the secondary—though a genuinely effective—dynamic factor and a ministerial agent.[4]

Aids Personal Integration. The teacher must learn, not only to present the matter well and clearly and to be equipped with facts, information, and principles, but also to promote and stimulate discussion and free exchange among the students. Unless the teacher is a skillful discussion leader, who can develop personal responsibility and creative thinking, the knowledge presented in the classroom remains dead. Together with guidance and teaching there must be a place in the school program for the personal integration of each student, if education is to produce fruits in action. Such integration is greatly aided by discussion.

[4]Jacques Maritain: *Education at the Crossroads,* New Haven, Yale University Press, 1943. p. 33.

We have seen, too, in our previous analysis of the counseling process that fear, hostility, and tension block insight and freeze the child's, or adult's, perception on a narrow aspect of reality.[5] The class that is teacher-centered, or the meeting that is taken over by one individual in the capacity of leader or chairman, is apt to produce resentment and hostility among the others. This will block insight, and prevent any of the knowledge presented from flowing through the persons and becoming active in their own choices.

A classroom atmosphere which has no limits will, of course, be inadequate for the promotion of knowledge, because reality itself implies limits and the acquiring of self-discipline. On the other hand, a rigid, teacher-centered discipline is apt to arouse fear and resentment in the students. They may be motivated to routine recitation and performance. But these alone do not result in integrated insight and may produce only memory action which, of itself, becomes no part of the person and disappears as soon as the pressure of the task has passed. We can see, too, that such a classroom situation could sometimes further personal maladjustment and confusion by increasing the fear of failure and sense of inadequacy in the student. His school day is then spent in strong emotional tensions. When we consider how often this same type of child is from a home where he constantly faces difficult personal and emotional situations, it is easy to see how the classroom task, and the fear and hostility which it may engender, can often be too much for him. Such a student, if he is aggressive, may go into truancy and ultimate delinquency. Alternately, he may withdraw and become increasingly insecure and inadequate. In any case, teacher-centered instruction seems only to develop a state of passive acquiescence in students, and not responsible virtue.

Responsible Lay Activity.   Besides their application to the classroom and educational functions, discussion methods are particularly applicable to all the broad programs of lay action which have become so prominent and important in Catholicity today. The laity must be instructed and guided, but they must also be enabled to assume personal responsibility and act on their own convictions and understanding. Consequently, any kind of leadership which promotes passivity and a "mass mind" on the part of people, is the very opposite of what is both Catholic and democratic. The following quota-

[5]See Chapter VII.

tion illustrates this method of centering everything on the leader, and making the whole group dependent on him for their ideas, and passively acquiescent to his will:

> It lies in the nature of an *organization* that it can only exist in a broad mass, where a more emotional attitude serves a high intellectual leadership. A company of two hundred men of equal intellectual ability would in the long run be harder to discipline than a company of a hundred and ninety intellectually less capable men and ten with higher education. . . . The new movement rejects in general and in its own inner structure, a principle of majority rule in which the leader is degraded to the level of a mere executant of other people's will and opinion. In little as well as big things, the movement advocates the principle of unconditional authority of the leader, coupled with the highest responsibility.[6]

On the contrary, the kind of leadership which is Catholic as well as democratic, must activate the personal responsibility of each individual. As Pope Pius XII has said, "The people lives by the fullness of life in the men that compose it, each of whom—at his proper place and in his own way—is a person conscious of his responsibility and of his own views."[7] Catholic as well as democratic leadership is, therefore, wedded to the quest for truth and reality, and to the active participation in public and social affairs through the stimulation of each individual's ability to think for himself. It is clearly opposed to any type of conditioning of a "mass" way of thinking, which merely creates passive acquiescence in people so that they follow wherever they are directed. For the promotion of such individual personal responsibility, discussion skills can be especially helpful.

Sharing Ideas. Moreover, the problems of living are now so complex that priests and other religious cannot be trained in all facets of knowledge. As Pope Pius XI pointed out,

---

[6]Adolf Hitler: *Mein Kampf*, translated by Ralph Manheim, Boston, Houghton Mifflin Co., 1943, pp. 456 and 344.

[7]*Op. cit.* Pope Pius XII: *Christmas Message,* 1944. Elsewhere Pope Pius XII says, ". . . the mentality of associates who consider themselves as inert wheels of a gigantic machine, incapable of moving of their own accord until the central force makes them rotate, would not be compatible with the proper idea of Catholic Action. Nor could it be admitted that the leaders of Catholic Action should be like the operators of an electrical plant merely waiting for the word of command to switch on or interrupt, to regulate or direct the current in the vast network." Pope Pius XII: "On Catholic Action," *The Catholic Mind,* August 1951, Vol. XLIX, p. 526.

Indeed, in all ages the Catholic clergy has distinguished itself in every field of human knowledge; in fact, in certain centuries it so took the lead in the field of learning that the word "cleric" became synonymous with "learned". . . . Today it could hardly be hoped that the clergy could hold a similar primacy in every branch of knowledge; the range of human science has become so vast that no man can comprehend it all, much less become distinguished in each of its numberless branches.[8]

Consequently, in many discussions, such as those of capital and labor, or in the highly complex questions of factory problems, the priest cannot understand as well as some laymen many of the intricacies of these problems. Comparatively few priests, for example, can be technically trained in economics. Even when they are, they will often not know, as thoroughly and accurately as the worker and management, the problems of a particular factory or department. So, too, in many other questions, such as the details of family living and of courtship, young people or married people are often better equipped to offer valid and accurate information about particular questions in these matters. If the discussion centers entirely on the leader, much valuable knowledge which the group possesses will be lost. But if the leader, whether he be a priest, other religious, or layman, can acquire discussion skills, he can facilitate the exchange of views and the growth in increased understanding of the whole group, as they profit from each other's knowledge and see all sides of the question through each one's particular contributions.[9]

Prepares the Way for Counseling. Discussion skills, too, can be particularly valuable with regard to that type of information which has personal implications. Here, a skilled discussion leader can promote a free and relaxed expression of ideas on subjects which often provoke only confused and embarrassed silences. Sometimes it may be felt wiser to break up a larger group into smaller units of about ten, to facilitate each individual's expression. If the leader is prepared for the situation, discussion groups can often lead to personal counseling interviews. Once the group has discussed a topic with the

---

[8]Pope Pius XI: *The Catholic Priesthood,* Encyclical Letter: Vatican Press Translation, 1936.

[9]This was found to be true in combat. One report indicated that those combat units in which the officers allowed free exchange of ideas proved to be much more efficient than those that were dictated to by the leaders. Often the newest member of the squadron observed the most significant things and made the sharpest contributions. Interestingly, also, St. Benedict in his rule has this to say, "We have said that all should be called to council, because it is often to the younger that the Lord revealeth what is best."

leader in a somewhat personal manner, it is much easier for an individual both to face the need of personal counseling and to approach the discussion leader, or someone whom he recommends, for an interview.

This same possibility—of discussion leading to counseling—always exists in any meeting of a society or organization, whenever the topic can be presumed to have personal meaning for many of the members, as, for example, some phase of family or marriage problems. If the talk is followed by a skillfully handled discussion, the way is open for a number of those present to seek individual counseling.

In such situations, it is often helpful for the leader to state openly that he realizes the personal nature of the material discussed and that he would be very glad to talk it over with any who might wish to see him individually. For such a personal interview to produce constructive results he must, of course, have some knowledge of the skills and other prerequisities essential to good counseling.

UNDERLYING FACTORS IN DISCUSSION

Before this kind of discussion is possible, the leader must be aware of a number of factors that are under the surface of any discussion group. While these people do not come for counseling as such; yet, behind what they say and do in the group, there are usually many of the same kinds of hidden and conflicting attitudes and feelings as were previously revealed in the various counseling interview excerpts. Although they may not come out into the open in a discussion group in the same way they do in counseling, these factors still play a part, and sometimes a major part, in the reactions of each individual who makes up any group.

Personal Needs. It is important to realize, therefore, that whenever a group of people get together—either as students in a classroom or as adults in a study club or group conference—they are not just themselves. They are all their cares, disturbances, arguments, rejections, successes, loves, and hates.[10] The way each one acts in

---

[10]Some parts of this chapter also appeared in a separate form as an article in Charles A. Curran, "The Leader's Skill in Group Discussion," *Am. Cath. Soc. Rev.*, 11, December 1950. See also: Nicholas T. Fouriezos, Max L. Hutt, and Harold Guetzkow, "Measurement of Self-Oriented Needs in Discussion Groups," *The J. Abnorm. and Social Psychol.*, Vol. 45, pp. 682–690. K. D. Benne and P. Sheets, "Functional Roles of Group Members," *J. Soc. Issues*, 1948, 4, No. 2, 41–49. R. W. Heyns, "Functional Analysis of Group Problem-solving Behavior," *Conference Research Staff Papers*, 1948–49, Microfilmed.

that group will be motivated by all these things. We all need to be accepted, to feel we belong, to have confidence in some success and achievement. The measure of our security and ease in any group is apt to be the degree to which we have these feelings of acceptance and achievement in our personal life, our home, school, work, play, and even in the previous experiences of that day or week.

The order or disorder of a group's discussion, then, can give us clues to the state of mind of those who make it up. If a teacher or student comes to class, or an individual arrives at a meeting emotionally upset or tense, he is apt to demand far more personal acceptance for what he says than his ideas are worth, or the group is capable of giving him. If so, he can readily become hostile to some individual who differs with him, and antagonistic to the group. In any emotional state of irritation or rejection, as we have seen, one's perception often narrows—one fixes on little phrases and minute points of difference, losing sight of the larger questions. That is, one comes to the class or group with the need to release emotion, and from the beginning is unconsciously seeking small issues or differences to offer an outlet for this release. Obviously, these kinds of needs can cause a few people to take over a discussion; the discussion gets nowhere, and others sit silently for awhile and then grow bored. Some of us, for periods of our life at least, are emotionally tense and on edge a good part of the time. Psychological research indicates that this is true of a good part of the population. At such times, unless we keep a tight hold on ourselves, we are not very capable of reasonable discussion ourselves and we will block it in others. If, then, reasonable discussion and difference of opinion are to take place without individuals becoming disagreeable and personally unpleasant, we must know ourselves, our emotional needs and weaknesses, and keep some measure of control of these as well as allow for them in others.

People Express Emotions as Well as Ideas. Obviously, people talk because they have something to say. What they say, however, is not always thought out. Any conversation carefully analyzed usually contains as many emotions as ideas. People are likely to say as much what they feel as what they think. A person's statement can be discerning analysis and careful judgment, or, it may be largely the release of feelings. Most people find it hard to talk without somehow introducing their own problems and often, too, their own emotional prejudices. We are not as conscious of this as we might be in our daily personal relationships. We tend to assume that whatever a person says, he really meant to say; that he had thought it out completely and was thoroughly convinced of it. Actually, this is seldom true. The firmness and emphasis of a statement is not necessarily a sign of conviction. On the contrary, a person may be firm, emphatic, and even angry because he is insecure and threatened either by the situation he is in, the other people, or the subject itself. In fact, we saw in the analysis of excerpts of interviews that people are apt to express even more emotion than content when they talk. This is especially true at first, when they are not sure of acceptance. Most people are quite unaware of this tendency in themselves.

Emotional conversation can go to two extremes. Generally, it takes the form of opposition. Whenever a person is tense, insecure, or irritable, his first reaction may be to oppose. Sometimes, however, emotions go the other way: at the outset some may find themselves enthusiastic about something, which, when they think it out, they are not really convinced of and not sure they want to support. These emotional expressions can, of course, be controlled simply by a person's forcing himself to be silent. They can be changed as people acquire a new point of view about the persons, places, or subjects that color their emotions.

Emotions Helped by Talking. Everyone, naturally, wants to be reasonable. This is true, as we saw, even in the play interviews of small children. No one wants to act solely on his feelings. But, the mere wish to change these emotional attitudes does not always prove effective. Many are not aware of the deep and blind feelings that motivate many of their judgments. A great aid to understanding one's emotional motives is the experience of talking about these feelings to another person or in a group. We have seen how talking about a feeling or prejudice gets it out of ourselves and we are able to see it more objectively. This increased self-understanding makes it easier for us to see when our position is unreasonable. Talking aloud seems also to release the strong hold which these feelings have on us and we are gradually able to control and change them.

THE LEADER'S SKILL

Acceptance Essential. But, as in individual counseling, for this talking process to be helpful in a discussion group, it is essential that the atmosphere be one of personal acceptance. If the group leader becomes involved in an argument when the attitudes are emotional, he only fixes a person's feelings all the more firmly and usually makes him further resistant and hostile. After a number of remarks such a person may become silent through embarrassment. But his silence is likely to be firm, negative disagreement, crystalized now by even stronger feelings and resentments.

The group leader must, then, not only be sensitive enough to recognize and allow for the emotional tone in a person's statement; he must also be skillful enough to respond in such a way that, instead of an increase of hostility, insecurity, and negativism, he can gradually stimulate insight and understanding. Like the counselor, the leader needs more than good intentions. He needs a precise method if he is to prevent his own emotions and personal prejudices and those of the group from running away with the discussion.

General Issues Contain Personal Tones. The discussion leader is both the idea co-ordinator and emotional reflector, as in counseling. But there are some differences. Persons coming for counseling are especially concerned with working out personal problems. This is not the immediate motive for a group discussion, since the group's concern is with more general issues. However, most general issues important enough for discussion usually involve sufficient personal elements so that some individuals in the group feel strongly about them. For example, in a religious inquiry class, the instructor may make a particular statement about another religion in an effort to clarify a point of Catholic teaching. This can touch one individual in the group very deeply because he may immediately think of a good father or mother who represents that particular religious group to him. Here we have a strong emotional tone on the part of one, which none of the others may feel, and which the instructor had no intention of arousing.

In the same way, discussions of labor encyclicals in groups that have representatives of both labor and management may involve intense emotional reactions as the members present their differing views. Marriage questions, too, as well as the discussion of child or adolescent problems, can have personal connotations for some of the participants when the group generally would be left unmoved. The leader may never know of this because these emotionally disturbed people may remain silently negative or guardedly defensive. They may, of course, become openly hostile and sometimes so strongly determined and insistent on the acceptance of their personal views that they carry the whole discussion.

Such attitudes call for a particular skill. People in this state of mind are usually only made more emotional by argument and their reaction, in turn, may set off tensions in the others. Differences of opinion can quickly become personal and offensive. The leader, if he is not careful, will become embroiled himself. What purposed to be an intelligent discussion ends in the emotional tone of a brawl and everyone will be at least somewhat upset and disturbed. If it is a discussion outside the classroom some of the members may be so irritated that they will not come again. In any event, there has been little or no intellectual clarification or stimulation and much of the time has been wasted.

SOME STEPS IN DISCUSSION

Beginning the Discussion. In the beginning the leader should remain quiet, leaving the responsibility for the opening of the discussion with the group. If it is in a classroom, and he has explained the matter well, he can assume the interest of the group and the spontaneity which will produce discussion. This will be especially evident as the class becomes aware that, after the explanation is given and the matter is presented, there is always a time for discussion. The students grow alert to this discussion time and mentally begin to prepare questions and contributions. Consequently, the discussion leader in the classroom should structure his relationship so that the students themselves can distinguish his function as instructor and teacher from his function as discussion leader. As they grow used to this, they rapidly sense the transitional stage when the instruction and explanation period ends and the discussion begins. In the first part of the class year, the teacher can indicate this by an opening statement that the discussion is for the students and that they may contribute whatever they wish toward the integration of the ideas. He may state the topic and say, in a relaxed way,

Suppose we discuss that together now and each one feel free to make his own contributions or present his difficulties or objections as he wishes.

He may also find it helpful to set a definite time limit for the discussion.

In a discussion group outside the classroom, we can assume that people would not come to a meeting without some interest. This interest, if allowed to develop, will produce an exchange of ideas and intellectual growth. The very presence of each person implies that he has unanswered questions and the urge for further understanding. The leader must be sufficiently relaxed and at ease to allow these urges to begin to express themselves.

Group Responsibility for Discussion. The group only gradually becomes aware that the leader really meant the opening statements indicating that the discussion is for them, that he is not going to take over, and that whatever ideas are contributed must come from them. The group's silence can be accepted by a direct response to the situation, for example,

It's a little hard to get started, isn't it?

The more accurate the leader is in responding to the feeling of the group in these beginning states of insecurity and hesitancy, the quicker the members will be at ease and begin freely to express themselves. By the leader's understanding manner, he shows his conviction that the discussion belongs to the group, that he is not going to take over, but is there to co-ordinate and reflect their expressions. The leader's silence is very effective in structuring his role.

Structuring Statements. In the first discussion or so, the leader may find it necessary to explain the kind of relationship that is to exist between himself and the group. Sometimes he will find it helpful to define his role briefly with a statement, such as,

I'd like you to feel these discussions are for you. The more people feel free to express themselves like this, the more it seems they get from the meeting.

After such a statement the leader should be quite willing to pause for some minutes. In most cases, someone in the group will have some question or comment. If not, the pause should not be so long that it becomes embarrassing. The leader might then propose the general topic of discussion—

Would you care to express your reaction on —————— point—just the way you feel about what you read, *or*, about what was explained?

Group Survey. Another approach that is sometimes helpful in beginning a discussion, is a survey of group opinions and suggestions. This may take the form of seeking from the members, their expression of the various aspects of a particular topic they would like to discuss or the order of importance of certain topics to them. In this way, too, questions on how to proceed, such as the arrangement of suitable time and similar practical issues that demand an immediate solution, can be presented to the group for comments and suggestions. While these points may appear in themselves comparatively insignificant, members of the group will, in the beginning, talk more readily about such things precisely because they are unimportant. The members only gradually take up more serious and personal issues, when they feel at ease with the leader and one another and are surer of the group's acceptance.

Pressure May Create Passivity or Resistance. In all this, the leader's relaxed, quiet, non-aggressive manner is most important. He must avoid overenthusiasm and any attempt at selling the discussion to the group. The attitudes of the group are delicately balanced between active interest and the general tendency to passivity which quickly settles over any audience when someone lectures. Aggressive pressure on the part of the leader often only seems to encourage this passivity.

In the classroom every student has many motives to wish to achieve further understanding and recognition by participating in discussion. In addition, there are the release and satisfaction he gets from being able to talk freely and express himself to the group. He is sometimes blocked from this by his fear of the group's rejection and ridicule. But the teacher's accepting manner allows him to feel that his ideas are understood even when other students differ, laugh, or perhaps ridicule him.

In adult discussion groups or those outside school hours, the sense of personal responsibility is strong enough to have caused each person present to leave his home and other activities. There was, therefore, a whole series of evaluations and choices necessary to bring him, finally, to this group on this particular evening. This responsibility is weakened or destroyed if the leader takes over either by attempting to talk the group into something or by aggressive suggestions to which they respond laconically. We then have the vicious circle in which the group's passivity calls for enthusiasm and encouragement from the leader, which further decreases group responsibility and necessitates more leader stimulation. This is the exact opposite of the individual, personal responsibility to which democratic leadership is dedicated.

Discussion Is the Group's Responsibility.   Good leadership must encourage personal initiative by keeping the responsibility squarely on the group. Silence, lack of discussion, are the group's problems— not the leader's. Here is a subtle pitfall that threatens the unwary. If the leader has not thought out his role, and vaguely assumes that the success of the discussion depends on him, the group's silence or hesitant comments will appear to be a reflection on himself. He is apt to feel rejected and threatened by the apparent failure. This will push him into more aggressive determination to make the discussion succeed. On the contrary, if he really feels that his role is to co-ordinate and reflect what others express, instead of being threatened, the leader leaves the problem of silence and sporadic discussion directly with the group.

Such difficulties can be faced honestly and presented in a brief statement:

We seem to find it hard to keep our discussion going,

or

Could we have suggestions about what we could do to help our discussion?

No group discussion can rise higher than the level of interest of those who make it up. The group leader does not pump-prime or stimulate artificially interest that is not there. Rather, he channels interest and enables the group to stimulate itself by its own enthusiasm.

The Leader's Position.   The leader's facial expression, as well as the various positions he may take in relation to the group, are often as important in aiding discussion as his words, especially in the beginning when the group feels somewhat strange. The leader must be alert to recognize a person's desire to speak by moving his eyes slowly back and forth over the whole group. Whether the leader sits or stands does not in itself appear important, so long as he can be seen easily. The turning of his head and even sometimes his walking slowly across the room in front of the group, if he has been standing, is itself an important first step in the group's feeling that he will accept their contribution. Since each member's line of vision is, or should be, centered on the leader, his failure to look at one or the other, may have slight tones of rejection and discourage their participation.

When one person has spoken, the leader can often encourage further comments from others by looking slowly from one to the other. If one person is speaking at some length, the leader can begin to do this before he finishes. Generally, this does not offend the speaker, but does indicate that others also now wish to be heard.

The Group's Position.   Generally a group will, when interested, tend to arrange itself around the leader. They usually take the form as near a half circle as the size of the group and the mobility of the chairs will permit. In the beginning, the group's insecurity will often show itself in a number of compromise expressions, in what might be called group design. One of the most common, in a group of large size, will be for the majority to sit as far away as possible from the speaker, so they can avoid being the center of attention. In a smaller group, of ten or fifteen, some individuals may demonstrate a slight resistance by sitting behind someone else. This may block the line of vision between the leader and themselves. Such people may also choose to sit so far to the right or left of the leader that he must turn his head to see them. For these reasons, some leaders have found it helpful not to assume their place until the design of the group is already set. Then they can take a position as near as possible in the center of the group's line of vision.

To illustrate how the position a person takes in a group can sometimes symbolize his resistance: in one small group of ten, two people at first sat at an angle to two others in such a way that the leader, who was seated, could not see them. The chairs, in this case, were unattached and could be moved. Later, as the group discussion began to unfold and a number had expressed themselves, the two whose chairs were outside the half circle design each contributed something to the discussion. As each of the two spoke, he also brought his chair forward so that he was now in the line of vision of the leader. In this particular group, while the discussion was about a topic important to the group, it was also being used to give them a demonstration of discussion skill. Afterwards, for the purpose of this demonstration and to illustrate the point we have just discussed, the leader was able, without giving offense, to question the two people about their attitudes when the discussion began. Both were surprised to realize that they had taken positions which symbolized their unexpressed resistance to the topic under discussion. It was only after they had begun to participate mentally, and then to contribute something to the discussion, that each felt the urge to be in the direct vision of the leader. Until it was pointed out, however, they were not consciously aware that, as they spoke, they in turn had moved their chairs into the half circle, away from the compromise position they had first taken.

In the conversation that followed this, one of the two, a young man, stated that it was one of the few times he had ever been able to express himself in a group; he had always felt resistant to and on the outside of any group he was in, even though people appeared to accept him. This elicited spontaneous comments from each of the other nine indicating that they had sensed this in him and felt it was a handicap to his own achievement but had never been able to tell him so. Such personal revelations, of course, will not always take place. But this does demonstrate how often even the design of the group may, in some way, be determined by some of the attitudes of those who make it up.

VARIOUS TYPES OF QUESTIONS

In the first discussion or so, particularly, the group's comments may include a number of questions. This may be due to various causes. Any form of discussion may be new to them and they may feel the need of a certain amount of information. Some questions, especially about arrangement and matters of procedure, obviously require the leader's answer, which should be brief and to the point. Such questions can easily be anticipated and the answers prepared.

Avoids Responsibility. A significant point about questions often overlooked, though, is this: *one takes no responsibility when one asks a question.* Group members are likely to feel somewhat insecure with one another and with the leader, and a question is a way of saying something and participating without actually involving one's self. Any other form of comment is apt to include some expression of opinion and some definite stand, but a question puts the responsibility right back on the leader and leaves the inquirer uninvolved.

Questions with Hidden Motives. Many questions, therefore, may not actually involve information. They are, upon analysis, subtly intended to get the leader to commit himself and, further, to take over the group. The questioner himself may not realize this. He may not be consciously aware of his own tendency to avoid responsibility in discussion. Sometimes, also, a person asks a question because he is cautiously feeling the leader out, having a very deep conviction or prejudice on the point himself. These kinds of questions demand the greatest keenness if they are to be handled well. Instead of searching for an answer, the leader keeps his mind fixed on the tone, as well as on the content, of the question and reveals it with a response. The questioner, for example, may say,

Do you think we can get anywhere in discussion on a topic like this?

And the leader responds simply and easily,

You wonder whether our discussion on a topic like this will have any value.

Such a response as this, keeping the responsibility on the questioner, readily calls forth further explanation by him and sometimes even a definite expression of opinion, with which the others agree or disagree, and the discussion is off. Direct questions, too, can be nicely turned over to the group with a brief statement like,

Mr. B. raises the question (Stating the point raised)—would the group care to comment on that?

Personal Attack. A more difficult kind of question is the one that has a veiled personal sting in it. This kind of question seldom occurs after a good discussion relationship has been established but it often arises when there is aggressive personal dominance, such as sometimes happens in a classroom. For example, a college student raises his hand and slyly asks,

Just what do you mean by a depth examination? I don't get what you mean. That's awfully vague.

The Professor replies:

Any intelligent college student should know what I meant. It's perfectly obvious.

We notice here that the innocent appearing question is actually an attack on the professor's vagueness. The professor senses this, is aroused to defense, and does not answer the question at all but impugns the student's intelligence. The other students, too, have not missed this sharp exchange and so the next question coming from another student begins,

Now I don't want to raise your ire, Dr. D., but there is a lot of material in this course and I'm just sweating trying to get it all in. Do we have to read everything you mentioned? We do have other classes and other activities, you know, and some of us veterans are married.

Here, we have open resistance probably shared by a good part of the group. A reading program which might have been both informative and stimulating has now the emotional tones of a burden and an inconsideration. If this were a free discussion, without the necessity of having to pass a course to get a degree, one would not be surprised if neither of these students came to the next class.

Much as we disapprove of Dr. D.'s handling of this situation, we may be surprised to find that in a similar position we have reacted in the same way. It is not hard to be objective when no one is threatening us, but faced with a personal affront, however slight, especially before others, our emotions are quick to take over. The handling of personal attack is one of the most difficult of skills in discussion as well as in counseling. Most leaders and counselors are at first overwhelmed and realize afterwards, with regret, that their own replies were defensive and resistant. Although the leader may think he has been successful in hiding his emotional attitudes, they are sensed by everyone. If he finds he has become defensive and consequently has aroused further attack from the one or two, it is better to face it openly with a phrase like,

Perhaps I may have been a little hasty or prejudiced on that point—you feel in a way that I was.

Much to be preferred, though, is the leader who can reflect hostile and critical attitudes towards himself as sincerely as he responds to any other opinions. As one grows more adept at the method of handling attack and more skilled in penetrating and responding to the attitudes expressed, he will become more and more aware how quickly negative and hostile emotions, even towards the leader, can become positive.

THE DISCUSSION PROCESS

Group Stimulation and Enthusiasm. The discussion will get rather rapidly under way if the leader has cautiously and skillfully avoided taking from the group the responsibility for contributing ideas. One is often surprised, not only at the quick response, interest, and free exchange among the members, but also at the amount of information and close reasoning of which they are capable. Thinking a problem out together stimulates each person's enthusiasm and sharpens wits. Different aspects are quickly pointed out and analyzed. This kind of discussion, well-structured in a self-directive way, is often a remarkable demonstration of the depth and breadth of group thinking. A point or fact missed by one person will be immediately supplied by his neighbor. This snow-ball movement can gather together an impressive amount of reasoning, even in the short time of an hour or two. What is often a slow and tedious process when done alone can, by the magic of association and sharing, become easy, enjoyable, and stimulating. Even after a single hour of this kind of group exchange, each person is apt to feel he has acquired new ideas and achieved greater integration. Enthusiastic reactions are common:

You know I never thought those things out before—I really got some new ideas today.

We really thought that through tonight, didn't we? I certainly enjoyed it.

I want to think that over a lot more, and do more reading on it.

A lot of those things pointed out never occurred to me before. I'm not nearly as set on that point as I was before this evening. Maybe I was a little more prejudiced than I realized.

Leader Co-ordinates Ideas. When the discussion is going along in this manner, the role of the leader is comparatively simple. He is the centerpiece around which the group's ideas are co-ordinated. He achieves this co-ordination by summarizing the intellectual content of each person's statement. The more precise and brief this kind of leader summary is, the better. The group's enthusiasm may crowd him somewhat, so that he cannot respond to every individual statement. He should, however, without being aggressive, be alert to any pause and fill it with a statement which combines the ideas just expressed by two or three.

Leader's Response Objectifies and Impersonalizes Each Contribution. This kind of leader response to idea content is very valuable. His restatement of an idea makes it the possession of the whole group and allows them to discuss it more objectively. Differences of opinion or further clarification by others in the group are now no longer so personal. This aids discussion because people can now argue without feeling they are making themselves offensive.

Record of Discussion. The leader, too, or someone else in the group, may find it helpful to make summarizing notes of each person's comment so that some record of the group's reasoning process is available. This kind of record tends further to objectify the ideas expressed, and wield all the thinking into one composite achievement. A record of this sort can also help the leader afterwards in examining the accuracy and thoroughness of his responses.

An even greater aid, particularly for the leader's examination of his methods, is the use of some recording device so that the complete interchange of an hour or two's discussion can be studied word for word. If such recordings are made, one is usually in for some great surprises when he hears some of his own responses. As we mentioned, accurate note-taking in the process of an interview, even by experienced counselors and social workers, produces at best one-third of what takes place. It is easy to see, then, how the memory may trick us; we may be amazed and chagrined at some of the things we really said, especially in an emotionally tense situation.

Blackboard and Code. A blackboard can often be an aid in summarizing different points of view. In using a blackboard, some leaders find it helpful to give code designations for the different points of view, rather than using people's names. For example, one person's proposal or idea is labelled A, the alternate or different view, B, etc. When additional suggestions are made by the group to one view or the other, they become A_1, B_1, A_2, etc. This both objectifies and centers the group's thinking around definite points and it also impersonalizes and unifies each person's contribution. By not using the person's name, discussion takes place around the ideas themselves, and objections or differences are less likely to be taken personally.

Response Gives Acceptance. A second advantage which follows from the leader's function of restating ideas is the feeling of being understood which each person gets from it. The leader's neutral acceptance often goes a long way in removing the personal sting and rejection a person experiences whenever others in the group disagree, as they may often do. Both sides of any question should be sincerely and accurately reflected.

Leader Must Control His Own Emotions. In this the leader must especially control his own emotional blind spots and prejudices lest he become embroiled in a dispute. A difference of opinion can be profitable for sharpening distinctions and clearing up confused ideas, but it also runs a risk of precipitating personal rejection and threat. Here, the line between an intellectual and an emotional statement is finely drawn. To allow for emotions as well as for differences of opinion, and yet keep the discussion on an objective and impersonal plane, calls for the highest concentration, alertness, sensitivity, and skill.

RELEASING AND CLARIFYING EMOTIONS

Even strong emotional expressions are lessened when released and accepted by an accurate restatement of such feelings. But, as in the counseling interview, this response to the emotion contained in a statement made in group discussion is also probably the most difficult of all skills for the leader to master. As we saw, many people at first do not recognize the difference between an intellecutal statement and an emotional one. Fewer still can recognize delicate emotional tones that a phrase or a word may reveal in an otherwise straightforward expression of ideas. No easy or quick answer to this can be given. Much as one might like to assure those in the role of discussion leaders or counselors that it is not hard, long experience in the training of counselors has shown otherwise. As we have seen, the mastering of the ability to handle emotional responses is the most difficult of all counseling skills. There is no "Open Sesame" to this. And, like many similar skills, it has a deceptive simplicity and ease when one sees it done by an expert counselor or group leader. However, this difficulty should not be discouraging. Just the awareness of emotional tones in intellectual statements and the conscious effort to catch them will steadily increase one's sensitivity and make one a far more effective group leader than he would otherwise have been. This sensitivity has great advantages, too, in personal relationships, which make it well worth the knowing. One is often surprised to see how much easier it is to get along with others, especially with persons who are emotionally tense.

Emotional Clarification Illustrated. We see this illustrated in the following classroom situation:

John has been given a written penance by the principal for misdemeanors on the playground. The teacher in the home-room has been assigned to collect the penance.

TEACHER: John, I have a note here that a penance is due today? (Pause)

Silence.

TEACHER: You don't care to answer.

JOHN: I haven't got it! (Eyes flashing)

TEACHER: You didn't care to answer because you do not have it. (Pause)

Silence.

(Tense alertness in all the students.)

TEACHER (Quietly and kindly): Would you care to tell us why you do not have the penance the principal assigned?

JOHN: Well—uh—uh—I just don't have it, that's all. (Long pause) I—uh—uh—don't think it's fair.

TEACHER: You don't have it because you don't think the penance was fair.

JOHN: No—it wasn't fair! (Boos and laughter from some of the boys.) Well, it wasn't! (John turns on them.) A lot of these other guys did just as much—they didn't get any penance.

TEACHER: You feel it was unfair because others should have had a penance too.

JOHN: That's right! They did just as much as me. (More boos, catcalls, laughter, "Aw, quit crabbing!") They never get any penance and I always do!

TEACHER: You resent their not getting penances when you always seem to.

JOHN: Well, I mean—uh, I shoulda done this penance I know but—well—I—just felt sore. I'll do it though if you give me another day.

The next day John smilingly submitted the penance.

Obviously, John is one of those unfortunate youngsters who is always getting into trouble. If we knew John's home it would not be difficult to understand why he is tense when he comes to school and why he is usually so hostile and obstinate. Here we have a typical situation, which might have resulted in a serious reprimand or possibly expulsion for John had it been carried to extremes. The teacher might readily have taken personal offense from John's silence. Instead, she accepts this silence. She might have gotten angry and rebuked John for his strong emotional statement, "I haven't got it!" This likely would only have made John more resistant and hostile and more determined to hold his ground against the teacher. We notice, however, that the teacher simply responds to the basic attitude and in no way involves herself. Her kind and quiet desire to have John express himself on the matter about which he feels so strongly takes John completely by surprise. He did not expect this kind of understanding acceptance and he is cautious. Finally, he blurts out his feeling of unfairness. We notice, too, how isolated he is from the other students by the group's opposition to him. Finding himself accepted and understood by the teacher, his negative emotions rapidly become positive and he is able to say that he should have done the penance and now clearly wishes to do it. One might raise the question: what would have happened to this resistent boy had the teacher taken the stand of personal rejection and reprimand, and attempted to compel him to do the penance or face the consequences? It probably is not an exaggeration to say that, in the tense state in which John was, such a situation as this could have been the beginning stage of a series of impolite and even completely unmanageable reactions that may ultimately have led to his expulsion from school.

Resistance as a Clue. A common difficulty for the discussion leader is the tendency to focus on the content of ideas and miss the intensity of feeling with which they were expressed. This is especially true when the discussion has been going along rather smoothly. We can tell we have missed this when our own response meets with a stronger assertion from the same person. Then, we need to be quickly alert and rephrase our statement to indicate that the emotion is accepted. For example, in a discussion of mixed marriages—a view that they should be discouraged is expressed by one member. Another, Mrs. M., disagrees. The leader responds:

LEADER: Mrs. M. thinks that attitude is too strict against mixed marriages.

MRS. M. (Breaks in): Well, I don't see why Catholics are so opposed to mixed marriages. My husband is a non-Catholic and our marriage has been a lot more successful than many Catholic marriages. Not all mixed marriages are no good as some Catholics seem to think.

LEADER: You feel, Mrs. M., that Catholics are too opposed to mixed marriages.

MRS. M.: Yes, I do. (Pause) Of course, I can see, maybe, where in some cases it's not good but that doesn't mean that every mixed marriage is going to turn out wrong.

LEADER: You can see where some might turn out badly but you don't think it should apply to all.

MRS. M.: Well, I mean just because a few are bad (Pause)—of course, maybe in some instances they do not turn out too well. I don't know just how it would be generally.

LEADER: In a way, you're just not too sure.

MRS. M.: Well, I suppose I don't really know, as I think about it. You naturally think of all marriages in terms of your own. Maybe our marriage has been more successful than many mixed marriages. I don't know.

LEADER: You feel that perhaps your marriage may be an exception.

MRS. M.: Well, I suppose perhaps it's—I—I suppose a lot of mixed marriages do not turn out as well as ours has. Perhaps my husband is an exception and our marriage has turned out a lot better than most mixed marriages do, I don't know.

MR. J.: Well, I think it's wise for the Church at least to point out the dangers of a mixed marriage. There seems to be a lot of evidence even from general statistics that mixed marriages are much less successful than the marriage of two Catholics. It seems to me that there is always going to be a barrier between the two people on so important a thing as religion even when they do love each other and share a great deal in other ways. Then, I think it affects the children, too.

Here, we have an illustration of skillful handling of an emotional attitude. Mrs. M. flatly disagrees. As her disagreement is accepted by the leader, she insists on her point. This is not offensive or disturbing for the leader, but only makes him more alert to the intensity of the resistance, and he carefully responds to Mrs. M.'s feeling. We observe that the leader makes no effort to soften the bluntness of Mrs. M.'s attitude. This is most important. As we saw in individual counseling, *a negative feeling, clearly responded to, is apt to become positive.* If, however, on very personal issues we try to encourage a person to positive attitudes by persuasion or, what is more common, by refusal to accept his negation, he is likely only to resist all the more. This would have probably happened if the leader had attempted persuasion with a statement like,

Well, Mrs. M., you *surely* don't think all mixed marriages are successful, do you?

He might have tried to turn Mrs. M.'s resistance with

Mrs. M. doesn't agree with this view. Could you tell us, Mrs. M., what do you think should be encouraged?

The leader makes no implication that Mrs. M. should change her attitude—he simply reflects Mrs. M.'s feeling. Mrs. M.'s pause might indicate her surprise at this. Probably she has grown to expect resistance from others when she expresses negations and was prepared for a stronger attack. Finding, however, that the leader is not going to oppose her, there is already a partially positive tone in her next negation. This, too, the leader reflects and Mrs. M. becomes openly ambivalent—not sure which view she has now. The leader responds to the ambivalent feeling. This enables Mrs. M. to reaffirm it. By the next response, Mrs. M. has emphasized the positive side of her double attitude when Mr. J. enters the discussion.

We notice here how smoothly these responses aid an openly resistant person to admit, in the short space of five statements, "Well, I suppose maybe a lot of mixed marriages don't turn out as well as ours." Obviously, the very fact of Mrs. M.'s presence at a discussion group of this sort indicates a definite interest in knowing more of the Catholic position. Covered over as it is with resistance and misunderstanding, this interest could only be expressed after the release of these negative feelings and their sensitive acceptance by the leader. Contrast this with what might have happened had Mrs. M. been forced to answer whether she thought mixed marriages should be encouraged. Is it likely, after Mrs. M.'s first sweeping statement, that she could have said that perhaps her marriage was an exception? Or, would she feel forced to defend herself and shift the discussion into a personal argument between herself and the leader? And, if so, would the other members have felt free, as Mr. J.

did, to enter what might readily have become a somewhat heated exchange?

Others Can Participate. We see how easy it is for the other members to enter this discussion at any time. Handled with skilled responses, discussions seldom become personal or restricted and the whole group feels free to join in. Differences of opinion flow through the leader's calm summarizing or reflective statements and personal tones are filtered out. Members can, therefore, disagree freely without being disagreeable and unpleasant.

Discussion between Two. Sometimes, after general participation by most of the group, the comments may narrow down to two members who may differ sharply. Usually, the group will be interested in these contrasting views as long as new ideas are developed. Others may join in again. However, the leader often becomes aware of a growing group restlessness after a discussion has gone on for some time. A simple response to this group feeling would be,

This seems to have narrowed down to two main opinions—would we want to leave it at that or should we continue to talk about this point?

This encourages comments from other members and a simple showing of hands will reveal the general group desire.

VOTING SHOWS GROUP OPINION

Voting is thus a very helpful tool when some revelation of the group's general attitude is necessary. Whenever possible, the group should decide all questions of procedure. If the group sets the time and even the place of the meeting, and the other details, each one is much more likely to feel it is his discussion. Even the arrangements have become each one's responsibility. In matters like this, where the vote goes against a few, the fact that they have expressed their opinion and have been heard will help them to accept an arrangement less desirable to them. As we have seen, any opportunity to express our opposition makes it easier to accept the other side, especially if we have heard their reasons. Even in such little details as the time of the meeting, the question of a recess, etc., the leader's evident desire to know the group-will by opinion and vote is a significant factor in making the group aware of their role of responsibility. By careful observation of these little things, a group relationship is skillfully structured.

LEADER PARTICIPATION

From time to time, the leader may himself wish to express an opinion. If he does so, he runs the risk of arousing personal opposition which, since it is directed against himself, will be hard to handle. This kind of personal attack, as we have seen, calls for special skill. The leader, in matters when opinions may differ, having committed himself to a particular side, will likely find it much more difficult to be entirely impersonal in reflecting opposition statements. Others, too, may find it harder to differ because they will not be sure of the leader's reaction. If, after a number of experiences in presenting his own views on a topic, the leader finds he does become somewhat emotional himself or takes advantage of his position to press his view, he would probably find it better to curb himself. Any leader expression of opinion calls for great skill if it is not to endanger the relationship between the leader and the group.

THE GENERAL COURSE OF LATER DISCUSSIONS

Two Types. Some of the points we have treated thus far will ordinarily only occur in the first few discussions. After this, as the group becomes familiar with the leader and with one another, and as the members grow to understand and enjoy their participation in the discussion, there is less need for these structuring statements. In the later stages discussion groups usually veer off in one of two directions, depending on the nature of the topic discussed and the degree of personality needs and conflicts in the members which make up a particular group. On the one side, the group's discussion may tend primarily in the direction of intellectual clarification and there may be comparatively few emotional tones. Alternately, the content may be made up largely of personal release that is somewhat emotional because each one is using the discussion mainly to gain greater self-understanding.

Begins with Disunity. In both types, the discussion generally begins with a somewhat disorganized series of statements around a topic. At first, some of the members are hesitant and the brunt of the discussion is usually borne by the remainder. The comments and contributions are, for the most part, impersonal, with the exception perhaps of expressions of resistance such as were indicated by the previous illustration. There is also little co-ordination in the ideas expressed. The general impression is one of disunity. In the beginning, too, the group probably does not have any cohesive or sympathetic feeling for one another. There is little or no thinking together. Gradually, as the discussion progresses, some signs of unity begin to appear. More members contribute until, before long, all are participating freely. There is a greater sense of sharing both ideas and feelings and mutual understanding grows.

General Intellectual Clarification. If the topic under discussion is, by its nature, somewhat impersonal, it may not involve the individual members emotionally. If they themselves get along well with one another and have no evident antipathies or confusions, there will be few occasions when any statements arouse emotions. In this case, the main course of the discussion will be in the direction of intellectual clarification and the co-ordination of ideas, as well as the rounding out of each one's knowledge about the topic.

Usually, as each person expresses his opinions on a question, common ground opens up and differences gradually fuse into an integrated statement that combines and clarifies each view. Opinions are apt to fall into two categories. Some individuals will have a broad, general view of a topic. This causes them to be indifferent, or, if they speak, to be vague and express themselves in platitudes. Others will have very narrow views, oftentimes drawing sweeping conclusions from a few facts. This group may be prejudiced and even somewhat hostile. These two views coming together in discussion create a dynamic and thought-provoking situation. Like complementary parts of a whole, each type of opinion fills out, defines and integrates the others. As the members one after another speak out, all sides of an issue are unfolded and fall into place in each one's mind. Individual questions and confusions expressed to the group become everyone's responsibility and the group thinks each problem through together. When differences remain, it has not been without a willingness to listen to and evaluate the other sides. This kind of discussion thus engenders an increasing awareness of the value of another person's opinion and a growing respect for our neighbor's right both to express himself and to make up his own mind.

Personal and Emotional Involvement. When, however, the topic itself is more immediately related to the members of the group, as, for example, a discussion on marriage for engaged couples or the raising of children for a group of young mothers, emotionally charged statements will come more quickly. Sometimes too, the group itself may be in conflict or disturbed for various reasons or it may, by chance, happen to have some or even a majority of strongly emotionalized persons in it. In these cases, the group's discussion may center more on personal clarification and integration than on the unfolding and delineating of ideas around the topic itself. Here, the discussion soon turns into what, in many respects, is really group counseling. In such situations, the emotional content of the members' statements will usually far outweigh their intellectual contributions. Even here, however, each will at first usually speak about the topic in an impersonal manner. But, gradually, as the members begin to apply the topic to themselves, they unfold their own problems around it. Here, too, some will speak more readily than others. But, as each one sees that his problems can be expressed and will be accepted both by the leader and the group, he is encouraged and stimulated by the group's growing understanding and sympathy. He becomes aware that problems, which he thought were peculiar to himself, are actually shared by some or all of the group. As he realizes this, he experiences great relief in expressing these problems to the group and getting the benefit of their clarification. Others will also contribute personal experiences around similar incidents or reactions. Deep gains in self-insight can come from such release and understanding. Even more than can be achieved in individual counseling interviews, the whole group's acceptance of a common problem has a powerful reassuring and normalizing effect. A person gets encouragement and satisfaction from being able to speak about factors that previously were considered so highly personal he always kept them carefully guarded from others. This is a great aid both in removing his feeling of being unusually different and in helping him overcome his previous tendency to withdraw himself. A person is often delighted by the discovery after one such discussion that, as he may say,

I'm not so bad off after all if some of you people have these same conflicts and feelings too!

Group Counseling Illustrated. The following excerpt is the exact reproduction of the third session of a discussion that has now become group counseling. The first two sessions lasted an hour and were composed of five members. At this present session, which lasts a half hour, one of the members (D) was unavoidably absent. She returned for later sessions. The counselor begins by making a resumé of the previous meeting. He might preferably have remained silent to see if some member would have spontaneously begun the discussion.

Co: To make a resumé of the last session, just sorta to get us on the way again (Pause), D began it and presented the problem of her insecurity and self-consciousness in any group, and the fear and withdrawal she had in any group, and A shared that very much. B shared it somewhat, but felt to some degree that she had taken steps away from that, and C shared the feeling of fear but expressed the idea that she had an entirely different method of coping with it. It was more of an aggressive taking over the group, or, if she couldn't do that she avoided the group situation entirely. (Pause) Perhaps that resumé will be suggestive of some thoughts for the group; either they may wish to continue on that point or that general topic or it may suggest some new area of discussion.

Two minute pause.

A: Well, maybe I can start it by saying that I think it was the same night, in fact I know it was the same night of the group discussion we had, that I had an individual discussion and after that I sorta decided I was going to be different—I mean feel differently about those inferiority feelings that I have all the time, and this self-consciousness that I have with a group, and I know that I still have those feelings, and just by feeling confident right now that doesn't, I mean, that's not the end of the whole thing, so, if, ah, I know that I'll have plenty of things to discuss if anyone else has anything to say.

Co: That is, the group session last time, perhaps the two group sessions and then the individual discussion put you on a kind of a positive plane or kind of positive attitude so that you haven't really been thinking any more about these insecurities although you are pretty sure that if the discussion continues on them, there are still quite a number of them there.

A: Yes, I do feel more positive about them but I'm sure that (Laughs) they are still there. I can't dismiss them that quickly.

Co: It won't succeed that quickly—the pattern won't be overcome that quickly.

A: No, I don't think so.

B: Well, I said to someone in the group sometime after—the day after. I had talked quite a bit about situations at school as they are now and after talking—it was hard for me to talk last time because I had been thinking about those things quite a bit and they were kind of deep for me, and the next day in class there was a situation where we were pretty free. I mean, there were quite a number there in the room together and I noticed that I didn't feel that way at all. It just seemed to sort of—it just helped tremendously. I just felt very relieved after having talked about it without doing anything else.

Co: You noticed a big difference in your ability in groups just by having talked about this feeling in the previous group session.

B: Of course the whole thing is very complex for me because, I mean, I am always working with about ten different aspects of myself and the situations that I never quite get together—what I was before I was sick and in the hospital for so long; what I was before I worked through interviews; what I was in the hospital as a patient where everything was more or less set up for me; what I was when I was able to be out again—that's why it's so complex because after I had interviews before and worked things out and in high school, too, I could always solve anything I felt about a group because I would go in and be very lively and get things sort of started and then I would be very much at ease and then the situation would flow. But, now with those five years that I lost when I was sick, I just don't exactly know what to do now that I'm a 24-year-old person.

Co: There's a kind of a lapse there in which your present-day reality and your plan of life, your life plan and the reality haven't got together yet. And you're still acting to some degree on a 19-year-old plan as a mature 24-year-old person.

B: Yes, I can't go in a group like I did before and be witty and sort of "cute"—was the high school way of acting—I can't be that now and I don't exactly know what else to do.

Co: You can't do what you did when you were comfortable before in a group and yet have no other way now of being comfortable.

B: That's one thing and the other thing that this is the first time that I've been in a large school and there are just so many factors of difference, little things that others are probably accustomed to that I'm not—that if I were in a small group as I was before I probably wouldn't notice so many differences.

Co: That is, there is a double factor of adjustment—both the mature experience and at the same time a completely different sort of environment or atmosphere that you must also get adjusted to that's also strange.

B: But, I've really made quite a beginning. I mean, it's not just as though I haven't done anything because I notice that—we have a room that we work in and when I'm there, just walking around meeting the different students that I'm in class with, I notice that I have an altogether different attitude than I had before. Nothing bothers me like it did. I didn't know whom to speak to and whom not to speak to, and little things like that, and I know that I am much more at ease than I was before.

Co: Actually notice a lot more social security so to speak in what were strange surroundings.

B: Yes. (Pause.)

C: Well, I don't—at present I don't have much experience with groups because the groups that I am in are mostly boys and they are mostly younger and so that I don't have that same social role that B does, I mean, where she is with a group of older people as a whole but I do notice that I used to, if I was afraid to go someplace because of people and I didn't know exactly what it would be like, I just didn't bother going. Well, I think that I've gotten over a lot of that, partly because through a confidence in my own competence, I mean, I don't think that I'm too good but just the reality that you can't know everything and I think through nursing especially—that's a situation in which I'm pretty sure. I mean, I don't think about my relationship with others and I think that I've been able to carry that over pretty well to outside, you know, but I do notice that once in a while I am kind of uncomfortable when I'm with a patient. What I have doesn't apply to groups yet but I think it's because I notice more or less recently and I think it's kind of a conflict. Like this week-end I was working with a nurse, well, I'm able now to be relaxed and not be feverishly active, and letting them rest and going on the assumption that if they want something, they're going to ask for it but the fact that she was a nurse, I suppose, there was an old conflict there that I should hurry up or that I should be very efficient when actually the poor woman really needed to rest and I knew that. And I mean, I figured it out, but I think it is those kinds of situations now that cause me to be uncomfortable when it's something from the old life that I, you know, am trying to be relaxed about it I feel that I shouldn't be like I was before, that's where the uneasiness comes in.

Co: That is, whenever a situation is at all suggestive of the old patterns of coping, by being very efficient and so on that you find a struggle then between this excessive efficiency and a more relaxed tone.

C: But it is only with people that I think would expect me to be efficient. Most people don't affect me that way anymore—even people that have stayed in the hospital a lot and have had nurses—that doesn't bother me because I figure well I know that I am good, and I give them good care, and everybody has different ways but it is just someone who is in the profession (Laughs) so to say, and I unconsciously feel that they would expect me to be very efficient.

Co: Kind of a challenge or even a little bit of a threat to make you demonstrate how efficient you can be, if it's a professional-medical sort of person.

C: Well, I think that's about all, I mean, it isn't about groups but at least it's about other people.

Co: Each one has a certain reaction to the previous sessions on this sort of self-consciousness pattern. A finds her outlook much more positive now although she's still conscious that the insecurities are there; and B has actually experienced a much greater easiness which is a result of the sessions; and C is aware in individual instances that the old patterns of efficiency with which she previously coped with any kind of insecurity, now come back much less often but only when a sort of professional challenge seems to be involved.

A: I know that I just finished saying that I'm trying to feel secure but I know now that I'm scared about tomorrow and this new job. (A is starting a new job tomorrow).

Co: Actually, now as you think about it, you're conscious that there is a real fear of this new job coming up.

A: Yes, and it's that old thing—I mean I know I'm very acceptable to them now but then after they know me (Laughs) maybe I won't be too acceptable and I'm afraid of that.

Co: It's an old pattern of being sure that you are very acceptable at first, somehow fearing that when people get to know you as you really are, they'll no longer accept you. That sort of constitutes a threat now.

A: Yes, it does. That way I'm afraid to let people know me and (Laughs nervously) when people don't know you, you're not very acceptable. I mean, you can't be so—maybe I should just see how tomorrow works out before I start worrying.

Co: While the fear is there, that fear of thinking that somehow when people do know you, they won't like you, they won't accept you. However as you give it a second thought now, it occurs to you that perhaps the thing to do is to wait until you experience tomorrow before you sort of anticipate how it is going to be.

A: Yes, (Laughs nervously) but I know that I'll be afraid.

Co: The thing is actually fearsome, isn't it, as you think about it now?

A: It isn't that I'm afraid of the work, I mean, it's the people that I am afraid of. If I can build my confidence up in this one thing then I mean, I'll be sort of going on the way to what I just said I wanted. But I know just saying that doesn't make it so and I know that oh, I'll just *have* to make this one come out right.

Co: Pretty determined with all the fear that's there, that it's going to be different from the other situations that you experienced.

A: Yes, I'm going to do everything I can to make it come out right but (Laughs) I'll be scared all the time.

The pauses indicate the slow, concentrated thought process that is taking place here. Generally, for this kind of intensely personal discussion to occur, the group should be small. However, in a surprising number of instances, such personal release and intense analysis can happen even in groups of twenty or thirty. While only five or six may participate in the discussion, the others will show their interest both by their concentrated manner and their later expressions of the personal value the discussion had for them. This seems to happen because all personal problems are shared in some way by each member of the group and therefore each one may, and often does, get value from the exchange even when he does not participate.

We notice, too, that the counselor responds primarily to the basic attitudes and underlying fears and conflicts that are expressed. The progress of B and C aids A by offering her a learning situation that is, however, not intended to be supportive or reassuring. We see how B and A, particularly, feel they have benefited by this half hour discussion from the following excerpt taken from the end of this third session:

Co: As you look back on it you have the recollection of having set up a plan of conduct you wanted to follow and actually carrying it out so that you have a feeling of satisfaction in it. (Pause)

B: That gives me an insight into something for the school situation I'm in now. There are so many unknown factors that I'm not sure of, but one thing is pretty definite, that a person should keep his own counsel, in a sense, and go ahead and be what you are and the other things just sort of take care of themselves. You don't have to be concerned about as many things as I'm being concerned about. When I followed this plan at work, that's one situation where it actually worked out.

Co: Putting the two together now, this work situation and the school, you can see if you apply that same pattern at the school you can be yourself and not try to solve everything and at the same time succeed there the same way. (Pause)

A: I think that if I could start in right now I would feel—I would be in a pretty good disposition to do well. If I can just carry this feeling over that I have right now! I mean, even though there is still that fear, this talking sort of recalls to my mind the things that I want to do. It makes me feel more sure that I'll know more the things that I have to watch out for, and to be really aware of my own self, and what I'm trying to do, so that if I could start right now I think I would be pretty much at ease.

Co: That is, this unfolding here has given you a confidence now and also an awareness of what you have to face and a kind of a security that you could face it if you could hold this.

A: Yes, it has and, well, I can tell more about it in a day or a week whether I can actually do that. But, I feel confident now. I feel that I can do it if I just stick to what I know and want.

Co: This has actually brought you a greater security than when we first started talking about it.

A: Yes, it has, because when I first started talking I really wasn't, I mean, these things have been in the back of my mind the whole day actually but they had never come out before. Just once, I mentioned it very early today but not to any length. I think just saying this much and hearing this little discussion has helped me a lot.

Co: It has been a very valuable half hour for you.

A: Yes (Laughs) but I didn't want to take the whole half hour for myself.

Co: A little self-conscious of that now.

A: I have been but not to the extent that I wouldn't go on with it.

Co: Still worthwhile, huh?

A: Yes.

B: That reproduces a feeling that I always have in these discussions. I enjoy talking so much that when I get started I never want to stop (Laughs), and then afterwards I'm sorry because I think I've blocked somebody else.

Co: You're also a little self-conscious that you talk too much.

B: Yes. I don't think it's too much but I'm afraid that it will take something from somebody else.

Co: Sort of rob someone else of the time they would want to talk. Well, our time is about up. Suppose we do call it off then.

While the discussion has centered primarily around the difficulty A raised, we see that B, too, expressed a definite gain in self-insight as a result of the discussion. C, while not so clearly indicating any immediate gain, obviously enjoyed her participation. This is typical of many such sessions where, in larger groups particularly, even those who may remain silent still find value and significance for themselves in the problems discussed.

In some instances when people have experienced both individual and group counseling, they find special advantages in the group sessions. The following comment of A immediately after this third session, indicates this:

A: Well, I think that today anyway this is more valuable than if I had been alone. In these group discussions, it always helps me to have other people's ideas around a subject because it gives me a little bit more to think over and I get around maybe to the same place a good bit faster than I would have in an individual interview. It seems to me that these are always more informal and I don't feel so tense for some reason. Maybe it is just because it is informal and I can feel pretty free. I don't say that I don't feel free when I'm alone, but anyway it's just an easy flowing feeling in this group that makes it easy to think and to say what I feel. I don't want to give the impression that I feel ill at ease in the individual interviews because I appreciate them very much but—the fact that it is a group—instead of making me feel nervous it makes me feel even more at ease than if I were alone. (Laughs) I mean, that seems like a reversal but that's the way it is.

The question might be raised whether A was actually more effective as a result of the group counseling. Her comment, three days later, indicates that she was:

A: Well, the first day, I was afraid before I started there but I was pretty satisfied with the way I acted (Laughs) and everything went very well. I was really pleased with myself. I think that I did everything that I should have done. Then, on Tuesday I sorta bogged down a little bit and I was dissatisfied with myself and I was really very unhappy. But, I think I corrected what I had done wrong in the morning. I think I sort of fixed that up and then the whole rest of the day went very well and this whole day too so I feel pretty good about it. I think it could be better but I think this is the best I've ever done. So, I think that I've handled it much better than I would have without that discussion we had and it's better than I ever have done before, too.

Individual Counseling. Sometimes the leader or group counselor can be aware of unexpressed emotions in one or the other members. This may produce an opportunity for individual counseling, if, after the discussion, he makes it a point to talk privately with each of these. Such apparently accidental meetings can often result in the type of approach to counseling described in Chapters XV and XVI. But such personal needs are not always detected in the group sessions. For this reason, sometime during the discussion series, the leader should try to have at least one short, private, but apparently unplanned, talk with each one of the group. Here, again, he must be alert to the various compromise means of approaching counseling that an individual may use.

Such an approach to counseling can also occur in another way. After the discussion proper, some usually wish to talk to the leader. They will not, however, as readily come to the front of the room to see him as they will go to the back or side. The best position for him to assume, after a discussion, seems to be near the exit but sufficiently over to the side that some element of privacy is possible. As the group begins to move towards the door, individuals can easily step over to talk with him. Here, as the individual proposes a question or difficulty, the leader should set appointments as quickly as he can, without making a person resistant by appearing to push him into an interview. He may use an expression like the following:

I'd be very glad to discuss that further with you. Could you come and see me, say tomorrow at 2:00?

We described this process in Chapter XV. If the leader is prepared for this by knowing his appointment schedule in advance, and efficient in setting an appointment, he may, in the ten or fifteen minutes people usually linger after a discussion, arrange interviews with as many as five or six people. Yet, it is possible to do this with such simple dispatch that none of those coming privately need feel the others know of it. Often, of course, members of a group are very free in discussing such interviews with one another. The need for individual counseling has, in some instances, been so accepted by groups that they appoint one person to set the time for the individual interviews as they fit in with the leader's schedule. It is better, however, for the leader to keep some measure of privacy in this until the individual himself, or the group, begin to talk openly of coming for counseling.

Discussion which in any way involves an individual personally is therefore an especially helpful means of promoting counseling. It may, for the first time, clearly focus his attention on his own problems and needs. Before, a person may have been only vaguely aware of feeling disturbed, without having any urge to change himself or his situation. But, when he can himself relaxedly talk about and hear others discuss a topic which in some way includes his own personal difficulties, he is already at the beginning of counseling. Usually, during the discussion itself, a person gets some opportunity to express his personal difficulties, at least in a general way. The satisfaction of the leader's accepting and penetrating responses then, often smooth the way for him to approach the leader for individual interviews. The leader's kind, sympathetic but skillful method of handling the discussion may make an individual feel, sometimes for the first time in his life, that he has finally met someone to whom he could talk freely about the things that are on his mind. In this way, discussion groups can be an effective means of preparing the way for group or individual counseling. Discussion and counseling going together can then be significant factors in a person's total life reorientation.

PART FIVE

CONCLUSION

CHAPTER XVIII

COUNSELING AND VIRTUE

Having now examined in detail the process and skill of counseling and the other functions which are related to it and can aid it, we are in a better position to evaluate some of the effects of counseling from the point of view of furthering more virtuous living. Previously, in Chapter I—in order to give an initial over-all view of the causes of personal difficulties—and at various other places throughout this book, we have considered how different phases of counseling have provided people with the means for a better and happier life. In the present chapter we will briefly draw some of these applications and conclusions together, particularly as they relate to certain basic virtues.[1]

Unfortunately, the word "virtue" has a confused meaning in modern terminology. Webster defines it as "an active quality, power, capacity adequate to the production of a given effect" and also as equivalent to "integrity of character." "Virtue causes an ordered operation," says St. Thomas.[2] It is in this sense of the permanent power to produce reasonable action that we use the concept "virtue" here. After a person has acquired the ability to play the piano, for example, he retains this power even when he is not playing. He does not lose it during the interim of an hour or a day, but keeps his power to play as long as it is actively exercised. Moreover, even though his playing ability may decrease somewhat due to lack of practice, yet some of this ability will usually perdure for a long time.

In the same way, between interviews and after a particular series of interviews are over, a person retains what he has achieved and

---

[1] We obviously do not mean to include here all the philosophical and theological aspects of virtue but only some limited implications of this type of counseling process. The interested reader may wish also to consult well-known Catholic manuals of philosophy and theology, especially those which treat directly of the moral virtues.

[2] St. Thomas Aquinas: *Summa Theologica*, I–II, Q. 55, a. 2, reply obj. 1, translated by Fathers of the English Dominican Province, New York, Benziger Brothers, 1947. Reprinted from the *Summa Theologica* with the permission of Benziger Brothers, Inc., Publishers and Copyright Owners.

is able to meet different life situations in a more reasonable manner. Counseling, as Rogers pointed out:

aims directly toward the greater independence and integration of the individual rather than hoping that such results will accrue if the counselor assists in solving the problem. The individual and not the problem is the focus. The aim is not to solve this problem, but to assist the individual to grow, so that he can cope with this problem, and with later problems, in better integrated fashion. If he can gain enough integration so that he can handle this problem in more independent, more responsible, less confused, better organized ways, then he will also handle new problems in that manner.[3]

Not all counseling is, of course, successful. In many instances, however, permanent effects do follow and a person is able, as a result of counseling, not only to solve particular problems, but to lead a generally more effective and achieving life. Consequently, there must be some capacities acquired during counseling which remain with a person after the fulfillment of the individual goals for which the counseling was inaugurated. In so far as such permanent qualities can and do result, they would come under the category of virtues.

SELF–KNOWLEDGE FOR REASONABLE LIVING

Knowledge Not Enough. Counseling is fundamentally a process of increasing self-knowledge. However, this self-knowledge is acquired, not simply for itself, but in order to produce more reasonable living. This was one of the main factors that brought about the development of counseling as something distinct from the other means of acquiring self-knowledge which we have called guidance. We saw how, in their recent research into ways of helping personality growth and development, psychologists, psychiatrists, social workers, and others soon learned that, no matter how accurate their diagnostic evaluation of a person was, they encountered repeated instances when, after this knowledge was given to him, it had little influence on his manner of living. This led them to conclude that other personality factors entered into the total process. They began to devise methods by which the person himself was encouraged and

[3]Carl R. Rogers: *Counseling and Psychotherapy*, New York, Copyright 1942, by Houghton Mifflin, pp. 28–29.

stimulated to put to use the knowledge he had by making his own self-evaluation, insight, and choice. We have, therefore, throughout this book, repeatedly referred to this assimilating or integrating aspect peculiar to counseling. This is its main characteristic and distinguishes it from other processes by which personal information is imparted.

Counsel, Prudence, and Moral Virtue. This awareness which modern research has uncovered, that knowledge as such—even highly personal knowledge—is insufficient for a better and happier life, is not, as we have seen, completely new. It corresponds to the path of reasoning St. Thomas follows when he makes counsel, prudence, and similar virtues of action, distinct from the speculative intellectual virtues. In the thinking of his own time and prior to it there was a point of view that focused on the imparting of knowledge, and considered this alone to be necessary.[4] But, as we discussed in Chapter I, experience itself had shown St. Thomas, and a long line of thinkers before him, that the process of reasonable action includes more than just an understanding of what is to be done. The emotions and instincts and the total psychosomatic personality enter in here.

This conflict between knowledge and the ability to carry out knowledge arises when a personal goal is seen as the object of *some action*. If something is seen as "good for me" and I have an appetite for it, I may run into a series of conflicts with my reason. The emotions, instincts, and various other physical factors are also aroused to act favorably or unfavorably in relation to the circumstances and conditions necessary to the act. They, too, play a major part in determining whether the act is carried out reasonably or not. It is only when a person, particularly through the use of available resources within himself, has brought all his reactions into line with his reasonable insight, that the final act conforms to the total good. The alternate is that one or the other instincts and emotions may take over and motivate him. They do this, either by narrowing his perception and focusing it on a pleasant aspect of some circumstance that leads him away from the goal; or, by holding up some unpleasant phase or condition, they cause him to shun the performance of an action necessary for reaching the goal. In either case

[4]St. Thomas, (D): I–II, Q. 58, a. 2.

he is moved to act against his reason. Unless a man has co-ordinated and integrated all these factors with his reasonable understanding of what he should do, he cannot be said to possess constructive and effective self-knowledge. It is precisely around this point of personal action that counsel, prudence, and the moral virtues have their distinctive characteristics.[5]

The enduring results of counseling are, therefore, said to be associated with good-counsel, prudence, and the moral virtues since they concern, not only knowledge itself, but the way by which this knowledge can be carried out in action. So St. Thomas explains that the speculative intellectual virtues such as wisdom, understanding, or science, once they have been acquired in any degree, confer a proportionate "aptness" for a good work. But, it is only through the acquisition of prudence and the moral virtues grouped around justice, courage, and moderation, that the "right use" is conferred.[6] Counseling is, then, productive of good-counsel, prudence, and moral virtue in so far as it not only enables a person to act better in a particular situation, but it helps him to acquire a power of consistently acting on a more mature and reasonable basis.

COUNSELING AND THE ART OF LIVING

Evaluation in Action. From this point of view, a good counseling process can also be said to improve a person's attainments in the art of living, for,

prudence stands in the same relation to such human actions, consisting in the use of powers and habits, as art does to external makings; since each is the perfect reason about the things with which it is concerned.[7]

To perform any work of art well it takes more than abstract knowledge; it takes a complex process of organized activity that can only be learned by repeatedly performing that particular art and, at the same time, carefully evaluating one's successes or errors in each action. More knowledge of the particular art alone will not do this.

---

[5]St. Thomas, (D): I–II, Q. 58, a. 2.
[6]*Ibid.*
[7]St. Thomas Aquinas: *Summa Theologica*, I–II, Q. 57, a. 4, in *Basic Writings of St. Thomas Aquinas*, Vol. II, translated by Anton Pegis, New York, Copyright 1945, by Random House.

The immediate evaluation in action is essential. Without such evaluation, one may never improve performance but continue at the same level.

If we apply these demands of a particular art to the whole field of living well, it helps us understand how any improvement of one's performance in the art of living requires, in addition to knowledge, the peculiar virtues which center around prudence. St. Thomas quotes St. Augustine on this:

> Augustine usually applies the term *art* to any form of right reason; in which sense art includes prudence which is the right reason about things to be done, even as art is the right reason about things to be made. Accordingly, when he says that virtue is the art of right conduct, this applies to prudence essentially; but to the other virtues, by participation, for as much as they are directed by prudence.[8]

Stages of Practical Learning. If, by way of illustration, we were to analyze the process a young girl might undergo in learning the art of cooking, it might be said to involve four stages. First, the girl would have to study and memorize the recipes in order both to understand the purpose of the various combinations of foods and to have at hand norms to guide her in the use of different ingredients and portions. Then, in the second stage, the girl might watch her mother cook, observing how her mother carried out in practice the things she saw in the recipe book. At the third stage, she might cook under her mother's direction doing what she was told. Yet, even here, although she may have produced an appetizing meal, she would not yet have acquired the art of cooking. The actual art was in her mother who directed her and not in the girl herself since the girl's main function was to be passively acquiescent to what she was told to do. She will only be a good cook herself after she has undergone a rather long series of experiences in which she takes the direct responsibility for each judgment and action that goes into the meal. At the same time she will have to evaluate each result to make sure she continues to do the things that produce success while she corrects the causes of particular failures. Gradually, from this experience and evaluation, she will acquire the combined qualities and abilities that make up the complex process of the culinary

[8]St. Thomas, (D): I–II, Q. 58, a. 2, reply obj. 1.

art. As she does, evaluation and correction will become less necessary except perhaps when she wishes to learn a new recipe.

So, in a similar way, the art of living well and virtuously cannot be learned simply by studying the rules of moral science and memorizing and understanding them, although this may be an important first stage. Nor is it sufficient either merely to observe another's acting out these moral principles or even to act them out oneself under immediate direction from someone else. For while the action itself may be prudent—as the young girl may cook a good meal under her mother's direction—yet the prudence is in the one directing. For virtue to complete itself in a good life, it must, like the final stage of a particular art, proceed by way of responsible action and repeated experience. It is, therefore, often a slow growth in the ability to co-ordinate impulses and urges around the reasonable determination of what we should do. In this sense, then, we can see how this final stage of the art of living agrees with Rank's contention that the important thing in counseling was, not the theory or the interpretation of the counselor, but the experience a person underwent in his own process of willing and feeling. Assuming that counseling can, as we have seen, objectify and clarify these feelings so that they can be more readily controlled and understood by the person's growing self-insight, we see how counseling and the art of virtuous living, go together.

PRUDENCE AND RELATED VIRTUES

Obviously, achievement in the art of good living, while similar, is much more complex and difficult than successful attainment in any particular art, even of a most exalted type. Consequently, since "prudence is of good counsel about matters regarding man's entire life"[9] and not merely, like art, about the means of making a particular thing, an important result of good counseling is the way it brings into play many of the factors which St. Thomas considered under the title of prudence and the virtues related to it. As he says,

Prudence is *right reason applied to action.* . . . Hence that which is the chief act of reason in regard to action must needs be the chief act of prudence. Now there are three such acts. The first is to *take counsel,* which belongs to discovery, for counsel is an act of inquiry. . . . The

[9]St. Thomas, (D): I–II, Q. 57, a. 4, reply obj. 3.

second act is *to judge of what one has discovered,* and this is an act of the speculative reason. But the practical reason, which is directed to action, goes further, and its third act is *to command,* which act consists in applying to action the things counseled and judged and since this act approaches nearer to the end of the practical reason, it follows that it is the chief act of the practical reason, and consequently of prudence.[10]

I. COUNSEL

We saw[11] how this first phase of prudence, the inquiry stage of counsel is, in a special way, connected with counseling. People who are in any degree of personal confusion and conflict, because of the disorganized state of their understanding of themselves and their problems, do not know what is the matter or what to do. They see their problems in a separated, unrelated fashion. They are often at cross-purposes with themselves. When they try to solve one problem it comes in conflict with another need. They are acting on a number of confused solutions none of which really solves anything. At the end of a series of actions, they are no better off than before. Few things are secure and definite.

Inquiry. The interviews begin, then, with a person's statement of his problems and the inquiring into causes. This includes the exploring of his present goals and values and the examining of various ways of acting which have proved unsatisfactory and disappointing. The purpose of this inquiry is that a person may see with greater clarity what he really is and what his genuine needs and capacities in a given situation are. As he grows more aware of himself and his abilities, he can devise ways of reaching goals that are within his scope.

Past and Present. In seeking to understand why many of his plans and actions have thus far failed, or proved only partially successful, the person in the interview tends naturally to go into the past as well as the present, especially when present attitudes are related to the past. As we have seen, he usually uncovers some deep experiences and relationships with significant persons in his home or early environment, which have fixed some of the ways he is reacting to the present. Many of his present confusions are, therefore, only understood after he has consciously connected them with the

[10]*Ibid.* II–II, Q. 47, a. 8.
[11]Pp. 24–25.

past. Some actions which he had not looked at carefully before, are now seen for the first time as carry-overs from the past. He may have been, as Rank theorizes, fearful of the present and unable to cope with it. Many of his judgments and actions, therefore, may have been strongly influenced by experiences fixed and buried in some earlier life stage. This conscious awareness of past factors and intelligent attention to present circumstances, St. Thomas makes two of the integral parts of prudence.

The Virtue of Good-Counsel. This survey and inquiry aspect, which is the first phase of prudence, is in itself so important that St. Thomas makes it a special virtue which he calls "good-counsel." This virtue results when a person has acquired the ability of deliberating well in pursuing the research of his reason about the actions, circumstances, and other means necessary for reaching any reasonable goal. St. Thomas says this virtue is especially needed because man is "unable by simple insight to comprehend with certainty the truth of things, especially in matters of action which are contingent."[12]

This particular virtue of good-counsel is so necessary in St. Thomas' consideration that he holds every sin to be due, in some way, to its absence. He says,

All sin is contrary to taking good-counsel. For good-counsel requires not only the discovery or devising of fit means for the end, but also other circumstances. Such are suitable time, so that one be neither too slow nor too quick in taking counsel, and the mode of taking counsel, so that one be firm in the counsel taken, and other like due circumstances, which sinners fail to observe when they sin. On the other hand, every virtuous man takes good-counsel in those things which are directed to the end of virtue.[13]

The counseling process, therefore, as we have seen demonstrated, can be especially helpful in furthering this virtue of good-counsel. Into the disorder of a person's conflicting urges and purposes, counseling brings him a broad survey of all the factors that enter into these major conflicts. As he grows in self-understanding, the person slowly relates these conflicting factors together into patterns. Instead of acting on a partial view of his problems, he can now begin to

---

[12]St. Thomas, (D): II–II, Q. 51, a. 2.
[13]*Ibid.* reply obj. 3.

judge and plan solutions that reach the deepest causes of his conflict. In place of the previous ineffectual and discouraging efforts to understand and reach his life goals he begins to get a defined grasp of his wants and needs and, accompanying this, he develops more courage and confidence to fulfill them.

II. JUDGMENT

Since, however, man acts as a unit in everything he does and since "good counsel is directed to prudence as to a principal virtue,"[14] the *inquiry* stage of the interviews fuses into the *judgment* stage. Somewhere in the process of getting out problems and relating the present to the past, a person also begins to make judgments about his present attitudes and their value. He will often reject many of the fixed attitudes carried over from the past as he begins to see that, while he has been acting on these attitudes for a good part of his life, they are not adequate to meet his present needs nor satisfying for him.

Here, the person is especially enabled to objectify and impersonalize his judgments about himself and his situation through the counselor's responses. By relating factors together, comparing them, seeking causes, judging certain solutions valid or invalid, and similar means, he begins to free himself from the emotions of the moment and the fixed perceptions that were previously warping his judgment. As the young man (V) says towards the end of his interview series:

But I think these talks here have done a great deal to bring me from the emotional and shocking outlook on these problems to the sensible or intellectual, or whatever you want to call it, outlook. That's been their big assistance.

Realistic Evaluation. One of the first effects of this phase of counseling is the growing realistic evaluation a person begins to make of himself. Previously, he has in some way held up an unreal picture of himself and his situation. But, as a result of counseling he begins to see and judge himself and his world as they really are.

This is evident, for example, in the young man who was so afraid of and insecure in the world of reality. This fear and inadequacy

[14]St. Thomas, (D): II–II, Q. 51, a. 2.

about the present seemed to bring on his urge to escape by various compensations, such as the apathy of letting others decide things for him and his giving in to earlier patterns of conduct that were no longer adequate. In this excerpt from the middle of the interview series, as he gets more self-confidence, he gradually realizes that he can have achievement in the real world. After some small positive experiences carried out as a result of his own reasoned judgment, he has an entirely different outlook on his present world. Now, for the first time, he can see value in just being ordinary (V):

P: I used to have the idea I wanted to amount to so much, and coming over today I happened to think, while there was always such a desire within me to be another Tom Edison or something, I've always had all these crazy ideas sort of promoting each one individually within me, daydreaming to be a great person, and well, lots better than anyone else. I might desire to be an awfully great person, but really just to be normal is something to be very much appreciative of because I was thinking it could very easily be that I could turn out to—to be a *bum*. I was watching some of the newsies, men about 35 or 40 uptown selling their papers, and I thought "Gee, just to be average really isn't such a little thing." For a man to have a respected position, he really doesn't need to be known even in his own community as a great figure, but to be average is really a very high position compared with how low a person could fall in the opposite direction where he would be a bum or a drunkard or something like that.

This is a sharp contrast to the attitudes which the young man had previously. Then, he could not face being average because he could not be himself. He had to compensate and avoid reality by building up excessive, exaggerated fantasy conceptions of his own abilities and possible achievements. Any small achievement in the real world was miserably insignificant compared to these fantasy goals. Now, however, he can propose some real goals for himself and already he sees that things are not as bad as they might be. He can also accept a moderate life goal and humbler ideal of success. This kind of goal, coming as a result of his coping with the real world on his own responsibility, he now sees as far more satisfying, reassuring, and integrating than his previous views of himself as an extremely brilliant and achieving personality, who would be able to equal or surpass his brother. Goals, which before had no significance because they seemed so far below his fantasy picture of himself, now become very meaningful. Realistic living is, in a way, possible for him for the first time.

Security and Certainty. The person, in a good counseling series, shows another consequence of the inquiry and evaluation processes of counsel and judgment. As he begins to see some relationship between his various problems and conflicts and gets some order into his understanding of himself and his circumstances, he exhibits a growing security and certainty in his judgments. While this in itself does not lead him to a better life, it prepares the way for the final phase in which he can plan more adequate solutions and carry these out in successful actions. St. Thomas indicates this:

> Different acts are directed in different degrees to the one end which is *a good life in general*: for counsel comes first, judgment follows, and command comes last. The last named has an immediate relation to the last end: whereas the other two acts are related thereto remotely. Nevertheless, these have certain proximate ends of their own, the end of counsel being the discovery of what has to be done, and the end of judgment, certainty.[15]

This growing certainty of judgment as a result of counseling is illustrated in the following excerpt from an interview with the naval ensign a year after the completion of the counseling series (S):

P: Let's see—it's been about a year since I saw you, hasn't it? Well, things have really been fine now and I have been swell. Oh, I've had some bad days, and depressed and discouraged moments, but I suppose everybody has that. My whole attitude towards my fiancee has changed a great deal. I am hopeful now. I think with a little more effort on my part things are going to work out fine.

C: You really have pretty much hope of being able to work this thing out completely and things have been sufficiently better to encourage you in that.

P: Yes, I believe very much so. . . . I feel certain I can work it out. We're going to be married in about a month now . . . You know—as I think of it now—something serious may have happened to me. I don't know where I would have ended up had not something been done about it. I had lost all confidence in myself but now I'm much surer than I ever was before. That's why I know our marriage will be okay now.

C: You feel that very deeply don't you?

[15] St. Thomas, (D): II–II, Q. 51, a. 2, reply obj. 2.

P: Yes, and I will always feel very grateful for the ease you have given me. I know you've saved my engagement and I want you to feel that all of this effort and time that you have given to me and all the effort I have put forth in trying to overcome this thing is not wasted.

Here his understanding of himself and his patterns of conduct make him no longer afraid to face the future, give him confidence that he can control his fears and confusions and that his personal life and future marriage can be successful. While he still has problems and difficulties which he has not entirely solved, this positive self-understanding and security is a noticeable step forward when compared with the disorganized state he was in when he first came to see the counselor.

III. COMMAND

In the final stage of the counseling process, as we have seen, a person's growing self-understanding and security in judgment fuses into the planning of new and better solutions and the making of more significant choices according to these new life plans. These choices may be small and hesitant at first because the person is insecure and has to grow in confidence and hope. Gradually, the solutions that are planned are acted on. These actions, because they have been carefully thought out and organized, usually prove more adequate and successful than previous life plans. If they still fail somewhat, the causes of failure can be calmly examined in subsequent interviews. Here especially takes place the evaluation in action so necessary to the perfection of any art, particularly the art of good living. As his plans begin to succeed, the person gains confidence in his judgments and often takes quite rapid strides in acquiring new ways of acting. The third aspect of prudence, "to command, which consists in applying to action the things counseled and judged," is, therefore, demonstrated in these last steps of the counseling process.

We see this evaluation in action illustrated in the following excerpt from the interviews with the young man (V):

P: Over last week I really accomplished more than I did any other time. I can say that. I really felt happy after the week-end was over, and thought I was quite a different person Monday morning, but now the end of the week, I'm blue a little bit. I don't know what to think of the whole thing. But I know this, things don't bother me so much any more.

C: Last week was a real success for you, wasn't it? You felt like a new person. Now while you're down some, these things don't bother you as much as they did.

P: But—I don't know—the way I started out last week, I guess that's the right way—to plan that you are going to do things and carry them through because that's the only way. Coming over here every week or going to anyone every week, would never settle the problem for me unless I took an active part in it. So maybe in going to this new job, if I forced myself and made up my mind that it was going to be a life and death proposition, I imagine that I could get through it and probably after the first few weeks I can come out all right. At least it would seem that way. (Pause)

C: You feel that if you were really determined, like you were able to be last week, you could stick it out and make a success of it?

His feeling of success in seeing his new way of life pay off even small dividends gives him more confidence, courage, and security in facing a new assignment that might otherwise have overwhelmed him.

OTHER PARTS OF PRUDENCE

Associated with these three main phases, other parts of prudence are revealed in counseling:

The things which need to concur for the perfect act of a virtue, are called the parts of that virtue. In this way, out of all the things mentioned, eight may be taken as parts of prudence. . . . Of these eight, five belong to prudence as a cognitive virtue, namely, *memory*, *reasoning*, *understanding*, *docility*, and *shrewdness*: while the three others belong thereto, as commanding and applying knowledge to action, namely, *foresight*, *circumspection*, and *caution*. The reason of their difference is seen from the fact that three things may be observed in reference to knowledge. In the first place, knowledge itself, which, if it be of the past, is called *memory*, if of the present, whether contingent or necessary, is called *understanding* or *intelligence*. Secondly, the acquiring of knowledge, which is caused either by teaching, to which pertains *docility*, or by *discovery* . . . of which *shrewdness* is a part. . . . Thirdly, the use of knowledge, in as much as we proceed from things known to knowledge or judgment of other things, and this belongs to *reasoning*. And the reason, in order to command aright, requires to have three conditions. First, to order that which is befitting the end, and this belongs to *foresight*; secondly, to attend to the circumstances of the matter in hand, and this belongs to *circumspection*; thirdly, to avoid obstacles, and this belongs to *caution*.[16]

Teachableness.   We have already considered how *memory* of the past and *intelligent consideration* of the present are evident in counseling. As people grow more secure in their judgments, they are also less resistant to others. When they see its necessity, they show increasing willingness to consult others who may be able to supply them with information which they themselves do not have. This state of *teachableness* or *docility* resulting from good counseling is quite different from the dependent tendencies and refusal to take responsibility which these same persons may have displayed in the opening interviews. Dependent people seek the advice of others, not to help them integrate their own power of evaluation and action, but to place the responsibility for the consequences of their actions on the adviser. Counseling interviews may sometimes cause a person to seek information which he does not possess. But he now uses this information in a responsible manner as an aid to reasonable choices.

We have also seen[17] how counseling often makes a person more alert to and appreciative of many factors in his present environment which previously he did not even consider. In this sense too he is more docile to, and therefore able to learn from, the reality of his own life experiences. He is also less defensive and therefore more willing to abide by reasonable and necessary limits and norms.

Shrewdness.   Since, as St. Thomas says, "prudence consists in a right estimate about matters of action," *shrewdness*, he also defines as "an apt disposition to acquire a right estimate by oneself."[18] People, with the aid of the counseling process, also display a remarkable amount of this *shrewdness* in the manner in which they can uncover significant elements in their difficulties and devise expedient methods for solving them. These would often never have occurred to even a most experienced adviser, since he could not know all the minute details of a person's life as the person himself knows them.

Foresight, Circumspection, and Caution.   When they come to the carrying out of these new solutions—the command phase of pru-

16St. Thomas, (D): II–II, Q. 48, a.
17Pp. 181–182.
18*Ibid*. II–II, Q. 48, a. 4.

dence—people, through counseling, are able to project themselves into the future with greater accuracy since they now have a better understanding of the past and present. Through this *foresight*, aided by the repeated experience of evaluating themselves and their environment, they often exhibit great facility at finding new ways of meeting future problems. As a person's focus on himself and others is broadened, his fixed ways of reaction and his rigid attitudes become unfrozen and fluid. He then acquires what is sometimes a remarkable increase in both *circumspection* through which he becomes alert to previously hidden circumstances and changing aspects, and *caution* in devising ways of circumventing new or previously insurmountable obstacles.

St. Thomas explains these three virtues this way:

. . . Nothing is subject to human providence except the contingent matters of actions which can be done by man for an end. Now the past has become a kind of necessity, since what has been done cannot be undone. In like manner, the present as such, has a kind of necessity. . . . Consequently, future contingents, in so far as they can be directed by man to the end of human life, are the matter of prudence: and each of these things is implied in the word *foresight*, for it implies the notion of something distant, to which that which occurs in the present has to be directed. . . . Since, however, prudence is about singular matters of action, which contain many combinations of circumstances, it happens that a thing is good in itself and suitable to the end, and nevertheless becomes evil or unsuitable to the end, by reason of some combination of circumstances. Thus to show signs of love to someone seems, considered in itself, to be a fitting way to arouse love in his heart, yet if pride or suspicion of flattery arise in his heart, it will not longer be a means suitable to the end. Hence the need of *circumspection* in prudence, viz., of comparing the means with the circumstances. . . . Even as false is found with true, so is evil mingled with good, on account of the great variety of these matters of action, wherein good is often hindered by evil, and evil has the appearance of good. Wherefore prudence needs *caution*, so that we may have such a grasp of good as to avoid evil.[19]

Avoid Precipitation. Having lived a good part of his life with many of the people directly involved in his judgments, a person, aided by the objectivity of the interviews, may unfold a surprising

[19]St. Thomas, (D): II–II, Q. 49, a. 7, 8.

amount of understanding of the temperaments, qualities, and peculiarities of these other people. As he evaluates these, he is aided to make shrewder choices about the proper time, place, and manner of getting their co-operation in accomplishing what he sees as a reasonable goal. Moreover, since the counseling process makes the person increasingly aware that he is making these choices himself and carrying them out on his own motivation and judgment, he grows cautious in not proceeding too swiftly, since he has a strong desire now to succeed. He is also more willing to allow himself sufficient time so that, when new obstacles arise which he did not at first foresee, he can gradually devise ways of coping with them and surmounting them. Instead of the precipitous, headlong plunging into simple solutions, which was so characteristic of his earlier life plans, he now has before him a broad perspective of the complexities of even comparatively small successes. He can allow for the possibility of a number of failures without getting discouraged, because he realizes that any significant achievement in reality is a more difficult and demanding process than the day-dream fantasies or quick solutions which previously led him only to discouragement and frustration. At the end of a successful interview series, a person displays a quiet, cautious evaluation, which is the exact opposite of the heedless, headlong rush that so often is typical of an emotionally tense and confused person when he first comes to the counselor. In this way, counseling helps a person avoid that precipitation which St. Thomas considers a violation of prudence.

General Alertness. Even when it is highly developed, a person's *caution* cannot, of course, prepare him for all possible contingencies that may arise in his life. But, since there is often a kind of consistency in the way things happen, a person, from his knowledge of the past and present, can be ready for such situations. Even when the unpredictable does occur, the general alertness which counseling has produced makes a person more able to cope immediately with such unforeseen events. So St. Thomas explains,

Of the evils which man has to avoid, some are of frequent occurrence; the like can be grasped by reason, and against them caution is directed, either that they may be avoided altogether, or that they may do less harm. Others there are that occur rarely and by chance, and these, since they are infinite in number, cannot be grasped by reason, nor is man able to take precautions against them, although by exercising prudence he is able to prepare against all the surprises of chance, so as to suffer less harm thereby.[20]

COUNSELING EFFECTIVENESS AND INTELLIGENCE

Since understanding and reasoning play such an important part in the process of counsel and prudence, another point we might consider here is the commonly proposed question of whether counseling success is determined by a person's intelligence. People usually grant the possibility of counseling being successful with people of average and superior intelligence but they are unsure of the degree to which it might apply to those of lower intelligence. Insufficient research has been done on this question to supply us with any definite answers. It seems likely that the degree to which a person is able to judge the various factors in his past and present life and to find better ways of meeting his difficulties in the future is somewhat determined by his native intelligence.

However, two other considerations enter in here. The first is that the state of a person's emotional conflicts seems to influence, to some degree at least, his score on even the most basic and accurate intelligence tests. Therefore, it is not as easy to determine precisely a person's intelligence as some psychologists were saying a decade or so ago. Secondly, granting that there are well-established, fundamental differences of intelligence in certain broad areas, such as between low-grade, normal, and extremely bright people, successful counseling might still be possible for all groups. For, while the degree of intelligence makes a noticeable difference in the general solving of problems, it may not be so significant in personal difficulties. The kinds of things that cause people to be in personal conflict, as well as the various goals they seek, will be determined for each primarily by each one's degree of intelligence. Children, for example, are not faced with the same problems as adults. Consequently, it seems that each person has the capacity to work out the problems which he himself sees just as children at various age levels can, through counseling, solve the problems peculiar to that stage in their development. The horizon of a person's problems seems to be determined in a large measure by the horizon of his

[20]St. Thomas, (D): II–II, Q. 49, a. 8, reply obj. 3.

abilities and especially of his intelligence. The person of low-grade intelligence does not seem ordinarily to see nor, therefore, to suffer intensely over problems which might be very evident to brighter people—such as the state of world conditions, the threat to civilization, and similar concepts which may seriously disturb people of higher intelligence. In this sense, then, it seems that the counseling process can be a help for the problems each one faces even though these problems, when compared together, vary greatly according to the intelligence of the person. This, however, is a question which demands much more research before any conclusive results could be stated.

Interestingly, St. Thomas seems to suggest this possibility when he says that good-counsel does not necessarily involve "grasping quickly what should be done" since

> A man may take good counsel, though he be long and slow in so doing, and yet this does not discount the utility of a happy conjecture in taking good counsel.[21]

Undoubtedly, the brighter person does move more quickly in his gaining of insights once he reaches this stage. But, though it may be longer and slower, the less bright person can often be helped by counseling too and his problems are apt not to be so numerous nor so complex as those of a more intelligent individual.

COUNSELING AND OTHER VIRTUES

Justice. The effects of counseling often relate to justice. A greater consideration for the rights of others is usually shown by people in the later stages of counseling, as in the interviews previously cited,[22] where the two married people saw, at the end of the series, the injustices that were being done to their partners. This follows from the broadening understanding of themselves and their circumstances and the more realistic evaluation and judgment which insight brings. They no longer have merely an egocentric point of view and see only an isolated segment of their world. The rights of others now begin to appear in their proper proportions. They are given more of the consideration that is due them.

21St. Thomas, (D): II–II, Q. 49, a. 8, reply obj. 2.
22Pp. 149–150, 183–190.

Courage and Moderation. More immediately, however, the effects of counseling are evident in the persons themselves, especially the noticeable increase in the courage with which they face difficulties. They have acquired more confidence and security. At the same time, they restrict their previous tendencies to compensate for failures by an exaggerated opinion of themselves and an unwillingness to face moderation and limitations.

Humility. Expressed in other terms, we might say that the self-understanding of the counseling process produces a growth in the virtue of humility. This word, too, is often misunderstood in our present use of it. Humility is not an Uriah Heep kind of servility and fawning obsequiousness. Since the word itself comes from "humus"—the ground—we might say that, in a sense, something of its realistic evaluation is implied in the popular description of a man as "having his feet on the ground." Such a man does not "float off into the clouds" of unreality but is capable of an accurate judgment about himself, his capacities, and what he is able to do in a given circumstance. Humility, then, is the middle way between an inferiority and superiority complex. As Carlson has pointed out,

> It will foster in every individual *either the self-assertion* or the *self-suppression* proportionate to the talents he has received, and thus bring about fruitful cooperation of the Mystical Body and its visible head on earth. . . . *Its essential purpose is simply to keep the quest of one's own excellence reasonable.* St. Thomas indicates this clearly. Properly speaking," he says, "humility is directive and moderative of the motion of the appetite." . . . The formal motive of humility is the special good which reason sees will be ordained by guiding the appetite firmly in its tendency toward excellence.[23]

Counseling Atmosphere Aids Humility. As we saw, the tendency both to over-evaluate his talents and the possibility of great achievement and, at the same time, to consider himself extremely inadequate and inferior is often characteristic of a person's attitude towards himself at the beginning of an interview series. Inferiority feelings seem usually to be behind the tendency to depend on others and to seek constant reassurance from others. Alternately, people may

---

[23]Sebastian Carlson, O.P.: "The Virtue of Humility," *The Thomist*, Vol. VII, No. 2, April 1944, pp. 136, 149, 150. (Italics mine.)

be resistant to taking advice because they fear to lean on another and are actually desirous of preserving their own responsible judgment. In either event the accepting and understanding manner of the counselor, coupled with his cautious skill, does not reject nor make more insecure the fearful, inferior person. But, it does not permit him to depend on the counselor and thereby destroy his urge and need of responsible self-determination. On the other hand, the nature of the counseling process is such that it offers an impersonal and objective help to the person who resists such dependency. He can feel that he himself is working out his own problems in a responsible and integrated way while, at the same time, he recognizes the valuable aid which the counselor's penetrating responses are giving him. This is also true of the various group skills which prepare the way for counseling. In both the individual interviews and group discussion there is a recognition of the real self-worth and personal dignity of each one so that each is encouraged to be what he is, not pretending to be more from emotional confusion and compensation nor failing to be what he could, through personal insecurity and feelings of worthlessness.

Humility Is Truth.   One time when St. Theresa, the Little Flower, was accused of being proud, she remarked with her incisive childlike wisdom, "I do not know whether I am humble or not, I only know that I am truthful." In this she had hit the heart of humility, truth with oneself. Christ's parable of the talents[24] makes it very clear that we must recognize the abilities, qualities, and potentialities which God has given us and that we are responsible for using them adequately. Such use of our talents is dependent on the degree of self-knowledge by which we know both what we are and what we can do. St. Thomas says, "the knowledge of truth is antecedent to humility; when one has considered the truth he does not lift himself up beyond his measure."[25]

The humble man, when he is aware of having great talent, recognizes from the very nature of things his dependency on God for all he has. Like St. Paul he knows: "what have we that we have not received and if we have received it why do we act as if we have received it not?" A man, therefore, need not feel any superiority to

---

[24]St. Matthew, C. 25.
[25]St. Thomas, (D): II–II, Q. 82, a. 3, reply obj. 3.

others even when he recognizes that his achievements excel theirs. In this he is simply being truthful with himself.[26]

Moreover, the self-confidence that comes from knowledge and understanding does not necessarily lead away from humility. The focus on acquiring knowledge in any particular field or the seeking of other achievements in such a way as to make them ends in themselves would be a hindrance.

> Science or anything else conducive to greatness, is to man an occasion of self-confidence, so that he does not wholly surrender himself to God. The result is that such-like things sometimes occasion a hindrance to devotion.[27]

A careful examination of himself, however, and an increased awareness of his weaknesses, will lead a man to God.

> The other consideration is that of man's own shortcomings on account of which he needs to lean on God . . . and this consideration shuts out presumption whereby man is hindered from submitting to God, because he leans on his own strength.[28]

In this sense, then, even the greatest achievements can be a source of growth in God. So, "If a man perfectly subjects his knowledge or any other perfection whatever, to God, from that very fact his devotion is increased."[29]

Self-Knowledge and Hope. In opening interviews we notice, too, a gradual movement away from discouragement and failure to a sense of hope. A person begins to feel that certain achievements are possible for him. In this way self-knowledge is directly related to hope. Confused and disorganized persons will either seek goals

---

[26]Humility thus conceived is based on truth, especially on the truth that there is an infinite distance between the Creator and the creature. The more this distance appears to us in a living and concrete manner, the more humble we are. However lofty the creature may be, this abyss is always infinite; and the higher we ascend, the more evident does this infinite abyss become for us. . . . We have been created from nothing; this is the basis of humility according to the light of right reason.

Humility is also based on the mystery of grace and on the necessity of actual grace for the slightest salutary act. This mystery exceeds the natural powers of reason; it is known by faith, and it is expressed in these words of the Savior: "Without Me you can do nothing" in the order of salvation.

Reginald Garrigou-Lagrange, O.P.: *The Three Ages of the Interior Life*, Vol. II, St. Louis, Copyright 1948, by B. Herder Book Co., pp. 118–119.

[27]*Ibid.*

[28]St. Thomas, (D): II–II, Q. 82, a. 3.

[29]*Ibid.*

beyond them or seek them in ways which cannot bring fruitful results. As a person begins to know himself he sees whether or not the
goals he is holding up for himself are beyond his abilities. If so,
he gradually reaches a more realistic understanding of what he can
achieve. Paralleling this he sees ways to reach particular goals, which
before were either hidden from him or not considered important. A
young high school student, for example, gradually sees that the
rejection she is receiving from others is due more to her own attitudes
towards them than to their unwillingness to accept her and make
her part of their activities and interests.[30]

The counseling process can, therefore, often enable a person to
see what is possible for him; and his hope of achievement becomes
actually realizable. Before, he was discouraged and frustrated because what he hoped for was either beyond him or was sought in
the wrong way. As his self-knowledge grows he gains both in humility and in a degree of hope, which gradually fulfill themselves
in real accomplishment and achievement. This in turn gives him
the courage to hope and strive for something more. As he continues
to look at himself, he becomes reasonably convinced that certain
desired objects are achievable if he employs the right means.

Without self-knowledge, there can be no humility; it is the old principle in a different vest, *nihil volitum nisi cognitum.* Unless man knows
what he should seek and avoid in the matter of personal aggrandize-
ment, he will neither seek nor avoid it rightly. His hope will be as sane
or as unbalanced as his understanding of his ego.[31]

Not Infantilism. Such humility is a far cry from the whimpering
kind of self-effacement that is sometimes thought to be characteristic
of an "umble man." This last seems more likely to be a mask for
an infantile type of immaturity that seeks to depend on others to
avoid the responsibility of making choices. We can distinguish, as
Kelly points out, the childlikeness that is characteristic of a
spiritually and psychologically mature person from the childishness
of the infantile or pusillanimous person.

The word "childish" is used designedly. For Our Lord Himself has told
us that we must all become as little children in order to gain the kingdom of heaven; hence there must be some sense in which the truly

[30] See p. 174.
[31] Carlson, *op. cit.,* p. 160.

spiritual man must always be a child. On the other hand, we have the words of St. Paul to the effect that we must grow up and put aside the things of a child. There can be no conflict between the words of Christ and the inspired words of Paul; and I take it that these two meanings are perfectly harmonized by distinguishing between "childlikeness" and "childishness." Even one who is fully grown in Christ must be childlike; he must possess the simplicity, the candor, the humility, the sweet trust in God that come so naturally to the child. But the adult should not be childish.[32]

Magnanimity. We have already discussed in some detail,[33] the importance of counseling in overcoming the inferiority attitudes characteristic of *infantilism* or *pusillanimity*. A person requires both temperance and humility to moderate his urges, especially his own exaggerated egoism and "the impetuosity of the emotions"[34] in those things he can achieve easily. Otherwise, he will seek them excessively as compensations for his failures in more difficult areas. But he also needs courage and magnanimity to give him the self-confidence and sustained drive to keep at the hard tasks that stand in the way of many reasonable goals. So St. Thomas says,

. . . The difficult good has something attractive to the appetite, namely the aspect of good, and likewise something repulsive to the appetite, namely the difficulty of obtaining it. In respect of the former there arises the movement of hope, and in respect of the latter, the movement of despair. . . . For those appetitive movements which are a kind of impulse towards an object, there is need of a moderating and restraining moral virtue, while for those which are a kind of recoil, there is need, on the part of the appetite, of a moral virtue to strengthen it and urge it on. Wherefore a twofold virtue is necessary with regard to the difficult good: one, to temper and restrain the mind, lest it tend to high things immoderately; and this belongs to the virtue of humility: and another to strengthen the mind against despair, and urge it on to the pursuit of great things according to right reason; and this is magnanimity.[35]

When successful counseling interviews are brought to a close, it is largely because the person has acquired a relaxed confidence in himself and a security that he can get along now on his own. Being

---

[32]Gerald Kelly, S.J.: "Emotional Maturity," *Review for Religious*, Copyright 1947, by Gerald C. Ellis, Vol. VII, No. 1, January 1947, pp. 3–4.

[33]Pp. 101–102.

[34]St Thomas, (D): II–II, Q. 61, a. 4.

[35]*Ibid.*, a. 1.

no longer so fearful and solicitous for the future, he does not feel the need of further counseling. He will, therefore, often suggest this with a phrase like, "I don't see that I have any more problems to talk about now. I got them pretty well worked out." This relaxed ease flows, not from indifference or false pride, but from reasonable confidence:

> The magnanimous man is said to be *slow* and *leisurely* not because he is solicitous about nothing, but because he is not over-solicitous about many things, and is trustful in matters where he ought to have trust, and is not over-solicitous about them: for overmuch fear and distrust are the cause of over-solicitude, since fear makes us take counsel.[36]

COUNSELING AND VIRTUOUS LIVING

In all this discussion of the effects of good counseling as they relate to prudence and the moral virtues, we are dealing largely with those factors peculiar to a person's individual self and all the immediate minute conditions and events of his day-by-day living. The life of virtue consists

> in virtuous doing, in doing the things a man does in that almost bewildering multitude of circumstances in which from year to year, in fact, from moment to moment a man finds himself. The very constancy and immutability of the first principles *prevent* their being of immediate usefulness. For the operations which a man performs, the operations which bring his nature to the fullness of goodness, take place in contingent and concrete circumstances—of times and places and persons and things, of weakness and strength, of past achievement and future promise, of all those things in all men's lives which conspire to make every human situation different from every other.

For action of this kind universal practical knowledge is clearly insufficient. Nature's universal illumination and fundamentally right ordination are indeed generous, but in that bewildering multitude of circumstances it is not the nature but the man that acts. His nature fixes his end; his nature enlightens him with respect to his end. But he himself must solve his bewilderment, he must introduce reason's order into the welter of circumstances; he must put reason's stamp of unity on their multiplicity and diversity.[37]

---

[36]St. Thomas, (D): Q. 47, a. 9, reply obj. 3.
[37]Charles J. O'Neil: "Prudence, the Incommunicable Wisdom," from *Essays in Thomism*, edited by Robert E. Brennan, O.P., Copyright by Sheed & Ward, Inc., New York, 1942.

Not Moral Science. In this context it is important to remember, as Merkelbach points out,[38] that prudence and actual moral virtue are clearly distinguished from moral science. Moral science, as science, still says what is to be done in an abstract and general sense. But prudence determines what is to be done by the individual person himself in all the extremely complex concrete circumstances and conditions that are often involved in even one completed action. The moral virtues are the resources he calls upon within himself to bring sufficient order within his many conflicting urges, so that he can carry out what moral science in general, and his own prudence in this particular case, determine he should do. Confusing moral science with prudence and moral virtue can perhaps cause a person to overlook the highly difficult process that is still necessary even after we have clearly determined in principle what should be done.

Each judgment a man makes is peculiarly personal and singular because he alone, in its execution, is the final judge of the events and circumstances of his life. But besides this, even the particular actions which the same man makes from day to day are also subject to the flux of events and their changes and are, therefore, themselves each in some way different. No two actions are exactly the same even when they are performed by the same person at approximately the same time. Countless changes are constantly taking place, not only in things around us, but in the attitudes within ourselves and others. Each action of one person in some way creates or changes attitudes in others, and results in shades of difference in their actions, which in turn may affect the attitudes and actions of many others within a comparatively short space of time.

Individual Evaluation. Consequently, when a man's judgments and actions are reasonably determined by consistent principles and he has made a broad survey of all the factors entering into his choices, he yet needs to evaluate each individual action as a separate and distinct unit. Maritain explains this:

> . . . the act of moral choice is so individualized (both by the singularity of the person from whom it emanates and by that of the context of contingent circumstance in which it takes place) that the practical judgment in which it is expressed and by which I declare to myself,

---

[38]Benedictus Henricus Merkelbach, O.P.: *Summa Theologiae Moralis*, Paris, Desclee de Brouwer & Cie., Vol. II, p. 13.

"This is what I need," can only be right if actually, *hic et nunc*, the dynamism of my willing is right and tends towards the genuine goods of human life. . . .

There are objective norms of morality, there are duties and rules, because the measure of reason is the formal constitutive element of human morality. However, I neither apply them, nor apply them well, unless they are embodied in the ends which actually attract my desire and in the actual movement of my will. In many cases man finds himself confronted by simple rules, such as those which forbid homicide or adultery. They set him no problem except the problem of effectively following them. Yet, in order that a man follow them, at the moment of temptation they must not merely resound in his head as mere universal rules which suffice to condemn him though not to set him in motion; but he must recognize in them (by a kind of painful labour of intussusception and reflection upon himself) an urgent demand of his most highly individuated, most personal desire, for the ends upon which he has made his life depend. If not, he will not do the good he loves (loves inefficaciously, only because he sees it to be good in itself), but he will do the evil he does not wish to do (he does not wish it as evil, though he will at present make of it his good). But in many cases, which, in truth, form the stuff of our moral life, man finds himself confronted by a diversity of conflicting duties and multiple rules which crisscross in a context of circumstance where the problem "What ought I really do?" is posed. This is the time when he must have recourse to the *regulae arbitrariae* of prudence; to those rules which not only take account of all the objective peculiarities of given conditions, but which become decisive only by reason of the subject's deepest attractions (which, by supposition, are duly orientated) and the inclinations of his virtues.[39]

Counseling Aids This. The counselor cannot dictate the prudent decisions which a person must make about the contingent singular events of that person's life. If, however, the person seeks it and the counselor has the skill, he can create a situation where the "conflicting duties and multiple rules which crisscross in a context of circumstance" can be talked out, objectified and reorganized. Through the unfolding of the counseling process, a person's "deepest attractions" and "inclinations" can gradually become duly orientated to his reason. The conflicting rights and duties then fall into their immediate relationship of reasonable priority. The new choices made

---

[39] Jacques Maritain: *Existence and the Existent*, New York, Copyright 1948, by Pantheon Books, Inc., pp. 50–53.

to meet each unique event flow now from the recognition of the "urgent demand of his most highly individuated, most personal desire" and are at the same time in more consistent conformity with the universal rules of reasonable conduct. Seen from the over-all and broad view of growing insight, the long-time reasonable goals are also the happiest and best. In this way the objective norms of morality can, through counseling, become "embodied in the ends which actually attract my desire and in the actual movement of my will."

The process of counseling, as we have described it, is not co-extensive with the virtue of counsel, which is larger and may or may not involve the aid of a counseling interview. Taken by itself, too, the counseling process is distinct from the gift of counsel, even though, in individual instances, the choices a person makes as a result of the interviews, such as accepting a religious vocation, may show the influence of the gift as well as the virtue of counsel. People obviously can make prudent judgments without feeling any need to undergo interviews. However, in particular circumstances, especially where emotional confusions and an extremely complex series of persons and events are involved, the counseling process seems to be a great aid in objectifying, separating, and integrating all the factors and in helping a person to come to a more reasonable judgment about them. In this way, the steps of prudence and the associated virtues may be helped by skilled counseling.

Knowledge and Guidance Necessary. As we have explained in detail, this does not do away with a person's need for information and guidance, particularly in matters of general knowledge—theology, philosophy, science, and the like—which the greater experience and study of others can reveal to him. But knowledge or factual information is pointless if it is presented in a manner that raises negative emotions and confusions which block the person's use of it. So, guidance and teaching must be given in such a way that the person can best integrate and act upon the knowledge given. Otherwise, such knowledge will not be fulfilled in a life of greater virtue.

Virtuous Living. The counseling process we have described reveals in some detail the steps which enter into virtuous living. As St. Thomas points out, the moral virtues are all united in prudence. Prudence, as we have seen, is an incommunicable virtue and as such cannot be taught. It must be lived. But counsel is essential to every prudent judgment as a man weighs the past and the present in order to meet the changing events of the future. Consequently, while prudence cannot be taught it can be greatly aided by a counseling skill which enables people to make more reasonable evaluation of the singular circumstances and unique conditions which enter into their own major life choices. Since such counseling can be productive of an increase in good-counsel, prudence, and moral virtue, the recent developments in counseling have, therefore, important implications for the whole of Catholic educational, parochial, and spiritual life.

CONCLUSION

Need for Prudence and Moral Virtue. Previously, we have quoted the opinion[40] that Catholic education has failed to produce a vital Catholic life in proportion to the effort spent on it. Assuming this to be so, perhaps the reason is that, in our school and parish programs, the focus has been too exclusively on the development of the intellectual virtues, particularly knowledge and understanding. We may not have been sufficiently conscious of the need for prudence and the moral virtues.

Commandments Tell What to Do. One reason why we may have been less conscious of prudence and the moral virtues could be that text books usually emphasize the commandments as a scheme for presenting moral virtues. Often, the explanations that are given of the different commandments, while valuable for moral guidance, do not contain all the fine delineations and active emphasis on positive virtue which are found in the treatment on the practical virtues in St. Thomas. In fact, many discussions of the commandments would appear largely to be concerned with understanding and knowledge rather than the active movement of self-responsible action which makes up prudence and the related moral virtues. This may also be a reason why we have not been as conscious as we might of fostering situations for responsible self-directed choices and reasonable judgments around personal problems.

For people to know what to do in principle or in terms of the commandments does not of itself imply that they have the virtue to carry out this knowledge in the singular events of their lives. The commandments taken by themselves simply tell what to do

40P. 5.

and do not give the complete unfolding of all the virtues that are concerned. They are also primarily concerned with the virtue of justice. So St. Thomas points out:

> Although prudence is simply foremost among all the moral virtues, yet justice, more than any other virtue, regards its object under the aspect of something due, which is a necessary condition for a precept. . . . Hence it behooves the chief precepts of the Law, which are those of the decalogue, to refer to justice rather than to prudence.[41]

Taking the commandments in themselves without adequate understanding and interpretation, a person may miss the important condition that to carry out the commandments adequately involves prudence and all the moral virtues and not simply justice.

Personal Factors. The focus on justice can be confusing particularly because the measure of justice, as also the measure of the intellectual virtues, is the objective thing involved, or what in the Latin phrase is called the "medium rei." But the measure of the other moral virtues, centering in temperance and fortitude, is the "medium rationis," that is, the complex circumstances, conditions, and singular contingencies which are different for each one in any particular action.[42] It is possible, therefore, for one person to pass a valid decision about a matter of justice concerning someone else since that decision can be based primarily on the thing involved. "Justice," says Merkelbach, "considers external things without respect to the diverse conditions of the one acting."[43] For example, if an object that a person destroys cost ten dollars, then justice is fulfilled by paying that ten dollars or replacing the thing with an object of equal worth. But in a matter that involves, for example, the courage to face various obstacles that impede a particular goal, what may be a threatening situation for one person may not be so for another, and what may be a means within the capacity and availability of one person may not be possible for another. Oftentimes, only the person himself can know these minute circumstances of difference and ultimately he must cope with them. Consequently, if we do not consciously recognize in each situation whether we are

---

41St. Thomas, (D): Q. 56, a. 1, reply obj. 1.
42Merkelbach, *op. cit.*, Vol. I, pp. 473–474; St. Thomas, (D): Q. 64, a. 1, 2, 3; De Virt. Q. 1, a. 13.
43*Ibid.* V. I, p. 474; see also V. II, 148 ff.

concerned with justice or with the other moral virtues, we may group them all together and apply the *medium rei*, that is, the measure of the thing, of the virtue of justice to matters which concern temperance or fortitude. For this reason, it is in matters of justice primarily that common judgments can be made. In questions of prudence, fortitude, and temperance regarding the means of carrying out a particular action, the measure is the peculiar circumstances, conditions, and capacities of the individual person involved. In these especially there is often a need for counseling.

A certain neglect of personal factors seems also inherent in the nature of mass education such as we have attempted in America. Any program aimed at the simultaneous educating of a large number, makes it difficult to reach the individual. It is understandable, then, why our main consideration may have been that people learn the Catholic way of life and know what they should do. There is, however, a growing awareness now of a need for more than this. It seems necessary for us to give more attention to the growth of personal responsibility and virtuous living. We need to create situations in our school and parish programs where responsible thinking takes place around the immediate circumstances of the different states in life and the individual personal difficulties of children and adults. The more we concern ourselves with the contingent singulars which vary with states of life and individual personalities, the more we are approaching the field of the moral virtues, and particularly of prudence and counsel. This does not mean, of course, any neglect of the intellectual virtues which are still, in a sense, the primary purpose of education as such. Knowledge, understanding, and wisdom, both natural and supernatural, are essential to a well-orientated life. But, in addition, there must also be the prudent ability to make reasonable self-directed choices in the particular events and circumstances which make up each person's life. Counseling, then, can be a further contribution to the development of the basic moral virtues founded in prudence and to each individual's growth in self-understanding and responsible, saintly living.

The Fruitful Development of the Individual Personality. It is the peculiar genius of Catholicity that it always penetrates and absorbs the culture in which it is. It both supernaturalizes and humanizes every culture because it endows it with the increased sense of the personal dignity of man as a creature of God. If

American culture may be noted for one outstanding characteristic, it is its emphasis on the dignity, freedom, and individual responsibility of each man. In this it stands as the hope of people everywhere. American democracy is founded on the basic Christian concept of man's worth as a creature of God. "We hold," said the framers of the Declaration of Independence, "these truths to be self-evident, that all men are created equal, that they are endowed by their Creator with certain unalienable Rights." This is fundamentally a religious concept based on a moral responsibility. As Bishop Wright has remarked:

Social stability and individual salvation still depend on the recognition of the central place of individual responsibility in whatever good may be accomplished or whatever evil must be suffered on the face of the earth over which God gave man dominion.

Specifically, it was the philosophy of responsibility that made America great. It is the basis of free self-government, as free self-government in turn has been the basis of American greatness. Woodrow Wilson said some wise things about the relationship of self-government to the kind of character produced by the philosophy of responsibility. He said, "Self government is not a mere form of institution, to be had when desired, if only the proper pains are taken. It is a form of character. It follows on the long discipline which gives a people self-possession, self-mastery, the habit of order and common counsel, and a reverence for law which will not fail when they themselves become the makers of law."[44]

Such an emphasis on personal responsibility and worth is also at the heart of Catholicity. In this sense, programs and methods which emphasize personal responsibility and self-reliant living in the realm of the moral virtues are contributing both to the growth in Catholic sanctity and to the preservation of those ideals of democracy which we hold so dear. The truly educated Catholic will not be in isolation from the culture in which he lives but will form a living, responsible part of it. As Pope Pius XII has recently pointed out:

The essence and the goal of education—to use the expression of Our immediate Predecessor—consist in collaboration with divine grace for the formation of the true and perfect Christian.

[44]Most Reverend John J. Wright, D.D.: "The Philosophy of Responsibility," *The Catholic Univ. of Am. Bull.*, Vol. 16, No. 5, March 1949, p. 6.

In this perfection is included the ideal that the Christian, as such, be in condition to face and to overcome the difficulties and to correspond to the demands of the times in which it is his lot to live.

That means that the work of education, since it must be carried on in a specific environment and for a specific background (milieu), must constantly adapt itself to the circumstances of this background, and of this environment wherein this perfection has to be obtained and for which it is destined.[45]

The manner of inculcating Catholic life in children and adults, the methods by which moral as well as intellectual virtues are developed to form the integrated Christian, demands steady growth in reasonable judgments and self-responsible living. Education has failed in its purpose if it has not achieved this. So, as Pope Pius XII continues:

But in this work, act with caution and prudence, so that it will be the youth himself who will always be seeking something more and, little by little, working by himself, will be learning to live and to practice his life of faith.[46]

By such methods which encourage self-responsible choices we will approach closer to the fusion and interaction of the natural and supernatural virtues which make up the perfection of Christian living. In this way we will have

. . . education which always gives first place to spiritual and moral values; both to the natural and, above all, to the supernatural ones. . . . But never forget that it is impossible to reach this goal without the powerful help of the Sacraments of Confession and of the Most Holy Eucharist, whose supernatural educative value can never be duly appreciated. . . . Thus, the Christian ideal of education is identified with the latest findings of psycho-pedagogical science, surrounding it with a light which perfects it and facilitating the educative process with *the complete and fruitful development of the individual personality*.[47]

---

[45]Pope Pius XII: "Education and the Modern Environment," a radio address to the Inter-American Congress on Catholic Education held at La Paz, Bolivia, October 15, 1948. *The Catholic Mind*, Vol. XLVII, p. 119.

[46]*Ibid.*

[47]*Ibid.* (Italics mine.)

BOOK LIST

ALLEN, M.D., FREDERICK H., *Psychotherapy with Children*, New York, Norton, 1942.

ALLERS, RUDOLPH, *The New Psychologies*, London, Sheed & Ward, 1932.

ARTHUR, GRACE, *Tutoring as Therapy*, New York, Commonwealth Fund, 1946.

AXLINE, VIRGINIA, *Play Therapy*, Boston, Houghton Mifflin, 1947.

BENJAMINS, J., "Changes in Performance in Relation to Influences upon Self-Conceptualization," Unpublished Doctoral Dissertation, Columbus, Ohio State University, 1949.

BLAKE, R. R., and RAMSEY, G. V., *Perception, An Approach to Personality*, New York, Copyright, 1951, by The Ronald Press Co.

BRAYFIELD, ARTHUR H., *Readings in Modern Methods of Counseling*, New York, Appleton-Century-Crofts, 1950.

BRENNAN, O.P., ROBERT E., ed., *Essays in Thomism*, New York, Sheed & Ward, 1942.

———, *General Psychology*, New York, Macmillan, 1937.

———, *History of Psychology*, New York, Macmillan, 1946.

———, *The Image of His Maker*, Milwaukee, Bruce, 1948.

———, *Thomistic Psychology*, New York, Macmillan, 1941.

BROWN, Ph.D., ESTHER LUCILE, *Nursing for the Future*, New York, Russell Sage Foundation, 1948.

BUGENTAL, J. F. T., An Investigation of the Relationship of the Conceptual Matrix to the Self-Concept, Unpublished Doctoral Dissertation, Columbus, Ohio State University, 1948.

CAMERON, N., *The Psychology of Behavior Disorders*, New York, Houghton Mifflin, 1947.

CARLSON, O.P., SEBASTIAN, *The Virtue of Humility*, Baltimore, J. H. Furst, 1949.

CHAUTARD, O.C.S.O., DOM JEAN-BAPTISTE, *The Soul of the Apostolate*, tr. J. A. Moran, S.M., Techney, Illinois, Mission Press S.V.D., 1945.

CURRAN, CHARLES A., *Personality Factors in Counseling*, New York, Grune & Stratton, 1945.

———, "Family and Marriage Counseling and the Catholic College Program" in R. J. Deferrari, ed., *Guidance in Catholic Colleges and Universities*, Washington, The Catholic University of America, 1949.

———, "Structuring the Counseling Relationship," in A. H. Brayfield, ed., *Readings in Modern Methods of Counseling*, Appleton-Century-Crofts, New York, 1950.

CURRAN, O.P., S.T.D., JOHN W., "Religion," in *Summa Theologica*, Vol. III, New York, Benziger Brothers, 1947.

DARLEY, JOHN G., *Testing and Counseling in the High-School Guidance Program*, Chicago, Science Research Associates, 1945.

DOLLARD, J., and MILLER, N., *Personality and Psychotherapy*, New York, Copyright 1950, by McGraw-Hill.

DUNBAR, M.D., HELEN FLANDERS, *Emotions and Bodily Changes*, New York, Columbia University Press, 1938.

——, *Mind and Body*, New York, Random House, 1947.

——, *Psychosomatic Diagnosis*, New York, Hoeber, 1943.

ENGLISH, O., and PEARSON, H. J. G., *Emotional Problems of Living*, New York, W. W. Norton, 1945.

GARRIGOU-LAGRANGE, O.P., REGINALD, *The Love of God and The Cross of Jesus*, Vol. III, tr. Sr. Jeanne Marie, O.P.

——, *The Three Ages of the Interior Life*, III Vols., St. Louis, B. Herder, 1947.

GLENN, PAUL J., *Psychology*, St. Louis, B. Herder, 1936.

HEALY, WILLIAM and BRONNER, AUGUSTA, *New Lights on Delinquency*, New Haven, Yale University Press, 1936.

HITLER, ADOLF, *Mein Kampf*, tr. Ralph Manheim, Boston, Houghton Mifflin, 1943.

HUNT, J. McV., *Personality and the Behavior Disorders*, Vol. I, II, New York, Ronald Press, 1944.

JOHNSON, WENDELL, "The Semantics Of Maladjustment," in L. A. Pennington and I. A. Berg, ed., *An Introduction to Clinical Psychology*, New York, Ronald Press, 1948.

KLAPMAN, J. W., *Group Psychotherapy*, New York, Grune and Stratton, 1946.

LECLERQ, GEORGES, *La Conscience du Chrétien*, Paris, Aubier, Editions Montaigne, 1946.

LILLE, RALPH S., *General Biology and Philosophy of Organism*, Chicago, University of Chicago Press, 1945.

LINDQUIST, E. F., *Statistical Analysis in Educational Research*, Cambridge, Riverside Press, 1940.

LOTTIN, DOM ODON, *Principes de Morale*, Tome II, Louvain, Belgium, Abbaye du Mont Cesar, 1946.

MAIER, NORMAN R. F., *Frustration*, New York, McGraw-Hill, 1949.

MARITAIN, JACQUES, *Education at the Crossroads*, New Haven, Yale University Press, 1943.

——, *Existence and the Existent*, New York, Pantheon Books, 1948.

——, *St. Thomas and the Problem of Evil*, Milwaukee, Marquette University Press, 1942.

MASLOW, A. H., and MITTLEMANN, BELA, *Principles of Abnormal Psychology*, New York, Harper, 1941.

MAYO, ELTON, *Human Problems of an Industrial Civilization*, Cambridge, Harvard University Press, 1945.

MERKELBACH, O.P., BENEDICTUS HENRICUS, *Summa Theologiae Moralis*, Paris, Desclee de Brouwer, 1935.

MOORE, DOM VERNER, *The Driving Forces of Human Nature*, New York, Grune & Stratton, 1948.

——, *The Nature and Treatment of Mental Disorders*, New York, Grune & Stratton, 1944.

——, *Personal Mental Hygiene*, New York, Grune & Stratton, 1944.

——, *Principles of Ethics*, 4th Ed., Philadelphia, Lippincott, 1937.

MORENO, M.D., J. L., *Group Method and Group Psychotherapy*, New York, Beacon House, 1932.

——, *Psychodramatic Treatment of Marriage Problems*, New York, Beacon House, 1945.

——, *Psychodrama, Collected Papers*, New York, Beacon House, 1945.

——, *Group Therapy*, New York, Beacon House, 1945.

MUENCH, GEORGE A., *An Evaluation of Non-Directive Psychotherapy by Means of Rorschach and Other Tests*, Applied Psychology Monograph, No. 13, 1947.

MULVEY, MARY J., *A Tutoring-Counseling Relationship between Teacher and Pupil for Removal of Emotional Blocks to Learning*, Masters Thesis, Columbus, Ohio State University, 1948.

NOLDIN, S.J., H., *Summa Theologicae Moralis*, Roma & New York, Fridericum Pustet, 1935.

NOLL, BISHOP JOHN F., "What is Wrong with Our Schools," in *From a Friend to a Friend*, Huntington, Indiana, Our Sunday Visitor Press, 1944.

O'BRIEN, C.M., PATRICK, *Emotions and Morals*, New York, Grune & Stratton, 1950.

PAVLOV, IVAN PETROVICH, *Conditioned Reflex*, G. V. Anrep tr. and ed., London, Oxford University Press, 1928.

PENNINGTON, L. A. and BERG, I. A., *Introduction to Clinical Psychology*, New York, Ronald Press, 1948.

POPE PIUS XI, *The Catholic Priesthood*, Encyclical Letter, tr. Vatican Press, 1936.

PORTER, E. H., *An Introduction to Therapeutic Counseling*, Boston, Houghton Mifflin, 1950.

QUIGLEY, THOMAS J., *Inquiry into the Religious Knowledge of Catholic High School Girls*, Diocese of Pittsburgh, Pennsylvania.

RAIMY, VICTOR C., *The Self-Concept as a Factor in Counseling and Personality Organization*, Ph.D. Thesis, Columbus, Ohio State University, 1943.

RANK, OTTO, *Truth and Reality*, New York, Knopf, 1936.

REGAN, ROBERT EDWARD, *Professional Secrecy in the Light of Moral Principles: with an Application to Several Important Professions*, Washington, D. C., Augustinian Press, 1943. Same, with title, *Moral Principles Governing Professional Secrecy with an Inquiry into some of the More Important Professional Secrets*, Studies in Sacred Theology No. 60, Washington, Catholic University Press, 1941.

ROBINSON, FRANCIS P., *Principles and Procedures in Student Counseling*, New York, Harper, 1950.

ROETHLISBERGER, F. J., and DICKSON, W. J., *Management and the Worker*, Cambridge, Harvard University Press, 1939.

ROGERS, CARL R., *Client-Centered Therapy*, New York, Houghton Mifflin, 1951.

——, *Clinical Treatment of the Problem Child*, New York, Houghton Mifflin, 1939.

——, *Counseling and Psychotherapy*, New York, Houghton Mifflin, 1942.

——, "Current trends in psychotherapy," in Wayne Dennis, ed., *Current Trends in Psychology*, Pittsburgh, University of Pittsburgh Press, 1947.

——, and WALLEN, J., *Counseling with the Returned Serviceman*, New York, McGraw-Hill, 1946.

SAUL, L. J., "Physiological Effects of Emotional Tension," in J. McV. Hunt, *Personality and the Behavior Disorders*, Vol. I, II, New York, Ronald Press, 1944.

SBABARO, JUDGE JOHN A., *Marriage is on Trial*, New York, Macmillan, 1947.

SEEMAN, JULIUS, "A Study of Preliminary Interview Methods in Vocational Counseling and Client Reactions to Counseling," Unpublished Ph.D. Thesis, University of Minnesota, 1948.

SHAW, CLIFFORD R., *Delinquency Areas*, Chicago, University of Chicago Press, 1929.

SHEED, F. J., *A Map of Life*, New York, Sheed and Ward, 1944.

SHEEN, BISHOP FULTON J., *Techniques for Convert Makers*, New York, Paulist League, 1949.

SHERMAN, HOYT L., *Drawing by Seeing*, New York, Hinds, Hayden & Elredge, 1947.

SHERMAN, MANDEL, "Emotional Disturbances and Reading Disability," in Gray, W. S., *Recent Trends in Reading:* Supplementary Educational Monographs No. 49, Chicago, University of Chicago Press, 1939.

SLAVSON, S. R., *Introduction to Group Therapy*, New York, Commonwealth Fund, 1943.

SNYDER, W. U., "An Investigation of the Nature of Non-Directive Therapy," Unpublished doctoral dissertation, Columbus, Ohio State University, 1943.

——, *Casebook of Non-Directive Counseling*, New York, Houghton Mifflin, 1947.

SNYGG, D., and COMBS, A. W., *Individual Behavior*, New York, Harper, 1949.

ST. FRANCIS DESALES, *Introduction to a Devout Life*, New York, Ross, Benziger, 1925.

ST. THOMAS AQUINAS, *Summa Theologica*, III Vols., tr. Fathers of the English Dominican Province, New York, Benziger, 1947.

——, *Basic Writings of St. Thomas Aquinas*, II Vols., tr. Anton Pegis, New York, Random House, 1945.

STRANG, RUTH, *Counseling Technics in College and Secondary Schools*, New York, Harper, 1949.

TANQUERY, A., *The Spiritual Life*, Tournai, Belgium, Desclee, 1930.

THORNE, FREDERICK C., *Principles of Personality Counseling*, Brandon, Vermont, Journal of Clinical Psychology, 1950.

WEISS, E., and ENGLISH, O. S., *Psychosomatic Medicine*, Philadelphia, W. B. Saunders, 1949.

WHITMER, HELEN L., *Teaching Psychotherapeutic Medicine; an Experimental Course for General Physicians*, New York, Commonwealth Fund, 1947.

WILLIAMSON, E. G., *Counseling Adolescents*, McGraw-Hill, 1950.

——, *How to Counsel Students*, New York, McGraw-Hill, 1937.

——, *Trends in Student Personnel Work*, University of Minnesota Press, 1949.

WRENN, C. G., and BELL, R., *Student Personnel Problems*, Farrar & Rinehart, 1942.

PERIODICAL REFERENCES

ALLPORT, G. W., "The Psychology of Participation," address given at the annual meeting of the Society for the Psychological Study of Social Issues at Columbia University (September 16, 1944).

——, and KRAMER, B. M., "Some roots of prejudice," *J. Abnorm. & Social Psychol.*, 41, 229–239 (July, 1946).

ARTZ, PHILIP K., M.D., "Psychosomatic medicine in general practice," *J. Lancet*, LXVIII (November, 1948).

ASSUM, A., and LEVY, S., "Analysis of a non-directive case with follow-up interview," *J. Abnorm. & Soc. Psychol.*, 43, 78–89, 1948.

AXLINE, VIRGINIA M., "Mental deficiency—symptom or disease?" *J. Consult. Psychol.*, 13, 313–327, 1949.

AXLINE, VIRGINIA M., "Nondirective therapy for poor readers," *J. Consult. Psychol., 11,* 61–69, 1947.

——, "Play therapy and race conflict in young children," *J. Abnorm. & Soc. Psychol., 43,* 300–310, 1948.

——, "Play therapy experiences as described by child participants," *J. Consult. Psychol., 14,* 53–63, 1950.

BACON, SELDON D., "The alcoholic: a study in the interplay of individual and social factors," from Lectures at the Forum Conference, Ohio State University, January 24, 1945, p. 13.

BARRY, JOHN R., "The relation of verbal reactions to adjustment level," *J. Abnorm. & Soc. Psychol., 45,* 647–658 (October, 1950).

BARTLEY, S. HOWARD, "Conflict, frustration, and fatigue," *Psychosom. Med., V* (April, 1943).

BARUCH, D. W., "Mental hygiene counseling as part of teacher education," *J. Psychol., 13,* 69–108, 1943.

BENNE, K. D., and SHEETS, P., "Functional roles of group members," *J. Sociol. Issues, 4,* 41–49, 1948.

BIXLER, R. H., "Limits are therapy," *J. Consult. Psychol., 13,* 1–11, 1949.

——, "Treatment of a reading problem through nondirective play therapy," *J. Consult. Psychol., 9,* 105–118, 1945.

——, and BIXLER, VIRGINIA H., "Clinical counseling in vocational guidance," *J. Clin. Psychol., 1,* 186–192, 1945.

——, ——, "Test interpretation in vocational counseling," *Educ. and Psychol. Measures, 6,* 145–155, 1946.

BOLLINGER, D. M., "Group therapy of the children's center," *Nervous Child., 4,* 221–227, 1945.

BORDIN, E. S., and BIXLER, R. H., "Test selection: a process of counseling," *Educ. and Psychol. Measures, 6,* 361–373, 1946.

BRUNER, J. S., and GOODMAN, C. C., "Value and need as organizing factors in perception," *J. Abnorm. and Soc. Psychol., 42,* 33–44, 1947.

BUTLER, JOHN M., "On the role of directive and non-directive techniques in the counseling process," *Educ. and Psychol. Meas., 8,* 201–209, 1948.

CARR, ARTHUR C., "An evaluation of nine nondirective psychotherapy cases by means of the Rorschach," *J. Consult. Psychol., 13,* 196–205, 1949.

COMBS, A. W., "Follow-up of a case treated by the nondirective play therapy," *J. Clin. Psychol., 1,* 148–154, 1945.

——, "Non-directive techniques and vocational counseling," *Occupations, 25,* 261–267, 1947.

——, "A phenomenological approach to adjustment theory," *J. Abnorm. & Soc. Psychol., 44,* 29–35, 1949.

——, "Some contributions of non-directive methods to college counseling," *J. Consult. Psychol.*, *9*, 218–223, 1945.

Corsini, R. J., "Non-directive counseling of prison inmates," *J. Clin. Psychol.*, *3*, 96–100, 1947.

Covner, B. J., "Nondirective interviewing techniques in vocational counseling," *J. Consult. Psychol.*, *11*, 70–73, 1947.

——, "Studies in phonographic recordings of verbal material," *J. Consult. Psychol.*, *6*, 105–115, 149–153, 1942.

Cowen, Emory L., and Combs, A. W., "Follow-up study of 32 cases treated by nondirective psychotherapy," *J. Abnorm. & Soc. Psychol.*, *45*, 233–257, 1950.

Cuber, J. F., "Functions of the marriage counselor," *Marriage and Family Living*, *2*, 116–120, 1945.

Curran, C. A., "The family and community living," *The Homiletic and Pastoral Review*, *48* (January, 1948).

——, "Family counseling," *Am. Cath. Soc. Rev.*, *9*, 152–161, 1948.

——, "The leader's skill in group discussion," *Am. Cath. Soc. Rev.*, *11* (December, 1950).

——, "Nondirective counseling in allergic complaints," *J. Abnorm. & Soc. Psychol.*, *43*, 244–251, 1948.

——, "Religion and the returned soldier," *The Homiletic and Pastoral Review*, *46* (March, 1946).

——, "Structuring the counseling relationship: a case report," *J. Abnorm. and Soc. Psychol.*, *39* (April, 1944).

——, "The virtue of counsel and nondirective counseling," *Nat. Cath. Educ. Assn.*, *College News Letter* (March, 1949).

——, in cooperation with Mitchell, J., et al, *International Correspondence of Allergy*, IX and X, 1947.

——, ——, "A method of approach to psychosomatic problems in allergy," *West Virginia Med. J.*, *42*, 1–24, 1946.

——, et al, "Personality factors in 'allergic disorders,'" *J. Allergy*, *18*, 337–340, 1947.

——, ——, "Some psychosomatic aspects of allergic complaints," *Psychosomat. Med.*, *9*, 184–191, 1947.

Darley, J. G., "Changes in measured attitudes and adjustments," *J. Soc. Psychol.*, *9*, 1938.

Eberle, E., O.F.M., "A technique of guidance," *Guidance Through Franciscan Spirituality*, *29*, 181–195, 1948.

Ellis, A., "A critique of the theoretical contributions of non-directive therapy," *J. Clin. Psychol.*, *4*, 248–255, 1948.

Fleming, L., and Snyder, W. U., "Social and personal changes following non-directive group play therapy," *Am. J. Orthopsychiat.*, *17*, 101–116, 1947.

FOULKES, S. H., "Principles and practices of group therapy," *Bull. Menninger Clinic, 10,* 85–90, 1946.

FOURIEZOS, N. T., HUTT, MAX L., and GUETZKOW, H., "Measurement of self-oriented needs in discussion groups," *J. Abnorm. & Soc. Psychol., 45,* 682–690, 1950.

GARRIGOU-LAGRANGE, O.P., R., "Eternal youth," *Cross and Crown, 2,* 17–23, 1950.

——, "Special grace of the spiritual director," *Cross and Crown, 2,* 411–428, 1950.

GATES, A. I., "The role of personality maladjustment in reading disability," *J. Genet. Psychol.,* 77–83 (September, 1941).

GOODRICH, FREDERICK W., and THOMS, HERBERT, "A clinical study of natural childbirth," *Am. J. Obs. & Gyn., 56,* 575–883, 1948.

HAIGH, GERARD, "Defensive behavior in client-centered therapy," *J. Consult. Psychol., 13,* 181–189, 1949.

——, and KELL, BILL L., "Multiple therapy as a method for training and research in psychotherapy," *J. Abnorm. and Soc. Psychol., 45,* 659–666, 1950.

HATHAWAY, STARKE R., "Some considerations relative to non-directive counseling as therapy," *J. of Clin. Psychol., 3,* 226–231, 1948.

HEWITT, H., and GILDEA, M. C. L., "An experiment in group psychotherapy," *Am. J. Orthopsychiat., 91,* 511–517, 1945.

HEYNS, R. W., "Functional analysis of group problem-solving behavior," in *Research Staff Papers,* 1948–49, microfilmed.

HOFFMAN, EDWARD, "A study of reported behavior changes in counseling," *J. Consult. Psychol., 13,* 190–195, 1949.

IVANCIC, MARY J., "A way to ease emotional blocks to learning," *Understanding the Child, 18* (April, 1949).

KAMM, R. B., and WRENN, C. G., "Client acceptance of self-information in counseling," *Educ. and Psychol. Measures, 10,* 32–42, 1950.

KELLY, GERALD, S.J., "Emotional maturity," *Review for Religious, 7* (January, 1947).

KEMBLE, R. P., "Constructive use of the ending of treatment," *Am. J. Orthopsychiat., 11,* 684–690, 1941.

LANGMUIR, IRVING, "Science, common sense and decency," *Science News Letter, 43* (January, 1943).

LIPKIN, STANLEY, "The client evaluates non-directive psychotherapy," *J. Consult. Psychol., 12,* 137–146, 1948.

LOWERY, L. Y., "Group therapy: special session meeting," *Am. J. Orthopsychiat., 13,* 648–691, 1943.

MADIGAN, VIRGINIA E., "An illustration of non-directive psychotherapy," *J. Clin. Psychol., 1,* 36–52, 1945.

MEISTER, R. K., and MILLER, H. E., "The dynamics of non-directive therapy," *J. Clin. Psychol.*, 2, 59–67, 1946.

MITCHELL, J. H., COHEN, S., and CURRAN, C. A., *International Correspondence of Allergy*, IX and X, 1947.

——, and CURRAN, C. A., "A Method of approach to psychosomatic problems in allergy," *West Virginia Med. Journ.*, 42, 1–24, 1946.

——, ——, MITCHELL, W. F., SIVON, IOLA, and MYERS, R., "Personality factors in 'allergic disorders,' " *J. Allergy*, 18, 337–340, 1947.

——, ——, and MYERS, R., "Some psychosomatic aspects of allergic complaints," *Psychosom. Med.*, 9, 184–191, 1947.

MOWRER, O. H., "Implications of a two-factor learning theory," *The Psychological Service Center Journal*, Vol. II (June, 1950).

MUENCH, G. A., and ROGERS, C. R., "Counseling of emotional blocking in an aviator," *J. Abnorm. & Soc. Psychol.*, 41, 207–215, 1946.

PALMER, GRETTA, "Marriage counsel from the church," *Look*, July 1, 1948.

PAUWELS, C. F., O.P., "Theological problems of conversion," *The Thomist*, 11 (October, 1948).

PATTERSON, C. H., "The Relationship of Bernreuter scores to parent behavior, child behavior, urban-rural residence, and other background factors in one hundred normal adult parents," *J. Soc. Psychol.*, 24, 3–49, 1946.

PERL, R. E., and SIMON, A. J., "Criteria of success and failure in child guidance," *Am. J. Orthopsychiat.*, 12, 642–658, 1942.

POPE PIUS XII, Christmas Message, 1944, *The Catholic Mind*, 43, 65–77, 1945.

——, "Education and modern environment," *The Catholic Mind*, 47 (December, 1948).

——, "On Catholic action," *The Catholic Mind*, 49 (August, 1951).

RAIMY, V. C., "Self references in counseling interviews," *J. Consult. Psychol.*, 12, 153–163, 1948.

RASKIN, NATHANIEL J., "An analysis of six parallel studies of the therapeutic process," *J. Consult. Psychol.*, 13, 206–220, 1949.

REDL, FRITZ, "Diagnostic group work," *Am. J. Orthopsychiat.*, 14, 53–68, 1944.

REDMOND, W., and STULBERG, B., "An analysis of the non-directive counselor's personal self," *Personal Counsellor*, 2, 13–21, 1947.

REID, DOROTHY K., and SNYDER, WILLIAM U., "Experiment on 'recognition of feeling' in non-directive psychotherapy," *J. Clinic. Psychol.*, 3, 128–135, 1947.

RIPLEY, H. S., and WOLF, S., "The intravenous use of sodium amytal in psychosomatic disorders," *Psychosom. Med.*, 19, 260–267, 1947.

ROGERS, CARL R., "The attitude and orientation of the counselor in client-centered therapy," *J. Consult. Psychol.*, *13*, 82–94, 1949.

——, "The clinical psychologist's approach to personality problems," *The Family*, *18*, 233–243, 1937.

——, "Divergent trends in methods of improving adjustment," *Harvard Educ. Rev.*, 209–219, 1948.

——, Presidential Address—American Psychological Association, *Am. Psychol.*, *2* (September, 1947).

——, "The process of therapy," *J. Consult. Psychol.*, *4*, 161–164, 1940.

——, "Significant aspects of client-centered therapy," *Am. Psychol.*, *1*, 415–422, 1946.

——, "Some implications of client-centered counseling for college personnel work," *Educ. and Psychol. Measures*, *8*, 540–549, 1948.

——, "Some observations on the organization of personality," *Am. Psychol.*, *2*, 358–368, 1947.

——, "Trends in the formation of client-centered therapy," Paper given at the National Symposium on New Trends in Counseling and Psychotherapy at the University of Illinois, February 25, 1949.

——, "The use of electrically recorded interviews in improving psychotherapeutic techniques," *Am. J. Orthopsychiat.*, *12*, 429–434, 1942.

ROSENBLITH, JUDY F., "A replication of some roots of prejudice," *J. Abnorm. & Soc. Psychol.*, *44*, 470–489, 1949.

SARGENT, H., "Non-directive counseling applied to a single interview," *J. Consult. Psychol.*, *7*, 183–190, 1943.

——, "Non-directive treatment of a motor block," *J. Abnorm. & Soc. Psychol.*, *42*, 243–252, 1947.

SCHMIDT, B. G., "The rehabilitation of feeble-minded adolescents," *School and Society*, *62*, 409–412, 1945.

SEEMAN, JULIUS, "Client reactions to vocational counseling," *J. Consult. Psychol.*, *13*, 95–104, 1949.

——, "The process of non-directive therapy," *J. Consult. Psychol.*, *13*, 157–168, 1949.

SHEERER, ELIZABETH T., "The relationship between acceptance of self and acceptance of others," *J. Consult. Psychol.*, *13*, 169–175, 1949.

SKEELS, H. M., "Some Iowa studies of the mental growth of children in relation to differentials of environment; a summary," *N.S.S.E. Yearbook*, 281–308, 1940.

SNYDER, WILLIAM U., "An investigation of the nature of non-directive psychotherapy," *J. Genet. Psychol.*, *33*, 193–223, 1945.

——, "The present status of personality counseling," *Psychol. Bull.*, *44*, 297–386, 1947.

——, "A short term non-directive treatment of an adult," *J. Abnorm. & Soc. Psychol.*, *38*, 86–137, 1943.

——, "Warmth in non-directive psychotherapy," *J. Abnorm. & Soc. Psychol.*, *41*, 491–495, 1946.

——, and REID, DOROTHY K., "Experiment on 'recognition of feeling' in non-directive psychotherapy," *J. Clin. Psychol.*, *3*, 128–135, 1947.

SLAVSON, S. R., "Differential methods of group therapy in relation to age levels," *Nervous Child*, 4, 196–210, 1945.

——, "Group therapy at the Jewish Board of Guardians," *Mental Hygiene*, *28*, 414–422, 1944.

——, "Some elements in activity group therapy," *Am. J. Orthopsychiat.*, *14*, 578–588, 1944.

——, "Treatment of withdrawal through group therapy," *Am. J. Orthopsychiat.*, *15*, 681–689, 1945.

STOCK, DOROTHY, "An investigation into the interrelations between the self-concept and feelings toward other persons and groups," *J. Consult. Psychol.*, *13*, 176–180, 1949.

STOGDILL, EMILY, "Techniques of student counseling," *J. Consult. Psychol.*, *4*, 176–180, 1940.

THOMAS, JOHN L., S.J., "The urban impact on Catholic families," *The Am. Cath. Soc. Rev.*, 258–267, 1949.

WAELDER, ROBERT, *et al*, "Areas of agreement in psychotherapy," *Amer. J. Orthopsychiat.*, *10*, 1940.

WHITE, H. C., "An adventure in group therapy in a family agency setting," *Mental Hygiene*, *28*, 422–430, 1944.

WILLIAMSON, E. G., and BORDIN, E. S., "A statistical evaluation of clinical counseling," *Educ. Psychol. Measures*, *1*, 117–132, 1941.

——, ——, "The evaluation of vocational and educational counseling: a critique of the methodology of experiments," *Educ. Psychol. Meas.*, *1*, 5–24, 1941.

WRIGHT, BISHOP JOHN J., "The philosophy of responsibility," *The Catholic Univ. of Am. Bull.*, *16* (March, 1949).

WYATT, F., "The self-experience of the psychotherapist," *J. Consult. Psychol.*, *12*, 82–88, 1948.

GLOSSARY

Acceptance response – Counselor conveys an attitude of acceptance of the person and an understanding of his statement, but does not crystallize it with any tone of agreement or disagreement with intellectual or logical content.

Adjustment – Moving out to reality and coping with it; the person moves away from self-deception, and his insights and actions are more in line with what is; movement of man's positive will in the line of being; (Rank) enables a person to meet the realities of the immediate present by uncovering and dispersing those fears of the present which may cause him to cling to attitudes of the past.

Art – Right reason about certain things to be made. "The art of living well" is prudence.

Choice – (St. Thomas) Follows the judgment of reason in matters of action. More adequate choices are possible after integrating the field of factors which enter into life experiences through the insight process.

Client – The person coming for counseling; in this book usually called "person"; generally used as synonymous with counselee or patient.

Client-centered – Term designating that the focus of counseling is on the client's or person's self-unfolding and responsible integration.

Conditioning – Reactions which are characteristically aroused by one stimulus may become attached to another stimulus not necessarily associated with the original one.

Conflict – Doubt and confusion or inability to make a choice between two or more plans of action.

Conscience – (Glenn) "Conscience is the intellectual consciousness or reasoned awareness of right or wrong in a situation here and now to be judged."

Contingent singulars – The particular, unique, or personal events that occur in an individual's life.

Counseling – A definite relationship where, through the counselor's sensitive understanding and skillful responses, a person objectively surveys the past and present factors which enter into his personal confusions and conflicts, and at the same time reorganizes his emotional reactions so that he not only chooses better ways to reach his reasonable goals, but also has sufficient confidence, courage, and moderation to act on these choices.

Counseling process – Follows certain general trends which can be separated into five phases: 1. Problem stating. The unfolding stage in which the person is negative towards himself and his problems. 2. Analysis. The more positive self-examination stage in which the person can look at previously hidden motives and values in a positive light after the negative emotion has been drained off. 3. Synthesis. The stage in which the person begins to relate his problems together and acquire from his past and present state an integrated understanding of how they came about. 4. Planning. With all factors of the situation before him in an integrated manner, the person plans new and more adequate choices and means of action. 5. Re-evaluation. This phase fuses with the fourth phase. The person re-evaluates the experiences which occurred when the new solutions were acted on.

Discussion leader – Not an instructor or lecturer, but one whose role and purpose are directly related to the discussion itself. His chief function is to promote a free exchange of the group's views.

Docility or teachableness – Willingness to consult others and to learn from them as well as learning from experience. This is not to be confused with the dependent seeking of advice.

Estimative power – Aquinas recognizes, in addition to the power to synthesize sensory percepts, another power which he calls *vis aestimativa*. This is the ability of the organism immediately to recognize an object as useful or harmful to it.

Fatigue – (Bartley) The desire to quit a given activity and turn to something else. It arises out of the discomfort or impairment involved in pursuing the task or in the relative failure in doing so for any reason.

Focal point – In counseling, the centering or concentration on the interviews themselves as a fixed and stable point from which to work out problems. Also, the changing relationships of various personal factors in the development of insight.

Forking response – This type of response does not channel the person in the direction of any one problem, solution, or path of reasoning, but lets him take up whatever he considers important at the moment.

Frustration – Results from an inability to reach a goal because of external factors, such as physical barriers, personal situations, economic reasons, etc., or because of internal factors such as emotional instability, confusion, etc.

Guidance – Particular application of knowledge and facts to special needs; applies generally to groups according to age, position, sex, etc.

Humility – (Carlson) The reasonable pursuit of one's own excellence.

Inquiry – 1. The first step in the virtue of counsel, examining of all factors which have a bearing on the present action; 2. In the counseling process, it is the exploring of present purposes and values as well as a survey of past plans, goals, and actions.

Insight – Involves both an increase in self-understanding and the ability to act on the knowledge one has acquired. The person either takes the knowledge he has or the new knowledge which he acquires and filters it through himself so that it becomes an integrated part of his whole plan of action.

Integrating response – Whenever two or more factors are related together in a statement, the counselor responds by not only reflecting the feelings expressed, but also by stating precisely whatever factors the person has disclosed which related these feelings to each other or to fundamental causes.

Negative emotion – Expressions of unhappiness; hostility to others and to self; feelings of rejection, fear, conflict, worry, anxiety, confusion, dependence, escape, insecurity, frustration, and the like.

Negative will – By willing to negate, a person wills in the direction of nothing. He wills something usually, but in relation to what he could have willed and what was best for him, it moves him further away from his goals. It produces discouragement, failure, and frustration.

Passive acquiescence – A state in which the individual takes no responsibility and does not exercise self-evaluation and direction.

Personal integration – Reasoned ordering of instincts, emotions, and actions around basic life achievements and purposes.

Play therapy – Interviews with children where clay, dramatics, or toys are used to aid the child's expression and self-understanding.

Positive emotion – Expressions of hope, courage, confidence, feeling better, happiness, and satisfaction, usually accompanying insights and new plans of action.

Positive will – The positive urge to take steps necessary to reach goals or to change one's plan of action in order to live a more adequate life. In counseling, it produces steady growth in direction of reasonable achievement and success.

Precipitation – Results when the steps of prudence are not fulfilled, particularly counsel.

Pride – (St. Thomas) The inordinate pursuit of one's own excellence; unreasonable self-esteem.

Prudence (acquired) – Understanding the immediate steps in our daily lives to reach any desired goal; an acquired virtue having three integral parts: 1) a survey of the best means and methods to reach our goals, 2) a choice of the means, and 3) action on the means.

Psychosomatic medicine – Medical treatment with the awareness of the substantial union of body and soul in man and their interaction.

Self-acceptance – Positive attitude of self-understanding in which a person accepts his abilities, successes, and achievements, and limitations or handicaps honestly and plans solutions around these realities.

Self-deception – The superficial explanations people give themselves for actions; sometimes synonymous with the negative aspects of problem-stating.

Self-direction – 1. The ability to judge and command ourselves well for the completion of prudent action. 2. In counseling, the person increases self-understanding and emotional control so that he can carry into action what he knows he should do.

Simple solution – The first immediate urge or perception of a situation or of the path to be taken in resolving a difficulty.

Stereotype reactions – People in prolonged states of frustration tend toward unvaried conduct, and their reactions to situations may become fixed so that they always react in the same way.

Structuring statements – Phrases which define simply and precisely the counseling relationship.

Summarizing response – A brief restatement of previously explored problems, insights, or solutions.

Virtue – (Webster) An active quality, power, capacity adequate to the production of a given effect. Equivalent to integrity of character. (St. Thomas) Virtue causes an ordered operation—the permanent power to produce reasonable action.

Virtue of counsel – To uncover the means for personal and responsible individual life action which applies primarily to the person himself as part of his own prudence. It involves self-coordination and control as well as knowledge concerning the single event.

AUTHOR INDEX

457

SUBJECT INDEX

Acceptance, and children, 62, 96, 297, 304; atmosphere of, 199, 231; in counseling, 65, 69–70, 210–213, 345; need of, 58–59; of adults, 111, 299

Achievement, 75, 130; reasonable, 73, 84, 163, 246, 272, 418

Adjustment, 171, 193, 452; measure of, 169; to reality, 169, 170–171, 193, 194, 246, Chapter VIII

Advice giving, 26–29, 62; limitations of, 28; resistance to, 27, 28, 44, 46, 73, 90, 166, 186

Advice, of team, 41–42

Advising attitudes, 293, 294–295

Alcoholism, 82

Aristotelian-Thomistic, concept of man, 131, 136, 159–160

Attitude check lists, 291, 293

Change, desire for, 84, 164, 194, 234; motivation for, 73

Child characteristics, 97–98; see also Dependency; fear, 73, 297–298, 300–302, 303–304; sensitivity, 297

Child counseling, 328, Chapter XIII; see also Counseling; and play, 300, 303; dramatic roles in, 314–315; insight in, 313–314; invoking limits, 309–311; limits of child's action, 308–309, 317–318, 363–364; setting of, 307–308

Choice, 148, 266, 452; adequate, 37, 175; through counseling, 160, 168, 188–189, 271; through insight, 139, 151, 158

Comparison, adult and child interview, 299, 302–303, 304, 313–314, 317

Compensation, 23, 26, 80, 91; by parents, 106–107

Compromise, 315, 339, 340–341, 344, 351; channeling, 340–342, 344–345; in interview, 346–347; references, 341

Conditioning, 136, 178, 452; and passivity, 130, 143; carry over of, 124–126, 132–133, 154; physical factors in, 125–127; studies of Pavlov, 122–123

Confidence, through counseling, 78, 100, 271

Confidences, adhering to, 204, 317–318, 327–328

Conflict, 23, 66, 72, 75, 110, 369, 452; and compromise, 345; between home and school, 108–109, 112; between parents, 102–103, 298–299; carry-over of, 95, 278; effects of, 56; in childhood, 74, 94; of goals, 26; of values, 95, 115–117; pressure of, 54–55; source of, 94; symbolized in clothes, 116–117

Conscience, 177–178, 180–181, 182, 452

Contingent singulars, 23, 25, 66, 157, 169, 434–435, 452; coping with, 19–20

Counsel, 21, 157, 435; and inquiry, 25, 157, 415, 417, 453; function of, 21, 29, 31; gift of, 35; in prudence, 25, 50, 412, 415; virtue of, 140, 156, 180, 192, 411, 435, 455

Counseling, 1–26, 40, 43–44, 48, 426, 452; acceptance in, 65, 69–70, 167, 199, 263, 327; adolescents, 175, 223–225, 229, 232–233, 358; and authority, 362–363; and disciplinary roles, 328; and guidance (see Guidance); atmosphere for, 199–201, 325, 326; children (see also Child counseling), 11, 60; development of, 32; fields for, 6, 438; group, 367, 368, 398–404; importance of, 1–2; process of analysis, 7–8; progress in, 47; research in, 7–8, 49, 53, 329, 410, 425. Self-directive counseling, 49, 84, 455; and Sacrament of Penance, 181; and virtue, Chapter XVIII; effects of, 192; five phases of, 244–246, 452–453; in emergency situations, 363–366; in medical setting, 358–362; limits of, 180–181; process of, 9, 194, 412, 428, 452–453 (Part Two); purpose of, 36, 334, 410; re-evaluation through, 120–121, 417–418; stages of, 9; successful, 70, 164, 200, 424; teachableness of, 8, 47; temporary relationship, 190–191

459

Counseling relationships, 202, 207, 326; attitude toward, 201–202, 334

Counseling skill, purpose of, 199–200

Counselor, and nurse, 361–362; and physician, 359–360; as tutor, 354–358; attitudes of, 205, 281, 286; attitudes, tests of, 289–293; crystallizing attitudes, 211; defensiveness of, 225, 269; effects of impatience in, 69, 336–337; honesty of, 261, 269, 282; improvement of skill, 223, 227, 250, 330–331, 332; manner of, 55, 69, 78, 209, 281; misstatement, 251; needs of, 227, 269, 336, 338; personal qualities of, 332–333; projection of self, 242–243; reassurance of, 335; resistance to, 217, 223, 240, 243, 253, 266; responses (*see also* Response), 10, 201, 364; role of, 84, 139, 209; sensitivity, 222, 310; sincerity of, 336; skill of, Part Three, 10, 13, 49, 50, 58, 64, 87, 164, 197–199, 259, 364, 365

Data, psychological or sociological, 355, 425

Delinquency, 107–108, 298

Democracy, 439–440

Dependency, 74, 99, 167, 204, 336; and passivity, 74; of childhood, 73, 74, 296–297, 299; on counselor 200–201

Diagram, Mother-Child Counseling, 319; Plan of Conduct, 173; Triangle, 18

Dignity of man, 14, 29, 330, 439

Discouragement, 23, 72–73, 429

Discussion groups, 11, 65, 211, 366, 368; and lay activity, 372–373; counseling through, 12, 374–375, 405–406; emotion in, 376; geometric position of, 383–384; in education, 371–372, 379; purpose of, 368; record of, 388–389; resistance in, 383–384, 391, 392–393; responsibility of, 379–380, 382; steps in, 379–382, 387; structuring, 380–381; types of later, 395–397; various uses of, 369–375

Discussion leader, 453; acceptance of, 378; function of, 368–369, 378–379, 383, 387–388; manner of, 381, 389; participation of, 395; skill of, 378–379

Discussion skills, 374, 385–387, 389–390; in classroom, 371–372; questions, 384–386; summarizing, 387–388; voting, 381, 394–395

Discussions, round-table, 41

Dynamics of counseling, 208, Chapter X

Dynamism, intrinsic, 73

Education, general, 19, 156, 371

Emotional conditioning, 122–123

Emotions, 74–75, 115; affect learning, 61, 135, 356; and choice, 75–76; and physical reactions, 122, 128–129, 143, 184, 305, 360; and punishment, 117; and reason, 24;

clarified, 87, 88–89; control of, 89, 136–137; narrow perception, 57, 141, 142, 172, 337, 411; negative, 69, 75, 83, 86, 245, 247, 248, 251, 454; positive, 74–75, 89, 163, 166, 178, 220, 223, 245, 246–249, 251, 265, 271, 454

Escape, 79, 91; daydreams, 66, 80

Evil, 165

Excerpt illustrating: accepting responses, 211–212; balancing response, 262; clarifying emotions, 88–89, 390; defining counseling relationship, 207; fear in children, 300–302; forking response, 255–257; group counseling, 398–404; inferiority, 85; information in interview, 349–350; limits with children, 310–312; need to talk, 59; parental conflict, 103–104; resistance to counselor, 267; resistance to learning, 119; response to basic feeling, 213–214, 219, 241; structuring group discussion, 380–381; structuring statements, 203; summarizing response, 231; unsuccessful counseling, 235–236, 238–239

Fatigue, 79, 453

Fear, 63, 73, 77, 297–298, 300–302

Fortitude, virtue of, 22, 427, 438

Freedom, personal, 14, 25, 439

Free will, Rank on, 46

Frustration, 73, 144–146, 153, 369, 453

Garrigou-Lagrange, R., on aid of Holy Spirit, 35; on grace, 161; on infused and acquired virtue, 33; on necessity of prayer, 34; on prudent action, 37; on spiritual director, 334–335

Goal, particular, 76; seeking, 25, 156; ultimate, 19, 76, 161

Goals, basic life, 84, 418–419

Group counseling, *see* Counseling and Discussion groups

Group discussion, *see* Discussion Groups

Guidance, 20, 40, 74, 435, 453; and counseling, 7, 11, 43, 254, 364; and information, 20; fields for, 20; in colleges, 3; realm of, 29; vocational, 20

Guilt, 166, 176–177, 180–181, 247

Happiness, 178

Home, and influence of parents, 95; and religious values, 101, 113; dominating personality, 98, 113; value of, 95

Humility, 12, 84–85, 101, 166, 427–429, 453

Infantile fixation, 45

Infantilism, 430–431

Inferiority, 84–85, 94

Influence, of companions, 107–108; of home,

Methods in Enzymology

Volume 121
IMMUNOCHEMICAL TECHNIQUES
Part I
Hybridoma Technology and Monoclonal Antibodies

METHODS IN ENZYMOLOGY

EDITORS-IN-CHIEF

Sidney P. Colowick   Nathan O. Kaplan

Methods in Enzymology

Volume 121

Immunochemical Techniques

Part I

Hybridoma Technology and
Monoclonal Antibodies

EDITED BY

John J. Langone

DEPARTMENT OF MEDICINE
BAYLOR COLLEGE OF MEDICINE
HOUSTON, TEXAS

Helen Van Vunakis

DEPARTMENT OF BIOCHEMISTRY
BRANDEIS UNIVERSITY
WALTHAM, MASSACHUSETTS

1986

ACADEMIC PRESS, INC.

Harcourt Brace Jovanovich, Publishers

Orlando   San Diego   New York   Austin
London   Montreal   Sydney   Tokyo   Toronto

ACADEMIC PRESS, INC.
Orlando, Florida 32887

United Kingdom Edition published by
ACADEMIC PRESS INC. (LONDON) LTD.
24–28 Oval Road, London NW1 7DX

Library of Congress Catalog Card Number: 54-9110

ISBN 0–12–182021–1

Printed in the United States of America

86 87 88 89   9 8 7 6 5 4 3 2 1

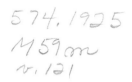

Table of Contents

Section I. Production of Hybridomas

A. Immunization and Cell Fusion

v

B. Growth and Cloning of Hybridomas

Section II. Monoclonal Antibodies

A. Screening Assays for Monoclonal Antibodies

B. Purification of Monoclonal Antibodies and Preparation of Antibody Fragments

Section IV. Summary

Contributors to Volume 121

Article numbers are in parentheses following the names of contributors.
Affiliations listed are current.

PAUL G. ABRAMS (10), *NeoRx Corporation, Seattle, Washington 98119*

W. STEVEN ADAIR (42), *Department of Biology, Washington University, St. Louis, Missouri 63130*

GUIDO ANTONI (16), *Sclavo Research Center, 53100 Siena, Italy*

DORETTA ARMELLINI (16), *Sclavo Research Center, 53100 Siena, Italy*

LEONIE K. ASHMAN (48), *Department of Microbiology and Immunology, The University of Adelaide, Adelaide 5000, Australia*

M. ZOUHAIR ATASSI (8), *Marrs McLean Department of Biochemistry, Baylor College of Medicine, Houston, Texas 77030*

ROBERT C. ATKINS (78), *Department of Nephrology, Prince Henry's Hospital, Melbourne, Victoria 3004, Australia*

M. L. BANQUERIGO (28), *The Johns Hopkins Oncology Center, The Johns Hopkins University School of Medicine, Baltimore, Maryland 21205*

FRANK BATTYE (71), *Flow Cytometry Laboratory, The Walter and Eliza Hall Institute of Medical Research, The Royal Melbourne Hospital, Parkville, Victoria 3050, Australia*

HERVÉ BAZIN (19, 59, 61, 63), *Experimental Immunology Unit, Faculty of Medicine, University of Louvain, B-1200 Brussels, Belgium*

ROSALIE BER (35), *Rappaport Family Institute for Research in the Medical Sciences, Faculty of Medicine, Technion-Israel Institute of Technology, Haifa 31096, Israel*

WILLIAM F. BIBB (38), *Division of Bacterial Diseases, Centers for Disease Control, Atlanta, Georgia 30333*

ROBERT J. BJERCKE (54), *Department of Medicine, Baylor College of Medicine, Houston, Texas 77030*

CLARE BLESSINGER (41), *Department of Rheumatic Diseases, Hospital for Joint Diseases, Mount Sinai Medical School, New York, New York 10003*

TIMOTHY BLOCK (73), *Department of Microbiology, Jefferson Medical College, Philadelphia, Pennsylvania 19107*

ALBERT BOEYÉ (30), *Department of Microbiology and Hygiene, Vrije Universiteit Brussel, B-1090 Brussels, Belgium*

D. J. BOLT (40), *Reproduction Laboratory, Animal Science Institute, Agricultural Research Service, Beltsville Agricultural Research Center, United States Department of Agriculture, Beltsville, Maryland 20705*

BARBARA D. BOSS (3), *Developmental Neurobiology Laboratory, The Salk Institute for Biological Studies and Clayton Foundation for Research-California Division, San Diego, California 92138-9216*

JOHN M. BOSWORTH, JR. (51), *Department of Pediatrics, Uniformed Services University of the Health Sciences, F. Edward Hébert School of Medicine, Bethesda, Maryland 20814-4799*

MARK BOTHWELL (73), *Department of Physiology and Biophysics, University of Washington, School of Medicine, Seattle, Washington 98195*

CLAUDE BOUCHEIX (55), *INSERM U.253, Hôpital Paul Brousse, 94800 Villejuif, France*

RÜDIGER W. BRAUN (70), *Institut für Virusforschung, Deutsches Krebsforschungszentrum, D-6900 Heidelberg, Federal Republic of Germany*

THOMAS BRODIN (25), *Department of Tumor Immunology, The Wallenberg Laboratory, University of Lund, S-220 07 Lund, Sweden*

TIMOTHY L. BROOKS (58), *Chromatography Business Unit, Bio-Rad Laboratories, Richmond, California 94801*

MCKAY BROWN (29), *Department of Microbiology and Immunology, Oregon Health Sciences University, Portland, Oregon 97201*

CLAUDINE BRUCK (56), *Department of Pathology, Harvard Medical School, Boston, Massachusetts 02115, Department of Medicine, New England Medical Center, Boston, Massachusetts 02110, and Laboratoire de Chimie Biologique, Department de Biologie Moleculaire, Universite Libre de Bruxelles, B-1640 Rhode-St-Genese, Belgium*

ABIGAIL BUENAFE (29), *Department of Microbiology and Immunology, Oregon Health Sciences University, Portland, Oregon 97201*

PAUL A. BUNN, JR. (65), *Division of Medical Oncology, University of Colorado Health Sciences Center, Denver, Colorado 80262*

SCOTT W. BURCHIEL (57), *College of Pharmacy, The University of New Mexico, Albuquerque, New Mexico 87131*

JENG-CHYH CHEN (58), *Chromatography Business Unit, Bio-Rad Laboratories, Richmond, California 94801*

MAURIZIO CIANFRIGLIA (16), *Laboratorio di Biologia Cellulare, Istituto Superiore di Sanita', 00161 Roma, Italy*

DANIEL R. CIOCCA (54), *Laboratorio de Reproducción y Lactancia (LARLAC), Consejo Nacional de Investigaciones Científicas y Técnicas (CONICET), Mendoza 5500, Argentina*

CURT I. CIVIN (28), *The Johns Hopkins Oncology Center, The Johns Hopkins University School of Medicine, Baltimore, Maryland 21205*

BRIAN R. CLARK (43), *Division of Pediatrics, City of Hope National Medical Center, Duarte, California 91010*

M. R. CLARK (52), *Department of Pathology, University of Cambridge, Cambridge CB2 1QP, England*

PATRICK H. CLEVELAND (50), *Department of Ophthalmology, University of California, San Diego, Veterans Administration Medical Center, San Diego, California 92161*

W. LOUIS CLEVELAND (9), *Department of Microbiology, Columbia University, New York, New York 10032*

DAVID COLCHER (76), *Laboratory of Tumor Immunology and Biology, National Institutes of Health, National Cancer Institute, Bethesda, Maryland 20892*

SUSAN P. C. COLE (11, 12), *Department of Microbiology and Immunology, Queen's University, Kingston, Ontario K7L 3N6, Canada, and Ontario Cancer Treatment and Research Foundation, Kingston Regional Centre, Kingston, Ontario K7L 2V7, Canada*

BARRY S. COLLER (37), *Division of Hematology, State University of New York at Stony Brook, Stony Brook, New York 11794*

HILARY A. COLLER (37), *Harvard/Radcliffe College, Cambridge, Massachusetts 02138*

DAWN E. COLWELL (5), *Department of Microbiology, University of Alabama at Birmingham, Birmingham, Alabama 35294*

EVERLY CONWAY DE MACARIO (49), *Wadsworth Center for Laboratories and Research, New York State Department of Health, Albany, New York 12201*

FRANÇOISE CORMONT (19, 59, 61), *Experimental Immunology Unit, Faculty of Medicine, University of Louvain, B-1200 Brussels, Belgium*

ROBERT S. CRISSMAN (15), *Department of Anatomy, Medical College of Ohio, Toledo, Ohio 43699*

CARLO M. CROCE (11), *The Wistar Institute of Anatomy and Biology, Philadelphia, Pennsylvania 19104*

A. C. CUELLO (17), *Department of Pharmacology and Therapeutics, Faculty of Medicine, McGill University, Montreal, Quebec H3G 1Y6, Canada*

JOHN M. DAVIS (27), *Division of Immunology, Department of Pathology, University of Cambridge, Addenbrooke's Hospital, Cambridge CB2 2QQ, England*

C. J. DEAN (6), *Section of Tumour Immunology, Institute of Cancer Research, Surrey SM2 5PX, England*

LIEVE DE CLERCQ (19, 59, 61), *Experimental Immunology Unit, Faculty of Medicine, University of Louvain, B-1200 Brussels, Belgium*

JEFFREY A. DREBIN (56), *Department of Pathology, Harvard Medical School, Boston, Massachusetts 02115, and Department of Medicine, New England Medical Center, Boston, Massachusetts 02110*

KENDRA B. EAGER (7), *The Wistar Institute of Anatomy and Biology, Philadelphia, Pennsylvania 19104*

WILLIAM C. EBY (74), *Department of Pathology and Microbiology, Loma Linda University, Loma Linda, California 92350*

PAUL H. EHRLICH (66), *Monoclonal Antibody Department, Sandoz Research Institute, Sandoz, Inc., East Hanover, New Jersey 07936, and Department of Obstetrics and Gynecology, University of Medicine and Dentistry of New Jersey, Piscataway, New Jersey 08854*

EDGAR G. ENGLEMAN (13), *Department of Pathology, Stanford University School of Medicine, Stanford University Medical Center, Stanford, California 94305*

BERNARD F. ERLANGER (9), *Department of Microbiology, Columbia University, New York, New York 10032*

DANIEL P. ESKINAZI (74), *Division of Research Grants, National Institutes of Health, Bethesda, Maryland 20892*

JOSE ESTEBAN (76), *Laboratory of Tumor Immunology and Biology, National Institutes of Health, National Cancer Institute, Bethesda, Maryland 20892*

PETER L. EY (48), *Department of Microbiology and Immunology, The University of Adelaide, Adelaide 5000, Australia*

S. FAZEKAS DE ST.GROTH (33), *Basel Institute for Immunology, CH-4005 Basel, Switzerland*

K. A. FOON (10), *Division of Hematology and Oncology, Simpson Memorial Research Institute, University of Michigan, Ann Arbor, Michigan 48109*

STEVEN K. H. FOUNG (13), *Department of Pathology, Stanford University School of Medicine, Stanford University Medical Center, Stanford, California 94305*

FRANTIŠEK FRANĚK (23, 60), *Department of Membrane Biochemistry, Institute of Molecular Genetics, Czechoslovak Academy of Sciences, CS-142 20 Prague 4, Czechoslovakia*

IAN H. FRAZER (71), *Division of Immunology, Department of Medicine, University of Queensland, Princess Alexandra Hospital, Brisbane, Queensland 4102, Australia*

J. GHEUENS (39), *Laboratory of Neuropathology, Born-Bunge Foundation, Universitaire Instelling Antwerpen, B-2610 Wilrijk, Belgium*

THOMAS J. GILL III (36), *Department of Pathology, University of Pittsburgh, School of Medicine, Pittsburgh, Pennsylvania 15261*

STEPHEN GINN (15), *Department of Anatomy, Medical College of Ohio, Toledo, Ohio 43699*

MARK C GLASSY (50), *Department of Medicine, University of California San Diego Cancer Center, University of California, San Diego, La Jolla, California 92093*

CORINNE GLINEUR (56), *Laboratoire de Chimie Biologique, Department de Biologie Moleculaire, Universite Libre de Bruxelles, B-1640 Rhode-St-Genese, Belgium*

L. MICHAEL GLODE (67), *Division of Medical Oncology, Department of Medicine,*

University of Colorado Health Sciences Center, Denver, Colorado 80262

RICHARD A. GOLDSBY (21, 40, 75), Department of Biology, Amherst College, Amherst, Massachusetts 01002

F. CARL GRUMET (13), Department of Pathology, Stanford University School of Medicine, Stanford University Medical Center, Stanford, California 94305

ALBERT J. GUIDRY (21), Milk Secretion and Mastitis Laboratory, Animal Science Institute, Agricultural Research Service, United States Department of Agriculture, Beltsville, Maryland 20705

L. A. GYURE (6), Section of Tumour Immunology, Institute of Cancer Research, Surrey SM2 5PX, England

J. G. HALL (6), Section of Tumour Immunology, Institute of Cancer Research, Surrey SM2 5PX, England

WAYNE W. HANCOCK (78), Department of Pathology, Brigham and Women's Hospital and Harvard Medical School, Boston, Massachusetts 02115

YOSHIYUKI HASHIMOTO (77), Department of Hygienic Chemistry, Pharmaceutical Institute, Tôhoku University, Aobayama, Sendai 980, Japan

RICHARD HAWKES (46), Department of Biochemistry and Laboratory of Neurobiology, Laval University, Quebec City, Quebec, Canada

NICHOLAS J. HOOGENRAAD (34), Department of Biochemistry, La Trobe University, Bundoora, Victoria 3083, Australia

KENNETH W. HUNTER, JR. (51), Departments of Pediatrics and Preventive Medicine/Biometrics, Uniformed Services University of the Health Sciences, F. Edward Hébert School of Medicine, Bethesda, Maryland 20814-4799

JAMES P. JAKWAY (45), Department of Microbiology and Immunology and the George W. Hooper Foundation, University of California, San Francisco, San Francisco, California 94122

ROBERT J. JOVELL (49), Wadsworth Center for Laboratories and Research, New York

State Department of Health, Albany, New York 12201

HECTOR JUAREZ-SALINAS (58), Chromatography Business Unit, Bio-Rad Laboratories, Richmond, California 94801

TOSHIO KAMIYA (77), Division of Cellular Immunology, Cell-Engineering Research Center, Osaka University, Suita, Osaka 565, Japan

H. W. D. KATINGER (32), Institute of Applied Microbiology, University of Agriculture, A-1190 Vienna, Austria

BENNETT KAUFMAN (75), Department of Biologics Research, Walter Reed Army Institute of Research, Walter Reed Army Medical Center, Washington, D.C. 20307-5100

TOMOYUKI KAWAMOTO (22), Department of Biochemistry, Okayama University Dental School, Okayama City 700, Japan

ROGER H. KENNETT (7), Department of Human Genetics, School of Medicine, University of Pennsylvania, Philadelphia, Pennsylvania 19104

JAN KOVÁŘ (23), Department of Membrane Biochemistry, Institute of Molecular Genetics, Czechoslovak Academy of Sciences, CS-142 20 Prague 4, Czechoslovakia

DANUTA KOZBOR (11, 12), The Wistar Institute of Anatomy and Biology, Philadelphia, Pennsylvania 19104

PATRICIA KRIEF (55), INSERM U.253, Hôpital Paul Brousse, 94800 Villejuif, France

GUNTHER KÜMEL (70), Abteilung Virusforschung, Zentrum der Hygiene, D-6000 Frankfurt am Main, Federal Republic of Germany

UDO KUMMER (64), Department of Immunology, Institute of Hematology, Gesellschaft für Strahlen- und Umweltforschung m.b.H., D-8000 Munich 2, Federal Republic of Germany

THOMAS J. KUNICKI (67), Platelet Research Laboratory, The Blood Center of Southeastern Wisconsin, Milwaukee, Wisconsin 53233

HEINZ W. KUNZ (36), *Department of Pathology, University of Pittsburgh, School of Medicine, Pittsburgh, Pennsylvania 15261*

MARGHERITA LAFATA (16), *Sclavo Research Center, 53100 Siena, Italy*

EDMUNDO LAMOYI (62), *Laboratory of Immunology, National Institute of Allergy and Infectious Diseases, National Institutes of Health, Bethesda, Maryland 20892*

RICHARD D. LANE (15), *Department of Anatomy, Medical College of Ohio, Toledo, Ohio 43699*

JOHN J. LANGONE (81), *Department of Medicine, Baylor College of Medicine, Houston, Texas 77030*

P. M. LANSDORP (80), *Terry Fox Laboratory, British Columbia Cancer Research Centre, Vancouver, British Columbia V5Z 1L3, Canada*

TORE LINDMO (65), *Department of Biophysics, Norsk Hydro's Institute for Cancer Research, Oslo 3, Norway*

DANIEL LOCKER (47), *Laboratory of Immunogenetics, CNRS, CSEAL, and University of Orleans, 45067 Orleans Cedex 2, France*

ALBERTO J. L. MACARIO (49), *Wadsworth Center for Laboratories and Research, New York State Department of Health, Albany, New York 12201*

DON B. MCCLURE (22), *Division of Molecular and Cellular Biology, Eli Lilly and Company, Indianapolis, Indiana 46285*

D. E. MCFARLIN (39), *Neuroimmunology Branch, National Institutes of Neurological and Communicative Disorders and Stroke, Bethesda, Maryland 20205*

JERRY R. MCGHEE (5), *Department of Microbiology, University of Alabama at Birmingham, Birmingham, Alabama 35294*

IAN R. MACKAY (71), *Clinical Research Unit, The Walter and Eliza Hall Institute of Medical Research, The Royal Melbourne Hospital, Parkville, Victoria 3050, Australia*

DAVID MALE (53), *Department of Neuropathology, Institute of Psychiatry, London SES 8AF, England*

PATRICK MANOUVRIEZ (59), *Experimental Immunology Unit, Faculty of Medicine, University of Louvain, B-1200 Brussels, Belgium*

J. MARBROOK (72), *Department of Immunobiology, School of Medicine, University of Auckland, Auckland, New Zealand*

MASSIMO MARIANI (16), *Sclavo Research Center, 53100 Siena, Italy*

ANNALISA MASSONE (16), *Sclavo Research Center, 53100 Siena, Italy*

SUZANNE M. MICHALEK (5), *Department of Microbiology, University of Alabama at Birmingham, Birmingham, Alabama 35294*

K. F. MILLER (40), *Reproduction Laboratory, Animal Science Institute, Agricultural Research Service, Beltsville Agricultural Research Center, United States Department of Agriculture, Beltsville, Maryland 20705*

KINGSTON MILLS (69), *Division of Immunology, National Institute for Medical Research, London NW7 1AA, England*

C. MILSTEIN (17), *Medical Research Council, Laboratory of Molecular Biology, Cambridge CB2 2QH, England*

MASSOUD MIRSHAHI (55), *Service de Médecine Interne et Oncologie, Hôtel Dieu, 75004 Paris, France*

DHIRENDRA N. MISRA (36), *Department of Pathology, University of Pittsburgh, School of Medicine, Pittsburgh, Pennsylvania 15261*

GIUSEPPE A. MOLINARO (74), *Department of Pathology and Microbiology, Loma Linda University, Loma Linda, California 92350*

PATRICIA K. A. MONGINI (41), *Department of Rheumatic Diseases, Hospital for Joint Diseases, Mount Sinai Medical School, New York, New York 10003*

ROBERT R. MONTGOMERY (67), *Hemostasis Research Laboratory, The Blood Center of Southeastern Wisconsin, Milwaukee, Wisconsin 53233*

FRANÇOISE MORNEX (76), *Laboratory of Tumor Immunology and Biology, National Institutes of Health, National Cancer Institute, Bethesda, Maryland 20892*

K. MOSBACH (32), *Pure and Applied Biochemistry, University of Lund, S-221 00 Lund, Sweden*

GENEVIÈVE MOTTA (47), *Laboratory of Immunogenetics, CNRS, CSEAL, and University of Orleans, 45067 Orleans Cedex 2, France*

WILLIAM R. MOYLE (66), *Department of Obstetrics and Gynecology, University of Medicine and Dentistry of New Jersey, Piscataway, New Jersey 08854*

GARTH L. NICOLSON (68), *Department of Tumor Biology, The University of Texas System Cancer Center, M. D. Anderson Hospital & Tumor Institute, Houston, Texas 77030*

K. NILSSON (32), *Pure and Applied Biochemistry, University of Lund, S-221 00 Lund, Sweden*

SAAD A. NOEMAN (36), *Department of Biochemistry (Immunology), Faculty of Medicine, University of Tanta, Tanta, Egypt*

LENNART OLSSON (25), *Department of Medicine A, State University Hospital, Copenhagen 2100, Denmark*

LARS ÖSTBERG (18), *Pharmaceutical Division, Sandoz Research Institute, Sandoz, Inc., East Hanover, New Jersey 07936*

GARY S. OTT (58), *Chromatography Business Unit, Bio-Rad Laboratories, Richmond, California 94801*

JEAN-YVES PERROT (55), *Service de Médecine Interne et Oncologie, Hôtel Dieu, 75004 Paris, France*

BEVERLEY L. PIKE (31), *Cellular Immunology Unit, The Walter and Eliza Hall Institute of Medical Research, The Royal Melbourne Hospital, Parkville, Victoria 3050, Australia*

DANIEL PORTETELLE (56), *Laboratoire de Microbiologie, Faculte des Sciences Agronomiques, B-5800 Gembloux, Belgium*

RIVO PRESENTINI (16), *Sclavo Research Center, 53100 Siena, Italy*

GARETH PRYCE (53), *Department of Immunology, Middlesex Hospital Medical School, London W1P 9PG, England*

JANET H. RANSOM (24), *Bionetics Research, Inc., Rockville, Maryland 20850*

CHRISTOPHER L. READING (2), *Departments of Tumor Biology and Hematology, The University of Texas System Cancer Center, M. D. Anderson Hospital & Tumor Institute, Houston, Texas 77030*

MARVIN B. RITTENBERG (29), *Department of Microbiology and Immunology, Oregon Health Sciences University, Portland, Oregon 97201*

JOHN C. RODER (11, 12), *Division of Molecular Immunology and Neurobiology, Mount Sinai Medical Research Institute, Toronto, Ontario M5G 1X5, Canada*

CLAUDE ROSENFELD (55), *INSERM U.253, Hôpital Paul Brousse, 94800 Villejuif, France*

JEFFREY L. ROSSIO (10), *Program Resources, Inc., National Cancer Institute, Frederick Cancer Research Facility, Frederick, Maryland 21701*

J. ROUSSEAUX (63), *Unité 409 du CNRS, Institut de Recherches sur le Cancer, 59045 Lille Cedex, France*

R. ROUSSEAUX-PREVOST (63), *Unité 409 du CNRS, Institut de Recherches sur le Cancer, 59045 Lille Cedex, France*

FRANCISCO SANCHEZ-MADRID (20), *Servicio de Inmunologia, Hospital de la Princesa, 28006 Madrid, Spain*

GORDON H. SATO (22), *W. Alton Jones Cell Science Center, Lake Placid, New York 12946*

J. DENRY SATO (22), *W. Alton Jones Cell Science Center, Lake Placid, New York 12946*

W. SCHEIRER (32), *Sandoz Forschungsinstitut Gmblt, A-1235 Vienna, Austria*

JOHN E. SHIVELY (43), *Division of Immunology, Beckman Research Institute of the City of Hope, Duarte, California 91010*

MICHAEL E. SIERZEGA (11), *The Wistar Institute of Anatomy and Biology, Philadelphia, Pennsylvania 19104*

HANS OLOV SJÖGREN (25), *Department of Tumor Immunology, The Wallenberg Laboratory, University of Lund, S-220 07 Lund, Sweden*

M. SPITZ (4), *Department of Immunology, National Institute for Biological Standards and Control, Hampstead, London NW3 6RB, England*

TIMOTHY A. SPRINGER (20), *Laboratory of Membrane Immunochemistry, Dana-Farber Cancer Institute, Harvard Medical School, Boston, Massachusetts 02115*

S. SRIKUMARAN (21), *Department of Veterinary Science, University of Nebraska, Lincoln, Nebraska 68583-0905*

LARRY H. STANKER (58), *Biomedical Sciences Division, Lawrence Livermore National Laboratory, University of California, Livermore, California 94550*

H. C. STEVENSON (10), *Biological Response Modifiers Program, National Cancer Institute, Frederick Cancer Research Facility, Frederick, Maryland 21701*

J. M. STYLES (6), *Section of Tumour Immunology, Institute of Cancer Research, Surrey SM2 5PX, England*

MINORU SUGAWARA (77), *Division of Biochemistry, Japan Roche Company Institute, Kajiwara, Kamakura 247, Japan*

M. R. SURESH (17), *Summa Biomedical Canada Ltd. and Faculty of Pharmacy, University of Alberta, Edmonton T6G 2N8, Canada*

SHINYA SUZUKI (77), *Department of Hygienic Chemistry, Pharmaceutical Institute, Tôhoku University, Aobayama, Sendai 980, Japan*

BRYAN M. TURNER (79), *Department of Anatomy, The University of Birmingham, Medical School, Birmingham B15 2TJ, England*

P. A. UNDERWOOD (26), *CSIRO, Division of Molecular Biology, North Ryde, New South Wales 2113, Australia*

TIMOTHY V. UPDYKE (68), *Department of Tumor Biology, The University of Texas System Cancer Center, M. D. Anderson Hospital & Tumor Institute, Houston, Texas 77030*

VERONICA VAN HEYNINGEN (44), *Medical Research Council Clinical and Population Cytogenetics Unit, Edinburgh EH4 2XU, Scotland*

P. VAN MOURIK (14), *Central Laboratory of the Netherlands Red Cross Blood Transfusion Service, 1006 AD Amsterdam, The Netherlands*

HELEN VAN VUNAKIS (81), *Department of Biochemistry, Brandeis University, Waltham, Massachusetts 02254*

CHRISTOPH WAGENER (43), *Abteilung Klinische Chemie, Universität Pathobiochemie der Mechizinischen, Fakultät der RWTH Aachen, D-5100 Aachen, Federal Republic of Germany*

DAVID E. WELLS (38), *Department of Microbiology, University of Alabama at Birmingham, Birmingham, Alabama 35294*

REGINE J. WESTERWOUDT (1), *Laboratory for Electron Microscopy, University of Leiden, 2333 AA Leiden, The Netherlands*

PAMELA L. WITTE (35), *Immunobiology and Cancer Research Program, Oklahoma Medical Research Foundation, Oklahoma City, Oklahoma 73104*

A. W. WOGNUM (80), *Central Laboratory of the Netherlands Red Cross Blood Transfusion Service and Laboratory for Experimental and Clinical Immunology, University of Amsterdam, 1006 AD Amsterdam, The Netherlands*

CHRISTOPHER J. WRAIGHT (34), *Department of Biochemistry, La Trobe University, Bundoora, Victoria 3083, Australia*

W. P. ZEIJLEMAKER (14, 80), *Central Laboratory of the Netherlands Red Cross Blood Transfusion Service and Laboratory for Experimental and Clinical Immunology, University of Amsterdam, 1006 AD Amsterdam, The Netherlands*

Preface

Since hybridoma technology for the purpose of eliciting monoclonal antibodies of predefined specificity was introduced by Köhler and Milstein in 1975, it has become a mainstay in most laboratories that utilize immunochemical techniques to study problems in basic, applied, or clinical research. In simplest terms, the steps leading to the production of hybridomas and their monoclonal antibody products suitable for a specific purpose remain the same: immunization, cell fusion, cell growth and cloning, propagation of stable hybridomas, and screening for antibody specificity and functional activity. The process is labor intensive and several months may be required before appropriate cell lines are obtained and monoclonal antibodies are fully characterized. It is not surprising that the widespread use of monoclonal antibodies has led to the rapid development of new techniques to improve the efficiency, sensitivity, and simplicity of the individual steps.

This volume is divided into three sections that cover the various aspects of producing and maintaining hybridomas as well as of detecting, characterizing, and utilizing monoclonal antibodies. It is not possible to cover every development in methodology. Therefore, we have included established techniques as well as selected newly developed approaches that we feel would be especially useful because of their general applicability. We have also included a list of articles from other volumes of *Methods in Enzymology* which are relevant to topics covered in this volume. We have cross-referenced these articles for the convenience of the reader and to avoid unwarranted duplication. As the field of hybridoma technology undergoes further development, publication of supplemental volumes will be considered.

We are grateful for the sound advice and constructive suggestions from Nathan Kaplan and Sidney Colowick during the preparation of this volume. The recent passing of Sidney Colowick has saddened his many friends and colleagues. He will always be remembered for his significant scientific contributions, his wise counsel, and his gentle humor.

JOHN J. LANGONE
HELEN VAN VUNAKIS

METHODS IN ENZYMOLOGY

EDITED BY

Sidney P. Colowick and Nathan O. Kaplan

VANDERBILT UNIVERSITY
SCHOOL OF MEDICINE
NASHVILLE, TENNESSEE

DEPARTMENT OF CHEMISTRY
UNIVERSITY OF CALIFORNIA
AT SAN DIEGO
LA JOLLA, CALIFORNIA

METHODS IN ENZYMOLOGY

EDITORS-IN-CHIEF

Sidney P. Colowick and Nathan O. Kaplan

Methods in Enzymology

Volume 121
IMMUNOCHEMICAL TECHNIQUES
Part I
Hybridoma Technology and Monoclonal Antibodies

Section I

Production of Hybridomas

A. Immunization and Cell Fusion
Articles 1 through 21

B. Growth and Cloning of Hybridomas
Articles 22 through 38

[1] Factors Affecting Production of Monoclonal Antibodies

By REGINE J. WESTERWOUDT

When "nonsecretor" myeloma cells are fused with splenic lympho-cytes, the hybrids produce a single immunoglobulin, thus demonstrating an ability inherited from the mouse splenic lymphocyte, and proliferate without limit, which is the contribution of the tumor cell. Hybridization followed by clonal expansion of the antibody-producing hybridoma makes possible the subsequent mass production of antibodies reactive with a single antigenic determinant. Although this technique seems rather sim-ple, a drawback frequently encountered during the procedure is loss of antibody production. Some knowledge concerning the mechanism of action of hybridization is essential to understand this problem.

Polyethylene Glycol (PEG)-Mediated Fusion

Little is known of the mechanism by which PEG operates, but it is likely that its effect on cell membranes is complex. When antioxidants and/or polymerization agents added to commercial PEG are removed, PEG becomes nonfusogenic when used at 1-min incubation time.[1-3] Wo-jcieszyn and co-workers[3] showed that membranes are brought together at closely opposed contact regions and lipid probes spread from one cell membrane to the other in the presence of both fusogenic or nonfusogenic PEG. Therefore, they assumed that the coordinate action of two distinct components is necessary and that the fusion stimulus is provided by the additives contained in commercial PEG. However, PEG purified by dialy-sis or recrystallization is not uniformly nonfusogenic, because hen eryth-rocytes fused following a 15-min incubation with purified PEG.[2]

Synkaryon Formation. A number of biological, physical, and chemical processes which affect cell surfaces and cell aggregation are known to result in formation of polykaryocytes. Cells at all stages of the cell cycle fuse with each other when exposed to PEG. Because of chromosomal abnormalities, a large number of polykaryons never reach mitosis or fail to complete a normal mitosis. Polykaryocytes can remain viable without dividing for several weeks under favorable conditions. However, contin-

[1] K. Honda, Y. Maeda, J. Sasakawa, H. Ohno, and E. Tsuchida, *Biochem. Biophys. Res. Commun.* **100**, 442 (1981).

[2] C. Smith, Q. Ahkong, D. Fisher, and J. Lucy, *Biochim. Biophys. Acta* **692**, 109 (1982).

[3] J. W. Wojcieszyn, R. A. Schlegel, K. Lumley-Sapanski, and K. A. Jacobson, *J. Cell Biol.* **96**, 151 (1983).

METHODS IN ENZYMOLOGY, VOL. 121

ued survival of most hybrid cells requires the formation of daughter cells with a single nucleus (synkaryons).[4]

Polykaryons containing nuclei of more than one stage are said to be heterophasic, whereas those which contain nuclei from only one stage of the cell cycle are classified as homophasic.

Synchronization of Nuclei in Interphase. The mechanisms responsible for synchronization have been analyzed by Rao and Johnson[5,6] by fusing cells in different phases of the cell cycle with each other. They found that in multinucleate cells containing only G_1 nuclei, all nuclei started DNA synthesis at the same time. In heterophasic G_1/S nuclei of HeLa cells, stimulating substances from the S phase cytoplasm migrate into the G_1 nucleus and DNA synthesis is induced. The greater the proportion of S nuclei, the faster DNA synthesis is induced in the G_1 nuclei. Nuclei in G_1 or G_2 do not inhibit the initiation of DNA synthesis in nuclei entering S phase. The nuclei of these multinucleate cells subsequently enter mitosis with almost perfect synchrony.[5]

The rate and pattern of DNA synthesis of genomes in mouse–Chinese hamster hybrids are regulated autonomously. The S periods of the hybrids are identical to that of the mouse parent, which has the longest S phase and appears to remain constant with time. However, hamster chromosomes complete DNA synthesis considerably earlier than most mouse chromosomes.[7]

Fusion between Mitotic and Interphase Cells. Problems associated with synchronization between mitotic and interphase cells result in a phenomenon called premature chromosome condensation (PCC). PCC is dependent on two events in the post-G_2 mitotic nuclei: (1) the normal condensation of chromosomes within these nuclei, and (2) the breakdown of the nuclear envelopes around these chromosomes.[8] When there is no induction of PCC in mitotic–interphase fused cells the mitotic chromosomes do not complete division, but form micronuclei which synthesize neither DNA nor RNA during the next cycle and are probably genetically inactive. However, in some M/G_1 fusions there is no induction of PCC and mitotic chromosomes can undergo division with one of the daughter cells inheriting the G_1 nucleus. PCC induction is described in more detail by other authors.[9,10]

[4] G. Poste, *Int. Rev. Cytol.* **33,** 157 (1972).
[5] P. N. Rao and R. T. Johnson, *Nature (London)* **225,** 159 (1970).
[6] P. N. Rao and R. T. Johnson, *Methods Cell Physiol.* **5,** 75 (1972).
[7] C. J. Marshall Graves, *Exp. Cell Res.* **73,** 81 (1972).
[8] S. P. Peterson and M. W. Berns, *Exp. Cell Res.* **120,** 223 (1979).
[9] N. R. Ringerts and R. E. Savage, "Cell Hybrids," Chapter VI. Academic Press, London, 1976.
[10] R. J. Westerwoudt, *J. Immunol. Methods* **77,** 181 (1985).

PCC and pH. Hybridization frequencies are elevated when the fusion is performed at pH 8.0.[11] The same pH induces nuclear envelope formation and suppresses PCC.[12,13] An elevated pH during the first days after fusion also improves the fusion frequency. Presumably, in this period viable hybrids are being formed from the multinucleated heterokaryocytes.[14]

Chromosome Analysis of Hybrid Cells

Chromosome analysis plays an important part in the discovery of hybrid cells. Intraspecific mouse hybrid cells may contain a total chromosome number which is very close to the sum expected if two cells, one of each parental type, have fused. Interspecific hybrids may show extensive chromosome elimination. This phenomenon, referred to as chromosome segregation, frequently involves the preferential elimination of chromosomes of one species, while the chromosomes of the other species are selectively retained.

Chromosome Stability. About 24 hr after fusion of a permanent mouse cell line and a diploid human cell line, the majority of the hybrid cells contain the complete genome of both parents. The loss of chromosomes increases markedly during the following days.[15] Analysis of hybrid cell lines that show karyotypic instability suggests that cells which eliminate chromosomes from the slower growing parent are at a growth advantage.[16–18]

Chromosome Segregation. Chromosome loss is moderate in mouse–mouse and mouse–rat lymphocyte hybrids, but extensive in mouse–human and mouse–rabbit lymphocyte hybrids.[19] It was found that chromosome segregation in mouse–mouse T-cell hybrids was greater than in rat–mouse B-cell hybrids. This suggests that the chromosome segregation is not merely a species-specific event, but also depends on the parental cells or cell lines used.

Chen[20] concluded that human chromosome loss in man–rodent cell hybrids appears random and the number of lost chromosomes varies

[11] J. Sharon, S. L. Morrison, and E. A. Kabat, *Somatic Cell Genet.* **6**, 435 (1980).
[12] Y. Obara, H. Yoshida, L. S. Chai, H. Weinfeld, and A. A. Sandberg, *J. Cell Biol.* **58**, 608 (1973).
[13] Y. Obara, L. S. Chai, H. Weinfeld, and A. A. Sandberg, *J. Cell Biol.* **62**, 104 (1974).
[14] C. M. Croce, H. Koprowski, and H. Eagle, *Proc. Natl. Acad. Sci. U.S.A.* **67**, 1953 (1972).
[15] J. Jami and S. Grandchamp, *Proc. Natl. Acad. Sci. U.S.A.* **68**, 3097 (1971).
[16] Y. Matsuya, H. Green, and C. Basilico, *Nature (London)* **220**, 1199 (1968).
[17] F. T. Kao and T. T. Puck, *Nature (London)* **228**, 329 (1970).
[18] L. J. Donald, H. S. Wang, and J. L. Hamerton, *Somatic Cell Genet.* **8**, 105 (1982).
[19] J. Schröder, M.-L. Sutinen, and H. A. Suomalainen, *Hereditas* **94**, 77 (1981).
[20] T. R. Chen, *Cytogenet. Cell Genet.* **23**, 221 (1979).

widely. Others, however, showed that chromosome loss is not random.[19,21] Survival of hybridomas in selective culture medium is possible when the human chromosomes carrying enzymes necessary for growth in such media (chromosome 17, thymidine kinase; chromosome X, hypoxanthine–guanine phosphoribosyltransferase[22]) are retained. It proved that mouse–human B-cell hybrids preferentially retain human chromosome 14, which carries the human immunoglobulin heavy-chain gene,[23] while mouse–human T-cell hybrids retain human chromosome 6, which carries several genes involved in the immune response.[24] Rushton[25] demonstrated by linear regression analysis of human chromosomes that segregation is concordant and nonindependent. Certain groups of human chromosomes appeared more frequently in the surviving hybrid cell line than others.

While environmental conditions can affect karyotypic stability, they do not explain the differential stability of different lines maintained under similar conditions. Karyotypic stability may be an inherent characteristic of each hybrid line, in that it depends on the integration of the two parental genomes. A balanced hybrid genome capable of survival in culture does not depend on the fusogen used.[26]

Segregation Reversal Genes on the X Chromosome. When the direction of chromosome loss in mouse–Chinese hamster hybrids was compared with the direction of segregation of the same hybrids, to which an additional murine X chromosome was introduced at the time of fusion, it was found that the addition of this X chromosome reversed the direction of chromosome segregation; that is, it led to loss of mouse chromosomes. The reversal in chromosome segregation is mediated by factors located on the X chromosome called segregation reversal genes. In the absence of a foreign X chromosome, mouse–Chinese hamster hybrids uniformly lose Chinese hamster chromosomes. In contrast, hybrids containing a Robertsonian translocation between an additional mouse X chromosome and Chinese hamster chromosome 16 switch their segregation and show loss of mouse chromosomes. This ability is not an *in vitro* acquired or transformation-related property.[27,28] Efforts to control the direction of chromo-

[21] G. Martin and L. Pugliatti-Crippa, *Exp. Cell Res.* **70**, 253 (1972).

[22] C. M. Croce, A. B. Knowles, and H. Koprowski, *Exp. Cell Res.* **82**, 457 (1973).

[23] C. M. Croce, M. Shander, J. Martinis, L. Cicurel, G. G. D'Ancona, and H. Koprowski, *Eur. J. Immunol.* **10**, 486 (1980).

[24] H. A. Suomalainen, R. A. Goldsby, B. A. Osborne, and J. Schröder, *Scand. J. Immunol.* **11**, 163 (1980).

[25] A. R. Rushton, *Cytogenet. Cell Genet.* **17**, 243 (1976).

[26] H. S. Wang, V. Niewezas, H. R. de S. Nazareth, and J. L. Hamerton, *Cytogenet. Cell Genet.* **24**, 233 (1979).

[27] D. D. Pravtcheva and F. H. Ruddle, *Exp. Cell Res.* **146**, 401 (1983).

[28] D. D. Pravtcheva and F. H. Ruddle, *Exp. Cell Res.* **148**, 265 (1983).

some segregation in mouse–Chinese hamster hybrids by irradiation of the murine parental genomes prior to fusion have met with little success.[29]

Interspecific Hybrids

Evolutionary divergence seems responsible for some events occurring during hybridization. From a number of publications it is evident that rodent–human hybrids lose chromosomes derived from one of the parental cells[30–32]; that is, chromosomes of the slower growing parent are either partly or completely lost after fusion. This is in contrast with rodent–rodent hybrids, in which chromosome loss hardly occurs.[33–35]

Aberrations at the Nucleic Acid Level. When human chromosomes are preferentially segregated, only mouse 28 S ribosomal RNA (rRNA) but no human 28 S rRNA is produced.[36] This happens even if human acrocentric chromosomes, where the nucleolus organizer regions (NOR) (containing the genes for rRNA) are located, are retained. The Ag–As silver staining method, which preferentially stains the NOR, only detects the 18 + 28 S rRNA gene sites which are active in the preceding interphase.[30,37,38] In these mouse–human hybrid cells only mouse, but no human 45 S, rRNA precursor gene sites are detected.[39] Results of some investigators suggested that nucleolar RNA synthesis was not suppressed during the first 48 hr in the nuclei of either species in any of the heterokaryons formed by fusion of human and mouse cells.[40] It is generally accepted that the suppression of rRNA synthesis occurs after synkaryon formation and is completed within a few days, the rate depending on the parental cell types and the ratio of their genomes.[41,42] Recently, Kaplan

[29] J. A. Marshall Graves, *Exp. Cell Res.* **125,** 483 (1980).
[30] O. J. Miller, D. A. Miller, V. G. Dev, R. Tantravahi, and C. M. Croce, *Proc. Natl. Acad. Sci. U.S.A.* **73,** 4531 (1976).
[31] C. M. Croce, *Proc. Natl. Acad. Sci. U.S.A.* **73,** 3248 (1976).
[32] C. M. Croce, A. Talavera, C. Basilico, and O. J. Miller, *Proc. Natl. Acad. Sci. U.S.A.* **74,** 694 (1977).
[33] G. L. Eliceiri, *J. Cell Biol.* **53,** 177 (1972).
[34] L. G. Weide, V. G. Dev, and C. S. Rupert, *Exp. Cell Res.* **123,** 424 (1979).
[35] O. J. Miller, V. G. Dev, D. A. Miller, R. Tantravahi, and G. L. Eliceiri, *Exp. Cell Res.* **115,** 457 (1978).
[36] G. L. Eliceiri and H. Green, *J. Mol. Biol.* **41,** 253 (1969).
[37] D. A. Miller, V. G. Dev, R. Tantravahi, and O. J. Miller, *Exp. Cell Res.* **101,** 235 (1976).
[38] R. Tantravahi, D. A. Miller, G. D'Ancona, C. M. Croce, and O. J. Miller, *Exp. Cell Res.* **119,** 387 (1979).
[39] R. P. Perry, D. E. Kelly, V. Schibler, K. Huebner, and C. M. Croce, *J. Cell. Physiol.* **98,** 553 (1979).
[40] J. S. Lipszyc, S. G. Phillips, and O. J. Miller, *Exp. Cell Res.* **133,** 373 (1981).
[41] C. J. Marshall, S. D. Handmaker, and M. E. Bramwell, *J. Cell Sci.* **17,** 307 (1975).
[42] V. G. Dev, D. A. Miller, M. Rechsteiner, and O. J. Miller, *Exp. Cell Res.* **123,** 47 (1979).

and Olstad[43] postulated that the complete cessation of NOR activity might occur soon after the hybridization. Chromatin condensation is not found to accompany inhibition of rRNA synthesis,[44] but "Ag-NOR" proteins are involved in the process of decondensation of NOR chromatin.[45]

A second phenomenon occurring in correspondence with chromosome segregation is suppression of histones, the DNA chain elongation proteins. Human–mouse somatic cell hybrids segregating human chromosomes express only mouse histones.[46,47] However, it is not clear whether species-specific suppression of the production of histones occurs at the transcriptional level as with rRNA[39] or whether it occurs at some post-transcriptional level of control. It may be possible that selective segregation of recessive parent cell chromosomes in interspecific hybrid cells could be induced, in part, by the absence of the appropriate species-specific histones during chromosome replication in hybrid cell lines.

A third phenomenon is the inability of mouse–human hybrids to replicate both species of mitochondrial DNA (mtDNA). mtDNA of the parent whose chromosomes are segregated is absent from the hybrid, even in the early stage when there is little chromosome loss.[48,49] The nucleus provides a major part of the information required for the synthesis of mitochondrial constituents. It is not yet established, however, whether a different mechanism is involved in the suppression of the genes required for mtDNA retention compared to the mechanism operating on the rRNA genes.

Fusion Frequency

Recently activated (probably dividing) B cells fuse preferentially compared to nonactivated B cells.[50,51] Activated peripheral blood cells (PBL) have very low fusion frequencies. This low fusion frequency (only 1 in 10 PBL are B cells) and the fact that only 5×10^{-4} cells produce a specific antibody are barriers to the hybridoma field.[52] The chance of obtaining a

[43] G. Kaplan and R. Olstad, *Exp. Cell Res.* **135**, 379 (1981).
[44] F. J. Medina, M. C. Risueño, M. A. Sánchez-Pina, and M. E. Fernández-Gómez, *Chromosoma* **88**, 149 (1983).
[45] M. A. Sánchez-Pina, F. J. Medina, M. E. Fernández-Gómez, and M. C. Risueño, *Biol. Cell.* **50**, 199 (1984).
[46] K. Ajiro, A. Zweidler, T. Borun, and C. M. Croce, *Proc. Natl. Acad. Sci. U.S.A.* **75**, 5599 (1978).
[47] P. Hohmann, L. K. Hohmann, and T. B. Shows, *Somatic Cell Genet.* **6**, 653 (1980).
[48] B. Attardi and G. Attardi, *Proc. Natl. Acad. Sci. U.S.A.* **69**, 129 (1972).
[49] L. de Francesco, G. Attardi, and C. M. Croce, *Proc. Natl. Acad. Sci. U.S.A.* **77**, 4079 (1980).
[50] J. Andersson and F. Melchers, *Curr. Top. Microbiol. Immunol.* **81**, 130 (1978).
[51] J. W. Goding, *J. Immunol. Methods* **39**, 285 (1980).
[52] R. H. Stevens, E. Macy, C. Morrow, and A. Saxon, *J. Immunol.* **122**, 2498 (1979).

specific hybridoma is of the order of 10^{-8}, and for unstimulated PBL even lower.[53,54]

Epstein–Barr virus (EBV)-transformed B cells, which have a doubling time of approximately 24 hr, are better fusion partners than resting PBL.[55] PBL from tetanus toxoid (TT)-immunized individuals, vaccinated with EBV, yielded cells which showed much higher frequencies of hybrid formation (36×10^{-7}) compared to nonstimulated PBL. Furthermore, a marked increase in immunoglobulin secretion was observed after hybridization while preselection of EBV subcultures for high anti-TT production prior to fusion resulted in a 5-fold increase in TT-specific hybridomas.[56]

Growth of Hybridomas

Four different growth stimulators for B-cell hybridomas are described and the efficiency discussed.

Lipopolysaccharides

Lipopolysaccharides (LPS) derived from the cell wall of various strains of *Escherichia coli* stimulate rodent B cells to divide and mature to immunoglobulin-producing B-cell stages. Lipid A, one of the three moieties of which LPS consists, possesses most of the polyclonal B-cell-stimulating activity. It is a mitogen for mature B lymphocytes from a variety of species including rodents, rabbits, chickens, cows, and hamsters, but not for human peripheral blood cells. Only 25–30% of the mature B cells of the spleen, the most prominent cells responding to LPS, generate antibody-secreting cells. Depending on the LPS concentration, two pathways of B-cell differentiation can be followed. At low doses, 20 μg/ml, the B cells differentiate into blast cells while at high doses, 100 μg/ml, the cells transform into plasma cells.[57] Furthermore, the efficiency of stimulation is definitely affected by the origin of the serum,[58,59] the density of the cell suspension, and the presence of accessory cells. In addition, LPS activity has been shown to be enhanced by dextran sulfate.[60]

[53] J. Davidson, S. Katzav, H. Ungar-Waron, Z. Eshkar, J. Haimovich, and Z. Trainin, *Mol. Immunol.* **19,** 893 (1982).
[54] J. Olsson, H. Kronstrøm, A. Cambon-de Mouzon, C. Honsik, T. Brodin, and B. Jakobsen, *J. Immunol. Methods* **61,** 17 (1983).
[55] D. Kozbor and J. C. Roder, *Immunol. Today* **4,** 72 (1983).
[56] D. Kozbor and J. C. Roder, *Eur. J. Immunol.* **14,** 23 (1984).
[57] D. Radoux, G. Goessens, and L. J. Simar, *Eur. J. Cell Biol.* **34,** 193 (1984).
[58] R. J. Westerwoudt, J. Blom, and A. M. Naipal, *Cell. Immunol.* **81,** 268 (1983).
[59] R. J. Westerwoudt, J. Blom, and C. M. H. Harrisson, to be published.
[60] J. Kettman and M. Wetzel, *J. Immunol. Methods* **39,** 203 (1980).

Preparation. Escherichia coli 055:B5 LPS, prepared by the Westphal technique, is dissolved in distilled water to a concentration of 5 mg/ml, and dextran sulfate (DxS; a sodium salt containing 17% sulfur; MW 500,000) is dissolved at a concentration of 4 mg/ml in distilled water. LPS, 0.1 ml, and DxS, 0.05 ml, are added to 10 ml of hybrid-selective medium.

Macrophage Supernatant

The influence of macrophages on host immune responses may be manifested directly via interaction with antigen, or indirectly through the synthesis and secretion of immunoregulatory molecules. Following appropriate stimulation *in vitro,* macrophages secrete effector molecules which are released into the culture medium. These highly potent secretory products may activate lymphocyte function. The macrophage-secreted effector molecules have been collectively defined as monokines. One monokine derived from monocytes that enhances *in vitro* plaque formation of murine spleen cells was named B-cell activation factor (BAF). Recently this monokine or BAF has been identified as interleukin I. Endotoxins have been demonstrated to be one of the most potent stimuli of macrophages leading to synthesis and secretion of monokines.[61]

Proliferation of B cells is sensitive to inhibition by the E-series prostaglandins (PGE). The production of PGE is increased by macrophages exposed to LPS, and is suppressed by the prostaglandin synthetase inhibitor, indomethacin.[62]

Preparation. BALB/c mice are injected with 1.5 ml thiogylcolate medium, and peritoneal exudate cells are harvested after 4 days. The peritoneal cavity is flushed with 4 ml of medium. The cells are cultured at a concentration of 1×10^5 cells/ml in culture medium supplemented with 20 μg LPS/ml and 0.05 μg indomethacin/ml. A stock solution of the latter is prepared by dissolving indomethacin in a minute amount of 95% ethyl alcohol and subsequent adjustment to 10 ml with PBS. Conditioned medium is harvested 2 days later and the cells removed by centrifugation. The conditioned medium is used at a 1 : 4 dilution in selective medium.

Human Endothelial Culture Supernatant

Vascular endothelial cells in culture are capable of producing a growth factor or factors. Activity, promoting proliferation or differentiation of B-cell hybridomas, has also been found in medium conditioned by human

[61] J. I. Kurland, *J. Reticuloendothel. Soc.* **24,** 19 (1978).
[62] J. I. Kurland and A. Bockman, *J. Exp. Med.* **147,** 952 (1978).

umbilical vein endothelium.[63] The nature of this mitogenic factor(s) is still unknown.

Preparation. Endothelial cells are obtained from human umbilical cord veins. The cord is severed from the placenta soon after birth, placed in a sterile container filled with cord buffer, and held at 4° until processing. The cord is inspected, and all areas with clamp marks are cut off. A cannula is inserted into the umbilical vein, and secured by clamping the cord over the cannula with an umbilical cord tie. Polyethylene tubing is slipped over the cannula and a syringe is connected. The vein is perfused with 100 ml of cord buffer to wash out the blood until almost all erythrocytes are removed. The other end of the umbilical vein is then cannulated with a blunt, hubless, needle shaft over which polyethylene tubing is slipped. Then 5–10 ml of 0.2% collagenase in Hanks'/HEPES buffer is infused into the umbilical vein, and the polyethylene tubing is clamped with hemostats. The umbilical cord, suspended by its ends, is placed in a water bath containing cord buffer and incubated at 37° for 20 min. After incubation, the collagenase solution containing the endothelial cells is flushed from the cord by perfusion with 30 ml of Hanks'/HEPES buffer. The effluent is collected in a sterile 50-ml conical tube. The cells are sedimented at 250 *g* for 10 min, washed once with 2 ml medium, and resuspended by trituration in 2.5 ml of fresh culture medium. The cell suspension is divided into one or more bottles. The bottles are incubated at 37° under 5% CO_2, and the medium changed after 4 hr. The cells are fed three times a week with a complete change of fresh culture medium. When the bottom of the bottle is well covered, the supernatant is harvested and called HECS (human endothelial culture supernatant).

Reagents

Cord buffer: 0.14 *M* NaCl. 0.004 *M* KCl, 0.001 *M* phosphate buffer (pH 7.4), 0.011 *M* glucose.

Medium: 30% human serum A, 2 m*M* gentamine, 10 m*M* glucose (end concentration), 50 μg/ml gentamicin, 70% medium 199 (Earle's).

Human Umbilical Cord Serum

Human umbilical cord serum (HUCS) increases the number of hybridoma colonies *in vitro*. The stimulatory effect is significantly greater than that of fetal or newborn calf serum. The stimulatory substances present in HUCS are still unknown. Compared to normal human serum, albumin concentration is decreased and the concentrations of most amino acids

[63] G. C. B. Astaldi, M. C. Janssen, P. Lansdorp, C. Willems, W. P. Zeylemaker, and F. Oosterhof, *J. Immunol.* **125,** 1411 (1980).

are increased.[64] Probably a growth-promoting factor produced by the endothelial cells, the same as in HECS, is also present in the serum.

Preparation. Placental blood is collected during delivery immediately after section of the umbilical cord. A pool of HUCS was made from 10–15 sera from healthy individuals. The serum is heat inactivated for 45 min at 56° and passed through a Millipore filter (0.45-μm pore size). Small aliquots are frozen at −20°.

Comparison of the Growth Promoters

Immediately after cell fusion hybridomas were dispensed into microtiter tissue culture plates with 10% fetal calf serum (FCS) or with 10% FCS and one of the four different growth promoters at a concentration of 10^5 spleen cells per well (Table I). As shown in Table I, it appears that with the addition of FCS and one of the growth promoters, both frequencies of spleen cells forming clones and of spleen cells forming antibody-producing clones are elevated. HUCS gives the most rapid growth of hybridomas, even at a concentration as low as 4%. It if is not available, a good alternative is LPS and DxS. HECS also is a good alternative, but it is quite laborious to produce. The frequency of antibody-producing clones cultured in macrophage supernatant is greater than with any other simulator. A disadvantage, however, is that it does not stimulate cells cultured separately in limiting dilution experiments. Figure 1 clearly shows that there is no significant difference between FCS and macrophage supernatant. However, LPS plus DxS, HECS, and HUCS increased the number of clones significantly. More details about the B-cell stimulators will be discussed elsewhere.[65]

Fusion Protocol

The manipulations of the fusion protocol have already been described in an earlier *Methods in Enzymology* volume.[66] There are, however, some additions.

It is my experience that the myeloma cells must be kept under good growing conditions and the medium changed three times a week. The day before fusion, medium is changed one additional time. Good culture conditions of the myeloma cell line improves the fusion frequency. I once

[64] M. H. Malloy, O. K. Rassin, and W. J. McGanity, *Biol. Neonate* **44,** 1 (1983).
[65] R. J. J. M. Westerwoudt, *in* "Hybridoma Formation: Mechanisms and Technical Aspects of Hybridoma Generation and Monoclonal Antibody Production" (A. H. Bartal and Y. Hirshaut, eds.). Humana Press, New York (in press).
[66] R. H. Kennett, this series, Vol. 58, p. 345.

TABLE I

EFFECT OF DIFFERENT FEEDER SYSTEMS ON RECOVERY AND YIELD OF ANTIBODY PRODUCTION BY HYBRIDOMA CELLS AFTER FUSION

Stimulators	Wells plated[a] (and number of fusions)	Wells with clones		Antibody-producing clones	
		Percentage of total plated	Frequency of spleen cells forming hybridoma clones[b] ($\times 10^5$)	Percentage of total plated	Frequency of spleen cells forming clones[b] ($\times 10^6$)
FCS	384 (4)	65	1.05	12	1.3
LPS + DxS	384 (4)	99	4.61	33	4.0
Macrophage supernatant	384 (4)	98	3.91	42	5.4
HECS	288 (3)	99	4.61	34	4.2
HUCA	384 (4)	99	4.61	33	4.0

[a] Concentrations of 10^5 spleen cells per well.

[b] Calculated from the logarithmic form of the zero term of the Poisson distribution ($-\ln Fo$) and the number of spleen cells per well, with the formula: ($-\ln Fo/10^5$ spleen cells).

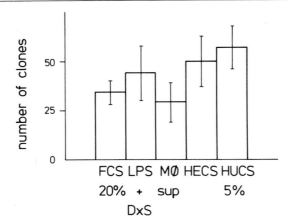

FIG. 1. A hybrid cell line cultured as single cells by limiting dilution to measure the influence of different feeder systems. Each column represents the mean of the number of wells containing hybrid clones (± SD) in four different experiments. Mφ Sup, macrophage supernatant.

used a myeloma cell line from which the medium was changed fortnightly for a long period. The fusion frequency was very low, about 10% of what it should be. When the cells were kept under optimal culture conditions for 2 months, they grew well, but the fusion frequency was still very low.

Spleens from immunized mice are squeezed with tweezers. Myeloma cells and spleen cells are washed in Hanks' buffer or PBS and fused at a ratio of 1 : 10 using 1 ml PEG at 4°. Two minutes after the addition of PEG the cells are slowly diluted with 40 ml RPMI 1640 at 37° and kept at this temperature for 15–30 min. The cells are pelleted, resuspended in HAT medium enriched with a growth promoter, and distributed into micro-plates. The plates should be put in the incubator as soon as possible and kept at 37° for at least 3 days, without opening the door of the incubator. One week after fusion an equal amount of HT medium is added.

Although the hybridomas are cultured in HAT medium immediately after fusion and I find high fusion frequencies, Ege[67] reported that the early division products of heterokaryons are sensitive to HAT medium and that the cloning efficiency is increased if exposure to the selective medium is delayed until 5 days after fusion.

[67] T. Ege, *Cell Biol. Int. Rep.* **8,** 599 (1984).

Reagents

Polyethylene glycol (PEG): 1 ml PEG 4000 and 0.1 ml dimethyl sulfoxide (DMSO) were added to 1 ml distilled water. The suspension was autoclaved 20 min at 120°.

Aminopterine, 4.4 mg, was diluted in 100 ml of 1 mM NaOH at 42°; 2 ml was added to 500 ml of culture medium and the pH adjusted.

Hypoxanthine, 340 mg, and thymidine, 100 mg, were diluted in 500 ml distilled water at 45°; 10 ml was added to 500 ml of culture medium.

Culture medium was supplemented with 1% nonessential amino acid solution, 1% sodium pyruvate, and 1% HEPES.

Antibody Production. Many investigators use the cell fusion technique to obtain monoclonal antibodies. One of the major problems encountered in this procedure is that clones that grow well and produce an apparent stable amount of antibody sometimes stop producing suddenly. One reason for loss of antibody production is inactivation or loss of the chromosome carrying the genes for heavy chains. To reduce this problem to a minimum the hybridomas should be kept under good growing conditions at an optimal pH. There is little growth either in terms of cell number or in terms of cell protein production at a low or high pH.[68] Also, loss of antibody production, mentioned by many investigators, may arise when more than one clone is present in a well. It has been postulated that a non-antibody-producing clone outgrows the antibody-producing clone.

Loss of Antibody Production. The stability of antibody-producing clones is investigated by limiting dilution experiments performed very soon after fusing the cells. Two weeks after fusion, the hybridomas from one antibody-producing clone are plated at one cell per well. Two weeks later, when the individual hybridomas of that clone also form clones so that the concentration of antibody in the well can be measured, supernatants are tested. This experiment is repeated with 36 different antibody-producing clones. In this way an estimation can be obtained of the percentage of clones that lose antibody production very soon after fusion. It appears that about half of the clones of which all hybridomas produce antibody in an initial stage lose this ability almost completely.

Overgrowth of Antibody-Producing Clones by Non-Antibody-Producing Clones. To investigate the overgrowth of antibody-producing clones by non-antibody-producing clones, three fusions were performed at five different concentrations ranging from a mean of 1.5 to a mean of 12 different clones per well. Two weeks after fusion, supernatants of wells

[68] C. Ceccarini and H. Eagle, *Proc. Natl. Acad. Sci. U.S.A.* **68,** 229 (1971).

TABLE II
STABILITY OF ANTIBODY-PRODUCING HYBRIDOMAS WHEN
MORE THAN ONE CLONE IS PRESENT IN THE WELL

Mean number of clones	Number of samples tested	Percentage of wells containing 90–100% pure Ab-producing clones
1.5	12	33
3	13	31
4.5	14	14
6	15	20
12	15	7

with clones were tested. From each concentration, clones from a number of wells showing antibody production were cultured by limiting dilution, and again antibody production from the individual hybridomas, grown to small clones, was tested. When at least 90% of the supernatants of the individual hybridomas contain antibody, the clone is considered to be pure. From these experiments it was calculated that 1 out of 7 hybrid clones produce specific antibody. If the antibody-producing clones are in a subordinate growth rate, certainly no antibody-producing clones would be detected at a mean of 3 or more clones per well. From the results of Table II it appears that at all concentrations, even at a mean of 6 or 12 different clones per well, there are antibody-producing clones without contamination of non-antibody-producing clones. Therefore, non-antibody-producing hybridomas are not favored over antibody-producing clones.

Contamination of Antibody-Producing Clones with Non-Antibody-Producing Clones. The question now is whether there is any contamination with non-antibody-producing clones at high hybridoma concentrations after fusion. This was tested in the same series of experiments as described above. If at least one-third of the supernatants of the wells in limiting dilution do not contain antibody it is considered that the clones have lost antibody production, or that non-antibody-producing hybridomas are present, or both. Loss of antibody production due to chromosomal segregation or inactivation was calculated to be 40%. From the results presented in Table III it was established that with increasing mean number of clones per well the percentage of negative wells increases, until at a mean of 12 clones per well, the percentage of negative wells decreases. This is due to a higher number of antibody-producing

TABLE III
STABILITY OF ANTIBODY-PRODUCING HYBRIDOMAS WITH
INCREASING NUMBER OF CLONES PER WELL

Mean number of clones per well	Number of samples tested	Percentage of Ab-negative wells (containing ≥33% Ab-negative clones)
1.5	9	44
3	11	55
4.5	8	63
6	8	75
12	9	56

clones per well rather than to a decreased number of non-antibody-producing hybridomas per well.

Comments

Cloning efficiency and maximal survival of hybridomas are important for the success of the fusion. During the whole process a number of events play a part: only binucleated hybridomas give rise to large colonies, no trinucleated or multinucleated cells give rise to continuously growing daughter cells,[67] and fusion of populations of cells which have been synchronized in the same phase of the cell cycle ensure maximal survival of the hybrids.[6,69] Also, Olsson and co-workers[54] have suggested that B lymphocytes should be in a certain stage of differentiation for successful hybridization. This may explain why the number of hybridomas depends on the number of spleen cells and not on the number of myeloma cells used for hybridization. Possibly, only those cells which are in interphase at the time of fusion can form stable hybridomas. It also appeared that suboptimal nutritional conditions led to asynchrony in DNA synthesis and mitosis in multinucleated cells.[70]

From the experiments described previously, it can be concluded that limiting dilution after fusion can be omitted. Similar observations have been made by others.[71] There is hardly any contamination by non-antibody-producing hybridomas. Stability of antibody production is depen-

[69] H. G. Coon, *J. Cell Biol.* **35**, 27A (1967).
[70] S. Ghosh, N. Paweletz, and I. Ghosh, *Chromosoma* **65**, 293 (1978).
[71] E. A. Klasen, personal communication.

dent on chromosome segregation. The stability of antibody-producing clones can be determined after freezing and thawing the hybridomas. Unstable hybrids stop antibody production and lose chromosomes after thawing.[28] Therefore if they do not withstand the freezing process, they cannot be stored and kept for long periods.

Acknowledgments

I wish to thank Dr. J. J. Haaijman and Dr. E. A. Klasen for their help in preparing this chapter, J. Blom and A. M. Naipal for technical assistance, and G. C. A. M. Spigt-van den Bercken for secretarial help.

[2] *In Vitro* Immunization for the Production of Antigen-Specific Lymphocyte Hybridomas

By CHRISTOPHER L. READING

Realization of the potential of antigen-specific monoclonal antibodies is often limited by failure to stimulate adequate numbers of antigen-specific B lymphocytes during the *in vivo* immunization procedure. This failure may be due to tolerance (antigen-specific nonresponsiveness) or to an antigen hierarchy response (selective responsiveness to one or a few components of the immunogen preparation) rather than to a lack of antigen-reactive precursor cells. After immunization with low levels of antigen, animals with high serum titers of specific antibodies may fail to yield the desired hybridomas because of the low splenic content of the appropriate cells. "Weak" immunogens may require the use of immunostimulating adjuvants that can induce polyclonal B-cell activation. Some of these problems are overcome through the use of *in vitro* immunization.[1,2] The procedures are described here in detail; the theoretical aspects are dealt with elsewhere.[3]

Cell Culture Procedure

All cells and hybrids are cultured in a supplemented Dulbecco's modified Eagle's medium (SDMEM). This is a medium rich in essential amino

[1] R. A. Luben and M. A. Mohler, *Mol. Immunol.* **17,** 635 (1980).
[2] C. L. Reading, *in* "Hybridomas and Cellular Immortality" (B. Tom and J. Allison, eds.), p. 235. Plenum, New York, 1983.
[3] C. L. Reading, *J. Immunol. Methods* **53,** 261 (1982).

acids and vitamins and supplemented with 23 mM sodium bicarbonate, 16 mM HEPES, 880 μM sodium pyruvate, 44 μM 2-mercaptoethanol, 8.8 μM MEM nonessential amino acids, 26 μM hypoxanthine, and 2.6 μM thymidine.

Reagents

1-liter package of Dulbecco's modified Eagle's medium (GIBCO 430-2100)

Sodium bicarbonate

HEPES buffer (Flow Labs)

1-liter bottle of sterile water for irrigation, USP (Travenol Laboratories, Deerfield, IL)

Sterile solution of 100 mM sodium pyruvate (GIBCO 320-1360)

5 mM 2-mercaptoethanol in water, prepared by diluting 35 μl of reagent-grade 2-mercaptoethanol in 100 ml of sterile water and filtering it through a 115-ml 0.20-μm disposable filter unit (Nalge 120-0020). This is stored as a sterile solution in the refrigerator.

Sterile solution of 10 mM MEM nonessential amino acids (GIBCO 320-1140)

Sterile solution of 3 mM hypoxanthine, 300 μM thymidine (stored at room temperature in the dark)

1-liter package of Hanks' balanced salts without NaHCO$_3$ (Flow Labs 17-101-20)

10 N NaOH solution

Type 100 rabbit serum (Diagnostic Biochemistry, San Diego, CA)

SDMEM. Dissolve the contents of a 1-liter package of Dulbecco's modified Eagle's medium in about 800 ml sterile water, and rinse out the package. Add 2.2 g NaHCO$_3$ and 4.29 g HEPES, and when dissolved, dilute to 1100 ml. Add 10 ml 100 mM sodium pyruvate, 10 ml 5 mM 2-mercaptoethanol, 10 ml MEM nonessential amino acids, and 10 ml 3 mM hypoxanthine, 300 μM thymidine. Adjust the pH to 7.3 with 10 N NaOH. Check the osmolarity, which should be about 290 mOsm. Deviations of more than 2% should be corrected by the addition of either sterile water or 5 M NaCl. Filter immediately through 0.2-μm filters and store in gastight sterile plastic 75-cm^2 tissue culture flasks (Corning 25116) at 4–10°.

HEPES-Buffered Hanks' Balanced Salt Solution. Dissolve a 1-liter package of Hanks' balanced salt solution in 960 ml of water and add 2.5 g HEPES buffer to produce HEPES-buffered Hanks' balanced salt solution (HHBSS). Adjust the pH to 7.2 with 10 N NaOH and check the osmolarity (it should be about 290 mOsm). Sterilize with 0.2-μm filters and store in 75-cm^2 tissue culture flasks at room temperature in the dark.

Type 100 Rabbit Serum. This serum is prescreened by the supplier to support growth of myeloma and hybridoma cells at 2% in SDMEM. It is heat inactivated and filtered with a 0.2-μm filter. It has a high lipid and lipoprotein content and a lipid layer tends to separate when the serum is left for prolonged periods after thawing. To prevent this separation, thaw 100-ml bottles of serum rapidly at 37° and freeze 10-ml aliquots in 15-ml snap-cap polypropylene tubes and thaw as needed. Rabbit serum from other suppliers has rarely worked for *in vitro* immunization, but an adequate serum can be prepared by sterile cardiac puncture of adult rabbits without anesthesia. (The commercial type 100 serum is from rabbits fed fresh vegetable matter. Animals fed laboratory feed may have a different serum lipid content than those raised on fresh vegetable matter.) Allow the blood to clot at room temperature for 2 hr and the clot to retract at 4° overnight. After centrifugation of the pooled sera to remove remaining erythrocytes, heat to 56° and maintain at 56° for 30 min. After cooling to room temperature, filter through nonsterile Millipore 0.8-, 0.45-, and 0.22-μm filters and then through sterile 0.2-μm absolute filters (Pall Corp., DFA 3001 FRP, Cortland, NY) into sterile 125-ml screw-cap glass bottles (Wheaton "400" media bottles). Chill 100-ml aliquots on ice and quick-freeze in a dry ice–ethanol bath and store at −70°. A bottle from each lot should be thawed, tested for mycoplasma,[3] and tested for growth with myeloma or hybridoma cells.

Preparation of Allogeneic Thymocyte Culture-Conditioned Medium (TCM)

Materials and Reagents

Three sets of surgical scissors and forceps
HHBSS
70% ethanol in a squeeze bottle
50-ml screw-cap polypropylene tubes (Corning Glass Works, No. 25331) and test tube rack
6- to 8-week-old female BALB/c and C57BL/6 mice
Dissection board and pins
Sterile 60 × 20-mm petri dishes
50-mesh stainless-steel screen with handle
Type 100 rabbit serum
SDMEM
Disposable plastic 12-ml syringe
Sterile plastic disposable tissue culture pipets (10 ml, 5 ml, 1 ml)
Humidified (5% CO_2 in air), 37° tissue culture incubator

Hemacytometer and coverslip
Inverted phase-contrast microscope
Centrifuge
Sterile gastight screw-cap glass vials

Procedure

Sterilize three sets of scissors and forceps by placing each set in a 50-ml polypropylene tube containing 40 ml of 70% ethanol at least 1 hr before use. Place 20 ml HHBSS in a sterile 50-ml tube. Obtain five 6- to 8-week-old female BALB/c and five 6- to 8-week-old C57BL/6 mice. Do not work with the mice in the tissue culture hood. Kill one mouse by cervical dislocation, pin limbs to the dissection board with the mouse on its back, and wash chest, abdomen, and neck with 70% ethanol from a squeeze bottle. With the first set of instruments, pick up the skin on the chest and cut a wide flap from the zyphoid process to each axillary region. Separate the skin from the muscle layer by spreading with the tips of the scissors, and pull the skin back over the head to expose the chest and neck. Replace the instruments in the 70% ethanol. Rinse the muscle layer with 70% ethanol. With the second set of instruments, cut the muscle and ribs from the zyphoid process to the axillary region on both sides and pull the flap up over the head. The thymus, which is a white bilobed organ just anterior to the heart, should now be exposed. Replace the instruments in the 70% ethanol. With the third set of instruments, remove the thymus and place it in the HHBSS. Replace the instruments in the 70% ethanol. Repeat these steps for the remaining mice, taking care not to contaminate the thymus glands. Dispose of the mice and wash your hands. Spray the HHBSS tube with 70% ethanol, and place it in a clean rack in the laminar flow hood. Open five 60 × 20-mm petri dishes in the hood. Fill the first with 70% ethanol. Spray the handle of a 50-mesh stainless-steel screen with 70% ethanol and soak the screen in the first petri dish. Leave the second dish empty and pipet 10 ml of HHBSS into the third and fourth petri dishes. Pipet 5 ml of SDMEM with 10% type 100 rabbit serum into the fifth dish. Transfer the screen to the second dish and pour the HHBSS and the thymus glands into the screen. Transfer the screen through the third and fourth petri dishes to rinse the glands, and place the screen containing the glands in the fifth dish. Remove the plunger from a sterile disposable plastic 12-ml syringe, and use the plunger to press the thymus tissue through the screen into the SDMEM with rabbit serum. Discard the remaining capsule and fat. Pipet the suspension repeatedly (five or six times) until a single-cell suspension is obtained. Transfer the cells to a

50-ml tube, dilute to 50 ml with SDMEM, and count the viable cells. Dilute the thymocytes with SDMEM plus 2% rabbit serum to 4×10^6/ml. Place 50-ml aliquots of the cell suspension in 75-cm² tissue culture flasks and place them horizontally in the incubator. After 48 hr harvest the medium and spin out the cells and debris at 500 g for 10 min. Filter the thymocyte culture-conditioned medium (TCM) through a 0.2-μm filter. Store the medium in 10-ml aliquots in gastight screw-cap glass vials at $-70°$.

In Vitro Immunization

Materials and Reagents

Three sets of surgical scissors and forceps
HHBSS
70% ethanol in a squeeze bottle
50-ml screw-cap polypropylene tubes and test tube rack
Dissection board and pins
Sterile 60 × 20-mm petri dishes
50-mesh stainless-steel screen with handle
Type 100 rabbit serum
SDMEM
Disposable plastic 12-ml syringe
Sterile plastic disposable tissue culture pipets (10 ml, 5 ml, 1 ml)
Humidified (5% CO_2 in air), 37° tissue culture incubator
Inverted phase-contrast microscope
10 ml TCM
One 6- to 8-week-old BALB/c mouse
Sterile antigen preparation (see below)
Cell irradiator

Procedure

Sterilize three sets of scissors and forceps and prepare 20 ml of HHBSS as for TCM preparation. Kill an unimmunized female BALB/c mouse by cervical dislocation, pin limbs to dissection board with the mouse on its back, and wash chest and abdomen with 70% ethanol from a squeeze bottle. With the first set of instruments, pick up the skin on the abdomen over the midline near the groin, and make a small incision through the skin but not the muscle. Spread with the tips of the scissors under the skin to separate the skin from the muscle layer. Cut a wide flap from the groin to the ribs on either side, and pull the skin up over the chest. Rinse the muscle layer with 70% ethanol. With the second set of instruments, cut a narrow flap of muscle from the peritoneum near the groin almost to the zyphoid process. With the third set of instruments, remove the spleen, which is an elongated dark red organ just below the stomach, and place it in the HHBSS. Dispose of the mouse, wash your hands, rinse the HHBSS tube with 70% ethanol, and place it in a clean rack in the laminar flow hood. Sterilize the screen, rinse the spleen, and prepare a cell suspension in SDMEM and 10% rabbit serum exactly as for the thymus glands. Transfer cells to a 50-ml tube and dilute to 20 ml with serum-free SDMEM containing 30–1000 μg of filtered (with 0.2-μm filter) soluble antigen or 10^7 sterile irradiated or alcohol-fixed cells. Cells to be used for immunization should be irradiated with 4500 rad of ^{137}Cs radiation or washed in HHBSS, resuspended in ice-cold 95% ethanol, left overnight at 4°, and washed three times with HHBSS before immunization. Successful immunizations have been performed with much lower amounts of soluble antigen, although the frequency of antigen-reactive hybrids decreases below about 1 μg. Add 10 ml freshly thawed TCM (thawed rapidly at 37°) and transfer the suspension to a 75-cm^2 tissue culture flask. Place the flask horizontally in the incubator and leave it for 5 days. After 5 days, numerous large blasts should be visible by phase-contrast microscopy. Dislodge the blasts by striking the side of the flask with the heel of your hand. The cells are now ready for fusion.

Fusion

Combine the immunized cells from one flask with 2×10^7 P3X63Ag8.653 cells and centrifuge. Wash the pellet once in HHBSS to remove serum. Fuse the cells in the washed pellet with 47% (v/v) polyethylene glycol in HHBSS containing DMSO at 37° as previously described.[3] Dilute the fused cells to 100 ml with SDMEM containing 2% rabbit serum, 4×10^{-7} M aminopterin, and 2×10^5 ^{137}Cs-irradiated (4500 rad) BALB/c spleen cells. Dissociated spleen cells, or another source of macrophages, are necessary for growth of the hybrids at low density, both immediately after fusion and at the limiting dilution cloning stages later. For *in vitro* immunized spleen cells, the addition of fresh adherent cells is an absolute necessity, because the original adherent cells remain attached to the flask from the immunization. The fused cells and feeder cells are plated in 96 1-ml cultures as previously described.[3]

Screening for Antigen-Specific Hybridomas

Because of the simplicity of the *in vitro* immunization technique, investigators are sometimes reluctant to have confidence in the results obtained. After initial testing by the enzyme-linked immunosorbant assay (ELISA) or a radioactive binding assay, it is necessary to retest the hybrids by another, distinct assay.[4] With cells and tissues, indirect immuno-fluorescence or indirect immunoperoxidase staining can give distinct and specific patterns for desired antibodies. Matched subclass mouse antibody controls should be used with unfixed cells to control for nonspecific and Fc-mediated binding. Immunoprecipitation with enzyme or radiolabeled antigens also allows identification of the desired antibodies. When worthwhile antibodies are identified, the hybrids should be cloned by limiting dilution and recloned until stability is achieved.[3]

Examples of in Vitro Immunization

In vitro immunization with alcohol-fixed murine tumor cells yielded 23 cultures reactive with the immunizing tumor cells out of 96 original cultures.[5] Immunization *in vitro* with 1 mg of *Sacchromyces cervisiae* X2180-1A mannan yielded 18 of 96 cultures with reactive antibodies.[6] We have also immunized BALB/c spleen cells with alcohol-fixed pooled acute myeloid leukemia (AML) cells from leukapheresis products from four patients using the *in vitro* technique.[7] Of 96 cultures, 31 produced antibodies reactive with a pool of AML cells from four other patients. After several reclonings, all 31 cultures yielded stable clones with the same reactivity. Six of these clones were unreactive with normal peripheral blood and bone marrow mononuclear cells in an ELISA. This result was distinct from fusions using mice immunized *in vivo* with leukemic cells. *In vivo* immunizations produce mostly antibodies reactive with major histocompatibility antigens or major myeloid differentiation antigens present on the majority of cells of a particular lineage. This procedure has also yielded hybrids reactive with highly conserved proteins such as calmodulin (30/96 cultures) and actin (20/96)[8] and with hapten–carrier complexes such as fluorescein (12/96) coupled to BSA.[2]

Other Methods for in Vitro Immunization

Luben and Mohler[1] originally described the use of thymocytes from 10-day-old mice for the preparation of TCM, based on the findings of Anders-

[4] C. L. Reading, *in* "Differentiation and Function of Hematopoietic Cell Surfaces" (V. T. Marchesi and R. C. Gallo, eds.), p. 277. Alan R. Liss, Inc., New York, 1982.

[5] K. M. Miner, C. L. Reading, and G. L. Nicolson, *Invasion Metastasis* 1, 158 (1981).

[6] C. L. Reading, *in* "Glycoconjugates" (T. Yamakawa, T. Osawa, and S. Handa, eds.), p. 382. Jpn. Sci. Soc. Press, Toyko, 1981.

[7] K. A. Dicke, S. E. Tindle, F. M. Davis, and C. L. Reading, *in* "Differentiation and Function of Hematopoietic Cell Surfaces" (V. T. Marchesi and R. C. Gallo, eds.), p. 283. Alan R. Liss, Inc., New York, 1982.

[8] R. L. Pardue, R. C. Brady, R. J. Dedman, and C. L. Reading, *J. Cell Biol.* 91, 81A (1981).

TABLE I

MURINE ANTIGEN-REACTIVE HYBRIDOMAS FROM *in Vitro* IMMUNIZATIONS

Antigen	Stimulator	Amount	Frequency[a]	Ref.
Osteoclast activating factor	10-day TCM	10–500 ng	0.34 (0.18–0.64)	1 11
Complement component	Peritoneal cells	10 μg/5 × 10^7 spleen cells, serum free	0.07–0.29 0	10
ALL cells	Peritoneal cells	10^5 cells/ml spleen cells, serum free	0.14–0.20 0	10
Alcohol-fixed lymphosarcoma cells	Mixed TCM	10^7 cells	0.24	5
Yeast mannan glycoprotein	Mixed TCM	1 mg	0.18	6
AML cells	Mixed TCM	10^7 cells	0.32	7
Calmodulin	Mixed TCM	300 ng	0.31	2
Actin	Mixed TCM	3 μg	0.21	12
Fluorescein	Mixed TCM	1 mg/FITC–BSA	0.13	12
Rat AML cells	Mixed TCM	10^7 cells	0.40	12
Insulin	Mixed TCM	3 mg	0.29	13
Benzopyrene–BSA	Mixed TCM	1.5 mg	0.18	13
Myoglobin	Mixed TCM	1.5 mg	0.22	13
Myoglobin	Mixed TCM	0.03–300 μg	0.05–0.17	14
Myoglobin	Mixed TCM	300 μg, serum free	0.26	13
Hemoglobin	Bovine TCM	300 ng	0.026	14

[a] All are measured by antigen-reactive cultures per total cultures, except the complement component and the ALL (acute lymphocytic leukemia) cells, which are measured by antigen-reactive clones per total clones.

son *et al.*[9] that thymocytes would support growth of antigen- or mitogen-stimulated B lymphocytes. Feder *et al.*[10] replaced TCM with peritoneal exudate cells and tested serum-free medium. With peritoneal exudate cells the number of hybrids with the desired reactivity was somewhat lower than that reported with TCM.[1] Under serum-free conditions, no antigen-reactive hybrids were formed.

An *in vitro* immunization kit is commercially available from Hana Biologics (Berkeley, CA), and contains frozen bovine thymocyte-condi-

[9] J. Andersson, A. Coutinho, W. Lenhardt, and F. Melchers, *Cell* **10**, 27 (1977).
[10] M. Feder, Z. L. Jonak, A. A. Smith, M. C. Glick, and R. H. Kennett, *in* "Hybridomas and Cellular Immortality" (B. Tom and J. Allison, eds.), p. 145. Plenum, New York, 1983.

TABLE II
HUMAN ANTIGEN-REACTIVE MONOCLONAL ANTIBODIES FROM *in Vitro* IMMUNIZATIONS[a]

Antigen	Stimulator	Amount	Frequency	Ref.
Fusions				
SRBC	PWM	100 μl 1% suspension/ml	0.04–0.54	15
SRBC	NR	NR	NR	16
Lipid fraction of endotoxin	NR	NR	NR	16
EBV transformations				
DNA-coupled SRBC	EBV	To rosette	0.20–0.30	17
Chicken RBC	EBV	To rosette	0.16–0.40	17
Breast adeno-carcinoma	EBV	Adherent monolayer	0.14	18
AML cells	EBV	Formaldehyde-attached cells	0.23	19

[a] Abbreviations: SRBC, sheep red blood cells; RBC, red blood cells; PWM, pokeweed mitogen; NR, not reported.

tioned medium for stimulation of murine cells. This kit also uses serum-free medium and may result in a lower frequency of antigen-reactive hybrids. A summary of results of *in vitro* immunization with murine spleen cells is presented in Table I.[11–14]

In Vitro Immunization with Human B Lymphocytes

A number of experimental *in vitro* stimulation systems exist for human B cells (reviewed in Ref. 3). Table II[15–19] lists a few attempts at *in vitro* immunization with human lymphocytes followed by fusion with myelo-

[11] R. A. Ruben and M. A. Mohler, *in* "Biochemical Characterization of Lymphokines" (A. L. de Weck, F. Kristensen, and M. Landy, eds.), p. 55. Academic Press, New York, 1980.
[12] C. A. K. Borrebaeck, *Scand. J. Immunol.* **18,** 9 (1983).
[13] C. A. K. Borrebaeck, *Mol. Immunol.* **21,** 841 (1984).
[14] Y. E. McHugh, Hana Biologics, Inc., Berkeley, California (personal communication).
[15] L. E. Strike, B. H. Devens, and R. L. Lundak, *J. Immunol.* **132,** 1798 (1984).
[16] L. Olsson and H. S. Kaplan, *Proc. Natl. Acad. Sci. U.S.A.* **77,** 5429 (1980).
[17] L. Winger, C. Winger, P. Schastry, A. Russell, and M. Longenecker, *Proc. Natl. Acad. Sci. U.S.A.* **80,** 4484 (1983).
[18] A. J. Roome and C. L. Reading, *Exp. Biol.* **43,** 35 (1984).
[19] C. L. Reading, M. Chandran, and L. Vellekoop, *J. Cell. Biochem.* **7A,** 73 (1983).

mas. Also presented are attempts at exposure of lymphocytes to antigen followed by Epstein–Barr virus (EBV) transformation. We have found antigen-specific B-cell selection followed by transformation with EBV to be a promising method for production of human monoclonal antibodies.[18] The extent to which this represents "immunization" is unclear. The B lymphocytes bind antigen through their surface receptors and are then stimulated by infection with EBV, which is a polyclonal B-cell activator.[20] The net result is an increase in antigen-specific B cells and immunoglobulin secretion. A similar procedure has been used by Winger *et al.*[17] Work is under way in numerous laboratories to improve the *in vitro* stimulation systems for generating human monoclonals. Whether it be by *in vitro* immunization followed by fusion or by preselection of antigen-specific B cells prior to transformation, we can expect great strides in the production of human monoclonal antibodies specific for predetermined antigens in the near future.

[20] A. Rosen, P. Gergely, M. Jondal, G. Klein, and S. Britoon, *Nature (London)* **267,** 52 (1977).

[3] An Improved *in Vitro* Immunization Procedure for the Production of Monoclonal Antibodies

By BARBARA D. BOSS

Coupling *in vitro* sensitization of lymphocytes with standard fusion techniques to yield hybridomas secreting specific monoclonal antibodies was first reported by Hengartner, Luzzati, and Schreier in 1978.[1] Two years later, Luben and Mohler[2] introduced the use of thymus-conditioned medium during the *in vitro* sensitization period and found a 3-fold increase in the number of hybridomas secreting antibody of the desired specificity (compared to *in vivo* immunization). Others have modified this *in vitro* system to produce specific immune responses to haptens, glycoproteins, and polysaccharides (see Reading[3] for reviews).

Many factors make such *in vitro* immunization of spleen cells preferable to *in vivo* immunization. These considerations include the reduced

[1] H. Hengartner, A. L. Luzzati, and M. Schreier, *Curr. Top. Microbiol. Immunol.* **81,** 92 (1978).
[2] R. A. Luben and M. A. Mohler, *Mol. Immunol.* **17,** 635 (1980).
[3] C. L. Reading, *J. Immunol. Methods* **53,** 261 (1982); this volume [2].

amount of antigen required for *in vitro* lymphocyte activation, the reduced amount of time required for *in vitro* activation, and the enhanced ability to break tolerance or overcome suppression found with *in vitro* systems. Moreover, breaking tolerance *in vivo* may lead to impaired viability of the immunized animals in some situations, and immunizing *in vitro* eliminates this concern. For all these reasons, I have sought to develop simplified *in vitro* immunization conditions which would permit workers unfamiliar with immunological techniques greater success in obtaining useful monoclonal antibodies. To this end, I describe an *in vitro* system which utilizes either Roswell Park Memorial Institute (RPMI) medium or Dulbecco's modified Eagle's medium (DMEM), involves the sole addition of commercially available adjuvant peptide *N*-acetylmuramyl-L-alanyl-D-isoglutamine,[4-6] and significantly increases the number of viable hybridomas as well as the number of hybridomas secreting antibody of the desired specificity (as judged by initial screening assays).[7] This method of immunization has been used repeatedly in this laboratory, as well as in others, over the last 2 years and has continued to yield valuable IgM monoclonal antibodies at greater frequency than do conventional methods of *in vivo* immunization.

Spleen Cell Culture

Lymphocyte Harvest

Following cervical dislocation, two spleens from young adult, female BALB/c mice are removed under sterile conditions and placed into a petri dish containing Hanks' buffered salt solution (HBSS; Grand Island Biological Co., Grand Island, NY) at room temperature. The spleens are washed by transferring them into and out of two other petri dishes (No. 1007; Falcon, Oxnard, CA) containing HBSS. Using a fourth dish, the lymphocytes are harvested by gently forcing the spleens through a stainless-steel wire mesh with the aid of a 5-ml syringe plunger. The cells are then transferred to a 15-ml conical tube (Corning Glass Works, Corning, NY) and the larger tissue fragments are allowed to settle out for a few minutes. The single-cell suspension is placed into a clean 15-ml tube and

[4] F. Ellouz, A. Adam, R. Ciobaru, and E. Lederer, *Biochem. Biophys. Res. Commun.* **59,** 1317 (1974).
[5] S. Kotani, Y. Watanabe, F. Kinoshita, T. Shimono, I. Morisaki, T. Shiba, S. Kusumoto, Y. Tarumi, and K. Ikenaka, *Biken J.* **18,** 105 (1975).
[6] F. Audibert and L. Chédid, *Cell. Immunol.* **21,** 243 (1976).
[7] B. D. Boss, *Brain Res.* **291,** 193 (1984).

centrifuged at 212 g for 5 min. The resulting lymphocyte pellet is resuspended in RPMI medium (GIBCO) containing 20% heat-inactivated fetal bovine serum (Lot No. 210631; Irvine Scientific Co., Santa Ana, CA) supplemented with 5×10^{-5} M 2-mercaptoethanol (Sigma Chemical Co., St. Louis, MO), 2 mM glutamine (GIBCO), 1 mM sodium pyruvate (GIBCO), 100 units penicillin/ml (GIBCO), and 100 μg streptomycin/ml (GIBCO). DMEM medium (GIBCO) can be substituted for RPMI here. When purchasing new serum, batches from several different suppliers should be tested for their ability to support the growth of both myeloma and hybridoma cell lines which are available.

Culture Conditions

Using trypan blue dye exclusion (GIBCO) to determine viability, the cells are counted in a hemacytometer, and diluted to 10^7/ml. Care should be taken not to include the smaller red blood cells in this count. For the sensitization, 1 μg or less of purified soluble antigen is added to a 20-ml suspension of lymphocytes together with 20 μg/ml of N-acetylmuramyl-L-alanyl-D-isoglutamine[8,9] (Calbiochem-Behring, San Diego, CA). The 20-ml suspension is placed into a 75-cm^2 tissue culture flask (Falcon) and incubated at 37° in a humidified 5% CO_2/95% air atmosphere for 4 days prior to fusion. When immunizing against intact cells which may not survive in lymphocyte medium, I have fixed a layer of the intact, adherent cells with 0.25% glutaraldehyde for 20 min and washed repeatedly with phosphate-buffered saline prior to adding the lymphocyte suspension containing adjuvant peptide. Most cells will adhere to such tissue culture flasks if the flasks are pretreated with 1 mg poly-L-lysine/ml (Sigma; 260,000 M_r) for 1 hr. For cells that could survive alongside the lymphocytes, fixation is not required. If the intact cells are tumorigenic and therefore capable of colony formation, it will be necessary to suppress their growth by means of γ-irradiation (^{60}Co, 3300 rad). When intact cells, fixed or unfixed, are incubated with the lymphocyte suspension, the period of culture incubation is reduced to 3 days.

Fusion Protocol

It should be possible to utilize any standard fusion protocol along with this system of *in vitro* immunization. For continuity, I will describe the protocol currently in use in this laboratory. This procedure is closely

[8] S. Specter, R. Cimprich, H. Friedman, and L. Chédid, *J. Immunol.* **120**, 487 (1978).
[9] J. Watson and C. Whitlock, *J. Immunol.* **121**, 383 (1978).

patterned after that described in the EMBO course on B-Lymphocyte Fusion held at the Basel Institute for Immunology in 1978.[10–12]

Macrophage Preparation

On the day before the fusion is to be carried out, 3×10^3 γ-irradiated (^{60}Co, 3300 rad) mouse peritoneal macrophages are plated in Costar microtiter wells (No. 3596; Costar, Cambridge, MA). For this, BALB/c mice are injected intraperitoneally with 5 ml cold HBSS under sterile conditions following cervical dislocation. The abdomen is gently massaged for several minutes, and the peritoneal fluid is withdrawn by Pasteur pipet from a small incision made into the peritoneal cavity. The fluids from several animals are pooled and kept on ice. The average yield is 10^6 peritoneal macrophages/animal. Following centrifugation at 212 g for 5 min, the macrophage pellet is rapped loose on the counter, 5 ml of cold lymphocyte medium containing 10^{-4} M hypoxanthine (Sigma), 4×10^{-7} M aminopterin (Sigma), and 1.6×10^{-5} M thymidine (Sigma) (HAT medium) is added, and the macrophages remaining on the sides of the 50-ml polypropylene conical tube (Corning) are recovered by vigorously squirting the medium in and out of a Pasteur pipet. The number of viable macrophages (as judged by trypan blue dye exclusion and their large size, as compared to lymphocytes) is then determined, the cells are irradiated, diluted to 6×10^4/ml in HAT medium using a glass pipet, and plated at 50 μl/well.

Myeloma Harvest

The Sp2/0-Ag14 myeloma line which is in use in this laboratory was obtained from The Salk Institute's Cell Distribution Center. On the day before the fusion, these cells are split to ensure that they will be in a logarithmic phase of growth on the following day. On the day of fusion, the myelomas are harvested off the flask (by squirting medium in and out of a Pasteur pipet), pooled, and washed three times in 15 ml cold HBSS by centrifugation. The final resuspension is in 15 ml of cold, serum-free RPMI with no additions. The viability of the cells is determined using trypan blue.

[10] G. Galfré, S. C. Howe, C. Milstein, G. W. Butcher, and J. C. Howard, *Nature (London)* **266,** 550 (1977).
[11] C. Milstein and G. Köhler, in "Antibodies in Human Diagnosis and Therapy" (E. Haber and R. M. Krause, eds.), p. 271. Raven Press, New York, 1977.
[12] M. M. Trucco, J. W. Stocker, and R. Ceppellini, in "Lymphocyte Hybridomas" (F. Melchers, M. Potter, and N. L. Warner, eds.), p. 66. Springer-Verlag, Berlin and New York, 1978.

Spleen Cell Harvest

On the day of fusion, the tissue culture flasks are gently harvested to remove loosely adherent lymphocytes, and the recovered cells are placed into a 50-ml conical tube. The lymphocytes are washed in tandem with the myelomas as described in the previous section.

Fusion Procedure

When the lymphocytes and myelomas have been counted, they are combined in a ratio of 4 spleen cells for every myeloma cell (10 spleen cells for every myeloma cell will also work). After the addition of another 20 ml of cold, serum-free RPMI to the 50-ml tube, the combined cells are centrifuged, the pellet is rapped loose, and the tube is placed into a 37° water bath (under sterile conditions). Then, 0.7 ml of a warm 45% polyethylene glycol (PEG; 4000 molecular weight; Merck, Darmstadt, West Germany) solution in DMEM is slowly added over the course of 1 min while the tube is rotated to gently mix the cells and PEG.

After a 90-sec interval of gently swirling the tube in the water bath, 3 ml of warm serum-free RPMI is added slowly over the next 3 min (with continued swirling). Over the next few minutes, an additional 12 ml of RPMI is added, the cells are centrifuged for 10 min at 310 g, and the pellet is resuspended in warm HAT medium so that each well receives 50 μl of medium containing approximately 1×10^5 total cells.

Hybridoma Maintenance

The microtiter plates are fed 50 μl HAT medium/well for the next 3 days following fusion. After that, 100 μl of medium/well is aspirated off and replaced every second or third day. Following 2 weeks in HAT medium, the cells are switched to hypoxanthine–thymidine medium for 2 weeks. Thereafter the cells are fed normal lymphocyte medium.

Visible colonies will begin to form as early as 9 days following plating, and should all be formed by 3 weeks. When colonies have reached the 1000-cell stage, 100 μl of supernatant is kept for testing while 100 μl of suspended hybridoma cells is transferred to 24-well Costar plates containing 0.5–0.7 ml medium (No. 3524). Additional medium is added to these wells over time until the cells are finally transferred to a 15-ml tissue culture flask (25 cm^2; Corning) containing 10 ml of medium. From this stage on, the cells can be frozen for storage or used to generate ascitic fluids.

Enzyme-Linked Immunosorbent Assay (ELISA)

Soluble Antigens

The reserved supernatant fluids are most easily screened in an ELISA.[13] For this, Microtest III flexible assay plates (No. 3912; Falcon) or vinyl assay strips (No. 2590; Costar) are incubated sequentially with (1) soluble antigen (usually 10–100 μg/ml) overnight at 4°, (2) 5% fetal calf serum for 2 hr at room temperature, and (3) the sample supernatant overnight at 4°. Volumes of 45 or 50 μl are used for antigen and supernatant. Volumes of 200 μl are used for the fetal calf serum and two brief washing steps (phosphate-buffered saline) prior to fetal calf serum addition. During any of these steps, the plates can be flicked over a sink to remove the liquid in the wells. Following the serum incubation, the wells can be stored for months at 4° in phosphate-buffered saline containing 0.05% sodium azide or used immediately. Once the test supernatants have been incubated in the wells, bound antibody is visualized by using a hybridoma screening kit (Bethesda Research Laboratories, No. 9502 AI) according to the instructions provided by the supplier. The positive wells can easily be scored by visualization of the colored reaction product. Background wells containing no antigen, but blocked as usual with serum, should be run alongside the antigen wells to screen for possible reactivity of the test supernatants to serum components. Some spurious background reactivities of this type can be eliminated by blocking for the same amount of time with 10% sheep serum containing 0.1 M lysine (Sigma) instead of fetal calf serum, by adding 2% sheep serum to the test supernatants and by adding 1% sheep serum to the hybridoma screening reagent (sheep anti-mouse Ig).

Intact Cells

Slight modifications of the above ELISA procedure are employed for whole-cell antigens. First, the cells are plated directly into the Microtest III flexible assay plates (sterilized with ethanol), cultured, and fixed prior to blocking with fetal calf serum. Light fixation (0.25% glutaraldehyde for 20 min) is recommended for most antigens. If the cells must be trypsinized prior to culture, one should wait an appropriate amount of time for all cell surface proteins to be synthesized and replaced prior to fixation. As before, the plates are treated with 1 mg poly-L-lysine/ml for at least 1 hr so that the cells will adhere to the wells. Second, because of the comparatively loose association of the cells with the surface of the wells, these

---

[13] A. Voller, A. Bartlett, and D. E. Bidwell, *J. Clin. Pathol.* **31,** 507 (1978).

plates should be blotted (upside down) to remove previous additions during the assay. Flicking these plates will result in uneven cell loss from the wells. Last, when the hybridoma screening reagent protocol is followed, it is best to omit all detergent from the wash buffers when whole cells are being used. This ensures less destruction of membrane-bound antigens on the cell surfaces.

Further Characterization of the Antibodies

Once it is known which of the hybridoma wells are secreting interesting antibodies, one should clone those wells to ensure their monoclonal nature (all progeny will behave equally when the parent is monoclonal). In addition, one may wish to test the subclass of these antibodies. Using a variation of the ELISA for this works very well with tissue culture fluids (taken from confluent cultures). Ouchterlony methodology requires concentrating these fluids approximately 10-fold. Biochemical and immunohistochemical characterization of the antibodies follows, as dictated by the needs of the laboratory.

Acknowledgment

The described procedure is covered by U.S. Patent Application No. 567,561 assigned to The Salk Institute for Biological Studies.

[4] "Single-Shot" Intrasplenic Immunization for the Production of Monoclonal Antibodies

By M. Spitz

The immunization schedule used to generate activated splenic lymphocytes is of prime importance for the production of monoclonal antibodies (MAbs). "Conventional" immunization schedules have been selected on the basis of their ability to generate polyclonal antisera but these procedures may not be the best choice for hybridoma production. Immunization for hybridoma production almost invariably involves a final injection of antigen 3–4 days before fusion, which is several days before serum antibodies reach maximal levels. This suggests that protocols suitable for producing high serum antibody titers may be different from those activating in the spleen large numbers of B cells which will fuse with myeloma cells to generate hybridomas.

Direct injection of the antigen into the target organ has been previously reported. Boyd and Peart[1] produced rabbit anti-angiotensin II antisera by injecting the immunogen directly into lymph nodes and spleen followed by an intramuscular course of angiotensin absorbed on carbon. Newbould[2] elicited adjuvant-induced arthritis and allergic encephalomyelitis in rats by intra-lymph-node injection. Goudie *et al.*[3] produced specific antisera by inoculating an estimated 20 μg of antigen in the form of an immunoprecipitate into the popliteal lymph nodes of rabbits. Sigel *et al.*[4] reported the production of rabbit anti-pituitary hormone antibodies by direct injection in the lymph nodes.

These considerations suggested that intrasplenic injection of the antigen might provide a good method of immunization for hybridoma production.[5]

Procedure

Intrasplenic Injection. The animal (mouse or rat) is anesthetized by intraperitoneal injection of 10 μl/g body weight (200–300 μl for a mouse, 2.5–3.0 ml for a rat) of the following anesthetic mixture: Nembutal 40 mg, saline 8 ml, absolute ethanol 2 ml. The animal is placed on its right side and may be immobilized on a cork board with rubber bands as shown in Fig. 1a; the fur is clipped and the skin swabbed with 70% ethanol. An oblique skin incision 1–1.5 cm long is made below the rib on the left. By blunt dissection the skin is separated from the muscle layer. The muscle layer and peritoneum are picked up with forceps and carefully incised to avoid cutting the intestine. The spleen can be seen as an elongated dark red organ adjacent to the stomach. The spleen is exteriorized by gently lifting its lower pole with the aid of forceps. A 12 × 0.4-mm (½ × 27-gauge) needle fitted to a 1-ml syringe is inserted deeply into the spleen and the antigen injected as the needle is pulled out, to distribute the antigen through a large part of the spleen. After injection the spleen is pushed back into the peritoneal cavity, the peritoneum and muscle layer sutured together with thread, and the skin edges closed with two to three stitches.

Preparation of the Immunogen. Soluble antigens were dissolved in phosphate-buffered saline (PBS) at about 0.02–0.04%, to give 20 μg of

[1] G. W. Boyd and W. S. Peart, *Lancet* **2,** 129 (1968).
[2] B. B. Newbould, *Immunology* **9,** 613 (1965).
[3] R. B. Goudie, C. H. W. Horne, and P. C. Wilkinson, *Lancet* **2,** 1224 (1966).
[4] M. B. Sigel, Y. N. Sinha, and W. P. Vanderlaan, this series, Vol. 93, p. 3.
[5] M. Spitz, L. Spitz, R. Thorpe, and E. Eugui, *J. Immunol. Methods* **70,** 39 (1984).

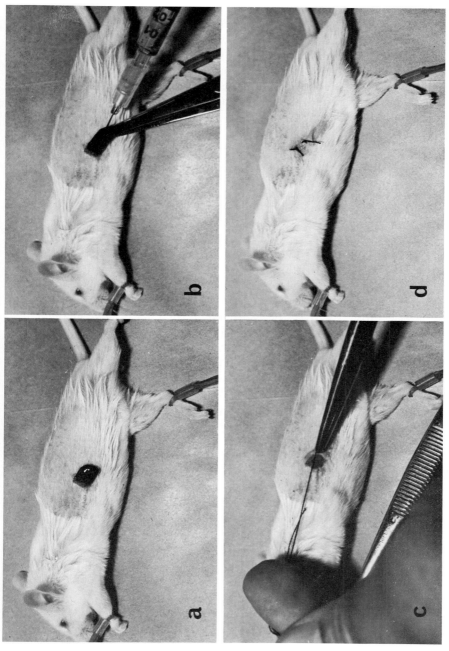

FIG. 1. Intrasplenic injection of antigen. Position of a mouse anesthetized and immobilized with rubber bands as described in the text. (a) Incision and exposure of the spleen; (b) injection of the antigen directly into the spleen; (c) suture of the peritoneum, usually two separate stitches; (d) suture of the skin with two or three stitches, depending on the size of the incision.

antigen in 50–100 μl. Cell suspensions were prepared to contain approximately 2.5–5 × 10^6 cells/ml. Fifty to one hundred microliters of this suspension containing 2.5 × 10^5 cells was injected. Antigen preparations obtained by extraction with detergents, e.g., membrane proteins, can be injected without further purification, and antigen which contains 0.02% sodium azide as preservative can also be injected without adverse effect. Detergent preparations sometimes produce a granuloma but this does not interfere with the production of hybridomas.

Although adjuvant is not required there is probably an advantage in using alum-precipitated immunogens as a different way of handling and presenting antigenic sites. In practice, to 2.5 ml of protein solution containing not less than 1 mg protein/ml, 1.5 ml 1 M sodium bicarbonate is added. To this solution 2.5 ml of a 10% alum preparation is added dropwise and with constant stirring. For injection this suspension is diluted with PBS to contain 10–20 μg of immunogen in 50 or 100 μl.

Production of Monoclonal Antibodies. The fusion procedure was that described by Galfré et al.[6] with some modifications. Spleen cell suspension was prepared by gently teasing the spleen as it was held with a pair of forceps in a petri dish, with a needle bent into a right angle on a 5-ml syringe. The cells were washed twice in RPMI 1640 supplemented with 3% fetal calf serum (FCS) and resuspended in 25 ml of the same medium. Myeloma cells (NS-O) were collected at logarithmic growth phase, washed once, and added to the spleen cell suspension in a 50-ml tube (Gallencamp). The mixture was pelleted at ~450 g (1500 rpm), the supernatant carefully aspirated, removing as much fluid as possible, and the pellet loosened by flicking the tube. Fusion was performed at room temperature by adding 1 ml of polyethylene glycol (PEG) 1500 (BDH) from a 1-ml pipet, with a pipet boy ARH (Arnold Horwell) over 1 min, constantly stirring with the tip of the pipet and rotating the tube between finger and thumb. The mixture was incubated for another minute. Then 1 ml of warm RPMI (30–37°) was added over 1 min followed by 5 ml of RPMI in 3 min and 10 ml more over another 3 min. The cell suspension was centrifuged and resuspended in ~200 ml of HAT selective medium[7] consisting of RPMI 1640 (GIBCO) supplemented with 100 U penicillin/ml, 100 μg streptomycin/ml, 20% FCS (Seralab), 100 mM hypoxanthine (Sigma), 0.4 mM aminopterin (Sigma), and 16 mM thymidine (Sigma).

The cell suspension was dispensed in 1-ml volumes into eight 24-well tissue culture plates (Flow) and incubated at 37° in a humid atmosphere with 5% CO_2–95% air for 8–10 days. Supernatants were aspirated and the

[6] G. Galfré, S. C. Howe, C. Milstein, G. W. Butcher, and J. C. Howard, *Nature (London)* **271,** 266 (1977).
[7] J. W. Littlefield, *Science* **145,** 709 (1964).

cells fed with 1 ml HAT medium per well. From then on the cells were fed every 2–3 days according to cell growth. Under these conditions cells grow in nearly every well.

The myeloma cell is the major factor in determining the growth of hybridomas. It is better to grow them in suspension. A simple procedure is to grow the myeloma cells in half-liter bottles (from medium or FCS) containing a magnetic bar (autoclaved or dry-sterilized together) on a magnetic stirrer in an incubator or a hot room (37°) or on a roller.

In a typical experiment with mouse cells, the spleen cell suspension contained 1.2×10^8 cells. To these cells 4×10^7 myeloma (NS-O) cells were added in a ratio of 3 : 1. In other experiments a ratio of 2 : 1 (spleen cells : myeloma cells) has been used.

Supernatants of confluent wells were screened for the presence of specific antibodies. Positive wells were cloned, usually on the same day as the assay, in soft agar and specific clones recloned, cryopreserved, and grown in tissue culture to produce MAb-containing supernatants, or injected intraperitoneally into pristane-primed BALB/c mice (0.5 ml pristane ip 8 days before injecting the cells).

Comparison of Conventional and Intrasplenic Immunizations

The advantage of the single-shot intrasplenic injection over conventional protocols for the production of MAbs was investigated in two experiments. These experiments compared the two procedures for the production of MAb anti-human immunoglobulin M (IgM) and anti-human fibrin degradation products (FDPs).

Conventional Immunization Protocol. A solution containing about 2–3 mg of antigen (human IgM or FDPs) per milliliter was emulsified with an equal volume of Freund's complete adjuvant (Difco) by repeatedly passing the mixture through a needle joining two syringes. A total of 0.4 or 0.6 ml of the emulsion was injected in multiple subcutaneous sites. Three to four weeks later, and again after another 3–4 weeks, the animals were boosted similarly with antigen in Freund's incomplete adjuvant. Ten days after the last injection, antibody levels were measured. The animals with the highest titer were given 50 μg antigen intramuscularly and 2 days later 50 μg intraperitoneally. Three days later 100 μg immunogen was given intravenously and spleen cells taken for fusion after another 3 days.

Anti-Human IgM MAbs. Single-shot intrasplenic immunization and conventional immunization were compared for the production of anti-human IgM MAbs.[8] Intrasplenic injection resulted in a lower number of positive wells than conventional immunization (Table I); all wells but one

---

[8] A. Gearing, R. Thorpe, L. Spitz, and M. Spitz, *J. Immunol. Methods* **76**, 332 (1985).

TABLE I
SUMMARY OF RESULTS OF TWO FUSIONS COMPARING INTRASPLENIC WITH
CONVENTIONAL IMMUNIZATION[a]

	Intrasplenic, NIBn 198	Conventional, NIBn 37
No. supernatants reacting with IgM	23	31
No. supernatants also reacting with IgG	1	30

[a] Fusion NIBn 198 was done with spleen cells from an animal immunized with human IgM by the single-shot intrasplenic injection and fusion NIBn 37 with spleen cells from an animal immunized by the "conventional" protocol as described.

were specific for human IgM. Conventional immunization gave 31 supernatants reacting with IgM. However, all but one were cross-reactive with IgG and the single non-cross-reactive antibody failed to react with other myeloma IgM or normal serum IgM and may have been idiotype specific.

Two clones of the most reactive supernatants were selected for further characterization. Both MAbs were IgM class as demonstrated by internal labeling with [³H]leucine followed by sodium dodecyl sulfate–polyacrylamide gel electrophoresis (SDS–PAGE). Both antibodies reacted with different myeloma IgMs, normal serum IgM, and monomer and pentamer Fcμ. No binding was seen with IgG, IgA, or IgD. By competitive binding between [³H]leucine-labeled and unlabeled antibodies, we established that the two MAbs bind to different antigenic determinants on Fcμ.

Monoclonal Antibodies to Fibrin Degradation Products. Previous experiments showed that fusions following conventional immunization with soluble fibrin degradation products (FDP) always yielded antibodies which were nonspecific, as in the case of fusion NIBn 97 where all of 42 monoclonal antibodies studied cross-reacted with fibrinogen. To overcome this problem mice were immunized with FDP intrasplenically and fusion carried out 3 days later. Table II shows that 6 out of 13 antibodies studied were specific.[9] Competitive binding between biosynthetically tritium-labeled and "cold" antibodies showed that the antigenic determinants recognized by the MAbs were different.

Monoclonal Antibodies against Human Lymphocyte Surface Components. Mice were immunized with 200,000 human peripheral blood mononuclear cells given intrasplenically. In one experiment 20% of the wells had antibody to lymphoid cells in the supernatant and FACS analysis

[9] R. Thorpe, M. J. Perry, M. Callus, P. J. Gaffney, and M. Spitz, *Hybridoma* **3**, 381 (1984).

TABLE II

NUMBER OF SPECIFIC AND NONSPECIFIC MAbs AGAINST
CROSS-LINKED FIBRIN DEGRADATION PRODUCTS

Fusion no.	Immunization	No. of cross-reactive MAbs[a,b]	No. of specific MAbs[a]
NIBn 97	Conventional	42	0
NIBn 196	Intrasplenic	1	3
NIBn 216	Intrasplenic	6	3

[a] Hybridoma supernatants were screened by ELISA.
[b] Cross-reactive MAbs were antibodies which reacted with either fibrinogen and/or non-cross-linked fibrin degradation products.

suggested that different subsets were being detected. One hybridoma which was subsequently cloned produced an antibody reacting with a polymorphic determinant on human platelets.

The time course of the appearance of spleen cells which acted as fusion partners generating specific MAb-producing hybridomas was interesting. Table III shows that specific antibody was found in ~5% of wells of a fusion with spleen cells 24 hr after a single intrasplenic injection and

TABLE III

TIME COURSE OF GENERATION OF SPECIFIC HYBRIDOMAS[a]

Hours after intrasplenic injection	Total no. of wells	No. of wells with hybrids	No. of specific wells	%
24	96	84	5	5.5
48	96	88	4	4.5
72	96	86	18	18.7
92	72	48	2	4.2
Double intrasplenic injection[b]	96	95	66	69.5

[a] Time between intrasplenic injection of 2×10^5 human peripheral blood cells and fusion. Supernatants have been studied by solid-phase radioimmunobinding, immunofluorescence, and cell sorting.
[b] The double intrasplenic injection was done by injecting the animal in the spleen, using the same procedure, on day 0 and day 12.

that this figure rose to 18.7% at 72 hr. In one experiment in which antigen was injected intrasplenically on day 0 and day 12 with fusion on day 15, 70% of the supernatants contained specific antibody.

Discussion

The fate of antigen in the body is influenced by many factors, among which is the route of immunization. When injected into the bloodstream very little soluble antigen becomes involved in the induction of the immune response, and the rest is removed from the body by natural clearance. When injected into the skin the antigen is filtered by the regional lymph nodes where most of it is taken up either by macrophages or dendritic reticular cells. The remaining antigen entering the bloodstream is taken to the spleen, liver, kidneys, and other organs of the reticuloendothelial system.[10]

In the hybridoma technique the spleen is the organ which provides the normal immunocyte partner of the fusion. By injecting the antigen directly into the spleen, uptake and elimination by other parts of the body are avoided. In addition, by fusing the spleen cells 3 days after one single injection, clonal expansion of activated B cells is very unlikely. Therefore, the spleen would not contain large clones derived from a single activated B cell and so fewer identical hybridomas would be generated.

There are two major practical advantage to the intrasplenic route of immunization. First, it is very economical of antigen. In particular, it is possible to use very small quantities of antigen, and although a dose–response curve is not available, 20 μg of human IgM produced class-specific monoclonal antibody. Similarly, as few as 200,000 cells activated a number of splenocytes to produce successful fusions. This makes it possible to work with cells which are difficult to obtain in large numbers, such as veiled cells. Moreover, experience so far suggests that nearly all animals respond and that there is no need to immunize a large number of animals. A second advantage is that the fusion can be undertaken 3 days after immunization. However, it is not known for how much longer fusion can be delayed. In fact other workers have obtained successful fusions at 3 days after intravenous injection of large numbers of human white cells.[11]

There are some interesting theoretical possibilities that arise from the finding that antigen will activate B cells for fusion as early as 1 day after immunization. Normally, activation of B cells, at least by T-dependent

[10] G. J. V. Nossal and G. L. Ada, "Antigens, Lymphoid Cells, and the Immune Response." Academic Press, New York, 1971.
[11] M. M. Trucco, J. W. Stocker, and R. Ceppellini, *Nature (London)* **273**, 666 (1978).

antigen, is envisaged as involving antigen presentation by macrophages to T cells, followed by activation of T cells with the production of antigen-nonspecific B-cell growth and differentiation factors, and perhaps antigen-specific T helper cells and factors. The B cell is then activated by the sequential effect of antigen (probably presented by antigen-presenting cells) and T-cell factors and products. It is possible, however, that the activation for fusion is due to a direct interaction of antigen with B cells or perhaps presentation of antigen to B cells by antigen-presenting cells.

Antigens, even very simple ones, usually have several antigenic determinants, and since different epitopes have different lag phases for the induction of antibody production, more and more antibody species are produced as the immunization progresses in time. It is general knowledge that the antiserum becomes more polyspecific and cross-reactive with time. Therefore with one single injection, activated lymphocytes against some antigenic determinants may be selectively generated.

On the basis of the present analysis we would predict that not all the antigenic determinants will behave similarly. Working conditions, with reference to time of fusion after antigen injection, amounts of antigen injected, and presentation of the antigen, may all influence the outcome of a fusion experiment.

Presentation of the Antigen. In addition to the use of soluble (proteins) and particulate antigens (cells), especially when working with small peptides or haptens, several attempts have been made to modify the presentation of the antigen. The precipitation of proteins or hapten–proteins with alum has been widely used in animal immunization and can be used with the intrasplenic route of injection. We also used peptides conjugated with CNBr-activated Sepharose beads. In this case a 0.6-mm needle was used for injection. Although adjuvants are not required in the intrasplenic immunization, the alum precipitation of Sepharose conjugation of antigens may act beneficially by altering the presentation of antigenic determinants. This intrasplenic form of immunization has potential not only for the production of MAbs against a wide range of antigens (detergent extracted, azide preserved, toxins, etc.), but also for studies of the early events in the immune response.

[5] Method for Generating a High Frequency of Hybridomas Producing Monoclonal IgA Antibodies

By Dawn E. Colwell, Suzanne M. Michalek, and Jerry R. McGhee

The mucosal membranes of the gastrointestinal and upper respiratory tracts of mammals are subject to continual exposure to ingested and inhaled antigens, including potentially pathogenic bacteria, viruses, and parasites, as well as food and other environmental antigens. Antibodies present in the external secretions which bathe mucosal surfaces represent a critical component of the host's immune response to such antigens. Immunoglobulin A (IgA) is the predominant isotype of immunoglobulin in external secretions[1,2] and exists primarily as 11 S secretory IgA (SIgA, molecular weight 400,000) which is composed of an IgA dimer linked to a molecule of J chain (molecular weight 15,600) and covalently bound to a molecule of secretory component (molecular weight 71,000).[3] A number of biological functions have been attributed to SIgA. These include the inhibition of bacterial adherence to and subsequent colonization of mucosal membranes, the neutralization of viruses and toxins, and the limitation of absorption of soluble antigens through the mucosal epithelium and into the circulation, a phenomenon termed "immune exclusion."[4] Definitive studies of the role of IgA in external secretions, however, have been limited because of the unavailability of sufficient quantities of purified, antigen-specific IgA antibodies.

The advent of hybridoma technology offered a means of generating large quantities of monoclonal IgA antibodies of various specificities for use in studying functional mechanisms of this isotype of immunoglobulin. Nevertheless, the generation of a significant number of somatic cell hybridoma lines which produce IgA antibodies has not been readily achieved, although several laboratories have reported a variety of successes in this endeavor.[5–12]

[1] J. R. McGhee and S. M. Michalek, *Annu. Rev. Microbiol.* **35,** 595 (1981).

[2] J. Bienenstock and A. D. Befus, *Immunology* **41,** 249 (1980).

[3] P. C. McNabb and T. B. Tomasi, *Annu. Rev. Microbiol.* **35,** 477 (1981).

[4] J. R. McGhee and J. Mestecky, "The Secretory Immune System," Vol. 409. N.Y. Acad. Sci., New York, 1983.

[5] J. L. Hurwitz, C. Coleclough, and J. J. Cebra, *Cell* **22,** 349 (1980).

[6] J. Sharon, E. A. Kabat, and S. L. Morrison, *Mol. Immunol.* **18,** 831 (1981).

[7] J. L. Claflin, S. Hudak, and A. Maddalena, *J. Exp. Med.* **153,** 352 (1981).

[8] C. J. Dean, L. A. Gyure, J. M. Styles, S. M. Hobbs, S. M. North, and J. G. Hall, *J. Immunol. Methods* **53,** 307 (1982).

A compilation of data from numerous laboratories[4] has provided evidence that oral administration of particulate antigen to experimental animals results in the induction of antigen-specific IgA plasmacyte precursors in gut-associated lymphoreticular tissue (GALT), e.g., Peyer's patches. These IgA-committed B cells leave GALT, pass through the mesenteric lymph nodes, thoracic duct lymphatics, bloodstream, and spleen, and preferentially localize in mucosal and glandular tissues where they differentiate into plasma cells secreting IgA antibodies with specificity to the antigen first encountered in GALT. Although other investigators have reported the use of cells from GALT in the generation of monoclonal IgA antibodies,[9,12] we describe the use of cells from the spleens of appropriately immunized mice or rats for generating a high frequency of IgA-producing hybridomas.

Immunization Regimen

We have previously shown that gastric intubation of mice with particulate antigen such as sheep erythrocytes (SRBC)[13] or whole bacterial cells[14] results in splenic IgA plaque-forming cell responses. Higher IgA responses are noted in germfree BALB/c mice and lipopolysaccharide (LPS)-hyporesponsive C3H/HeJ mice than in conventional LPS-responsive mice following intragastric immunization, suggesting that lipopolysaccharide from the indigenous gut microflora influences IgA responses to orally administered antigen.[15] Based upon these results, we have adapted the use of orally immunized germfree BALB/c mice to our model (outlined in Fig. 1) for generating IgA-producing hybridomas.[10]

For the immunization of mice, antigen is suspended immediately prior to use in intubation medium, which consists of four parts Hanks' balanced salt solution [Grand Island Biological Company (GIBCO), Grand Island, NY] and one part 7.5% sodium bicarbonate solution (GIBCO). The mouse is grasped at the back of the neck and is held in a vertical position so that

[9] J. L. Komisar, J. A. Fuhrman, and J. J. Cebra, *J. Immunol.* **128**, 2376 (1982).
[10] D. E. Colwell, K. A. Gollahon, J. R. McGhee, and S. M. Michalek, *J. Immunol. Methods* **54**, 259 (1982).
[11] D. E. Colwell, K. A. Gollahon, I. Morisaki, J. R. McGhee, and S. M. Michalek, *Ann. N.Y. Acad. Sci.* **409**, 794 (1983).
[12] J. L. Komisar, J. A. Fuhrman, and J. J. Cebra, *Ann. N.Y. Acad. Sci.* **409**, 833 (1983).
[13] H. Kiyono, J. L. Babb, S. M. Michalek, and J. R. McGhee, *J. Immunol.* **125**, 732 (1980).
[14] H. Kiyono, S. M. Michalek, L. M. Mosteller, M. Torii, S. Hamada, and J. R. McGhee, *Scand. J. Immunol.* **16**, 455 (1982).
[15] J. R. McGhee, S. M. Michalek, H. Kiyono, J. L. Babb, M. P. Clark, and L. M. Mosteller, *in* "Recent Advances in Mucosal Immunity" (W. Strober, L. A. Hanson, and K. W. Sell, eds.), p. 57. Raven Press, New York, 1982.

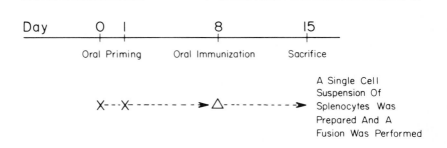

FIG. 1. Basic regimen for orally immunizing mice to generate a high frequency of hybridomas producing monoclonal IgA antibodies to particulate antigens. An alternate regimen includes systemic immunization on day 8.

its head is stationary and upright. An intubation needle (22 gauge; Popper and Sons, New Hyde Park, NY) attached to a 1-ml syringe is introduced into the esophagus and gently inserted into the stomach, where 0.25 ml of the antigen suspension is delivered. In this manner, antigen is administered to mice daily for 2 consecutive days and then once 1 week later. One week following the final administration of antigen, the mice are sacrificed by cervical dislocation, and the spleens are aseptically removed and processed into a single-cell suspension for fusion (see below).

A second immunization regimen which has also been used successfully in the generation of a high frequency of IgA-producing hybridomas involves long-term intravenous (iv) injection of conventional mice with increasing doses of particulate antigen. Antigen for iv injection is suspended in pyrogen-free saline or an equivalent physiologic buffer. The mouse is carefully warmed under a heating lamp or its tail is immersed for 5–10 sec in a container of hot water in order to dilate the veins. The mouse is then placed in a restraining device and 0.1 ml of the antigen suspension is injected into either lateral tail vein with the aid of a 27-gauge hypodermic needle. Daily injection of antigen for 2 consecutive days per week for at least 4 weeks is an effective immunization regimen for stimulating an immune response which supports the generation of IgA-producing hybridomas when immune spleen cells are fused with non-immunoglobulin-producing murine myeloma cells (see below).

The rat may also be used for generating somatic cell hybridomas. We have previously shown that oral immunization of germfree rats with particulate antigen forms of *Streptococcus mutans* results in IgA immune

EXPERIMENTAL DESIGN

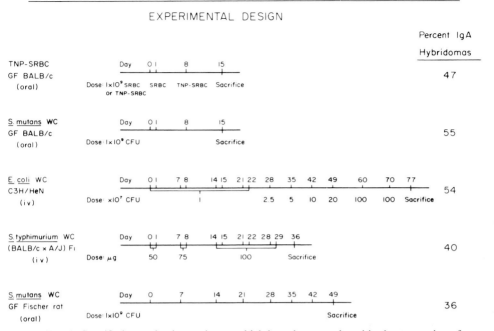

FIG. 2. Specific immunization regimens which have been employed in the generation of monoclonal IgA antibodies. The proportion of hybridomas producing IgA antibody is indicated as a percentage of the total number of hybridomas producing antibody specific for the immunogen used.

responses[16] and that fusion of their spleen cells with murine myeloma cells results in the generation of stable IgA-producing hybridomas.[11] Young (20- to 30-day-old) germfree rats are given antigen weekly for 7 weeks by gastric intubation. One week after the last administration of antigen, the rats are sacrificed by cervical dislocation, and the spleens are aseptically removed and processed into a single-cell suspension for fusion (see below).

Figure 2 summarizes several immunization protocols used in the generation of hybridomas producing IgA antibodies according to the methods described above. When murine myeloma cells were fused with spleen cells from germfree (GF) BALB/c mice (8 to 12 weeks old) orally primed with SRBC and immunized with trinitrophenyl-haptenated SRBC (TNP–SRBC) or immunized with formalin-killed *Streptococcus mutans* whole cells (WC), 54% (27/50) or 40% (52/131), respectively, of the total number

[16] I. Morisaki, S. M. Michalek, C. C. Harmon, M. Torii, S. Hamada, and J. R. McGhee, *Infect. Immun.* **40,** 577 (1983).

of immunogen-specific monoclonal antibodies were of the IgA isotype. Approximately 50% of the hybridomas generated using spleen cells from conventional mice hyperimmunized with either killed *Escherichia coli* WC or killed *Salmonella typhimurium* WC also produced antibodies of the IgA isotype.

In recent studies, we have shown that mice which are orally primed with particulate antigen and systemically boosted 1 week later have higher splenic IgA responses than mice to which antigen is provided only by the oral route.[17,18] To test the effectiveness of this immunization regimen for the generation of monoclonal antibodies of the IgA isotype, germ-free BALB/c mice were given formalin-inactivated X-73 influenza virus vaccine by gastric intubation followed by an iv injection of the viral vaccine 1 week later.[19] Fusion of spleen cells with NSI/1 murine myeloma cells 1 week later resulted in nine hybridomas producing antibodies to the internal nucleoprotein and matrix protein of the virus, and 3 (33%) of these hybridomas produced antibody of the IgA isotype.

Fusion Procedure

The basic procedure used by our laboratory for generating hybridomas has been described previously.[10,11,20] We routinely immunize two animals for each fusion. On the specified day following immunization, mice (or rats) are sacrificed by cervical dislocation and their spleens are aseptically removed. A single-cell suspension of pooled spleen cells is prepared by processing the spleens through a 60-mesh stainless-steel screen into a 60 × 15-mm petri plate containing 10 ml of RPMI 1640 (GIBCO). The cell suspension is transferred into a 15-ml test tube and is left undisturbed for 8–10 min to allow clumps to settle. The supernatant portion of the cell suspension is then carefully transferred into a 50-ml centrifuge tube, and the cells are washed by centrifugation in RPMI 1640 (4°, 1200 rpm, 10 min). Following centrifugation, the supernatant fluid is discarded, the cell pellet is resuspended in fresh RPMI 1640, and the cell concentration is determined. Non-immunoglobulin-producing X63-Ag8.653 murine

[17] H. Kiyono, L. M. Mosteller, J. H. Eldridge, S. M. Michalek, and J. R. McGhee, *J. Immunol.* **131**, 2616 (1983).

[18] E. Jirillo, H. Kiyono, S. M. Michalek, and J. R. McGhee, *J. Immunol.* **132**, 1702 (1984).

[19] K. L. van Wyke, J. W. Yewdell, S. M. Michalek, J. R. McGhee, and B. R. Murphy, *in* "Segmented Negative Strand Viruses. Arenaviruses, Bunyaviruses, and Orthomyxoviruses" (R. W. Compans and D. H. L. Bishop, eds.), p. 307. Academic Press, New York, 1984.

[20] G. Hammerling, V. Hammerling, and J. F. Kearney, "Monoclonal Antibodies and T Cell Hybridomas." Elsevier/North-Holland, New York, 1981.

myeloma cells[21] grown at 37° in tissue culture plates (100 × 15 mm) in a humidified atmosphere of 10% CO_2 in air are harvested, washed twice by centrifugation in RPMI 1640, resuspended in fresh RPMI 1640, and counted. Spleen cells and myeloma cells are added to a 50-ml centrifuge tube at a ratio of 5 to 1, respectively, and are again washed by centrifugation in RPMI 1640. The supernatant fluid is discarded and the cell pellet is resuspended in the residual RPMI 1640 by tapping the bottom of the tube, resulting in a cell slurry. One ml of warmed (37°) polyethylene glycol (PEG; molecular weight 4000; Sigma Chemical Company, St. Louis, MO) solution is added with gentle mixing to the cell slurry over a 1-min interval. Cells are incubated in a 37° water bath during the next minute, and the PEG in the cell suspension is slowly diluted during the next 3–5 min by the dropwise addition of 7 ml of RPMI 1640. The cell suspension is then pelleted by centrifugation (4°, 1200 rpm, 10 min), the supernatant fluid is discarded, and the cell pellet is resuspended to a concentration of 4×10^5 spleen cells/ml in HAT media.[22] One milliliter of the cell suspension is dispensed into each well of 24-well, 16-mm flat-bottomed tissue culture plates, and the plates are incubated at 37° in a humid atmosphere of 10% CO_2 in air. After 2 weeks, the HAT media is eliminated by gradual replacement with complete culture media, and supernatant fluids from the hybridoma cultures are tested for the presence of antibody specific for the immunogen used (see below). Antibody-producing hybridomas are then subcloned by limiting dilution using 96-well flat-bottomed tissue culture plates containing a feeder layer of spleen cells (0.1 ml/well, 4×10^5 cells/ml) from normal nonimmunized BALB/c mice. Two to three weeks later, culture fluids from growing subclones are tested for the presence of specific antibody, and positive subclones are expanded *in vitro*. Stocks of each hybridoma cell line are prepared by suspending cells in freezing media and dispensing the cell suspension into plastic freezing vials. The vials are placed in a −70° freezer overnight, and then are transferred into liquid nitrogen. Monoclonal antibodies may be produced at high concentrations by growing the hybridomas as ascitic tumors in mice. BALB/c mice (or other appropriate histocompatible mouse strains) are injected intraperitoneally with 0.2 ml of pristane (2,6,10,14-tetramethylpentadecane; Aldrich Chemical Company, Milwaukee, WI). One week later, mice are injected intraperitoneally with freshly harvested and washed hybridoma cells (2×10^7 cells in 2 ml serum-free RPMI 1640). The rate of hybridoma growth and fluid production *in vivo* varies with each cell line,

[21] J. F. Kearney, A. Radbruch, B. Liesgang, and K. Rajewsky, *J. Immunol.* **123,** 1548 (1979).
[22] J. W. Littlefield, *Science* **145,** 709 (1964).

but a sufficient quantity of ascites to allow collection usually accumulates in the peritoneal cavity within 9–10 days. Ascites is removed by inserting a 20- to 22-gauge hypodermic needle into the peritoneal cavity of the mouse and collecting the fluid which drains out. The ascites is then clarified by centrifugation, and the ascitic fluid is stored frozen at $-20°$. Monoclonal antibody may be purified from the ascitic fluid in milligram amounts by a variety of conventional means.

Media and Reagents

Polyethylene glycol: Place 20 g PEG in a 100-ml bottle, and sterilize in the autoclave for 20 min. Add 28 ml sterile 0.02 M PBS (pH 7.2) containing 15% dimethyl sulfoxide. Mix and store at $4°$.

Complete culture media: To RPMI 1640, add 20% heat-inactivated ($56°$, 30 min) fetal calf serum, 2 mM glutamine, 100 units penicillin/ml, and 100 μg streptomycin/ml. Store at $4°$.

HAT media

   100× stock hypoxanthine and thymidine (HT): To 200 ml distilled H_2O, add 272.2 mg hypoxanthine + 7.65 mg thymidine. Hypoxanthine does not dissolve well. Adjust to pH 8.1–8.5 with NaOH. Sterilize by Millipore filtration. Store at $4°$.

   100× stock aminopterin (A): To 200 ml distilled H_2O, add 3.82 mg aminopterin. Sterilize by Millipore filtration. Store at $4°$.

   To 98 ml complete culture media, add 1 ml HT 100× and 1 ml A 100×. Store at $4°$.

Freezing media: To RPMI 1640, add 20% heat-inactivated ($56°$, 30 min) fetal calf serum and 15% dimethyl sulfoxide. Store at $4°$.

Assay Methods

A number of different methods can be used for the detection and characterization of antibody in hybridoma culture supernatants. We have commonly used an enzyme-linked immunosorbent assay (ELISA) to identify both the isotype and specificity of such antibodies. The ELISA outlined below was developed for the detection of murine antibodies directed against antigens displayed on intact bacteria[23] and is a modification of the procedure of Engvall and Perlmann.[24] While the basic procedure could be applied universally, optimal antigen concentrations and conditions for coating plates may vary depending upon the properties of the antigen used. Flat-bottomed Linbro EIA plates (Flow Laboratories,

[23] D. E. Colwell, S. M. Michalek, D. E. Briles, E. Jirillo, and J. R. McGhee, J. Immunol. **133,** 950 (1984).

[24] E. Engvall and P. Perlmann, J. Immunol. **109,** 129 (1972).

McLean, VA) are coated with 100 μl/well of a suspension of killed bacteria (5 × 10^8 equivalent colony-forming units/ml) in carbonate–bicarbonate buffer (pH 9.6). After overnight incubation at 37°, plates are washed five times with 0.9% saline containing 0.05% Tween 20 (Tween–saline). A solution of 1% bovine serum albumin in carbonate–bicarbonate buffer is then added to the wells, and plates are incubated at 25° for 90 min. The plates are again washed five times with Tween–saline, 100 μl of undiluted supernatant fluid from hybridoma cultures or dilutions of ascites fluid is added to the wells, and plates are incubated at 37° for 90 min. Plates are then washed five times with Tween–saline, and anti-mouse immunoglobulin heavy chain class (μ, γ, or α)- or γ subclass (γ_1, γ_{2a}, γ_{2b}, or γ_3)-specific reagents (Bionetics Laboratory Products, Kensington, MD) coupled to alkaline phosphatase (type VII; Sigma) by the method of Engvall and Perlmann[24] are added (100 μl/well) to appropriate wells. After overnight incubation at 4°, plates are washed five times with Tween–saline and p-nitrophenyl phosphate (1 mg/ml; Sigma 104 phosphatase substrate) freshly dissolved in diethanolamine buffer is added to each well. Absorbance is read at 405 nm using a Titertek Multiskan photometer (Flow), and wells are scored as positive or negative based upon a comparison of the level of absorbance measured for unknown samples with that obtained for negative controls. In the initial screening of supernatant fluids from hybridoma cultures it is often desirable to use an enzyme-labeled anti-mouse immunoglobulin reagent in order to detect antigen-specific antibodies of any isotype. When using such a reagent, however (particularly for the detection of IgA antibodies), one must be careful to determine the level of reactivity of the reagent with each isotype of murine immunoglobulin.

Buffers and Reagents for ELISA

Carbonate–bicarbonate buffer, pH 9.6: 1.59 g Na_2CO_3 anhydrous, 2.93 g $NaHCO_3$, and 0.2 g NaN_3. Bring volume up to 1 liter with distilled water. Store at 4° for no more than 2 weeks.

Tween–saline: 8.77 g NaCl, 0.5 g Tween 20, and 0.2 g NaN_3. Bring volume up to 1 liter with distilled water. Store at 25°.

Diethanolamine buffer, pH 9.8: 48 ml diethanolamine, 400 ml distilled water, 24.5 mg $MgCl_2 \cdot 6H_2O$. Adjust to pH 9.8 with 1 M HCl. Bring total volume up to 500 ml with distilled water. Store at 4° in the dark. Warm to 25° before use.

We have used column chromatography and a solid-phase radioimmunoassay to determine the molecular form and quantity of IgA in supernatant fluids from our hybridoma cultures. Figure 3 summarizes results obtained with fluid from three representative IgA-producing hybridomas. Supernatant fluid from hybridoma cultures containing antigen-specific an-

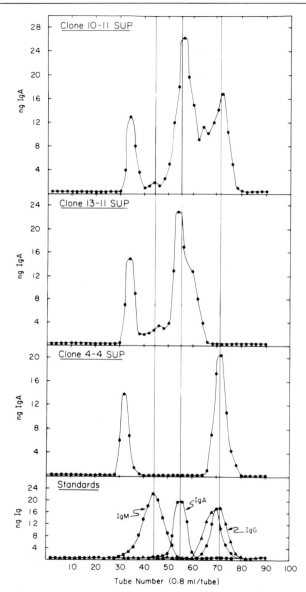

FIG. 3. Ultrogel AcA 22 column fractionation of culture supernatants from three hybridomas producing IgA antibody. The level of IgA in each fraction was determined by RIA (see text). Standards are IgG (7 S, ▲), MOPC 315 IgA (7 S and 11 S, ●), MOPC 104E IgM (19 S, ■).

tibody of the IgA isotype was concentrated 10-fold using an Amicon Diaflo ultrafiltration system (Amicon, Lexington, MA) and a Diaflo YM30 membrane (Amicon). One milliliter of concentrated supernatant fluid was fractionated by gel filtration on a 1.6 × 48-cm column of Ultrogel AcA 22 (LKB Instruments) which had been equilibrated in 0.01 *M* PBS and calibrated with purified IgM, IgA, and IgG murine myeloma proteins. Column fractions (0.8 ml/fraction) were collected, and the amount of monoclonal IgA antibody in each was determined by a solid-phase radioimmunoassay (RIA). Briefly, dilutions of each fraction and known concentrations of a purified IgA myeloma protein (MOPC 315) standard were added in triplicate to polystyrene Removawell strips (Dynatech Laboratories, Alexandria, VA) which had been coated with monospecific anti-mouse IgA, washed, and blocked with a 1% solution of RIA-grade BSA in 0.02 *M* PBS (pH 7.2). Following incubation of samples overnight at 4°, wells were washed, and ^{125}I-labeled monospecific anti-mouse IgA (prepared by the chloramine-T method[25]) was added. Wells were then incubated overnight at 4°, washed, separated, and counted in a Gamma 4000 gamma counter (Beckman Instruments, Palo Alto, CA). As shown in Fig. 3, clone 10-11 produced monomeric, dimeric, and polymeric IgA; clone 13-11 produced dimeric and polymeric IgA; while clone 4-4 produced monomeric and polymeric IgA.

Concluding Remarks

A method is described for generating mouse or rat antigen-specific monoclonal antibodies of the IgA isotype. The availability of large quantities of monoclonal IgA antibodies will allow further studies of the mechanisms of IgA function in host defense against infections at mucosal surfaces and the role of IgA in serum. The availability of these reagents will also be useful in studies aimed at determining the cellular mechanisms involved in the induction and regulation of IgA responses.

Acknowledgments

The authors wish to thank Drs. David Briles, William Koopman, and John Volanakis for their helpful comments, Dr. Katherine Gollahon for her scientific help, and Yvonne Noll for typing the manuscript. The work was supported by USPHS Grants DE 02670, AI 19674, CA 13148, and DE 00092 and Contracts DE 02426 and DE 42551. This manuscript is submitted by D.E.C. in partial fulfillment of the requirements for the degree of Doctor of Philosophy in the Department of Microbiology in the Graduate School, The University of Alabama at Birmingham.

[25] W. M. Hunter, *in* "Handbook of Experimental Immunology" (D. M. Weir, ed.), 14.1. Blackwell, Oxford, 1978.

[6] Production of IgA-Secreting Rat × Rat Hybridomas

By C. J. DEAN, L. A. GYURE, J. G. HALL, and J. M. STYLES

Hybridomas secreting specific antibodies of the IgM and IgG classes can be prepared readily after conventional immunization by using spleen cells as the lymphoid source.[1] Specific IgA- and IgE-secreting hybridomas are rarely obtained using these protocols, although it is clear that IgA-producing cells can be demonstrated in the spleens of immune animals.[2] This failure is most likely due to the absence of IgA-committed cells that are capable of fusing with myeloma cells, and our experience suggests that special immunization procedures are necessary to obtain these cells with any frequency. In this report, we discuss our experience in the rat and detail protocols which have enabled us to prepare specific monoclonal antibodies of the IgA class by fusing the rat myeloma Y3 Ag1.2.3[3] with lymphoid cells taken from peripheral intestinal lymph, mesenteric nodes, or spleens of immune animals.

After antigens are injected into the Peyer's patches, the mesenteric nodes of rats are rich in IgA-secreting plasma cells[2] and specific antibodies of this class can be detected in the bile.[4,5] Although IgA-secreting hybridomas can be prepared using cells from the mesenteric nodes, good yields of hybridomas are only obtained if the lymphoid cells are taken shortly after antigenic challenge (7–10 days). At later times IgG-producing hybridomas are usually obtained. These findings[6] have been exploited for the preparation of antibodies of different isotypes that are directed against the same antigen. Higher yields of IgA-secreting hybridomas can be obtained from animals immunized via the Peyer's patches[7] by collecting and using for fusion the lymphocytes present in peripheral intestinal lymph that normally drains into the mesenteric nodes ("afferent mesenteric lymph"). These findings suggest that the IgA-committed cells in the mesenteric nodes of hyperimmunized animals are too far along the differ-

[1] G. Köhler and C. Milstein, *Nature* (*London*) **256,** 495 (1975).

[2] E. M. Andrew and J. G. Hall, *Immunology* **45,** 169 (1982).

[3] G. Galfré, C. Milstein, and B. Wright, *Nature* (*London*) **277,** 131 (1979).

[4] J. G. Hall, E. Orlans, J. Reynolds, C. Dean, J. Peppard, L. Gyure, and S. Hobbs, *Int. Arch. Allergy Appl. Immunol.* **59,** 75 (1979).

[5] L. A. Gyure, C. J. Dean, J. G. Hall, and J. M. Styles, *Br. J. Cancer* **41,** 640 (1980).

[6] C. J. Dean, J. M. Styles, L. A. Gyure, J. Peppard, S. M. Hobbs, E. Jackson, and J. G. Hall, *Clin. Exp. Immunol.* **57,** 358 (1984).

[7] J. M. Styles, C. J. Dean, L. A. Gyure, S. M. Hobbs, and J. G. Hall, *Clin. Exp. Immunol.* **57,** 365 (1984).

entiation pathway to plasma cells to undergo successful fusion with the rat myeloma Y3 Ag1.2.3. In the rat it is a relatively simple matter to remove the mesenteric nodes by blunt dissection and, when the lymphatic vessels have regenerated, to collect the peripheral intestinal lymph by cannulation of the thoracic duct.

Materials for Cell Culture

Medium. For a general description of the preparation of monoclonal antibodies the reader is referred to the comprehensive article by Galfré and Milstein that appears in an earlier volume in this series.[8] For medium we use Dulbecco's modified Eagle's medium (DMEM) which we prepare from dry powder (Gibco-Europe, Paisley, Scotland) and filter sterilize. Sufficient medium is prepared to last for about 2 weeks, and antibiotics (500 IU penicillin, 50 μg streptomycin, and 100 μg neomycin/ml) are added prior to sterilization. Medium is stored in 100- and 500-ml batches at 6°.

HAT Selective Medium. 100× HT: 136 mg of hypoxanthine (Sigma, Poole, Dorset, England) and 38.75 mg of thymidine (Sigma) are dissolved in 100 ml of 0.02 N NaOH, filter sterilized, and stored in 1-ml aliquots at −20°.

100× aminopterin: 1.9 mg aminopterin (Serva Feinbiochimica, Heidelberg, West Germany) is dissolved in 100 ml 0.01 N NaOH, filter sterilized, and stored in 1-ml aliquots at −20°.

1× HAT, 20% fetal calf serum (FCS): 80 ml DMEM, 20 ml FCS, plus 1 ml each of 100× HT and 100× aminopterin.

1× HT, 10% fetal calf serum: 90 ml DMEM, 10 ml FCS, 1 ml 100× HT.

Serum. Batches of fetal calf serum vary widely in their ability to support the growth of hybridomas and it is important to select a batch of serum that has been carefully tested using several hybridoma lines as described in Ref. 8.

PEG Solution. Fifty grams of polyethylene glycol (1500 MW; Hopkins and Williams, Chadwell Heath, Essex, England) is weighed into a capped 150-ml bottle, 1 ml of water is added, and the solution is then autoclaved for 30 min at 120°. After cooling to about 70°, 50 ml of DMEM is added, mixed, and allowed to cool. The pH is adjusted to about 7.2 with NaOH and 1-ml aliquots are stored at −20°.

Myeloma Cell Culture. If good yields of hybridomas are to be obtained it is important that the Y3 myeloma is properly grown to produce cells

[8] G. Galfré and C. Milstein, this series, Vol. 73, p. 3.

competent for fusion, and in our experience it is essential to grow the cells in spinner culture. We maintain stocks of the Y3 Ag1.2.3 myeloma frozen in liquid nitrogen, as 1-ml aliquots in 95% FCS–5% dimethyl sulfoxide (BDH, Poole, Dorset, England), directly from spinner culture. When setting up a fresh spinner flask, about 4×10^6 cells are thawed from liquid N_2, washed in 10 ml DMEM–10% FCS, and then placed in 100 ml of this medium into a 100- or 200-ml Bellco Spinner Flask (Bellco Glass, Vineland, NY). The flask is placed in a 37° incubator on a Bellco magnetic stirrer, and after allowing the cells to stand for 2 days the culture is then stirred at about 160 rpm. The cells are maintained at a maximum density of between 5×10^5 to 10^6 cells/ml by daily 4-fold dilution with fresh medium. When established in suspension culture (2–3 days after commencement of stirring) the cells are suitable for fusion and the cultures remain competent for several weeks under these conditions.

Feeder Cells for Fusion Cultures. Although cells from the spleen or thymus provide some feeder capacity, we find that the yields of hybridomas are greatly enhanced when the fusion cultures are plated onto subconfluent monolayers of irradiated rat fibroblasts obtained from xiphoid cartilage. Xiphoid cartilages (which terminate the xiphisternum) from six to eight adult or weanling rats are chopped with a scalpel and then stirred for 75 min at room temperature in 15 ml DMEM containing 0.5% trypsin (bovine pancreas type III, Sigma) and 1% collagenase (type II, Sigma). Debris is filtered off by passing the suspension through sterile gauze placed over the mouth of a sterile capped centrifuge tube, and the cells harvested by centrifugation at 400 g for 5 min. After plating into DMEM containing 10% FCS, the fibroblasts are routinely passaged in this medium and stocks frozen in liquid nitrogen as aliquots of $2–4 \times 10^6$ cells in 95% FCS–5% DMSO.

Feeder cells are prepared the day before the fusion either by thawing frozen cells or by treating monolayers grown in Nunc 80-cm^2 flasks (GIBCO) for 5 min at room temperature with 10 ml of phosphate-buffered saline (PBS), pH 7.4, containing 0.04% disodium EDTA and 0.025% trypsin. After centrifugation for 2 min at 400 g the cells are resuspended in 10 ml DMEM–10% FCS in a 25-ml plastic universal and irradiated with about 30 Grays (3000 rad) of X rays from a Marconi 250 kVp X-ray generator (Picker International, Wembley, Middlesex, England). After suitable dilution in DMEM–10% FCS the fibroblasts are plated as 1-ml aliquots, each containing about 2×10^4 cells, into four 24-well Costar plates (Costar, Cambridge, MA) and incubated overnight at 37° in 5% CO_2. The medium in each well is aspirated off just before plating out the fusion mixture.

Surgical and Immunization Procedures

Those unfamiliar with the surgery and anatomy of small animals may find it helpful to first visualize the mesenteric lymphatic system by injecting a small amount of lymphography dye (Guerbet's patent blue V, May and Baker, Dagenham, England) into a Peyer's patch.

Removal of Mesenteric Nodes

Four-week-old Hooded Lister/Cbi or Wistar/Ola rats, taken in our case from a positive-pressure isolator-maintained colony, are fasted for 24 hr and then anesthetized with diethyl ether. The lower abdomen is opened by making a 2-cm incision along the central line. The small intestine and cecum are carefully exteriorized and, after location, the lymph nodes on either side of the mesenteric bed are removed by blunt dissection using a pair of curved forceps. Bleeding is controlled using light finger pressure on the vessels. The intestine is then replaced and about 2 ml of 0.9% NaCl (containing antibiotics if necessary) added to prevent the formation of adhesions. The abdomen is closed with sutures and the animals are kept for 5–6 weeks to allow the lymphatics to regenerate before immunization is commenced.

Immunization

Rats are anesthetized and the lower abdomen opened along the central line. For animals that have undergone surgery previously the second incision is made to one side of the first. The small intestine is carefully extended and the 12–16 Peyer's patches that lie along the peritoneal wall of the small gut are located. For soluble antigens, e.g., horseradish peroxidase, the material (at concentrations up to 10 mg/ml) in saline or PBS is emulsified with an equal volume of Freund's complete adjuvant (Difco Laboratories, Detroit, MI) and taken up in a 1-ml syringe. Between 10–15 μl of this mixture is injected via a 27-gauge needle into every other Peyer's patch, to give a total dose to each animal of about 0.1 ml. Precipitated antigens in PBS can also be used and are often easier to administer than the viscous Freund's adjuvant. Administration of antigens is facilitated if the region of the gut containing the Peyer's patch is gently squeezed between thumb and forefinger so that the hypodermic needle can be inserted just beneath the capsular membrane of the Peyer's patch.

When viable cells are used for immunization,[9] they are suspended in either 0.9% NaCl or DMEM at between 10^6–10^7 cells/ml and about 0.1 ml

[9] C. J. Dean, L. A. Gyure, J. M. Styles, S. M. Hobbs, S. M. North, and J. G. Hall, *J. Immunol. Methods* **53**, 307 (1982).

is distributed between alternate Peyer's patches. For hyperimmunization the procedures described are repeated using the unchallenged patches as recipient for antigen.

If tumor cells syngeneic to the host are used they will grow in the Peyer's patches and provide a continuous source of antigen for stimulation. When using the Hooded rat sarcomata HSN and MC24,[6,7] the total numbers of cells injected has been kept to between 5×10^5 to 10^6 so that the animals become hyperimmunized by growth of the tumors over a period of 2–3 weeks. With some tumors viable cells are shed into the afferent mesenteric lymph and reach the mesenteric nodes.[10] With metastasizing tumors this can be a real problem and may lead subsequently to overgrowth of the hybridoma cultures by tumor cells.

Peripheral Intestinal Lymph

Rats of about 12 weeks of age which have had their mesenteric nodes removed are anesthetized and the upper abdomen opened by making a transverse incision. The thoracic duct is located and the cisterna chyli cannulated with a polyethylene cannula (Portland Plastics, Hythe, Kent) of approximately 1 mm o.d., after the method of Bollman, Cain, and Grindlay.[11] About 5 ml of 0.9% NaCl is placed in the peritoneal cavity to promote initial lymph flow and the abdominal wall closed. The rats are placed in a standard Bollman restricting cage and the cannula tubing is passed into a sterile aluminum-capped 150-ml bottle containing 50 ml DMEM supplemented with 10% FCS and 500 IU heparin to prevent cell death and clot formation. The rats are fed *ad libitum* with water containing 0.6% NaCl, 0.05% KCl, and 2.5% glucose[12] and with food pellets. When flowing well, up to 100 ml of lymph can be collected over a 24-hr period at room temperature (20–25°) and continuous collection of samples over a period of several days is possible. Up to 2×10^8 lymphocytes can be collected from a single rat over a 24-hr period, an amount which is ample for cell fusion.

Hybridoma Production

Preparation of Cells for Fusion

Exponentially growing cells of Y3 Ag1.2.3 are centrifuged in 50-ml aliquots for 5 min at 400 g, washed twice in serum-free DMEM, and then resuspended in DMEM to about $1–2 \times 10^7$ cells/ml.

[10] L. A. Gyure, J. M. Styles, C. J. Dean, K. Nagy, and J. G. Hall, *Br. J. Cancer* **51**, 379 (1985).
[11] J. L. Bollman, J. C. Cain, and J. H. Grindlay, *J. Lab. Clin. Med.* **33**, 1349 (1948).
[12] E. J. Delorme, J. Hodget, J. G. Hall, and P. Alexander, *Proc. R. Soc. London, Ser. B* **174**, 229 (1969).

Thoracic duct lymphocytes collected over a period of 16–24 hr are centrifuged for 5 min at 400 g, washed twice in serum-free DMEM, and then resuspended to 3–5 × 10^7 cells/ml in this medium.

Mesenteric lymph nodes removed by blunt dissection or spleens are disaggregated by forcing through a fine stainless-steel sieve (fine tea strainers from hardware stores are ideal), using a spoon-headed spatula, and collected into serum-free DMEM. After two washes a total leukocyte count is made and the cells resuspended in medium to a concentration of 3–5 × 10^7 cells/ml.

Fusion Protocol

About 10^8 lymphocytes from thoracic dust lymph, mesenteric nodes, or spleens are mixed with 5 × 10^7 Y3 Ag1.2.3 in a 10-ml sterile capped tube (Falcon No. 2001, Becton-Dickinson, Cockeyville, MD), and the cells pelleted by centrifugation for 5 min at 400 g. The supernatant medium is poured off and excess liquid on the walls of the tube carefully removed with a Pasteur pipet. After gently tapping the base of the tube to release the cell pellet, 1 ml of 50% PEG is stirred into the cells over a period of 1 min. Mixing is continued for another minute either by stirring or by gently rocking the tube. Then the cells are diluted with DMEM (2 ml over a period of 2 min, then 5 ml added over 1 min). After centrifugation for 5 min at 400 g, the cells are resuspended in 200 ml of HAT selection medium containing 20% FCS and plated at 2 ml/well into four 24-well Costar plates seeded with irradiated fibroblasts.

The plates are examined after 6 days of incubation at 37° in 5% CO_2 for the presence of hybridoma colonies and then daily until the supernatants are to be tested. Hybridomas produced with this rat myeloma do not grow as cell clusters but are highly mobile, so that to the inexperienced eye it is often difficult to detect the diffuse colonies that are formed early. The hybridomas exhibit a wide variation in initial growth rates and it may be necessary to test supernatants for specific antibody on several occasions. Cultures are not fed until testing for antibody commences, usually after 7–10 days of incubation.

Screening for Specific Antibody

One-milliliter samples of culture supernatant are removed from each well using separate Pasteur pipets, and then aliquots are screened for specific antibody using standard procedures, e.g., RIA, ELISA, or immunofluorescence, on target cells or on antigen-coated plates. For a general description of the methods used the reader is referred to earlier volumes in this series[13] and to Refs. 4 and 6. The cultures are fed at this

---

[13] J. J. Langone and H. Van Vunakis, eds., this series, Vols. 73, 74, and 92.

time, and subsequently until the hybridoma colonies are fully established out of the fusion wells, with HT medium containing 10% FCS. Wells that are positive for specific antibody are examined under an inverted microscope, and if more than one hybridoma colony is present, then cells from individual colonies are aspirated off the well bottom and transferred separately into 24-well Costar plates. The secondary cultures are then retested and the specific antibody-producing cells are cloned.

Cloning of Hybridomas

Specific hybridomas are cloned twice using Nunc 96-well plates (Gibco-Europe, Paisley, Scotland) containing 5×10^3 irradiated fibroblast feeders per well either by limiting dilution or by plating out a total of about 50 cells. If large numbers of hybridomas are to be cloned, the sampling and feeding of the cultures are greatly facilitated by use of the Costar Transplate 96, a 96-well pipetting device.

When selecting clones for bulking up it is important to select not only for antibody specificity but also for antibody affinity and maximum output of immunoglobulin. Also, since the Y3 myeloma produces κ light chains the specific clones may vary in their output of antibodies containing the myeloma light chain.

Bulk Culture

When fully established we find that bulk cultures of rat $\times$ rat hybridomas grow well in either roller bottles or spinner flasks, where the FCS concentration can be reduced to 3%. Many of the hybridomas that we have produced grow well in the peritoneal cavity of athymic rats and up to 30 ml of ascitic fluid containing 1–5 mg/ml of monoclonal antibody can be obtained from one animal. However, rats have a particularly efficient hepatic transport system for IgA,[14,15] and with hybridomas secreting this class of antibody it may be better to use culture supernatants as a source of antibody.

Comments

In several hundred fusions using conventionally immunized rats (i.e., by intravenous, intraperitoneal, intramuscular, or subcutaneous challenge), we have never obtained specific IgA-secreting hybridomas using spleen cells as a source of lymphoid cells. With soluble antigens, such as

[14] E. Orlans, J. Peppard, J. Reynolds, and J. G. Hall, *J. Exp. Med.* **147**, 588 (1978).
[15] G. D. F. Jackson, I. Lemaitre-Coelho, J. P. Vaerman, H. Bazin, and A. Beckers, *Eur. J. Immunol.* **8**, 123 (1978).

horseradish peroxidase, immunization via the Peyer's patches has yielded specific IgA-secreting hybridomas from both spleens and mesenteric nodes.[6]

Our experience suggests that while mesenteric nodes are a source for hybridoma production of IgA-committed cells early after primary challenge (up to 10 days), their frequency is much lower in hyperimmunized animals than are the IgG-committed cells. In hyperimmune animals, peripheral intestinal lymph appears to be the best source of IgA-producing cells for hybridoma production.

[7] The Use of Conventional Antisera in the Production of Specific Monoclonal Antibodies

By KENDRA B. EAGER and ROGER H. KENNETT

Köhler and Milstein's[1] technique for generating hybrid myelomas to make antibody to an antigen of one's choice has had a major impact in biochemistry. The production of monoclonal antibodies has proved to be an important technique in biochemical research and clinical immunology.[2,3] One drawback to the procedure is the relative difficulty of obtaining monoclonal antibodies to a specific antigen. Immunization with relatively impure immunogens can give rise to numerous antibody-producing clones, although the difficulty in identifying the relevant antigen from the complex mixture of antigens persists. It is advantageous, therefore, to be able to use an immunogen which is as homogeneous as possible. Often it is difficult to obtain sufficient quantities of the purified antigen of interest to use for immunization and screening. One method to eliminate the superfluous antigens from the immunization and screening procedures is to use a conventionally produced antiserum to precipitate the desired antigen of interest. We describe here the procedures for such a purification of an antigen and the screening of the resulting monoclonal antibodies. The example described is the production of monoclonal antibodies to human α_2-macroglobulin, a serum glycoprotein, using a conventionally produced goat anti-human α_2-macroglobulin (α_2M) antiserum.[4]

[1] G. Köhler and C. Milstein, *Nature (London)* **256**, 495 (1975).

[2] G. Eisenbarth, *Anal. Biochem.* **111**, 1 (1981).

[3] E. D. Sevier, G. S. David, J. Martinis, W. J. Desmond, R. M. Bartholomew, and R. Wang, *Clin. Chem. (Winston-Salem, N.C.)* **27**, 1797 (1981).

[4] K. B. Eager and R. H. Kennett, *J. Immunol. Methods* **64**, 157 (1983).

Rationale—Principle of the Method

We have demonstrated that specific monoclonal antibodies can be generated against an antibody–antigen complex. Conventionally generated antisera against a wide range of antigens are available from a variety of sources. When one decides to produce monoclonal antibodies against one of these antigens, it is often tedious to prepare sufficient quantities of the purified antigen needed for multiple immunizations of the animals and for the screening of the resulting hybridomas. Using this technique, a conventional antiserum "purifies" the antigen of interest. The antiserum is used to precipitate the antigen, immunoprecipitates are injected into animals, the spleens are removed as the source of cells to be fused with a myeloma partner, and the resulting clones producing antibodies are screened against the injected immunoprecipitate and the immunoprecipitating antiserum. Using a conventional antiserum containing antibodies of various specificities, it is unlikely that a specific region of the α_2M molecule will be blocked and thereby not recognized by the animal's immune system. It is likely that in this system the immunization with the immune complex presents the mouse with a more immunogenic form of the antigen with the goat immunoglobulin acting as a form of "carrier protein."[5]

Methods

Preparation of Proteins for Immunization

An antiserum from goats immunized with human α_2M (Cappel Laboratories, Cochranville, PA) was used to precipitate α_2M from human plasma. The antiserum was titrated to determine the maximum amount of human α_2M that could be precipitated from a given volume of human plasma. Using these optimal conditions, α_2M was precipitated at 4° either directly by mixing the antiserum and plasma in Eppendorf tubes or by immunodiffusion in double-diffusion plates (Kallestad, Chaska, MN). The reactions were left undisturbed for 24–48 hr. A property of α_2M is that it binds proteases with resulting biochemical and conformation changes.[6,7] When immunoprecipitations were done directly, protease inhibitors [Trasylol (aprotinin) (FBA Pharmaceuticals) and soybean trypsin inhibitor (Type 1S) (Sigma) at 500 KIU (kallikrein inactivator units) and 0.1 mg per milliliter, respectively] were added to the human plasma. The immuno-

[5] H. N. Eisen, *Methods Med. Res.* **10**, 94 (1964).
[6] P. C. Harpel, *J. Exp. Med.* **138**, 508 (1973).
[7] P. M. Starkey and A. J. Barrett, *in* "Proteinases in Mammalian Cells and Tissues" (A. J. Barrett, ed.), p. 663. Elsevier/North-Holland, Amsterdam, 1977.

precipitate formed by mixing the antiserum and the plasma in Eppendorf tubes was centrifuged for 5 min at 4° in a Beckman microfuge, and the pellet was washed three times by resuspending in phosphate-buffered saline (PBS), pH 7.2. Immunoprecipitates formed in double-diffusion plates were washed at 4° by submersion in PBS to remove unreacted proteins from the gel. The plates were washed for several days until protein staining of a sample plate indicated that the only proteins remaining were the immunoprecipitin bands.

Female BALB/c mice (Ace Animal Suppliers), approximately 1–2 months of age, and female Brown Norway rats (Dr. David Gasser, University of Pennsylvania) of the same age were immunized for several weeks with the α_2M–antibody complex. The mice were immunized with the amount of α_2M immunoprecipitated from 15 μl of serum (i.e., 20–30 μg). Either washed immunoprecipitate was diluted in PBS to 0.2 ml, or precipitin bands were cut from the diffusion plates and homogenized by passage through a syringe with a 26-gauge needle to remove large pieces of gel. Twice this amount of antigen was injected into the rats. Conventional immunization schemes yielded few anti-α_2M-producing hybridomas. To increase the frequency of α_2M-specific hybridomas, we adapted the procedure described by Stahli et al.[8] The injections were carried out at weekly intervals; the route of immunization alternated between subcutaneous and intraperitoneal injection. For the 3 days preceding the day of fusion, the animals were immunized intravenously through the tail vein with double the quantity of antigen used for immunizing in previous weeks. On the day of the fusion, blood was collected for titration of anti-α_2M antibodies to be used as a positive control and the spleen removed aseptically.

Generation of Hybridomas

Preparation of Myeloma Cells for Fusion. The mouse myeloma cell line Sp2/0-Ag14,[9] a non-immunoglobulin-producing cell, was used for all fusions. The cell line was maintained in suspension culture in Dulbecco's modified Eagle's medium with high glucose (4.5 g/liter) (DMEM) supplemented with 10% fetal calf serum and 0.06% glutamine with 8% CO_2 at cell densities between 10^5 and 10^6 per milliliter. The cells were periodically grown in the presence of 8-azaguanine (0.1 mM) to eliminate any revertants. We have found that cells in the mid log phase (4–6 × 10^5/ml) are better fusion partners.

[8] C. Stahli, T. Staehelin, V. Miggiano, J. Schmidt, and P. Haring, *J. Immunol. Methods* **32**, 297 (1980).
[9] M. Shulman, C. D. Wilde, and G. Köhler, *Nature (London)* **276**, 269 (1978).

Preparation of Spleen Cells for Fusion. As described above, the spleen was aseptically removed from an immunized animal and placed in a 60-mm petri dish (Falcon) with DMEM containing 20% fetal calf serum (DMEM-S20). Several holes were poked in the spleen with a 26-gauge needle, and medium injected forcing out the spleen cells. The cells were collected by centrifugation for 10 min at 1000 rpm (IEC-HN-S) and the pellet resuspended in 5 ml of sterile cold 0.17 mM ammonium chloride. The cells were incubated for 10 min on ice and diluted with 10 ml of DMEM-S20. Viability and cell number were determined by phase microscopy. With this procedure, cell viability is usually greater than 95%.

Fusion. The fusion was carried out according to the procedure reported by Kennett *et al.*[10] with modifications. Approximately 10^8 spleen cells and 10^7 mouse plasmacytoma cells were mixed in a round-bottomed test tube (Falcon) and washed in DMEM without serum. Following centrifugation at 1000 rpm for 10 min, all media was removed and the pellet loosened by gentle tapping of the tube. Next, 0.2 ml of a solution of 35% polyethylene glycol 1000 (PEG, J. T. Baker), 5% dimethyl sulfoxide (Sigma) in DMEM without serum, pH approximately 7.5 and warmed to 37°, was slowly added to the cells. The cells were exposed to the PEG solution for a maximum of 8 min, included in this time period was a centrifugation at 1000 rpm for 5–6 min. At the end of the incubation time, 5 ml of DMEM without serum was added slowly to disperse the pellet. An additional 5 ml of DMEM-S20 was added and the cells gently resuspended and pelleted. The pellet of cells was subsequently resuspended in 30 ml of HY media [HY media; DMEM-S20, 10% NCTC 109 (Microbiological Associates), 0.2 units bovine insulin/ml (Sigma), 0.06% glutamine, 0.45 mM pyruvate, 1 mM oxaloacetate, 0.1% gentamicin] and distributed into six 96-well microtiter plates (Linbro Scientific Company, Hamden, CT) with one drop of suspension per well. The following day, one drop of HY media containing hypoxanthine ($1 \times 10^{-4} M$), aminopterin ($4 \times 10^{-5} M$), and thymidine ($1.6 \times 10^{-5} M$) was added to each well. Two drops of HY media were added 6 days later and every 3–4 days thereafter. Clones appeared macroscopically 10–20 days after the fusion.

Collection of Supernatants for Assays. Supernatants were collected when cell growth covered at least 25–50% of the surface area of the well. Prior to the collection of the supernatant, most of the media was removed and fresh media added. This procedure was repeated at least twice. Following the final change of media, the media remained on the cells for 4 days and then was removed and tested for antibody activity. Sodium

---

[10] R. H. Kennett, K. A. Denis, A. S. Tung, and N. Klinman, *Curr. Top. Microbiol. Immunol.* **81,** 77 (1978).

azide may be added to a final concentration of 0.1%, and the supernatants stored at 4° for at least a few weeks and possibly longer depending upon the stability of the particular monoclonal antibody.

Screening by Solid-Phase Immunoassays

Supernatant from those microtiter wells containing hybridomas was collected (~200 μl) and screened for anti-human α_2M antibodies using a radioimmunoassay (RIA) and an enzyme-linked immunoassay (ELISA).[11] The source of human α_2M was an immunoprecipitate prepared from reacting human plasma with goat anti-human α_2M sera. The precipitate was prepared in Eppendorf tubes as described earlier.

Materials and Reagents

Microtiter plates (96-well): poly(vinyl chloride) flat-bottomed or V-bottomed plates (Dynatech Laboratories, Alexandria, VA) and polystyrene Microelisa plates (Dynatech)

Plastic plate sealers (Dynatech)

RIA protein coupling buffer: 0.2 M sodium phosphate (pH 8.0)

RIA wash buffer: PBS (pH 7.2)

RIA blocking buffer: PBS (pH 7.2) with 1% bovine serum albumin (BSA)

ELISA protein coupling buffer: 0.05 M sodium carbonate (pH 9.8)

ELISA wash buffer: PBS (pH 7.2) with 0.5% Tween 80 (Sigma) (Tw80/PBS)

ELISA antibody dilution buffer: Tw80/PBS with 0.05 M EDTA and 2% additional sodium chloride

ELISA substrate solution: 0.1 M sodium citrate (pH 4.5), 5.5 mM o-phenylenediamine (Sigma), 0.012 M hydrogen peroxide. A 1 M stock of sodium citrate can be prepared, but the o-phenylenediamine and hydrogen peroxide should be added immediately prior to dispensing the substrate solution.

ELISA stop solution: 0.1 M sodium fluoride

Competition assay incubation and wash buffer: 0.1 M sodium phosphate (pH 8.0), 0.15 M sodium chloride, 0.02% sodium azide, 0.25% BSA, and 2% calf serum.

Peroxidase-conjugated goat anti-mouse immunoglobulin (Cappel). Antibody dilution must be titrated for each lot. In general, 1/200–1/1000 dilutions work well. Lyophilized antibody is reconstituted with sterile distilled water, dispensed in 50-μl aliquots, and stored frozen at −70°.

---

[11] E. Engvall and P. Perlmann, *Immunochemistry* **8**, 871 (1971).

Radioimmunoassay (RIA). α_2M immunoprecipitate from 100 μl of plasma was washed in PBS (pH 7.2) and then diluted to 10 ml in 0.2 M phosphate buffer (pH 8.0). Fifty microliters of this solution was added to each well of a 96-well poly(vinyl chloride) (PVC) microtiter plate (Dynatech). Of the protein applied per well, 0.75–1 μg was expected to be α_2M. Control plates were prepared using goat anti-human α_2M alone at the same concentration used in the immunoprecipitations. The plates were covered with plate sealers (Linbro) and incubated at 4° for 18 hr. The wells were then filled with 1% BSA in PBS (pH 7.2) for 1 hr at room temperature followed by two washings with PBS. The BSA saturates the nonspecific protein binding sites on the plate. Monoclonal antibody, 30–50 μl, was added in the form of culture supernatant and incubated at room temperature for 2 hr. The wells were washed four times with cold PBS by filling the wells with approximately 400 μl and flicking out the solution. The plates were drained to remove any excess PBS and ^{125}I-labeled anti-mouse Fab was added to each well (200,000 cpm/well). Following a 2-hr incubation at room temperature, the unbound iodinated protein was removed by washing the plates six times with cold PBS as described above. The plates were dried under a heat lamp and the wells cut from the plate using a hot wire and counted in a gamma scintillation counter.

Enzyme-Linked Immunosorbent Assay (ELISA). α_2M immunoprecipitate from 100 μl of plasma washed in PBS was diluted in 0.05 M sodium carbonate (pH 9.8) to 10 ml and 50 μl of this solution dispensed into wells of a 96-well protein binding polystyrene plate (Microelisa plates, Dynatech Laboratories). Control plates were prepared using the goat anti-human α_2M alone (1/100 dilution). These plates were rinsed several times with distilled water before application of the protein to eliminate contaminants and reduce surface tension. After the protein solutions were added to the wells, the plates were covered and incubated at 4° for 18 hr. The plates were washed twice in PBS containing 0.05% Tween 80 (Sigma). After 50 μl of monoclonal antibody was added, the plates were incubated for 2 hr at room temperature and then washed four times in Tw80/PBS. Peroxidase-conjugated goat anti-mouse Ig (Cappel) was pretreated for 18 hr at 4° with an equal volume of purified human Ig (Cappel) (5 mg/ml) to remove cross-reacting antibodies prior to dilution in Tw80/PBS containing 0.05 M EDTA and 2% additional NaCl. Peroxidase-conjugated antisera, 100 μl per well, was added and the plates incubated 2 hr at room temperature and then washed five to seven times with Tw80/PBS. Then, 150 μl of substrate solution (0.1 M Na citrate, pH 4.5, containing freshly added 5.5 mM o-phenylenediamine and 0.012 M hydrogen peroxide) was added to each well. The enzyme reaction proceeded for 15–20 min and was stopped by the addition of 25 μl of 0.1 M sodium fluoride.

The absorbance of the colored reaction was quantitated on a Multiscan spectrophotometer (Flow Laboratories) at 450 nm. Sodium azide should not be added to any of the solutions used for the ELISA procedure with the exception of the monoclonal antibodies, as it inhibits the peroxidase activity. We have found that as low as 0.1 μg of purified α_2M is detected by specific antibodies using the ELISA method.

Competition Binding Assay. [^{35}S]Methionine-labeled immunoglobulin was obtained by incubating healthy cultures of hybridomas with L-[^{35}S]methionine (Amersham). Cells are washed in methionine-deficient RPMI 1640 (Grand Island Biological Co.) supplemented with 30 mg glutamine/ml (Sigma) and 5% fetal calf serum, 250 μCi of [^{35}S]methionine was added to 10^7 cells (4×10^5 cells/ml), and the cells incubated for 18 hr in a 5% CO_2 incubator. Methionine (10 mM), 0.1 ml, was added 20 min before harvesting the supernatant. Sodium azide was added to 0.1% and the labeled supernatants were stored at 4°.

α_2M immunoprecipitate was prepared as described previously and dissolved in 0.2 M phosphate buffer (pH 8.0) to a final concentration of 2.5 μg/50 μl. To each well of a 96-well PVC plate, 50 μl of this solution was distributed, and the wells were covered with a plate sealer and incubated at 4° for 18 hr. The plates were blocked the following day for 1 hr at room temperature with 0.1 M Na phosphate (pH 8.0), 0.15 M NaCl, 0.02% NaN$_3$, 0.25% BSA, and 2.0% calf serum. Unlabeled antibody in the form of dense culture supernatant was added (50 μl/well) and incubated for 2 hr at room temperature. Subsequently, 50 μl of biosynthetically labeled antibody (approximately $2-3 \times 10^3$ trichloroacetic acid-precipitable counts/5 μl) was added and the plates incubated an additional 2 hr. The wells were washed several times with the above buffer, air dried, and counted in toluene/POPOP-PPO (Liquifluor, New England Nuclear).

Results and Discussion

Generation of Anti-α_2M Monoclonal Antibodies

Hybridomas were produced from four independent fusions. The results of these fusions and the immunization schedules used are shown in Table I. Fusions preceded by a conventional immunization scheme of one or more intraperitoneal/subcutaneous injections followed by a single intravenous injection 3 days prior to the fusion resulted in a low number of clones. All of the fusions produced hybridomas making anti-goat Ig antibodies. The supernatants from these fusions were quantitated for the amount of antibody activity to human α_2M by radioimmunoassay and enzyme-linked immunoassay. α_2M immunoprecipitate and goat antisera

TABLE I
PRODUCTION OF ANTIBODIES AGAINST HUMAN α_2M–GOAT IMMUNOGLOBULIN COMPLEX[a]

| Fusion | Origin of spleen cells | Immuni-zation protocol | Total | Number of hybrids | | Hybrids with activity to α_2M after 30 days in culture (%) |
				Anti-goat Ig (%)	Anti-α_2M (%)	
1	BALB/c	3 sc/ip 1 iv	34	4 (12)	6 (18)	0
2	BALB/c	8 sc/ip 3 iv	44	2 (4.5)	0	—
3	BALB/c	8 sc/ip 3 iv	313	16 (5)	39 (12.5)	18 (46)
4	Brown Norway	6 sc/ip 3 iv	316	41 (13)	30 (9.5)	8 (27)

[a] Reproduced with permission from Eager and Kennett.[4]

to human α_2M were attached to either polystyrene or poly(vinyl chloride) plates, depending on the assay. Colonies that were considered as positive in the radioimmunoassay were also positive by the standards set for the enzyme-linked radioimmunoassay (Table II). Antibody 74 is included to represent those clones whose antibodies react with both the immunopre-cipitate and the antisera. Figure 1, reproduced from Eager and Kennett,[4] shows the binding of several anti-α_2M monoclonal antibodies and their

TABLE II
SAMPLE OF ANTI- α_2M HYBRIDOMA SUPERNATANTS SCREENED BY RIA AND ELISA

| Monoclonal antibody | RIA (cpm) | | ELISA (OD$_{450}$) | |
| | Antigen | | Antigen | |
	Immuno-precipitate (α_2M–Ig)	Antisera (Ig)	Immuno-precipitate (α_2M–Ig)	Antisera (Ig)
SAM4	319	49	0.382	0.146
SAM34	185	79	0.329	0.081
SAM35	491	67	0.867	0.067
SAM74	177	266	0.180	0.239
SAM56	317	62	0.717	0.051
SAM85	463	69	0.564	0.128
Sp2/0 (negative control)	51	71	0.031	0.076

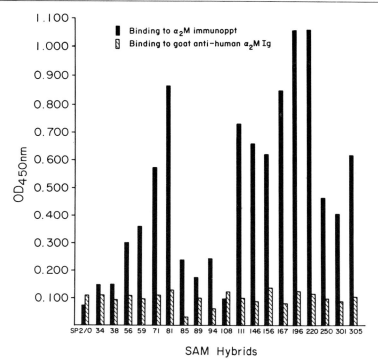

SAM Hybrids

Fig. 1. Binding of mouse anti-α_2M (SAM hybrids) supernatants to immunizing proteins. Bar graphs are representative of duplicate samples from a single assay. Immunoprecipitate and immunoglobulin were bound to wells of a polystyrene plate and tested for the binding of supernatants to the two proteins by the ELISA method. Shown here are those monoclonal antibodies that react with the immunoprecipitate but do not bind significantly to goat immunoglobulin. (Reproduced with permission from Eager and Kennett.[4])

degree of binding to the α_2M immunoprecipitate versus the goat immunoglobulin. Although this method of immunizing with the α_2M–immunoglobulin complex does produce specific hybridomas, we note that α_2M appears to be a poorer immunogen than other antigens we have used and generally yields reduced numbers of hybridomas.

Characterization of Antibodies

The antibodies with an activity toward only the α_2M immunoprecipitate were further analyzed to determine if these antibodies reacted solely with the α_2M and not with a contaminant of the immunoprecipitate or a structure unique to the antibody–antigen complex. This has been previ-

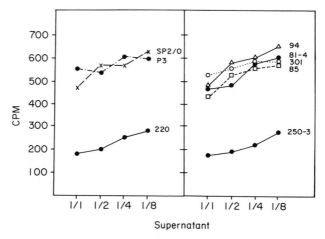

FIG. 2. Competitive binding inhibition of ³⁵S-SAM220. Fifty microliters of serial dilutions of SAM unlabeled antibody (in the form of dense culture supernatant) was incubated with 2.5 μg of human α_2M immunoprecipitate attached per well of a poly(vinyl chloride) plate at room temperature. Then 50 μl of biosynthetically labeled antibody, [³⁵S]methionine-labeled SAM220, was added and incubated for an additional 2 hr. Wells were washed, dried, and counted. The left panel shows the binding of unlabeled SAM220 antibody with labeled ³⁵S-SAM220. Sp2/0 and P3 supernatant do not show any inhibition, as expected. The right panel shows the binding of dilutions of several monoclonal antibodies; only SAM250-3 demonstrates any inhibition with ³⁵S-SAM220.

ously reported by Eager and Kennett.[4] All antibodies react with purified α_2M and immunoprecipitate a protein of the expected molecular weight.

Since numerous anti-α_2M antibodies were generated, it was of interest to determine the nature of the antigenic determinants recognized by the antibodies. A competition assay using a labeled monoclonal antibody and excess unlabeled monoclonal antibodies allowed us to look at the individual antibody binding sites. A graph of one of these competition experiments is shown in Fig. 2. Monoclonal antibodies SAM220 and SAM250-3 compete for the same or spatially close antigenic sites. From these competition experiments, we recognize a minimum of 11 distinct antigenic sites identified by 19 monoclonal antibodies. These antibodies also have different reactivities toward α_2M from other species as well as different reactivities toward chemically modified α_2M.[12] Consequently, the generation of antibodies using an immune complex does not severely restrict the antigenic sites identified by the animal's immune system.

[12] K. B. Eager and R. H. Kennett, *Ann. N.Y. Acad. Sci.* **421,** 154 (1983).

Summary

We have shown here that conventionally produced antisera aids in the production of specific monoclonal antibodies. The complex of immunoglobulin plus antigen acted as an effective immunogen in both rats and mice. Stable cell lines producing anti-human α_2M monoclonal antibodies to numerous antigenic sites on the α_2M molecule have been generated by this method. This method has also been used to produce monoclonal antibodies to human complement components.[13] This procedure of immunizing mice with an immunoprecipitated product derived from conventionally produced antisera is a unique approach in that the antigen is conveniently enriched without tedious and time-consuming biochemical purification. In addition, the use of the immunoprecipitated product in conjunction with the immunoprecipitating antisera allows for rapid screening of the hybridomas in the initial stages when cell growth and maintenance is critical. This method thus further simplifies the task of obtaining a specific monoclonal antibody from a complex mixture. A final consideration is the wide availability of conventionally produced antisera to numerous proteins and other biological substances that could be used in the production of monoclonal antibodies, and consequently these antibodies could be used in more detailed studies of these same molecules.

Acknowledgments

The authors would like to thank Dr. Douglas Holsclaw, Hahnemann University, Philadelphia, for providing human plasma samples. This work was supported by NSF Grant 26757.

[13] Z. Jonak, personal communication.

[8] Preparation of Monoclonal Antibodies to Preselected Protein Regions

By M. Zouhair Atassi

Introduction

Monoclonal antibodies produced by the techniques of somatic cell hybridization[1,2] are being used in many areas of fundamental research and

[1] G. Köhler and C. Milstein, *Nature (London)* **256,** 495 (1975).
[2] G. Köhler and C. Milstein, *Eur. J. Immun.* **6,** 511 (1976).

clinical medicine (for reviews, see Refs. 3–16). Most of these applications have taken advantage of the precise binding specificities expressed by monoclonal antibodies to distinct antigenic determinants. Yet in spite of recent developments in cell fusion and tissue culture techniques,[15,17–22] as well as in hybridoma screening methods,[23–26] the production of monoclonal antibodies that express desired submolecular binding specificities to single antigenic sites remains a time-consuming and often expensive endeavor. Large numbers of hybridoma cultures must first be screened for the production of relevant antibodies to the native molecule. Once obtained in sufficient quantities, these antibodies must be tested again to determine if they express the desired submolecular binding specificity. Since many hydridomas secrete antibodies with irrelevant or undesired

[3] F. Melchers, M. Potter, and N. L. Warner, in "Current Topics in Microbiology and Immunology—Lymphocyte Hybridomas," Vol. 81.IX-XXIII. Springer-Verlag, Berlin, 1978.

[4] D. E. Yelton and M. D. Schraff, Am. Scient. 68, 510 (1980).

[5] J. W. Goding, J. Immun. Meth. 39, 285 (1980).

[6] N. Z. Staines, Immunology 40, 287 (1980).

[7] W. C. Raschke, Biochim. Biophys. Acta 605, 113 (1980).

[8] B. A. Diamond, D. E. Yekton, and M. D. Schraff, New Engl. J. Med. 302, 1344 (1981).

[9] R. Lewin, Science 212, 767 (1981).

[10] E. D. Sevier, G. S. David, J. Martinins, W. J. Desmond, R. M. Bartholomew, and R. Wang, Clin. Chem. 27, 1797 (1981).

[11] M. D. Schraff, S. Roberts, and P. Thammana, J. Infect. Dis. 143, 346 (1981).

[12] D. Lane and H. Koprowski, Nature (London) 296, 200 (1982).

[13] N. Wade, Science 215, 1073 (1982).

[14] D. Eilat, Molec. Immun. 19, 943 (1982).

[15] H. S. Kaplan, L. Olsson, and K. Raubitschek, in "Monoclonal Antibodies in Clinical Medicine" (A. J. McMichael and J. W. Fabre, eds.), pp. 17–35. Academic Press, London, 1982.

[16] C. Milstein, in "Monoclonal Antibodies in Clinical Medicine" (A. J. McMichael and J. W. Fabre, eds.), pp. 3–16. Academic Press, New York, 1982.

[17] D. M. Kranz, P. A. Billing, J. N. Herron, and E. W. Voss, Jr., Immun. Commun. 7, 639 (1980).

[18] M. Shulman, C. D. Wilde, and G. Köhler, Nature (London) 276, 269 (1978).

[19] S. Fazekas de St. Groth and D. Scheidegger, J. Immun. Meth. 35, 1 (1980).

[20] A. L. DeBlas, M. V. Ratnaparkhi, and J. E. Mosimann, J. Immun. Meth. 45, 109 (1981).

[21] J. M. Davis, J. E. Pennington, A.-M. Kubler, and J.-F. Conscience, J. Immun. Meth. 50, 161 (1982).

[22] H. Murakami, H. Masui, G. H. Sato, N. Sueoka, T. P. Chow, and T. Kanosueoka, Proc. Natl. Acad. Sci. U.S.A. 79, 1158 (1982).

[23] M. D. Schneider and G. S. Eisenbarth, J. Immun. Meth. 29, 331 (1979).

[24] D. R. Parks, V. M. Bryan, B. T. Oi, and L. A. Herzenberg, Proc. Natl. Acad. Sci. U.S.A. 76, 1962 (1979).

[25] D. Buchanan, J. Kamarck, and N. H. Ruddle, J. Immun. Meth. 42, 179 (1981).

[26] R. H. Yolken and F. J. Leister, J. Immun. Meth. 43, 209 (1981).

specificities, it is apparent that the preparation of monoclonal antibodies to specific antigenic sites can be tedious and elusive.

It is highly desirable, therefore, to have a direct approach that would be less tedious and more fruitful in the preparation of monoclonal antibodies of predetermined specificities to protein regions selected by the investigator. This can be accomplished by using the protein region of interest, prepared synthetically or by protein cleavage, as the immunizing antigen, in some suitable form. One way is to immunize with the conjugate of peptide and a protein carrier. It has long been a standard practice in immunology that, in order to prepare antibodies against a small peptide from a given protein, the peptide is coupled to a large molecular weight carrier prior to immunization (see Ref. 27 for review). The antibodies thus prepared can react with the region represented by the peptide in the native parent protein if this region is accessible on the protein surface.[28]

Frequently, however, in the coupling of a peptide to a carrier, side chains on the peptide that are used for the covalent attachment to the carrier are also important for immune recognition, specificity, and binding to antibodies. Thus, the immune recognition of a region is often altered by coupling the region to a carrier and antibodies against a conjugated peptide will react only weakly, or not at all, with the intact protein. This shortcoming would be completely avoided if small peptides were immunogenic in their free form. It has been believed that free small peptides are not immunogenic. However, we have recently discovered that small (six residues or longer) synthetic peptides are in fact immunogenic in their *free* (i.e., without conjugation to any carrier) form. These discoveries were initially stimulated by our studies that were aimed at investigating whether the antigenicity of certain protein regions (i.e., the antigenic sites) was related to any uniquenesses in their primary structures.

Studies in this laboratory have resulted in the determination of the first complete protein antigenic structures to be defined. These were the antigenic structures of sperm whale myoglobin (Mb) in 1975[29] and of hen egg white lysozyme in 1978.[30] Also, we have recently localized and synthesized all the antigenic sites of the α and β chain of human adult Hb,[31–34] the

[27] D. M. Weir, *in* "Handbook of Experimental Immunology," Vol. 3, 2nd ed., pp. A2.10-A2.11. Blackwell Scientific Publications, Oxford, 1973.

[28] M. Z. Atassi and A. F. S. A. Habeeb, *in* "Immunochemistry of Proteins" (M. Z. Atassi, ed.), Vol. 2, pp. 177–264. Plenum, New York, 1977.

[29] M. Z. Atassi, *Immunochemistry* **12**, 423 (1975).

[30] M. Z. Atassi, *Immunochemistry* **15**, 909 (1978).

[31] A. L. Kazim and M. Z. Atassi, *Biochem. J.* **191**, 261 (1980).

[32] A. L. Kazim and M. Z. Atassi, *Biochem. J.* **203**, 201 (1982).

[33] N. Yoshioka and M. Z. Atassi, *5th Int. Congr. Immunol. Abstr.* (232) 0023 (1983).

[34] N. Yoshioka and M. Z. Atassi, *Biochem. J.* (1986) in press.

major antigenic sites of serum albumin,[35-38] the antigenic and allergenic sites of ragweed allergen Ra3,[39,40] and many (12) of the major sites of influenza virus hemagglutinin.[41,42] Our determination of the antigenic structure of Mb[29] and then that of lysozyme[30] answered many questions relating to the molecular immune recognition of native proteins with surprising accuracy.[29] Many of the observations and findings first made from our Mb work[29,43] have since become established concepts that have been confirmed with a variety of other proteins.

Sperm whale Mb is a single polypeptide chain comprising 153 amino acids.[44] Because this was the first protein for which the entire antigenic structure was determined,[29] it has served as a valuable system for investigating parameters of the mechanism and regulation of the immune response to protein antigens. The native protein has five antigenic sites located in exposed, conformationally sensitive, continuous portions of the polypeptide chain (Fig. 1). The five antigenic sites occupy the following regions (Fig. 2): site 1, residues 15 through 22; site 2, residues 56 through 62; site 3, residues 94 through 99; site 4, residues 113 through 119; site 5, residues 145 through 151.

Following the determination of the entire antigenic structure of Mb,[29] we have carried out detailed studies designed to investigate the antigenicity, in their free form (i.e., without coupling to any carrier), of the synthetic antigenic sites and peptides representing other selected surface regions of Mb that are not antigenic when the intact protein is used as the immunizing antigen, and to examine the factors controlling any such antigenicity. These studies showed that the immunization with free peptides will evoke *in vivo* antibody responses.

With the demonstration that it is possible to elicit antibodies with preselected submolecular binding specificities to protein regions by immunization with free peptides, it appeared possible to produce monoclonal antibodies with similar predetermined specificities by the use of free synthetic peptides as immunogens. The salient features in the development of this approach are (1) the use of a model protein whose antigenic structure is known in detail; (2) immunization with free synthetic peptides rather

[35] M. Z. Atassi, S. Sakata, and A. L. Kazim, *Biochem. J.* **179,** 327 (1979).

[36] S. Sakata and M. Z. Atassi, *Biochim. Biophys. Acta* **625,** 159 (1980).

[37] S. Sakata and M. Z. Atassi, *Mol. Immunol.* **17,** 139 (1980).

[38] M. Z. Atassi, *Biochim. Biophys. Acta* **704,** 552 (1982).

[39] H. Atassi and M. Z. Atassi, *FEBS Lett.* **88,** 96 (1985).

[40] H. Atassi and M. Z. Atassi, *Eur. J. Immunol.* (1985) in press.

[41] M. Z. Atassi and R. G. Webster, *Proc. Natl. Acad. Sci. U.S.A.* **80,** 840 (1983).

[42] M. Z. Atassi and J. I. Kurisaki, *Immunol. Commun.* **13,** 539 (1984).

[43] M. Z. Atassi, *in* "Specific Receptors of Antibodies and Cells" (D. Pressman, T. B. Tomasi, A. L. Grossberg, and N. R. Rose, eds.), pp. 118–136. Karger, Basel, 1972.

[44] A. B. Edmundson, *Nature (London)* **205,** 883 (1965).

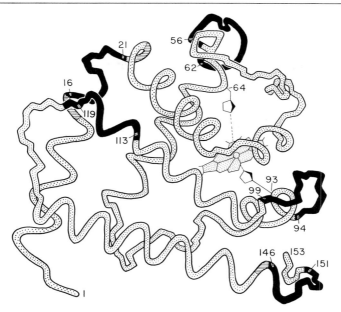

FIG. 1. Sperm whale myoglobin. The five antigenic sites are shown in black. (From Atassi.[29])

Site	Structure and location	No. of residues
1	15 16 21 22 (Ala)–Lys–Val–Glu–Ala–Asp–Val–(Ala)	6 (or 7)
2	56 62 Lys–Ala–Ser–Glu–Asp–Leu–Lys	7
3	94 99 Ala–Thr–Lys–His–Lys–Ile	6
4	113 119 His–Val–Leu–His–Ser–Arg–His	7
5	145 146 151 (Lys)–Tyr–Lys–Glu–Leu–Gly–Tyr	6 (or 7)

FIG. 2. Covalent structures of the five antigenic sites of sperm whale Mb. Residues in parentheses are part of the antigenic site only with some antisera. Thus for site 1, the reactive region invariably comprises residues 16–21 and with some antisera Ala–15 is part of the region (which will then correspond to residues 15–21), while with other antisera Ala–22 is an essential part of the region (which will then correspond to residues 16–22). This site occupies either six or seven residues depending on antiserum. A shift in site 2 by two residues to the left was recently found with a monoclonal antibody to Mb. For sites 3 and 4 no such "displacement" or "shift" has been observed yet (at least with the antisera so far studied). In the case of site 5, Lys-145 can be part of the antigenic region only with some antisera and this site will therefore comprise six or seven residues, depending on the antiserum. (From Atassi.[29])

than peptide–carrier conjugates; (3) hybrid selection and maintenance using traditional hybridoma tissue culture techniques; (4) submolecular binding specificities determined by, and entirely directed to, the synthetic regions used for immunization; and (5) an apparent similarity between the monoclonal antibodies secreted by the subcloned hybrids and the serum anti-Mb antibodies produced by the donor mice spleen cells.

In the following sections, representative procedures for the preparation of antisera and monoclonal antibodies to peptides will be described. These will be followed by a brief presentation and discussion of some of the parameters that control and regulate the responses to free peptides.

Procedure

The following methods[45,46] employed in the preparation of antisera and monoclonal antibodies to the synthetic antigenic sites (Fig. 2) of sperm whale Mb will serve as a representative example of the procedure employed in such studies.

Mice and Immunizations. Adult male and female mice (Jackson Laboratories, Bar Harbor, ME) are immunized at 3-week intervals with optimum dose of free synthetic antigenic sites 1–5 (one site/animal) by means of an intradermal injection in the hind footpads with an emulsion (0.1 ml) consisting of equal volumes of peptide dissolved in PBS and complete Freund's adjuvant containing 1 mg/ml heat-killed *Mycobacterium tuberculosis* H37Ra (Difco Laboratories, Detroit, MI). (PBS made as 0.01 M sodium phosphate buffer, pH 7.2, with 0.15 M NaCl.) The mice are bled from the tail at biweekly intervals and the sera tested for anti-Mb antibody by solid-phase RIA. Mice that have positive sera are injected with uncoupled peptide (50 μg/0.1 ml, ip in PBS) 4–5 days before the animals are killed and their spleens excised for hybridization.

Myeloma Cells. Fa/O cells, a hypoxanthine–guanine phosphoribosyltransferase (HGPRT)-negative hybridoma variant that does not produce Ig components,[19] are maintained under 5% CO_2 in air at 37° in a complete medium (CM) consisting of Iscove's modified Dulbecco's medium (IMDM) supplemented with 10% (v/v) γ-globulin-free newborn calf serum (NCS), 100 units penicillin/ml, 100 μg streptomycin/ml, and 0.002 mM L-glutamine (GIBCO Laboratories, Grand Island, NY). Cultures are tested for revertants by exposure to 100 μM hypoxanthine, 0.4 μM aminopterin, and 16.0 μM thymidine (Sigma Chemical Co., St. Louis, MO) in CM (CM-HAT).

[45] H. E. Schmitz, H. Atassi, and M. Z. Atassi, *Mol. Immunol.* **19,** 1699 (1982).
[46] H. E. Schmitz, H. Atassi, and M. Z. Atassi, *Mol. Immunol.* **20,** 719 (1983).

Monoclonal Antibody Production. Somatic cell fusions are performed essentially by the method of Frazekas de St. Groth and Scheidegger.[19] Spleen cells (5×10^7 cells) are added to 1×10^8 Fa/O cells in 50 ml IMDM, pelleted at 200 g, and mixed gently with 1.0 ml 50% (v/v) polyethylene glycol (PEG 1540; J. T. Baker Chemical Co., Phillipsburg, NJ) in IMDM for 1 min at room temperature. After an additional $1\frac{1}{2}$ min, the suspension is diluted dropwise with 12.0 ml IMDM, pelleted, resuspended in 48.0 ml CM-HAT, and distributed in 1.0 ml volumes to Costar 24-well tissue culture plates (Bellco Glass, Vineland, NJ) containing $1.0–1.5 \times 10^6$ nonimmune BALB/cByJ irradiated (3200 rad) spleen cells in 1.0 ml CM-HAT/well. Cultures are fed every 7–8 days with 1.0 ml fresh CM-HAT until hybrids demonstrated vigorous growth. These cultures are screened for anti-Mb antibody production at appropriate intervals by solid-phase RIA. Positive cultures are cloned by limiting dilution into 96-well flat-bottomed plates (Nunc, GIBCO), scored for growth, screened for specific antibody production, and expanded in CM containing 100 mM hypoxanthine and 16.0 μM thymidine (CM-HT). Clones are then subcloned by the same procedures and expanded in CM.

Hybridoma antibodies are collected in media supernatants by the method of Oi and Herzenberg.[47] Expanded subclones are also injected ip into BALB/cByJ mice (2.0×10^6 cells/1.0 ml fresh CM) that had been primed with 2,6,10,14-tetramethyl pentadecane (pristane, Sigma Chemical Co.). Ascites fluids are collected, clarified, and purified by protein A-Sepharose (Pharmacia Fine Chemical, Uppsala, Sweden) affinity chromatography essentially by the method of Ey *et al.*[48]

The homogeneity of the monoclonal antibody preparations is confirmed by isoelectric focusing electrophoresis[49] on thin-layer polyacrylamide gels (LKB, Gaithersburg, MD) using a heme-specific (Mb) benzidine stain (Kodak Co., Rochester, NY).

RIA Plates. Poly(vinyl chloride) protein assay plates (Costar, Cambridge, MA) are incubated for 3 hr at 37° with excess (1.5 μg in 50 μl/well) test and control antigens, following which they are washed extensively with PBS, and blocked with 1% bovine serum albumin (BSA) in PBS (100 μl/well) for 1 hr at 37° to prevent nonspecific binding of subsequent reagents.

Radiolabeling of Protein A. Purified protein A (Pharmacia) is radiolabeled with ^{125}I (Amersham Corp., Arlington Heights, IL) using the chlor-

[47] V. T. Oi and L. A. Herzenberg, *in* "Selected Methods in Cellular Immunology" (B. B. Mishel and S. M. Shiigi, eds.), pp. 351–372. Freeman, San Francisco, 1980.

[48] P. L. Ey, S. J. Prowse, and C. R. Jenkin, *Immunochemistry* **15**, 429 (1978).

[49] A. R. Williamson, *in* "Handbook of Experimental Immunology" (D. M. Weir, ed.), 2nd ed., pp. 8.1–8.23. Blackwell, London, 1973.

amine-T method.[50] Unbound ^{125}I is separated from the radiolabeled protein A by gel filtration on Sephadex G-25 (Pharmacia). At least 95% of the protein A associated ^{125}I is precipitable with 10% (w/v) trichloroacetic acid).

Screening and Determination of Antigen Binding Specificities. Sera, culture supernatants, and clarified ascites fluids are screened for anti-Mb antibodies using a solid-phase RIA described by Sakata and Atassi[51] as modified by Schmitz *et al.*[45] This assay is also used to determine antibody binding specificities. Briefly, RIA plates that had been coated with the appropriate test antigens (Mb or peptide conjugates) are incubated for 3 hr at 37° with an antibody preparation (50 μl/well) appropriately prediluted in PBS containing 0.1% BSA (PBS–BSA) to maximize specific binding. The plates are subsequently washed with PBS and amplified with excess (1 : 1000 dilution of the stock reagent in PBS–BSA) rabbit anti-mouse IgG + IgM antisera (Litton Bionetics, Kensington, MA) for 2 hr at 37°. After washing, the plates are developed with excess (200,000 cpm in 50 μl PBS–BSA/well) ^{125}I labeled protein A for 2 hr at room temperature, washed with PBS, and then separated into individual wells that are counted in a gamma scintillation counter (Beckman Instruments, Irvine, CA). Results are corrected for nonspecific (0.1–2%) binding detected in control wells not coated with test antigen but blocked with BSA.

Determination of Antibody Class. Solid-phase RIA is also used to determine the class of each antibody preparation obtained by this procedure. In these assays, Mb is used as the plate antigen for the test antibody and the latter is followed by a panel of rabbit anti-mouse immunoglobulin class-specific antisera (Litton Bionetics), which are used to amplify the murine anti-Mb antibody binding, or Mb is followed by normal rabbit serum or PBS–BSA. These antisera are diluted 1 : 100–1 : 1000 in PBS–BSA. The specificities of the anti-class antisera are first confirmed by RIA and in Ouchterlony immunodiffusion plates in which class-specific myeloma proteins (Zymed Laboratories, San Francisco, CA) are used as antigens.

Antibody Responses to Free Peptides

Optimum Peptide Dose

It is of practical importance to know the optimum amount of a given peptide that will evoke a maximum antibody response in a particular host.

[50] W. M. Hunter, *in* "Handbook of Experimental Immunology" (D. M. Weir, ed.), p. 608. Davis, Philadelphia, 1969.
[51] S. Sakata and M. Z. Atassi, *Mol. Immunol.* **18**, 961 (1981).

This question has been investigated[52] in detail for the antigenic sites of Mb following immunization into BALB/cByJ mice. Separate groups of BALB/cByJ mice were immunized with different amounts of each of the free synthetic antigenic sites (Fig. 2) to determine the optimum immunizing dose for eliciting serum antibodies that bind specifically to Mb. The dose range used in immunization of each antigenic site was from 6 to 100 μg per mouse. Radioimmune antibody binding studies indicated that there is an optimal immunizing dose for each of the five antigenic sites[52] which was smaller than anticipated. The optimal immunizing dose for each of the antigenic sites, in their free state, was 50 μg for site 1, 25 μg for site 2, 12 μg for site 3, 25 μg for site 4, and 25 μg for site 5. A summary of the antibody binding of antisera raised following immunization with the optimal dose of each of the antigenic sites is shown in Tables II and III. It was also clear from these studies[52] that some antigenic sites are more immunogenic than others. Thus, there is no general optimum peptide dose and, for an unknown peptide, this must be determined for each host strain or species used. At present it is unknown why some peptides are more immunogenic than others. In all likelihood, this is dependent on their covalent structures (i.e., the amino acids constituting the peptide and the sequence of the amino acids).

Effect of Peptide Size

To study the effect of size on the antigenicity of free peptides, several synthetic peptides of increasing length and carrying site 5 of Mb (Fig. 3) were injected into $H\text{-}2^d$ and $H\text{-}2^s$ mice, and their ability to evoke antibodies that will react with native Mb was examined.[53] We had previously shown, when Mb is used as the immunogen, that $H\text{-}2^d$ strain mice are high responders to Mb and respond to sites 1, 2, 3, and 5 and that $H\text{-}2^s$ strain mice are high responders to Mb and respond to sites 1, 2, and 5.[54] Immunization with peptides of 22 amino acids (peptide 132–153), 11 amino acids (peptide 143–153), 9 amino acids (peptide 145–153), or even 7 amino acids (peptide 145–151), each of which contains only one antigenic site within Mb, at least when the native protein is used as the immunizing antigen, is effective in eliciting antibodies capable of binding to the native protein.[53] The specificity of these antibodies was rigorously established.[53] In general, the 22- and 11-residue peptides elicited higher antibody responses than the 9- and 7-residue peptides. The responses to the latter two pep-

[52] C. R. Young, H. E. Schmitz, and M. Z. Atassi, *Immunol. Commun.* **12**, 419 (1983).

[53] C. R. Young and M. Z. Atassi, *Immun. Commun.* **11**, 9 (1982).

[54] K. Okuda, S. Twining, C. S. David, and M. Z. Atassi, *J. Immunol.* **123**, 182 (1979).

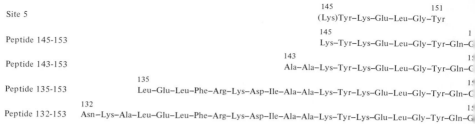

FIG. 3. Structure of the synthetic Mb peptides that were first used to study effect of peptide size on antibody response to immunization by free peptides (site 5, peptides 145–153, 143–153, 135–153, and 132–153. The residue in parenthesis is not required as part of the antigenic site in all antisera. (From Young and Atassi.[53])

tides were essentially of comparable magnitude. The response to peptide 145–151 (site 5) was improved by further boosting and the antibody titer was maintained in the serum for an extended period.

These were the first reports that immunization with a free (i.e., not coupled to a carrier) synthetic antigenic site, of only seven amino acids, can elicit antibodies that will bind to the native protein.[53] It should be noted that subsequent studies[55] have shown that even a six-residue peptide (peptide 1–6 of Mb) will evoke antibody responses of considerable titer which bound specifically to Mb. Examination of smaller peptides (corresponding to Mb residues 1–5, 1–4, and 1–3) for antigenicity in their free form in mice has shown that no significant antibody responses to the peptides are obtained below the pentapeptide size (M. Z. Atassi, unpublished results).

Adjuvants, Antibody Titer, and Immunoglobulin Class

It is well known that antibody responses induced experimentally to antigens are dependent on the adjuvant used. Similarly, adjuvant effects on peptide immunogenicity should be expected. We have examined the effect of adjuvants on the antibody responses to several of the Mb peptides (M. Z. Atassi and C. R. Young, unpublished results). In general, to a given peptide, the highest antibody responses were obtained by immunization of peptide in complete Freund's adjuvant. Immunizations with diphtheria–pertussis–tetanus toxoid produced somewhat lower responses to that peptide, which were a little higher than responses to immunization of the same peptide in aluminum hydroxide. Peptide immunizations with incomplete Freund's adjuvant or without any adjuvant (in PBS) usually

[55] C. R. Young, H. E. Schmitz, and M. Z. Atassi, *Mol. Immunol.* **20**, 567 (1983).

gave little or no antibody responses. In all the other studies described here, peptides were injected as an emulsion of equal volumes of the peptide solution in PBS and complete Freund's adjuvant.

It should be noted that the titer of the anti-protein antibody elicited with a short immunization schedule by a free peptide is usually lower than that raised by immunization with the native protein. The titers of anti-Mb antibodies evoked by free small peptides are low. However, if the size of the synthetic peptide employed in immunization is increased or the immunization schedule lengthened, the levels of antibody titer become comparable to the titers directed to those regions, obtained after immunization with native protein. For example, for site 5, the antibody titer obtained in response to immunization with a 7-residue peptide (peptide 145–151) is lower (0.2 mg/ml) than that elicited by immunization with a 22-residue peptide (peptide 132–153) (0.5 mg/ml).[53] After several boosters with the 7-residue peptide, the levels of antibody titer become comparable to those obtained with the 22-residue peptide. Also, it was shown recently that following immunization with synthetic influenza hemagglutinin antigenic sites,[41,42] antibody titer increased steadily with several boosters, reaching levels comparable to the antibody titers to these regions in antisera obtained by immunization with intact hemagglutinin. Immunizations with synthetic peptides of other proteins gave similar results. In general, the level of antibody response to immunization with a free peptide is elevated with periodic (every 3–5 weeks) boosting, usually reaching maximum titer in about 2–3 months.

In the early stages of the response, most of the antibodies are usually IgM (κ), together with some IgG_1 and IgG_{2a}.[46] Periodic boosting (usually three to six times), while it causes an increase in antibody titer, also effects a gradual switch to IgG antibodies until in fact the IgG antibodies predominate. Usually, but not always, IgG_1 and IgG_{2b} titers are higher than IgG_{2a} and IgG_3 titers.

Antigenicity of Free Peptides Is Unrelated to Antigenicity of These Regions in Intact Protein When the Whole Protein Is Used as Immunogen

The finding that a free synthetic antigenic site of only a few amino acids will elicit antibody responses posed the question[55] whether such antigenicity can be evoked by any synthetic protein antigenic site. If so, will such antigenicity be confined to free synthetic peptides representing the antigenic sites of a protein, or can it also be expressed by free synthetic peptides representing surface regions which are nonantigenic when the whole protein is used as the immunogen (Fig. 4)?

Peptide 1-6

$\overset{1}{\text{Val}}$–Leu–Ser–Glu–Gly–$\overset{6}{\text{Glu}}$

Peptide 121-127

$\overset{121}{\text{Gly}}$–Asn–Phe–Gly–Ala–Asp–$\overset{127}{\text{Ala}}$

FIG. 4. Structure of the synthetic Mb peptides representing two surface regions to which no detectable antibody responses are found when intact Mb is the immunizing antigen. (From Atassi.[29])

Again, for these studies, Mb served as an excellent model. The results clearly showed[55] that immunization with each of the synthetic peptides that represent the antigenic sites of Mb elicited specific antibodies that bind to native Mb exclusively at the region of the peptide used for immunization (Table I). The antibody responses to these peptides were detectable within 14 days after the first immunization and persisted throughout the immunization period up to 224 days. Later bleedings were not tested.

It is very important to note that immunization with free synthetic peptides 1–6 and 121–127 produced specific antibodies that bind to native Mb[55] (with the binding being exclusively at the region used for immunization; Table II). These two peptides represent surface regions within the Mb molecule that are not antigenic when intact Mb is the immunizing antigen.[29] Thus it would appear that the lack of antigenicity of these surface regions in the native protein[55] does not preclude their being antigenic in the free state. Clearly the lack of antigenicity of these surface regions within Mb is not caused by some specific structural features that render the regions nonantigenic. These findings pose many questions concerning our understanding of the molecular and cellular factors that contribute to produce an immune response to proteins and peptides.

The antigenic structure of Mb has shown that the antigenic sites are all surface regions but that not every region of the surface is an antigen site.[29] Knowledge of the antigenic structures of Mb,[29] lysozyme,[30] the α and β chains of human hemoglobin,[31–34] and the major antigenic sites of serum albumin,[35–38] ragweed allergen Ra3,[39,40] and influenza virus hemagglutinin[41,42] have revealed (for review see Ref. 56) that the antigenicity of the sites in a protein is largely inherent in their conformational locations[57] (i.e., the conformational locations of the regions determine the potential for their immune recognition, while the sequence and nature of the side chains constituting the "contact" residues determine the specificity of the recognition). Furthermore, other cellular factors, external to the molecule, regulate the immune response. The immune responses to Mb are

[56] M. Z. Atassi, *Mol. Cell. Biochem.* **32**, 21 (1980).
[57] M. Z. Atassi and A. L. Kazim, *in* "Immunobiology of Proteins and Peptides" (M. Z. Atassi and A. G. Stavitsky, eds.), Vol. 1, pp. 19–40. Plenum, New York, 1978.

TABLE I

SPECIFICITY OF SERUM ANTIBODIES OBTAINED BY IMMUNIZATION WITH FREE
SYNTHETIC ANTIGENIC SITES OF Mb[a]

Serum antibody[c]	Antibodies bound (cpm) to Mb and peptide–BSA conjugates[b]					
	Site 1	Site 2	Site 3	Site 4	Site 5	Mb
Anti-site 1	16,737 ± 711	0	0	0	0	17,398 ± 1586
Anti-site 2	0	16,859 ± 1457	0	0	0	20,784 ± 2214
Anti-site 3	0	0	17,881 ± 1163	0	0	20,117 ± 1973
Anti-site 4	0	0	0	16,437 ± 695	0	21,455 ± 1305
Anti-site 5	0	0	0	0	19,246 ± 611	20,632 ± 2358
Prebleed[d]	0	0	0	0	0	0

[a] From Schmitz et al.[46] by permission.

[b] Values represent means (± SEM) of three to four replicate analyses (by direct solid-phase RIA) and have been corrected for binding to baseline control antigens. Baseline control antigen for peptide–BSA conjugates was peptide 121–127–BSA conjugate. Baseline control antigen for Mb was BSA. No binding was detected against a control protein, hen egg white lysozyme. Values that were not significantly greater than 0 by Student's t test ($p < 0.05$) are reported as 0.

[c] Serum antibodies were obtained by immunization with free peptide in complete Freund's adjuvant.

[d] Prebleed sera was a pooled sera obtained from the spleen cell donor mice before they were injected with any synthetic peptides.

TABLE II

SERUM ANTIBODIES OBTAINED BY IMMUNIZATION
WITH FREE SYNTHETIC PEPTIDES REPRESENTING
SURFACE REGIONS THAT ARE NONIMMUNOGENIC IN
WHOLE Mb[a]

Peptide/protein[c]	Antibodies bound (cpm)[b] to	
	Anti-peptide 1–6 antisera[d]	Anti-peptide 121–127 antisera[d]
Site 1	0	0
Site 2	0	0
Site 3	0	0
Site 4	0	0
Site 5	0	0
Peptide 1–6	26,050 ± 2281	0
Peptide 121–127	0	17,082 ± 3282
Mb	33,058 ± 2983	29,608 ± 1542

[a] From Schmitz et al.[73] by permission.
[b] Values represent mean (± SEM) of three to four replicates (by direct solid-phase RIA) and have been corrected for binding to the baseline control antigen, BSA. Values not significantly greater than 0 by Student's t test ($p < 0.05$) are reported as 0. No significant binding was detected using prebleed sera preparations obtained from the spleen cell donor mice prior to immunization. Representative data shown.
[c] Peptides were conjugated to BSA before use in RIA.
[d] Serum antibodies were obtained by immunizations with *free* peptide emulsified in complete Freund's adjuvant.

controlled by genes in the I region of the major histocompatibility complex,[58] with the responses to each of its antigenic sites being under separate genetic control.[54,59] Further, the overall response to a protein is regulated by intersite influences, among site-specific cells, which could either be cooperative (helping) or suppressive in nature.[60] Because of these complex factors, the reason for the antigenicity of certain surface regions within a protein molecule is not clearly understood.

[58] K. Okuda, P. Christadoss, S. S. Twining, M. Z. Atassi, and C. S. David, *J. Immunol.* **121,** 866 (1978).
[59] S. S. Twining, C. S. David, and M. Z. Atassi, *Mol. Immunol.* **18,** 447 (1981).
[60] M. Z. Atassi, S. Yokota, S. S. Twining, H. Lehmann, and C. S. David, *Mol. Immunol.* **18,** 945 (1981).

TABLE III
BINDING TO α CHAIN AND TO Hb OF
ANTIBODIES OBTAINED BY IMMUNIZATION WITH
FREE SYNTHETIC α PEPTIDES[a]

Immunizing peptide	Antibodies bound (cpm) to	
	α chain	Hb
α1–15	13,430	29,450
α15–23	17,760	38,840
α49–56	12,540	23,960
α121–127	9,620	21,960
Prebleed	0	0

[a] Procedures are the same as for Tables I and II, except that SEM values have been deleted here.

It is necessary to note that, although more studies have been done with the Mb system, the finding that small synthetic peptides are antigenic in their free form has not been confined to Mb peptides. Synthetic peptides of other proteins have been found to elicit, when injected in their free form, anti-peptide antibodies that will bind specifically to the parent protein. We have obtained similar results with free synthetic peptides of human Hb[61] (Table III), bovine serum albumin, ragweed allergen Ra3[39] (Table IV), and influenza virus hemagglutinin[41,42] (Tables V and VI and Fig. 5). So far, 41 different synthetic peptides belonging to these and other protein systems have evoked, without exception, *in vivo* antibody responses in rabbits and/or mice. The anti-peptide antibodies thus obtained invariably bound to the respective protein (Tables I–VI). Table VI shows an example of the change of antibody response with time after immunization with a free synthetic peptide which represents an antigenic site within influenza virus hemagglutinin, and the binding of these antibodies to immunizing peptide and to the virus.

Genetic Control of the Response

It has been shown that the immune responses to Mb[58] and to other protein antigens[62–66] are under genetic control. More importantly, the re-

[61] D. McCormick and M. Z. Atassi, unpublished results (1983).
[62] K. Okuda, S. Sakata, M. Z. Atassi, and C. S. David, *J. Immunogen.* **6,** 447 (1979).

TABLE IV
BINDING TO Ra3 OF ANTI-PEPTIDE
ANTIBODIES[a,b]

Immunizing peptide[c]	Antibodies bound (Δ cpm) to	
	Immunizing peptide	Ra3
1–15	3,119	3,313
21–35	6,320	6,340
31–45	3,140	3,840
51–65	3,340	3,510
71–85	18,670	17,530

[a] From Atassi and Atassi.[39]
[b] Anti-peptide antisera were elicited in four out-bred mice by immunization with free (i.e., not coupled to any carrier) peptides. For RIA plate assay, the peptides were used as conjugates on succinylated bovine serum albumin.
[c] Peptides are designated by the position number of the first and last residues in its sequence within the primary structure of ragweed allergen Ra3.

sponses to each individual sites within a protein are under separate Ir gene control.[54,59] In the use of small peptides as free immunogens for the production of antisera and monoclonal antibodies of desired specificities to preselected protein regions, it is highly relevant to know whether the immune responses to free peptides are under genetic control and whether this genetic control resembles the control of the responses to these regions when the whole protein is used as an immunogen. A protein of known antigenic structure and whose parameters of genetic control have been mapped out in detail is needed as a model to investigate these questions in an unambiguous manner. Again, Mb has served as an excellent model for these studies because, in addition to knowledge of its entire

[63] C. J. Krco, A. L. Kazim, M. Z. Atassi, and C. S. David, *J. Immunogen.* **8,** 315 (1981).
[64] C. J. Krco, A. L. Kazim, M. Z. Atassi, R. Melvold, and C. S. David, *J. Immunogen.* **8,** 471 (1981).
[65] M. Z. Atassi, P. M. Long, K. Beisel, S. Sakata, T. Peters, Jr., and C. S. David, *Mol. Immunol.* **19,** 313 (1982).
[66] M. Z. Atassi, *Eur. J. Biochem.* **145,** 1 (1984).

TABLE V
BINDING TO INTACT VIRUS OF ANTI-PEPTIDE
ANTIBODIES[a,b]

Immunizing antigen	Antibodies bound (Δ cpm)[c] to	
	Immunizing peptide	X-31 virus
Peptide 1	19,390	18,688
Peptide 2	20,065	18,320
Peptide 3	12,530	11,340
Peptide 4	14,920	11,420
Peptide 5	8,860	3,190
Peptide 6	24,230	19,430
Peptide 7	20,480	18,490
Peptide 8	13,600	9,840
Peptide 9	16,390	22,130
Peptide 10	16,800	15,380
Peptide 11	22,300	21,910
Peptide 12	22,660	20,890

[a] From Atassi and Kurisaki.[42]
[b] Anti-peptide antisera were elicited in three outbred mice by immunization with free (i.e., not coupled to any carrier) synthetic peptides of the hemagglutinin A molecule of X-31 influenza virus. For RIA plate assays, the peptides were used as protein conjugates. Anti-peptide antisera (60-day bleedings) were diluted 1 : 100 to 1 : 1000 with PBS–0.1% BSA for these assays. The results, which have been corrected for nonspecific binding (1–2% of total label) of BSA, represent the average of triplicate analyses which varied ±1.6% or less.
[c] Note that none of these antisera showed any significant binding ($p < 0.05$, by Student's t test) to Mb and Hb controls.

antigenic structure,[29] the Ir gene control of its sites has been investigated in detail.[54,59,60,67–69] A detailed account of the genetic control of the immune response to Mb was the subject of a recent review.[68]

[67] S. Yokota, C. S. David, and M. Z. Atassi, *Mol. Immunol.* **17,** 1079 (1980).
[68] C. S. David and M. Z. Atassi, *Adv. Exp. Med. Biol.* **150,** 97 (1982).
[69] G. S. Bixler and M. Z. Atassi, *J. Immunogen.* **11,** 339 (1984).

TABLE VI
EXAMPLE OF ANTIBODIES AGAINST INFLUENZA VIRUS ELICITED BY
IMMUNIZATION WITH FREE SYNTHETIC ANTIGENIC SITES[a,b]

Antigen	Harvest day	Antibody bound (Δ cpm $\times$ 10^{-3}) to	
		Virus (A/Port Chalmer's)	Virus (X-31)
Peptide 1–11 of	51	9.72	9.60
HA 2, strain A	80	40.64	39.71
	108	43.29	46.59
	125	64.68	61.32
		HA (B/ Hong Kong)	Virus (B/ Hong Kong)
Peptide 1–11 of	66	11.99	11.19
HA 2, strain B	108	16.32	17.30
	125	24.41	25.86

[a] From Atassi and Webster,[41] by permission.
[b] Antibody binding to hemagglutinin (HA) or to virus was determined by direct solid-phase RIA. Lysozyme and bovine serum albumin were used to correct for nonspecific binding (3% or less). Values are means of triplicates which varied ±1.4% or less. Binding studies were carried out with antiserum dilution of 1 : 1000.

Previously, studies had shown[54] that following immunization with Mb, BALB/cByJ strain mice are high responders to Mb, responding predominantly to sites 1, 2, 3, and 5. Furthermore in immunization with Mb, the sites that are recognized by mouse B cells are also recognized by mouse T cells.[54,59] However, we found[55] that BALB/cByJ mice when immunized with any of the five free synthetic antigenic sites will produce antibodies that bind to native Mb and exclusively to the corresponding immunizing peptide (Table I). Thus the genetic control of the B-cell (antibody) responses to the antigenic sites which operates following immunizing with native Mb seemed to be different from the control following immunization with the free antigenic sites.

These findings prompted us to investigate[70] the genetic control of the response, of mouse antibodies that bind to Mb, following immunization with free (i.e., not coupled to a carrier) synthetic antigenic sites (Fig. 2) or

[70] C. R. Young, H. E. Schmitz, and M. Z. Atassi, J. Immunogen. 10, 453 (1983).

X-31 Hemagglutinin Peptides

HA 1 Peptides

Peptide 1	23 36 GTLVKTITDDQIEV
Peptide 2	124 134 GFTWTGVTQNG
Peptide 3	138 152 AGKRGPGSGFFSRLN
Peptide 4	154 167 LTKSGSTYPVLNVT
Peptide 5	175 188 DKLYIWGVHHPSTN
Peptide 6	183 199 HHPSTNQEQTSLYVQAS
Peptide 7	201 218 RVTVSTRRSQQTIIPNIG
Peptide 8	272 288 APIDTGISEGITPNGSI
Peptide 9	300 315 ITYGAGPKYVKQNTLK

HA 2 Peptides

Peptide 10	1 11 GLFGAIAGFIE
Peptide 11	56 68 IEKTNEKFHQIEK
Peptide 12	68 84 KEFSEVEGRIQDLEKYV

FIG. 5. Covalent structures of the surface peptides of the hemagglutinin A molecule of X-31 influenza virus that we have synthesized and studied (see Table V).[41,42] In the synthetic peptides, the residues Cys-277, Cys-281, and Cys-305 were replaced by glycine. It is not implied that the antigenic sites constitute the full size of the peptides shown, but rather that the sites reside within the boundaries of these peptides. The single letter notation of the amino acids is A, alanine; D, aspartic acid; E, glutamic acid; F, phenylalanine; G, glycine; H, histidine; I, isoleucine; K, lysine; L, leucine; N, asparagine; P, proline; Q, glutamine; R, arginine; S, serine; T, threonine; V, valine; W, tryptophan; Y, tyrosine. (From Atassi and Kurisaki.[42])

with other peptides (Fig. 4) representing surface regions of Mb which are not immunogenic when the native protein is used as the immunizing antigen. Anti-peptide antibodies in the antisera were measured by a radioimmune plate-binding assay in which Mb was used as the solid-phase plate antigen. A distinct genetic control of the antibody response was found[70] following immunization with the free synthetic Mb peptides. This genetic control is different when intact Mb is used as the immunogen.[70] For example, following immunization with native Mb,[54] mice of strain B10.R11(72NS) are nonresponders to Mb and do not respond to any of the five antigenic sites, peptide 1–6, or peptide 121–127. However, the same strain of mice are low responders following immunization with free site 3, peptide 1–6, or peptide 121–127 and intermediate responders following immunization with free site 1, site 2, site 4, or site 5.[70] Table VII gives a summary of results with some representative strains following immunization with peptides or with Mb.

At the present, reasons for the differences in the genetic control of the submolecular (site) responses to intact Mb and to the free synthetic peptides are not known. Some factors should be noted here concerning the molecular aspects of the genetic control of the immune response to Mb and its antigenic sites. The overall response to Mb is regulated by intersite influences which can either be cooperative (helping) or suppressive in nature.[60] Also, the Ir gene control of the responses to Mb and its antigenic sites is dependent on antigen dose.[71] Thus, following immunization with Mb or with the free peptides, the differences in the genetic control of the B-cell responses could be caused by either or both of these factors. Furthermore, even though the same five antigen sites that are recognized by mouse B cells are also recognized by mouse T cells,[54,59] Mb has additional T-cell recognition sites that are not recognized by B cells.[69,72] These may also contribute via T-helper or T-suppressor cells to the regulation of the overall immune response to Mb.[59,60]

The relevance of these findings, in practical terms, to the experimental situation is that when the preparation of antisera and/or monoclonal antibodies to a new peptide is being contemplated, the response of a few mouse strains (at least several independent haplotypes) to the free peptide should be examined. The mouse strain selected for the eventual antibody preparation should be a high responder to the immunizing free peptide. Strain selection should be based not only on the quantity of the antibody response, but also on the basis of the quality (immunoglobulin class) of the response.

Monoclonal Antibodies with Predetermined Specificities

After antisera have been obtained with desired specificities to preselected protein regions by immunization with the corresponding free syn-

---

[71] C. R. Young and M. Z. Atassi, *J. Immunogen.* **9,** 343 (1982).
[72] G. S. Bixler and M. Z. Atassi, *Immunol. Commun.* **12,** 593 (1983).

TABLE VII

COMPARISON OF THE RESPONSE PROFILES IN SELECTED MOUSE STRAINS FOLLOWING IMMUNIZATION WITH FREE PEPTIDES OR WITH INTACT Mb[a]

| | Response and its level following | | | | |
| | Immunization with Mb[b] | | Immunization with free synthetic peptides[c] | | |
Mouse strain	High	Low	High	Intermediate	Low
B10.R11(72NS)	No response to Mb or peptide	No response to Mb or peptide	—	Sites 1, 2, 4, 5	Site 3, peptides 1–6, 121–127
C57BL/10J	Site 4	Sites 1, 2, 3, 5, Mb	—	Site 1, peptide 121–127	Sites 2, 3, 4, 5, peptides 1–6
B10.A(2R)	Mb, sites 1, 2, 4	Sites 3, 5	—	—	Sites 1, 2, 3, 4, 5, peptides 1–6, 121–127
B10.A(5R)	Mb, sites 1, 2	Site 5	—	Sites 2, 3, 5	Sites 1, 4, peptides 1–6, 121–127
B10.D2/n	Mb, sites 1, 2, 3, 5	Site 4	Sites 1, 2, 3, 4, peptide 121–127	Peptide 1–6	Site 5

[a] From Young et al.[70] by permission.

[b] This is a summary of the findings when the mouse strains shown are each immunized with Mb and the responses subsequently tested with the synthetic peptides. Upon immunization with Mb, no response is detectable to peptides 1–6 and 121–127 in any of these strains.

[c] The column represents a summary of the findings when a given mouse strain is immunized with each of the synthetic peptides (Figs. 2 and 4) in their free form.

thetic peptides, it will then be relatively easy to prepare monoclonal antibodies possessing the same specificity. The specificity of the monoclonal antibodies thus prepared is a function of peptide immunization and not of tedious hybrid selection and screening. B-cell hybridomas will have to be tested only for antibody production (by screening with intact parent protein) and not for specificity of those antibodies, because the specificity will be exclusively directed against the peptide region employed in the immunization. The following results with Mb demonstrate the preparation of monoclonal antibodies to Mb antigenic sites and to selected surface regions of the protein that are normally nonantigenic when intact Mb is used as the immunogen.

Monoclonal Antibodies against the Antigenic Sites

Initially, two monoclonal antibodies with preselected submolecular binding specificities to sperm whale Mb were prepared[45] by hybridization of Fa/O mouse myeloma cells with spleen cells from mice which had been immunized with free (not coupled to any carrier) synthetic peptides 132–153 or 145–151 (antigenic site 5) of Mb. Both monoclonal antibodies were IgG$_1$ (κ), and their binding specificities were exclusively directed to determinants present in Mb and in the immunizing peptides. The results indicated that monoclonal antibodies with preselected submolecular binding specificities can be readily obtained by somatic cell hybridization when the corresponding free synthetic sites are used as immunogens.[45]

Subsequent studies showed[46] that the finding was not due to a peculiarity in antigen site 5 of Mb but was in fact a general phenomenon fully applicable to other peptides. By immunization of separate groups of BALB/cByJ mice with the five synthetic antigenic sites of Mb (Fig. 2) that were in their free form (i.e., not coupled to any carrier), each group of mice made antibodies that bound specifically to Mb at exclusively the region of the respective immunizing antigenic site. Hybridization of Fa/O mouse myeloma cells with spleen cells derived from each group of mice[46] enabled the preparation of monoclonal antibodies to each of the five antigenic sites. These monoclonal antibodies expressed the same isotypes [either IgM (κ) or IgG$_1$ (κ)] as the antigen-specific serum antibodies obtained from the mice whose spleen cells were used for hybridization.[46] Analyses by solid-phase RIA also indicated that each monoclonal antibody, like the antisera of the respective parent animals, bound specifically to Mb and exclusively to the synthetic peptide used in immunization (Table VIII). These results demonstrated that the submolecular binding specificities of the monoclonal antibodies were the result of peptide immunization rather than hybrid selection. It is therefore concluded[45,46] that

TABLE VIII

MONOCLONAL ANTIBODIES FROM IMMUNIZATION WITH FREE SYNTHETIC ANTIGENIC SITES OF Mb[a]

Monoclonal antibody	Antibody bound (cpm) to Mb and peptide–BSA conjugates[b]					
	Site 1	Site 2	Site 3	Site 4	Site 5	Mb
MB1-4-15 (anti-site 1)	4414 ± 167	0	0	0	0	20,288 ± 613
MB2-5-4 (anti-site 2)	0	9353 ± 745	0	0	0	29,667 ± 933
MB3-5-13 (anti-site 3)	0	0	9735 ± 792	0	0	52,190 ± 2030
MB4-3-22 (anti-site 4)	0	0	0	4357 ± 510	0	17,103 ± 201
MB5-16-1 (anti-site 5)	0	0	0	0	13,392 ± 643	62,763 ± 2010
MB5-14-5 (anti-site 5)	0	0	0	0	27,203 ± 3789	30,570 ± 1410

[a] From Schmitz et al.[46] by permission.

[b] Values represent means (± SEM) of four replicate analyses by direct solid-phase RIA and have been corrected for binding to baseline control antigens. Baseline control antigen for peptide–BSA conjugates was peptide 121–127–BSA conjugate. Baseline control antigen for Mb was BSA. No binding was detected against a control protein, hen egg white lysozyme. Values not significantly greater than 0 by Student's t test (p < 0.05) are reported as 0. Representative data shown.

monoclonal antibodies with predetermined submolecular binding specificities to preselected protein antigenic sites can be produced by the techniques of somatic cell hybridization when the corresponding free synthetic peptides are used as immunogens.

Production of Monoclonal Antibodies to Regions That Are Nonimmunogenic in a Protein

Other studies[73] have examined even wider applications by investigating whether monoclonal antibodies with preselected submolecular binding specificities can be prepared to surface regions of a protein that are ordinarily not immunogenic, when the intact protein is used as the immunogen, by immunization with corresponding synthetic peptides (six to seven residues) in their free form. Such monoclonal antibodies, which possess specificities that cannot otherwise be obtained, should have great value in basic research and in clinical and diagnostic applications.

Two surface regions of Mb (Fig. 4) that are not antigenic when the native molecule is used as immunogen were synthesized and injected in their free form (i.e., not coupled to any carrier) into separate groups of BALB/cByJ mice. Each group of mice made antibodies that bound specifically to Mb, exclusively at the region corresponding to the immunizing peptide (Table II). Monoclonal antibodies to each of the two surface regions were prepared from hybrids of Fa/O mouse myeloma cells with spleen cells derived from each group of mice. These monoclonal antibodies expressed the same isotype [IgM (κ)] as the antigen-specific antisera of the mice whose spleen cells were used for hybridization. Each monoclonal antibody, like the antiserum of the parent animal, bound specifically to Mb and exclusively to the respective synthetic peptide that was used as immunogen (Table IX). These results demonstrate that the binding specificities were the result of peptide immunization rather than hybrid selection. Thus, monoclonal antibodies having binding specificities to preselected surface regions in a protein molecule that are not immunogenic when the whole protein is used as the immunizing antigen can be produced by the techniques of somatic cell hybridization when the respective free synthetic peptides are used as immunogens.[73]

Conclusions

The finding that free synthetic peptides as small as six to seven amino acids in size are able to elicit an antibody response that enables the production of monoclonal antibodies is somewhat counter to the traditional

[73] H. E. Schmitz, H. Atassi, and M. Z. Atassi, *Immunol. Commun.* **12,** 161 (1983).

TABLE IX
SPECIFICITY OF MONOCLONAL ANTIBODIES FROM IMMUNIZATION WITH
FREE PEPTIDES REPRESENTING SURFACE REGIONS THAT ARE
NONANTIGENIC IN WHOLE Mb[a]

Peptide/protein[c]	Antibodies bound (cpm)[b] to		
	MB16-6-1	MB16-8-21	MB121-2-5
Site 1	0	0	0
Site 2	0	0	0
Site 3	0	0	0
Site 4	0	0	0
Site 5	0	0	0
Peptide 1–6	14,231 ± 861	29,665 ± 1060	0
Peptide 121–127	0	0	7,477 ± 374
Mb	18,094 ± 1662	36,390 ± 1095	15,205 ± 1508

[a] From Schmitz et al.[73] by permission.
[b] Values represent mean (± SEM) of three to four replicate analyses by direct solid-phase RIA. Results have been corrected for binding to baseline control antigen (BSA). Values not significantly greater than 0 by Student's t test (p < 0.05) are reported as 0. Representative data shown.
[c] Peptides were conjugated to BSA before use in the RIA.

concepts concerning the immunogenicity of small peptides. The mechanisms for recognition and responses to small peptides are yet to be elucidated.

Studies with the Mb peptides showed that the incidence of positive growth fusion wells which initially secreted anti-Mb antibodies indicated a frequency of antigen-specific fusible B cells in the spleens of the peptide-immunized mice that was sufficient to permit the establishment of several cell lines. It was thus evident that the production of hybrid lines by the free synthetic peptide approach does not require selective enrichment for antigen-specific B cells and is in this respect similar to conventional procedures.

During immune recognition, these results would suggest that, in addition to sequence identity, some conformational similarity must also exist between the free synthetic peptides and the corresponding regions in the native molecule. A free peptide in solution exists in a conformational equilibrium comprising a multitude of dynamic conformational states, the time average of which is random.[74] These states, however, are not all equally favored, and each peptide is able to assume, even for some frac-

74 M. Z. Atassi and B. J. Saplin, Biochemistry 7, 688 (1968).

tion of the time, a favorable conformational state that resembles the shape of the corresponding region in the native protein.[74] Binding to cell receptors, as in binding to antibody,[29,30] may also induce the peptide to assume this favorable conformational state,[74] because it shifts the conformational equilibrium in favor of that state.[74] This would allow for both the molecular and submolecular binding specificities expressed by the antisera and monoclonal antibodies that are prepared through immunization with free peptides. The fact that neither region 1–6 nor 121–127 on the surface of Mb is immunogenic in the native molecule but that they can induce antibodies when used as immunogens suggests that some molecularly intrinsic and host constraints must be placed on the immune recognition of these regions during the immune response to the whole protein. These constraints may in part be related to intersite influences[60] but their exact nature(s) is not yet fully understood.

It is evident from the foregoing that the binding specificities of the monoclonal antibodies obtained via immunization with free synthetic antigenic sites or even with nonimmunogenic regions of a protein were the result of peptide immunization rather than hybrid selection. The isotype of each monoclonal antibody was also the same as the isotype that predominated in the serum antibodies of the respective animal, suggesting that the monoclonal antibodies were also an adequate representation of antibody clonotypes produced in the animals. The ability to produce large quantities of antibodies whose binding specificities are preselected by immunization and not by hybridization obviates the costly and time-consuming screening of a large number of hybridoma cultures for the presence of antibodies that possess the desired specificity. It also avoids the need for coupling of the synthetic peptide to a large molecular weight carrier and the shortcomings of these conjugates. Furthermore, it does not require any special tissue culture technique other than those associated with hybrid selection. Because specificity is determined by, and is exclusively directed against, the immunizing peptide it will be unnecessary to use the peptide for screening of the antibodies. Rather, the protein antigen can be used exclusively for screening, and no further examination of specificity should ordinarily be needed.[46,45,73]

The ability to produce antisera and monoclonal antibodies which express predetermined binding specificities to preselected protein regions, even to those that are otherwise nonimmunogenic when the protein is used as the immunogen, affords valuable reagents that may be employed as powerful probes of the conformation of essentially any surface region of a protein, irrespective of whether that region is immunogenic in the native molecule. With this remarkable versatility, the monoclonal antibodies produced will help elucidate the molecular basis of immunity. As stated earlier, they should also have enormous value in clinical and diagnostic applications. Thus, they should assist in the development of sensitive therapeutic and diagnostic reagents that have precise binding capabilities and that would otherwise be difficult or impossible to obtain.

Acknowledgments

The work was supported by Grants AI-21336 from the National Institutes of Health, U.S. Public Health Service. The author holds the Robert A. Welch Chair of Chemistry, endowed by the Welch Foundation, and this support is gratefully acknowledged.

[9] The Auto-Anti-Idiotypic Strategy for Preparing Monoclonal Antibodies to Receptor Combining Sites

By W. Louis Cleveland and Bernard F. Erlanger

Introduction

A unique property of immunoglobulin molecules is the enormous diversity of their *v*-region sequences within a single organism. This property, as appreciated by Lindenmann[1] and Jerne,[2] raises the possibility that *v*-region idiotopes may imitate antigenic determinants on nonimmunoglobulin molecules. The existence of immunoglobulin idiotopes that imitate or cross-react with antigenic determinants on other species of molecules has been demonstrated in a number of studies in which antibodies to receptor combining sites have been raised without using the receptor for immunization.[3] Instead a ligand of the receptor has been used to raise an anti-ligand antibody (Ab1). The Ab1 has then been used to raise a second, anti-idiotypic antibody (Ab2). In accordance with the possibility pointed out by Lindenmann[1] and by Jerne,[2] some of the anti-idiotypic antibodies have been found to react with the receptor combining site.

In our laboratory, an alternative anti-idiotypic strategy[4] has been developed on the basis of the idiotypic network theory proposed by Jerne.[2] An essential prediction of this theory is that immunization with antigen induces not only antibodies that recognize the antigen (i.e., Ab1), but also

[1] J. Lindenmann, *Ann. Immunol. (Inst. Pasteur)* **124C**, 171 (1973).
[2] N. K. Jerne, *Ann. Immunol. (Inst. Pasteur)* **125C**, 373 (1974).
[3] N. R. Farid and T. C. Y. Lo, *Endocrine Rev.* **6**, 1 (1985).
[4] W. L. Cleveland, N. H. Wassermann, R. Sarangarajan, A. S. Penn, and B. F. Erlanger, *Nature (London)* **305**, 56 (1983).

auto-anti-idiotypic antibodies (i.e., auto-Ab2) that recognize the Ab1 set.[2] We have immunized mice with ligands of receptors and have immortalized the resulting antibody-secreting cells with the hybridoma technique of Köhler and Milstein.[5] Among the hybridoma clones, we have found cells secreting not only Ab1s, but also auto-Ab2s, as predicted by Jerne's theory. In accord with previous studies, some of the Ab2s have been found to react with receptor. Thus, anti-receptor antibodies could be induced by immunization with a ligand of a receptor rather than the receptor itself. In this communication we discuss methodological aspects of the auto-anti-idiotypic strategy.

Immunogens

Ligands of receptors can be divided into two categories: haptens and macromolecules. Haptenic ligands must be coupled to a protein carrier in order to impart immunogenicity. It is of critical importance to couple the ligand at a site that preserves its specificity for the receptor combining site. This point is well illustrated by experience with adenosine. Adenosine coupled to protein by periodate oxidation of the vicinal ribose hydroxyls proved ineffective as a ligand of the adenosine receptor, whereas an N-6 linkage preserved reactivity with receptor.[6]

In our studies, several different carrier proteins have proved effective for immunization of mice: bovine serum albumin, porcine thyroglobulin, and keyhole limpet hemocyanin. As yet our experience is inadequate to determine if Ab2 induction is best achieved with very foreign proteins, such as hemocyanin, or with carriers that are analogs of proteins found in the recipient animal.

Macromolecular ligands differ from haptens in that they may possess multiple epitopes, only one of which reacts with the receptor combining site. This feature creates a problem in the two step procedure that has been used in other laboratories. With this technique monoclonal Ab1 is made in one animal, purified, and injected into a second animal to make Ab2. If the wrong monoclonal Ab1 is chosen, much time and effort can be wasted. As demonstrated by the studies of Noseworthy et al., identification of the correct monoclonal Ab1 can involve considerable effort.[7] An

[5] G. Köhler and C. Milstein, *Nature (London)* **256,** 495 (1975).

[6] B. F. Erlanger, W. L. Cleveland, N. H. Wassermann, B. L. Hill, A. S. Penn, H. H. Ku, and R. Sarangarajan, *in* "Molecular Basis of Nerve Activity" (J.-P. Changeux, F. Hucho, A. Maelicke, and E. Neumann, eds.) p. 523. de Gruyter, Berlin and New York, 1985.

[7] J. H. Noseworthy, B. N. Fields, M. A. Dichter, C. Sobotka, E. Pizer, L. L. Perry, J. T. Nepom, and M. I. Greene, *J. Immunol.* **131,** 2533 (1983).

advantage of the auto-anti-idiotypic procedure is that selection of the correct Ab1 is not necessary.

Immunization Protocol

The protocol used in our initial study dealing with the acetylcholine receptor (AChR) consisted of an ip injection of 100 μl of complete Freund's adjuvant containing 1 mg/ml of the hapten–carrier conjugate. An identical boost was given 21 days later. Splenocytes were harvested 5 days after the boost and used to prepare hybridomas. A strong auto-Ab2 response was observed. Out of approximately 1000 wells, 7.4% were positive for Ab2 in the initial screen, as compared with 14% for Ab1. On the basis of this initial success, we have used this protocol with minor variations in more recent studies. In one case the mouse was boosted twice at 3 week intervals and splenocytes harvested 4 days after the boost for fusion. In another, a mouse initially immunized on day 0 was, for reasons of convenience, boosted on days 148, 155, and 161 (saline). Splenocytes were harvested on day 162.

While these protocols have been successful, it is not known if they are optimal. It should be noted that one of the basic predictions of Jerne's theory is that the levels of Ab1 and Ab2 should oscillate with time, possibly with an inverse phase relationship. If so, then the time chosen to harvest splenocytes for fusion may be of critical importance. In addition to their value in clarifying the role of physiological idiotype regulation, studies of the kinetics of the auto-Ab2 response in relation to the Ab1 response should also be useful to those using the auto-anti-idiotypic strategy to prepare anti-receptor antibodies. Unfortunately, very little data on the kinetics of auto-Ab2 responses at the cellular level are currently available.

Preparation of Hybridomas

To maximize the probability of obtaining the desired anti-receptor antibodies, we have attempted to optimize procedures for preparing hybridomas. This optimization is based, in part, on an improved culture medium developed in this laboratory.[8] The medium, which consists of an improved basal medium (BM) supplemented with trace elements (1/2 TE I + TE II), is further supplemented with 5 or 10% FCS for the initial cultivation of hybrids. Established hybrids can then be adapted to grow in

---

[8] W. L. Cleveland, I. Wood, a id B. F. Erlanger, *J. Immunol. Meth.* **56,** 221 (1983).

this medium without FCS or protein supplements of any kind. Monoclonal antibodies can be produced under protein-free conditions for long periods.

Fusion Protocol. In this laboratory, fusions are carried out using a modified version of the protocol described by Sharon *et al.*[9]

1. The polyethylene glycol (PEG) (av. MW = 1000, J. T. Baker) solution (35% v/v) is made with Tris-buffered Dulbecco's medium without $NaHCO_3$ and without antibiotics, as follows: the 0.044 mol of $NaHCO_3$ normally added to a 1 liter packet of the Gibco formulation [catalog # 430-2100] is replaced with 0.03 mol of NaCl + 0.014 mol of Tris base and the pH is adjusted to 8.1 at room temperature with HCl.

2. The PEG solution is sterile filtered, avoiding the need to autoclave PEG.

3. Cells are treated with the modified PEG solution as described by Sharon *et al.*[9] Briefly, splenocytes, depleted of erythrocytes with NH_4Cl,[10] are mixed with P3x63-Ag8.653 myeloma cells[11] in a 10:1 ratio and centrifuged at 500 *g* for 6 min at room temperature in a 50-ml plastic conical centrifuge tube. After aspirating the supernatant, the pellet is resuspended by hitting the tube. Then, 2 ml of the PEG solution (at room temperature) is immediately added. The cells are further resuspended by pipetting in and out 2 or 3 times with a 10-ml pipet. The mixture is immediately centrifuged at 500 *g* for 3 min at room temperature. Without removing the supernatant, 5 ml of BM + 1/2 TE I + TE II is added and the cells are gently resuspended. Immediately following this, the mixture is centrifuged at 230 *g* for 6 min at room temperature. After aspiration of the supernatant, the fusion mixture is diluted to 100 ml with 90 ml of BM + 1/2 TE I + TE II + 10% FCS and 10 ml of 10 × HAT[12] medium. Untreated spleen cells (10^7 from the same animal used for fusion) have been added as feeder cells in some experiments, but appear unnecessary. Medium conditioned by growth of myeloma cells has been used in some experiments, but this also appears unnecessary.

4. The diluted fusion mixture is then distributed into approximately 1000 microplate wells, 100 μl/well. The microplates are wrapped along the crack between the plate and the lid with several layers of parafilm to prevent evaporation.

[9] J. Sharon, S. L. Morrison, and E. A. Kabat, *Proc. Natl. Acad. Sci. U.S.A.* **76,** 1420 (1979).

[10] B. B. Mishell, S. M. Shiigi, C. Henry, E. L. Chan, J. North, R. Gallily, M. Slomich, K. Miller, J. Marbrook, D. Parks, and A. H. Good, *in* "Selected Methods in Cellular Immunology" (B. B. Mishell and S. M. Shiigi, eds.), p. 23. Freeman, San Francisco, 1980.

[11] J. F. Kearney, B. L. Radbruch, and K. Rajevsky, *J. Immunol.* **123,** 1548 (1979).

[12] J. W. Littlefield, *Science* **145,** 709 (1964).

5. After 1 week, 100 μl/well of BM + 1/2 TE I + TE II + 10% FCS + HT[12] was added. Alternatively, this step can be eliminated if the initial fusion mixture is diluted to 200 ml and 200 μl is added to each well.

6. After 2 weeks, if clone size is judged adequate, supernatants are harvested by the replica transfer technique described below, and screened.

Replica Transfer Technique for Harvesting Supernatants. In our studies we have used 1000 microplate wells for the initial cloning of hybrids made from one spleen because of a concern that the presence of many clones in a single well might lead to the production of both Ab1 and Ab2 in the same well. Simultaneous production of both Ab1 and Ab2 might lead to immune complexes that would interfere with detection in screening assays. The use of 1000 wells avoids this problem since fusion efficiency is such that the number of colonies per well seen before feeding is usually in the 2–5 range. However, with 1000 wells, harvesting and screening supernatants is extremely laborious if done manually with single channel or even eight channel pipets. We have therefore developed a replica transfer technique that eliminates this problem. This technique requires no special equipment and allows the supernatants from a single plate to be harvested in about 1 min. Leakage from individual wells is rare, and when it occurs, it is not of concern, since subcloning is always necessary, as most wells are likely to contain several clones. According to our experience the transfer technique does not degrade sterility. It is carried out in a laminar flow sterile hood. Polyvinylchloride gloves, dipped in 70% ethanol and air-dried, are worn during all steps.

1. The cover of the 96-well culture plate is removed and placed on a sterile, empty microplate bottom, which is used as a convenient sterile support. Then a sterile microplate with round bottom wells (supplied in a sterile package without a cover, Corning #25855) is placed on the culture plate (Corning #25860). The plates are picked up and aligned so that the well openings coincide (Fig. 1). Misalignment can best be detected by touch at the edges where the plates meet.

2. Using both hands to maintain alignment of the plates and a tight seal at each well opening, the plates are tilted 90°. Then an impact is transmitted to the plates by a gentle shake or by gently bumping one's elbows on the table of the hood. This causes the supernatants to move to a new position (Fig. 1).

3. Next, the plates are tilted an additional 90° in the same direction so that the culture plate is now on top. In a few moments, most of the supernatant drains into the other plate, which shall henceforth be referred to as the "storage plate." Without changing their orientation, the plates are placed on the table of the hood. The culture plate is removed and

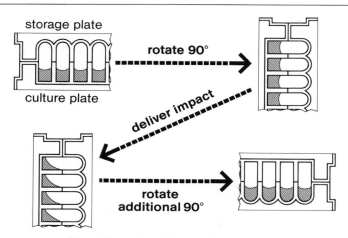

Fig. 1. Steps in replica transfer procedure.

placed in its normal orientation. After placing a sterile cover (i.e., an old cover sterilized by UV light) on the storage plate, 200 μl of BM + 1/2 TE I + TE II + 10% FCS are added to each well of the culture plate using a repeating dispenser pipet.

Cloning Procedures. In most of our work we have recloned hybridoma lines by limiting dilution or in soft agarose. Although adequate, these procedures must be repeated one or more times in order to ensure monoclonality. Recently, we have developed a micromanipulation procedure which is sufficiently rigorous to ensure monoclonality with only a single cloning step. Though tedious, this procedure avoids the waiting time associated with the multiple cloning steps required for other procedures. It is performed using an inverted microscope (e.g., Olympus IMT) as follows. In wells 12A through 12H, 100 μl of BM + 1/2 TE I + TE II + 10% FCS + 0.1% nigrosine is added. Then, 100 μl of a culture supernatant containing the cells to be cloned is added to well 12A. Serial dilutions are made into the other wells containing nigrosine. After the cells have settled, the wells are examined at low power to identify those containing cells at a convenient concentration for micromanipulation. Then a pipet, prepared as described below and coupled to a mouth tube, is used to pick up several cells, e.g., 5–10. The pipet is then used to transfer a tiny drop into the middle of an empty well. This is done while observing the pipet tip at 60× magnification. The liquid is expelled until a single viable (nigrosine-excluding) cell emerges. Then the drop is examined quickly (1–3 sec) at 200× to confirm the identification of a single viable cell and immediately covered with 100 μl of BM + 1/2 TE I + TE II + 10% FCS. This is easily done using a stepping syringe coupled to a "Butterfly" (Abbott Hospitals #4492), the needle of which is mounted directly above the well. After the desired number of cells have been micromanipulated, 100 μl of BM + 1/2 TE I + TE II containing 1000 P3x63-Ag8.653 cells and 2× HAT is added to each well. The myeloma cells serve as convenient feeder cells.

When the pipet is lowered into the well, care is taken to ensure that it does not touch the sides of the well. The volume of the expelled liquid is kept sufficiently small as to remain entirely in the field of view of the low power objective and to avoid contact with the wall of the well. In this way it is ensured that all cells added can be observed. If the cells were added to a well already containing 100 μl of medium, it would not be possible to exclude the possibility that some cells were floating above the focal plane of the objective. If more than one cell is expelled, excess cells can be picked up again. A cell whose viability is questionable can also be picked up again. To facilitate easy lowering and raising of the pipet, the condenser of the inverted microscope is removed and a transparent fixture for holding the pipet is inserted in its place. Illumination without the condenser is still adequate. The pipet can be centered relative to the microplate well using the mechanical stage of the microscope. Although possible, for reasons of convenience, we have not carried out micromanipulation in a sterile hood. Contamination of micromanipulated wells has still been less than 1 in 50. Cloning efficiency has been found to vary with individual cell lines, but it has frequently been greater than 50%.

Pipettes are conveniently made from 10 μl glass micropipets (Clay Adams #4616). The pipets are first sterilized by flaming with a bunsen burner; then forceps are used to pull the end of the pipet to a small diameter, the tip of which is broken off.

Screening to Identify Anti-Id Clones

A key element in our strategy for screening hybridomas is the use of affinity-purified polyclonal anti-ligand antibodies as a surrogate receptor. This maneuver was based on our finding that polyclonal anti-BisQ antibodies showed a fine specificity that was parallel to the fine specificity of the AChR in its excited state.[13] Agonists were bound well and antagonists were bound poorly. Moreover the rank order of binding of a panel of ligands was similar for both AChR and rabbit anti-BisQ antibodies.

Another point to be noted is that the use of polyclonal antibodies

[13] N. H. Wassermann, A. S. Penn, P. I. Freimuth, N. Treptow, S. Wentzel, W. L. Cleveland, and B. F. Erlanger, *Proc. Natl. Acad. Sci. U.S.A.* **79,** 4810 (1982).

instead of a single monoclonal anti-ligand antibody biases the screening assay to favor detection of anti-idiotypic antibodies that recognize public idiotypic determinants. This follows from the fact that private idiotypic determinants associated with a single clonotype are likely to be present at low concentration in a polyclonal population of antibodies specific for a particular ligand. The category of anti-idiotypic antibodies that recognize public immunoglobulin idiotypic determinants shared across species has been found to contain those which cross-react with receptor combining sites.

The speed and convenience of ELISA techniques, especially when the replica transfer technique described previously is used, make them the method of choice for screening fusions. Most convenient is an indirect assay in which microplate wells are coated with affinity-purified anti-ligand antibody from a species other than mice (e.g., rabbit). Then, an enzyme-labeled anti-mouse Ig second antibody can be used to detect mouse monoclonal antibodies that react with the coated wells. Enzyme-labeled reagents must be selected or else adsorbed to reduce binding to coated plates, in the absence of mouse antibody, to a satisfactory level.

Screening to Identify Anti-Receptor Clones

General Considerations

In our studies of AChR, anti-receptor antibodies were detected by ELISA using highly purified preparations of receptor from *Torpedo californica* and *Electrophorus electricus* and also with crude preparations of acetylcholine receptor from rat muscle.[4,13] The idiotypic nature of the immunization route led to the expectation that anti-receptor clones would be a subset of those identified as anti-Id with the above assay. This was confirmed experimentally. Approximately 7.4% of the wells were found to be positive using ELISA plates coated with affinity-purified rabbit anti-BisQ antibody. About 1/3 of these were also positive for receptor. Moreover, all wells positive for receptor were also positive for anti-BisQ. This suggests that only those hybridoma supernatants that are positive for anti-Id reactivity need to be screened for reactivity with receptor. An important advantage of this strategy is that the number of supernatants to be screened with receptor is much less than the total number of wells, allowing the more difficult and time-consuming assays that need to be performed when receptor has not been isolated or when only very crude preparations are available.

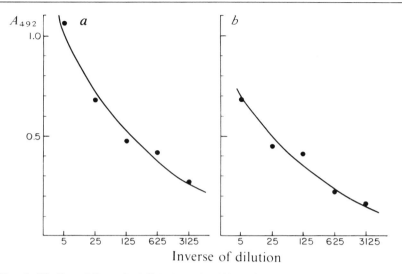

FIG. 2. Binding of *Torpedo* AChR (*a*) and rabbit anti-BisQ (*b*) by F8-D5. Taken from Cleveland *et al.*[4]

Detection of Monoclonal Antibodies to AChR by ELISA

Wells of polystyrene microplates (Corning #25855, round bottom wells, not tissue culture treated) were coated by adding 150 μl of either 400 ng/ml affinity-purified rabbit anti-BisQ antibody in 0.1 M NaHCO$_3$, pH 9.3, or 3 μg/ml purified AChR from *Torpedo californica* in the same buffer. For coating, the plates were incubated for 2 hr at 37° in a humid box. After washing twice with 0.01 M phosphate buffer–0.14 M NaCl, pH 7.2, containing 0.05% Tween 20 (PBS-Tween), the wells were exposed to various dilutions of hybridoma-antibody-containing supernatant in PBS-Tween for 2 hr at 37°. The wells were then washed three times with PBS-Tween and filled with 200 μl of a 1 : 1000 dilution of peroxidase-labeled goat anti-mouse immunoglobulin (Sigma) in PBS-Tween. After incubation at 37° for 1 hr, the wells were washed three times with PBS-Tween and assayed for peroxidase. The substrate used was *o*-phenylenediamine (7 mg in 10 ml of 0.1 M citrate-phosphate buffer, pH 4.8, containing 5 μl of 30% H$_2$O$_2$). After 10 min, the reaction was stopped with 50 μl per well of 4 M H$_2$SO$_4$. Optical density was determined at 490 nm with a Multiscan Titertek apparatus. Typical results are shown in Fig. 2. Values given have been corrected for a PBS blank, which was never higher than 0.150. Since Ig concentration in most hybridoma supernatants is usually greater than

0.1 μg/ml, we optimized our assay for speed and convenience rather than sensitivity.

Characterization of Specificity

Hybridoma supernatants identified as positive in the initial screening of a fusion must be further assayed to confirm the specificity. This is normally done after the hybridoma line has been subcloned to ensure monoclonality. A specificity assignment becomes convincing when different kinds of immunochemical assays give similar results and when inhibition studies give expected results. These principles are illustrated in our characterization of a clone F8-D5, which secretes an auto-anti-idiotypic antibody that was induced by immunization with a BisQ-BSA conjugate. The F8-D5 antibody was shown to react with AChR by the following studies.

1. The binding of F8-D5 to purified rabbit anti-BisQ could be inhibited by *Torpedo* AChR BisQ, 50% inhibition occurring with 8.1 μg of affinity purified antibody per well. F8-D5 was preincubated with inhibitor as follows. Two rows of six wells were used, one row serving as a control. To the first well of each row was added 110 μl of PBS-Tween, and to the remaining wells 100 μl was added. Then 15 μl of *Torpedo* AChR (purified) (1.52 μg/ml) was added to the first well of each row. Then 5-fold serial dilutions were made by transferring 25 μl from the first to the second well, and so on. Finally 5 μl portions of F8-D5 (2 μg/ml) were added to one row of wells and 5 μl of PBS to the other row, which served as a control (blank) for each of the concentrations of AChR used as inhibitor. Wells containing PBS only and PBS + F8-D5 were also included. The remainder of the assay was done as described above.

2. The binding of F8-D5 to *Torpedo* AChR could be inhibited by purified rabbit anti-BisQ, 50% inhibition occurring with 3 μg.

3. The binding of F8-D5 to AChR and to rabbit anti-BisQ could be inhibited by ligands known to bind to the AChR combining site, as shown in the table.

4. In addition to ELISA, F8-D5 was found to bind to AChR using immunofluorescence to detect binding to sections of electric organ. The staining pattern seen with F8-D5 was similar to that obtained with a conventional rabbit anti-AChR antiserum, as shown in Fig. 3.

5. In collaboration with J. Lindstrom, F8-D5 was also found to block [134]Cs influx in a vesicle system containing reconstituted *Torpedo* AChR.[14]

[14] B. A. Suarez-Isla, K. Wan, J. Lindstrom, and M. Montal, *Biochemistry* **22**, 2319 (1983).

INHIBITION OF BINDING OF F8-D5 TO ANTI-BisQ
AND TO *Torpedo* AChR[a]

Inhibitor	IC$_{50}$ (mM)[b]	
	Torpedo	Anti-BisQ
BisQ	0.04	0.04
Decamethonium Br	0.06	0.07
Carbamylcholine Cl	0.05	0.1
Hexamethonium Br	0.37	0.29
α-Bungarotoxin	5.5×10^{-3}	0.7×10^{-3}

[a] Taken from Erlanger *et al.*[22]
[b] IC$_{50}$ = concentration that caused 50% inhibition.

6. Preliminary results indicate that F8-D5 bound to Sepharose beads can be used to isolate AChR. In addition to their importance with regard to specificity, these results also indicate that anti-receptor antibodies made by the auto-anti-idiotypic route can be used to isolate receptor preparatively.

Discussion

An important question concerns the nature of the idiotypic determinant recognized by F8-D5. As defined by the classical studies of Oudin[15] and Kunkel[16] and their respective co-workers, idiotypic determinants are unique antigenic specificities that are presumably associated with clonally unique aspects of *v*-region sequences. Antibodies from different animals immunized with the same antigen share idiotypic determinants only rarely.[17] In addition to classical anti-idiotypic antibodies there is another type of anti-idiotypic antibody referred to as an internal image[2] or homobody.[1] Internal images have the property that they recognize all antibodies of a particular specificity, regardless of the individual or species of origin.[17–20] By operational criteria, these antibodies are anti-idiotypic since they are not usually absorbed with normal serum and since they are inherently site-specific. Since an internal image recognizes essentially all

[15] J. Oudin and M. Michel, *C. R. Seances Acad. Sci. Paris* **257**, 805 (1963).
[16] H. G. Kunkel, M. Mannik, and R. C. Williams, *Science* **140**, 1218 (1963).
[17] J. Urbain, M. Slaoui, B. Mariamé, and O. Leo, *in* "Idiotypy in Biology and Medicine" (H. Köhler, J. Urbain, and P.-A. Casenave, eds.), p. 15. Academic Press, Orlando, 1984.
[18] A. Nisonoff and E. Lamoyi, *Clin. Immunol. Immunopathol.* **21**, 397 (1981).
[19] N. K. Jerne, J. Roland, and P.-A. Casenave, *EMBO J.* **1**, 243 (1982).
[20] A. A. Augustin, G. K. Sim, and C. Bona, *Surv. Immunol. Res.* **2**, 78 (1983).

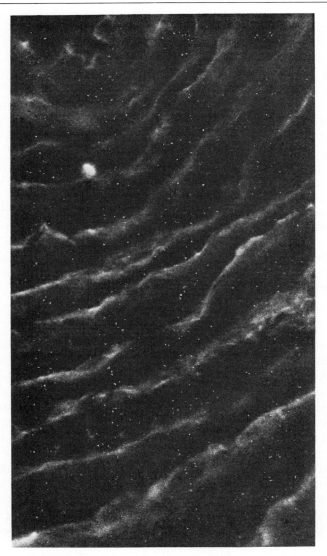

FIG. 3. Immunofluorescence pattern of reaction of F8-D5 with *Torpedo* electric tissue. Taken from Erlanger *et al.*[22]

antibodies of a particular specificity, it can be regarded as an "image" or copy of the antigenic determinant recognized. Since F8-D5 recognizes an idiotope that is shared across species and with a nonimmunoglobulin receptor, it is likely that F8-D5 is an internal image of BisQ.

Another important question concerns the probability of success when using the auto-anti-idiotypic strategy to prepare anti-receptor antibodies. With the BisQ ligand, 24 wells positive for AChR were identified in a single fusion. More recently, we have applied this strategy to the adenosine receptor.[6] In three fusions, a total of 18 auto-anti-Id wells were identified in initial screens. Five auto-anti-Ids from one of the fusions were screened for anti-receptor activity, and two were found to be positive. For the glucocorticoid receptor, two fusions were done before a well positive for receptor was found.[21] Although more experience is necessary, these three successes encourage the expectation that the auto-anti-idiotypic strategy may have wide applicability.

In conclusion, we wish to point out that the very strong auto-anti-idiotypic response observed in the BisQ system raises the possibility that monoclonal antibody technology can be used to study idiotype regulation under physiological conditions.

Acknowledgment

This work was supported by NIH Grants AI-17949 and NS-15581 and grants from the Muscular Dystrophy Association.

[21] E. Cayanis, R. Rajagopalan, W. L. Cleveland, I. S. Edelman, and B. F. Erlanger, *J. Biol. Chem.* (in press).

[22] B. F. Erlanger, W. L. Cleveland, N. H. Wassermann, B. L. Hill, A. S. Penn, H. H. Ku, and R. Sarangarajan, *in* "Investigation and Exploitation of Antibody Binding Sites, Vol. 15 Methodological Surveys in Biochemistry and Analysis" (E. Reid, G. M. W. Cook, and D. J. Morre, eds.). Plenum, New York, in press.

[10] Optimal Strategies for Developing Human–Human Monoclonal Antibodies

By PAUL G. ABRAMS, JEFFREY L. ROSSIO, H. C. STEVENSON, and K. A. FOON

The importance of developing human monoclonal antibodies has not been vitiated by the great strides of the last 2 years in applying murine antibodies to the treatment of human disease.[1–3] Some of the deficiencies

[1] P. G. Abrams, A. C. Morgan, Jr., R. W. Schroff, C. S. Woodhouse, J. Carrasquillo, H. C. Stevenson, M. F. Fer, R. K. Oldham, and K. A. Foon, *in* "Monoclonal Antibodies and Cancer Therapy" (R. A. Reisfeld and S. Sell, eds.), p. 233. Alan R. Liss, Inc., New York, 1985.

and problems encountered in the clinical application of murine antibodies, such as lack of antitumor effect,[4] antiglobulin responses,[5] serum sickness,[6] and RES uptake,[7] may be largely overcome by substituting their human counterparts. Indeed, the very successes of murine antibodies despite these problems has made the quest for human monoclonal antibodies with similar specificities even more alluring. Besides their actual clinical application, human antibodies may also help unlock mysteries of autoimmune disease, B-cell differentiation, and host responses to tumors.

As is true of murine monoclonal antibodies, difficulties encountered in the production of human monoclonal antibodies depend in part on the purpose for which the antibodies are intended. There are greater challenges in producing human monoclonal antibodies against tumor-associated antigens than against antigens that are targets of autoimmune diseases, where the underlying antibody production is already programmed in the patient and the task is to immortalize those cells accounting for it. Development of human antibodies against tumor-associated antigens depends upon overcoming the additional hurdle of generating sufficient numbers of human B cells programmed to produce the appropriate antibodies.

Part of the problem that has plagued human monoclonal antibody development has been the source of B cells. This is not surprising for, unlike mice, humans cannot be immunized repeatedly with virtually any antigen to increase the prefusion B-cell population programmed to make specific antibody. In addition, human antibodies, except in very circumscribed experimental settings, have depended upon peripheral B cells (PBLs) or draining lymph node cells. There is some evidence that PBLs may be a poor source of memory cells when compared to splenocytes.[8]

---

[2] R. A. Miller, D. G. Maloney, R. Warnke, and R. Levy, *N. Engl. J. Med.* **306,** 517 (1982).

[3] K. A. Foon, R. W. Schroff, P. A. Bunn, D. Mayer, P. G. Abrams, M. Fer, J. Ochs, G. C. Bottino, S. A. Sherwin, D. J. Carlo, R. B. Herberman, and R. K. Oldham, *Blood* **64,** 1085 (1984).

[4] R. K. Oldham, K. A. Foon, A. C. Morgan, Jr., C. S. Woodhouse, R. W. Schroff, P. G. Abrams, M. F. Fer, C. S. Schoenberger, M. M. Farrell, E. S. Kimball, and S. A. Sherwin, *J. Clin. Oncol.* **2,** 1235 (1984).

[5] R. W. Schroff, S. M. Beatty, K. A. Foon, R. K. Oldham, and A. C. Morgan, Jr., *Cancer Res.* **45,** 879 (1985).

[6] M. F. Fer, unpublished observations.

[7] R. W. Schroff, J. A. Carrasquillo, K. A. Foon, A. M. Keenan, A. C. Morgan, Jr., P. A. Bunn, J. C. Reynolds, P. Perentesis, S. M. Larson, and P. G. Abrams, *FASEB Abstr.* (1985).

[8] R. Callard, G. McCaughan, J. Babbage, and R. Souhami, *J. Immunol.* **129,** 153 (1982).

Immunizations of humans with many antigens are not possible on ethical grounds. We developed a protocol[9] to produce human monoclonal antibodies by utilizing PBLs from patients who were participating in a clinical trial in which they received irradiated, autologous colon carcinoma cells as a tumor vaccine. This protocol was used to develop human antibodies that react with considerable specificity for colon carcinoma,[10] indicating that, in the right circumstances, these problems are not insurmountable.

The human B lymphoblastoid or myeloma lines, the other side of the fusion equation, have also created more difficulties than their murine counterparts. One problem is that most of the lines are not true myelomas, and lack the rough endoplasmic reticulum, abundant mitochondria, and well-developed Golgi apparatus associated with the high levels of immunoglobulin production and secretion of true myelomas.[11] Many of the human–human hybridomas created secrete low levels of immunoglobulin.[12] Secondly, most of the lines are Epstein–Barr virus (EBV) positive, so that the B cells may be infected with EBV rather than fused to form a true hybridoma; the presence of EBV raises additional issues for the eventual *in vivo* use of the antibody.

Each of the first two human lines reported to be used successfully for constructing human hybridomas presented difficulties when employed by subsequent investigators. SKO-007, derived from an IgE-secreting myeloma U-266, fused poorly, was only modestly sensitive to HAT medium, and was found to be contaminated heavily with mycoplasma; human antibodies to dinitrochlorobenzene (DNCB) were produced using splenocytes from Hodgkin's disease patients undergoing staging laporotomy who had been immunized with DNCB as part of routine testing for immunological status prior to surgery.[13] GM1500, an IgG-secreting B lymphoblastoid line, grew slowly and was infected with EBV; Croce produced anti-measles antibodies using PBLs from a patient with subacute sclerosing panencephalitis who had high circulating titers of anti-measles

[9] P. G. Abrams, J. A. Knost, K. A. Foon, A. C. Morgan, Jr., J. Rossio, M. Hanna, H. C. Hoover, Jr., and R. K. Oldham, unpublished observations.

[10] M. G. Hanna, M. V. Haspel, R. P. McCabe, N. Pomato, and H. C. Hoover, Jr., in "Monoclonal Antibodies and Cancer Therapy" (R. A. Reisfeld and S. Sell, eds.), p. 505. Alan R. Liss, Inc., New York, 1985.

[11] D. Kozbor, D. Dexter, and J. C. Roder, *Hybridoma* **2**, 7 (1983).

[12] P. G. Abrams, J. J. Ochs, S. L. Giardina, A. C. Morgan, Jr., S. B. Wilburn, A. R. Wilt, R. K. Oldham, and K. A. Foon, *J. Immunol.* **132**, 1611 (1984).

[13] L. Olsson and H. S. Kaplan, *Proc. Natl. Acad. Sci. U.S.A.* **77**, 5429 (1980).

antibody.[14] These encouraging results led to the search for superior human lines.

Human Monoclonal Antibodies: Strategies

Continuous production of a human immunoglobulin by a human lymphocyte immortalized by fusion to a mouse myeloma line was first reported by Schwaber and Cohen,[15] 2 years prior to Köhler and Milstein's work describing murine hybridomas producing antibodies of predefined specificity.[16] There are now a number of strategies that may be employed to achieve the desired goal of a human monoclonal antibody: (1) EBV transformation of human lymphocytes; (2) fusion of human lymphocytes with murine myeloma; (3) fusion of human lymphocytes with human "myeloma"; (4) fusion of human lymphocytes with human–murine myeloma hybrid; (5) transfection of human lymphocytes with DNA from human tumor; (6) transfection of murine hybridoma with human constant and variable region DNA.

EBV transformation of lymphocytes has been used successfully, for example to produce human IgM monoclonal antibodies to a melanoma-associated antigen (OFA),[17] but these transformants generally suffer from a limited secretion of human antibody and limited survival as secretors; this may be because of the difficulty in growing true clones. Human–murine hybridomas often cease Ig secretion within 12 weeks,[12] a factor that can produce very frustrating results. We were able, for example, to produce a human antibody that reacted strongly to small-cell carcinoma of the lung (Table I), but could not maintain secretion despite six subclonings. Croce has assigned the genes for human heavy chain to chromosome 14, and those for κ and λ chains to numbers 2 and 22, respectively; in addition, he has demonstrated that chromosome 2 is preferentially segregated in human–mouse hybridomas so that those that produce human antibodies that have κ light chains are much less stable than those with κ.[18,19] Nonetheless, human–mouse hybridomas have been developed that secrete antibody for limited periods of time that were specific for a num-

[14] C. M. Croce, A. Linnenback, W. Hall, Z. Steplewski, and H. Koprowski, *Nature (London)* **288,** 488 (1980).

[15] J. Schwaber and E. P. Cohen, *Nature (London)* **244,** 444 (1973).

[16] G. Köhler and C. Milstein, *Nature (London)* **256,** 495 (1975).

[17] R. Irie, L. Sze, and R. Saxton, *Proc. Natl. Acad. Sci. U.S.A.* **79,** 5666 (1982).

[18] C. M. Croce, M. Shander, J. Martinis, L. Cicurel, G. G. D'Ancona, T. W. Dolby, and H. Koprowski, *Proc. Natl. Acad. Sci. U.S.A.* **76,** 3416 (1979).

[19] J. Erikson, J. Martinis, and C. M. Croce, *Nature (London)* **294,** 173 (1981).

TABLE I

BINDING OF HUMAN MONOCLONAL ANTIBODY
CLONES TO HUMAN SMALL-CELL CARCINOMA
CELL LINES NCI-H69 AND NCI-H128

Clone	Binding ratios[a]	
	NCI-H69	NCI-H128
605H4	9	16
605G5	7	5
605H6	3	5
605G8	7	7
605G9	8	7
605G10	5	5
605H10	7	7
605G12	9	9
604H8	12	17
604D10	9	15
604G10	15	28
604H11	15	15

[a] Counts/background.

ber of antigens, including human glioma,[20] human breast cancer,[21] the Forssman antigen,[22] tetanus toxoid,[23] and keyhole limpet hemacyanin.[24]

Human–Human Hybridomas

There are many reports in the literature now describing human–human hybridomas secreting antibodies. The problem with most of these is the paucity of data proving specificity. We have, for example, performed over 30 separate fusions using PBLs and another 15 employing draining lymph nodes from patients with malignancy. Most of the fusions have been successful, yielding up to 90% of the wells with hybrid growth in some instances, with a substantial percentage that secreted human Ig. Most of these antibodies have been IgM, reacted strongly with human

[20] K. Sikora and J. Phillips, *Br. J. Cancer* **43,** 105 (1981).
[21] J. Schlom, D. Wunderlich, and Y. A. Teramoto, *Proc. Natl. Acad. Sci. U.S.A.* **77,** 6841 (1980).
[22] R. Nowinski, C. Berglund, J. Lane, M. Lostrom, I. Berstein, W. Young, and S. Hakomori, *Science* **210,** 537 (1980).
[23] F. Gigliotti and R. Insel, *J. Clin. Invest.* **70,** 1306 (1982).
[24] H. C. Lane, D. J. Volkman, G. Whalen, and A. S. Fauci, *J. Exp. Med.* **154,** 1043 (1982).

tumor cells, but cross-reacted with normal human tissues or fibroblasts. Schoenfeld *et al.*[25] found that monoclonal autoantibodies to double-stranded DNA (dsDNA) from lupus patients cross-reacted with synthetic molecules and one-third of them with cardiolipin. Littman *et al.* were able to rescue an antibody by the hybridoma technique that bound specifically to dsDNA,[26] illustrating the difficulties in drawing conclusions where hybridoma efficiency is low and that the source of lymphocytes may not be representative of the state of the patients' immune responses.

An insight into the obstacles encountered in producing human hybridomas may be gained by a quick survey of the statistics. Obtaining 10^3 hybrids from a fusion of 10^8 murine splenocytes with 10^7 myeloma cells is an excellent fusion. If 30 of these prove to produce antibodies of interest that are stable secretors, it is considered a job well done. These splenocytes are, as a rule, not only individually ripe for fusion, but contain expanded populations of cells stimulated by the immunizing antigen. The 10^4 "loss" that occurs in the best of circumstances makes more acute any compromise involving poorer fusion efficiency myeloma lines, poorer immunized lymphocytes, or less expanded populations of lymphocytes immunized against a particular antigen. That is one reason why production of antigen-specific human antibodies derived from lymphocytes from patients with autoimmune diseases, who have greater numbers of stimulated B cells, has generally been more successful than those against tumor-associated antigens made from lymphocytes from patients with cancer, who at best have a small number of cells programmed to make antibody against the appropriate antigen.

Approaches to Comparing the Human Myeloma Cell Lines

The range of antigens to which human monoclonal antibodies have been developed with human–mouse fusions demonstrates the existence of a suitable immune response and the ability of hybridoma technology to facilitate cloning and immortalization of these antibodies. The stability problems with the interspecies hybridomas prompted a search for a suitable "myeloma" partner of human origin. As mentioned above, most of the human lines are not true myelomas but rather B lymphoblastoid lines; they are referred to as myeloma lines only for ease of communication. The important parameters in assessing the relative merits of a given

[25] Y. Shoenfeld, J. Rauch, H. Massicotte, S. K. Data, J. Andre-Schwartz, B. D. Stollar, and R. S. Schwartz, *N. Engl. J. Med.* **308**, 414 (1983).

[26] B. H. Littman, A. V. Muchmore, A. D. Steinberg, and W. C. Greene, *J. Clin. Invest.* **72**, 1987 (1983).

myeloma line are efficiency of hybrid formation, percentage of Ig-secreting hybrids, cloning efficiency, stability, and the percentage of specific antibody-producing clones.

The first problem with the human myeloma lines is their relative paucity. It became relatively easy to induce murine plasmacytomas[27] and a large battery was available to test and select for high fusion efficiency and stability of secretion. There are, in contrast, only a relatively few human lines that are suitable for the role of myeloma parent; again, most of these are not true plasma cells but rather B lymphoblastoid. Second, human cells do not generally grow as fast as their murine counterparts so that selection of appropriate mutants, growth of initial hybridomas, and cloning simply take more time. Third, it was difficult to ascertain that true hybridomas, rather than EBV-transformed lymphocytes, were growing out in the cultures. Fourth, perhaps based on this consideration, true cloning with less than a single cell per well was difficult, and feeder layers required definition. Finally, screening assays for human antibodies to tumor-associated antigens cannot routinely use PBLs as a negative control because the detecting anti-human antibody will usually cross-react with surface membrane Ig on these cells.

There are two strategies that can be employed to define the optimal human cell lines for human–human hybridoma development. The first is to take a relatively small number of myeloma lines and perform multiple fusions with human lymphocytes from a variety of sources. Cote et al.[28] compared SKO-007[13] and LICR-LON-HMy2 (HMy2)[29] in more than 75 fusions using PBLs, splenocytes, lymph node and infiltrating mononuclear cells of tumors. Murine plasmacytoma NS-1 was used as a control. They found that HMy2 was superior to SKO-007, but that NS-1 was better than both in fusion efficiency, and were equal in the other parameters. They also reported that the human–murine hybridomas were as stable as the human–human, but only tested this over 2–3 months. Most of the antibodies detected intracellular antigens. One antibody was extensively subcloned and found to react with a cell surface antigen present on a minority of tumor cell lines. Houghton et al. performed a similar study adding GM4672 to the contest, with comparable results.[30]

[27] M. Potter, J. G. Humphrey, and J. L. Walters, J. Natl. Cancer Inst. (U.S.) **49**, 305 (1972).

[28] R. J. Cote, D. M. Morrissey, A. N. Houghton, E. J. Beattie, Jr., H. F. Oettgen, and L. J. Old, Proc. Natl. Acad. Sci. U.S.A. **80**, 2026 (1983).

[29] P. A. W. Edwards, C. M. Smith, A. M. Neville, and M. J. O'Hare, Eur. J. Immunol. **12**, 641 (1983).

[30] A. N. Houghton, H. Brooks, R. J. Cote, M. C. Taormina, H. F. Oettgen, and L. J. Old, J. Exp. Med. **158**, 53 (1983).

Methods

We took the opposite approach,[31] identifying a human chronic lymphocytic leukemia (CLL) cell that fused well with NS-1 and produced stable hybrids secreting its surface membrane IgMκ, as a "standard" human B cell that could be used to compare the human myeloma cell lines available to us at the time. Cote *et al.* not unexpectedly found substantial variability in fusion efficiency depending upon the source of lymphocytes. Our CLL cells, on the other hand, could be obtained in large quantities from 50 ml of peripheral blood, were virtually 100% identical, required no immunization, and could not be transformed by EBV so that any growth in the wells could be attributed to true hybridoma formation.[31] In addition, since the cells uniformly expressed a single Ig that was not expressed by the myeloma lines (except in very low levels, 10 ng/ml, by UC729-6), screening for hybridoma secretion was simple. The major drawback to this strategy is that hyperimmunized lymphocytes might behave differently; nonetheless, it seemed reasonable to presume that those human cells lines that performed the best with these CLL cells generally would also be superior for hyperimmunized lymphocytes.

Cells. Using this strategy we tested seven different cell lines for the above-mentioned parameters. Rather than use the mycoplasma-infected SKO-007, we selected our own aminopterin-sensitive mutant of U-266, and did the same for RPMI 8226. In addition to the GM4672 and HMy2, we used UC729-6[32] and HF2,[33] and NS-1 for comparison. The cell lines were all brought out of the freezer at the same time and reestablished in tissue culture and maintained in log phase growth with either 6-thioguanine (6-TG) or 8-azaguanine (8-AG) to maintain aminopterin sensitivity. Three days prior to fusion, the cells were taken off the drugs and grown in log phase with daily replenishment of the medium. Roswell Park Memorial Institute medium 1640 (RPMI 1640) supplemented with sodium pyruvate (1 mM), L-glutamine (2 mM), and 15% fetal calf serum (growth medium) with or without 6-TG or 8-AG was used to grow the cells. Fusions were plated in this growth medium plus 132 μg/ml oxaloacetic acid and HAT (100 μM hypoxanthine, 10 μM aminopterin, and 30 μM thymidine).[34]

Fusions. The PBLs of 50 ml of blood obtained from a patient with CLL were isolated on a Ficoll-Hypaque gradient and 99% were found to

[31] P. G. Abrams, J. A. Knost, G. Clarke, S. Wilburn, R. K. Oldham, and K. A. Foon, *J. Immunol.* **131**, 1201 (1983).

[32] H. Handley and I. Royston, *in* "Hybridomas in the Diagnosis and Treatment of Cancer" (M. Mitchell and H. Oettgen, eds.). Raven Press, New York, 1982.

[33] R. Lundack, unpublished observations.

[34] B. W. Littlefield, *Science* **145**, 709 (1964).

express surface membrane IgMκ by cytofluography. After washing twice with serum-free growth medium, 10×10^8 CLL cells and 1×10^7 myeloma cells were pelleted together. The cell pellet was dislodged and 1 ml of polyethylene glycol 1000 (PEG 1000) was added gradually to the cell slurry over 60 sec and then stirred for an additional 60 sec. The PEG was gradually diluted to 6% over 6 min, and the cells gently pelleted, resuspended in HAT medium, and seeded into 96-well plates (2.5×10^5 cells/ well). The cells were incubated in 5% CO_2 at 37°).

Cloning. As indicated above, the human myelomas did not clone as readily by limiting dilution as the murine hybridomas. We used a two-stage process to establish the monoclonal nature of the hybridomnas. First, the contents of one well from the 96-well plate were dispersed into the first column (8 wells) of another 96-well plate. Using a multitip pipetter, the cells were serially diluted across the plate. Growth medium was diluted 1 : 1 with conditioned medium from parental myeloma cell lines for cloning. Plates were examined periodically and those in which there was growth of a single colony were then cloned formally.

Testing. To determine efficiency of immunoglobulin secretion, initial fusion plates were tested after the appearance of hybrids for the production of human IgMκ, using an enzyme-lined immunosorbent assay (ELISA). Unlike fusions with lymphocytes in cancer patients that require testing for tumor reactivity, screening in this system requires only detection of the surface IgMκ from the CLL cell. Since none of the myeloma lines secrete IgM with the exception of UC729-6 (10 ng/ml), and all the CLL cells express the same surface membrane IgMκ, detection of secreted IgMκ is a simple, valid method of assessing hybridomas for Ig secretors. Ninety-six-well soft vinyl plates were coated with goat anti-human Ig (Cappell, Cochranville, PA), diluted 1 : 3000 in 0.1 M Tris buffer (pH 8.3), and then washed in Tris–0.2% bovine serum albumin–0.2% sodium azide–0.05% Tween 20 (TBTA), and nonspecific binding to plastic was then blocked with TBTA minus Tween (TBA) with 1% chicken serum. After blocking, the plates were washed again with TBTA, and test supernatants diluted 1 : 10 in TBA plus 1% chicken serum were then added. After incubating for 1 hr at room temperature, the plates were washed with TBTA and p-nitrophenyl phosphate (Sigma 104; prepared immediately before use as 1 mg/ml in 1 M Tris, pH 9.8, plus 0.3 mM $MgCl_2$) was added and incubated for 30 min. Optical densities were read at 405 nm on a microELISA reader, with the blank being the well containing RPMI alone. Any wells $\geq$ 30% of positive control after subtraction of backgrounds were scored as positive. Calculation of the level of IgM secretion was determined by comparison of serial dilutions of a known concentration of human IgMκ with those of clone supernatants.

Results

As shown in Table II, U-266 produced hybrids in 38% of the wells in two-thirds of the fusions (0% in the third) and these were ready for testing on day 32. Only three, however, secreted IgM. Three fusions with HMy2 produced hybrids in 17% of the wells, and were ready for testing on day 20; 67% of these, however, secreted IgM. A mean of 46% of wells produced hybrids when HF2 was the myeloma parent, 24% of these being secretors. Fifty-one percent of seeded wells yielded hybrid growth with UC729-6 as the myeloma parent, and 43% were secretors. No hybrids were produced either with GM4672 or RPMI 8226. Fusions with murine myeloma NS-1 yielded a hybrid efficiency of 80%, and 60% of these secreted human IgM. Cloning efficiencies varied from 11 to 33%, but the numbers tested were too small to make any definitive comparison of this parameter. Immunoglobulin secretion varied from 0.8 μg/ml per 10 cells for an HMy2 clone to 1.5 μg/ml per 10 cells for an HF2 or UC729-6 clone. The NS-1 clone tested secreted 2.4 μg/ml per 10 cells of human IgM. The clones derived from the human–human fusions continued to produce the IgMκ for more than 12 months, but the human–mouse clone ceased secretion at 20 weeks.

Discussion

These data indicate that GM4672 and RMPI 8226 are poor at forming hybrids with human lymphocytes. U-266 formed hybrids with considerable efficiency, but their rate of appearance was slow and, most importantly, very few secreted the Ig from the human lymphocyte. This line should not, however, be summarily dismissed as a potentially useful fusion partner. We performed another series of experiments using *in vitro* sensitization to create a substantial number of B cells hyperimmunized to tetanus toxoid.[35] Cultures of lymphoid cells revealed maximum IgG production at days 11 and 12 of incubation, with appearance of antibody first seen on day 6. Fusions of these cells with U-266 produced hybrids in 4% of the wells using the day 6 cells, and 33% of the wells using the day 10 cells. This only includes the hybridomas secreting antibody specific for tetanus toxoid. Thus, it appears as if U-266 secretes specific antibody with equal efficiency as the others but only if the fusing lymphocytes have been adequately differentiated, which the CLL cells apparently were not. For this cell line at least, the ideal time for fusion is just prior to maximum antibody secretion. It may be that this cell, being the true myeloma,

---

[35] J. Rossio, J. Knost, S. Pickeral, and P. Abrams, *J. Clin. Invest.* (in press).

TABLE II

Combined Results of Three Separate Fusions of CLL Cells with Human and Murine Cell Lines

	Parent cell line (secretion)						
	U-266 (IgE)	HMy2 (IgG)	HF2 (nonsecretor)	UC729-6 (IgM)	GM4672 (IgG)	RPMI 8226 (λ chain)	NS-1 (murine)
Wells seeded	968	880	1012	846	804	1012	352
Wells with growth in HAT	264	132	485	422	0	0	270
% Hybrids[a]	38	17	46	51	0	0	80
Secretors[b]	3	88	130	179	0	0	164
% Secretors among hybrids[c]	1	67	24	43	0	0	60
Hybrids cloned	3	3	9	8	0	0	6
Cloned hybrid secretors	0	1	1	2	0	0	1
% Stable clones[d]	0	33	11	25	0	0	17

[a] (Number of hybrids/number of wells seeded) × 100.
[b] Optical density ≥ 30% of positive control (100 ng/well of IgM κ).
[c] (Number of hybrids secreting IgM/number of hybrids) × 100.
[d] (Number of clones secreting IgM/number of hybrids cloned) × 100.

requires a more differentiated cell than the CLL cells for successful fusion and secretion.

The HMy2 cell line fused inefficiently, but a high proportion of the hybrids secreted immunoglobulin. The strategy with this line is to develop superior fusion protocols to increase hybrid efficiency. Investigations of alternative PEGs, different percentages of PEGs, different incubation times, or other modifications of the fusion protocols are worthwhile because this line appears to be a highly efficient secretor.

The UC729-6 and its clone, HF2, produced hybrids with the greatest efficiency, that grew out the quickest, and that had a high percentage of secretors. The total numbers of secreting hybrids was greater with this line than any of the others. That the secreted antibody was of CLL cell origin and not parental myeloma line origin was demonstrated by production of an anti-idiotype monoclonal antibody to the secreted IgMκ that reacted strongly, and exclusively, with the CLL cells used and no other CLL cells and no other human IgMκ, and were negative against surface membrane or internal IgM in the parental myeloma cell line.[36] Since these parental myeloma cells are really B lymphoblastoid, and not true myelomas, they may fuse and secrete more efficiently with relatively undifferentiated cells such as CLL than, for example, true myelomas such as U-266 (see above). This may explain why the overwhelming majority of antibodies produced using these lines have been IgMs compared to the tetanus toxoid experiment with U-266 where there were 75% IgGs. In order to establish this fact, identical *in vitro* sensitization experiments using UC729-6 and HF2 would have to be performed with U-266 repeated as an appropriate control.

Future Directions

Two new approaches to developing human or human–mouse chimeric antibodies have recently proved successful. Foung *et al.* developed a human–mouse myeloma line by fusing human lymphocytes with murine myeloma SP2/0, and selecting an 8-azaguanine-resistant mutant. The clone selected was monitored for human gene retention by its continued expression of human HLA backbone antigen on the chimeric cell surface. This line has been used to develop stable human hybridomas secreting antibodies to varicella-zoster virus.[37] This myeloma appears to have the positive growth and cloning efficiencies of the murine myeloma but an improved retention of human chromsomes. Its utility in capturing and

---

[36] P. Abrams, in preparation.
[37] S. K. H. Foung, S. Perkins, A. Raubitschek, J. Larrick, G. Lizak, D. Fishwild, E. G. Engleman, and F. C., Grumet, *J. Immunol. Methods* **70**, 83 (1984).

maintaining secretion of human antibodies directed at tumor-associated antigens remains to be proved.

The second approach was pioneered by Oi et al.[38] They cloned genes for human constant and murine variable regions into cells already producing a murine antibody of desired specificity and were able to obtain rearrangements that produced antibodies of the human constant region with the murine hypervariable region that imparted specificity to the antibody. Thus, it is now possible to produce a human–mouse chimeric antibody that contains mostly human immunoglobulin but retains the engineered specificity of the original murine antibody.

Summary

Human monoclonal antibodies are desirable, especially as therapeutic agents, but the best means of producing them is still a matter of investigation. It is clear that human antibodies of predicted specificity from patients with autoimmune disease can be derived, and this may help unlock some of the mysteries of these illnesses.

Human monoclonal antibodies against tumor-specific antigens for use in in vivo diagnosis and therapy remain desirable goals. Problems involved in their routine development include the lack of available, adequately immunized, and differentiated lymphocytes and the nature and paucity of the available human "myeloma" cell lines. These lines have been compared now by a number of authors who have reached similar conclusions. Our study directly compared the greatest number of cell lines and found UC729-6 and HF2 to be the best; on the other hand, our success in developing IgG-secreting hybridomas from U-266, using hyperimmunized lymphocytes, suggests that this line may only be capable of secretion with the more differentiated cell, the human equivalent of those hyperimmunized murine spleens. Hence both sides of the fusion equation must be made optimal. Two new approaches to circumvent this problem involve the use of either a human–murine myeloma chimera as the parental myeloma line or, more recently, genetic engineering techniques to substitute human constant regions for the murine while retaining the murine hypervariable region, preserving the binding specificity of the murine antibody.

Acknowledgment

The work reported here was supported in part by Department of Health and Human Services Contract NO1-CO-23910.

[38] S. L. Morrison, M. J. Johnson, L. A. Herzenberg, and V. T. Oi, Proc. Natl. Acad. Sci. U.S.A. **81,** 6851 (1984).

[11] Comparative Phenotypic Analysis of Available Human Hybridoma Fusion Partners

By DANUTA KOZBOR, JOHN C. RODER, MICHAEL E. SIERZEGA, SUSAN P. C. COLE, and CARLO M. CROCE

The technology for production of murine monoclonal antibodies has advanced enormously since its introduction by Köhler and Milstein in 1975.[1] However, the production of human monoclonal antibodies by fusion technologies has been hampered, mainly by the paucity of suitable human cell lines that can serve as fusion partners and support the secretion of immunoglobulin (Ig). Hypoxanthine–aminopterin–thymidine (HAT)-sensitive murine plasmacytomas have been fused instead with human lymphocytes to yield mouse × human hybrids that secrete human antibody against the Forssman antigen,[2] keyhole limpet hemocyanin,[3] tetanus toxoid (TT),[4,5] human tumor-associated antigen,[6-8] and multiple endocrine organs.[9] These interspecies hybridomas preferentially segregate human chromosomes, making it difficult to derive stable lines secreting human antibody. However, the loss of human chromosomes from mouse × human hybridomas is not random. It is known, for example, that human chromosomes 14 (heavy chain) and 22 (λ light chain) are preferentially retained, whereas chromosome 2 (κ chain) is preferentially lost.[10,11]

Since the chromosomal constitution of intraspecies hybrids is much more stable, human × human hybridomas are more likely to be a useful source of specific human monoclonal antibodies. However, the plasmacytomas, which represent the most differentiated of lymphoid malignancies,

[1] G. Köhler and C. Milstein, *Nature (London)* **256**, 495 (1975).

[2] R. Nowinski, C. Berglund, Y. Lane, M. Lostrom, I. Bernstein, W. Young, S. Hakomori, L. Hill, and M. Cooney, *Science* **210**, 537 (1980).

[3] H. C. Lane, J. H. Shelhamer, H. S. Motowski, and A. S. Fauci, *J. Exp. Med.* **155**, 333 (1982).

[4] D. Kozbor, J. C. Roder, T. H. Chang, Z. Steplewski, and H. Koprowski, *Hybridoma* **1**(3), 323 (1982).

[5] Y. L. Butler, H. C. Lane, and A. S. Fauci, *J. Immunol.* **130**, 165 (1983).

[6] J. Schlom, D. Wunderlich, and Y. A. Teramoto, *Proc. Natl. Acad. Sci. U.S.A.* **77**, 6841 (1980).

[7] K. Sikora and R. Wright, *Br. J. Cancer* **43**, 696 (1981).

[8] K. Sikora and J. Phillips, *Br. J. Cancer* **43**, 105 (1981).

[9] J. Satoh, B. S. Prabhakar, M. V. Haspel, F. Ginsberg-Fellner, and A. L. Notkins, *N. Engl. J. Med.* **309**, 217 (1983).

[10] C. M. Croce, M. Shander, J. Martinis, L. Cicurel, G. G. D'Ancona, T. W. Dolby, and H. Koprowski, *Eur. J. Immunol.* **10**, 486 (1979).

[11] J. Erikson, J. Martinis, and C. M. Croce, *Nature (London)* **244**, 173 (1981).

TABLE I
HUMAN PLASMACYTOMA CELL LINES

Parent plasmacytoma cell line	Tissue of origin	Class of Ig produced *in vitro*	Ref.	Fusion partner (HGPRT-deficient derivative)	Ref.
RPMI 8226	Peripheral blood	λ	12	8226-8AG[R]	13
U-266	Peripheral blood	ε, λ	14	SKO-007 (U-266AR1)	15
				U-266 (8AG[R])	13
				FU-266	16
LA49	Pleural effusion	δ, λ	17	ND[a]	
Oda	Subcutaneous plasmacytoma	δ, λ	18	ND	
L 363	Peripheral blood	λ	19	ND	
KMM56	Pleural effusion	λ	20	ND	
Karpas 707	Peripheral blood and bone marrow	λ	21	ND	
KMM-1	Subcutaneous plasmacytoma	λ	22	ND	

[a] Not done.

seem to be one of the most difficult types of human cells to establish in continuous culture. Despite numerous effort in several laboratories, only few long-term cultures of human plasmacytomas have been established and two of them have been used for fusion with human lymphocytes (Table I).[12–22]

[12] Y. Matsuoka, G. E. Moore, Y. Yagi, and D. Pressman, *Proc. Soc. Exp. Biol. Med.* **125,** 1246 (1967).

[13] P. G. Abrams, J. A. Knost, G. Clarke, S. Wilburn, R. K. Oldham, and K. A. Foon, *J. Immunol.* **131,** 1201 (1983).

[14] K. Nilsson, H. Bennick, S. G. O. Johansson, and J. Pontén, *Clin. Exp. Immunol.* **7,** 477 (1970).

[15] L. Olsson and H. S. Kaplan, *Proc. Natl. Acad. Sci. U.S.A.* **77,** 5429 (1980).

[16] N. N. H. Teng, K. S. Lam, F. C. Riera, and H. S. Kaplan, *Proc. Natl. Acad. Sci. U.S.A.* **80,** 7308 (1983).

[17] M. E. Jobin, J. L. Fahey, and L. Price, *J. Exp. Med.* **140,** 494 (1974).

[18] N. Ishihara, T. Kiyofuri, and S. Oboshi, *Proc. Jpn. Cancer Assoc.* **36,** 120 (1977).

[19] V. Diehl, M. Schaadt, H. Kirchner, K. P. Hellriegel, F. Gudat, C. Fonatsch, E. Iskewitz, and R. Guggenheim, *Blut* **36,** 331 (1978).

[20] T. Shibuya, Y. Niho, K. Yamasaki, K. Nakayama, Y. Oka, K. Arase, and T. Yanase, *Acta Haematol. Jpn.* **43,** 256 (1980).

[21] A. Karpas, P. Fischer, and D. Swirsky, *Lancet* **1,** 931 (1982).

[22] A. Togawa, N. Inoue, K. Miyamoto, H. Hyodo, and M. Namba, *Int. J. Cancer* **29,** 495 (1982).

TABLE II
HUMAN LYMPHOBLASTOID CELL LINES

Parent cell line	Class of Ig produced	Ref.	Fusion partner (HGPRT-deficient derivative)	Ref.
GM1500	γ_2, κ	23	GM1500-6TG-A1-2	23
			GM1500-6TG-A1-1	23
			GM4672	24
			GK-5	25
ARH-77	γ, λ	26	LICR-LON-HMy2[a]	27
			LICR-LON-HMy2/CAM1[a]	28
WI-L2	μ, κ	29, 30	UC729-6	31
	γ, κ		UC729-6-HF$_2$	13
			LTR228	32, 33
			H351.1	34
			WI-L2-727-HF2-6TG[a]	35
PGLC33H	μ, λ	36	GMO467	36, 34
MC/CAR	γ, κ	37	MC/MNS-1,2,3	37

[a] Reported as γ, κ.

The lack of available human plasmacytoma lines prompted efforts to construct human × human hybrids using lymphoblastoid cell lines as fusion partners (Table II).[23-37] In this article, we briefly summarize the

[23] C. M. Croce, A. Linnenbach, W. Hall, Z. Steplewski, and H. Koprowski, *Nature (London)* **228**, 488 (1980).

[24] Y. Shoenfeld, S. C. Hsu-Lin, J. E. Gabriels, L. E. Silberstein, B. C. Furie, B. Furie, B. D. Stollar, and R. S. Schwartz, *J. Clin. Invest.* **70**, 205 (1982).

[25] D. S. Dwyer, J. R. Bradley, C. K. Urguhart, and J. F. Kearney, *Nature (London)* **301**, 611 (1983).

[26] K. H. Burk, B. Drewinko, J. M. Trujillo, and M. J. Ahearn, *Cancer Res.* **38**, 2508 (1978).

[27] P. A. W. Edwards, C. M. Smith, A. M. Neville, and M. J. O'Hare, *Eur. J. Immunol.* **12**, 641 (1982).

[28] K. Sikora, T. Alderson, J. Ellis, J. Phillips, and J. Watson, *Br. J. Cancer* **47**, 135 (1983).

[29] J. A. Levy, V. Viroloinen, and V. Defendi, *Cancer* **22**, 517 (1968).

[30] J. A. Levy, D. N. Buell, C. Creech, Y. Hirshaut, and H. Silverberg, *J. Natl. Cancer Inst. (U.S.)* **46**, 647 (1971).

[31] M. C. Glassy, H. H. Handley, H. Hagiwara, and I. Royston, *Proc. Natl. Acad. Sci. U.S.A.* **80**, 6327 (1983).

[32] D. W. Buck, J. W. Larrick, A. Raubitschek, K. Truitt, G. Senyk, J. C. N. Wang, and B. J. Dyer, *in* "Hybridomas: A New Dimension in Biological Analyses" (R. H. Kennett, T. J. McKearn, and K. B. Bechtol, eds.), p. 275. Plenum, New York, 1984.

[33] J. W. Larrick, K. E. Truitt, A. Raubitschek, G. Senyk, and J. C. N. Wang, *Proc. Natl. Acad. Sci. U.S.A.* **80**, 6376 (1983).

phenotypic characteristics of human lines of B-cell lineage which have been successfully used as fusion partners.

Morphology of Plasmacytoma and Lymphoblastoid Cells

The basis for classification of myeloma cells lies in the identity of the myeloma protein *in vivo* with Ig synthesized *in vitro*. In addition, as shown in Fig. 1A, plasmacytoma cells have abundant rough endoplasmic reticulum (RER), few free polyribosomes, numerous mitochondria, and a well-developed Golgi apparatus. The rate of Ig secretion is high. These cells never carry Epstein–Barr virus (EBV) and are usually aneuploid.[38,39] Most of these cells have doubling times of 36–73 hr and are difficult to grow in tissue culture, often requiring a plasmacyte-stimulating factor for proliferation.[17] Most plasmacytoma cell lines are derived from myeloma patients with very advanced disease, and are often established from extramedullary sites, such as pleural effusions or subcutaneous (sc) plasmacytomas. It also appears that most of these lines are established from the more unusual forms of myeloma, such as IgD or IgE, and it is curious that the Ig light chain type has always been λ rather than κ.

The lymphoblastoid cell lines (LCL) established from malignant or normal hematopoietic tissue are much more easily maintained in tissue culture, with population doubling times of 20–30 hr. They show a constant association with EBV, polyclonal derivation, and diploidy.[38,39] They have numerous free polyribosomes and poorly developed RER and Golgi apparatus (Fig. 1B), and secrete less Ig than plasmacytoma cells. The lymphoblastoid cells can be generally distinguished from plasmacytoma cells on the basis of characteristics listed in Table III. Some of these phenotypic features are characteristic for certain stages in B-cell differentiation and may play a crucial role in supporting the production of antibodies when fused with normal B cells.

[34] N. Chiorazzi, R. L. Wasserman, and H. G. Kunkel, *J. Exp. Med.* **156,** 930 (1982).

[35] D. Emanuel, J. Gold, J. Colacino, C. Lopez, and U. Hammerling, *J. Immunol.* **133,** 2202 (1984).

[36] K. Sato, R. S. Slesinski, and J. W. Littlefield, *Proc. Natl. Acad. Sci. U.S.A.* **69,** 1244 (1972).

[37] R. E. Ritts Jr., A. Ruiz-Arguelles, K. G. Weyl, A. W. Bradley, B. Weihmeir, D. J. Jacobsen, and B. L. Strehlo, *Int. J. Cancer* **31,** 133 (1983).

[38] K. Nilsson and J. Pontén, *Int. J. Cancer* **15,** 321 (1975).

[39] K. Nilsson, *in* "Human Lymphocyte Differentiation: Its Application to Cancer" (B. Serrou and C. Rosenfeld, eds.), INSERM Symp. No. 8, p. 307. Elsevier/North-Holland Biomedical Press, Amsterdam, 1978.

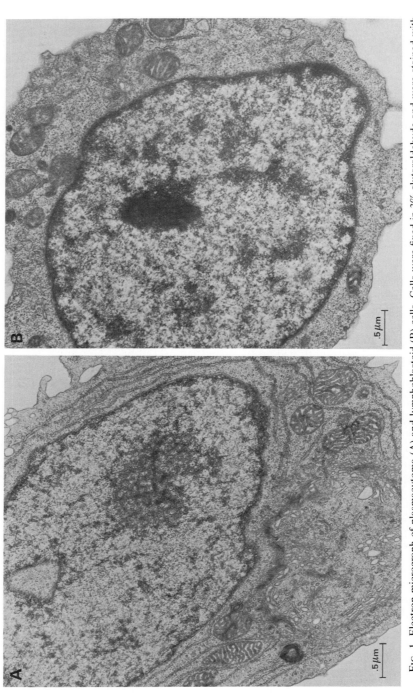

FIG. 1. Electron micrograph of plasmacytoma (A) and lymphoblastoid (B) cells. Cells were fixed in 3% glutaraldehyde and were stained with uranyl acetate and lead citrate. (A) RPMI 8226 cells show abundant RER, well-developed Golgi apparatus, and prominent mitochondria. The nuclear membrane is regular. (B) KR-4 cells show prominent polyribosomes with scant RER. Moderate numbers of mitochondria are seen.

TABLE III
PHENOTYPIC CHARACTERISTICS OF PLASMACYTOMA AND
LYMPHOBLASTOID CELLS

Characteristic	Plasmacytoma	Lymphoblastoid
Electron microscopy	Abundant RER and prominent Golgi apparatus	Sparse RER, free polyribosomes
EBNA[a]	Negative	Positive
Rate of Ig production	High	Low
Surface Ig expression	±	++
Doubling time	36–73 hr	20–30 hr
Karyotype	Aneuploid	Usually diploid
Growth in culture	Single-cell suspension or loose clumps	Clumps
Cell morphology	Round, regular	Irregular, elongated with prominent pseudopodia

[a] EBNA, Epstein–Barr virus-induced nuclear antigen.

Procedure for Electron Microscopy

The ultrastructure of plasmacytoma and lymphoblastoid cells can be examined by electron microscopy. (1) Cell pellets are fixed in 3% glutaraldehyde in PIPES buffer (pH 7.2) for 1 hr at room temperature, washed in PIPES, and postfixed in 1% osmium tetroxide in PIPES for 1 hr at room temperature. (2) The pellet is then washed in distilled H_2O and block-stained in 1% aqueous solution of uranyl acetate overnight at 60°, followed by dehydration through an ethanol series (70, 90, 95%, absolute) and in propylene oxide. (3) Samples are then embedded in Epon-812 and sectioned with a diamond knife on a Sorvall MT-2 ultramicrotome. (4) Sections are stained with lead citrate and examined with a Hitachi 11-E or Zeiss M-10 electron microscope.

Procedure for EBV-Induced Nuclear Antigen (EBNA) Assay

All lymphoblastoid cells carry EBV DNA and express EBNA. On the other hand, EBNA has never been detected in any human plasmacytoma cells and therefore expression of this antigen can be used to distinguish lymphoblastoid cells from plasmacytomas. EBNA can be assayed by anti-complement immunofluorescence as described by Reedman and Klein.[40] (1) Cells are suspended in a hypotonic glycerin-containing solution (0.8 mM $MgCl_2 \cdot 6H_2O$, 1 mM $CaCl_2$, 30 mM glycerin, pH 7.0, with 4 drops of fetal bovine serum added per milliliter) for 2–3 min, and smears are prepared. (2) Smears are fixed in methanol : acetone (1 : 2) at $-20°$ for 5 min. (3) Fixed cells are treated with an anti-EBNA-positive serum at 37° for 15 min, washed three times with BSS (0.8% NaCl, 0.014% $CaCl_2$, 0.04% KCl, 0.02% $MgSO_4 \cdot 7H_2O$, 0.06% KH_2PO_4, 0.06% $Na_2HPO_4 \cdot 2H_2O$, pH 6.9), and incubated with an anti-EBNA-negative human serum (as a source of complement) at 37° for 15 min. (4) After washing with BSS, the cells are stained with a fluorescein isothiocyanate (FITC)-conjugated rabbit anti-human β_1C/β_1A reagent (Hyland Laboratories, Los Angeles, CA; diluted 1 : 20) at room temperature for 30 min. Smears are counterstained with an aqueous solution of 0.01% Evans blue at room temperature for 10 min. Parallel controls are exposed to an EBNA-negative reference serum. (4) The EBV-carrying Raji and EBNA-negative Ramos lines are used as positive and negative controls. Raji and Ramos lines are available from the American Type Culture Collection, 12301 Parklawn Drive, Rockville, MD 20852-1776.

Human Plasmacytomas as Fusion Partners

The first reported human hybridoma produced monoclonal antibodies against 2,4-dinitrophenyl (DNP) hapten and was constructed with the HAT-sensitive plasma cell line U-266AR1 (later renamed SKO-007),[15] derived from the IgE-producing plasmacytoma U-266 (Table IV). The U-266AR1 cells were fused with the uninvolved splenic lymphocytes from a Hodgkin's lymphoma patient sensitized with dinitrochlorobenzene. Average fusion frequencies were 37×10^{-7}. Approximately 28% of wells containing hybrids produced IgG and 1.7% of all hybrids were specific for DNP. Hybrids produced 3–11 $\mu g/ml$ per day of monoclonal IgG, anti-DNP antibodies. These results were not reproducible for several years, probably due to mycoplasma contamination of the cells. Abrams et al.[13] derived a second HAT-sensitive subline from the U-266 cell line and Ig-secreting hybrids were obtained, but fusion frequencies were very low. A third HAT-sensitive derivative of U-266, FU-266,[16] has not yet been characterized in terms of its fusion properties in human × human hybridomas.

Another HAT-sensitive fusion partner of putative plasmacytoma origin, 8226-8AG^R,[13] was derived from the RPMI 8226 line.[12] The cells did fuse with lymphocytes from a patient with Crohn's disease, but no Ig-

[40] B. M. Reedman and G. Klein, *Int. J. Cancer* **11**, 499 (1973).

secreting hybrids were recovered. Other hypoxanthine–guanine phosphoribosyltransferase (HGPRT)-deficient cells originated from the RPMI 8226 as potential fusion partners[41] have been found to be of nonhuman origin.

Human Lymphoblastoid Cell Lines as Fusion Partner

The first LCL fusion partner was derived by Croce et al.[23] from a B-cell line, GM1500 (IgG$_2$ κ), established from a patient with multiple myeloma. This line, GM1500-6TG-2, was fused with peripheral blood lymphocytes (PBL) obtained from a lethally infected patient with subacute sclerosing panencephalitis (SSPE) who had an extremely high serum titer (10^{-6}) of anti-measles antibody. Six clones secreting IgM specific for measles virus were obtained and hybridization frequencies of 18×10^{-7} were estimated. In another study, GM1500-6TG-2 was used as a fusion partner with peripheral blood mononuclear cells from a patient with type I diabetes mellitus of 5 months' duration.[42] Only one out of three attempted fusions was successful, and in this case a hybridization frequency of 25×10^{-7} was obtained. One clone (4.5% of all hybrids) produced IgM specific for islet cells in the pancreas. This clone was stable for over 1 year and secretes approximately 0.4 μg IgM/ml. Osband et al.[43] fused GM4672, an LCL subline of the GM1500 line, with peripheral blood mononuclear cells sensitized in vitro with Rh(D) erythrocytes. Hybrids secreted Rh(D)-specific IgG at approximately 0.01–0.1 μg/ml. Shoenfeld et al.[24] fused GM4672 with blood lymphocytes stimulated with pokeweed mitogen (PWM). Cells from patients with autoimmune disorders such as systemic lupus erythematosus and cold agglutinin disease yielded hybridization frequencies of 17×10^{-7}. Out of 108 hybridomas, 16 produced autoantibodies (15%), all of the IgM class. Seven were specific for single-stranded DNA, six for platelets, and seven produced cold agglutinins specific for erythrocytes. All hybridomas except the cold agglutinin-secreting lines were stable for 7 months and secreted in the range of 1–15 μg IgM antibody/ml.

Another derivative of GM1500, GK-5, has been used to construct hybridomas which secreted a monoclonal anti-idiotypic antibody to the nicotinic acetylcholine receptor,[25] using PBLs from a patient with myasthenia gravis. Satoh et al.[9] used GK-5 cells to generate hybridomas with PBLs from patients with a variety of autoimmune diseases, including

[41] J. W. Pickering and F. B. Gelder, *J. Immunol.* **129,** 406 (1982).

[42] G. S. Eisenbarth, A. Linnenbach, R. Jackson, R. Scearce, and C. M. Croce, *Nature* (*London*) **300,** 264 (1982).

[43] M. Osband, J. Cavagnaw, and H. Z. Kupchick, *Blood* **60**(5), Suppl. 1, 81a (abstr.) (1981).

TABLE IV
HUMAN HYBRIDOMAS CONSTRUCTED WITH MYELOMAS AND LCLs AS FUSION PARTNERS

Fusion partner	Fusion partner Cell type	Class of Ig produced	Drug resistance[a]	Source of donor lymphocytes[b]	Fusion frequency (× 10^-7)[c]	Ig secretion (µg/ml)	Specificity Antigen	Specificity Ig class	Hybridomas Cloning efficiency (%)[d]	Hybridomas Stability (months)	Ref.
SKO-007	Plasmacytoma	ε, λ	8-AG	Immune spleen (Hodgkin's)	37	3–11	DNP	IgG	ND[e]	ND	15
GM1500	LCL[f]	γ₂, κ	6-TG	Immune PBL (SSPE)	18	ND	Measles virus	IgM	ND	ND	23
				PBL, type 1 diabetes	25	0.4	Islet cells	IgM	ND	>12	42
GM4672	LCL	γ₂, κ	6-TG	Immune PBL	ND	0.01–0.1	Rh(D)	IgG	ND	ND	43
				Autoimmune disorders	17	1–15	ssDNA	IgM	ND	>7	24
GK-5	LCL	γ₂, κ	6-TG	PBL, spleen PBL, insulin-requiring diabetes, autoimmune disorders	ND	1–20	Multiple organ reactivity	IgM	ND	>6	9
				Myasthenia gravis	ND	ND	Acetyl-choline receptor	IgM	ND	>4	25
LICR-LON-HMy2	LCL	γ₁, κ	8-AG	Normal PBL, tonsil, lymph node	0.1–10	0.5–8	None	IgG	25	>12	27
				TIL	ND	ND	Glioma cells	ND	ND	ND	44
GM0467.3	LCL	µ, λ	8-AG	Immune tonsil (PWM)	22	0.4–2.8	TT	IgM	High	>9	34

Cell line	Type	Ig	Selection	Lymphocytes	%	Cloning	Antigen	Ig class	Secretion		Ref.
H351.1	LCL	μ, κ	8-AG	Normal PBL, spleen (PWM)	22	ND	None	ND	High	ND	34
LTR228	LCL	μ, κ	6-TG	Immune PBL, B-cell blasts	100	1–5	TT	IgG	ND	>11	33
WI-L2-727-HF2-6TG	LCL	γ, κ	6-TG, Oua	EBV line (CMV)	ND	5	CMV	IgG	High	>12	35
KR-4	LCL	γ₂, k	6-TG, Oua	TT, specific EBV line	112	3–10	Tetanus toxoid	IgM	70	>20	49
UC729-6	LCL	μ, κ nonsecretor	6-TG	PBL, lymph node (cancer patients)	29	3–9	Carcinoma lines	IgM	ND	>9	31
MC/CAR	LCL	γ, κ nonsecretor	8-AG	Immune PBL (rubella)	100	ND	Rubella	ND	ND	ND	37
RH-L4	B-cell lymphoma	γ, κ nonsecretor	8-AG	PBL (PWM)	96	5–15	Human leukemic cells	IgG	ND	>24	58
Heteromyelomas: FU-266neoᴿ × X63-Ag8.653, clone D-33	Hybrid myeloma (human–mouse) nonsecretor	ε, λ	6-TG, Oua, G-418	Activated B cells	20–100	2–36	DNP, TT, ds-DNA, ss-DNA, ribosomal RNA, Rh factor, E. coli 0111:84 (T5)	IgM/IgG	ND	>9	16
KR-12	Hybrid myeloma (human–human)	γ, κ, λ	6-TG	EBV line (TT, cancer patients)	100	5–30	TT, carcinoma cell lines	IgM	70	>12	50

[a] AG, Azaguanine; TG, thioguanine; Oua, ouabain.
[b] PBL, Peripheral blood lymphocytes; SSPE, subacute sclerosing panencephalitis; TT, tetanus toxoid; EBV, Epstein–Barr virus; TIL, tumor-infiltrating lymphocytes; PWM, pokeweed mitogen; CMV, cytomegalovirus.
[c] Estimate based on assumptions made concerning the number of cells seeded per well.
[d] Cloning efficiency determined by limiting dilution.
[e] ND, Not done.
[f] LCL, Lymphoblastoid cell line.

insulin-requiring diabetes mellitus. Monoclonal antibodies from seven of the hybridomas obtained reacted with antigens in multiple endocrine organs.

Another lymphoblastoid fusion partner that has been used by a number of investigators is the LICR-LON-HMy2 line (IgG$_1$ κ)[27] or its clone adapted for growth in serum-free medium, LICR-LON-HMy2/CAMI. LICR-LON-HMy2 has been reported as an IgG$_1$ κ producer, although the parental LCL ARH-77 was described as an IgG λ-positive cell line.[26] Lymphocytes from peripheral blood, tonsil, or lymph node all fused with LICR-LON-HMy2 cells with frequencies of approximately 10^{-7}. Hybrids secreted 0.5–8 μg IgG/ml. LICR-LON-HMy2 has also been fused with tumor-infiltrating lymphocytes from glioma patients. A hybridoma was obtained which secreted antibody that bound to glioma surface components and not to normal brain cells[44] and, after intravenous injection of radiolabeled antibody, localized in the area of the recurrent cystic glioma.[45] Other investigators have fused LICR-LON-HMy2 cells with lymph node lymphocytes[46] from melanoma patients. Several of the hybrids secreted antibody which showed some binding specificity for melanoma cell lines but grew slowly, were relatively unstable, and produced low amounts of Ig.

Chiorazzi *et al.*[34] cloned H351.1 (IgM κ) from the parental line WI-L2-AG^{R}35scl, and GM0467.3 (IgM λ) from the parental line PGLC33H. These clones hybridized equally well at estimated frequencies of 22 × 10^{-7} with lymphocytes from spleen, tonsil, or peripheral blood stimulated *in vitro* with PWM. Most (89%) of the hybrids secreted IgM, whereas few (11%) secreted IgG. In one case, tonsil lymphocytes from a donor immunized with TT 1 week before surgery was fused with GM0467.3, but of 21 hybrids (4.7%), one secreted anti-TT and subclones secreted levels of 0.4–2.8 μg/ml for the duration of the study (9 months). A separate group[47] has also reported success in deriving IgA, IgG, and IgM monoclonal antibodies against sheep erythrocytes by fusing WI-L2-729-HF2 with tonsil lymphocytes immunized *in vitro*. A human monoclonal antibody to cytomegalovirus (CMV) has been obtained by fusion of an EBV-transformed cell line making antibody to CMV and a HAT-sensitive, ouabain-(Oua)-resistant variant of WI-L2, 727-HF2-6TG.[35] Sixty-five percent of the hybrids remained positive for CMV antibody IgG κ (5 μg/ml) over a period of 12 months.

[44] K. Sikora, T. Alderson, J. Phillips, and J. V. Watson, *Lancet* 1, 11 (1982).
[45] J. Phillips, K. Sikora, and J. V. Watson, *Lancet* 2, 1214 (1982).
[46] H. M. Warrenius, J. W. Taylor, B. E. Durack, and P. A. Cross, *Eur. J. Cancer Clin. Oncol.* 19, 347 (1983).
[47] L. Strike, B. H. Devens, and R. L. Lundak, *Immunology* 163(2–4), 272 (abstr.) (1982).

Another LCL, LTR228,[33] is a spontaneous 6-thioguanine (6-TG)-resistant mutant which has been reported to fuse efficiently (fusion frequency 10^{-5}) with PWM-stimulated peripheral blood B cells from individuals boosted with TT. Five percent of the hybrids produced anti-TT antibody. After cloning and subcloning, the hybridomas produced 1–5 μg of specific IgG κ antibody per 10^6 cells for a period of more than 11 months.

Lymphoblastoid versus Plasmacytoma Cells as Fusion Partners

The majority of fusion partners described for the production of human hybridomas (Table IV) are LCLs and one (or its variants) is a definite plasmacytoma. A comparison of hybridization frequencies, yield of antigen-specific hybridomas, growth rate, stability, and cloning efficiencies does not delineate a clear superiority of LCLs or plasmacytomas as fusion partners. The apparent limitation of LCL as fusion partners rests in the lack of sustained levels of human monoclonal antibody production in these hybrids. However, in many cases, this may be attributed to the status of the B lymphocytes with which they are fused. A relationship exists between cell morphology and the amount of Ig being produced;[38] plasma cells contain abundant RER which correlates well with the larger amounts of Ig being synthesized (1–10 μg/ml) as compared with LCLs with less developed RER and, hence, lower levels of Ig production (<1 μg/ml). However, it is well known that following the establishment of tumor cell lines in tissue culture, some differentiation and morphologic changes may occur, so that the phenotype of the passaged cell may not closely resemble the original tumor. For example, the level of IgE production by the SKO-007 myeloma cell line was lower (~200 ng/ml) than that of the parental U-266 myeloma (1–5 μg/ml).[15] A very low level of Ig (λ chain) production by RPMI 8226, despite the abundant RER and Golgi apparatus, has been reported.[48] To investigate the significance, if any, of morphology relative to other parameters important for production of monoclonal antibody-producing hybrids, we produced somatic cell hybrids between the KR-4 LCL line (γ_2, κ) which is HGPRT deficient and Oua resistant,[49] with the RPMI 8226 human plasmacytoma cell line, which produces only λ light chains.[12] Hybrid selection was done in HAT medium containing 10^{-5} M Oua. These hybrids were phenotypically similar to the human plasmacytoma parental cells (well-developed RER, high levels of Ig production, 5 μg/ml) and grew as well as the KR-4 cells.

[48] D. Kozbor, D. Dexter, and J. C. Roder, *Hybridoma* **2**(1), 7 (1983).
[49] D. Kozbor, A. E. Lagarde, and J. C. Roder, *Proc. Natl. Acad. Sci. U.S.A.* **79**, 6651 (1982).

Following counterselection in 6-TG, mutants that were 6-TG and Oua resistant were obtained, one of which, the KR-12 line, was used as a fusion partner to construct hybridomas with EBV-transformed B-cell lines as well as with non-EBV-transformed lymphocytes from peripheral blood of colorectal carcinoma patients.[50] The KR-12 cells had a high frequency of hybrid formation with LCLs (10^{-5}) (Table V) and, when fused, were able to support specific antibody production for a period of more than 12 months. Thus, a fusion partner was obtained that exhibited characteristics of both the plasmacytoma and lymphoblastoid cells desirable in human fusion partners. The hybrids constructed between KR-12 cells and anti-TT antibody-secreting lymphoblastoid cell line B6[51] produced 5–30 μg antibodies/ml, which is approximately 2- to 3-fold the amount of Ig produced by KR-4 × B6 hybrids (1–10 μg/ml). Electron microscopy revealed that the KR-4 × B6 hybrids resembled their lymphoblastoid parents and the KR-12 × B6 hybrid more closely resembled the plasmacytoma phenotype. Both human hybrids produced anti-TT antibody continuously for more than 12 months. Therefore, the increased number of chromosomes does not necessarily impair long-term stability.

In order to increase antibody production, the anti-TT antibody-producing hybrids (KR-4 × B6 and KR-12 × B6 cells) were grown as solid tumors in irradiated BALB/c nude mice and then adapted to ascites growth in irradiated, pristane-primed animals after a brief *in vitro* passage (Fig. 2).[52] Following this procedure, described in detail in the accompanying chapter,[53] ascites growth of hybrids was observed in 50% of irradiated and pristane-primed mice. As shown in Table VI, the KR-4 × B6 hybrids secreted on average 0.5–0.9 mg human Ig/ml ascites fluid, whereas the average Ig production by Kr-12 × B6 hybrids was 1.3–6.7 mg/ml. Approximately half of the total human Ig detected in the ascites fluid was IgM with specificity for TT. Repassage of ascites-recovered hybrids in BALB/c nude mice resulted in a 2-fold increase in human Ig production. Irradiation of mice improved the sc tumor growth (from 25% in nonirradiated to 85% in irradiated animals, respectively) and was essential for ascites growth of hybrids).

The more than 100-fold higher production of antibody by the hybrids *in vivo* compared to results in tissue culture could rest in the higher cell density in ascites fluids. In tissue culture, both hybrids grew to a density

[50] D. Kozbor, P. Tripputi, J. C. Roder, and C. M. Croce, *J. Immunol.* **133**, 3001 (1984).

[51] D. Kozbor and J. C. Roder, *J. Immunol.* **127**, 1275 (1981).

[52] D. Kozbor, W. Abramow-Newerly, P. Tripputi, S. P. C. Cole, J. Weibel, J. C. Roder, and C. M. Croce, *J. Immunol. Methods* **81**, 31 (1985).

[53] J. C. Roder, S. P. C. Cole, and D. Kozbor, this volume [12].

TABLE V

CHARACTERIZATION OF HYBRID HUMAN PLASMACYTOMA KR-12

Cell line	sIg, cIg[a]	Secreted Ig (μg/ml)[b]	Electron microscopy[c]	Division time (hr)	Frequency of hybrid formation at 10^{-6} mean ± SEM	
					EBV cell line	PBL[d]
KR-4	γ, κ	0.4	LCL	22–24	9.8 ± 2.5	0.1 ± 0.01
RPMI 8226	λ	0.3	Plasmacytoma	32–38	—	—
KR-12	γ, κ, λ	5.0	Plasmacytoma-like	24–28	10 ± 2.2	0.8 ± 0.07

[a] Surface Ig (sIg) and cytoplasmic (cIg) Ig were determined by direct immunofluorescence.

[b] Secreted Ig was quantitated by a solid-phase ELISA.

[c] In electron micrographs, well-differentiated cells with abundant RER, prominent Golgi, and condensed nuclear chromatin were considered "plasmacytomas." Less differentiated cells with small amounts of RER, moderately developed Golgi, and extended nuclear chromatin were considered "lymphoblastoid."

[d] Frequency was calculated from the fraction of negative wells with the Poisson equation. Mean frequency is given for three plates. The lymphocytes and lymphoblastoid cell lines were obtained from the peripheral blood of donors immunized with TT or from colorectal carcinoma patients.

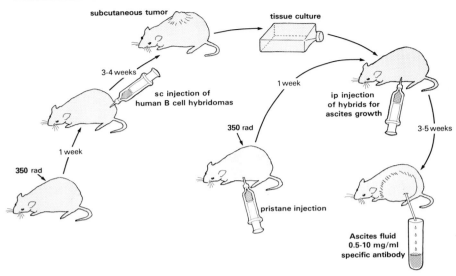

FIG. 2. Ascites growth of human hybridomas. Per mouse 10^7 cells of tetanus-specific human hybrids (KR-4 × B6 and KR-12 × B6) were injected subcutaneously into irradiated (350 rad) BALB/c nude mice 1 week prior to injection of cells. Animals developed tumors within 3–6 weeks. Cells from solid tumors were expanded in tissue culture for three to five passages and reinjected intraperitoneally into pristane-primed, irradiated (350 rad) mice. Ascites growth was observed within 3–4 weeks following injection of cells.

of 10^6 cells per milliliter culture medium, whereas in the mouse peritoneum, the cell density was 20–30 × 10^6 cells per milliliter of ascites fluid. However, the increased production of human Ig during the ascites growth may not only reside in increased cell density since morphological changes were also observed in these cells. Electron microscopy revealed that the majority of the KR-4 × B6 hybrids have a lymphoblastoid appearance during *in vitro* growth in tissue culture. However, these hybrids, after passage in the mouse peritoneum during ascites growth, showed ultrastructural changes associated with differentiation of at least 10% of lymphoblastoid cells toward a myeloma lineage, which correlated with increased human Ig production.

These results suggest that some characteristic(s) associated with plasmacytoma morphology may contribute to higher Ig production; however, the regulatory mechanism is still unknown and, particularly with the hybrids, it can vary from fusion to fusion. The polyploid human hybrids are not inherently unstable, but certain differentiated functions including pro-

TABLE VI

COMPARISON OF HYBRIDS BETWEEN EBV-TRANSFORMED CLONE B6 OR LYMPHOBLASTOID KR-4 AND HUMAN PLASMACYTOMA KR-12 USED AS FUSION PARTNERS

Hybrids	Secreted Ig (µg/ml)	Electron microscopy	Cloning efficiency (%)	Modal chromosome number[a]	Stability (months)	Production of human Ig in the ascites fluid (µg/ml)[b]
KR-4 × B6	1–10	LCL	63	89 (74–99)	>12	500–900
KR-12 × B6	5–30	Plasmacytoma-like	54	120 (95–150)	>12	1300–6700

[a] Range is shown in parentheses. A minimum of 40 metaphase spreads were counted for each cell line.

[b] Tetanus-specific human hybrid clones (KR4 × B6 and KR-12 × B6), which were grown as a sc tumor and then in vitro for three to five passages, were injected ip into irradiated BALB/c nude mice (10^7 cells per mouse) and ascites fluid was collected 3–5 weeks later from individual mouse and titered in an ELISA assay. Ascites fluid from P3X63Ag8 mouse myeloma was used as a negative control.

duction of Igs are often lost after fusion[54] or can undergo more complex regulatory mechanisms.[55]

Search for Non-Ig-Secreting Fusion Partners

The limitation of human hybridoma technology appears to lie in the variable and often low fusion frequency, the erratic levels of human monoclonal antibody production by these hybrids, and the presence of Ig molecules composed of heavy and/or light chains from both the plasmacytoma or lymphoblastoid fusion partner and the B-cell donor.

The presence of secreted Ig molecules synthesized by the parental fusion partner dilutes the specific antibody of interest. In the murine system, this difficulty was overcome by the development of two kinds of variants: those that synthesize but do not secrete Ig[56] and those that do not synthesize Ig.[57] Several laboratories are engaged in developing HAT-sensitive human myeloma and lymphoblastoid cells that do not secrete Ig. Glassy *et al.*[31] fused the UC729-6 lymphoblastoid cell line, which does not secrete Ig but is cytoplasmic and surface IgM κ positive, with the draining lymph node cells of cancer patients. Those authors obtained two hybrids secreting 3–10 μg of IgM or IgG antibody/ml, which reacted with human tumor cell lines but not with normal cells. The UC729-6 cells were recently found to secrete low amounts of IgM (30 ng/ml per 10^6 cell[13]).

Another LCL, MC/CAR, although reported as a nonsecretory plasmacytoid cell line, has features more characteristic of lymphoblastoid cell lines, such as expression of EBV, and was found to express cytoplasmic IgG κ.[37] These cells were fused with mononuclear cells from a donor known to have high titers of circulating antibodies to rubella after additional *in vitro* stimulation with the antigen. Two out of 95 Ig-positive cultures were found to have anti-rubella antibody.

Larrick *et al.*[33] used the reverse-plaque technique to select for a non-producer variant of the LTR228 lymphoblastoid cell line. Initial experiments suggest that these variants can produce hybrids with an efficiency similar to that of the LTR228 parental cells.

Most recently, Olsson *et al.*[58] obtained human × human hybrids be-

[54] B. D. Bengtsson, M. Nabholz, R. H. Kennett, and W. F. Bodmer, *Somatic Cell Genet.* **1**, 41 (1975).

[55] R. Ber, G. Klein, M. Moar, S. Povey, A. Rosén, A. Westman, E. Yefenof, and J. Zeuthen, *Int. J. Cancer* **21**, 707 (1978).

[56] G. Köhler, S. G. Howe, and C. Milstein, *Eur. J. Immunol.* **6**, 292 (1976).

[57] J. F. Kearney, A. Radbrusch, B. Liesegang, and K. Rajewski, *J. Immunol.* **123**(4), 1548 (1979).

[58] L. Olsson, R. B. Andreasen, A. Ost, B. Christensen, and P. Biberfeld, *J. Exp. Med.* **159**, 537 (1984).

tween RH-L4 B lymphoma (IgG κ producer, nonsecretor) and human B lymphocytes from patients with acute myeloid leukemia to study the antigenic repertoire of the humoral immune response against the patients' own leukemia cells and against leukemic cells from other patients. Although Ig production (5–15 μg) was detected in more than 50% of the hybrids, only 10% of these secreted Ig specific for human leukemia cells.

In another approach to obtaining a better fusion partner, Teng et al.[16] constructed mouse × human hybrid myelomas ("heteromyelomas"), reasoning that such hybrids would retain the superior fusion characteristics of the mouse myeloma and confer greater stability to hybrids generated with them because of the presence of the human chromosomes in the heteromyeloma fusion partner. The HAT-sensitive variant of U-266 human myeloma, FU-266, was rendered resistant to the antibiotic G-418 by transfection with the recombinant plasmid vector pSV2-neo^R, and one of the resultant neo^R clones, E-1, was subsequently fused with the non-Ig-secreting and HAT-sensitive mouse myeloma cell line X63-Ag8.653.[56] Selection was done in medium containing the antibiotic G-418 to eliminate the mouse parent and containing ouabain to kill the human cells. Because Oua and G-418 resistance are dominant traits, only hybrids survived the selection. The hybrids, in addition to being Oua and G-418 resistant, preserved the HAT sensitivity marker for both parents. Selected hybrid clones were then tested as fusion partners in a series of fusions with polyclonally activated human B lymphocytes, with antigen-primed human B lymphocytes, and, in some instances, after transformation of the latter with EBV. Hybrids producing 2–10 μg Ig/ml per 10^6 cells per day were stable for more than 6 months, and several antigen-specific monoclonal antibodies have been generated. In some instances, isolated clones have produced as much as 21–36 μg Ig/ml per 10^6 cells per day. The frequency of hybrid formation with heteromyelomas, i.e., 6–100% positive wells for hybrid outgrowth, was higher than that when human myelomas were used as fusion partners. Moreover, some of the heteromyelomas, e.g., D-33, became nonproducers after a few weeks in culture; others, e.g., D-36, ceased ε heavy chain production but retained a low level of λ light chain secretion. Although the heteromyelomas are routinely grown in the presence of G-418 to promote retention of human chromosomes with integrated bacterial genes for neomycin resistance, it is not clear how this influences the stability of new hybrids in which human chromosomes carry no drug markers and chance being segregated in the same fashion as in human × mouse hybrids. Thus, human × human hybrids are likely to be preferable and the recently produced human hybrid myeloma KR-12 attests to the superiority of this type of hybrid.

A fusion partner that is HAT sensitive and does not synthesize Ig has not yet been described. We have tried to select a non-Ig-producing variant from human hybrid myeloma KR-12 cells, based on some chromosomal segregation observed in these hybrids. Our efforts have included repeated killing of Ig-positive cells with rabbit anti-Ig antibody plus complement and repeated fluorescence-activated cell sorter selection of KR-12 cells labeled with fluorescein-conjugated rabbit anti-human IgA, IgG, IgM, κ, and λ antibody followed by cloning of selected Ig-negative cells by limiting dilution. After 20 cycles of such selection we have obtained clones negative for Ig expression, and studies are in progress to test the stability of such non-Ig-producing variants.

Limitations and Future Developments

An issue that has frequently been raised relates to the presence of either EBV or retroviruses in monoclonal antibody preparations intended for human use. Xenotropic retroviruses which are known to be infectious for human cells[59] are present in mouse plasmacytomas and are found in hybrids descending from the mouse myeloma cells.[60,61] We have not observed retrovirus particles either in human fusion partners KR-4 and KR-12 or in hybridomas, but discovery of a human C-type virus, HTLV, in certain T-cell leukemias/lymphomas[62,63] warrants a closer look at human fusion partners. Indeed, recent results suggest that HTLV may be associated with a broader range of host cells than previously recognized. For example, human T-cell leukemia virus type II (HTLV-II) was found to be capable of infecting both B and T cells.[64] HTLV-I has been isolated from a HTLV-transformed B-lymphocyte clone from a patient with HTLV-associated adult T-cell leukemia.[65] A strain of lymphadenopathy-associated retrovirus (LAV) passaged *in vitro* was used to infect a lymphoblastoid cell line, and the virus produced from this line (B-LAV) was also able to grow in some other LCLs as well as a Burkitt's lymphoma line.

The EBV used for human hybridoma work is derived from the B95-8 marmoset cell line.[66] The virus transforms human B lymphocytes *in vitro*

[59] R. A. Weiss, *Immunol. Today* **3**, 292 (1982).
[60] G. L. C. Shen-Ong and M. D. Cole, *J. Virol.* **42**(2), 411 (1982).
[61] D. Stavrou, T. Bilzer, J. Jsangaris, E. Durr, M. Steinecke, and A. P. Anzil, *J. Cancer Res. Clin. Oncol.* **106**(1), 77 (1983).
[62] B. J. Poiesz, F. W. Rusceth, A. F. Gazdar, P. A. Bunn, J. D. Minna, and R. C. Gallo, *Proc. Natl. Acad. Sci. U.S.A.* **77**, 7415 (1980).
[63] I. Miyoshi, E. Kubonishi, S. Yoshimoto, T. Akagi, Y. Ohtsuki, Y. Shiraishr, K. Nagata, and Y. Hinuma, *Nature (London)* **294**, 770 (1981).
[64] I. S. Chen, S. G. Quann, and D. W. Golge, *Proc. Natl. Acad. Sci. U.S.A.* **80**, 7006 (1983).
[65] D. L. Longo, E. P. Gelmann, J. Cossman, R. A. Young, R. C. Gallo, S. J. O'Brien, and L. A. Matis, *Nature (London)* **310**, 505 (1984).
[66] G. Miller and M. Lipman, *Proc. Natl. Acad. Sci. U.S.A.* **70**, 190 (1973).

and the EBV nuclear antigen, EBNA, is expressed but the viral cycle is not completed. Consequently, infectious virus is not released, although the possibility of contaminating hybridoma supernatants with transforming viral DNA does exist at least in theory. However, virus and viral DNA can easily be inactivated or removed from antibody preparations,[67] which can then be monitored by sensitive B-cell transformation tests and possibly by injection into marmosets, a species in which EBV is rapidly fatal. By analogy, hyperimmune serum from hepatitis patients is currently used for γ-globulin prophylaxis after removal of contaminating virus. As an additional safeguard, potential recipients of human monoclonal antibodies could be screened for serum antibodies to EBV. Most adults in Western countries are positive, having been exposed to infectious mononucleosis. Only in the very rare X-linked lymphoproliferative syndrome[68] would EBV infection be life threatening. Some patients have already been exposed to EBV-carrying human hybridomas growing in patients within implanted, cell-impermeable chambers.[44] As in all novel therapies, the potential benefits to the patient will have to be weighed against any potential risks.

The application of recombinant DNA techniques to the production of human monoclonal antibodies is still in its infancy. Jonak et al.[69] have immortalized splenocytes derived from mice immunized with human cells by transfection with human leukemia DNA. Several transfectants obtained secreted mouse antibodies reacting with the human cells used for immunization and with other human cell types. Whether this type of approach may be adapted to the production of human monoclonal antibodies remains to be determined.

Using a different application of recombinant DNA technology, several laboratories have reported Ig light chain[70–74] and heavy chain[75,76] expression after transfection of various cell types with cloned light and heavy chain genes, respectively. More recently, Ochi et al.[77] have demonstrated

[67] D. H. Crawford, E. R. Huehns, and M. A. Epstein, *Lancet* **1**, 1040 (1983).

[68] J. L. Sullivan, K. S. Byron, F. F. Brewster, and D. Purtilo, *Science* **210**, 543 (1980).

[69] Z. L. Jonak, V. Braman, and R. H. Kennett, *Hybridoma* **3**, 107 (1984).

[70] A. Ochi, R. G. Hawley, M. Shulman, and N. Hozumi, *Nature (London)* **302**, 340 (1983).

[71] V. T. Oi, S. L. Morrison, L. A. Herzenberg, and P. Berg, *Proc. Natl. Acad. Sci. U.S.A.* **80**, 825 (1983).

[72] D. Rice and D. Baltimore, *Proc. Natl. Acad. Sci. U.S.A.* **79**, 7862 (1982).

[73] F. G. Falkner and H. G. Zachau, *Nature (London)* **298**, 286 (1983).

[74] D. Picard and W. Schaffner, *Proc. Natl. Acad. Sci. U.S.A.* **80**, 417 (1983).

[75] S. D. Gillies, S. L. Morrison, V. T. Oi, and S. Tonegawa, *Cell* **33**, 717 (1983).

[76] M. S. Neuberger, *EMBO J.* **2**, 1373 (1983).

[77] A. Ochi, R. G. Hawley, T. Hawley, M. Shulman, A. Traunecker, G. Köhler, and N. Hozumi, *Proc. Natl. Acad. Sci. U.S.A.* **80**, 6351 (1983).

functional mouse IgM production after transfection of cloned Ig heavy and light chain genes into selected murine lymphoid cells; these cells possessed all the biochemical machinery for IgM production except the structural genes for the μ and κ chains. Thus it now appears possible to produce whole mouse Ig molecules by recombinant DNA methods, and the technology is being adapted to human monoclonal antibody production. For example, Boulianne et al.[78] have recently obtained functional chimeric antibodies consisting of mouse V regions and human C regions.

Acknowledgments

This work was supported by Grants 1-522 from the March of Dimes, CA-16685 and CA-36521 from the National Cancer Institute (C.M.C), and by grants from the NSERC, MRC, and the T. Fox Program of the National Cancer Institute of Canada (J.C.R.). Danuta Kozbor is supported by a postdoctoral fellowship from the National Cancer Institute of Canada.

[78] G. L. Boulianne, N. Hozumi, and M. J. Shulman, *Nature* (*London*) **312**, 643 (1984).

[12] The EBV–Hybridoma Technique

By J. C. Roder, S. P. C. Cole, and D. Kozbor

Human monoclonal antibodies (Mabs) will become essential for the prophylaxis and treatment of human disease. There are three conceptual approaches to producing human MAbs including (1) transformation of antigen-specific B lymphocytes by Epstein–Barr virus (EBV), as first carried out by Steinitz et al.,[1] (2) hybridization of 6-thioguanine-resistant (6-TG^r) human plasmacytomas or lymphoblastoid fusion partners to immune human lymphocytes, as first demonstrated in the mouse by Köhler and Milstein[2] and adapted to the human by Olsson and Kaplan[3] and Croce et al.,[4] and (3) a combination of the EBV and hybridoma techniques which combines the strengths of each system alone and avoids the weaknesses, as first shown by Kozbor et al.[5] We have reviewed the human hybridoma system in the accompanying chapter[6] and in this chapter we will summa-

[1] M. Steinitz, G. Klein, S. Koskimies, and O. Mäkelä, *Nature* (*London*) **269**, 420 (1977).
[2] G. Köhler and C. Milstein, *Nature* (*London*) **256**, 495 (1975).
[3] L. Olsson and H. S. Kaplan, *Proc. Natl. Acad. Sci. U.S.A.* **77**, 5429 (1980).
[4] C. M. Croce, A. Linnenbach, W. Hall, Z. Steplewski, and H. Koprowski, *Nature* (*London*) **288**, 488 (1980).
[5] D. Kozbor, A. Lagarde, and J. C. Roder, *Proc. Natl. Acad. Sci. U.S.A.* **79**, 6651 (1982).
[6] D. Kozbor, M. E. Sierzega, S. P. Cole, C. M. Croce, and J. Roder, this volume [11].

rize our own experience with the EBV and EBV–hybridoma systems for producing human MAbs.

EBV Immortalization

Epstein–Barr virus is a herpesvirus originally isolated in 1964 from a cultured cell line derived from an African Burkitt's lymphoma biopsy[7] and has been shown to be the etiological agent of infectious mononucleosis.[8] In infectious mononucleosis there is a pronounced increase in antibody of polyclonal specificity including autoantibodies.[9] This observation suggested that EBV infection could lead to polyclonal activation of the infected lymphocytes, which was first confirmed experimentally by Rosen *et al.*[10] who demonstrated that direct *in vitro* infection of purified human blood lymphocytes with EBV stimulated polyclonal secretion of immunoglobulin. This EBV-induced immunoglobulin production in B lymphocytes is T lymphocyte independent, although activated T lymphocytes can serve as modulators of the response.[11]

Within the lymphoid system, EBV is specific for small, resting B cells[12] bearing EBV receptors which are closely associated with, but distinct from, C3 receptors.[13,14] These receptors can be transferred by plasma membrane vesicle fusion to EBV receptor-negative cell types, thereby allowing EBV to expand its host cell range.[15] The infection *in vitro* of B lymphocytes leads to permanent stimulation of cell growth, a phenomenon termed *transformation,* or *immortalization.* This immortalization preserves the characteristics of the original B cells, including EBV receptors, complement receptors, surface immunoglobulin, and secretory immunoglobulin. Those cells which grow out *in vitro* and carry EBV DNA are termed lymphoblastoid cell lines (LCLs).

All such LCLs express the EBV-specific nuclear antigen (EBNA) and the amount of EBNA is directly proportional to the average number of EBV genomes per cell.[16] EBNA is a DNA-binding tetrameric structure of

---

[7] M. A. Epstein, B. G. Achong, and Y. M. Barr, *Lancet* **1,** 702 (1964).

[8] G. Henle, W. Henle, and V. Diehl, *Proc. Natl. Acad. Sci. U.S.A.* **59,** 94 (1968).

[9] F. A. Wollheim and R. C. Williams, *N. Engl. J. Med.* **274,** 61 (1966).

[10] A. Rosen, S. Britton, P. Gergely, M. Jondal, and G. Klein, *Nature (London)* **267,** 52 (1977).

[11] A. G. Bird and S. Britton, *Immunol. Rev.* **45,** 41 (1979).

[12] P. Aman, B. Ehlin-Henriksson, and G. Klein, *J. Exp. Med.* **159,** 208 (1984).

[13] M. Jondal, G. Klein, M. B. A. Oldstone, V. Bokish, and E. Yefenof, *Scand. J. Immunol.* **5,** 401 (1976).

[14] E. Yefenof and G. Klein, *Int. J. Cancer* **20,** 347 (1977).

[15] D. J. Volsky, I. M. Shapiro, and G. Klein, *Proc. Natl. Acad. Sci. U.S.A.* **77,** 5453 (1980).

[16] I. M. Shapiro, J. Luka, M. Andersson-Anvert, and G. Klein, *Intervirology* **12,** 19 (1979).

180,000 MW.[17] Normally, some EBV-infected B cells should also express both early (EA) and late antigens (VCA) of the viral cycle and release virus particles. However, the EBV recommended in hybridoma work is derived from the B95-8 marmoset cell line and is defective[18] in that it induces transformation in human B lymphocytes but does not induce early viral protein synthesis. Consequently viral replication is blocked, presumably as a result of a 12-kb deletion in an *Eco*RI fragment in the 3' end of the molecule.[19]

The early events after viral infection have been characterized by Einhorn and Ernberg.[20] Virus adsorbs to the EBV receptors of the cell, penetrates, and after 5 hr a small amount of RNA is synthesized. After 12–25 hr, EBNA can be detected, and 40 hr postinfection, there is an increase in RNA and DNA synthesis. At this stage, polyclonal immunoglobulin production is initiated, and finally at 48 hr, mitosis takes place.

Thus, *in vitro* transformation with EBV may be employed to obtain LCLs secreting antibodies to selected antigens. In fact, this method has been exploited successfully in numerous laboratories since the first report of Steinitz *et al.*,[1] who established anti-hapten antibody-producing human cell lines after preselection for hapten binding followed by EBV transformation. LCLs secreting specific human MAbs against streptococcal carbohydrate A,[21] Rhesus antigen D,[22-24] and tetanus toxoid[25]—to mention but a few—have been established this way. As summarized in Table I,[26-47] EBV does not appear to bias the immune repertoire since (1) specific

[17] J. Luka, W. Siegert, and G. Klein, *J. Virol.* **22**, 1 (1977).
[18] G. Miller and M. Lipman, *Proc. Natl. Acad. Sci. U.S.A.* **70**, 190 (1973).
[19] G. W. Bornkamm, H. Delius, U. Zimber, J. Hudewentz, and M. A. Epstein, *J. Virol.* **35**, 603 (1980).
[20] L. Einhorn and I. Ernberg, *Int. J. Cancer* **21**, 157 (1978).
[21] M. Steinitz, F. Seppala, K. Eichman, and G. Klein, *Immunobiology* **156**, 41 (1979).
[22] A. W. Boylston, B. Gardner, R. L. Anderson, and N. C. Hughes-Jones, *Scand. J. Immunol.* **12**, 355 (1980).
[23] D. H. Crawford, M. J. Barlow, J. F. Harrison, L. Winger, and E. R. Huehns, *Lancet* **1**, 386 (1983).
[24] S. Koskimies, *Scand. J. Immunol.* **11**, 73 (1980).
[25] D. Kozbor and J.C. Roder, *J. Immunol.* **127**, 1275 (1981).
[26] D. Kozbor, M. Steinitz, G. Klein, S. Koskimies, and O. Mäkelä, *Scand. J. Immunol.* **10**, 187 (1979).
[27] O. Yoshie and Y. Ono, *Cell. Immunol.* **56**, 305 (1980).
[28] D. H. Crawford, R. E. Callard, M. I. Muggeridge, D. M. Mitchell, E. D. Zanders, and P. C. L. Beverley, *J. Gen. Virol.* **64**, 697 (1983).
[29] J. M. Seigneurin, C. Desgranges, D. Seigneurin, J. Paire, J. C. Renversez, B. Jacquemont, and C. Micouin, *Science* **221**, 173 (1983).
[30] L. Evans, C. Maragos, and J. May, *Immunol. Lett.* **8**, 39 (1984).
[31] V. R. Zurawski, E. Haber, Jr., and P. M. Black, *Science* **199**, 1439 (1978).

TABLE I

SPECIFIC ANTIBODIES OBTAINED FROM EBV-IMMORTALIZED CELLS

Antigen			Cell line		Isotype[a]	Ref.
Class	Type	Name	Uncloned	Cloned		
Chemicals	Haptens	NNP	+	−	IgM	1
		TNP	+	−	IgM	26
		Phosphorylcholine	+	−	IgM	27
Proteins	Viral	Influenza nucleopeptide	−	+	IgG$_1$	28
		HSV glycoprotein D	−	+	IgG$_1$	29, 30
	Bacterial	Tetanus toxoid	+	+	IgM, IgG	25, 31, 32
		Diphtheria toxoid	+	−	IgG	33
	Chlamydia	Genus antigen	+	+	IgG$_1$	34
	Protozoa	Malaria	+	+	IgM	35
	Blood group	Rh D	+	+	IgM, IgG	22–24
	Autoantigens	Rheumatoid factor	+	+	IgM	36, 37
		Acetylcholine receptor	+	+	ND[b]	38
		Thyroglobulin	+	+	IgM	39
	Alloantigens	Maternal T cells	−	+	IgM	40
	Tumor antigens	Melanoma	−	+	IgM	41, 42
		Carcinoma	+	−	IgM	43
		Osteosarcoma	+	+	IgM	44
Nucleic acids	Autoantigens	DNA	−	+	IgM	45, 46
Carbohydrates	Bacterial	Strep. A	+	−	IgM	21
		Pneumococcal	−	+	IgM	47

[a] Light chains are usually κ, although production of λ has been reported.
[b] ND, Not determined.

antibodies against a wide range of antigens have been obtained, representing chemically defined haptens, proteins, carbohydrates, and nucleic acids, and (2) antibodies of both IgM, IgG, and κ and λ types are represented. However, little information is available on the affinity of antibodies produced by EBV lines.

An alternative strategy involves the EBV transformation of the total B-cell population (i.e., no preselection) followed by cloning and testing for specific antibody-producing cultures. This method has been used to isolate LCLs producing MAbs against diphtheria toxoid,[33] acetylcholine receptor,[38] tetanus toxoid,[25,31,32] phosphorylcholine,[27] melanoma antigens,[41,42] bacterial[34] and viral[28,29] antigens, as well as many other antigens.

A major disadvantage of the EBV immortalization technique is that bulk cultures of EBV-transformed lines frequently lose their ability to produce specific antibody after long-term culture.[25,28] The reason for this instability is not clear but may be due, at least in part, to the overgrowth of nonproducing cells within the culture. Thus, in some cases, early cloning by limiting dilution has been reported to result in a stable antibody-producing cell line.[23,25,28,34] Several investigators have reported varying successes in cloning EBV-transformed cell lines. This variation is largely unexplained but may be influenced by the immune status of the donor and the tissue from which the lymphocytes were derived, as well as the source of feeder layer cells used in cloning.[23,45,48] However, more complex intra-

[32] V. R. Zurawski, S. E. Spedden, Jr., P. Black, and E. Haber, *Curr. Top. Microbiol. Immunol.* **81,** 152 (1978).

[33] S. Tsuchiya, S. Yokoyama, O. Yoshie, and Y. Ono, *J. Immunol.* **124,** 1970 (1980).

[34] A. Rosen, K. Persson, and G. Klein, *J. Immunol.* **130,** 2899 (1983).

[35] K. Lundgren, M. Wahlgren, M. Troye-Blomberg, K. Berzins, H. Perlmann, and P. Perlmann, *J. Immunol.* **131,** 2000 (1983).

[36] M. Steinitz, G. Izak, S. Cohen, M. Ehrenfeld, and I. Flechner, *Nature (London)* **287,** 443 (1980).

[37] D. Haskard and J. Archer, *J. Immunol. Methods* **74,** 361 (1984).

[38] I. Kamo, S. Furukawa, A. Tada, Y. Mano, Y. Isawaki, and T. Furuse, *Science* **215,** 995 (1982).

[39] P. Delves and I. Roitt, *Clin. Exp. Immunol.* **57,** 33 (1984).

[40] Y. Miyagawa, *J. Immunol.* **133,** (1984).

[41] R. F. Irie, L. L. Sze, and R. E. Saxton, *Proc. Natl. Acad. Sci. U.S.A.* **79,** 5666 (1982).

[42] D. B. Watson, G. F. Burns, and I. R. MacKay, *J. Immunol.* **130,** 2442 (1983).

[43] S. Hirohashi, Y. Shimosato, and Y. Ino, *Gann* **73,** 345 (1982).

[44] K. Tsang, J. Pan, and H. Fudenberg, *Immunol. Lett.* **7,** 267 (1984).

[45] L. Winger, C. Winger, P. Shastry, A. Russell, and M. Longenecker, *Proc. Natl. Acad. Sci. U.S.A.* **80,** 4484 (1983).

[46] T. Sasaki, F. Endo, M. Mikami, Y. Sekiguchi, K. Tada, Y. Ono, N. Ishida, and K. Yoshinaga, *J. Immunol. Methods* **72,** 157 (1984).

[47] M. Steinitz, S. Tamir, and A. Goldfarb, *J. Immunol.* **132,** 877 (1984).

[48] L. D. Stein, C. J. Ledgley, and N. H. Sigal, *J. Immunol.* **130,** 1640 (1983).

cellular events likely also play a role in the stabilization of specific antibody production since cloning does not always stabilize the lymphoblastoid cell lines.[25,45] We have found that one anti-tetanus toxoid clone produced specific monoclonal antibody for 8 months of culture and then suddenly shut off light chain synthesis, thereby precluding recovery of antigen-binding activity in culture supernatants.[25] In addition to the instability of specific antibody production, a second limitation of the EBV immortalization technique is that low quantities of antibody (<1 μg/ml) are generally produced. In combination with EBV immortalization, cell fusion (hybridoma) techniques may be employed to rescue high levels of stable MAb production from EBV lines.

Procedure

EBV Transformation. Epstein–Barr virus is collected from the B95-8 cell line that was established by exposure of marmoset blood leukocytes to EBV extracted from a human leukocyte line.[18] The B95-8 line can be obtained from the American Type Culture Collection, Rockville, MD (ATCC CRL 1612). When cultured in standard RPMI 1640 medium (10% fetal bovine serum) this line releases large quantities of transforming EBV. Viral activity can be assessed by incubating various concentrations of supernatant with BJAB cells and measuring the percentage of EBNA-positive cells after 48 hr, as described in the accompanying chapter.[6] Concentrated, partially purified virus stocks can be obtained from Showa University Research Institute, 5180 113th Avenue North, Clearwater, FL 33520. This virus is titered and tested for transformation of human cord blood lymphocytes, and concentrations greater than 10^8 transforming units/ml are available (phone Dr. Lau, 813-576-6675). Cell lines producing EBV should be mycoplasma free. Human lymphocytes are isolated from peripheral blood, tonsils, lymph nodes, spleen, or bone marrow by centrifugation (800 g) on Ficoll–Hypaque (density 1.077 g/cm^3, Pharmacia).

Steps: (1) The B95-8 cells are grown to near-confluence and the culture supernatants are then harvested as a source of EBV. (2) Varying dilutions of B95-8 supernatant (1/2, 1/10, 1/50) or concentrated virus (10^7 transforming units per 10^6 lymphocytes) are incubated 2 hr with human peripheral blood lymphocytes (PBL) at concentrations of 2 × 10^6 cells/ml. Infected PBLs are then washed and cultured at 10^6 cells/ml in 24-well Costar plates (No. 3524) in RPMI 1640 medium (GIBCO) supplemented with 10% fetal bovine serum, L-glutamine (4 × 10^{-3} M), and 5 × 10^{-5} M 2-mercaptoethanol. (3) After 8 days, the cells are transferred to Falcon flasks (3013) and fed twice weekly by diluting to a density of 2 × 10^5 cells/ml. (4) We find that 1/5 dilutions of B95-8 culture supernatants usually give the maximum yield of transformed colonies. Stock supernatants can be stored at 4°

for 4 weeks or more, and can be frozen at $-70°$ although this results in some loss of activity. Supernatants should be filtered at pore sizes >0.45 μm due to the large size of the virion.

Cloning. EBV-transformed cell lines can be cloned in 96-well Linbro culture plates by limiting dilution on feeder layers of irradiated (3000 rad) mouse spleen cells (5×10^5/well) or human peripheral blood mononuclear cells (0.5×10^6/well).[25] Cells are seeded at 20, 10, 5, and 1 cells per well and only plates giving less than one-third of wells positive for growth are considered cloned. Inclusion of 10% human growth factor (supernatants of Con A-stimulated PBL cultures) will give a small (25%), but significant, improvement in cloning efficiencies. However we do not use it routinely. In contrast, colonies cannot be obtained from single EBV-transformed cells in the absence of feeder layers or on irradiated human fetal fibroblasts. In addition, cloning in 0.35% agarose will not be successful unless more than 5×10^4 cells are plated in 2.5 ml, in which case aggregates of growing cells, rather than single cell-derived colonies, appear. The best cloning results are obtained using irradiated feeder layers of autologous, allogeneic, or xenogeneic mononuclear cells with cloning efficiencies of approximately 30%, but this varies widely depending on the patient or sample.

Selection of Antigen-Specific Cells

In the EBV technique, as in the hybridoma procedure, it is important to use lymphocytes of individuals who have previously been immunized with the antigens and have increased numbers of specific antibody-producing cells in their circulation. The EBV procedure involves two steps: (1) the enrichment of cells with receptors for the given antigens, and (2) immortalization of these cells by EBV infection. Preselection of antigen-specific cells may facilitate the establishment of specific cell lines since even after immunization *in vivo,* only a small fraction (10^{-4}) of the B lymphocytes produce the desired antibody.[49] Several methods of preselection have been tried, including procedures in which (1) antigen-specific lymphocytes were enriched by rosetting with antigen-coupled erythrocytes, followed by separation on a density gradient,[1,21,22,26,36,50] (2) biotinylated antigen was bound to the surface of the antigen-specific cells and those cells binding fluorescein-coupled avidin were subsequently separated electronically on a fluorescence-activated cell sorter (FACS),[25] (3) antigen was bound to solid surfaces in a panning technique,[45] and (4) cells

[49] R. H. Stevens, E. Macy, C. Morrow, and A. Saxon, *J. Immunol.* **122**, 2498 (1979).
[50] M. Steinitz and S. Tamir, *Eur. J. Immunol.* **12**, 126 (1982).

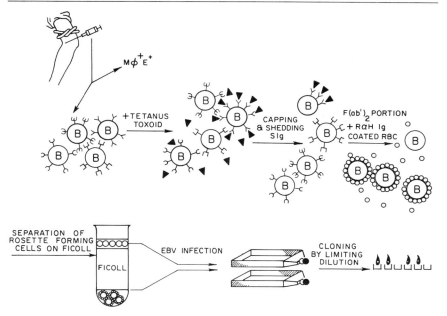

FIG. 1. Enrichment for tetanus-toxoid-binding B cells by negative preselection. This technique was first performed in the mouse by Walker et al.[51] and is based on the observation that B cells, upon binding of antigen, usually shed their surface Ig receptors and become nude (stripped). Those B cells not binding antigen, and therefore maintaining their surface Ig, are removed by rosetting with anti-human Ig-coated SRBC; this is followed by EBV infection of remaining B cells.[25] The established antigen-specific cell line is cloned by limiting dilution on a feeder layer. The B-cell-enriched fraction is obtained by the removal of monocytes (Mϕ^+) and cells rosetting with SRBC (E$^+$).

which did not bind antigen were removed.[25] This negative preselection technique was first performed in the mouse by Walker et al.,[51] and is based on the observation that B cells, upon binding to antigen, usually shed their surface Ig receptors and become nude or stripped. In the human, the B-cell-enriched fractions were obtained by the removal of monocytes and cells rosetting with SRBC, as shown in Fig. 1. Those B cells not binding antigen, and therefore maintaining their surface Ig, are removed by rosetting with sheep erythrocytes coated with the F(ab')$_2$ fragment of anti-human Ig. The nonrosetting B cells remaining are then EBV infected and the resulting antigen-specific cell line is cloned within 3 weeks by limited dilution on a feeder layer or fused directly with a TG^r, Oua^r fusion partner such as KR-4.

[51] S. M. Walker, G. C. Meinke, and W. O. Weigle, J. Exp. Med. 146, 445 (1977).

However, despite the success of these techniques, it is not yet clear which type of B cell can be infected and triggered by EBV to secrete imunoglobulin. Therefore, some methods of enrichment of antigen-binding cells may lead to the selection of cells which are at an inappropriate stage of maturation for Ig secretion after EBV transformation. An alternative strategy involves the transformation of the total B-cell population with subsequent cloning and testing for antibody-producing cultures.

Procedure

1. Select a blood donor with a history of one or more vaccinations with tetanus toxoid, or other antigen, during the previous year and boost again with the same antigen. Two to three weeks later is the optimum time to collect peripheral blood.[25] Take 100–200 ml of blood and separate the PBLs on Ficoll-Hypaque. Monocytes are removed by plastic adherence and T cells are removed by E rosetting, as described in the following section. The nonadherent, E^- fraction usually consists of 80–90% surface Ig^+ B cells.

2. Purified protein antigen (tetanus toxoid, TT) can be obtained by Connaught Laboratories, Willowdale, Ontario, and coupled to biotin by standard procedures.[52] Biotinylated tetanus toxoid (100 μg/ml) is incubated 30 min on ice with 10^6 cells/ml in PBS, washed, and incubated a further 30 min on ice with fluorescein isothiocyanate-conjugated avidin (Vector Labs, F/P ratio 3.7, 85% active conjugate) (100 μg/ml PBS), followed by washing. The tetanus toxoid-treated B cells are then incubated 6 hr (optimum) at 37° in culture medium to allow capping and shedding of tetanus toxoid-specific cell surface Ig receptors. Capping is monitored at intervals under the UV microscope.

3. In order to remove the sIg^+, nonstripped (and presumably non-TT-specific) B cells, rosettes are formed with 5% SRBC coated with the $F(ab')_2$ fraction of rabbit anti-human Ig (Cappel Laboratories, Cochranville, PA) by the $CrCl_3$ technique (0.05% $CrCl_3$, 500 μg/ml protein, 50% SRBC in 0.9% NaCl, 4 min, 20°). These anti-human Ig-coated SRBC usually form 90% rosettes with the sIg^+ cell line BJAB, whereas the sIg^- cell lines, K562 and Molt-4, form no rosettes. B-cell rosettes are separated by centrifugation on Ficoll-Hypaque (density 1.077 g/cm³). SRBC are lysed by a brief (10-sec) hypotonic shock with distilled H_2O. This technique is capable of removing over 75% of the sIg^+ cells in a B-cell-enriched fraction of PBLs. In addition, the cells in the pellet and band are depleted and enriched (severalfold), respectively, in the frequency of TT-binding cells. The fractions are routinely left 18 hr to recover before

[52] M. Wilchek and E. A. Bayer, *Immunol. Today* **5**, 39 (1984).

assay. It should be noted that removal of sIg⁺ B cells by treatment with anti-human Ig and rabbit complement was not nearly as effective.

4. Fractionated PBLs are transformed with EBV as described under "EBV Immortalization" above, and 8 days later, supernatants can be assayed for anti-tetanus antibodies.

5. As an alternative to step 3 above, tetanus toxoid-binding B cells can be enriched 20-fold to purities of 80% using positive selection on the FACS. However, the concentrations of anti-tetanus toxoid antibodies (1 μg/ml) obtained 8 days after EBV transformation were no greater than using the negative preselection technique above.

In Vitro Immunization

One limitation of EBV and human hybridoma technology is the requirement, thus far, to use lymphocytes from hyperimmunized donors. Sources of parental cells have included peripheral blood lymphocytes from measles virus-infected, subacute sclerotizing panencephalitis patients,[4] spleen cells from dinitrochlorobenzene-sensitized Hodgkin's patients,[3] and tumor-infiltrating lymphocytes[53] and tonsils from tetanus-vaccinated donors.[54] It is apparent that PBLs from humans offer the only readily available source of normal lymphocytes for fusion. However, only 1 in 10 PBLs are B cells. As reported by Stevens et al.,[49] the frequency of B cells in the circulation capable of responding to pokeweed mitogen (PWM) by producing anti-tetanus toxoid antibody of the IgG class was only 1×10^{-4}, 2–4 weeks after booster injection. This low number, together with typical fusion frequencies of 10^{-6} and a B-cell frequency of 10^{-1}, makes the chance of obtaining a specific hybridoma in the order of 10^{-11}, or 10^{-9} if we allow for an estimated 100-fold greater fusion frequency with antigen-stimulated B cells than resting B cells. It is clear that further improvements are necessary to increase the yields and proportions of immune B cells.

We have compared the usefulness of specific antigens (TT) and two polyclonal mitogens (PWM, EBV) in stimulating cultures of PBLs prior to fusion.[55] Stimulation with EBV yielded cells with much higher frequencies of hybrid formation (36×10^{-7}) compared to unstimulated PBLs (10^{-7}) or cells cultured with PWM (6×10^{-7}) or TT antigen (3×10^{-7}). The proportion of hybridomas (approximately 1%) producing anti-TT antibody was similar in EBV- and TT-stimulated cultures, although one would expect that antigen-driven cultures would yield higher affinity anti-

[53] K. Sikora, T. Alderson, J. Phillips, and J.V. Watson, *Lancet* **1,** 11 (1982).

[54] N. Chiorrazzi, R. L. Wasserman, and H. G. Kunkel, *J. Exp. Med.* **156,** 930 (1982).

[55] D. Kozbor and J. C. Roder, *Eur. J. Immunol.* **14,** 23 (1984).

bodies. Preselection of EBV subcultures for high anti-TT production prior to fusion resulted in a 5-fold increase in TT-specific hybridomas ($p <$ 0.001). Most (20/21) specific hybrids produced IgM anti-TT, whereas one (1/21) produced IgG anti-TT, possibly due to the immature stage of differentiation in EBV-stimulated parental cells. Immunized cultures can be transformed with EBV and used for hybridoma construction (unpublished observations). The ability to choose an antigen, immunize, and expand the rare antigen-specific B cells from PBLs *in vitro* prior to EBV immortalization and fusion should yield an increasing spectrum of human monoclonal antibodies for diagnostic, therapeutic, or basic studies.

Procedure

The following procedure was optimized in our laboratory for generating primary antibody responses to protein antigens[56] and the conditions are similar to those developed in other laboratories.[57,58]

PBLs are collected from 100–200 ml of blood by centrifugation on Ficoll-Hypaque (1.077 g/cm³).

Monocytes. Monocytes are removed by adherence to plastic culture dishes precoated with autologous serum as described by Fischer *et al.*[59] The nonadherent cell fractions usually contain 2–5% monocytes, as determined by immunofluorescent staining with monocyte-specific Mo2 monoclonal antibodies,[60] nonspecific esterase activity, and phagocytosis of latex beads. The adherent cells, recovered by trypsinization, consist of 90–95% monocytes by these criteria.

B Cells. Nonadherent mononuclear cells are rosetted with neuraminidase- (Sigma Chemical Co., St. Louis, MO) treated SRBC (0.1 U/ml, 2% SRBC, for 30 min at 37°), and the rosetting cells (E⁺) are depleted by centrifugation on Ficoll-Hypaque (1.077 g/cm³). The recovered E⁻ cells are <5% E⁺, and always >85–90% sIg positive, as detected by immunofluorescence.

T Helper Cells. PBLs are rosetted with SRBC as described above and centrifuged on Ficoll-Hypaque. The SRBC are removed from the E⁺ cells in the pellet by hypotonic shock with distilled H_2O (20 sec). In order to remove T cells bearing Fc receptors for IgG, E⁺ cells are rosetted with ox erythrocytes coated with an optimum concentration (20 μg/ml) of rabbit

[56] D. Kozbor and J. Roder, *Int. Arch. Allergy Appl. Immunol.* **72,** 260 (1983).
[57] D. J. Volkman, H. C. Lane, and A. S. Fauci, *Proc. Natl. Acad. Sci. U.S.A.* **78,** 2528 (1981).
[58] C. Morimoto, E. L. Reinherz, and S. F. Schlossman, *J. Immunol.* **127,** 514 (1981).
[59] D. Fischer, W. J. Hubbard, and H. S. Koren, *Cell. Immunol.* **58,** 426 (1981).
[60] R. F. Todd, L. M. Nadler, and S. F. Schlossman, *J. Immunol.* **126,** 1435 (1981).

anti-ox RBC (IgG fraction) and centrifuged on Ficoll-Hypaque. This interface is collected as a source of enriched T helper cells (Tγ^-),[61] which are positive for OKT3 (90–97%) monoclonal antibody, OKT4 (70–75%), OKT8 (24–49%), and sIg (0.5%). The Tγ^+ fraction is positive for T3 (20–25%), OKM1 (65–70%), T8 (10–12%), and T4 (10–15%).

Culture Conditions. Optimum ratios of B cells (2×10^5/well) are mixed with T8$^-$, T4$^+$ helper cells (4×10^5/well) and monocytes (3×10^4/well), and cultured in RPMI 1640 medium supplemented with 15% heat-inactivated fetal calf serum (FCS) (GIBCO), 4 mM L-glutamine, gentamicin (0.01 mg/ml), and 5×10^{-5} M 2-mercaptoethanol. An optimum concentration of tetanus toxoid (0.5 μg/ml) is added and cells are cultured in a stationary mode for 4 days in a total volume of 200 μl/well in flat-bottomed microtiter plates (Falcon, Oxnard, CA) at 37° in a humid atmosphere with 5% CO_2. The cells are then washed three times to remove excess tetanus toxoid, resuspended in fresh culture medium, and incubated for an additional 5 (optimum) days. Culture supernatants are assayed for levels of anti-TT antibody in an enzyme-linked immunosorbant assay which is sensitive to 1 ng specific antibody/ml.

Cultured cells are harvested and transformed with EBV as described under "EBV Immortalization."

Selection of a Fusion Partner

Many human fusion partners are available for study, as outlined in Tables I and II of the accompanying chapter.[6] Lines should be chosen which yield high fusion frequencies, high levels of specific immunoglobulin production, high proportions of antigen-specific hybridomas, and long-term stability. If high yields of monoclonal antibody are needed, then a line is preferred which has a proven ability to form hybridomas that grow as ascites tumors in nude mice. The fusion partner must be HAT sensitive, and it is suggested that cells be rendered resistant to 6-thioguanine (6-TG^r) rather than 8-azaguanine (8-AG^r) since, as outlined by Evans and Vijayalaxim,[62] (1) 6-TG is more stable than 8-AG, (2) 6-TG has a higher affinity for the substrate HGPRT than 8-AG, (3) exogenous purines present in serum reduce the selection exerted by 8-AG, but not 6-TG, and (4) almost all 6-TG^r mutants are HGPRT$^-$, whereas many 8-AG^r mutants have normal levels of enzyme (HGPRT$^+$). Both 6-TG and 8-AG are purine analogs and are converted into their respective toxic nucleotides by HGPRT (EC 2.4.2.8, hypoxanthine–guanine phosphoribosyltransferase).

[61] L. S. Morretta, S. R. Webb, C. E. Grossi, P. M. Lydyard, and M. D. Cooper, *J. Exp. Med.* **146**, 184 (1977).

[62] H. J. Evans and Vijayalaxim, *Nature (London)* **292**, 601 (1981).

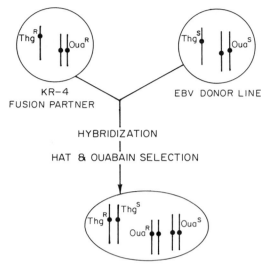

EXPRESSED PHENOTYPE OF HYBRID: Thg^S, Oua^R

FIG. 2. Basis for hybrid selection in HAT medium containing ouabain. 6-Thioguanine resistance: 6-Thioguanine-resistant (Thg^R; TG^r in text) cells lack the enzyme HGPRT, which is coded by genes on the X chromosome. There is only one functional X chromosome per cell [♂, XY], [♀, X(X)]. Thg^R cells die in HAT medium and, due to a recessive trait of the Thg^R mutation, only the Thg^S cells and hybrids with the Thg^S phenotype expressed can survive in HAT medium. Ouabain resistance: Ouabain resistance is an autosomal dominant trait, so only cells which carry this mutation, Oua^R, and hybrids will grow in ouabain-containing medium. Oua^S cells die in the presence of ouabain due to the inhibition of plasma membrane Na$^+$,K$^+$-ATPase by this drug.

6-TG is incorporated into DNA and can be used effectively in cell lines in which death occurs following cell division. 8-AG, on the other hand, is incorporated into RNA and is more appropriate in short-term lymphocyte cultures in which only limited cell proliferation is possible.

The fusion partner should also have a dominant selectable marker such as ouabain or neomycin resistance to allow selection of hybrids after fusion with EBV-transformed donor lymphocytes, a procedure which improves hybridization frequencies 10 to 100-fold. KR-4 is one line which meets all of these requirements, as shown in Fig. 2. It is a cell line originally derived from a 6-TG^r variant of GM1500, by a procedure which may be of general use for deriving Oua^r mutants of other fusion partners as well.[5] γ-Irradiation was chosen because of its known mutagenic action in deriving 8-AG^r human lymphocytes.[62] The alkylating agent, ethyl methane sulfonate (EMS), was also used, but without success. Mitomycin C

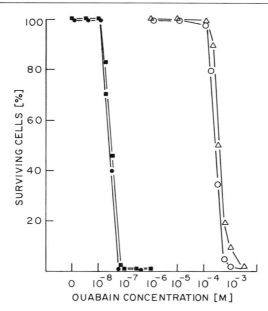

FIG. 3. Ouabain resistance of the KR-4 fusion partner. Triplicate samples of 2×10^5 cells were seeded in 24-well Costar plates containing ouabain at concentrations ranging from 10 nM to 5 mM and in control wells without drug. Viable cells were counted after 6 days of culture by trypan blue exclusion. Survival was expressed as the percentage of control growth without drug. Oua^r KR-4 cells were grown 4 weeks in the presence ($\triangle$) or absence ($\bigcirc$) of 100 μM ouabain. ($\bullet$) Oua^s parental GM1500 6TG^r cells; ($\blacksquare$) Oua^s EBV-transformed B6 line.

was avoided since resulting drug-resistant variants are often not true mutants[62] and therefore may be less stable.

Two hundred rads of γ-irradiation was found in our hands to increase the frequency of Oua^r mutants to 10.7×10^{-7}, from levels of 2.0×10^{-7} in untreated cultures. Higher or lower doses of γ-irradiation had less effect and EMS caused no significant increase in the frequency of spontaneous Oua^r mutations. As shown in Fig. 3, the concentration of ouabain required to kill 50% of the Oua^r KR-4 cells was 5×10^{-3} M, compared to 5×10^{-7} M for nonmutagenized parental cells, normal human lymphocytes (not shown), and EBV-transformed lymphoblastoid cell lines. This represents a remarkable level of drug resistance (10,000-fold) and ouabain can now be used at high concentrations as a very effective selective agent for hybridomas. The Oua^r marker was stable in these lines in the absence of ouabain for 1 month (Fig. 3), and even lines grown continuously in our laboratory for over a year maintain the same level of ouabain resistance.

Nevertheless, we routinely subculture the line in the presence of ouabain (5×10^{-4} M) and 6-TG (30 μg/ml) every few weeks to select against possible revertants.

Procedure

(1) Cells of the desired type (lymphoblastoid or plasmacytoma) are mutagenized with 200 rad of ionizing radiation (γ or X rays) at a cell concentration of 10^6/ml. (2) Mutagenized cells are grown in tissue culture medium (RPMI 1640, 10% fetal calf serum) for a period of 10 days. (3) Cells are then seeded into 96-well microculture plates (Linbro) in 0.2-ml volumes at a cell concentration of 2×10^6/ml, and ouabain is added to a final concentration of 10^{-7} M. (4) Cultures are fed every 4 days with fresh medium and ouabain and after 2 weeks, wells with viable colonies are scored. Surviving cells are transferred to 24-well culture plates (Costar) and subsequently expanded in culture flasks (Falcon) in gradually increasing concentrations of ouabain. Dead cells are removed periodically by centrifugation at room temperature (800 g) for 20 min on Ficoll-Hypaque at a density of 1.077 g/cm^3.[63] (5) Five months after mutagenesis, the cells should be totally resistant to concentrations as high as 10^{-4} M ouabain. (6) The Oua^r cell line should be grown for 1 month or more in the presence or absence of ouabain, and retested for toxicity at increasing concentrations of ouabain along with parental controls. Cells are seeded at 2×10^5/well in Costar 24-well plates and cultured 6 days with or without ouabain, after which time cell survival is determined by counting viable cells excluding trypan blue. If the marker is stable, the concentration of ouabain required to kill 50% of the cells should be identical in the Oua^r line grown in the presence or absence of ouabain, as shown in Fig. 3. (7) Several Oua^r lines should be fused with EBV-transformed lymphocytes (by the procedure outlined in the following section) and the line yielding the highest frequency of viable hybrids should be selected as the best fusion partner.

Human Hybridomas Constructed with EBV Lines

The first human hybridomas were constructed in 1980 by Olsson and Kaplan[3] and by Croce et al.[4] However, the efficiency of these systems was low and they were not adapted for general use. As described in the preceding chapter,[6] most of the human fusion partners developed since also have serious deficiencies. EBV-transformed cell lines and clones

---

[63] A. Boyum, *Scand. J. Clin. Lab. Invest.* **21,** Suppl. 97, 51 (1968).

have also provided a source of human monoclonal antibodies since the pioneering work of Steinitz *et al*. in 1977,[1] but poor stability and low rates of Ig secretion have posed limitations to the approach. In our laboratory, we have combined both the EBV immortalization method and conventional hybridoma technology to develop a system which we feel combines the strengths and overcomes the weaknesses inherent in each system alone.[5] We simply hybridize our plasmacytoma, or LCL fusion partner, with donor lymphocytes that have been transformed by EBV and established as a cell line. In this system, both parental cells are immortal and therefore it was necessary to have a fusion partner with appropriate drug markers to counterselect against the parental cells (Fig. 2). Thus, thioguanine-resistant GM1500 lymphoblastoid cells were rendered oubain resistant, as discussed under "Selection of a Fusion Partner," and the resulting line was designated KR-4. In our first study,[5] KR-4 was fused with an EBV-transformed, anti-tetanus toxoid-producing clone, B6, and hybrids selected in medium containing HAT and oubain. The hybridomas produced 8-fold more anti-tetanus toxoid antibody at a much higher rate, and cloned more efficiently than the parental B6 line. Furthermore, specific antibody production has remained stable for more than 2 years. Our total experience with the system is summarized in Table II.[64–66]

In a second study[66] we have established EBV-immortalized cells lines from lymphocytes derived from peripheral blood, tumor-draining lymph nodes, bone marrow aspirates, tumors, and pericardial effusions from lung cancer patients. Clones from a number of these lines were screened for tumor-specific antibody production but none were positive, suggesting that B lymphocytes specific for tumor antigens are rare in lung cancer patients. The EBV lines were then fused with KR-4 in an attempt to rescue low frequency B-cell precursors specific for tumor cells. More than 8% of hybridomas screened showed significant levels of activity although most were not tumor cell specific since they also reacted with EBV-infected cells from the lymphocyte donor. Two hybridomas showed apparent specific binding early after fusion but this activity was lost upon continued growth, although in general, hybrids continued to secrete high levels (up to 50 μg/ml) of IgM, in some cases beyond 18 months in culture. Thus the EBV–hybridoma system should be useful for rescuing low-frequency tumor-reactive B-cell precursors.

[64] D. Kozbor, J. C. Roder, T. H. Chang, Z. Steplewski, and H. Koprowski, *Hybridoma* **1**, 323 (1982).
[65] T. Atlaw, D. Kozbor, and J. C. Roder, *Infect. Immun.* **49**, 104 (1985).
[66] S. P. C. Cole, B. G. Campling, I. H. Louwman, D. Kozbor, and J. C. Roder, *Cancer Res.* **44**, 2750 (1984).

TABLE II

A COMPARISON OF THE EBV AND EBV–HYBRIDOMA SYSTEMS FOR PRODUCING HUMAN MONOCLONAL ANTIBODIES

Lymphocyte source[a]	Selection[b]	Donor[c]	EBV transformation[d]	Fusion partner[e]	No. of hybrids or clones screened[f]	Antigen[g]	Fusion frequency[h] (× 10^{-7})	% Antigen-specific hybrids or clones[i]	Specific Ig secretion[j] (μg/ml)	Ig class[k]	Cloning efficiency[l] (%)	Stability[m] (months)	Ref.
PBL	+	Vacc.	+	None	96	TT	NA[n]	3.1	0.7	IgM	30	6	25
PBL	+	Vacc.	+	P3X63Ag8	200	TT	100	70.0[o]	1.8	IgM	ND[p]	6	64
PBL	+	Vacc.	+	KR-4	395	TT	112	94.0	4.2	IgM	64	>24	5
PBL	-	Vacc.	+	KR-4	936	TT	36	0.7	2.6	IgM/ IgG	ND	>6	55
PBL	-	Vacc.	-	KR-4	20	TT	2	0.0	0.0	—	ND	ND	55
Tonsils	-	Vacc.	-	KR-4	32	TT	8	0.0	0.0	—	ND	ND	55
PBL	-	Lepr.	+	KR-4	4,400	Lep.	126	8.2	10.0	IgM	90	>12	65
PBL	-	Lepr.	-	KR-4	5	Lep.	2	0.0	0.0	—	ND	ND	65
PBL	-	Lepr.	+	None	10,000	Lep.	NA	0.42	0.0	ND	ND	2	65
PBL, LN, BM, TIL, PE	-	Ca	+	KR-4	4,500	Tum.	166	8.0	44	IgM	20	>12	66
PBL, LN, BM, TIL, PE	-	Ca	+	None	140	Tum.	NA	0.7	ND	ND	1	ND	66
PBL	-	Neuro.	+	None	300	MAG	NA	0.6	ND	ND	ND	ND	66

[a] Source of lymphocytes: PBL, fresh peripheral blood lymphocytes; pokeweed mitogen-stimulated tonsilar lymphocytes; L.N. draining lymph node cells; BM, bone marrow cells; TIL, tumor-infiltrating lymphocytes; PE, pericardial effusion cells.

[b] EBV lines were selected for anti-tetanus toxoid reactivity and one clone, B6, from such a line was used on the donor cell in hybridization experiments.

[c] Normal donors (Vacc.) were vaccinated with tetanus toxoid 2–3 weeks prior to fusions. Lepromatous leprosy patients (Lepr.) were selected with high levels of circulating antibody against *Mycobacterium leprae*. Lung cancer patients (Ca) with small-cell, large-cell, adeno, squamous, and bronchoalveolar carcinoma were also used as lymphocyte donors. Peripheral neuropathy patients (Neuro.) with IgM paraproteinemia and high titers of anti-myelin-associated glycoprotein antibody were also used as PBL donors.

[d] Lymphocytes were transformed with Epstein–Barr virus (B95-8).

[e] Donor lymphocytes were fused with a TG^r murine plasmacytoma P3X63Ag8.653 or a TG^r, Oua^r human lymphoblastoid cell line, KR-4, for hybridoma studies, or were not fused for studies of EBV clones.

[f] Number of hybrids or clones screened for reactivity with antigen in an enzyme-linked immunosorbent assay (ELISA). Hybridization was confirmed by analysis of chromosomes and codominant expression of phenotypic markers in selected hybridomas. Clonality was confirmed by isoelectric focusing of secreted immunoglobulins in selected cases.

[g] TT, Purified tetanus toxoid; Lep., glycolipid or protein extracts from *M. leprae*; Tum., glutaraldehyde-fixed human lung tumor cells; MAG, purified human myelin-associated glycoprotein (MW 110,000).

[h] Fusion frequency (f.f.) was calculated from the following formula using 96-well plates having less than the Poisson number (66%) of wells positive for growth: f.f. $= (\ln \Delta/96)/\chi$, where Δ is the number of wells negative for growth and χ is the number of cells plated per well divided by 2 since equal numbers of lymphocytes and fusion partner cells were hybridized.

[i] The proportion of all wells positive for growth which secreted antibody reacting with the antigen in question.

[j] The quantity of antigen-reactive antibody secreted from 10^5 hybridoma cells grown in a logarithmic fashion over a 7-day growth period. Values are means of several high-producing hybridomas selected for further study.

[k] Most hybridomas secreted antigen-specific antibody of the IgM class, although occasionally (1/20) IgG hybridomas were also found.

[l] Cloning was performed by limiting dilution on feeder layers, and cloning efficiency was calculated using the formula in footnote *h* above.

[m] The length of time in continuous culture that hybridomas or EBV clones continued to produce specific antibody before becoming unstable and ceasing specific Ig secretion. ">" signifies that an end point was not reached and cultures secreted antibody beyond the time indicated.

[n] NA, Not applicable.

[o] Only one-fifth of these were stable for the 6-month period of study.

[p] ND, Not done.

We have also constructed human hybridomas which produce antibodies against a number of antigen preparations of *Mycobacterium leprae*.[65] EBV-transformed cell lines from lepromatous leprosy patients were fused with KR-4 and hybrids screened for antibodies against three antigen preparations of armadillo-derived *M. leprae*, including (1) a soluble sonicated antigen, (2) a detergent extract of insoluble sonicated *M. leprae*, and (3) a phenolic glycolipid antigen. A number of reactive MAbs were obtained which were further screened for specificity on a panel of antigens from four other mycobacteria. A total of nine cloned stable hybrids have been obtained with specificity for *M. leprae*. In comparison, 10,000 EBV-transformed lymphocyte clones from lepromatous patients were screened for anti-*M. leprae* antibody production, and all the 42 clones that were initially positive lost their ability to produce antibodies within 6 weeks in culture. These results suggest that the EBV–hybridoma system is superior to the EBV system for production of human MAbs from leprosy patients.

We are also using the EBV–hybridoma system to produce human monoclonal antibodies against autoantigens such as myelin-associated glycoprotein (MAG). MAG is a minor glycoprotein component of the myelin sheath comprising less than 1% of the total protein present. It has a molecular weight of approximately 110,000 and consists of 30% carbohydrate. The IgM gammopathy detected in some peripheral neuropathy patients has been found to recognize an epitope on MAG which is, in part, formed by the carbohydrate residues.[67] Peripheral blood from a well-characterized neuropathy patient (ARM) was separated on Ficoll-Hypaque and transformed with EBV. This EBV line was cloned at 10 cells/well in 96-well plates on irradiated mouse spleen cells as a feeder layer. Screening of the clones was begun at 3 weeks using an ELISA system with MAG in the solid phase as the antigen (2 μg/ml). Dilutions of ARM serum and normal serum served as controls. Positive wells were detected at 5 weeks in 2 out of 400 wells tested. The strongest MAG-reactive well (clone 1) was grown up and fused with KR-4. Hybrids are currently being screened (R. McGarry).

Procedure

Solutions

Ouabain. A 10 mM solution of oubain is made by dissolving 365 mg in 20 ml tissue culture-distilled H_2O with gentle heating and vortexing and then made up to 50 ml with RPMI 1640 medium, filter sterilized,

[67] P. E. Braun, D. Frailand, and N. Latov, *J. Neurochem.* **39**, 1261 (1982).

and stored in aliquots at 4°, protected from light. For KR-4 cells (5 × 10^{-4} M ouabain resistant), 5 ml of 10 mM ouabain is added to 95 ml complete medium. For hybrids, 100 μl of 10 mM oubain is added to 100 ml of complete medium (final concentration is 1 × 10^{-5} M).

Thioguanine. Thioguanine, 100 mg, is dissolved in 10 ml 0.1 N NaOH, filter sterilized, and stored at 4° in plastic tubes. For KR-4 cells, grow at 30 μg/ml by adding 300 μl to 100 ml complete medium.

Hybridoma medium. RPMI 1640, with 20% heat-inactivated FCS, l-glutamine (4 mM), and 2-mercaptoethanol (50 μM). New hybrids frequently do not thrive well in less than 20% serum; the percentage serum can be decreased after 2 weeks or so, if desired.

50× HAT medium. Obtain from Flow Laboratories and stored at 4°, or make up as follows:

Hypoxanthine–aminopterin–thymidine (HAT) 100× solution. Dissolve 130.0 mg hypoxanthine, 1.9 mg aminopterin, and 39.0 mg thymidine in 100.0 ml NaOH (0.1 N), filter through a 0.22-μm filter, and add 1.0 ml HEPES buffer (1 M). Store at 4°. Stable for several months.

Hypoxanthine–thymidine (HT), 100× solution. Dissolve 130.0 mg hypoxanthine and 39.0 mg thymidine in 100.0 ml NaOH (0.01 N). Store at 4°. Stable for several months.

Cells

KR-4 Cells. Ouabain and thioguanine resistance markers are fairly stable; however, we usually maintain the cells on ouabain and thioguanine at least 1 week per month; alternatively, the cells are put on drugs several days before fusion (5 × 10^{-4} M ouabain, 30 μg thioguanine/ml) and taken off drugs 24–48 hr before fusion.

EBV Lines. These cells are usually checked a day or so before fusion to ascertain viability; if there are a large number of dead cells (>15%), then the cells are centrifuged on Ficoll-Hypaque to clean them up.

Feeder Cells. We have established a routine of using both irradiated spleen cells and peritoneal exudate cells (PECs) (either irradiated or not), although each cell population alone would likely be sufficient. Spleen cells are seeded at 2–5 × 10^5/microtiter well, while PECs are seeded at approximately 5 × 10^3 cells/microtiter well. We have found that low ratios of spleen cells to PECs are preferable. One mouse spleen routinely yields about 100 × 10^6 spleen cells (±10%). In most cases, we obtain the PECs and spleens the same day as the fusion, but it should be possible to seed them the day before. Check the viability of these cells on the day of the fusion.

PECs are obtained by injecting and then withdrawing about 10 ml of sterile RPMI medium into the mouse abdominal cavity. The spleens are aseptically removed and placed in about 3 ml of sterile medium in a 15-ml tube. The spleen cells are gently dispersed with a loosely fitting, sterile, Teflon homogenizing pestle. An additional 5 ml of medium is added and the cells pipetted up and down to suspend. After allowing the debris to settle briefly (1 min), the supernatant cell suspension is transferred to a sterile tube and centrifuged, and the pellet resuspended in fresh medium. The tube is capped tightly, parafilmed and double-bagged, and irradiated for 35–50 min (about 4000 rad). The PECs are also centrifuged and resuspended in fresh medium and may be irradiated, but it is not necessary. Following irradiation, the cells are centrifuged and are resuspended in 10 ml RPML 1640/20% FCS (hybridoma medium).

Fusion

(1) Polyethylene glycol (PEG) solution: PEG 4000 (Sigma), 2 g, is weighed in a glass tube and capped with aluminum foil for autoclaving. Prepare three or four extra for backup. The PEG is autoclaved (15 min) and can then be maintained at 60° for immediate use or allowed to solidify for future use (remelt in 60° water bath). Just before use, 2.4 ml of warm (37°) serum-free RPMI medium is added to the liquid PEG and well mixed. The pH is adjusted, if required, with sterile 0.1 N NaOH solution so that a pink color is obtained.

(2) Mix 10^7 KR-4 cells and 10^7 EBV-transformed lymphocytes in a 50-ml conical centrifuge tube and centrifuge; wash the cell pellet three times with serum-free RPMI 1640 medium; after the final wash, remove medium completely. (3) Add PEG solution (0.5 ml) over a 1-min period to the cell pellet, stirring *gently* with the pipet tip. (4) After allowing the tube to sit at room temperature for an additional $1\frac{1}{2}$ minutes with occasional gentle mixing, add prewarmed (37°) RPMI 1640 medium (10 ml) very slowly with gentle mixing over a 6- to 10-min period. (5) Cap the tube and incubate at 37° for 20 min to 1 hr. (Note: additional fusions may be done at this time if desired.)

(6) Centrifuge the cells and wash once with RPMI 1640 medium and resuspend in RPMI 1640/20% FBS with 20 mM L-glutamine and 5×10^{-5} M 2-mercaptoethanol. (7) Plate cells into 96-well plates (Linbro 76-032-05) in a total volume of 0.1 ml per well with 3000 rad-irradiated mouse spleen cells ($2–5 \times 10^5$/well) and mouse peritoneal exudate cells ($\leq 5 \times 10^3$/well). Plate control wells (parental cells).

(8) Twenty-four hours after fusion, add 0.1 ml of 2× HAT, 1× ouabain medium [4 ml 50× HAT (Flow Laboratories) and 100 μl 10 mM ouabain

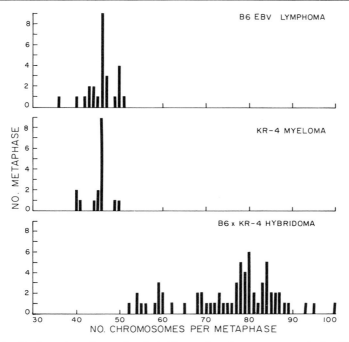

FIG. 4. Confirmation of putative hybridomas by chromosome analysis. Metaphase spreads of cells in the exponential phase of growth were stained for chromosomes by the method of Worton and Duff.[68]

per 100 ml medium] to each well. (9) Three days after fusion, remove half the medium and replace with 0.1 ml 1× HAT, 1× ouabain medium per well. Thereafter, feed hybrids every 4–6 days with HAT–ouabain medium. The first putative hybrids may be detected microscopically 7–12 days after fusion on the basis of large size and shape (tapering, fishlike morphology) and viability. In control wells, parental cells should be dead 8–10 days after fusion. Wells containing viable hybridomas can usually be screened 18–30 days after fusion.

 Confirmation of Hybrids. Because of the tendency for rare EBV-transformed cells to sometimes grow out of human lymphocyte populations, it is necessary to confirm the hybrid nature of putative hybridoma wells. One or both of the following criteria should be met: (1) hybridomas should have a near-tetraploid number of chromosomes as shown in Fig. 4,[68] or a 2-fold greater DNA content on FACS analysis, and (2) hybridomas should

[68] R. G. Worton and C. Duff, this series, Vol. 58, p. 322.

codominantly express HLA haplotypes and immunoglobulin isotypes of either parent (but HLA typing of these lines is often difficult).

Interspecies Hybrids

Murine MAbs are obtained by the fusion of murine myeloma cells with specific antibody-forming B lymphocytes from the spleen of immunized mice. The myeloma cell confers immortality onto the antibody-producing B lymphocytes and allows it to grow in culture and as a tumor in mice, whereas the B lymphocyte determines the specificity of the antibody produced by the hybridoma.[2] In 1975, Schwaber[69] noted that some hybrids of mouse myeloma cells and normal human peripheral blood lymphocytes secreted human immunoglobulin. Thus, before the availability of human myeloma fusion partners, it appeared feasible to generate human antibodies by fusing human lymphocytes with murine myeloma cells, i.e., interspecies hybrids.[70] In fact, mouse × human hybrids have been described that secrete human antibody against tetanus toxoid,[64,71] human tumor-associated antigens,[72–74] multiple endocrine organs,[75] and other antigens.

A limitation of interspecies hybrids lies in their preferential segregation of human chromosomes (Fig. 5), and thus stable hybrids secreting specific human antibodies are generally difficult to obtain. However, the stable production of human anti-tetanus antibody from an interspecies hybrid for more than 8 months after fusion has been reported at least in one case.[70] Loss of human chromosomes from mouse × hybrids does not appear random; human chromosomes 14 (heavy chain) and 22 (light chain λ) are preferentially retained whereas chromosome 2 (light chain κ) is preferentially lost.[76,77] The stability of the chromosomal constitution is much greater in hybrids derived from parental cells of the same species;

[69] J. Schwaber, *Exp. Cell Res.* **93,** 343 (1975).
[70] R. Levy, J. Dilley, S. Brown, and Y. Bergman, *in* "Monoclonal Antibodies. Hybridomas: A New Dimension in Biological Analysis" (R. B. Herberman, ed.), p. 137. Plenum, New York, 1980.
[71] F. Gigliotti and R. A. Insel, *J. Clin. Invest.* **70,** 1306 (1982).
[72] K. Sikora and R. Wright, *Br. J. Cancer* **43,** 696 (1981).
[73] K. Sikora and J. Phillips, *Br. J. Cancer* **43,** 105 (1981).
[74] J. Schlom, D. Wunderlich, and Y. A. Teramoto, *Proc. Natl. Acad. Sci. U.S.A.* **77,** 6841 (1980).
[75] J. Satoh, B. S. Prabhakar, M. V. Haspel, F. Ginsberg-Feblner, and A. L. Notkins, *N. Engl. J. Med.* **309,** 217 (1983).
[76] C. M. Croce, M. Shander, J. Martinis, L. Circurel, G. G. d'Ancoma, and H. Koprowski, *Eur. J. Immunol.* **10,** 486 (1980).
[77] J. Erikson, J. Martinis, and C. M. Croce, *Nature (London)* **294,** 173 (1981).

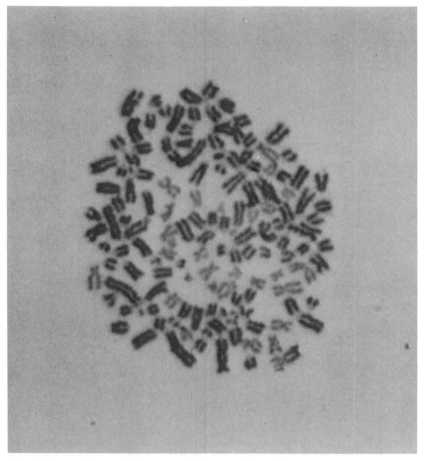

FIG. 5. Loss of human chromosomes in interspecies hybridomas. Metaphase spreads of interspecific (P3X63Ag8.653) × (B6) hybrid clones containing human (light) and mouse (dark) chromosomes stained by the G-11 banding method.[64]

thus, to produce stable human × human hybridomas, establishment of fusion partners of human origin became necessary.

Large-Scale Production of Human MAbs

Ascites Production

One of the problems remaining in human MAb technology is that of bulk production. Mouse hybridomas may be grown as ascites tumors in mice, increasing the yield of antibody up to 1000-fold. With human hybridomas, the use of immunodeficient mice is required to avoid xenograft rejection. Abrams *et al.*[78] have reported that murine × human hybridomas secreting human immunoglobulin grow readily in doubly pristane-primed nude mice. In our hands, this approach is not successful with human × human hybridomas. Instead, we and others[79] have found it necessary to passage the hybridoma in nude mice as a subcutaneous solid tumor, followed by *in vitro* culture, before intraperitoneal inoculation of the cells to grow as ascites.[80] In our studies, the appearance of ascites was not significantly affected by pristane pretreatment of mice alone nor by depletion of natural killer cells with anti-asialo GM_1. On the other hand, irradiation of the mice together with pristane treatment enhanced tumor takes, and ascites growth of human hybridomas was observed in 50% of the mice injected.[81] Repassage of ascites recovered cells resulted in a 2-fold increase in human Ig production by EBV hybridomas.

As shown in Table III, approximately half of the total human Ig detected in the ascites fluid was specific for tetanus toxoid. The other half probably represents production of human parental chains by the KR-4 and KR-12 fusion partners.

Procedure. (1) Harvest hybridomas and inject 10^7 cells into a subcutaneous site on each of two, 350-rad-irradiated, BALB/c nu/nu mice (available from Harlan-Sprague Dawley, Indianapolis, IN). (2) Remove the growing tumor 3–4 weeks after injection, using sterile technique. The tumor is then cut into fine pieces and cultured *in vitro* for several passages until enough cells have been grown up for cryopreservation and *in vivo* passage. (3) Cultures of readapted hybridoma cells are harvested and injected intraperitoneally into irradiated (350 rad) BALB/c nude mice pretreated 2 weeks prior with 0.5 ml undiluted pristane ip (2,6,10,14-tetramethylpentadecane, Aldrich Chemical Co., Milwaukee, WI). (4) Mice which develop distended abdomens are sacrificed approximately 4 weeks after injection and the ascites fluid is collected for analysis. Assay systems, such as ELISA, should employ reagents that are human Ig specific and do not cross-react with mouse Ig. As a control, we use ascites fluid from mice injected with a murine fusion partner such as Sp2/0 or

---

[78] P. G. Abrams, J. J. Ochs, S. L. Girardina, A. C. Morgan, S. B. Wilburn, A. R. Wilt, R. K. Oldham, and K. A. Foon, *J. Immunol.* **132,** 1611 (1984).

[79] K. E. Truitt, J. W. Larrick, A. A. Raubitschek, D. W. Buck, and S. W. Jacobson, *Hybridoma* **3,** 195 (1984).

[80] S. P. C. Cole, B. G. Campling, T. Atlaw, D. Kozbor, and J. C. Roder, *Mol. Cell. Biochem.* **62,** 109 (1984).

[81] D. Kozbor, W. Abramow-Newerly, P. Tripputi, S. P. C. Cole, J. Weibel, J. C. Roder, and C. Croce, *J. Immunol. Methods* **81,** 31 (1985).

TABLE III
ANTIBODY PRODUCTION BY HYBRIDOMAS IN ASCITES[a]

| | | Antibody concentration (μg/ml) | | | |
| | | In Vitro | | Ascites ($n = 6$) | |
Parents	Hybridoma	Total Ig	Anti-TT	Total Ig	Anti-TT
KR-4 × B6	1	5	3	933 ± 215	450 ± 125
	2	6	4	1130 ± 235	550 ± 104
KR-12 × B6	1	15	7	1766 ± 368	866 ± 172
	2	16	8	7050 ± 1162	5358 ± 1046

[a] Tetanus toxoid-specific human hybridoma clones from B6 × KR-4 and B6 × KR-12 were grown as a solid sc tumor followed by in vitro passage and reinjection ip into irradiated BALB/c nu/nu mice. Ascites fluid was collected 4 weeks later from three mice per group and measured for total human immunoglobulin and specific anti-TT antibody content using an ELISA assay. Ascites cells were repassed into an additional three mice per group which were again measured for Ig and anti-TT. Antibody content in ascites passage II was only about 2-fold higher than in ascites passage I and therefore the data have been pooled for both groups. Values represent the mean ± SE of six individually assayed mice. These data have been published in full in Ref. 81.

P3X63Ag8, since neither KR-4 nor KR-12 grow readily as ascites tumors. A discussion of the enhanced tumorigenicity of human hybridomas and a flow chart (Fig. 2) can be found in the preceding chapter.[6]

Serum-Free Culture

As an alternative to ascites production, hybridomas may be grown in large-scale tissue culture systems. However to be practical and economically feasible, a serum-free culture system is essential. Furthermore, elimination of serum would facilitate rapid purification of human immunoglobulins. Several systems have been described for growing human lymphocytes under serum-free conditions.[82,83] We have adapted several human hybridomas to grow in serum-free RPMI 1640 medium in a stepwise fashion.[84] The hybrids did not grow well when the percentage of fetal bovine serum was decreased to less than 5%, and essentially failed to thrive at 1% FCS. However, the cells readily adapted to growth in RPMI 1640 medium supplemented with 0.5% bovine serum albumin, transferrin

[82] M. D. Sharath, S. B. Rincerknecht, and J. M. Weiter, *J. Lab. Clin. Med.* **103,** 739 (1984).
[83] J. Rarrant, C. A. Newton, M. E. North, C. Weyman, and M. K. Brenner, *J. Immunol.* **68,** 25 (1984).
[84] S. P. C. Cole, E. H. Vreeken, and J. C. Roder, *J. Immunol. Methods* **78,** 271 (1985).

(10 μg/ml), and 2-mercaptoethanol (5 × 10^{-5} M). Attempts to grow human hybrids in completely protein-free culture medium are in progress and include adaptation of hybrids to growth in a 1 : 1 mixture of Hanks' F-12 medium and high-glucose Dulbecco's modified Eagle's medium (DMEM) supplemented with transferrin (5 μg/ml) and HEPES buffer (10 mM), pH 7.2. Thus it appears entirely feasible to grow human hybridomas in serum-free culture and it is likely that this will become the method of choice for large-scale production of human MAbs.

The Advantage of Human Monoclonal Antibodies

Human monoclonal antibodies are desirable and have advantages over the conventional murine fusion products for several reasons. (1) Human monoclonal antibodies are preferable for γ-globulin therapy because of the risk of sensitization with xenoantisera. Almost half of the 20 patients treated to date in various centers with murine monoclonal antibodies have developed an antibody response to the mouse Ig, which prevented effective treatment.[85–90] Human Ig would be far less immunogenic in humans than xenogeneic mouse Ig. In the past, the serum for γ-globulin prophylaxis for infections (tetanus, rabies) was switched from horse antiserum to human antiserum, which elicits far fewer adverse reactions. Even human Ig, however, may be expected in some cases to stimulate a response to allotypic or idiotypic sites. (2) Autoantibodies or naturally occurring human antibodies could be used as antigens to select and develop human monoclonal anti-idiotypic antibodies, which would potentially be useful for suppressing the response to autoantigens or transplant antigens. (3) The human immune response would generate a wider range of antibodies against HLA and other polymorphic surface determinants than immunization across species barriers. (4) From the biological standpoint, human monoclonal antibodies would tell us more than murine monoclonal antibodies about the spectrum of the human B-cell specificity repertoire. However, the difficulties encountered in the murine hybridoma field are

[85] R. A. Miller and R. Levy, *Lancet* 2, 226 (1981).
[86] R. A. Miller, D. G. Maloney, R. Warnke, and R. Levy, *N. Engl. J. Med.* 306, 517 (1982).
[87] J. Ritz, J. M. Pesando, S. E. Sallan, L. A. Clavell, J. Notis-McConarty, P. Rosenthal, and S. F. Schlossman, *Blood* 58, 141 (1981).
[88] H. R. Sears, B. Atkinson, D. Herlyn, C. Ernst, J. Matteis, Z. Steplewski, and H. Koprowski, *Lancet* 1, 762 (1982).
[89] L. M. Nadler, P. Stashenko, R. Hardy, W. D. Kaplan, L. N. Button, D. W. Kufe, K. H. Antman, and S. F. Schlossman, *Cancer Res.* 40, 3147 (1980).
[90] R. O. Dillman, D. L. Shawler, R. E. Sobol, H. A. Collins, J. C. Beauregard, S. B. Wormsley, and I. Royston, *Blood* 59, 1036 (1982).

relevant to the human system as well. Potential limitations of the EBV–hybridoma system have been dealt with in the accompanying chapter.[6]

Conclusions

A number of human fusion partners have been described for the production of human hybridomas but the majority are lymphoblastoid cell lines and only two are definite plasmacytomas. A detailed comparison of hybridization frequencies, yield of antigen-specific hybridomas, immunoglobulin secretion levels, cloning efficiencies, division times, and stability[6] leads to the conclusion that the EBV–hybridoma system described here is near optimal and approaches the murine system in efficiency, with mean fusion frequencies of 1.54×10^{-5} in four independent studies and *in vitro* secretion levels of >5 μg/ml specific antibody (Table II). Lymphocytes from lymph nodes, tonsils, bone marrow, and peripheral blood of hyperimmune patients or *in vitro* immunized cultures have been fused effectively, and human monoclonal antibodies against *M. leprae*, tetanus toxoid, and lung tumor cells have been generated in our laboratory. A plasmacytoma-like fusion partner has been constructed and we have successfully adapted our human hybridomas for growth in serum-free medium *in vitro* or as ascites tumors in nude mice. We are currently developing a non-Ig-secreting fusion partner. Other systems, such as electrofusion, may in theory produce higher affinity monoclonal antibodies and should be investigated.[91]

The EBV–hybridomas technique offers a high degree of flexibility since the use of EBV (1) immortalizes the donor B cells for future use and repeated fusions, (2) aids the expansion of rare antigen-specific B cells in the peripheral blood prior to fusion, and (3) increases hybridization frequencies over 10-fold. One limitation of the system is that the majority of hybridomas obtained in this way secrete antigen-specific IgM, rather than IgG. Recent developments may allow induction of an IgM-to-IgG switch in these hybrids using UV light[92] or a gene transfer.[93] We believe that human monoclonal antibodies produced by the EBV–hybridoma technique will become useful tools for the diagnosis and treatment of human disease.

[91] M. Lo, T. Tsong, M. Conrad, S. Strittmatter, L. Hester, and S. Snyder, *Nature (London)* **310**, 792 (1984).
[92] A. Rosen and G. Klein, *Nature (London)* **306**, 189 (1983).
[93] G. Boulianne, N. Hozumi, and M. Shulman, *Nature (London)* **312**, 643 (1984).

[13] Generation of Human Monoclonal Antibodies by Fusion of EBV-Activated B Cells to a Human–Mouse Hybridoma

By STEVEN K. H. FOUNG, EDGAR G. ENGLEMAN,
and F. CARL GRUMET

Since the now classic observation of Köhler and Milstein in 1975 on the generation of murine hybridomas secreting predefined antibodies, monoclonal antibodies have been useful in many areas, including (1) the characterization of phenotypically and functionally distinct lymphocyte subpopulations, (2) as clinical tools for diagnostic testing (e.g., tissue typing and diagnosis of infectious agents), (3) the identification of tumor-associated antigens, and (4) their potential use as therapeutic agents in the treatment of cancer.[1-4] However, murine monoclonal antibodies suffer from three major limitations in application to human diseases. First, the majority of antibodies produced when human cells are injected into a mouse or rat are against species-specific rather than polymorphic determinants. Second, species-specific carbohydrate portions of immunoglobulins are important in several antibody effector functions.[5] Last, when murine antibodies are used therapeutically, it is likely that a human anti-murine antibody response will occur and potentially induce serum sickness.[4] Because of these reasons, it is important to develop technologies to produce stable human monoclonal antibodies.

Two basic approaches have been explored extensively for the production of human monoclonal antibodies: (1) viral transformation of human B cells with Epstein–Barr virus (EBV) and (2) hybridization of human B lymphocytes with appropriate mouse or human myeloma and human lymphoblastoid cell lines.[6-9] While a number of antigen-specific human monoclonal antibodies have been produced with EBV transformation, major problems of low-level antibody secretion and difficulty in establishing

[1] G. Köhler and C. Milstein, *Nature* (*London*) **256,** 495 (1975).

[2] F. C. Grumet, B. M. Fendly, L. Fish, S. K. H. Foung, and E. G. Engleman, *Hum. Immunol.* **5,** 61 (1982).

[3] N. K. Damle and E. G. Engleman, *J. Exp. Med.* **158,** 159 (1983).

[4] R. A. Miller, A. R. Oseroff, P. T. Strattle, and R. Levy, *Blood* **62,** 989 (1983).

[5] M. Nose and H. Wigzell, *Proc. Natl. Acad. Sci. U.S.A.* **80,** 6632 (1983).

[6] M. Steinitz, G. Klein, S. Koskimies, and O. Mäkelä, *Nature* (*London*) **269,** 620 (1977).

[7] R. Levy and J. Dilley, *Proc. Natl. Acad. Sci. U.S.A.* **75,** 2411 (1978).

[8] L. Olsson and H. S. Kaplan, *Proc. Natl. Acad. Sci. U.S.A.* **212,** 767 (1980).

[9] C. M. Croce, A. Linnenbach, W. Hall, Z. Steplewski, and H. Koprowski, *Nature* (*London*) **288,** 488 (1980).

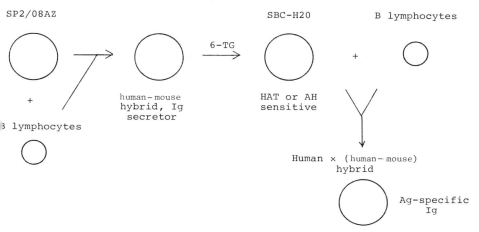

FIG. 1. Diagrammatic representation of the generation of a human–mouse fusion partner and production of antigen-specific human monoclonal antibodies.

stable antibody-secreting hybridomas are common.[10,11] Fusion of human B cells to murine cell lines will yield a high number of hybrids, but these are quite unstable in maintaining immunoglobulin secretion because of preferential loss of human chromosomes in the mouse–human hybridoma.[12] Routine generation of human–human hybridomas is still rare due to a general lack of suitable fusion partners.

To overcome some of these problems, we have developed a strategy to produce antigen-specific human monoclonal antibodies which involves initial EBV activation and expansion of the antigen-specific B-cell population, and subsequent fusion to a human–mouse hybridoma cell line (Fig. 1).[11]

Production of a Human–Mouse Hybridoma

As outlined (Fig. 1), the SBC-H20 cell line was derived from a fusion between a mouse myeloma line and human B lymphocytes isolated from a normal donor. Mutants from a human–mouse hybridoma with stable immunoglobulin production were subsequently selected by exposure to in-

[10] D. Kozbor, J. C. Roder, T. H. Chang, Z. Steplewski, and H. Koprowski, *Hybridoma* **1,** 323 (1982).

[11] S. K. H. Foung, S. Perkins, A. Raubitschek, J. Larrick, G. Lizak, D. Fishwild, E. G. Engleman, and F. C. Grumet, *J. Immunol. Methods* **000,** 83 (1984).

[12] R. Nowinski, C. Boglund, J. Lane, M. Lastrum, I. Bernstein, W. Young, S. Hakomori, L. Hall, and M. Cooney, *Science* **210,** 537 (1980).

creasing concentrations of 6-thioguanine-containing medium. To derive these mutants 10^8 cells in log phase growth were placed in Iscove's medium (IMDM) with 10% fetal calf serum supplemented with 2 mM glutamine, 100 units of penicillin and 10 mg streptomycin/ml, and 2 μM 6-thioguanine. The cells were placed in 24-well trays at 10^6 cells/ml per well. On the following day an additional milliliter of medium is placed in each well. A progressive decrease in cell viability was observed over the following 2 weeks and during this interval, medium was changed every 3–4 days by aspirating and replacing with 1 ml volume. At 2 weeks when microscopic colonies of viable cells were observed the concentration of 6-thioguanine was increased to 4 μM. When enhanced cell growth was observed between 3 and 4 weeks the viable cells were separated by Ficoll-Hypaque gradient centrifugation and again placed in 4 μM 6-thioguanine-containing medium. During the subsequent 4–6 weeks, the concentration of 6-thioguanine was progressively increased to a final concentration of 20 μM. After the establishment of 6-thioguanine resistance, monoclonal populations were isolated by standard limiting dilution and expanded prior to testing for sensitivity to hypoxanthine–aminopterin–thymidine (HAT) or azaserine–hypoxanthine (AH) selection. Generally, 100% cell death was observed by day 7 in HAT or AH selection before the particular cell line was used as a fusion partner. Since these mutants were partially of mouse origin, it was expected that they would be relatively ouabain resistant (100 nM), which was a necessary characteristic in selecting for hybridomas from a fusion with EBV-activated cells.[11] Unfused EBV-transformed cells should not survive in 100 nM ouabain. By using this approach, we developed a human–mouse cell line, SBC-H20, that fuses efficiently to stimulated normal human B lymphocytes and produces stable human immunoglobulin secreting hybridomas.

EBV Transformation

Epstein–Barr virus from the marmoset cell line B95-8 is commonly used to transform human B lymphocytes.[13] Spent supernatants are used as the virus source by growing the marmoset cell line in IMDM medium as stated above, but without 6-thioguanine. Supernatant is harvested and sterile filtered through a 0.2-μm filter prior to storage in 1-ml aliquots in liquid nitrogen. Once thawed, the virus is used immediately for transformation. Peripheral blood lymphocytes are isolated by a standard Ficoll-Hypaque density gradient and T cells are removed by a single-step rosetting method using 2-aminoethylisothiouronium bromide hydrobromide.[14]

[13] W. S. Sly, G. S. Sekhon, R. Kennett, W. F. Bodmer, and J. Bodmer, *Tissue Antigens* 7, 165 (1976).
[14] A. Saxon, J. Feldhaus, and R. A. Robins, *J. Immunol. Methods* 12, 285 (1976).

The residual non-T, or B lymphocytes are plated at 10^5 cells per well in microtiter plates and cultured in the above medium with 50% spent supernatant containing EBV for at least 14 days prior to initial assay. At this point, marked microscopic growth of EBV-transformed cells should be observed. Cells in wells containing supernatants positive for the antibodies of interest are either expanded or cloned by the standard limiting dilution method in liquid medium culture.

Fusion Protocol

EBV-transformed lymphocytes are mixed with SBC-H20 at a 1 : 1 ratio and washed three times in medium without serum. Approximately 10^7 total cells are pelleted in a 50-ml conical tube and gently resuspended in 1 ml of IMDM with 45% polyethylene glycol, molecular weight 1430–1570 (BDH Chemicals, Poole, England), prewarmed to 37°. After 2 min at room temperature, 1 ml of IMDM without serum is added over 30 sec followed with 5 ml over an additional 30 sec. The cell suspension is centrifuged at 350 g for 3 min. At 8 min from the onset of fusion, the cell pellet is washed once in IMDM with 10% fetal calf serum (10 ml). The fused cells are then plated in microtiter trays at various cell densities of 10^4 to 10^5 cells per well. Depending on the method of selection it is recommended that fused cells are placed in HT or H medium for 24 hr prior to the addition of aminopterin or azaserine. The two selection media are IMDM with 20% fetal calf serum and 100 μM hypoxanthine, 800 nM aminopterin, 15 nM thymidine, and 100 nM ouabain or 2 μg/ml azaserine, 100 μM hypoxanthine, and 100 μM ouabain. Usually by day 7, unfused SBC-H20 and EBV-transformed cells are dead. Hybridomas should be observed by light microscopy after 2–3 weeks from the onset of fusion. Selection medium is maintained for 2 weeks, at which point it is then switched to the corresponding medium without aminopterin or azaserine.

Human Monoclonal Anti-A Red Blood Cell Antibody

B lymphocytes were isolated from splenocytes of a type O individual requiring splenectomy because of severe hemolytic disease. T cells were removed by a standard sheep erythrocyte rosetting technique, and residual cells were transformed by EBV-containing supernatant from the marmoset B-958 lymphoblastoid line. Cells were plated at 10^5/well in microtiter trays and cultured 14 days prior to initial assay. Positive wells were expanded in liquid medium culture. Thereafter, lymphocytes producing anti-A and SBC-H20 or mouse myeloma (SP2/08AZ) cells were mixed at a ratio of 1 : 10 and fused with a solution of polyethylene glycol in a standard protocol. Supernatants from wells containing growing hybrids were

TABLE I
FREQUENCY AND TITER OF HYBRIDOMAS SECRETING
HUMAN ANTI-A ANTIBODY[a]

Secreting line	Number of wells with anti-A activity	Titer[b]
EBV line		2,000
SP2 hybrids		
Parents	19/22	32
Clones	0/23	0
SBC-H20 hybrids		
Parents	27/29	8,192
Clones	13/21	16,384
Subclones	36/53	32,768

[a] All antigen-specific Ig of IgM class with κ light chains.
[b] Maximum titer detected.

tested against type A_1 and B red blood cells (RBC) (Table I). Of 23 colonies of SP2-derived hybrids isolated, none contained cells that secreted anti-A antibody. Cloning of the SBC-H20-derived hybrids resulted in greater than 50% of clones secreting the antibody and, more importantly, the isolation of a number of clones with antibody titers substantially greater than that of the original EBV anti-A clone. These SBC-H20-derived hybrid clones produced antigen-specific immunoglobulin continuously for over 12 months prior to storage in liquid nitrogen. As determined by an enzyme-linked immunoassay, the class was IgM and the amount of immunoglobulin produced was approximately 3.5 μg/10^6 cells per 24 hr. The antigen specificity of the antibody produced by one of the clones was confirmed by testing against 133 RBC samples of groups A_1, A_2, A_{int}, A_1B, A_2B, and B (Table II). Positive reactions were observed with all type A RBC, but with no other groups. The quality of the reactions was as good or better than with the commercial antisera in current use.

Human Monoclonal Anti-Rh$_0$(D) Antibodies

Using techniques similar to those above, multiple anti-Rh$_0$(D) red cell human monoclonal antibodies have been produced. Whole blood was obtained from women known to be immunized to Rh$_0$(D) red cells and peripheral lymphocytes were isolated on a Ficoll-Hypaque density gradient. After removal of T lymphocytes by a standard sheep erythrocyte rosetting technique, the residual non-T lymphocytes were activated by

TABLE II
REACTIVITY OF HUMAN MONOCLONAL ANTI-A ANTIBODY
AGAINST RANDOM DONOR CELLS

Positive cells	Number tested	Negative cells	Number tested
A_2	12	B	13
A_1	44	0	54
A_1B	6		
A_2B	2		
A_{int}	2		

Epstein–Barr virus. The cells were cultured at an initial density of 10^4 to 10^5 cells per well for 6–12 days in a humidified incubator with 6% CO_2 at 37°. Proliferation of cells was observed by light microscopy and supernatants were harvested and assayed for anti-$Rh_0(D)$ activity. Supernatants from wells containing growing EBV-activated cells were tested against $Rh_0(D)$-positive and -negative red cells by a hemagglutination assay as previously described.[11] Reactivity was determined at three different phases: after addition of supernatant and red blood cells (initial spin), after a 25-min incubation at 37°, and after three washes and the addition of IgG-specific anti-human globulin. From two different individuals a significant portion of the wells contained supernatants with anti-$Rh_0(D)$ activity. Some of these cells were expanded and fused to SBC-H20 as described. Two human hybridomas from different parent wells, after multiple cloning to ensure monoclonality by limiting dilution, were selected for further characterization of secreted immunoglobulin. The initial reactivity pattern of these two antibodies against various red cells is illustrated in Table III. Both human antibodies reacted only with Rh-positive and not Rh-negative cells in this limited panel. Furthermore, in testing these antibodies against commercially available red cells, both reacted with Du cells with Rh(C) in trans to $Rh_0(D)$. Reactivity was not detected with Du cells of the mosaic type or any other specificity.

TABLE III
REACTIVITY TO Rh-TYPED RED BLOOD CELLS

Antibody	$Rh_0(D)$ positive	$Rh_0(D)$ negative
SC-01	4/4	0/6
SC-02	4/4	0/6

Comments

We have described a strategy to produce human monoclonal antibodies and the production of antigen-specific antibodies to two well-described red cell antigens. The approach that has been most successful involves the use of EBV to activate and expand human B lymphocytes, *in vitro,* prior to fusion with the SBC-H20 cell line. In addition to these two groups of antibodies, we have succeeded in producing human monoclonal antibodies to a variety of herpesviruses, *Mycobacterium leprae,* and autoantibodies from patients with autoimmune disorders. This strategy incorporates the observation that EBV activation of B cells appears capable of initial expansion of antigen-specific B cell clones. Furthermore, by fusion to an appropriate partner, SBC-H20, stabilization of antibody secretion is achieved. The combination of stability and specificity achieved with this system will be important factors in facilitating wider clinical applications of human monoclonal antibodies.

Acknowledgments

We thank Susan Perkins for her superb technical assistance and Angelina Pearson Miyamoto, who typed this chapter. The work was supported in part by Grants HL29572, A32075, and CA24607 from the National Institutes of Health and a grant from the Cetus Corporation, Berkeley, CA.

[14] Improved Hybridoma Technology: Spleen Cell Separation and Soluble Growth Factors

By P. van Mourik and W. P. Zeijlemaker

The development of hybridoma technology for the production of monoclonal antibodies has been a step forward in immunology.[1] Thus, large numbers of murine monoclonal antibodies against all kinds of immunogens have been produced, although the production of monoclonal antibodies against weak and impure imunogens is still difficult.

Several investigators have tried to increase the yield of hybrid clones producing antibodies of the desired specificity. Two approaches can be followed. The first approach is the expansion of cells of the desired specificity. This can be achieved by antigen-specific stimulation *in vitro* of the

[1] G. Köhler and C. Milstein, *Nature (London)* **256,** 495 (1975).

spleen cells prior to fusion.[2] Alternatively, primed spleen cells can be transferred into irradiated syngeneic recipients, together with antigen, leading to a 10-fold increase in the proportion of hybrid clones producing the desired antibody.[3] However, a major disadvantage of this method is the low recovery of living spleen cells. Recently, it was reported[4] that intrasplenic injection of the immunogen significantly increases the number of hybrid clones producing the desired antibodies.

A second approach is to increase the overall fusion frequency. This has been tried in several ways: with polyethylene glycol of various molecular weights,[5] with various types of culture media,[5,6] with various ratios of spleen cells to myeloma cells,[5] with various myeloma lines as fusion partners,[5,7] and with feeder systems, such as thymocytes[8] and soluble factors,[9-11] all with more or less success.

We describe here a technique based on the separation of spleen cells prior to fusion over a Percoll solution, to prevent overgrowth of hybrid cells by macrophages, fibroblasts, and P cells.[12] The overgrowth by these cells frequently hampers the recovery of hybridomas. At the same time, the density separation leads to a higher yield of immunoglobulin-secreting hybridoma cells.

Description of Methods and Reagents

Preparation of Percoll Solution. To prepare a Percoll solution of the required osmolality (about 290 mOsm at 25°), 7 ml of sterile Percoll (cat. no. 17-0891-01; Pharmacia, Uppsala, Sweden) is mixed with 93 ml of a 10 times concentrated sterile Earle's balanced salt solution (Earle's BSS; cat. no. 15-884-15; Flow Laboratories, Irvine, Scotland). The osmolality

[2] H. Hengartner, A. L. Luzzati, and M. Schreier, *Curr. Top. Microbiol. Immunol.* **81**, 92 (1978).

[3] P. C. Fox, E. H. Berenstein, and R. P. Siraganian, *Eur. J. Immunol.* **11**, 431 (1981).

[4] M. Spitz, L. Spits, R. Thorpe, and E. Eugui, *J. Immunol. Methods* **70**, 39 (1984).

[5] S. Fazekas de St. Groth and D. Scheidegger, *J. Immunol. Methods* **35**, 1 (1980).

[6] J. M. Davis, J. E. Pennington, A. M. Kubler, and J. F. Couscience, *J. Immunol. Methods* **50**, 161 (1982).

[7] D. E. Yelton, B. A. Diamond, S. P. Kwan, and M. D. Scharff, *Curr. Top. Microbiol. Immunol.* **81**, 1 (1978).

[8] J. Andersson and F. Melchers, *Curr. Top. Microbiol. Immunol.* **81**, 130 (1978).

[9] G. C. B. Astaldi, M. C. Janssen, P. M. Lansdorp, C. Willems, W. P. Zeijlemaker, and F. Oosterhof, *J. Immunol.* **125**, 1411 (1980).

[10] R. J. Westerwoudt, J. Blom, A. M. Naipal, and J. J. van Rood, *J. Immunol. Methods* **62**, 59 (1983).

[11] L. Aarden, P. Lansdorp, and E. de Groot, *Lymphokines* **10**, 175 (1985).

[12] P. van Mourik, R. A. Rivero, T. H. van der Kwast, P. M. Lansdorp, and W. P. Zeijlemaker, *J. Immunol. Methods* **68**, 45 (1984).

of the mixture is then measured and, if necessary, adjusted to the desired value.

Next, the density of the Percoll mixture is adjusted to the desired value, by dilution with Earle's BSS of normal concentration, according to the following formula:

$$V_e = V_p \times (D_p - D_d)/(D_d - D_e)$$

where V_e is the volume of normal Earle's BSS; V_p, the volume of the Percoll mixture; D_p, the density of the Percoll mixture (about 1.125 g/cm^3 at 25°); D_d, the desired density; and D_e, the density of the normal Earle's BSS (about 1.006 g/cm^3 at 25°).

The density of the solution is then measured and, if necessary, adjusted to the required value. The resulting Percoll solution is ready for use and can be kept in small aliquots at 4° for months. Sterilization of the final solution is no longer possible. Therefore, sterile conditions should be maintained throughout.

Immunization. In general, when protein is used as immunogen, the mice (BALB/c) are first primed intraperitoneally with 100 μg of protein mixed with an equal volume of Freund's complete adjuvant (FCA). After 4 weeks, the mice with the highest serum antibody titers are boosted intravenously with 10 μg of protein. When cells are used as immunogen, priming is performed with 5×10^7 cells without adjuvant. For boosting, 10^7 cells are given intravenously.

Preparation of Spleen Cell Suspensions. Suspensions of mouse splenocytes are prepared by teasing the cells from the spleens with a 2-ml syringe filled with Earle's BSS supplemented with 10% (all percentages by volume) fetal calf serum (FCS; Boehringer, Mannheim, West Germany). Next, the cells are centrifuged (10 min, 300 g, room temperature) and the pellet is resuspended in 4 ml of a Percoll solution of the required density. The suspension is then carefully overlayered with 1 ml of Earle's BSS supplemented with 10% FCS, to prevent drying of the low-density cells appearing on top of the gradient.

It is very important that the Percoll solution and the Earle's BSS have the same osmolality to avoid changes in the specific gravity of the cells during centrifugation. Next, the cell mixture is centrifuged (20 min, 450 g, room temperature), and cells from the ring and pellet fraction are collected separately. Both cell fractions are counted electronically and differentiated by size analysis (Coulter Counter with Channelyzer; Coulter Electronics, Dunstable, United Kingdom) according to Loos *et al.*[13] The cell viability is determined by the trypan blue exclusion test.

[13] J. A. Loos, B. Blok-Schut, B. Kipp, R. van Doorn, and L. J. Meerhof, *Blood* **48,** 743 (1976).

In our laboratory, hybridization experiments are routinely performed with cells derived from the pellet fraction after separation on a Percoll solution of 1.065 g/cm³. These cells have been proven to give the best overall results.

Cell Fusion. Murine plasmacytoma cells (Sp2/0 Ag14) and the spleen cells from the pellet fraction after Percoll centrifugation are mixed in neat Iscove's medium at a ratio of 1:4 and spun down (10 min, 90 g, room temperature). Cell hybridization is induced by addition of 0.5 ml of a 50% (v/v) solution of polyethylene glycol 4000 (art. no. 9727; Merck, Rahway, NY) in Dulbecco's medium (cat. no. 320-1965/1960; GIBCO) for 30 sec at room temperature, followed by a 30-sec incubation at 37°. The cell suspension is then slowly mixed with 10 ml of neat Iscove's medium. The cells are again centrifuged (10 min, 90 g), gently resuspended in culture medium containing growth-promoting activity (e.g., 10% human endothelial cell supernatant, HECS), and dispensed into 96-well tissue culture plates (7.5 × 10⁵ cells/well). HAT selection of hybrid cells is performed according to established procedures.[9] All cultures are performed in the presence of 10% HECS as growth-promoting activity, although other growth factors may also be used (see under "Examples").

Limiting Dilution. Cells from wells with hybrid cell growth are resuspended and a sample is drawn to count the number of viable cells in a hemacytometer. Next, to 5 ml of culture medium containing the desired growth-promoting factor, a fixed volume of the suspension is added, to obtain a final cell concentration of 50 cells/ml. About 4 ml of this suspension is used to dispense aliquots of 100 μl into 36 wells of a 96-well tissue culture plate. To the remaining 1 ml suspension, 4 ml culture medium is added, resulting in a cell concentration of 10 cells/ml. Again, 4 ml is used to fill 36 wells. To the remaining 1 ml, 1 ml of culture medium is added, and the suspension is dispensed into 24 wells.

Growth-Promoting Factors. For the preparation of HECS, cultures of smooth muscle cells are prepared from umbilical cord arteries. Conditioned medium of typical smooth muscle cell cultures, obtained after several passages, is used as HECS.[9] Human umbilical cord serum (HUCS) is prepared by dissection of umbilical cords immediately after delivery. The blood is centrifuged and passed through a 0.22-μm filter. Normal human serum (NHS) is prepared by pooling serum samples of six healthy blood donors. Hybridoma growth factor (HGF) is prepared from human peripheral blood mononuclear cells; after 24 hr of protein-free culture, the supernatant is used as a source of HGF.[11] Before use, all growth-promoting factors are treated for 45 min at 56°.

Tests for Antibody Production by Hybridomas. The supernatants of hybridoma cultures are tested for the presence of immunoglobulins and/ or specific antibodies by standard ELISA procedures.

TABLE I
CELL DISTRIBUTION IN DIFFERENT FRACTIONS AFTER SEPARATION OF
SPLEEN CELLS ON PERCOLL

Cell fraction	Cells with specific gravity of (g/cm³)	Cell distribution[a]	Percentage of cell viability
O	Unseparated		90
A	<1.060	67×10^6 (16.8)	60
B	1.060–1.065	50×10^6 (12.5)	80
C	1.065–1.070	53×10^6 (13.3)	>95
D	1.070–1.075	83×10^6 (20.8)	>95
E	>1.075	83×10^6 (20.8)	>95
		Total (84.2)	

[a] In parentheses, percentage of the cell number applied to the first gradient.

Examples

Density Gradient Separation of Spleen Cells

The effect of fractionation of spleen cells prior to the cell fusion was studied in model experiments, using splenocytes from BALB/c mice immunized with human serum albumin (HSA). Spleen cells were fractionated by centrifugation over series of Percoll solutions of increasing specific gravity. The results are shown in Table 1.

In these experiments, each pellet cell fraction was subjected to centrifugation on a Percoll solution with a higher specific gravity. The overall recovery of cells was about 80%, with a more or less equal distribution over the five fractions, A–E. Viability of the cells was good throughout, except for fraction A. The cells of the different fractions also differed in size (see Fig. 1).

Effect of Density Gradient Separation on Fusion Frequency and Cell Growth

Next, cells of the different fractions were tested for their fusion frequency. A constant number (35×10^6) of cells from each fraction were fused with SP2/0 cells, and plated at 0.75×10^5 cells/culture well. Twelve days after fusion, the wells were microscopically scored for cell growth. As shown in Fig. 2, the recovery of growing hybridomas was highest when cells of fractions B, C, and D were fused. In our experience, overgrowth of hybridomas by cells with the morphology of macrophages,

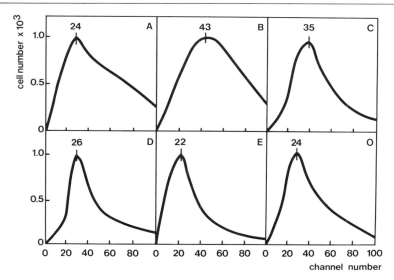

FIG. 1. Size distribution of Percoll density-separated mouse splenocytes. (A) <1.060 g/cm³; (B) 1.060–1.065 g/cm³; (C) 1.065–1.070 g/cm³; (D) 1.070–1.075 g/cm³; (E) >1.075 g/cm³; (O) unseparated. The size distributions were measured with a Coulter Channelyzer. Pulses were stored until 1000 pulses had been collected in the top channel.

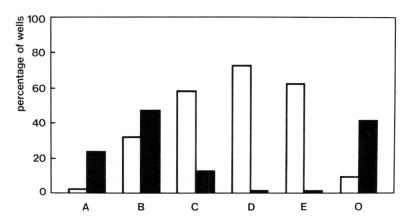

FIG. 2. Overgrowth by macrophages, fibroblasts, and/or P cells after fusion with fractionated cells. (A) <1.060 g/cm³; (B) 1.060–1.065 g/cm³; (C) 1.065–1.070 g/cm³; (D) 1.070–1.075 g/cm³; (E) >1.075 g/cm³; (O) unseparated. (□) Wells containing mainly hybrid cells; (■) wells containing mainly other cells.

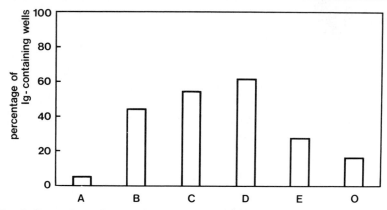

FIG. 3. Comparison of Ig-producing hybrid cells in different Percoll-separated fractions, tested in an ELISA. (A) <1.060 g/cm³; (B) 1.060–1.065 g/cm³; (C) 1.065–1.070 g/cm³; (D) 1.070–1.075 g/cm³; (E) >1.075 g/cm³; (O) unseparated.

fibroblasts, and so-called persistent cells (P cells)[14] frequently occurs. As shown in Fig. 2, fusion with unfractionated spleen cells or with the low-density (A) fraction cells yielded a high proportion of culture wells with growth of the "undesirable" cell types, but such overgrowth was very low with cells from fraction C, and absent with cells from fractions D and E.

Effect of Density Gradient Separation on the Proportion of Ig-Producing Hybridomas

It was found that density gradient separation of spleen cells also influences the recovery of Ig-producing hybrid cells after fusion. As shown in Fig. 3, the proportion of Ig-producing culture wells is highest in fusions of spleen cells from fractions B, C, and D, indicating an enrichment over the nonfractionated spleen cells.

On the basis of these results, we developed a standard method in which spleen cells are separated in a single centrifugation step on a Percoll solution of 1.065 g/cm³. This procedure has proved successful in over 100 cell fusions. However, there are differences in cell distribution in different experiments with spleens from mice injected with different antigens. As seen in Table II, the percentage of cells with a specific gravity smaller than 1.065 g/cm³ (i.e., the interphase cells to be discarded) ranged from less than 10 to about 40% of the total cell number. However, cell yields are generally sufficient to perform fusions.

[14] J. W. Schrader and G. J. V. Nossal, *Immunol. Rev.* **53**, 61 (1980).

TABLE II
FRACTIONATION OF SPLEEN CELLS OF MICE INJECTED WITH DIFFERENT ANTIGENS

Immunogen	Percentage of cells < 1.065 g/cm³	Immunogen	Percentage of < 1.065 g/cm³
Nonimmunized ($n = 7$)	13.5 ± 7.6	Human IgG₄	22.0
	(mean ± SD)	Human IgE	11.0
Human serum albumin	35.0	*Lolium perenne* L.	13.5
Human interferon	38.5	*Dermatophagoides pteronyssinus*	18.0
Human coagulation factor VIII	44.0	Human myeloblasts	6.0
		Human monocytes	9.5
Human neutrophil cytochrome *b*	26.0	Human B-cell-line cells	17.0
		Human cALL cells	30.0
Human λ chain	26.0	Total immunized	21.4 ± 12.4
Human IgG₃	24.0		(mean ± SD)

Comparison of Hybridoma Growth-Promoting Factors

We have reported that hybridoma cells can be cultured at the single-cell level in the absence of feeder cells, provided a growth-promoting activity, such as human endothelial cell supernatant (HECS), is present.[9] Since then, other growth promoters have been described, such as human umbilical cord serum (HUCS)[10] and hybridoma growth factor (HGF).[11]

We compared the effect of HECS, HUCS, HGF, and normal human serum (NHS) in supporting hybridoma growth. First, we tested the effect of growth factors in supporting hybridoma growth under limiting dilution conditions. At the optimal concentrations (1% for HGF and 10% for HECS, HUCS, and NHS), all these additives supported cell growth under limiting dilution conditions (data not shown).

Next, the effect of growth factors was tested under fusion conditions. Spleen cells of a mouse immunized with human thymocytes were separated on a Percoll solution of 1.065 g/cm³ (see above) and fused with myeloma cells. The mixture was divided into five equal parts and then plated in culture medium containing the optimal concentration of the growth factors. The percentage of wells with hybridoma cell growth and the percentage of cultures secreting immunoglobulins were examined on days 12, 15, and 20 after fusion. Figure 4 shows that the presence of growth factors is essential for the growth of hybridoma cells and the secretion of immunoglobulins. Furthermore, the data indicate that HUCS and NHS have only marginal growth-promoting activity that becomes manifest after 15 days of culture. The strongest effects were seen with HGF and HECS. Although HECS appears to be more potent than HGF

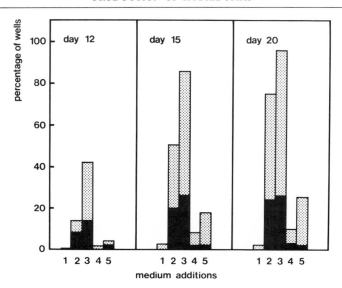

FIG. 4. Effect of growth-promoting factors on hybridoma growth and Ig production after fusion. Mice were immunized with human thymocytes, and spleen cells were collected and separated on Percoll of 1.065 g/cm³ density. After fusion under standard conditions, the percentage of wells with cell growth (stippled) and the percentage of wells with Ig production (solid) were scored, in the presence of different growth factors. (1) No growth-promoting factor (10% FCS only); (2) 1% HGF; (3) 10% HECS; (4) 10% HUCS; and (5) 10% NHS.

when analyzed after 12 days of culture, only small differences are observed after prolonged culture.

In conclusion, under fusion conditions, HUCS and NHS proved to be very poor growth promoters, whereas a satisfactory outgrowth of hybridoma cells occurred in the presence of HECS and HGF. Under limiting dilution conditions, the growth of already established hybridoma cells could be maintained in the presence of HECS, HGF, HUCS, and NHS, indicating that these cells have less stringent growth-factor requirements. When the effects of HECS and HGF are compared, it should be kept in mind that HGF is prepared serum free, whereas HECS contains 30% human serum by volume. It may well be that the addition of NHS to cultures containing HGF may have an additive growth-promoting effect.

Acknowledgment

We thank J. Wichers for his contribution on the work with the growth factors and R. van Lier for the helpful suggestions.

[15] High Efficiency Fusion Procedure for Producing Monoclonal Antibodies against Weak Immunogens

By RICHARD D. LANE, ROBERT S. CRISSMAN, and STEPHEN GINN

Successful production of monoclonal antibodies of a particular specificity is largely dependent upon the production of sufficient numbers of stimulated lymphoblasts in the donor spleen for use in the lymphocyte myeloma cell fusion procedure. Factors such as the antigen's size, relative concentration, and presence of foreign determinants affect the degree to which lymphoblast production is stimulated. Unfortunately, many of the moieties against which researchers wish to produce monoclonal antibodies are weak immunogens that fail to stimulate production of enough lymphoblasts for a successful fusion. With commonly used polyethylene glycol (PEG) fusion procedures,[1,2] it is generally necessary to repeatedly immunize the mice with the antigen until they have developed serum dilution titers near 1×10^5 as measured by an enzyme-linked immunosorbent assay (ELISA) before successfully producing the desired monoclonal antibody-secreting hybrids. Several procedures have been developed to increase the number of specific immunoblasts produced by weak immunogens with normal immunization procedures. These include the following: transferring spleen cells from immunized animals to X-irradiated mice followed by further *in vivo* antigen boosting[3]; culturing of spleen cells from immunized mice with the antigen for several days before fusion[3]; or use of a multiple high-dose immunization procedure.[4]

Another approach to successfully producing monoclonal antibodies against weak immunogens is to use a more efficient fusion procedure. One very efficient procedure utilizes electrical fields to produce antibody-secreting hybridomas from purified lymphoblasts and myeloma cells.[5] However, the equipment needed for this method is currently quite expensive. Another approach is to improve the fusion efficiency of the PEG procedure. It is apparent that current PEG techniques are extremely inefficient since highly immunized donor spleens contain many thousands of stimulated B lymphoblasts and less than 1% of these fuse with myeloma cells to become antibody-secreting hybridomas.

[1] S. Fazekas de St. Groth and D. Scheidegger, *J. Immunol. Methods* **35**, 1 (1980).
[2] R. D. Lane, R. S. Crissman, and M. F. Lachman, *J. Immunol. Methods* **72**, 71 (1984).
[3] R. P. Siraganian, P. C. Fox, and E. H. Berenstein, this series, Vol. 92, p. 17.
[4] C. Stähli, T. Staehelin, and V. Miggiano, this series, Vol. 92, p. 26.
[5] R. Bischoff, R. M. Eisert, I. Schedel, J. Vienken, and U. Zimmerman, *FEBS Lett.* **147**, 64 (1982).

This laboratory has worked to improve the fusion efficiency of the PEG fusion procedure in order to produce a greater yield of hybridomas producing monoclonal antibodies against weak immunogens. We have evaluated the effects of a number of different factors on the fusion efficiency, including the type of PEG used in the fusion solution, the pH and PEG concentration of the fusion solution, the myeloma cell line used as the fusion partner, and finally the exposure period of the myeloma–lymphocyte mixture to the fusion solution. In these studies, we used splenic lymphocytes from mice briefly immunized against a strong immunogen, sheep red blood cells (SRBC), to simulate the immune response to a weak antigen. Finally, we tested the optimal procedure for its ability to produce monoclonal antibodies against a weak immunogen, a murine tumor protein. The net result of these studies is the shorter PEG fusion procedure described below. We have successfully used this procedure to produce monoclonal antibodies from donor animals that had serum dilution titers 100–1000 times lower than previously required.

Materials

Media

Standard medium: RPMI 1640 (GIBCO 430-1800) with 10 mM HEPES, 15% (v/v) fetal bovine serum (HyClone Laboratory), and penicillin–streptomycin antibiotics (GIBCO 600-5140).

Selection medium for Sp2/0 fusions consisted of the standard medium plus 1.6×10^{-5} M thymidine (Sigma T9250), 4×10^{-7} M methotrexate (Lederle), and 1×10^{-4} M hypoxanthine (Sigma H9371).

Selection medium for FOX-NY fusions consisted of the standard medium plus 1.6×10^{-5} M thymidine, 4×10^{-7} M methotrexate, and 7.5×10^{-5} M adenine (Sigma A8751). All media were sterile filtered through a Nalgene 0.2-μm filter unit.

Cells

Spleen cells: Adult BALB/c mice of either sex received immunizing vaccinations until a serum dilution titer of approximately 1×10^3 was achieved as measured by an ELISA assay. Three days after the final peritoneal boost the mice were killed and their spleens aseptically removed. The spleen cells were isolated by first injecting the spleen at multiple sites with serum-free medium and then by teasing the spleen apart and dispersing the pieces by pipetting them through the syringe with the needle removed. The suspended cells were collected, centrifuged at 300 g for 5 min, and resuspended in 5 ml of cold 0.17 M ammonium chloride with 0.12% Na_2HCO_3 and 0.0037% EDTA for 10 min on ice to lyse SRBC. The lymphocytes were then diluted in 10 ml of serum-free medium, washed, and counted.

Peritoneal macrophages: Three or four adult BALB/c mice were killed, the abdominal skin was soaked with 70% alcohol and then removed, and 10 ml of cold serum-free medium was vigorously injected peritoneally. The lavage medium was immediately removed, pooled, and centrifuged for 5 min at 300 g; the cells in the pellet were counted and stored on ice until needed.

Myeloma cells: The BALB/c myeloma cell line Sp2/0 was obtained from the NIHMS Human Genetic Mutant Cell Repository (Camden, NJ). The FOX-NY myeloma cell line was obtained from the HyClone Laboratories (Logan, UT). Cultures were grown in 10 ml of the standard medium in 25-cm² standing flasks in a 8% CO_2, 95% humidity, and 37° incubator. Cells pooled from 10 flasks provided the number needed for the fusion.

Fusion Solution. The solution contained 5 ml of either Merck 4000 or Kodak 1450 PEG, 0.5 ml dimethyl sulfoxide, and 4.5 ml of phosphate-buffered saline. After warming and dissolving this mixture the pH was adjusted to 7.0 by the addition of 1 N NaOH or 1 N HCl, and the solution was sterilized by filtering through 0.22-μm filter unit.

Equipment

Microwell 96-well plates, Nunclon Delta (Nunc, Denmark)
Phase-contrast microscope, inverted (Olympus Microscope Co., Japan)
Sterile self-refilling syringe (Wheaton Instruments) fitted with a manifold for filling one row (eight wells) of a microwell plate (Drummond Scientific Instruments)
Small animal dissecting board
Sterile surgical instruments: scissors, toothed forceps
Sterile syringes (10 ml) and needles (21 gauge)
Sterile disposable centrifuge tubes (50 ml)
Sterile pipets (1, 10 ml)
Sterile filter unit, type LS, 0.2 μm (Nalgene)
Sterile filter unit, 0.22 μm Millex-GV (Millipore)
70% alcohol
Waterbath at 37°
Sterile hood
Incubator set at 37°, 8% CO_2, and 95% humidity
Hemacytometer

Procedure

Approximately 6×10^7 myeloma cells are combined with 1×10^8 spleen cells in a 50-ml centrifuge tube, which is then topped off with serum-free medium. After centrifugation at 300 g for 4 min, the medium is poured off by inverting the tube for approximately 5 sec. Then the tube is gently tapped until the cell pellet becomes resuspended in the remaining small amount of medium. Prior to fusion, the cells are warmed in a 37° water bath for 1 min. While still in a beaker of 37° water, the cells are transferred to a sterile hood where 1.0 ml of fusion solution (also maintained at 37°) is added to the cell suspension over a 45-sec period while gently shaking the tube. Beginning immediately at the end of that period, the fusion process is halted by slowly adding 50 ml of serum-free medium (3 ml over the first 30 sec, 9 ml over the next 30 sec, and the remainder over the last 30 sec). The cell suspension is then allowed to stand for 8 min at ambient temperature followed by 2 min in the 37° water bath. After a gentle centrifugation at 200 g for 4 min, the cells are resuspended in a bottle containing 120 ml of selection medium, to which 6×10^6 peritoneal macrophages are then added. The sinker of the refilling syringe is then placed in the bottle and the cells are gently pumped through the manifold to place 0.15 ml of cell suspension in each well of the microwell plates. The bottle is occasionally stirred to keep the cells suspended during this process. After 5 or 6 days of undisturbed culture in the incubator, numerous colonies should be visible through an inverted phase-contrast microscope. Another 0.15 ml of warm selection medium should be added per well at this time and the plates returned to the incubator for 5 more days. Between days 10 and 14, conditioned medium (50 μl) from each well is screened by the appropriate assay (usually an ELISA) for the presence of the desired antibody. It is generally a good idea to clone[6] or freeze[6] the cultures from positive wells within a few days of the initial assay to prevent the possible overgrowth of positive cultures by non-antibody-secreting colonies.

Comments

As anyone familiar with hybridoma techniques will realize, the fusion technique just described is based upon the common procedures described in the literature.[1,2,6,7] However, there are certain aspects of this procedure which are of critical importance if the procedure is to yield hybridomas in numbers far in excess of those of the common procedures.

[6] G. Galfré and C. Milstein, this series, Vol. 73, p. 3.
[7] V. T. Oi and L. A. Herzenberg, in "Selected Methods in Cellular Immunology" (B. B. Mishell and S. M. Shirgi, eds.), p. 351. Freeman, San Francisco, California, 1980.

TABLE I
COMPARISON OF PEGs[a,b]

Preparation	Hybrid[c]	Wells containing anti-SRBC-producing hybrids[d]
Aldrich 1000	43	3
Aldrich 3400	76	6
Aldrich 8000	128	4
Baker 1000	4	0
Baker 3350	81	6
Kodak 1450	127	9
Kodak 6000	94	4
Merck 4000	65	6

[a] From Lane et al.[2]

[b] After two immunizations 1 week apart with 0.25 ml of sheep red blood cells (SRBC), spleen cells (1.25×10^7) from the stimulated donor spleen, and cultured Sp2/0 myeloma cells (1.25×10^7) were fused with 0.3 ml of PEG fusing solution (adjusted to pH 7.0) over 1 min at 37°. After a further 90-sec incubation period with stirring, 15 ml of Hanks' buffered salt solution (HBSS) was slowly added to the cells over 90 sec and the suspension then stood undisturbed for 10 min. The cells were then pelleted at 200 g for 5 min, resuspended in hypoxanthine–aminopterin–thymidine (HAT) medium with peritoneal cells, and distributed into a 96-well plate.

[c] Total hybrids per plate were counted on day 6 after fusion.

[d] The presence of anti-SRBC-producing hybrids was determined by an ELISA assay on day 10 after fusion.

The culture medium which is used to initially culture the freshly fused cells must have been made within 2 weeks of the date of fusion. We have noted a greater than 90% loss of hybridoma colonies when using older medium. However, for maintenance of established cell lines, these older media work as well as the freshly prepared ones.

The composition of the fusion solution plays a major role in the efficiency of the fusion procedure. Initially, we compared eight different PEGs using a long (2.5 min) fusion procedure and found that Kodak 1450 produced the largest number of antibody-producing hybrids when using the highly immunogenic entity of sheep red blood cells (SRBC) as the test antigen (Table I). This PEG is also available from the Human Genetic

TABLE II

COMPARISON OF FUSION CONDITIONS[a]

Preparation	Fusion conditions	Hybrids[b]
Kodak 1450	90-sec incubation	125
Kodak 1450	90-sec centrifugation	107
Kodak 1450	4-min incubation + 3-min centrifugation	63
Kodak 1450	3-min incubation + 6-min centrifugation	10

[a] Spleen cells (1.25×10^7) and 1.25×10^7 Sp2/0 myeloma cells were fused with preparations of Kodak 1450. After adding the fusion solution over a 1-min period at 37°, the above combinations of fusion conditions (at 37° with gentle agitation), with or without additional 300 g centrifugation periods, were compared for their influence upon the fusion efficiency. The fusion process was halted by slowly adding 14 ml of HBSS over a 90-sec period. Each cell suspension was then allowed to stand for 10 min before being placed in HAT medium and distributed into a 96-well microwell plate with peritoneal cells.

[b] The number of hybrids produced per plate was counted on day 6 after fusion.

Mutant Cell Repository in lots which have been screened for cytotoxicity. Adjusting the pH of the fusion solution to 7.0 also improved the fusion efficiency.[2] Sterile filtration of the fusion solution avoids the possible production of toxic aldehyde groups generated during autoclaving.[8,9]

Early in our studies, we had noted that prolonged exposures and centrifugation of the lymphocyte and Sp2/0 myeloma cells in the fusion solution did not increase the fusion efficiency (Table II) but rather decreased the fusion efficiency. One explanation for this is that the cells fuse very quickly upon exposure to the fusogen and longer exposure periods only serve to increase the cytotoxic effects of the fusogen upon the newly formed hybridomas. This possibility is supported by our finding that a total exposure period to the fusion solution of 60 sec or less achieved dramatic improvements in fusion efficiency (Fig. 1A) compared to a common (2.5-min exposure) fusion period. At short fusion periods (60 sec or less adding period with no incubation period), we also noted a significant difference in the number of hybridomas produced by the two different

[8] J. L. Kadish and K. M. Wenc, *Hybridoma* **2**, 87 (1983).
[9] R. J. Klebe and M. G. Mancuso, *Somatic Cell Genet.* **7**, 473 (1981).

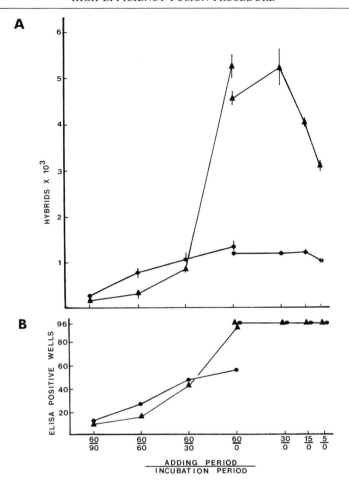

FIG. 1. Effect of the fusion period upon the fusion efficiency. The data represent two separate experiments in which splenic lymphocytes (1×10^8) from one SRBC immunized mouse were collected, divided equally, and mixed with 3×10^7 Sp2/0 or FOX-NY cells. These two mixtures were each divided evenly between four conical Falcon 2025 tubes and centrifuged, the medium was poured off, and 0.3 ml of fusion solution was placed in each tube over a particular adding period (measured in seconds) with or without an additional incubation period (in seconds). The fusion process was stopped by diluting the mixture in 15 ml of RPMI. Each mixture was then supplemented with peritoneal macrophages and distributed in one microwell plate containing the appropriate selection medium. In (A) the number of Sp2/0 (●) or FOX-NY (▲) hybrid colonies for each fusion period was estimated by a sample counting of colonies in 6 wells/plate (bars represent the standard error) on day 6 after fusion. In (B) the number of wells per plate that contain anti-SRBC Ig-producing hybrids was determined by collecting 50 μl of medium from each well on day 10 after fusion and assaying with an anti-SRBC ELISA. (From Lane.[10])

myeloma cell lines. Preparations of FOX-NY cells and stimulated lymphoblasts from the same donor spleen produced more than 30 times as many hybrids using a 1-min fusogen exposure than they did when exposed for 2.5 min. The Sp2/0 cells fused with lymphoblasts from the same donor spleen as above were only five times more efficient at the shorter fusion period. ELISA analysis of the number of wells per plate which contained anti-SRBC-secreting hybrids showed a corresponding increase in positive wells as the fusion efficiency of the procedure increased (Fig. 1B).[10] At the shorter fusion periods (60 sec or less adding period, no incubation period) all 96 wells of the plates for both myeloma cell lines tested positive, which based on Poisson statistics indicates that many of the wells should contain four or more antibody-secreting hybrids.

Next, we evaluated which PEG concentration was most effective when used in a short fusion period. Figure 2 indicates that a 50% (v/v) PEG concentration of Kodak 1450 is optimal for the FOX-NY cells. PEG concentrations between 40 and 70% work equally as well with the Sp2/0 cells.

Finally, the fusion efficiency of the eight different PEGs were retested using the short (45 sec) fusion procedure. The FOX-NY myeloma cells were used as the fusion partners for spleen cells from a mouse given a single ip injection of SRBC 3 days prior to fusion. At the time of fusion this mouse had an ELISA serum dilution titer of 1×10^1. Under these conditions the Merck 4000 outperformed the Kodak 1450 both in the total number of hybrid colonies produced and more significantly in the number of wells containing antibody-secreting hybrids (Table III).

With this higher efficiency fusion procedure, we have produced approximately 40 stable antibody-producing hybrids from a fusion of FOX-NY cells with spleen cells from a single BALB/c mouse immunized against shed murine tumor cell proteins (ELISA serum dilution titer of 1×10^3). Previous fusions of similar spleen cells immunized against this weak immunogen using a common procedure[2] had been unsuccessful at producing monoclonal antibodies.

A further increase of severalfold in the number of stable antibody-producing hybridomas obtained may be achieved by using RBF/Dn mice as the source of immunized lymphoblasts fused with the FOX-NY cells. The RBF/Dn mice have a translocation of chromosomes 8 and 12 that links the immunoglobulin heavy chain gene to the adenine phosphoribosyltransferase gene which is needed for the hybrids to grow in aminopterin–adenine–thymidine (AAT) selection medium. This linkage increases the genetic stability of the hybridomas.[11]

---

[10] R. D. Lane, J. Immunol. Methods 81, 223 (1985).

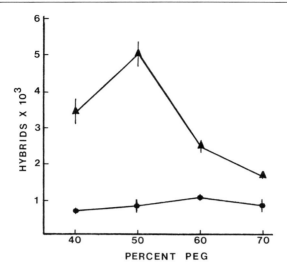

FIG. 2. Effect of PEG concentration on the fusion efficiency. Splenic lymphocytes (1×10^8) from one SRBC immunized mouse were collected and divided into aliquots with either Sp2/0 or FOX-NY cells as in Fig. 1. Four fusion solutions composed of 40–70% PEG (Kodak 1450), 0.5 ml dimethyl sulfoxide (DMSO), and phosphate-buffered saline (pH 7.0) making up the remainder were tested. The fusion procedure consisted of a 30-sec fusion solution adding period, followed by immediate dilution. Each test group was distributed into one microwell plate containing macrophages and selection medium. After 5 days of culture, the number of Sp2/0 (●) or FOX-NY (▲) hybrid colonies present per plate was estimated from a count of 6 sample wells/plate (bars represent the standard error). All the wells of the microplates from each test condition were found by ELISA to contain anti-SRBC Ig.

Based on our own success with this new fusion procedure, we believe other researchers trying to produce monoclonal antibodies against weak immunogens or specific epitopes may find it very useful. Furthermore, by combining this fusion procedure with one of the techniques for increasing the number of specific lymphoblasts available as fusion partners[3,4] it should be possible to increase the percentage of antigen-specific antibody-secreting hybridomas by 300- to 1500-fold over common procedures. This high efficiency fusion procedure also allows for fewer immunizations with stronger immunogens and thus reduces the time and expense of producing monoclonal antibodies.

[11] R. T. Taggart and I. M. Samloff, *Science* **219,** 1228 (1983).

TABLE III
REEVALUATION OF PEGs[a]

Preparation	Hybrid[b]	Wells containing anti-SRBC-producing hybrids[c]
Aldrich 1000	173	4
Aldrich 3400	39	1
Aldrich 8000	49	1
Baker 1000	10	0
Baker 3350	278	4
Kodak 1450	438	5
Kodak 6000	33	0
Merck 4000	537	13

[a] Three days after a single immunization with 0.15 ml of SRBC, spleen cells (1.0×10^7) from the stimulated donor spleen and cultured FOX-NY cells (1.0×10^7) were fused with 0.3 ml of a PEG fusing solution (pH 7.0) over a 45-sec interval, followed by a gradual dilution with 15 ml of HBSS over 90 sec. After a 10-min standing period, the cells were pelleted at 200 g for 5 min, resuspended in AAT medium with peritoneal cells, and distributed into a 96-well plate.

[b] Total hybrids per plate were counted on day 6 after fusion.

[c] The presence of anti-SRBC-producing hybrids was determined by an ELISA on day 14 after fusion.

Acknowledgments

This work was supported by the American Cancer Society, Ohio Division, The G. M. Jones and C. O. Miniger Memorial Foundations, and PHS Grant 1 R23 CA 33 903-01A1 awarded by the National Cancer Institute, DHHS.

The authors thank Joel Flora and Shelley Gupta for their excellent technical assistance, Dr. Ronald Mellgren for his valuable suggestions in preparing this chapter, and Joan Knighton for typing the manuscript.

[16] Methods for High Frequency Production of Soluble
Antigen-Specific Hybridomas; Specificities and Affinities of
the Monoclonal Antibodies Obtained

By Maurizio Cianfriglia, Massimo Mariani, Doretta Armellini,
Annalisa Massone, Margherita Lafata, Rivo Presentini, and
Guido Antoni

The production of hybrid cell lines secreting immunoglobulins of pre-determined specificity has been successfully applied in different fields of basic as well as clinical research. This methodology can be regarded as being in its infancy; thus a number of technological problems remain to be solved for a full exploitation of its potential. In the murine system, the major technical problem is the difficulty in obtaining a reasonable number of antibody-forming hybrids against antigens which either are available in small amounts and/or are weak immunogens or soluble. This problem could be overcome by increasing the efficiency of fusion or by developing methods which would significantly enrich the pool of normal antibody-forming cells or their precursors prior to fusion.

Table I contains a brief summary of the procedures used to enrich the population of antibody-forming cells where paucity, weak immunogenicity, and the soluble form of an antigen are factors negatively affecting the specific efficiency (SE, calculated as the total number of primary hybrid clones producing antibodies of predetermined specificity, divided by the total number of primary hybrid clones tested) of a fusion experiment. In this context, the large amount of literature which has been published after more than two decades of research in somatic cell genetics represents a useful source of cell culture techniques and methods.

As an example, Table I[1-6] reports an alternative hybrid selection system able to retain preferentially murine chromosome 12 (of the competent parental cell), which carries the gene coding for immunoglobulin heavy chains (Ig_H).[7] The strategy we adopted to increase the efficiency of a

[1] J. L. Sternick and A. M. Sturmer, *Hybridoma* **1**, 74 (1984).

[2] P. A. Kenny, A. C. McCaskill, and W. Boyle, *Aust. J. Biol. Med.* **59**, 427 (1981).

[3] N. Sakato and H. N. Eisen, *J. Exp. Med.* **141**, 1411 (1975).

[4] C. Stahli, T. Staehlin, V. Miggiano, J. Schmidt, and P. Hering, *J. Immunol. Methods* **32**, 279 (1980).

[5] M. M. S. Lo, T. Y. Tsong, M. K. Conrad, S. M. Strittmatter, L. O. Hester, and S. H. Snyder, *Nature (London)* **310**, 792 (1984).

[6] R. T. Taggert and I. A. Samloff, *Science* **219**, 1228 (1983).

[7] H. Hengartner, T. Meo, and E. Müller, *Proc. Natl. Acad. Sci. U.S.A.* **75**, 4494 (1978).

TABLE I

SUMMARY OF PROCEDURES ADOPTED TO INCREASE THE YIELD OF
ANTIGEN-SPECIFIC HYBRIDOMAS[a]

| Brief description of the procedure | Useful for | | | | Ref. |
	LAA	WIA	SA	PCR12	
Immunization using nanograms of antigen bound to nitrocellulose filter disks and intraperitoneally implanted in mice	+	−	+	−	1
Spleen cells of immunized mice injected into irradiated recipient. Restimulation of the recipient mice	−	+	+	−	2
Immunization with antigen conjugated to highly immunogenic carriers	−	±	±	−	3
Repeated daily immunizations prior to fusion in mice presensitized a long time beforehand	−	−	+	−	4
B-cell-antigen–avidin complex and myeloma cell–biotin complex electrically fused	+	−	+	−	5
Immunization of 5Bnr mice, which have a Robertsonian translocation involving both chromosome 12 and 8, where the APRT-selectable marker is located	±	±	±	+	6

[a] Abbreviations: LAA, low amount of antigen; WIA, weak immunogenicity of antigen; SA, soluble antigen; PCR12, preferential retention of chromosome 12, which carries the Ig_H gene; APRT, adenine phosphoribosyltransferase (EC 2.4.2.7).

fusion is based on the results of previous experiments demonstrating that if two distinct cell populations are fused, the fraction of proliferating cells forms viable hybrids with a higher frequency when compared to the remaining cells.[8] Thus the immunization protocol we adopted (see Table II) is aimed to enrich the splenic pool of rapidly proliferating antigen-specific B blast cells. Also, myeloma cells to be fused are harvested in the log phase of growth and the fusion procedure is carefully performed at 37°, using a fusion protocol which will minimally interfere with cell proliferation. In this manner the cellular fusion procedure represents, per se, a selective system for proliferating lymphocytes, most of which are antigen-specific cells.

[8] M. Cianfriglia, unpublished (1982).

TABLE II
IMMUNIZATION PROTOCOL[a]

| Immunization | Days from fusion | Amount of antigen dispensed (μg) and conditions[b] | |
		A (1300 μg total)	B (115 μg total)
1	−15	50, CFA, ip	50, CFA, ip
2	−8	50, CFA, ip	50, CFA, ip
3	−3	400, S, ip	5, S, ip
4	−2	200, S, ip + 200, S, iv	2.5, ip + 2.5, S, iv
5	−1	200, S, ip + 200, S, iv	2.5, ip + 2.5, S, iv

[a] Reproduced from Ref. 10 with permission of the publishers.
[b] CFA, Complete Freund's adjuvant; S, saline; ip, intraperitoneally; iv, intravenously.

The direct consequences of the selective fusion of large populations of proliferating antigen-specific B lymphocytes are the following: (1) the fusion frequency is one viable hybrid per 2×10^4 polyethylene glycol (PEG)-treated parental cells [this fusion frequency is about 10 times higher than those reported in the literature and is similar to the fusion frequency obtained using lipopolysaccharide (LPS)-stimulated spleen cells[9]]; and (2) the specific efficiency is high, varying between 0.52 and 0.78 for pure soluble antigens.

This previously undescribed high yield of specific hybridomas and the short (2 weeks) and simple immunization protocol we adopted demand a detailed description of the methods used as well as of the characteristics, such as the specificity and affinity, of monoclonal antibodies (MAbs) we have produced.

Antigens and Immunization Protocol

BALB/c mice (age 12 weeks) are immunized as indicated in Table II.[10] The following pure proteins have been used as soluble antigens: human prostatic acid phosphatase (hPAP, EC 3.1.3.2), 102,000 MW; human chorionic somatomammotropin (hCS), 22,000 MW; human growth hormone (hGH), 22,000 MW. The synthetic nonapeptide corresponding to fragment 166–174 of hCS and hGH (Cys-Phe-Arg-Lys-Asp-Met-Asp-Lys-

[9] J. Andersson and F. Melchers, *Curr. Top. Microbiol. Immunol.* **81**, 130 (1975).
[10] M. Cianfriglia, D. Armellini, A. Massone, and M. Mariani, *Hybridoma* **2**, 451 (1983).

Val-Gly), 1167 MW, and the hexapeptide corresponding to sequence 135–140 of hCS (Thr-Gly-Glu-Ile-Leu-Lys), 659 MW,[11] were used as synthetic soluble antigens. The synthetic peptides are injected in their free form, not conjugated to any carrier. Human cytokeratins (insoluble antigens) are extracted from human foot sole epidermis according to the method described by Franke et al.[12]

Cell Culture, Fusion Procedures, and Hybridoma Production

Maintenance of Cell Lines. The basic medium (BM) used for cell culture is RPMI 1640 supplemented with 10 mM HEPES, 2×10^{-5} M 2-mercaptoethanol, 2 mM L-glutamine, and 5% selected fetal calf serum (FCS). The FCS is inactivated at 60° for 90 min to eliminate possible contamination by mycoplasma. The capacity of these heat-inactivated sera to sustain cell growth is completely maintained.

Myeloma cell lines and hybrids derived from these are cultured at 37° in a humid incubator in the presence of 5% CO_2 in air, and using the standardized conditions for cells growing in suspension. Cell lines appear free of mycoplasma infection as revealed by the method described by Haas and Von Boehmer.[13] For an easier detection of mycoplasma infection, we culture all cell lines without the addition of antibiotics to the BM.

Parental Cells: Myeloma. The characteristics of the cell lines used in fusion experiments as incompetent parental cells are shown in Table III. The myeloma cell lines used are mycoplasma free. The cells are grown in BM containing 8-azaguanine to eliminate possible HAT-resistant revertants. They are harvested in the log phase of growth; when observed by phase microscopy, they appear to be of regular shape with clear outlines and more than 95% are viable cells.

Parental Cells: Spleen Cells. To prepare single-cell suspensions from the spleens of immunized mice we slightly modified the method described by Siranganian et al.[14] Our procedure is strictly performed at 37° using prewarmed BM serum-free medium (BMSF) to prepare and wash spleen cells. After the last washing, the cell pellet is resuspended in a plastic tube with 10 ml of prewarmed BM (10^7 cells/ml) and left in an incubator (for 2 hr) prior to cell fusion.

[11] P. Neri, G. Antoni, G. Barbarulli, M. Mariani, L. Nencioni, R. Presentini, and A. Tagliabue, *Mol. Immunol.* **21**, 151 (1984).
[12] W. W. Franke, K. Weber, M. Osborn, E. Schmid, and C. Freudenstein, *Exp. Cell Res.* **116**, 429 (1978).
[13] W. Haas and H. Von Boehmer, *J. Immunol. Methods* **52**, 137 (1982).
[14] R. P. Siranganian, P. C. Fox, and E. H. Berenstein, this series, Vol. 92, p. 17.

TABLE III
CHARACTERISTICS OF MYELOMA CELL LINES[a]

Name	Immunoglobulins secreted	No. of chromosomes	Origin
P3X63Ag8.653	None	65 (1 metacentric)	MOPC 12, BALB/c tumor
Sp2/01-Ag8	None	73 (1 metacentric)	Derived from a fusion of P3X63Ag8 with BALB/c spleen cells

[a] Common marker: deficient in hypoxanthine–guanine phosphorylribosyltransferase (HPRT; EC 2.4.2.8) gene activity, thus resistant to 20–40 μg/ml of 8-azaguanine and sensitive to HAT (hypoxanthine–aminopterin–thymidine).

In these culture conditions, the spleen cells continue to proliferate in the presence of growth factors released by the lymphoid cell population. Only 1×10^7 spleen cells are required for a fusion experiment; the remaining cells are frozen using the following method. The tube containing the spleen cell suspension is chilled and centrifuged, and the cell supernatant (CS) kept for thawing frozen spleen cells. The pellet is resuspended by adding dropwise a chilled solution consisting of nine parts of FCS and one part of dimethyl sulfoxide (DMSO). The cells are distributed in chilled vials (0.5 ml; 1×10^7 cells), allowed to stand overnight at $-80°$, and then stored in liquid nitrogen. For thawing, the vials containing frozen cells are incubated at 37° (bath), washed once with prewarmed BM, incubated for 1–2 hr in 1–2 ml of CS, and then processed for fusion.

Cell Fusion. Myeloma cells and splenocytes are washed two to three times with BMSF at 37° to remove debris from the cell membrane and maximize the fusion activity of PEG.[15] Mix 1×10^7 splenocytes with an equal number of myeloma cells in a tube with a wide-angle conical tip. Cells are spun down, the supernatant is poured off, and the tube is kept inverted until as much as possible of the remaining liquid is removed by suction with a Pasteur pipet (this is important, as the fusion efficiency is strongly dependent on the PEG concentration). Add 400 μl PEG solution (37°), consisting of 2 g PEG 1550 (SERVA) mixed with 2 ml of BMSF, to the drained pellet in a dropwise manner over 1 min, shaking carefully. After tapping the bottom of the tube for 1 min in order to obtain a homogeneous cell suspension, add 5 ml of prewarmed BMSF over a period of 5 min. Add 40 ml prewarmed BM to the cell suspension over a further 1- to

[15] G. Pontecorvo, *Somatic Cell Genet.* **4,** 397 (1975).

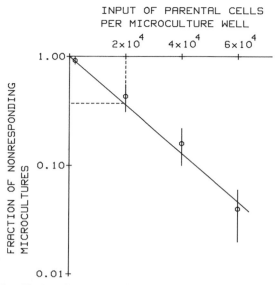

FIG. 1. Limiting dilution of parental cells to calculate the fusion frequency. The input of parental cells for each cell dilution was calculated as the average of the values found in 90 wells ± one standard deviation.

2-min period. The cells are then distributed in two 24-well Costar plates (Costar, 3524) fed with macrophages. Four hours later, 1 ml of 2× HAT (hypoxanthine $10^{-4} M$, aminopterin $5 \times 10^{-7} M$, thymidine $1.6 \times 10^{-5} M$) containing BM is added to each well to obtain the correct selective condition for hybrid cells.

Determination of Fusion Frequency. To calculate the lowest number of parental cells required to form hybrids, a microculture experiment in which only a fraction of microcultures (wells) respond with hybrid cell growth is performed. Since the precursor parental cells forming hybrids are independently distributed throughout the wells, the number of hybrids per well follow a Poisson distribution. If N is the average number of precursor cells per well, the frequency F_0 of wells without growth is given by $F_0 = e^{-N}$. When $N = 1$, we obtain $F_0 = e^{-1} = 0.37$, which represents the frequency of nongrowing cultures when a single clone is growing in each well. If we plot F_0 (on a logarithmic scale) as a function of the cell input, the experimental points are expected to fit a straight line. Results of a typical experiment to determine the number of parental cells per microculture well required to obtain one hybridoma per well are shown in Fig. 1. Parental cells are seeded soon after the fusion in 96-well flat-bottomed microtiter plates (Costar 3596) fed with macrophages (2×10^4/well) in BM + HAT medium (100 μl BM containing cell suspension plus 100 μl BM + 2× HAT) at the densities indicated in the figure. The cell concentration (lymphocytes plus PEG-treated myeloma cells) is determined by serial dilution and without taking into account cell losses due to the fusion procedures. Interpolating at the level of $F_0 = 0.37$, which corresponds to one hybridoma/well, we found a cell input value of 2×10^4. Thus 2×10^4 parental cells contain, on average, one "precursor" hybrid cell.

The fusion frequencies obtained reveal that the "culture unit" (in our case the well of the 24-well Costar plates) contain an average of about 10 different hybrid clones derived from distinct fusion events. This value is calculated by dividing the total number of parental cells by the fusion frequency and by the total number of wells in which the fused cells are distributed, e.g., $10^7/[(2 \times 10^4) \cdot 48] = 10.4$. Thus the "culture unit" may give rise to several distinct hybridoma clones with different specificities and affinities (see Table V).

Determination of Specific Efficiency in Fusion Experiments in Which Growth of the Hybrid Cell Population and Production of Specific MAbs Are Present in Every Well

Two different classes of cell hybrids are generated from a fusion: one producing immunoglobulin of predetermined specificities (positive), the other not secreting antibodies (negative). Their ratio (positive versus negative secretors) gives a value which we define as specific efficiency (SE). This value should not be affected by those cell culture conditions amplifying one of the two classes when screening is carried out. We considered the SE of a fusion reliable when the following conditions were fulfilled: (1) The two different classes of clones to be tested derive randomly from several distinct hybrid cell populations; (2) the screening is performed on a high number (statistically significant) of several distinct series of independent clones; and (3) the experimental procedures used to derive primary hybrid clones from hybrid cell populations are close enough to the time of the fusion to prevent one class of hybrids or possible negative variants to overtake the other class during the time of cocultivation[16] (nonproducing variants generally arise as an effect of segregation of chromosomes 6 and/or 12 of the competent parental cell; these variants have a shorter generation time).

To compare the specific efficiency calculated following the criteria

---

[16] A. Piazza, in "Immunological Methods" (I. Lefkovitz and B. Pernis, eds.), p. 419. Academic Press, New York, 1979.

described above with those obtained according to Poisson statistics, the products of two distinct cell fusions (see Table IV) are seeded in 1920 wells of 20 flat-bottomed Costar (3596) plates, using the standard conditions for hybrid cell selection. In these experiments the wells with growing hybrid cells are about 60% of the total wells (one hybrid cell/well is the proportion according to Poisson statistics). The fraction of positive wells (reported in Table IV as SE) are in good agreement with those calculated with the standard procedures described above.

To calculate the SE in a fusion experiment we proceed in the following manner: 5–10 hybrid cell populations (each contained in one culture unit), positive in solid-phase radioimmunoassay,[10] are cloned (0.3 cell/well) in 96-well flat-bottomed microtiter plates in HT medium. Five to ten series of independent clones (100–200 clones in all) are tested for the production of monoclonal antibodies of predefined specificity. The number of positive clones is divided by the total number of clones tested. The values obtained are those reported in Table IV. Usually, 10 days after the fusion the supernatants of hybrid cell populations are tested and the cells cloned; 24–30 days after the fusion the primary hybrid clones are tested.

The hybridoma clones give a stable production of specific immunoglobulins (mass culture or tumor ascites). A loss of antibodies production was found in 10–12 clones out of 135–140 grown continuously for 3–6 months. In fusion experiments in which the immunizing antigen was an intact protein, the immunoglobulin class produced by hybridomas was chiefly IgG, in spite of the short immunization protocol. IgM did not constitute more than 5–7% of the total.

Specificities and Affinities of Monoclonal Antibodies

Solid-Phase Double-Antibody Screening

The specificity and affinity of MAbs are first checked by a solid-phase double-antibody screening of cell culture supernatants.[17] The screening is performed in a poly(vinyl chloride) 96-well microplate coated with goat IgG that is anti-mouse immunoglobulin. In order to coat the IgGs to the plastic, an IgG solution, 100 μg/ml in 0.005 M glycine buffer, pH 9.2 (250 μg/well), is left in the plate at 4° overnight and the plate is then washed 10 times with PBS (pH 8.0) containing 0.125 ml Tween 20 (PBS–Tween) per liter. The dried plates may be stored at −20° for a few months before being used. The screening of each clone is then carried out in duplicate by

---

[17] M. Mariani, P. Neri, M. Cianfriglia, D. Armellini, G. Barbarulli, and G. Antoni, *J. Immunol. Methods* **71**, 43 (1984).

TABLE IV

SPECIFIC EFFICIENCY OBTAINED IN FUSION EXPERIMENTS[a]

Fusion	Antigen used	Type of immunization	Myeloma[b]	Wells with growth[c]	Positive wells[c]	Fusion frequency[d]	Specific efficiency[e]
DAM 2	hCS	A	S	48	48	2×10^4	0.66
DAM 3	hCS	A	P	48	48	2×10^4	0.59
DAM 10	hPAP	A	S, S	48	48	2×10^4	0.70; 0.61
DAM 11	hPAP	A	P, S	48	48	2×10^4	0.68 (0.70)
DAM 14	IF	A	S	48	48	2×10^4	0.55
DAM 15	IF	A	P	48	48	2×10^4	0.62
DAM 20	hGH	A	S, S, S	48	48	2×10^4	0.52; 0.57 (0.61)
DAM 21	hGH	B	S, S	48	48	2×10^4	0.78; 0.74
2N	166–174[f]	A	S	46	12	7×10^4	0.09
2E	135–140[f]	A	S	46	5	7×10^4	0.03

[a] Adapted from Ref. 10 with permission of the publishers.

[b] S, Sp2/0l-Ag8; P, P3X63Ag8.653.

[c] Out of a total of 48 wells.

[d] Lowest number of parental cells forming heterokaryons required for hybrid growth to be observed.

[e] Specific efficiency (SE) determined as positive primary hybrid clones divided by primary hybrid clones tested. Second values given are from a fusion experiment performed using frozen spleen cells from immunized mice. In parentheses are SE values calculated when the product of the fusion was distributed in 1920 wells (20 × 96-well flat-bottomed Costar plates). In the 2N and 2E fusion experiments the SE was calculated according to Poisson statistics, as follows. At an average number of three hybridomas per cell the proportion of wells with growth is 95% (46 wells with growth out of 48). Thus the percentage of positive hybrid cell populations is divided by the average number of hybrid cell per well.

[f] Synthetic peptides corresponding to the sequences 166–174 and 135–140 of hCS.

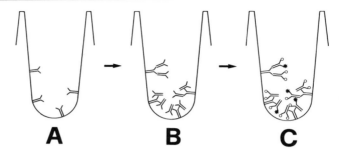

FIG. 2. Scheme of the screening method. (A) Insolubilization of goat anti-mouse immunoglobulin IgG on the plastic well; (B) binding of MAb to the anti-mouse-immunoglobulin IgG; (C) competitive binding of labeled and unlabeled antigen with MAb. (Reproduced from Ref. 17 with permission of the publishers.)

distributing the supernatant (200 μl) in six wells; in addition to two assay wells, two further wells are needed for each possible cross-reacting antigen to be tested, and PBS is added to two other wells for the measurement of nonspecific binding. Plates are incubated overnight at 4° and then washed 10 times with PBS–Tween.

The following additions (100 μl) are made to the different wells: PBS (pH 8.0) containing 10% fetal calf serum (PBS–FCS), for the measurement of the maximum binding; immunization antigen at two different concentrations (for example, 10 and 500 ng/ml) in two separate wells; and a more concentrated solution (for example, 5000 ng/ml) of each possible cross-reacting antigen. To the control wells 100 μl of PBS–FCS is added, and finally, 100 μl of ^{125}I-labeled antigen (about 50,000–100,000 cpm) is added to all other wells.

The microplate is incubated for 3 hr at 37° and then washed 10 times with PBS–Tween. Wells are cut out and counted in a gamma counter. The radioactivity counted in the wells is expressed as the ratio between counts per minute of the sample containing cold antigen and counts per minute of the maximum binding wells (B/B_0). The ratio of bound cpm/total cpm may also be used as a measurement of the degree of binding, which is dependent, however, on the concentration of MAbs in the supernatant and may be related to the culture conditions. Figure 2 shows schematically the screening method.

Purification of Monoclonal Antibodies

In the case of MAbs belonging to the IgG class, purification is carried out by affinity chromatography on protein A-Sepharose 4B[18] (Pharmacia

[18] P. L. Ey, S. J. Prowse, and C. R. Kenkin, *Immunochemistry* **15**, 429 (1978).

Fine Chemicals, Sweden); for MAbs of the IgM class, purification is performed by affinity chromatography on a column of Sepharose linked to the antigen.

The immunoglobulins are precipitated from the ascitic fluid with a 50% saturated solution of $(NH_4)_2SO_4$. The precipitate is dissolved in distilled water and dialyzed against running water for 3 hr and then against PBS (pH 8.0) overnight at 4°. The solution is then applied to the column and after removal of the unadsorbed material by elution with PBS (pH 8.0), the antibodies are eluted at acid pH. The pH used for the elution depends on the class or subclass of the antibodies. Phosphate buffer, 0.1 M (pH 5.0), gives a good recovery for IgG_1; lower pHs are needed for the other IgG subclasses. In the case of IgM adsorbed on antigen–Sepharose, 0.1 M glycine–HCl buffer (pH 3.0) may be used. In any case, it is worth collecting the eluates in tubes containing a small amount of solid tris(hydroxymethyl)aminomethane, to reduce to a minimum exposure of the antibody to strongly acidic conditions. Chaotropic agents such as KSCN may also be used as eluants. The eluate is then dialyzed against PBS (pH 8.0), and after spectrophotometric determination of the protein content ($E_{1\,cm,\,280\,nm}^{1\%}$ = 14.0 for IgG; $E_{1\,cm,\,280\,nm}^{1\%}$ = 13.3 for IgM), it is distributed in vials and lyophilized.

Epitope Specificity

To test the epitope specificity of the MAbs produced, the "sandwich assay" and solid-phase antibody competition assay procedures described in the literature[19,20] are used with purified MAbs and antigens.

In the sandwich assay an unlabeled monoclonal antibody (MAb 1) is adsorbed on polyvinyl plates (50 μl/well) as described above, and the wells are then saturated with 250 μl of a 2.5% (w/v) solution of BSA in glycine buffer (pH 9.2). After 1 hr incubation at 37°, the plates are washed with PBS–Tween and dried. The plates are incubated with 25 μl/well of antigen solution in PBS–FCS. Antigen concentrations in the range of 50–5000 ng/ml are generally appropriate. After 3 hr at 37°, plates are washed again with PBS–Tween, and 50 μl of ^{125}I-labeled monoclonal antibody (MAb 2) (30,000 cpm/well) is added. Control wells are prepared for each MAb by adding PBS–FCS instead of antigen solution. After overnight incubation at 4°, the plates are washed and the wells cut out and counted in a gamma counter. Results are considered significant when bound radio-

[19] C. Stähli, V. Miggiano, J. Stocker, T. Staehelin, P. Häring, and B. Takacs, this series, Vol. 92, p. 242.
[20] M. Mariani, M. Cianfriglia, P. Neri, M. Lafata, and G. Antoni, *J. Immunol. Methods* **75**, 395 (1984).

activity is 2- to 3-fold above background values, which demonstrates that the two antibodies react with two different epitopes.

In the solid phase antibody competition binding assay, the wells of a microplate are coated with 50 μl/well of a 100 μg/ml antigen solution in PBS (pH 8.0), and then saturated with BSA as described above. Then 50 μl/well of increasing concentrations of a solution of MAb 1 in PBS–FCS is added. A wide range of concentrations of MAb 1 (i.e., 0.1–1000 μg/ml) may be required, as otherwise partial overlapping or steric proximity of epitopes may give erroneous results; a similar problem arises when the affinity constant of MAb 2 is much higher than that of MAb 1. A solution of normal mouse immunoglobulins is added to the control wells, instead of MAb 1. After overnight incubation, 10 μl of ^{125}I-labeled MAb 2 is added to each well (50,000–100,000 cpm) without removing MAb 1. Plates are left to incubate for 4–5 hr at 37°. Then, after several washings, wells are cut out and counted in a gamma counter. The radioactivity bound in the wells containing MAb 1 divided by the radioactivity bound in the control wells gives the B/B_0 ratio, allowing typical competition curves of the monoclonal antibodies tested to be drawn. The interaction of both MAbs with the same epitope is proved when competition is observed.

Radioimmunoassay

Radioimmunoassay of the MAbs produced is performed by absorbing or coupling a purified MAb to a plastic surface and allowing it to react with labeled antigen in competition with increasing concentrations of cold antigen. In general, MAbs are bound to the plastic by simple adsorption; however, when MAbs with very low affinity are tested, a covalent linkage of the MAbs to the plastic is required.

In the adsorption method, we coat poly(vinyl chloride) microplates with purified MAbs.[17] In practice, 250 μl/well of a 100 μg/ml solution of MAb in 0.05 M glycine buffer (pH 9.2) is incubated for 20 hr at 4°. Plates are then repeatedly washed with PBS–Tween and dried. Competition assays are carried out by the addition to 100 μl of ^{125}I-labeled antigen (50,000–100,000 cpm) of 100 μl of increasing concentrations of unlabeled immunization antigen, or of a suspected cross-reacting antigen in order to verify this possibility. The range of concentrations of cold competitor is very wide and varies from one MAb to another, according to its specificity and affinity constant. In any case, concentrations ranging from 10^{-1} to 10^5 ng/ml may be used in a first trial, and later a more appropriate range may be chosen. All reagents are diluted in PBS–FCS. After overnight incubation at 4° and repeated washings, bound radioactivity is counted in a gamma counter.

When a covalent linkage of the MAb to the plastic is required, we use macroporous polystyrene/1% divinylbenzene resin XA-225 (Rohm and Haas, PA). The resin is chloromethylated[21] to give a derivative containing 0.9 meq chlorine/g dry resin and a glycine residue is added by esterification with Boc glycine (Fluka) using the cesium salt method.[22] The Boc group is then removed by treatment of the resin with 50% trifluoroacetic acid in dichloromethane. The resin (30 mg) is then swollen in N,N-dimethylformamide and treated with 30 mg of adipic acid disuccinimidyl ester, prepared as described by Hill *et al.*[23] The resin is then shaken for 1 hr at room temperature, filtered, washed 3 times × 2 min with N,N-dimethylformamide, then 3 times × 2 min with isopropyl alcohol, and 3 times × 2 min with N,N-dimethylformamide. The moist resin is added to a solution of 3 mg of lyophilized MAb, prepared as described above, dissolved in 0.5 ml of distilled water. After standing overnight at room temperature the resin is filtered and washed several times with PBS (pH 8.0). The beads, suspended in 6 ml of PBS, are very finely ground to give a homogeneous suspension with a glass Dounce rod. The slurry, 100 μl, is incubated overnight in a rotating shaker with 100 μl of ^{125}I-labeled antigen (100,000–200,000 cpm), 100 μl of increasing concentrations of cold antigen and, to allow more effective shaking, 300 μl of PBS–FCS. After incubation, the tubes are centrifuged and decanted, and the resin is washed twice with 2 ml of PBS–Tween and counted in a gamma counter. The radioactivity measured in the presence of a large excess of cold antigen is assumed as nonspecific binding. If no displacement is obtained up to very high concentrations of cold antigen, the experiment must be repeated using a more diluted MAb–resin slurry.

Calculation of the Affinity Constants

The affinity constants of monoclonal antibodies are calculated from the radioimmunoassay data obtained as described above. The reaction of the antigen with the unsolubilized antibody may be described with the general equation representing the interaction of a ligand with a protein[24]:

$$N_{Ag}/N_{Ab} = nK[Ag]/(1 + K[Ag]) \qquad (1)$$

where N_{Ab} is the number of moles of antibody linked on the solid phase, N_{Ag} the number of moles of antigen bound to the antibody, n the number

[21] R. B. Merrifield, *Biochemistry* **3**, 1385 (1984).
[22] B. F. Gisin, *Helv. Chim. Acta* **56**, 1476 (1973).
[23] M. Hill, J.-J. Bechet, and A. D'Albis, *FEBS Lett.* **102**, 282 (1979).
[24] I. M. Klotz, *in* "The Proteins: Chemistry, Biological Activity and Methods" (H. Neurath and K. Bailey, eds.), p. 727. Academic Press, New York, 1953.

of independent binding sites, K the affinity constant, and [Ag] the concentration of antigen in solution.

The amount of antigen bound to the antibody may be calculated as $Q_b = Q_t B/T$, where Q_t is the total amount of antigen added, B the counts measured in the sample, and T the total counts. The amount of free antigen is given by $Q_t - Q_b = Q_t(1 - B/T)$, from which $[Ag] = (Q_t(1 - B/T)/(V + V_m)$, where V is the volume of the solution of cold antigen and V_m that of labeled antigen.

Substituting W for $1 - B/T$, H for $(V + V_m)/K$, and A for nN_{Ab}, Eq. (1) may be rewritten as

$$B/T = AW/(H + Q_t W) \tag{2}$$

We adopted a nonlinear regression method to calculate the binding parameters A and K using Eq. (2). The linearization of the data with a Scatchard's plot generally does not give satisfactory results, due to the wide dispersion of the experimental points of the plot. Among the various nonlinear regression methods available, we chose the median method, which gives good results without the need for a preliminary approximate evaluation of the parameters.[25,26]

This method consists of the calculation of the values of A and H from Eq. (2) by resolving the two necessary nonlinear simultaneous equations for all the possible pairs of points. These equations are

$$H = W_1 W_2(B_2 Q_2 - B_1 Q_1)/(B_1 W_2 - B_2 W_1)$$
$$A = (B_1/T)(H + Q_1 W_1)/W_1$$

The values of H and A are median biased and must be transformed to the median-unbiased values H/A and $1/A$. The values are then ranked, and the median values are determined and then transformed again to the binding parameters A and K.

A computer program for the calculation of the affinity constants has been written in BASIC, using a Hewlett Packard 9845A desk-top computer. The program calculates the binding constants and their 95% confidence limits and draws a plot representing the radioimmunoassay data.[17,27] The program allows verification of the effective homogeneity of the MAb used, as a mixture of different antibodies may give an unsatisfactory curve fit when analyzed with this method.[28]

[25] R. Eisenthal and A. Cornish-Bowden, *Biochem. J.* **139**, 715 (1974).
[26] R. G. Duggleby, *Anal. Biochem.* **110**, 9 (1981).
[27] G. Antoni and M. Mariani, *J. Immunol. Methods* **86**, 61 (1985).
[28] G. Antoni, P. Neri, M. Lafata, M. Mariani, and M. Cianfriglia, *Mol. Immunol.* **22**, 75 (1985).

*Affinity and Specificity Characterization of Anti-hCS
Monoclonal Antibodies*

Studies are in progress in our laboratories on the characterization of the antigenic structure of human chorionic somatomammotropin (hCS),[11,17,20,29–31] a protein hormone which shares a high degree of homology with human growth hormone (hGH). In the course of these studies we prepared a suitable panel of different MAbs against this protein, adequately characterized with regard to the class to which they belong, epitope specificity, cross-reactivity with hGH, and affinity constant. These antibodies were prepared by immunizing the mice either with the whole protein or with synthetic peptides corresponding to fragments of the primary structure of the molecule.

Monoclonal antibody production was followed by the solid-phase double-antibody screening, and thereafter the binding constants of purified MAbs were determined by the radioimmunoassay techniques, elaborating the results of these measurements with the computer program described above. Table V shows the comparative results of screening and RIA of the antibodies under study.

The solid-phase antibody competition binding assay was used to determine the epitope specificity of the MAbs, which were found to belong to four different groups distinguishing four different epitopes on the hCS molecule. The competition curves of four representative antibodies, i.e., one selected for each group, are shown in Fig. 3. DAM 2.9.2 showed a clear difference from the other monoclonals as the competition never reached values below 50–60% with the addition of up to 900 μg MAb 1/ml.

Radioimmunoassay curves for these four representative monoclonals are shown in Fig. 4. The data of these curves were used for the calculation of the binding constants as described above. The figure shows the cross-reactivity of DAM 2.9.8.2 with hGH; the two corresponding binding curves are almost overlapping and the calculated affinity constants are identical (Table V). In fact, we have recently shown[29] that this antibody is directed against an antigenic determinant common to hCS and hGH, corresponding to the sequence 166–174.

---

[29] G. Antoni, P. Neri, R. Presentini, and M. Mariani, *Annali Sclavo* **2,** 71 (1984).

[30] G. Antoni, M. Mariani, R. Presentini, M. Lafata, P. Neri, and M. Cianfriglia, *Mol. Immunol.* **22,** 1237 (1985).

[31] C. Casagli, G. Borri, P. Neri, and G. Antoni, *Am.-East. Eur. Symp. Liq. Chromatog.,* 4th, in press.

TABLE V
COMPARATIVE RESULTS OF SCREENING AND RADIOIMMUNOASSAY OF ANTI-hCS
MONOCLONAL ANTIBODIES[a]

MAbs	Immunizing antigen	Screening evaluation	Cross-reaction with hGH	$A \times 10^{12}$	$K \times 10^{-7}$ (M^{-1})
2.4.2	hCS	±	−	2.9	2.2
2.4.5	hCS	−	−	1.7	8.0
2.4.8	hCS	+	−	1.5	24.6
2.4.9	hCS	+ +	−	1.8	17.0
2.6.22	hCS	−	−	0.1	15.0
2.6.30	hCS	±	−	6.2	2.4
2.6.40	hCS	+ +	−	1.4	15.6
2.9.1	hCS	+ +	−	0.9	77.6
2.9.2	hCS	+ +	−	0.2	316.0
2.9.6	hCS	+ +	−	0.4	40.8
2.9.8.2	hCS	±	+	$0.3 (0.1)^b$	$5.4 (5.5)^b$
2.9.8.15	hCS	+	−	0.6	17.3
2.9.12	hCS	±	−	1.8	21.0
1N 4.3	166–174	n.d.	n.d.	102.0	0.03
2N 29.4	166–174	n.d.	n.d.	209.0	0.01
1E 13.14	135–140	n.d.	n.d.	11.3	0.22
2E 17.12	135–140	n.d.	n.d.	62.5	0.05

[a] Adapted from Ref. 17 with permission of the publishers. n.d., Not done.
[b] Values for hGH.

Anti-hCS MAbs with predetermined specificity have also been prepared, using as immunizing agents two synthetic peptides corresponding to the sequences 135–140 and 166–174. The immunizations were carried out using the synthetic peptides in the free form, i.e., not conjugated to any carrier. As shown in Table IV, the fusion experiments gave satisfactory specific efficiencies. The MAbs produced in this way were characterized by radioimmunoassay by coupling them covalently to the solid phase as described above. This method allows relatively large amounts of immunoglobulins to be linked to the plastic and it can be used for both IgG and IgM antibodies. The affinity constants were also calculated, as shown in Table V.

Conclusions

The findings reported in this chapter allow us to draw the following conclusions. (1) Hybridomas secreting imunoglobulins of predefined specificity may be recovered with a high SE regardless of the structure and

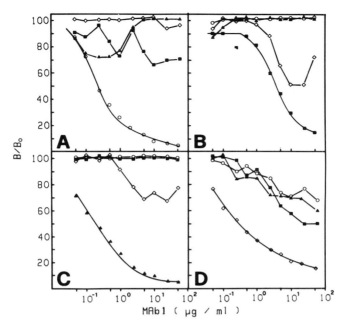

FIG. 3. Solid-phase antibody competition binding assay curves. MAb 2: (A) 2.9.8.2; (B) 2.6.30; (C) 2.9.8.15; (D) 2.9.2. MAb 1: (○) 2.9.8.2; (■) 2.6.30; (▲) 2.9.8.15; (◇) 2.9.2. (Reproduced from Ref. 20 with permission of the publishers.)

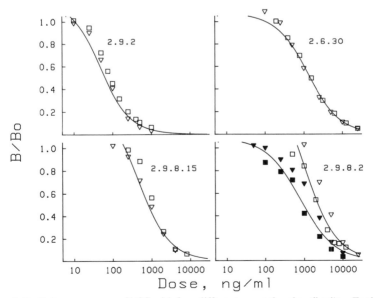

FIG. 4. Radioimmunoassay of hCS with four different monoclonal antibodies. Each point is the mean of triplicate measurements and each symbol represents a separate determination. The plotted curves were calculated with the computer program described, each curve being the geometric mean of two separate curves. In the case of DAM 2.9.8.2, the closed symbols represent the RIA obtained using hGH as cold antigen.

amount of antigen (similar high SEs are obtained administering either 1400 or 115 μg of antigen). (2) The short immunization time adopted allows us to identify hybridoma clones secreting MAbs of predefined specificity 5–6 weeks after the first immunization. (3) The B-lymphocyte populations stimulated with our immunization scheme cover the complete repertoire of the possible epitopes of the antigen. (4) The hybridoma clones secreting MAbs recognizing different epitopes are uniformly distributed in the repertoire of positive hybrids. MAbs against four different epitopes of the hCS molecule have been identified in two culture units (1/24 of the total fusion). (5) The MAbs obtained have high affinity constants, which is of particular interest for their possible employment in immunochemical studies and immunoassays. (6) Our immunization scheme proves to be very effective also with weak immunogens such as synthetic peptides, and good SEs have been obtained in the fusion experiments. The immunizations with the synthetic peptides not coupled to a carrier avoid the presence of a high fraction of undesired hybridoma populations.

Acknowledgment

The authors wish to thank Mrs. G. Ancilli and Mrs. M. Bartalini for their skillful technical assistance and Mr. G. Corsi for drawing the graphs. Dr. P. G. Natali and Dr. M. Nuti (Roma) are also acknowledged for helpful suggestions in preparing the manuscript.

[17] Bispecific Monoclonal Antibodies from Hybrid Hybridomas

By M. R. SURESH, A. C. CUELLO, and C. MILSTEIN

Hybrid hybridomas are derived by fusing at least two cells, each producing a different antibody of predefined specificity. The resulting hybrid cell secretes not only the immunoglobulins of both parents but also hybrid molecules manifesting the binding characteristics of the individual fusion partners.[1,2] These unique molecular chimeras or bispecific monoclonal antibodies (bsMAb) are structurally bivalent, exhibiting functional univalency. The possible applications of these heterobifunctional noncovalent cross-linking agents are numerous in biology and medicine and offer con-

[1] C. Milstein and A. C. Cuello, Nature (London) 305, 537 (1983).
[2] C. Milstein and A. C. Cuello, Immunol. Today 5, 299 (1984).

siderable advantages over chemical cross-linking methods. Immunohisto-chemical applications and advantages of bsMAb have been demonstrated as well as their utility in immunoassays.[1,2] Other possible uses such as target-directed chemotherapy, toxin therapy, radiotherapy, and radioimmunoimaging can be foreseen.[2,3]

Theoretical Considerations

The theoretical basis for isolating cell lines secreting bsMAb is implicit in the general method of deriving hybridomas. Thus, if two antibody-secreting cells are fused, the resulting hybrid codominantly expresses the immunoglobulin heavy and light chains of both its parents. The variable and constant regions of each chain are in a single transcriptional unit and remain in the same configuration in the hybrid hybridoma cell. Thus, the protein biosynthetic machinery generates a pool of heavy and light chains in the cisternae of a hybrid hybridoma cell, where assembly allows the formation of both parental and hybrid immunoglobulins.

A number of molecular species can be theoretically predicted to assemble under various conditions. Total absence of association between the two heavy chains of the individual parents will not generate bsMAb. Three patterns of chain association to generate HL pairs can be envisaged in hybrid hybridomas.

Type 1: Total random association of the two heavy (H_1H_2) and light (L_1L_2) chains generates all 10 different species, as diagrammatically represented in Fig. 1. Cis associations (defined as HL pairs derived from the genes of a single parent) forming functional Fab arms are indicated by a shaded box or circle and the various molecular forms are identified by Roman numerals for further reference. Inactive or nonfunctional combinations generally arise as a result of the trans association of heavy and light chains (each chain originating from different parental genes). However, exceptions have been described in which the trans-associated pair retained some activity.[4]

Type 2: Random heavy chain association with fully restricted light chain association. This gives rise to molecular forms I, VI, and VII (Fig. 1). It is apparent that this ideal pattern of chain association would generate the best yields of the highest specific activity of bsMAb. In such

[3] J. Martinis, J. F. Kull, G. Franz, and R. M. Bartholomew, *in* "Protides of the Biological Fluids" (H. Peeters, ed.), Vol. 30, pp. 311–316. Pergamon Press, Oxford, 1983.

[4] C. Milstein, K. Adetugbo, N. J. Cowan, G. Köhler, D. S. Secher, and C. D. Wilde, *in* "Cold Spring Harbor Symposia on Quantitative Biology," Vol. 41, Part 2, p. 793. Cold Spring Harbor Laboratory, New York, 1977.

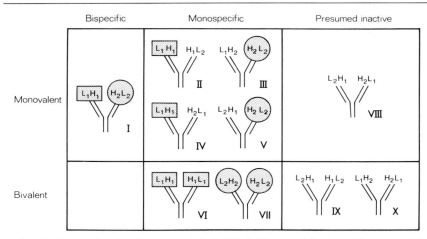

FIG. 1. Expected molecular species in hybrid hybridomas arising by random association of heavy and light chains. The parental antibody chain compositions are H_1L_1 and H_2L_2 and these functional associations are boxed or circled, while the presumed nonfunctional combinations are not (modified from Ref. 2).

clones up to 50% of the secreted immunoglobulins would be the desired bsMAb.

Type 3: Random heavy chain association with partly restricted light chain assembly. Here H_1 can associate with L_2 as well as L_1, whereas H_2 does not combine with L_1 but only with its homolog L_2. In this situation molecular species III, IV, VIII, and X would not be generated. Conversely, II, V, VIII, and IX would not be formed if H_2 associates with both L chains while H_1 is found associated only with L_1.

The three types of assembly capable of generating bsMAb are stereotypes of a more complex *in vivo* situation. Quantitative features in the preferential association of homologous vis-à-vis heterologous chains and differential rates of chain synthesis ultimately determine the relative abundance of each molecular species.

Derivation of Hybrid Hybridomas

Two general methods of deriving hybrid hybridomas are described below. Most of the general reagents used and the fusion protocols employed are comprehensively dealt with in an earlier volume in this series[5] and may be consulted for specific details and preparation methods.

[5] G. Galfre and C. Milstein, this series, Vol. 73, p. 3.

Hybridoma X Spleen Cell Fusions

The principle of this method involves the utilization of a HAT-sensitive hybridoma secreting the desired antibody as a fusion partner for spleen cells of animals immunized with the second antigen of choice. The same general methods of immunization, cell culture, cell fusion, and selection of hybrids in HAT medium described earlier[5] for the hybrid myelomas are applicable here. One of the first prerequisites is to generate an 8-azaguanine- or 6-thioguanine-resistant clone of the desired hybridoma. Clones resistant to bromodeoxyuridine or 6-chloropurine would also be HAT sensitive, being aberrant in thymidine kinase and adenine phosphoribosyltransferase, respectively.

Procedure to Isolate Azaguanine-Resistant Hybridoma Lines. Hybridomas are usually derived by fusion of an 8-azaguanine-resistant myeloma with spleen cells. They therefore usually contain the hypoxanthine–guanine phosphoribosyltransferase (HGPRT)-defective chromosome. Since chromosome losses occur at high frequency (particularly when the hybridoma clones have not been grown for long periods) it is usually easy to derive HAT-sensitive lines by loss of the HGPRT chromosome.

(1) Prepare 20 mM stock (3 mg/ml) 8-azaguanine by dissolving 300 mg of the purine in 99 ml H_2O and 1 ml 1 N NaOH. Filter sterilize, and store in aliquots at $-20°$. (2) Prepare 24 subconfluent wells (6 columns × 4 rows) of vigorously growing hybridoma. (3) Prepare a serial dilution of medium containing 8-azaguanine at the following doubling dilutions—30, 15, 7.5, 3.75, 1.88, 0.94 μg/ml—in 10% FCS–DMEM (Dulbecco's modified Eagle's medium with fetal calf serum) and equilibrate in CO_2 incubator for 1 hr. (4) Feed the various azaguanine concentrations in triplicate to the subconfluent hybridoma plate, keeping the last rows as controls. (5) Change medium every 2 days, removing cells if excess growth is seen. (6) Select culture growing at highest drug concentration and repeat above procedure with these cells.

(7) When cells appear to have adapted to the 30 μg/ml drug level, clone on soft agarose[5] containing 30 μg azaguanine/ml. (8) Pick about 24 clones and expand them in duplicates. Add HAT medium (for preparation, see Ref. 5) to one set and discard those clones which do not die. (9) Assay the remaining clones for production of antibody. Select a few and reclone. Choose the clone with best growth characteristics. (10) After several weeks of continuous growth, select the line which gives highest fusion efficiency.

Employing the above procedure we have derived several azaguanine-resistant hybridomas, notably the YP4 anti-horseradish peroxidase line which exhibits excellent fusion properties.[1] Not all clones exhibit equally good performance in test fusions.

Fusion Protocol. The preparation of parental fusion partners, namely, the spleen cells from an immunized animal and the azaguanine-resistant hybridoma cells, and fusion method are essentially as described earlier for fusion of cells in suspension (Ref. 5, Section IV,B,1). The only suggested difference is the use of 45% PEG–10% DMSO instead of 50% PEG in the cell fusion step with 10^8 spleen cells and 5×10^7 hybridomas. This is in accord with earlier observations[6] on the enhanced frequency (~100%) of hybridoma formation by employing two membrane active agents instead of PEG alone. The fused cells are plated in DMEM with or without feeder layers and after 6–24 hr, 1 volume of 2× HAT medium is added to the cells. Hybrid hybridoma clones would be apparent after 2–4 weeks, and when the supernatants turn yellow they are ready to be screened for bsMAb and parental immunoglobulin activity (see "Screening Assays for Hybrid Hybridomas").

This method of obtaining hybrid hybridomas has been successfully employed to generate to date a variety of bsMAb, for example, antisomatostatin–antiperoxidase, antibiotin–antiperoxidase, anti-alkaline phosphatase–antiperoxidase, and anti-β_2-microglobulin–antiperoxidase. While this procedure may be the best way of deriving hybrid hybridomas, it suffers from the disadvantages of the need to generate HAT-sensitive hybridoma lines. In addition, the contribution of the spleen partner (hence quality and affinity of the bsMAb) is a matter of chance.

Hybridoma × Hybridoma Fusions

In this method two established hybridoma lines whose antibody specificities and avidities are well characterized represent the two fusion partners. Fusion between two myeloma cells was achieved[7] earlier by making one line resistant to azaguanine and the other to bromodeoxyuridine and selecting hybrids in HAT medium. Below we describe a faster method to generate hybrid hybridomas by fusing two previously established cell lines, each secreting a well-recognized monoclonal antibody.

Chemical Inactivation Method. The principle of this procedure involves the use of two distinct site-specific irreversible inhibitors of macromolecular biosynthesis.[8] In this way independent metabolic pathways of each of the two cell lines are inhibited. Fused cells apparently survive by

[6] T. H. Norwood, C. J. Zeigler, and G. M. Martin, *Somatic Cell Genet.* **2,** 263 (1976).
[7] R. G. H. Cotton and C. Milstein, *Nature (London)* **244,** 42 (1973).
[8] T. Osawa, *Trends Biotechnol.* **2,** 39 (1984).

complementing each other. The fusion between the antiperoxidase YP4 (rat line secreting IgG$_1$) and anti-substance P NC1/34 (rat × mouse, secreting rat IgG$_{2a}$) hybridomas is described as a representative example applicable to other fusions.[9]

First, the sensitivity of both cell lines to emetine (Sigma; an inhibitor of protein synthesis blocking the translocation step) and to actinomycin D (an inhibitor of RNA synthesis) was determined. Other inhibitors can also be tested (hydroxyurea, ouabain, cycloheximide, edine, sparsomycin, fusidic acid, etc). Typically, 10^6 cells were incubated with doubling dilutions of emetine (beginning at 1 mM) or actinomycin D (starting at 1 μg/ml) for 1 hr at 37° in 10 ml of DMEM. The cells were collected by centrifugation, washed, and resuspended in 10 ml DMEM at 37° for 15–30 min to allow efflux of any residual free drug in the cell. Cells were again collected by centrifugation, resuspended in DMEM, and plated for further observations. At a certain doubling dilution (= critical drug concentration) less than 1% of cells survive, and beyond this drug level no cell growth is observed. The critical drug concentrations for NC1/34 and YP4 lines were found to be 200 μM emetine and 100 ng/ml actinomycin D, respectively.

(1) Using emetine for NC1/34 and actinomycin D for YP4, 5 × 10^7 cells of each line were treated with the respective critical drug concentrations in 50 ml DMEM for 1 hr. (2) Cells were centrifuged, washed, resuspended in DMEM, and collected after 15 min at 37°. (3) Cells were resuspended in 10 ml DMEM, mixed in 1 : 1 ratio, centrifuged, and fused in 1 ml of 45% PEG (MW 1400, Merck)–10% DMSO in DMEM as described in Ref. 5, Section IV,B,1. The final pellet after fusion was gently resuspended in 50 ml of 20% DMEM and incubated at 37° for 4–6 hr recovery. (5) An aliquot was cloned on the same day on soft agarose at four dilutions.[5] (6) The remaining cells were plated in two 24-well plate for parallel observations and assays. Here limiting dilution plating could also be chosen to supplement agarose cloning.

Clones were visible after 2–4 weeks and were clearly pleomorphic (compact, broken, diffuse, and irregular shaped). An appropriate plate was chosen, and about 100 clones (primary clones) were picked and expanded in 24-well plates with 10% FCS–DMEM. Supernatants of these primary clones were assayed for the two parental and the hybrid antibodies (see "Screening Assays for Hybrid Hybridomas") and the best clones were recloned again at least twice.

Combination of Chemical and HAT Selection. Another procedure also successfully employed was to kill the NC1/34 line with 200 μM emetine (its critical concentration) and fuse it with the azaguanine-resistant YP4

[9] M. R. Suresh, A. C. Cuello, and C. Milstein, in preparation.

line, followed by selection of hybrids in HAT medium. More than one drug can also be employed to kill the HAT-resistant (NC1/34) line.

(1) Obtain logarithmically growing 5×10^7 cells (100–200 ml culture) of NC1/34 by centrifugation and wash once with DMEM. (2) A 20 mM stock solution of emetine dihydrochloride in DMEM is prepared, filter sterilized, and stored at 4°. Incubate cells at 37° for 1 hr in a sterile conical tube (Falcon, Cat. No. 2070) with 50 ml DMEM containing 200 μM emetine. (3) Harvest cells and wash with DMEM. Incubate the cells again at 37° with DMEM to allow efflux of residual drug for 15 min and collect cells by centrifugation.

(4) Harvest the azaguanine-resistant YP4 cells and wash with DMEM twice to remove FCS proteins. (5) Mix YP4 and NC1 cells in a 1 : 1 ratio ($\sim$5 $\times 10^7$ each) by gently vortexing them and centrifuge. (6) Add 1 ml of 45% PEG–10% DMSO in DMEM prewarmed to 40° and perform cell fusion as described in Ref. 5, Section IV,B,1. (7) Clone an aliquot in HAT on semisolid support such as agar or agarose (Ref. 5, Section VII,2). Plate the rest of the fused cells in two 24-well plates for observations and subsequent assay of supernatants. (8) Pick clones when they appear (2–3 weeks) and transfer them to 24-well plates and expand in 10% FCS–DMEM until the supernatants are ready to be screened for antibody production.

Screening Assays for Hybrid Hybridomas

Hybrid hybridomas are highly polyploid and exhibit a higher propensity to lose chromosomes than hybridomas. During the first few divisions asymmetric chromosome loss would result in a pleotypic genotype in the daughter cells of the clone. Random chromosome loss can also involve one or more of the immunoglobulin loci, generating hybrid hybridomas which do not secrete all the expected immunoglobulin chains in a given clone. Hence there is the need to clone at very early stages and to reclone the primary clones at least twice. In order to screen for the desired hybrid hybridoma, several assays can be performed. Below we describe as examples the ones we used for the isolation of the anti-substance P–antiperoxidase hybrid hybridomas.[9] With minor adaptations the methods can be used for other antigenic specificities. It should be noted that bsMAb are competing with the monospecific species also secreted by the cell. For this reason, poor activity observed with the method designed to test directly for the presence of bsMAb may be encountered with unpurified tissue culture supernatants. Therefore, separate assays for the individual specificities are also performed.

HYBRID OR BISPECIFIC MONOCLONAL ASSAY

Immunochemical Procedure. This assay facilitates the rapid screening of supernatants for the presence of bsMAb. The principle of the hybrid MAb assay is diagrammatically represented in Fig. 2 along with a representative assay sheet showing positive clones. It is a modified version of the method described for screening hybridomas.[5]

Reagents

Nitrocellulose sheet, Schleicher & Schüll, 0.45 μm
Substance P–BSA conjugate 100 μg/ml in PBS (antigen A as in general case)
5% BSA in PBS
Horseradish peroxidase (HRPO) type II, Sigma (antigen B as in general case)
4-Chloro-1-naphthol (chloronaphthol, Sigma) and H_2O_2
Hybrid hybridoma supernatants

Procedure. (1) Mark a rectangular piece of nitrocellulose with a pencil or pointed instrument to identify 1 × 1-cm squares (24–96 as required). (2) Spot 2–5 μl of substance P–BSA conjugate at 100 μg/ml in PBS (or antigen A in general case) at the center of each square and dry the sheet for 5 min at room temperature. (3) Block additional protein binding sites by flushing the sheet with 10–20 ml of 5% BSA in PBS and gentle shaking for 15 min. (4) Blot the sheet between two filter papers gently to remove excess blocking solution and place it on the blue wax paper that is supplied along with the nitrocellulose sheet by the manufacturer. Make sure the antigen-coated side is on top. (5) Before the sheet dries up completely, spot 2–5 μl of the hybrid hybridoma supernatants directly on the antigen spot. (6) Wash sheet 2–5 min later with excess PBS (~200 ml) three times to remove all the unbound proteins from the supernatant. Obviously, both the monospecific anti-substance P antibodies and the bispecific anti-substance P–antiperoxidase antibodies in the supernatant bind the antigen immobilized on the nitrocellulose. However, they bind with a crucial difference, as diagrammatically shown in Fig. 2. Unlike any other molecular species secreted by the clone, only one Fab arm of the bsMAb binds to the support, leaving the other arm still available to bind the second antigen. The antiperoxidase antibodies fail to bind to the substance P–BSA-coated sheet and are washed away by PBS.

(7) Immerse the washed nitrocellulose sheet in 20 ml of 20 μg HRPO/ml (antigen B in a general case labeled with an enzyme or radioactive marker) in 5% BSA–PBS for 15 min with shaking. (8) Wash the sheet with

a

α – substance P   bsMAb α – Peroxidase

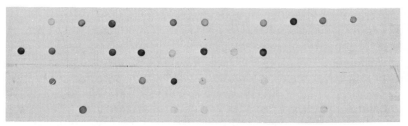

b

FIG. 2. Bispecific monoclonal antibody (bsMAb) assay. The principle of the assay is diagrammatically shown (a) along with a typical assay performed (b) with supernatants of P4C1, primary clones derived by fusing the antiperoxidase-secreting YP4 and anti-substance P-secreting NC1/34 hybridoma lines. Substance P–BSA conjugate was spotted onto a nitrocellulose sheet divided into squares, additional protein binding sites were blocked with BSA, and supernatants were spotted (see text for details). Only monovalent or bivalent antisubstance P antibodies bind to the substratum. The bsMAb binds with one Fab arm and the other is available for peroxidase binding in a subsequent step. Color development was with chloronaphthol and H_2O_2.

100 ml PBS for 5 min. Repeat this twice. Longer washes may be necessary in some cases to reduce background activity of enzyme or radioactive marker. (9) Identify bsMAb-secreting clones by the blue-black color developed in such squares with 10 ml of 0.4 mg/ml chloronaphthol and 0.03% H_2O_2 in PBS. Chloronaphthol is soluble in methanol or dimethyl formamide and a $20\times$ or $50\times$ stock can be prepared and stored at 0–5° for 2–3 weeks.

The above assay can be performed on microtiter plates as well, but in our experience the nitrocellulose sheet assays exhibit excellent signal-to-noise ratios. In addition, after completion of the assay, the dried sheet provides a handy permanent record for future reference. This hybrid or bsMAb assay could also be adapted to screen clones in the petri dishes using antigen-coated nitrocellulose filter disks as described elsewhere,[10] prior to picking clones extensively.

Immunohistochemical Procedure. In general, a tissue containing the antigen under investigation and in which cellular locations are well established is selected for screening bsMAb. In the case of antisomatostatin–antiperoxidase antibodies the median eminence of the rat was selected while for anti-substance P–antiperoxidase antibodies the substantia gelatinosa of the spinal trigeminal nucleus of the rat was chosen. Tissues were obtained from animals under equithesin anesthesia. The animals were perfused intracardially with 20 ml phosphate buffer (0.1 M, pH 7.2) followed by 300 ml of the same buffer containing 4% freshly prepared paraformaldehyde. The selected areas were kept in the fixative for a maximum of 5 hr and transferred to cold phosphate buffer (as above) containing 5–30% sucrose. After 24–96 hr, tissue samples were cut at 10 μm in a cryostat ($-20°$) and mounted on glass slides coated with chrome alum gelatin.

Staining is performed as follows: (1) Rinse with 0.1 M phosphate-buffered saline (pH 7.2), containing 0.02% Triton X-100 for 10 min at room temperature. (2) Incubate overnight with either test samples (hybrid hybridoma supernatants), control supernatants, or known primary antibodies against the antigen under investigation. Test supernatants were diluted 1 : 1 in 0.1 M phosphate buffer–Triton X-100 containing 5 μg HRPO/ml (Grade VI, Sigma). Control samples were prepared in 0.1 M phosphate-buffered saline at previously established dilution. Incubations were carried out in humid chambers at approximately 4°. (3) Rinse in 0.1 M phosphate buffer–Triton X-100 for 30 min. (4) Incubate for 15 min in 0.05 M Tris–HCl buffer (pH 7.6) containing freshly dissolved 0.06% 3,3′-diaminobenzidine (DAB, Sigma). Use gloves and a fume cupboard. (5) Incubate for further 15 min in the same solution as above but containing 0.01% H_2O_2. (6) Rinse in Tris buffer or PBS. Transfer sequentially to ethanol 50, 70, and 90%, for 15 min each, followed by two to three changes in absolute ethanol. (7) Transfer to xylene for 15 min. (8) Mount in De Pex or equivalent medium and observe with a bright field microscope. Immunoreactive sites are identified by the presence of precipitated brown products in the cellular elements known to contain the antigen under investigation.

---

[10] J. Sharon, S. L. Morrison, and E. A. Kabat, *Proc. Natl. Acad. Sci. U.S.A.* **76**, 1420 (1979).

INDIVIDUAL ANTIBODY ASSAYS

Individual antibody assays for the two parental specificities are similar in principle to general monoclonal antibody assays.[5] For some of the hybrid hybridomas we have used immunocytochemical assays for individual or parental antibodies as described above, with necessary adaptations. Below we describe two binding assays only as brief examples.

Anti-substance P Assay. The initial steps of the preparation of the antigen-coated nitrocellulose sheet, blocking, and subsequent spotting of the individual supernatants in each square are the same as described for the "Hybrid or Bispecific Monoclonal Assay." Following step 6, (7) incubate the assay sheet with shaking for 15–30 min with 10 ml of a 1 : 100 dilution in 5% BSA–PBS of rabbit (or sheep) anti-rat IgG (whole molecule) conjugated to HRPO (Bio Yeda, Israel). The second antibody conjugate recognizes the bsMAb as well as monospecific (monovalent or bivalent) anti-substance P antibodies bound to the sheet. (8) Decant the solution, which if stored in the cold can be used again at least five times if utilized within a 2- to 3-week period. Avoid adding azide as a preservative since it inhibits HRPO. (9) Wash the sheet with 100 ml PBS for 15 min with shaking. (10) Identify positive clones with chloronaphthol and H_2O_2 (see "Hybrid or Bispecific Monoclonal Assay," step 9) as substrates for peroxidase.

Clones which were positive in the bsMAb assay will always be positive in this assay, while the converse may not be true. If the antigen in question is available in limited amounts, the same assay sheet used for identifying the bsMAb in the hybrid assay can be used in this individual or parental antibody assay. Make a photographic or Xerox copy of the nitrocellulose sheet after step 8 of bsMAb assay for records and wash extensively with PBS to remove the residual enzyme substrates. Now perform the parental antibody assay as described in this section to identify additional positive clones secreting only the anti-substance P antibodies.

Antiperoxidase Assay. The principle of this assay provides yet another interesting variation of performing immunoassays,[11] eliminating the need for enzyme-labeled or radiolabeled second antibody conjugates. (1) Mark a nitrocellulose sheet with pencil to identify 1 × 1-cm squares. (2) Spot 5 μl of supernatant along with appropriate controls onto the center of each square. Allow 5 min for proteins to bind to nitrocellulose. (3) Wash with 100 ml PBS to remove any excess unbound proteins for 10 min. (4) Block additional protein binding sites with 20 ml 5% BSA–PBS for 15 min and decant blocking solution (which can be reused again five times within 2–3 weeks). (5) Incubate sheet with 20 ml of 20 μg HRPO/ml in 5% BSA–PBS

---

[11] M. R. Suresh and C. Milstein, unpublished data.

(or any radiolabeled or enzyme-labeled antigen) for 15–30 min and decant antigen solution. (6) Wash the assay sheet with 100 ml PBS three times, 10 min each wash. (7) Identify antiperoxidase-containing supernatants by developing the sheet in chloronaphthol and H_2O_2 (as described above, step 9).

Routinely, we perform the three assays (one bsMAb and two parental antibody assays) simultaneously while screening supernatants to identify hybrid hybridomas. Clones exhibiting strong positive reaction in at least both individual antibody assays and preferably in all the assays are chosen and recloned twice. Some hybrid hybridomas do not give rise to bsMAb due to incompatibility of heavy chain classes (see below under "Heavy Chain Compatibility in bsMAb Assembly").

Purification of Bispecific Monoclonal Antibodies

Large-Scale Preparations of bsMAb

Large-scale preparations can be made by growing hybrid hybridomas as tumors in the peritoneal cavity of pristane-primed animals or by large-scale tissue culture methods.[5] Hybrid hybridomas having a complex biological origin such as P4C1 clones [(mouse × rat) × rat] can be grown in the peritoneal cavity of a nude mouse or rat to obtain ascites. Alternatively, we have also prepared sufficient quantities of bsMAb from these clones by incubating cells obtained from a vigorously growing culture in serum-free tissue culture medium, at densities of about 2×10^6 for 24–48 hr.[5] Analysis of ascites or concentrated culture supernatants by cellulose acetate electrophoresis in 0.04 M veronal buffer (pH 8.6) using a Beckman microzone electrophoresis apparatus typically exhibits three prominent immunoglobulin bands (Fig. 3d): the middle band is the bsMAb and the other two are the parental antibodies. The preparation of crude antibody fractions from ascites or tissue culture supernatants suitable for DEAE column chromatography is described below.

Processing of Ascites. The volume of ascites from the peritoneal cavity of a single rat (20–30 ml) is higher than that obtained from a mouse. This advantage would be appreciated even more with hybrid hybridomas, where at best only 30–50% of the secreted immunoglobulins represent the desired bispecific class. (1) Clarify the tapped ascites by centrifugation to remove cells and other particulate matter. (2) Dilute ascites 1:1 with saline. (3) Add an equal volume of saturated $(NH_4)_2SO_4$, gradually with stirring to achieve a 50% salt saturation. Stir for 1 hr. (4) Collect precipitated proteins by centrifugation and discard supernatant (which may include residual oil droplets). (5) Dissolve the precipitate in a minimum

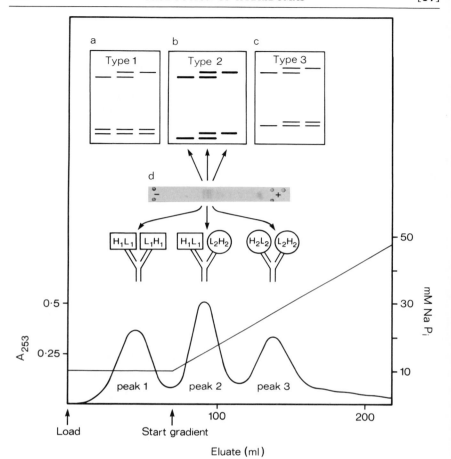

FIG. 3. Resolution pattern of hybrid hybridoma products on a DE-52 column. The crude antibody was loaded, and the three peaks shown were obtained with a linear phosphate gradient. In immunoassays, peaks 1 and 3 were found to be mainly the individual parental antibody activities, while the middle peak was the bispecific species. Insets (a–c) diagrammatically show the expected SDS–PAGE pattern of the three peaks in the three types of heavy and light chain associations (see "Theoretical Considerations"). Inset (d) depicts the cellulose acetate electrophoretic pattern of the ascites of one of the hybrid hybridomas, showing the three antibody bands. Note the higher intensity of the middle band.

amount of PBS (5 ml for every 10 ml ascites) and exhaustively dialyze with two changes of 100 volumes of 10 mM sodium phosphate buffer (pH 7.5).

Processing Serum-Free Tissue Culture Supernatants. The presence of FCS proteins in tissue culture supernatants presents problems while purifying the bsMAb and hence there is an advantage to serum-free supernatants. (1) Centrifuge to remove cells and pour the supernatant into a beaker. (2) Add solid $(NH_4)_2SO_4$ gradually with stirring to achieve 90% salt saturation (662 g/liter). Stir for 2 hr; the solution will become mildly turbid. (3) Centrifuge at 10,000 g for 15 min and discard the supernatant. (4) Dissolve the pellet with a minimum amount of PBS (20 ml/liter of original supernatant) and dialyze exhaustively with two changes of 100 volumes of 10 mM sodium phosphate buffer (pH 7.5).

Anion-Exchange Chromatography. The dialyzed crude antibody fraction obtained either from ascites or from serum-free supernatants can often be fractionated by DEAE column chromatography to obtain relatively pure bsMAb substantially free of contamination by the individual parental antibody species. (1) Prepare a DE-52 (Whatman, microgranular form) column measuring approximately 2 × 9 cm for processing the crude antibody fraction from 8–10 ml of ascites or 2 liters of serum-free supernatants. (2) Equilibrate the column by washing extensively (50 bed volumes) with 10 mM sodium phosphate (pH 7.5). (3) Load the crude antibody fraction and start collecting 6-ml fractions. A UV monitor continuously recording the effluent absorption is convenient. (4) Wash column with 1 bed volume of 10 mM sodium phosphate (pH 7.5).

(5) Elute antibody fractions by connecting the column to a linear gradient of 10–100 mM sodium phosphate (pH 7.5) (150 ml each). In favorable cases (see below) three peaks are obtained[1-3] as shown in an idealized example of such a resolution (Fig. 3). This profile of three peaks on DEAE columns and three bands on cellulose acetate electrophoresis has been observed for a number of hybrid hybridomas isolated in our laboratory. (6) Assay the fractions for bsMAb and individual antibody activities (see earlier sections). The middle peak will exhibit the bispecific activity flanked by the two parental antibody activities. (7) Analyze the purity and chain composition of the peak fractions (every third tube) by SDS–PAGE. We perform this on mini-gels to obtain results in less than 3 hr. Representative results are shown in Fig. 3, a–c. (8) Pool the appropriate fractions to obtain the purified bsMAb, make aliquots, and store at −20°. If the protein concentration is too low, we recommend addition of BSA to achieve 1–2 mg/ml.

It is pertinent to emphasize at this juncture that although it seems logical to expect better quality and quantity of bsMAb by obtaining hybrid hybridomas secreting the two heavy chains of the same subclass, purification of the desired species free of the parental classes may not be so straightforward. The idealized resolution pattern (Fig. 3) was observed in all our hybrid hybridomas wherein fortuitously two different heavy chain subclass combinations were involved (IgG_1 × IgG_{2a}, as in anti-substance

P–antiperoxidase, or $IgG_1 \times IgG_{2b}$, as in antisomatostatin–antiperoxidase), making it relatively easy to obtain the bsMAb.

Chain Composition of bsMAb

SDS–PAGE. Analysis of the three peaks obtained by ion-exchange chromatography (Fig. 3, a–c) of immunoglobulins secreted by hybrid hybridomas allows an easy analysis of the different molecular species secreted. It is very encouraging that among the examples we have studied, we find type 2 and 3 association patterns (see "Theoretical Considerations") as diagrammatically represented in Fig. 3, a–c. Type 2 is of course the most favorable in terms of bsMAb.

For instance, the anti-substance P–antiperoxidase hybridoma exhibits the type 2 association pattern described earlier. Here peaks 1 and 3 of the DEAE–cellulose column upon SDS–PAGE analysis show no cross-contamination of the light chains, indicating restricted light chain association with its corresponding heavy chain (Fig. 3b). Since there is no trans HL association, peak 2 is essentially pure bsMAb. If there is random association of heavy chains, the yield of bsMAb will approach 50% of the total secreted immunoglobulin, resulting in the higher intensity of the middle band in the cellulose acetate electrophoretic pattern of the ascites (Fig. 3d).

The antisomatostatin–antiperoxidase hybrid hybridoma belongs to the type 3 restricted HL association (Fig. 3c). In this example, peak 3 exhibits antiperoxidase activity. It contains the corresponding heavy chain as well as both light chains. Peak 1 has antisomatostatin activity and the composition is indistinguishable from the parental antisomatostatin IgG, with a single band in the position of the light chain. Thus, the antiperoxidase IgG peak has a certain proportion of its heavy chains associated with the light chain of the antisomatostatin antibody molecule (a presumed inactive combination). It follows that peak 2 containing the bsMAb includes molecules with the inactive trans association. This results in a reduced specific activity of the peak fraction containing the bispecific species, a feature also borne out in immunohistochemical assays.[1,2,11] A more refined method of purification is required to eliminate undesirable molecular forms of this type. A better alternative is to avoid the problem altogether by screening for a more suitable clone giving a type 2 pattern.

Heavy Chain Compatibility in bsMAb Assembly. Restriction in the ability of different classes of heavy chain to form stable dimers characteristic of the complete Ig molecule is well documented. In particular, γ and μ chains do not associate to form hybrid molecules.[1,12]

---

[12] G. Köhler, H. Hengartner, and M. J. Shulman, *Eur. J. Immunol.* **8**, 82 (1978).

On the other hand, γ chains of different subclasses do give rise to heterodimers. Mouse heterodimers have been suggested between γ_1/γ_{2a}, γ_1/γ_{2b}, γ_{2a}/γ_{2b}, and γ_{2b}/γ_3.[12–15] Other examples are discussed below. It is, however, not fully established how general this phenomenon is, and there are probably exceptions. Our recent experience, particularly with rat immunoglobulins, throws some light on the problem. For instance, hybrid hybridomas derived by fusion of a rat IgG$_{2c}$ hybridoma (YC5/45, antiserotonin) with hybridomas secreting rat IgG$_1$ or IgG$_{2a}$ did not seem to assemble bispecific molecules, perhaps due to structural constraints.[9]

Although heavy chains of different subclasses can give rise to hybrid dimers, the relative yield of symmetric versus asymmetric molecules may not be the one expected by random association. In some cases (rat γ_1 and γ_{2b} pair[1,2] and mouse γ_3 and γ_{2b} pair[15]), the expected ratio $1:2:1$ was not observed, while in other examples (rat γ_1 and γ_{2a} pair[9] and an unknown mouse subclass pair[3]) the ratio approximated the random $1:2:1$. In spite of this, the use of hybrid molecules of different heavy chain subclasses can be a definite advantage. Heavy chain hybrid formation between IgG$_1$ and either IgG$_{2a}$ or IgG$_{2b}$ has been exploited to resolve the desired bsMAb by a simple ion-exchange chromatography step since the different charge characteristics of the various secreted immunoglobulins are principally contributed by the two heavy chains. More elaborate purification methods have to be devised if the bsMAb were composed of heavy chains of the same subclass such as employing two affinity chromatography steps. The formation of hybrid molecules between heavy chains across species barriers has already been reported in mouse × rat hybridomas.[16] Thus, mouse IgG$_1$ has been found to associate with rat IgG$_{2a}$ and IgG$_{2b}$, generating the bispecific species. Such interspecific hybrid formation may also facilitate convenient purification of the desired bsMAb. It is well established that mouse, unlike most rat, immunoglobulins bind to protein A columns.

General Applications of bsMAb

The cross-linking ability of bsMAb to any two defined antigens makes the use of them a better alternative to the widely used chemical covalent cross-linking methods, at least in two major areas of applied immunology: immunoassays and immunohistochemistry. As with MAb, bsMAb are likely to greatly improve batch-to-batch reproducibility in the quality of

[13] G. Köhler and C. Milstein, *Nature* (*London*) **256**, 495 (1975).
[14] D. H. Margulies, M. W. Kuehl, and M. D. Scharff, *Cell* **8**, 405 (1976).
[15] D. Eilat and R. Laskov, *Mol. Immunol.* **18**, 589 (1981).
[16] J. C. Howard, G. W. Butcher, G. Galfre, C. Milstein, and C. P. Milstein, *Immunol. Rev.* **47**, 139 (1979).

the reagents, a feature of considerable importance particularly in industry. Furthermore, the functional univalency of bsMAb could confer some additional advantages such as lower degree of antigenic modulation and better complement-mediated cytotoxicity.[17]

Immunohistochemistry

The *in situ* localization of antigens with bsMAb was first demonstrated utilizing the antisomatostatin–antiperoxidase and more recently with antisubstance P–antiperoxidase.[1,2,9] These reagents identify neuropeptides in thin sections of the brain at the light and electron microscopic level with remarkable clarity and excellent signal-to-noise ratios. There was a complete absence of background staining, and phase-contrast microscopy was necessary to identify tissue landmarks which are generally obvious when a certain degree of nonspecific staining is observed with other methods of immunohistochemistry. The results were better than those obtained with direct, indirect, or peroxidase–antiperoxidase (PAP) methods of antigen localization, to the extent that hitherto unrecognized substance P-reactive sites have been identified. Methods employing second and third antibody conjugates to increase the sensitivity may occlude less accessible antigenic sites. Evidence was also obtained to suggest that bsMCA was even superior to the biotin–streptavidin method of antigen localization.[9]

Apart from these qualitative improvements, the practical advantages were shortening of incubation times and a one-step incubation of all the reagents preceding the enzyme reaction. However, the one-step reaction is less sensitive than a two-step process. For instance, we were unable to demonstrate extrahypothalamic somatostatin in a one-step incubation reaction. This is probably due to the larger molecular size of the preformed bsMAb–HRPO complex (~190,000 Da) hindering penetration through the tissues. Better sensitivity is obtained when the tissue section is first incubated with bsMAb alone followed by HRPO. This difference due to one or two incubation steps was not observed in immunoassays for which antigen accessibility is not a problem. Apart from size of the complex influencing antigen localization, it should be remembered that the bsMAb peak obtained by DE-52 column, as discussed above, may contain a monovalent monospecific impurity which binds to the tissue antigen but not to peroxidase[1,2] (see type 3 chain association, under "Theoretical Considerations"). This impurity, being smaller than the bsMAb–HRPO complex, can presumably penetrate tissues better and block identification of potential sites.

[17] S. P. Cobbold and H. Waldmann, *Nature (London)* **308**, 460 (1984).

Finally, bsMAb open new vistas in immunohistochemistry by allowing simultaneous identification of two or more antigens in a given tissue or cell by a judicious combination of several markers. Toward this goal, at the electron microscopic level we have successfully utilized a bsMAb along with a ^{3}H-labeled MAb for autoradiography to generate different electron-dense signals.[1,2] At the light microscopic level the simultaneous detection of more than one antigen may be simpler using bsMAb specific for different enzyme markers such as peroxidase, alkaline phosphatase, or β-galactosidase. Appropriate substrates would generate different insoluble colored products characteristic of each enzyme: red with 3-amino-9-ethyl carbazole and HRPO[18]; pink with 5-bromo-4-chloro-3-indolyl phosphate, NBT, and alkaline phosphatase[19]; blue with 5-bromo-4-chloro-3-indolyl β-D-galactoside, potassium ferri- and ferrocyanide, and β-galactosidase.[20]

Immunoassays

These assays usually involve the chemical modification of either the MAb or the second antibody with an enzyme or radioactive marker. Chemical cross-linking or modification procedures are generally random events resulting in the observed variability of reagent quality, not to mention the partial inactivation of the binding sites and short shelf life of the reagents. The use of bsMAb as a component in either competitive or "sandwich" immunoassays eliminates the drawbacks of chemical conjugation methods.

We have demonstrated[2,11] the utility of bsMAb in immunoassays designed to measure somatostatin and substance P. These antipeptide–antiperoxidases were used along with HRPO in one step to detect the presence of somatostatin or substance P bound to a solid support. Increasing inhibition of this binding obtained by competing free peptide was a measure of its concentration with reference to a standard curve. An important prerequisite for the success of this procedure involves the need to obtain the pure bispecific species from hybrid hybridomas. The various molecular forms secreted by hybrid hybridomas (Fig. 1), if used as unfractionated material, could result in competition between different antibody species. The monovalent forms may be preferentially displaced by bivalent species having a higher avidity. Antigenic density could play an important part in

[18] R. C. Graham, U. Lundholm, and M. J. Karnovsky, *J. Histochem. Cytochem.* **13**, 150 (1965).

[19] J. J. Leary, D. J. Brigati, and D. C. Ward, *Proc. Natl. Acad. Sci. U.S.A.* **80**, 4045 (1983).

[20] A. Bondi, G. Chieregatti, V. Eusebi, E. Fulcheri, and G. Bussolati, *Histochemistry* **76**, 153 (1982).

such interactions. For instance, there was no evidence for preferential divalent to monovalent binding in the antisomatostatin–antiperoxidase hybrid hybridoma supernatant to a somatostatin–BSA conjugate.[2] However, in a mouse–rat bispecific species recognizing a rat alloantigen on red cells, a low signal with marked prozone was observed, perhaps due to better binding by the competing bivalent species.[16]

Acknowledgments

M. R. Suresh was supported by an Usher Fellowship. A. C. Cuello acknowledges financial support from the Medical Research Council, The Wellcome Foundation, and the E.P.A. Trust (Oxford).

[18] Human × (Mouse × Human) Hybridomas

By Lars Östberg

As a very detailed report on the preparation of monoclonal antibodies has already been published in this series,[1] the following text deals mainly with features distinguishing human × (mouse × human) hybridomas from mouse × mouse hybridomas.

Introduction

After the first report[2] describing mouse hybridomas capable of permanent production of antibody with predetermined specificity, it was expected that a similar technique for the production of human monoclonal antibodies would soon emerge. However, despite a large number of reports describing hybrids with plasmacytoma[3] or lymphoblastoid[4–7] cell lines, none of these cells have been able to yield hybridomas comparable

---

[1] G. Galfré and C. Milstein, this series, Vol. 73, p. 3.

[2] G. Köhler and C. Milstein, Nature (London) 256, 495 (1975).

[3] L. Olsson and H. S. Kaplan, Proc. Natl. Acad. Sci. U.S.A. 77, 5429 (1980).

[4] C. M. Croce, A. Linnenbach, W. Hall, Z. Steplewski, and H. Koprowski, Nature (London) 288, 488 (1980).

[5] M. C. Glassy, H. H. Handley, H. Hagiwara, and I. Royston, Proc. Natl. Acad. Sci. U.S.A. 80, 6327 (1983).

[6] P. A. W. Edwards, C. M. Smith, A. M. Neville, and M. J. O'Hare, Eur. J. Immunol. 12, 641 (1982).

[7] Y. Shoenfeld, S. C. Hsu-Lin, J. E. Gabriels, L. E. Silberstein, B. C. Furie, B. Furie, B. D. Stollar, and R. S. Schwartz, J. Clin. Invest. 70, 205 (1982).

to mouse × mouse hybrids in stability, productivity, clonability, and ability to give hybrids producing immunoglobulins other then IgM. Another approach to make human monoclonals has been to use human × mouse hybrids. This has had some limited success.[8,9] However, due to the preferential loss of human chromosome 2,[9,10] which carries the gene for the κ light chain,[11] the procedure is very laborious and yields few long-term growing hybrids.

As a human × mouse hybrid still retains some human chromosomes[10] after losing its ability to produce complete antibodies, we undertook to study if such a "humanified" mouse cell would create a more favorable environment for reintroducing a complete human genome where all immunoglobulin gene-carrying chromosomes could be retained at a workable level.[12]

Materials

Media. Commercially available medium (Dulbecco's modified Eagle's medium, DMEM) and fetal bovine serum (FBS) (GIBCO, Glasgow, Scotland) is used throughout. Batches of FBS are always pretested to ensure their usefulness for hybridoma growth. Typically, the FBS is used at 10%, but in stressful situations (after fusion, cloning, thawing) the serum concentration is increased to 20%, and 10% NCTC 109, additional amino acids, insulin, pyruvate, and oxalacetic acid are added.[13] Mouse thymocytes are used as filler cells.[14]

The HAT medium is prepared according to Littlefield[15] with 4×10^{-7} M aminopterin, 1.6×10^{-3} M thymidine, and 1×10^{-4} M hypoxanthine (all from Sigma, St. Louis, MO). For selecting clones deficient in hypoxanthine phosphoribosyltransferase (HPRT), we used 8-azaguanine (Sigma) at 20 μg/ml.

Antibiotics. In the early stages, before liquid nitrogen storage can be established, a mixture of 20 μg gentamicin (Schering, Kenilworth, NJ)

[8] R. Nowinski, C. Berglund, J. Lane, M. Lostrom, I. Bernstein, W. Young, S.-I. Hakomori, L. Hill, and M. Cooney, *Science* **210**, 537 (1980).
[9] J. Schlom, D. Wunderlich, and Y. A. Terramoto, *Proc. Natl. Acad. Sci. U.S.A.* **77**, 6841 (1980).
[10] C. M. Croce, M. Shander, J. Martinis, L. Cicurel, G. G. D'Ancona, and H. Koprowski, *Eur. J. Immunol.* **10**, 486 (1980).
[11] S. Malcolm, P. Barton, C. Murphy, M. A. Ferguson-Smith, D. L. Bentley, and T. H. Rabbitts, *Proc. Natl. Acad. Sci. U.S.A.* **79**, 4957 (1982).
[12] L. Östberg and E. Pursch, *Hybridoma* **2**, 361 (1983).
[13] R. H. Kennett, K. A. Denis, A. S. Tung, and N. R. Klinman, *Curr. Top. Microbiol. Immunol.* **81**, 77 (1978).
[14] J. Andersson, A. Coutinho, W. Lenhardt, and F. Melchers, *Cell* **10**, 27 (1977).
[15] J. W. Littlefield, *Science* **145**, 709 (1964).

and 100 U penicillin G (Biochemie, Kundl, Austria) per milliliter is used. Use of any type of antifungal agent is not encouraged as they seem to promote loss of antibody production in recently established hybrids. Large-scale culture is always done without any antibiotics.

Equipment. Small-scale cultures are grown in microtiter plates or cluster plates in humidified incubators at 37° in an atmosphere of 10% CO_2. Larger cultures are grown in closed tissue culture flasks or roller bottles in a 37° room.

Parental Cells. The parental mouse cell line is the SP2/0.[16] Human cells for fusion can be obtained either from organs such as tonsils, lymph nodes, or spleens by pressing the cells through a fine-mesh steel net, or from peripheral blood (PBLs) by centrifugation on a 1.089 g/ml density cushion of Percoll (Pharmacia, Uppsala, Sweden). The 1.089 g/ml Percoll frequently gives a better hybridoma yield than the frequently used 1.077 g/ml Ficoll-Paque, probably due to better retention of heavy B cells. A slight contamination with erythrocytes is not important.

Experimental Procedures

The general method for producing mouse × human and human × (mouse × human) hybridomas is essentially identical to the method used for mouse × mouse hybrids.[1,2]

Preparation of Mouse × Human Parent

The SP2/0 myeloma cells and PBLs are separately washed free of serum and debris by repeated centrifugations for 5 min at 400 g. The cells are mixed at a myeloma to PBL ratio of 1 : 5 to 1 : 1. The cell mixture is spun in a 50-ml conical tube at about 400 g for 5 min and then the serum-free medium is meticulously removed. The fusion is executed by dropwise addition of 1 ml of 50% PEG 4000 (Roth, Karlsruhe, West Germany) in serum-free DMEM to the disrupted pellet. In order to quench toxic aldehydes[17] in the PEG, it is sometimes helpful to add 400 mg L-lysine (Sigma) per liter to the fusion medium. After incubating the cells in PEG for 1 min, 1 ml of serum-free DMEM is added over 1 min. That is followed by 10 ml of serum-containing DMEM over the following minute. After collecting the cells at 400 g for 5 min, the pellet is suspended at about 2×10^6 cells/ml in reinforced DMEM[13] containing 20% FCS and HAT. The cells are seeded into 96-well microtiter plates at 150 μl/well. A large number of growing hybrids are observed after 2–3 weeks. When tested for

[16] M. Shulman, C. D. Wilde, and G. Köhler, *Nature (London)* **276**, 269 (1978).
[17] J. L. Kadish and K. M. Wenc, *Hybridoma* **2**, 87 (1983).

production of human Ig, they are mostly positive. However, when the assay for human Ig is repeated over the coming weeks, the levels of human Ig go down and eventually reach zero. At that time, rapidly growing cells are selected for reintroduction of the HPRT⁻ marker by treatment with 20 μg 8-azaguanine/ml. Fresh 8-azaguanine-containing medium is added every 4 days.

Surviving cells are recovered after 3 weeks and tested for their susceptibility to HAT medium. Typically, all cells selected by this procedure up to now have been HAT sensitive, confirming their HPRT⁻ status. The most useful of these cells has been named SPAZ-4[12] and is the cell parent with which all our experiences with human × (mouse × human) hybridomas have been obtained. However, considering the nonrandom pattern of chromosome loss in mouse × human hybrids, it is very likely that other useful cell lines could be established using the same approach.

Preparation of Human × (Mouse × Human) Hybridomas

The preparation of cells and the fusion are performed identically as for the mouse × human hybrids described above. With the SPAZ-4, all nonfused cells are dead or moribund within 48 hr. As the loss of the human X chromosome, where the HPRT gene is located,[18] could occur without any disadvantages to the antibody production, it is well advised not to use HAT medium any more than absolutely necessary. The human × (mouse × human) hybridomas typically grow substantially slower than mouse × mouse hybridomas in the early stage of *in vitro* establishment, but a mature hybridoma (more than 3 months *in vitro*) grows as well as a mouse hybridoma. The preparation of a human × (mouse × human) hybridoma is schematically shown in Fig. 1.

Testing of Antibody Production

Gross Antibody Production. The most convenient way for testing large numbers of cultures for antibody production is usually some type of enzyme-linked immunoassay (ELISA)[19]; a rabbit anti-human Ig preparation is adsorbed in a microtiter plate and allowed to interact with the hybridoma supernatant. After washing, the presence of human antibody is detected with enzyme-conjugated rabbit anti-human Ig and a suitable enzyme-activated color reagent. The amount of antibody produced is comparable to that produced by mouse hybridomas (see below, "Large-Scale Production of Human Monoclonal Antibodies").

[18] M. F. Lyon, *Nature (London), New Biol.* **232,** 229 (1971).
[19] E. Engvall and P. Perlman, *Immunochemistry* **8,** 871 (1971).

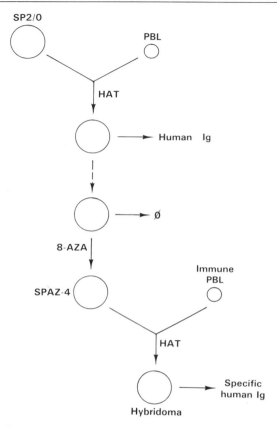

FIG. 1. Flow diagram to produce human × (mouse × human) hybridomas. (Modified from Ref. 12.)

Specific Antibody Production. It is quite meaningless to give any recommendations for specific tests because that obviously is intimately dependent on which antigen is being used and the potential application of the antibody. An additional helpful fact, however, is that even long-term functional tests can be performed in the early screening stage, as the cells accept freezing quite well. When the hybridomas in microwell cultures have grown to an optimal density, the supernatant is sampled so that approximately 100 μl of medium remains in the wells. After storing the plate on ice for 10–15 min, ice-cold medium containing 20% FBS and 20% dimethyl sulfoxide (DMSO) is added, 100 μl per well. The plates can then be sealed with a sterile adhesive sheet (Flow, Glasgow, Scotland) and stored at −70° for several months while waiting for test results. When the test data are available, the cultures are thawed and the positive cultures picked and reseeded in fresh medium with filler cells.

Large-Scale Production of Human Monoclonal Antibodies

A major difference between human × (mouse × human) hybridomas and mouse × mouse hybridomas is that large-scale production in mouse ascites fluid is not practical. It is possible to grow this type of cell in athymic nude mice or in lethally irradiated normal BALB/c mice. However, considering the cost of nude mice or the cost of routine irradiation, it is unlikely that such production is cost-effective compared to large-scale tissue culture. The risk of introducing contaminating viruses from the mice should also be considered. Removal of mouse immunoglobulin is complicated and is, of course, crucial, since any contamination of the human antibody preparation with animal proteins defeats much of the advantages of human monoclonals in therapeutic applications.

The largest scale for human monoclonal antibody production using this type of human × (mouse × human) hybrids has been 500-ml roller bottles. Such cultures routinely grow and produce well, reaching concentrations above 50 mg antibody per liter. Considering that this type of hybridoma in its *in vitro* behavior is indistinguishable from mouse hybridomas, there is no reason to assume that they will not be able to grow in even larger scale, allowing due time for adaptation.

The purification of human monoclonals is, in most cases, easily achieved by chromatography on Sepharose–protein A columns (Pharmacia). The use of that method for purification gives a preparation which contains only immunoglobulin molecules. However, as FBS is known to contain bovine Ig reactive with protein A,[20] this convenient method might compromise the purity of the final product. In order to obtain a pure final product, it might be worthwhile to spend the effort of adapting the cells to a protein-free, chemically defined medium, e.g., as described by Cleveland et al.[21]

Recently, Teng et al.[22] have described another method of constructing human × (mouse × human) hybridomas, using a human myeloma instead of PBLs in the first fusion step, and using another selection procedure after the first fusion to reserve the HAT selection markers for the second

[20] P. A. Underwood, J. F. Kelly, D. F. Haman, and H. M. MacMillan, *J. Immunol. Methods* **60**, 33 (1983).

[21] W. L. Cleveland, I. Wood, and B. F. Erlanger, *J. Immunol. Methods* **56**, 221 (1983).

[22] N. N. H. Teng, K. S. Lam, R. C. Riera, and H. S. Kaplan, *Proc. Natl. Acad. Sci. U.S.A.* **80**, 7308 (1983).

fusion without the need to reintroduce this marker by 8-azaguanine treatment. A paper by Foung et al.[23] describes a method identical to the one outlined in this chapter except that an EBV-transformed B cell was used in the second fusion. Interestingly, Tucker et al.[24] have constructed bovine × (mouse × bovine) hybridomas stably producing bovine Ig, indicating that a technique using a xenogeneic hybrid as myeloma parent might be generally applicable in order to obtain functional hybridomas in species for which no useful myeloma is available.

[23] S. K. H. Foung, S. Perkins, A. Raubitschek, J. Larrick, G. Lizak, D. Fishwill, E. G. Engleman, and F. C. Grumet, J. Immunol. Methods **70**, 83 (1984).
[24] E. M. Tucker, A. R. Dain, S. W. Clarke, and R. A. Donker, Hybridoma **3**, 171 (1984).

[19] Generation of Rat–Rat Hybridomas with the Use of the LOU IR983F Nonsecreting Fusion Cell Line

By LIEVE DE CLERCQ, FRANÇOISE CORMONT, and HERVÉ BAZIN

Since introduction of the cell fusion technique between a suitable myeloma cell and a lymphoid cell from an immunized animal,[1] specific monoclonal antibodies (MAb) have been produced in a large number of laboratories. The most common animal model is the mouse–mouse model, using cell lines derived from BALB/c plasmacytomas.[2] Rat–mouse hybrids have also been obtained by the fusion of rat spleen cells with one of the mouse myelomas.[3,4] In most cases, these hybrids are not very stable, nor can they be easily transplanted into animals. The LOU rat IR983F fusion cell line is nonsecretory[5]; its growth capacity and fusion efficiency are close to those of the mouse Sp2/0 myeloma.[6] The rat–rat model of hybridization has the advantage of offering a different antigen range than the mouse model, and is, moreover, more productive when

[1] G. Köhler and C. Milstein, Nature (London) **256**, 495 (1975).
[2] M. Potter, Physiol. Rev. **52**, 631 (1971).
[3] J. A. Ledbetter and L. A. Herzenberg, Immunol. Rev. **47**, 63 (1979).
[4] C. Verwaerde, J. M. Crzych, H. Bazin, M. Capron, and A. Capron, C.R. Hebd. Seances Acad. Sci. **289**, 725 (1979).
[5] H. Bazin, in "Protides of the Biological Fluids" (H. Peeters, ed.), p. 615. Pergamon, Oxford, 1982.
[6] A. Schulman, C. D. Wilde, and G. Köhler, Nature (London) **276**, 269 (1978).

transplanted *in vivo*. Finally, extremely simple techniques of purification[7,8] can be applied to the MAb derived from the LOU rat model.

The technique of rat–rat hybridoma generation with the use of the IR983F cell line is derived from that of the mouse–mouse system[1,9–12] with only minor modifications. However, even a small difference in hybridoma technology can considerably influence the results. The present description is based not only on mouse–mouse technology but also on our experience with *in vivo* LOU/C immunocytoma (plasmacytoma) transplantations since 1969[13] and with *in vitro* culture of the same tumors since 1972.[14]

IR983F Fusion Cell Line

As described in Bazin,[5] the IR983F cell line is derived from the LOU/C rat strain. The initial tumor, IR983, a nonsecreting immunocytoma (plasmacytoma), was first adapted to ascitic growth in rats,[13] before its development into a permanent azaguanine-resistant *in vitro* cell line, the IR983F or the thereafter abbreviated 983 cell line.

Animals

The spleen cells which serve as partners to the 983 cells in the fusion experiments are provided by syngeneic LOU/C or LOU/M rats which have developed an immune response. The LOU/C or LOU/M rats (abbreviated to LOU) are bred in our own colonies, which constitute the original breeding of these two strains as described in Bazin *et al.*[15] LOU/C.IgK-1b(OKA) is a congeneic line to the LOU/C strain, having the κ light chain locus from the OKA strain in LOU/C background.[8]

Immunizations

For fusion purposes, the classical immunization procedures are usually not applicable as such. One must obtain a serum with a high density

[7] H. Bazin, L. M. Xhurdebise, G. Burtonboy, A. M. Lebacq, L. De Clercq, and F. Cormont, *J. Immunol. Methods* **66,** 261 (1984).
[8] H. Bazin, F. Cormont, and L. De Clercq, *J. Immunol. Methods* **71,** 9 (1984).
[9] G. Galfré, C. Milstein, and B. Wright, *Nature (London)* **277,** 131 (1979).
[10] S. Fazekas de St. Groth and D. Scheidegger, *J. Immunol. Methods* **35,** 1 (1980).
[11] J. W. Goding, *J. Immunol. Methods* **39,** 285 (1980).
[12] G. Galfré and C. Milstein, this series, Vol. 73, Part B, p. 3.
[13] H. Bazin, C. Deckers, A. Beckers, and J. F. Heremans, *Int. J. Cancer* **10,** 568 (1972).
[14] G. Burtonboy, H. Bazin, C. Deckers, M. Lamy, and J. F. Heremans, *Eur. J. Cancer* **9,** 259 (1973).
[15] H. Bazin, A. Beckers, C. Deckers, and M. Moriame, *J. Natl. Cancer Inst. (U.S.)* **51,** 1359 (1973).

of blast and plasma cells[11,16] rather than a serum with a high antibody titer. But, the immunization schedule remains antigen dependent. For soluble antigens—in most of our cases, immunoglobulins—adjuvants are generally needed. The currently used immunization procedure consists of two intraperitoneal injections of about 100–500 μg immunoglobulin in 250 μl saline emulsified with the same volume of complete Freund's adjuvant. A booster injection of 200 μg of purified immunoglobulin in 0.5 ml of saline was given 4 days before fusion by the intravenous route. A long rest between initial immunization and the booster before fusion is a good general rule to follow: the longer the rest, the better the response to the booster, at least for the soluble antigens and within the limits of 6 to 12 months.

Examples of LOU rat immunization schedules for other antigens are given by Crzych et al.[17] for *Schistosoma mansoni* antigens, Burtonboy et al.[18] for canine parvovirus antigens, Lebacq and Bazin[19] and Lebacq-Verheyden et al.[20] for human leukemic lymphoblast antigens, Hirsch et al.[21] for autoantigens, and Bazin et al.[7] for dinitrophenylated soluble or insoluble carriers.

Media

For the fusion itself, Eagle's minimum essential medium or MEM (REGA 3) without L-glutamine (GIBCO, cat. No. 045-9993), buffered with 10 mM HEPES (GIBCO, cat. No. 043-5630) and supplemented with 50 mg gentamicin/liter (GIBCO, cat. No. 043-5750), gives good results.

The 983 cells grow well in DMEM without HEPES (Dulbecco's modified Eagle's medium; GIBCO, cat. No. 041-1965) supplemented with 5% heat-inactivated (30 min at 56°) fetal calf serum (GIBCO), 5% heat-inactivated horse serum (Flow), 1% nonessential amino acids (GIBCO, cat. No. 043-1140), 1% sodium pyruvate 100 mM (GIBCO, cat. No. 043-1360), and 0.1% gentamicin sulfate 50 mg/ml (GIBCO, cat. No. 043-5750).

All serum batches used for culture purposes are tested for 3 weeks on the 983 cell line for growth efficiency. An optimal doubling time of ~17 hr or less is required.

[16] C. Stähli, T. Staehelin, V. Migginao, J. Schmidt, and P. Häring, *J. Immunol. Methods* **32**, 297 (1980).

[17] J. M. Crzych, M. Capron, H. Bazin, and A. Capron, *J. Immunol.* **129**, 2739 (1982).

[18] G. Burtonboy, H. Bazin, and N. Delferrière, *Arch. Virol.* **71**, 291 (1982).

[19] A. M. Lebacq and H. Bazin, *Bull. Cancer* **70**, 93 (1983).

[20] A. M. Lebacq-Verheyden, A. M. Ravoet, H. Bazin, D. R. Sutherland, N. Tidman, and M. F. Greaves, *Int. J. Cancer* **32**, 273 (1983).

[21] F. Hirsch, F. Cormont, C. Sapin, H. Bazin, and P. Druet, *Proc. Int. Congr. Immunol. 5th. 1983* Book Abstr. No. 616-06, p. 166 (1983).

For the selection media, hypoxanthine–aminopterin–thymidine (HAT) (50×) and hypoxanthine–thymidine (HT) (50×) are used. The concentrations of aminopterin (Sigma, A-2255), hypoxanthine (Sigma, H-9377), and thymidine (Sigma, T-9250) are 20, 5, and 0.8 mM, respectively.

The concentration of the PEG (polyethylene glycol) solution used for fusion is 41.6% in fusion medium containing 8.75 ml dimethyl sulfoxide (Merck 802912) added to 100 g of initial PEG solution to improve the fusion efficiency. Two-milliliter final PEG solution aliquots are sterilized by autoclaving or filtration and stored in an incubator at 37° for a maximum of 3 months.

Feeder Layer

Feeder layers of rat peritoneal cells are prepared the day before fusion in HAT medium, or 1–4 days before development or cloning in HT medium. The cells are seeded at a concentration of 2×10^5 cells/ml on the basis of 0.1 ml/microwell (96-well plates, Costar cat. No. 3596) or 1 ml/macrowell (24-well plates, Costar cat. No. 3524 or Nunc cat. No. 168357). At no later stage, e.g., during mass culture or additional cloning, are peritoneal cells added. The origin of the rats used as the source of the feeder layers seems to have no importance, and outbred Wistar rats are therefore routinely used.

Fusion Experiment

The fusion capacity of the 983 cells depends, as with Sp2/0 cells, on the growth conditions. To ensure a high yield of hybrids, the myeloma cells used for the fusion must be in a strictly exponential growth phase for at least a week. The different ways to obtain this are either to add medium every day to the culture vessel (spinner or plastic flasks), adjust the cell concentration to 5×10^5 cells/ml,[22] or adjust the cell concentration back to 10^5 cells/ml on days 0, 3, and 5 (G. Burtonboy, University of Louvain, personal communication). On day 7, cells may be collected for hybridization.

After anesthesia, an immunized LOU rat is bled via the carotid artery. Its spleen is removed and immersed in EMEM without serum. The organ is teased under sterile conditions on a metal grid supported by a beaker. The cell suspension is allowed to stand for 10 min and the large fragments that settle are discarded.

The 983 cells and the spleen cells are centrifuged for 5 min at 250 g. The pellet is washed twice with fusion medium EMEM without serum.

[22] A. M. Lebacq-Verheyden, A. Neirynck, and H. Bazin, *Hybridoma* **2,** 355 (1983).

Cells are mixed in a ratio of one 983 cell to every five spleen cells. After centrifugation (5 min at 250 g), the supernatant is discarded and the cell pellet detached by gentle shaking. One milliliter of warmed PEG solution (37°) is added dropwise to 2×10^7 cells during 90 sec of gentle shaking. After another 30 sec of shaking, 2 ml of EMEM is added during the following 90 sec to the cell mixture. Finally, 20 ml of EMEM is progressively added to dilute the PEG solution. Centrifugation for 5 min at 180 g precedes the resuspension of all cells in the selection serum-rich HAT culture medium. The cell density is adjusted to 10^6 cells/ml, and the cell suspension is distributed over 24 (1 ml)- and 96 (0.1 ml)-well plates containing peritoneal cells in the selection HAT medium. The medium is renewed four times before starting the screening procedure.

Screening

The screening of supernatants generally begins on the tenth day after fusion, after four renewals of medium. Depending on the type of immunogen, one can utilize different screening procedures: radioimmunoassay, enzyme-linked immunoassay, hemagglutination, or immunofluorescence.

Cloning

Each positive hybrid is frozen in 7.5% DMSO in culture medium and stored in liquid nitrogen after one or two cloning steps by limiting dilution, as described by Goding.[23] Cells, 5×10^6 to 10^7, are also injected subcutaneously into a syngenic LOU rat or, even better, into a LOU/C.IgK-1b(OKA) rat[8] for propagation of the hybridoma *in vivo,* and purification by immunoaffinity chromatography. Hybridomas developed in LOU rats can also be frozen and stored in liquid nitrogen, as described for the LOU/C immunocytomas.[13]

Acknowledgments

This work was supported in part by the Fonds Cancérologique de la CGER (Belgium), the F.R.S.M. (Belgium), Contract No. 3.4518.76, and EURATOM Contract No. Bio-c-358-81-B (publication No. 2189). The authors wish to express their thanks to their colleagues A. M. Lebacq and G. Burtonboy (University of Louvain, Faculty of Medicine, Belgium) for their helpful suggestions. They appreciated the excellent technical assistance of D. Bourgois, C. Genart, F. Nisol, T. Goffart, J. P. Kints, and J. M. Malache. They also thank F. Bolle for her great help in preparing the chapter. H. B. is a staff member of the Commission of the European Communities.

[23] J. W. Goding, "Monoclonal Antibodies: Principles and Practice" p. 86. Academic Press, London, 1984.

[20] Production of Syrian and Armenian Hamster Monoclonal Antibodies of Defined Specificity

By FRANCISCO SANCHEZ-MADRID and TIMOTHY A. SPRINGER

Interspecies hybridomas have been generated using mouse myeloma cell lines as fusion partners with rat, human, rabbit, and bovine spleen cells. Rabbit × mouse hybrids rapidly lose secretion of rabbit Ig chains, probably due to the high rate of chromosome loss.[1] In contrast, fusions of mouse myeloma cells with mouse or rat spleen cells yield mouse and rat hybridomas which represent stable sources of mouse and rat monoclonal antibodies (MAbs).[2,3] Rat MAbs secreted by rat–mouse hybrids have been utilized to study mouse cell surface antigens.[3,4] However, identification of some surface molecules could be hampered by the evolutionary proximity of the rat and mouse. Many antigenic structures may remain conserved in these two species, which belong to the same Murinae subfamily.

In the search for animals evolutionarily distant from the mouse, we found that B lymphocytes from two different species of hamster (Cricetidae family) are excellent fusion partners with mouse myelomas.[5] Here, the production of hamster MAbs is described. Since the methods are in great part identical to those for mouse and rat MAbs, only the variations are described. A MAb reactive with Armenian and Syrian κ chains, which is a very useful screening reagent, is additionally described.

Generation and Characterization of Hamster–Mouse Hybridomas

Parental Cells

Myeloma Lines. The characteristics of mouse myeloma lines used in fusion experiments have been described in detail.[2] NSI (NSI/1.Ag4.1) and P3X63Ag8.653 are variant myelomas that synthesize κ light chain or no

[1] J. A. Sogn, M. C. Kuo, and T. J. Kindt, *Fed. Proc.* **41,** 595 (1982).
[2] G. Galfré and C. Milstein, this series, Vol. 73, p. 3.
[3] R. H. Kennett, T. J. McKearn, and K. B. Bechtol, "Monoclonal Antibodies." Plenum, New York, 1980.
[4] T. A. Springer, D. Davignon, M. K. Ho, K. Kürzinger, E. Martz, and F. Sanchez-Madrid, *Immunol. Rev.* **68,** 111 (1982).
[5] F. Sanchez-Madrid, P. Szklut, and T. A. Springer, *J. Immunol.* **130,** 309 (1983).

chain, respectively. These parental lines are maintained in logarithmic growth in suspension cultures or in spinner cultures. As medium for growth, we use either RPMI 1640 or Dulbecco's modified Eagle's medium (DME) supplemented with glutamine and 10% fetal calf serum (FCS).

Immunization of Animals. Syrian (*Mesocricetus auratus*) and Armenian (*Cricetulus migratorius*) hamsters can be obtained from Charles River Laboratories (Wilmington, MA) and Cambridge Diagnostics (Cambridge, MA 02139) or Dr. George Yerganian, Newton-Wellesley Hospital (Newton, MA 02162), respectively. Outbred animals from 2 months to 1 year old are used. Animals usually are primed with antigen intraperitoneally on day -30 and boosted intravenously on day -3 prior to fusion on day 0. For soluble antigens which equilibrate between extravascular and vascular spaces, it may be more convenient to boost intraperitoneally. Relative to mice, Armenian hamsters have short (2-in.), puny tails. Unless caged individually after the age of 8 weeks, female Armenian hamsters bite one another's tails off. Males are less aggressive. If tails are present, investigators with skill in the technique can successfully inject in the tail vein. Alternatively, boosting in the jugular vein is described.

Materials

Xylazine (Rompun; Haver-Lockhart, Cutter Labs, Shawnnee, KA 66201)
Ketamine (Ketaset; Bristol Labs, Syracuse, NY 13201)
Anesthetic: 1.6 mg Xylazine/ml, 1.6 mg ketamine/ml, in sterile water, in 1-ml syringe
27-gauge needles
1-ml syringe containing antigen in 0.2 ml saline
Tweezers and scissors
Wound clips (autoclip, Clay-Adams)

Procedure. Inject 0.1-ml aliquots of anesthetic intramuscularly with a 27-gauge needle. Wait several minutes after each injection, and test for lack of any response to squeezing the foot with tweezers. Typically, this occurs after about 0.3 ml for Armenian hamsters (about 30 g). Make a vertical incision along sternocleido-mastoid line using blunt-pointed scissors, exposing the submaxillary and sublingual glands. These are separated with blunt scissors to expose the jugular vein. Injection is with a 27-gauge ½-in. needle, bent slightly to facilitate a more shallow penetration of the vein. The incision is then cleaned and closed with 9-mm wound clips.

Fusion

The fusion procedure was not varied from the standard conditions for mouse–mouse and rat–mouse fusions.[2,6,7] Briefly, 50% (w/w) PEG (polyethylene glycol, MW 1,500, BDH) was prepared by autoclaving 10 g, cooling to 50°, and adding 10 ml of DME. The pH was adjusted to pH 7.4. The solution was prepared at least 1 day before fusion and could be kept at least 2 months. On day 0, hamsters were killed with CO_2 in a chamber with dry ice and water, and washed with 70% ethanol. Peritoneal cells were removed by intraperitoneal lavage with 10 ml or 5 ml of 10 units heparin/ml in PBS per Syrian or Armenian hamster, respectively. Hamster spleens were removed and cell suspensions prepared and fused with NSI or P3X63Ag8.653 mouse myeloma cells at a 1:4 myeloma to spleen cell ratio according to the Galfré procedure.[2,6,7] Syrian hamsters yielded about 6×10^7 white cells/spleen. Armenian hamsters yielded 2×10^7 to 10^8 white cells/spleen. After fusion, cells were resuspended directly in HAT selection medium and distributed in flat-bottomed microculture 96-well plates (Costar, No. 3596) at 2×10^5 spleen cells per well. Hamster peritoneal cells were added as feeder cells at a concentration of 2×10^4 cells/ml in the final hybrid cell suspension.

Growth Characteristics of Hybrids

The feeding schedule of cultures is similar to that described for rat–mouse hybrids.[5] Cultures are fed by replacing about one-half the medium on days 7 and 11 after fusion. After 2 weeks, cultures are fed every 3 days with the same medium lacking aminopterin (HT medium) until the medium becomes yellow. Then, feeding is carried out every 2 days. Visible growth is observed 1 week after fusion.

Compared to mouse and rat hybrids, Armenian hamster hybrids grow at a similar or slightly slower rate, and Syrian hamster hybrids grow somewhat more slowly during the first 2 weeks. After cloning (in soft agar), growth rates of both types of hamster hybrids are excellent. The doubling time was measured for one Armenian hybrid and found to be 15 hr. The frequency of wells with growing hybridomas was measured in four independent fusions[5] (and unpublished). Hybridomas grew in 50% of Syrian hybrid cultures seeded with 1.6 to 2.1×10^5 spleen cells and in

[6] G. Galfré, S. C. Howe, C. Milstein, G. W. Butcher, and C. J. Howard, *Nature (London)* **266**, 550 (1977).
[7] Z. Eshhar, *in* "Hybridoma Technology in the Biosciences and Medicine" (T. A. Springer, ed.), p. 3. Plenum, New York, 1985.

100% of American hybrid cultures seeded with 1.4 to 5×10^5 cells. Thus, the frequency of Armenian hybrids is $>0.7 \times 10^{-5}$, which is similar to that of murine hybrids.

In Syrian hamster fusions, adherent cells with a fibroblast-like morphology proliferated in 20–60% of the cultures. These cells were readily distinguished morphologically from the round, nonadherent B-cell hybrids and did not secrete Ig. Proliferation was so vigorous that this cell type appeared to often overwhelm the hybridomas. Such rapidly proliferating adherent cells were not observed in Armenian fusions in our hands, but have been found by others, and overgrew the hybridomas (J. Unkeless, U. Rockefeller, and R. Schreiber, Scripps Clinic, La Jolla, CA 92037). Thus far, the reasons for the predominance of this undesirable cell type in some but not other fusions are not clear. It is possible that the fusion conditions or growth factors in serum influence its appearance. Growth of this fibroblast-like cell type has not been seen in fusions with mouse or rat spleen cells.

Cloning

Hamster hybrids secreting antibodies of desired specificity are cloned in soft agar or in microtiter wells.[2] Stability has been measured by recloning and determining the percentage of active subclones. Subclones are almost always 100% active, showing hamster hybridomas are at least as stable as mouse or rat hybridomas.

Screening

The usual types of screening procedures can be applied to hamster MAbs. We have selected for MAbs which inhibit T-lymphocyte-mediated killing in functional screening, and have also used an indirect cell binding assay.[5] A potential disadvantage of the hamster is the limited commercial availability of antibodies to hamster Ig. Antisera to Syrian hamster (usually listed simply as "hamster" or "golden hamster") but not Armenian hamster IgG are available.

Fortunately, an anti-hamster Ig MAb has been produced which serves as an excellent reagent for use with hamster MAbs.[8] Labeled with ^{125}I, it can be used as a second antibody[8] to detect hamster MAbs of desired antigen specificity. It can be coupled to Sepharose to purify Ig or to isolate antigen–hamster MAb complexes for biochemical analysis of antigens.[5] This MAb, RG7/7, was originally selected as an antibody to rat κ Ib

[8] T. A. Springer, A. Bhattacharya, J. T. Cardoza, and F. Sanchez-Madrid, *Hybridoma* **1**, 257 (1982).

MAb	Class[a]	Hamster	Antigen polypeptide chain(s)[b] (MW × 10⁻³)	Antigen name	Cell distribution[c]
M21/3	IgM	Syrian	—	—	B and T lymphocytes, macrophages, brain
M22/3	IgG	Syrian	35	Lyt-2,3	T lymphocytes
M23/3	IgM	Armenian	—	—	B and T lymphocytes, macrophages, brain
M24/1	ND[d]	Armenian	180, 95	LFA-1	Leukocytes
M24/2	ND	Armenian	25	Thy-1	T lymphocytes, brain
M24/5	ND	Armenian	200, 160	—	T and B lymphocytes, macrophages
M24/6	ND	Armenian	12	—	Lymphocytes
M24/8	ND	Armenian	25	Thy-1	T lymphocytes, brain

[a] Determined by mobility of heavy chains in SDS–PAGE.
[b] Determined by SDS–PAGE of reduced, ¹²⁵I-labeled, immunoprecipitated antigen.
[c] Determined by indirect binding assay with ¹²⁵I-RG7/7.[8]
[d] Not done.

isotype light chains, but binds with even higher affinity to κ light chains of Armenian and Syrian hamster Ig.[5,8] It does not cross-react with Chinese hamster, human, rabbit, guinea pig, or mouse IgG. Four of four hamster MAbs which we identified by functional screening reacted in indirect binding assays with this MAb. It thus appears that most hamster MAbs contain the κ light chain, in similarity to the mouse and rat, where the κ to λ ratio is >9 : 1. The RG7/7 anti-Syrian and Armenian hamster κ chain hybridoma cell line may be obtained from the American Type Culture Collection, 12301 Parklawn Dr., Rockville, MD 20852. Purified RG7/7 IgG may be obtained from Boehringer-Mannheim or Hybritech, 11085 Torreyona Rd., San Diego, CA 92121. RG7/7 is a mouse IgG$_{2a}$ MAb, and can be purified on *Staphylococcus aureus* protein A–Sepharose.[9]

Hamster Ig subclasses are only in the initial stages of characterization. Syrian hamster IgG$_1$ and IgG$_2$ have been reported to both bind to protein A at pH 8 and to be differentially eluted at low pH.[10] Syrian hamster Ig binds to protein A with an affinity intermediate between that of rat and mouse Ig.[11] IgM and IgG hamster hybridomas can be differentiated by the

[9] P. L. Ey, S. J. Prowse, and C. R. Jenkin, *Immunochemistry* **15**, 429 (1978).
[10] M. J. Escribano, H. Haddada, and C. De Vaux Saint Cyr, *J. Immunol. Methods* **52**, 63 (1982).
[11] D. D. Richman, P. H. Cleveland, M. N. Oxman, and K. M. Johnson, *J. Immunol.* **128**, 2300 (1982).

mobility of their heavy chains in SDS–PAGE.[5] Secreted Igs can be conveniently analyzed after labeling with radioactive amino acids.

Conclusion

A number of hamster MAbs have thus far been obtained which recognized mouse T-lymphocyte surface antigens (table). Hamster MAbs to mouse γ-interferon have also been obtained.[12] Hamster hybridomas are an excellent and stable source of MAbs of predefined specificity. Their primary use thus far has been for the preparation of anti-mouse MAb, but they have the potential for much wider applications.

Acknowledgments

This work was supported by NIH Grant CA-31798. The superb technical assistance of P. Szklut is acknowledged.

[12] R. D. Schreiber, L. J. Hicks, A. B. Celada, and P. W. Gray, *J. Immunol.* **134,** 1609 (1985).

[21] Production and Characterization of Bovine Immunoglobulins from Bovine × Murine Hybridomas

By ALBERT J. GUIDRY, S. SRIKUMARAN, and RICHARD A. GOLDSBY

Introduction

Characterization of the classes and subclasses of immunoglobulins (Ig) is important for the study of humoral immune response and the structure–function relationship between Ig classes and subclasses and effector mechanisms. In human, murine, and a few other species, such characterization has been facilitated by the availability of homogeneous Ig produced by multiple myelomas.[1] Except for an isolated report of the appearance of Bence-Jones proteins in the bovine[2] species there have been no reports of bovine myelomas to date. The lack of availability of myelomas has made the characterization of bovine Ig difficult. Characterization of bovine Ig has been based on studies made with heterogeneous Ig preparations purified from serum, colostrum, and other exocrine secretions, em-

[1] M. Potter, *Adv. Immunol.* **25,** 141 (1977).
[2] S. Rodkey and A. T. Kimmel, *Immunochemistry* **9,** 23 (1972).

ploying physicochemical purification procedures.[3,4] However, because of the similar or overlapping physicochemical properties of Ig classes and subclasses, these procedures do not yield pure preparations of bovine Ig. Regardless of physicochemical purity, such preparations could not be used for detailed immunological and structural studies nor serve as reference standards, because they contain different molecular species of Ig secreted by different clones of B lymphocytes. However, if the homogeneous Ig-secreting ability of a single clone could be "immortalized" by hybridizing with an established cell line, unlimited quantities of pure and homogeneous Ig could be obtained.[5]

This chapter describes interspecific hybridization of a nonsecreting murine hybridoma with *normal* bovine spleen cells to produce stable hybridoma cell lines secreting monoclonal bovine Ig molecules.[6,7] Davidson *et al.*[8] recently reported the production of monoclonal bovine IgM by bovine × murine hybridomas. However, these workers employed bovine leukemic lymphocytes, which are unable to produce Ig of a predefined specificity. The procedure described here yields bovine B lymphocyte hybrids with *normal* secretory function, thus adding a new dimension to the field of bovine immunology. In addition to producing homogeneous bovine Ig isotypes, this approach allows for the continuous cultivation of hybridomas secreting bovine Ig of predefined antigenic specificity. Antigenic specificity is obtained by using normal bovine spleen cells from appropriately immunized donors, or spleen cells stimulated *in vitro* by the antigen, as fusion partners. In fact we were able to produce a bovine × murine hybridoma that secreted bovine antibodies to DNP by fusing normal spleen cells, from calves immunized with DNP–ovalbumin, with the murine × murine hybridoma cell line SP2/0; however, it was lost later in culture.

Production of Bovine × Murine Hybridomas

Bovine × murine hybridomas were derived by the polyethylene glycol (PEG)-induced fusion of normal bovine lymphocytes to SP2/0,[9] which

[3] H. Fey, H. Pfister, J. Mesierli, N. Sturzenegger, and F. Grolimund, *Vet. Med. B* **23**, 269 (1976).

[4] J. E. Butler and C. F. Maxwell, *J. Dairy Sci.* **55**, 151 (1972).

[5] G. Kohler and C. Milstein, *Nature (London)* **256**, 495 (1975).

[6] S. Srikumaran, A. J. Guidry, and R. A. Goldsby, *Science* **220**, 522 (1983).

[7] S. Srikumaran, A. J. Guidry, and R. A. Goldsby, *Vet. Immunol. Immunopathol.* **5**, 323 (1983/1984).

[8] I. Davidson, S. Katzav, H. Ungar-Waron, Z. Eshnar, J. Haimavich, and Z. Trainin, *Mol. Immunol.* **19**, 893 (1982).

[9] M. Shulman, C. D. Wilde, and G. Kohler, *Nature (London)* **276**, 269 (1978).

neither secretes nor internally produces murine Ig, using a protocol described by Goldsby et al.[10]

Media and Buffers

Tissue-grade deionized double-distilled water was used to prepare the following media and buffers:

RDG: 1 part RPMI 1640[11] (5 g/liter) to 1 part Dulbecco's modified Eagle's medium (DMEM)[11] (5 g/liter) supplemented with glucose (4.5 g/liter) and $NaHCO_3$ (2.85 g/liter) and sterilized by pressure filtration. Glutamine[11] (292 mg/liter), penicillin[11] (100,000 units/liter), and streptomycin[11] (100 mg/liter) were added before use.

RDGS: RDG supplemented with 10% γ-globulin-free *horse* serum.[11]

8-Ag: RDGS containing 25 μg 8-azaguanine/ml.[12]

HT: RDGS containing 1×10^{-4} M hypoxanthine[12] and 3×10^{-5} M thymidine.[12]

HAT: HT plus 4×10^{-7} M aminopterin.[12,13]

PBS: 8.0 g NaCl, 2.16 g $Na_2HPO_4 \cdot H_2O$, 0.2 g KCl, and 0.2 g K_2PO_4/liter; pH 7.2.

PEG: 52% solution (w/v) of polyethylene glycol 1540[14] in RDG.

Fusion and Growth of Hybridomas

Bovine lymphocytes were obtained from the spleen of an adult Holstein cow by mincing six randomly selected 2-cm cubes of spleen with scissors and grinding the mince between the frosted surfaces of microscope slides in RDG. The tissue was allowed to settle and the supernatant, containing the splenic lymphocytes, was saved. The lymphocytes were washed two times by centrifuging at 400 g for 15 min and resuspending in RDG. They were then resuspended in RDG to a concentration of 1×10^8 cells/25 ml.

Sp2/0 cells, which were grown in RDGS, were harvested, washed two times and resuspended in serum-free RDG to a concentration of 1×10^8 cells/25 ml RDG.

Murine thymocytes were prepared by mincing a mouse thymus between frosted glass slides and isolating and washing as described above, except that the final suspension was 1×10^6 cells/ml in HAT.

---

[10] R. A. Goldsby, B. A. Osborne, E. Simpson, and L. A. Herzenberg, *Nature (London)* **267**, 707 (1977).

[11] GIBCO, Grand Island, New York.

[12] Sigma, St. Louis, Missouri.

[13] J. W. Littlefield, *Science* **45**, 709 (1964).

[14] Baker Chemicals, Phillipsburg, New Jersey.

Fusion was performed by mixing 25 ml of the SP2/0 with an equal volume of the bovine lymphocytes and copelleting the mixed cell population by centrifugation at 400 g for 10 min. The supernatant was decanted and the cell pellet was rapidly slurried in 1 ml of 37° 40% PEG (MW 1300–1500) in RDG and then diluted to 5 ml with 37° 40% PEG. The slurry was immediately centrifuged for 4 min at 400 g. The fused pellet was gently reslurried by the addition, with stirring, of 5 ml of 37° RDG to the system. After 2 min, the 10 ml mixture was diluted to 20 ml with RDG, allowed to stand at 37° for 2 min, and then diluted to 50 ml with RDG and centrifuged at 400 g for 10 min. The fused cells were resuspended in 150 ml HAT[15,16] and distributed in 100-μl aliquots to wells of several 96-well microtiter plates containing murine thymocytes (1 × 10⁵/well) in 100 μl HAT, using a mechanical device[16] for pipetting and replicating.

At approximately weekly intervals, one-half of the medium in each well was removed and 100 μl of fresh HAT was added to feed the cells and to dilute the Ig secreted by the parent bovine nonfused spleen cells. Between 14 and 21 days postfusion, hybrid clones were visible to the naked eye. At this point, supernatants from the hybrid clones were assayed for the presence of bovine Ig by competitive radioimmunoassay (cRIA) (see "Testing for Positive Clones"). The clones which secreted bovine Ig were recloned by limiting dilution with HT in 96-well microtiter dishes as described by Goldsby and Zipser.[17]

Hybridoma Testing

Iodination of Affinity-Purified Immunoglobulins

Labeling of affinity-purified polyclonal bovine Ig isotypes[18] with ¹²⁵I was carried out according to the procedure described by Hunter,[19] with slight modifications. Briefly, 1 μCi ¹²⁵I[20] was added to 100 μl of 0.5 M phosphate buffer (1.11 g KH_2PO_4 and 14.96 g $Na_2HPO_4 \cdot 12\ H_2O$/100 ml deionized water, pH 7.5). One hundred micrograms of affinity-purified Ig in 100 μl phosphate-buffered saline (PBS) was then added to 50 μl of 0.01 M chloramine-T (10 mg chloramine-T/5 ml 0.05 M phosphate buffer). Iodination was allowed to take place at 0° in an ice bucket for 10 min and

[15] E. H. Szybalska and W. Szybalska, *Proc. Natl. Acad. Sci. U.S.A.* **48**, 2026 (1962).
[16] R. A. Goldsby and N. Mandell, *in* "Methods in Cell Biology" (D. M. Prescott, ed.), p. 261. Academic Press, New York, 1973.
[17] R. A. Goldsby and E. Zipser, *Exp. Cell Res.* **54**, 271 (1969).
[18] J. P. Flook and A. J. Guidry, unpublished results.
[19] R. Hunter, *Proc. Soc. Exp. Biol. Med.* **133**, 989 (1970).
[20] New England Nuclear, Boston, Massachusetts.

then at room temperature for 5 min. Two hundred microliters 0.01 M sodium metabisulfite (12 mg sodium methabisulfite/5 ml 0.05 M phosphate buffer, pH 7.5) was added to stop the reaction. The mixture was then allowed to stand at room temperature for 10 min. Potassium iodide (500 μl), 0.18 M, was added and the total volume of the reaction mixture made up to 1.5 ml with 3% (w/v) BSA in PBS. Unbound ^{125}I was separated from labeled protein on an anion-exchange column containing 1 g of Dowex[21] anion-exchange resin, Ag1-X8, in deionized water. Phosphate buffer (0.05 M, pH 7.5) was used to elute the protein. Fractions (1 ml) were collected in tubes containing 0.3 ml of 3% (w/v) PBS–BSA. The radioactivity of the effluent fractions was determined by counting 2 μl of the fractions in a Beckman Gamma 4000 gamma counter.[22]

Testing for Positive Clones

Supernatants from the bovine × murine clones were tested for the presence of bovine Ig using a competitive radioimmunoassay (cRIA). Affinity-purified rabbit anti-bovine Ig light chain (antiBIg$_{LC}$)[18] antibody was coated onto poly(vinyl chloride) (PVC) microtiter wells by adding 20 μl of the affinity-purified antibody (50 μg/ml PBS) to each well and incubating the plate for 1 hr at room temperature. The plate was then washed three times with 1% BSA in PBS (PBS–BSA). Culture supernatants (20 μl) and ^{125}I-labeled bovine IgG (20 μl, specific activity 10 μCi/μg) were added to the antibody coated wells. Culture supernatant from the parent cell line SP2/0 served as the negative control. Known amounts of bovine Ig in PBS served as positive controls. After 1 hr incubation, the wells were washed three times with PBS–BSA and counted in the gamma counter. Bovine Ig, if present in the culture supernatants, competes with the ^{125}I-labeled bovine IgG for binding sites on rabbit antiBIg$_{LC}$-coated plates. Therefore, the counts per minute (cpm) (i.e., radioactivity bound) is inversely proportional to the bovine Ig content of the culture supernatants. The percentage inhibition of binding of the ^{125}I-labeled bovine Ig by the hybridoma culture supernatant was calculated as indicated below:

$$\% \text{ Inhibition} = \frac{\begin{array}{c}\text{cpm of SP2/0}\\\text{culture supernatant}\end{array} - \begin{array}{c}\text{cpm of hybridoma}\\\text{culture supernatant}\end{array}}{\text{cpm of SP2/0 culture supernatant}}$$

Samples giving over 25% inhibition were considered as positive (Fig. 1). In the example presented in Fig. 1, 21 of the 63 clones tested were positive for bovine Ig.

---

[21] Dow Corning Corporation, Midland, Michigan.
[22] Beckman Instruments, Irvine, California.

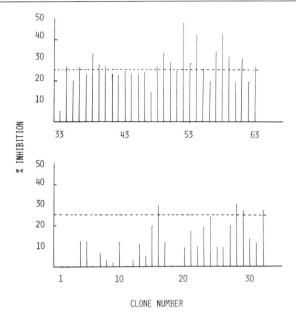

CLONE NUMBER

FIG. 1. Competition radioimmunoassay of culture supernatants from bovine × murine initial clones. Culture supernatants from cloned hybrids were tested for their ability to inhibit the binding of ^{125}I-labeled bovine Ig to immobilized rabbit antibody to bovine light chains. Culture supernatant from the parent cell line SP2/0 was used as control and percentage inhibition calculated. The horizontal slashed line represents 25% inhibition.

Initial Screening of Hybridomas for Isotype

A panel of affinity-purified murine × murine monoclonal antibodies (MAbs) with known specificities for bovine Ig isotypes was used in a cRIA, similar to that described above, to determine the isotype of the bovine × murine hybridomas. The panel consisted of DAS-1 which reacted with IgG_1, IgG_2, and IgM, and DAS-2 and DAS-6,[23] which were specific for IgG_2 and IgM, respectively.

DAS-1, DAS-2, or DAS-6 was coated onto the bottom of the wells of PVC microtiter plates as in the previous section. Culture supernatants (20 μl) from the bovine × murine hybridomas and the parent cell line Sp2/0, respectively, and ^{125}I-labeled bovine IgG_1, IgG_2, and IgM (20 μl, specific activity 10 μCi/μg) were added to the microtiter wells simultaneously. After 1 hr incubation and washing three times with PBS–BSA, the wells were cut out and radioactivity counted. The percentage inhibition of bind-

[23] S. Srikumaran, Ph.D. Thesis, University of Maryland (1982).

TABLE I
COMPETITION RADIOIMMUNOASSAY TO DETERMINE THE ISOTYPE OF MONOCLONAL
BOVINE IG

Immobilized monoclonal antibody	Specificity	Tracer antigen	Percentage inhibition by		
			LHRB-1	LHRB-2	LHRB-3
DAS-1	IgG_1, IgG_2, IgM (trace)	$^{125}I\text{-}IgG_1$	60	67	0
DAS-2	IgG_2	$^{125}I\text{-}IgG_2$	0	42	0
DAS-6	IgM	$^{125}I\text{-}IgM$	0	0	81

ing of the ^{125}I-labeled Ig by the hybridoma Ig in the culture supernatant was calculated. The results are shown in Table I.

Specific Immunoabsorption of [^{35}S]Methionine-Labeled LHRB-1, LHRB-2, and LHRB-3 Ig

A specific immunoabsorption analysis was used to establish that LHRB-1, LHRB-2, and LHRB-3 were secreting bovine Ig heavy chains. Bovine × murine hybridoma cells (1×10^7) were biosynthetically labeled by culturing in 2 ml of labeling media (Earle's minimum essential medium[11]) containing 0.5 mCi[^{35}S]methionine in a 60-mm tissue culture dish for 4 hr at 37° in 90% air/10% CO_2.[24] The cells were removed by centrifugation at 400 g for 15 min and the supernatant was dialyzed two times in 4 liters of PBS for 24 hr.

Six milligrams of affinity-purified murine monoclonal antibody DAS-1 was coupled to 1 g CNBr-activated Sepharose 4B (DAS-1–Sepharose),[25] according to the manufacturer's protocol,[25] and suspended in 15 ml PBS containing 0.05% polyoxyethylene sorbitan monolaurate (Tween 20). The [^{35}S]methionine-labeled culture supernatant (100 μl) was added to 1 ml of the DAS-1–Sepharose and mixed slowly for 30 min. The reacted DAS-1–Sepharose was washed three times with PBS containing 0.05% Tween 20 and the counts per minute of the bound [^{35}S]methionine determined. The ability of bovine or murine serum to inhibit the binding of the [^{35}S]methionine-labeled supernatant to DAS-1 was tested by repeating the above procedure after preincubation of the DAS-1–Sepharose with 50 μl of bovine and murine serum, respectively. As shown in Table II, [^{35}S]methionine-labeled LHRB-1, LHRB-2, and LHRB-3 binding to DAS-

[24] P. P. Jones, *in* "Selected Methods in Immunology" (B. B. Mishell and S. M. Shiigi, eds.), p. 398. Freeman, New York, 1980.
[25] Pharmacia Fine Chemicals, Upsalla, Sweden.

TABLE II

SPECIFIC IMMUNOABSORPTION OF [^{35}S]METHIONINE-LABELED MONOCLONAL BOVINE IG
BY DAS-1-CONJUGATED SEPHAROSE 4B

Sample treatment	Counts per minute + SD		
	LHRB-1	LHRB-2	LHRB-3
No preincubation	41,610 ± 60	9,302 ± 22	6,245 ± 305
Preincubation with bovine serum	3,473 ± 41	1,214 ± 107	2,891 ± 180
Preincubation with murine serum	40,226 ± 370	8,948 ± 127	6,216 ± 299

1–Sepharose was inhibited by whole bovine serum, but not by whole murine serum.

In a similar experiment, 6 mg of affinity-purified polyclonal sheep anti-murine Ig antibody was coupled to 1 g CNBr-activated Sepharose 4B (S-Sepharose) and suspended in 15 ml PBS containing 0.05% Tween 20. The [^{35}S]methionine-labeled culture supernatant, from the hybridomas or the parent cell line SP2/0 (equal amounts of trichloroacetic acid-precipitable cpm), was added to 1 ml of this suspension, and the mixture agitated slowly for 30 min. The S-Sepharose was washed three times with PBS containing Tween 20 and the cpm bound was counted. The results are shown in Table III. These results show that the [^{35}S]methionine-labeled products of LHRB-1, LHRB-2, and LHRB-3 are not murine Ig.

Affinity Purification and Characterization of Bovine Ig Isotypes

Affinity Purification

Monoclonal bovine IgG$_1$ (LHRB-1), IgG$_2$ (LHRB-2), and IgM (LHRB-3) were isolated, from RDG in which the respective hybridomas were

TABLE III

IMMUNOABSORPTION OF
[^{35}S]METHIONINE-LABELED MONOCLONAL
BOVINE IG BY SHEEP ANTI-MURINE
IG-CONJUGATED SEPHAROSE 4B

Sample	cpm ± SD
SP2/0 culture supernatant	4035 ± 466
LHRB-1 culture supernatant	2853 ± 150
LHRB-2 culture supernatant	2240 ± 66
LHRB-3 culture supernatant	4787 ± 257

TABLE IV
AFFINITY PURIFICATION OF MONOCLONAL BOVINE IG
FROM SERUM-FREE CULTURE MEDIUM

Hybridoma secreting	Volume of serum-free culture medium used (ml)	Ig isolated (mg)
LHRB-1	500	1.10
LHRB-2	500	1.76
LHRB-3	500	1.05

cultured, using an affinity column of guinea pig antibody to bovine light chains[18] coupled to CNBr-activated Sepharose 4B.[24] Serum-free culture medium in which the hybridomas were grown was passed over the affinity column (1 ml/min). The column was then washed with PBS until the optical density of the effluent fractions became zero. The protein bound to the column was eluted by glycine–HCl buffer (0.2 M glycine, pH 2.8) and the effluent fractions adjusted to pH 7 with Tris–HCl buffer (1 M Tris, pH 8). Table IV gives a summary of the volume of culture medium used and the amount of Ig recovered.

Identification of Isotype

cRIA. The affinity-purified monoclonal Ig from bovine × murine hybrids were tested for Ig isotype by cRIA as previously described. Samples (20 μl) of affinity-purified monoclonal bovine Ig from bovine ×murine hybrids and ^{125}I-labeled bovine IgG$_1$, IgG$_2$, and IgM (20 μl, specific activity 10 μCi/μg) were added to microtiter wells coated with DAS-1, DAS-2, or DAS-6, respectively. After 1 hr incubation and washing three times with PBS–BSA, the wells were cut and radioactivity counted. The percentage inhibition of binding of the ^{125}I-labeled antigens by the hybridoma Ig in the affinity-purified sample was calculated. As shown in Table V, the results of this assay confirmed that the affinity-purified LHRB-1, LHRB-2, and LHRB-3 Ig were bovine IgG$_1$, IgG$_2$, and IgM, respectively.

Immunodiffusion in Agarose Gels. Immunodiffusion in agarose gels was carried out as described by Ouchterlony and Nilsson.[26] Clean glass plates ($8\frac{1}{2}$ × $9\frac{1}{2}$ cm) were coated with 9 ml of 1% (w/v) Seakem[27] agarose

[26] O. Ouchterlony and L. A. Nilsson, *in* "Handbook of Experimental Immunology" (D. M. Weir, ed.), p. 19, 16 Blackwell Scientific Publication, London, 1978.
[27] Seakem, Marine Colloids, Inc., Rockland, Maine.

TABLE V

COMPETITION RADIOIMMUNOASSAY OF AFFINITY-PURIFIED MONOCLONAL BOVINE Ig

Immobilized monoclonal antibody	Specificity	Tracer antigen	Percentage inhibition by affinity-purified		
			LHRB-1	LHRB-2	LHRB-3
DAS-1	IgG$_1$, IgG$_2$, IgM (trace)	^{125}I-IgG$_1$	60.8	97.0	0
DAS-2	IgG$_2$	^{125}I-IgG$_2$	0	60.3	0
DAS-6	IgM	^{125}I-IgM	0	0	54.2

in 0.85% (w/v) NaCl and allowed to solidify at 4° in a humidified chamber for 4 hr. Sets of six wells, 4 mm in diameter and equidistant (4 mm) from a center well, were punched in the agarose, using a template and hole puncher. Six microliters of the antigens and antiserum at various concentrations was distributed to the wells. The plates were incubated in a humidified chamber at room temperature for 24 hr. The affinity-purified LHRB-1, LHRB-2, and LHRB-3 were placed in the center wells, and polyclonal guinea pig antibody to bovine IgG$_1$, IgG$_2$, IgM, and IgA and sheep antibody to murine Ig[18] were placed in the outer wells (Fig. 2). The plates were then immersed in 0.85% (w/v) NaCl solution for another 6 hr to "leach out" the nonprecipitated protein. The plates were then stained with 0.1% (w/v) Coomassie blue G-250 in 50% (w/v) trichloroacetic acid (TCA) for 20 min and destained in 7% (v/v) acetic acid. The plates were then dried at room temperature overnight.

The results shown in Fig. 2 clearly demonstrate both species and isotype specificity.

Sodium Dodecyl Sulfate–Polyacrylamide Gel Electrophoresis (SDS–PAGE). To assay the molecular weight of the bovine Ig isotypes produced by the LHRB$_x$ hybrids, affinity-purified bovine Ig from supernatants of the LHRB$_x$ hybrids, grown in serum-free media, were analyzed via SDS–PAGE analysis as described by P. P. Jones[24] using the Laemmli buffer system. Both the stacking and running acrylamide gels were prepared from a stock solution of 30% (w/v) acrylamide and 0.8% (w/v) *N,N'*-bismethylene acrylamide. The upper (stacking) gel contained 4.75% acrylamide, 0.1% SDS, and 0.125 *M* Tris–HCl (pH 6.8). The lower (running) gel contained 10% acrylamide, 0.1% SDS, and 0.375 *M* Tris–HCl (pH 8.8). The gels were polymerized chemically by the addition of 0.025% (v/v) tetramethylethylenediamine (TEMED) and ammonium persulfate. The running buffer contained 0.025 *M* Tris, 0.192 *M* glycine, and 0.1% SDS (pH 8.3). The samples (20 µl of 1 mg affinity-purified LHRB$_x$ Ig/ml

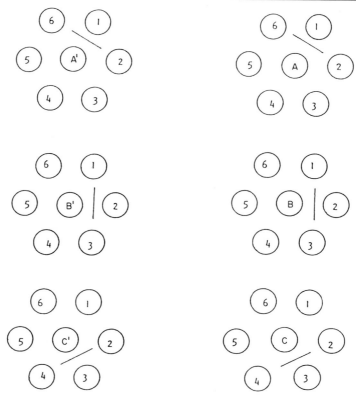

FIG. 2. Ouchterlony immunodiffusion analysis of monoclonal bovine Ig. Affinity-purified monoclonal bovine Ig were tested against guinea pig antisera to bovine IgG$_1$ (1), IgG$_2$ (2), IgM (3), IgA (4) and against sheep antibody to murine Ig (5) and PBS (6). The center wells in A, B, and C contained affinity-purified LHRB-1, LHRB-2, and LHRB-3, respectively, while the center wells in A′, B′, and C′ contained polyclonal bovine IgG$_1$, IgG$_2$, and IgM, respectively.

solution) contained 0.0625 M Tris–HCl (pH 6.8), 2% SDS, 10% glycerol, and 0.001% bromphenol blue. The reducing sample buffer also contained 5% 2-mercaptoethanol. The proteins were completely dissociated by immersing the samples for 1.5 min in boiling water. Electrophoresis was carried out at 20 mA/gel until the dye front was approximately 5 mm above the bottom edge of the gel. Gels were stained for 30 min in 50% TCA containing 0.1% Coomassie blue G-250 and destained with several changes of 7% acetic acid. Gels were then dried in a Bio-Rad[28] gel drier.

To assess the molecular weight of unreduced Ig molecules, the Ig

[28] Bio-Rad, Richmond, California.

samples were electrophoresed on a 4% acrylamide gel, cross-linked with *N*,*N'*-diallyltartardiamide (DATD) as described by Ziegler *et al.*[29] This system was similar to the one described above except for the following: (1) there was no separate stacking gel; samples were loaded onto the wells formed in the 4% running gel itself; (2) the gels contained 4% acrylamide, 0.7% (w/v) DATD, 0.1 M Tris–Bicine (equimolar), and 0.1% SDS; (3) polymerization was initiated by 0.075% (v/v) TEMED and 0.075% (w/v) ammonium persulfate; and (4) the running buffer was 0.1 M Tris–Bicine (equimolar) containing 0.1% (w/v) SDS (pH 8.3).

The affinity-purified LHRB$_x$ Ig, along with polyclonal Ig, were subjected to SDS–PAGE on 10% polyacrylamide gel slabs before and after reduction with 2-mercaptoethanol (to disrupt the disulfide bonds and to convert the intact Ig molecule into component Ig chains). Figure 3 shows the SDS–PAGE of LHRB-1. Before reduction it gave a single band corresponding to the unreduced Ig molecule. After reduction it gave two bands corresponding to the heavy and light chains. The unreduced molecule as well as the reduced heavy and light chains electrophoresed similar to the polyclonal IgG$_1$. It appears that LHRB-1 heavy chain is slightly larger and LHRB-1 light chain is slightly smaller than the polyclonal IgG$_1$ heavy and light chains, respectively. This discrepancy was attributed to the fact that LHRB-1 is a single molecular species, while the polyclonal preparation represents a mixture of a number of different molecules in which this particular Ig molecule may be present in trace amounts or not at all. The apparent molecular weights of the monoclonal LHRB-1 heavy and light chains appear to be around 63,000 and 25,800. The apparent molecular weight of the unreduced IgG$_1$ molecule appears to be in the region of 200,000. However, it should be recognized that a fair estimate of apparent molecular weight cannot be made in the upper region of the gel where the proteins have not migrated a considerable distance. When electrophoresed on a 4% acrylamide gel (Fig. 4) the unreduced LHRB-1 migrated similarly to the polyclonal IgG$_1$, indicating that it is an intact bovine IgG$_1$ molecule.

Similarly, before reduction LHRB-2 gave a single band corresponding to the unreduced molecule, and after reduction gave two bands corresponding to the heavy and light chains (Fig. 5). They showed an apparent molecular weight of 56,200 and 26,600. The unreduced LHRB-2 molecule migrated in the region of MW 200,000. The LHRB-2 heavy and light chains and the unreduced molecule migrated similarly to the polyclonal IgG$_2$ heavy and light chains and the unreduced molecule, indicating that LHRB-2 is an intact bovine IgG$_2$ molecule. When unreduced LHRB-2 Ig

[29] A. Ziegler and H. Hengartner, *Eur. J. Immunol.* **7**, 690 (1977).

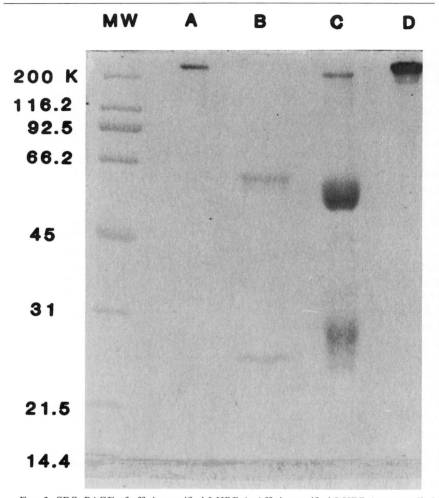

FIG. 3. SDS–PAGE of affinity-purified LHRB-1. Affinity-purified LHRB-1 was applied on a 10% polyacrylamide gel before (A) and after (B) reduction. Polyclonal IgG₁ was co-electrophoresed before (D) and after (C) reduction. Molecular weight standards (MW) were also included.

was electrophoresed on a 4% acrylamide gel, it migrated similarly to polyclonal IgG$_2$ (Fig. 4).

LHRB-3, after reduction, gave two bands corresponding to heavy and light chains which migrated similarly to the polyclonal IgM heavy and light chains (Fig. 6). The LHRB-3 heavy and light chains showed an

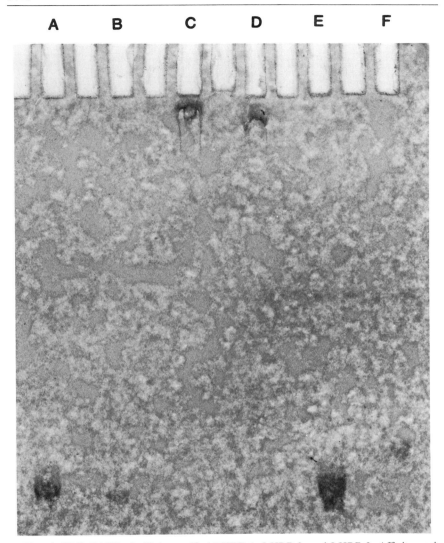

FIG. 4. SDS–PAGE of affinity-purified LHRB-1, LHRB-2, and LHRB-3. Affinity-purified, unreduced LHRB-1 (B), LHRB-2 (F), and LHRB-3 (D) were co-electrophoresed with
polyclonal IgG$_1$ (A), IgG$_2$ (E), and IgM (C), on a 4% polyacrylamide gel.

apparent molecular weight of 76,000 and 29,400. The unreduced LHRB-3,
like the polyclonal IgM, did not migrate into this 10% polyacrylamide gel.
When the unreduced LHRB-3 Ig and polyclonal IgM were co-electrophoresed in 4% polyacrylamide gels, LHRB-3 Ig migrated similarly to

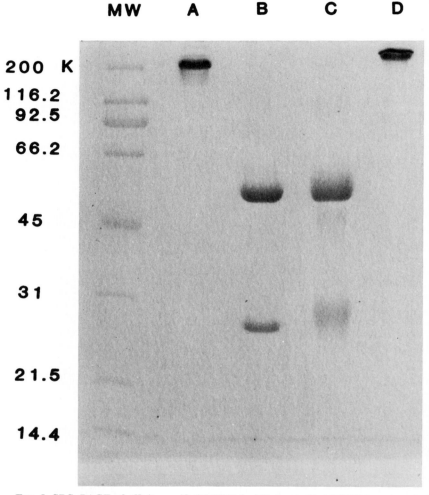

FIG. 5. SDS–PAGE of affinity-purified LHRB-2. Affinity-purified LHRB-2 was applied on a 10% polyacrylamide gel before (A) and after (B) reduction. Polyclonal IgG₂ was co-electrophoresed before (D) and after (C) reduction. Molecular weight standards (MW) were also included.

the polyclonal IgM preparation, indicating that it is a pentameric IgM (Fig. 4).

Isoelectric Focusing. The isoelectric focusing (IEF) experiments were performed in the LKB[30] Multiphor apparatus for flat-bed IEF, along the

[30] LKB, Copenhagen, Denmark.

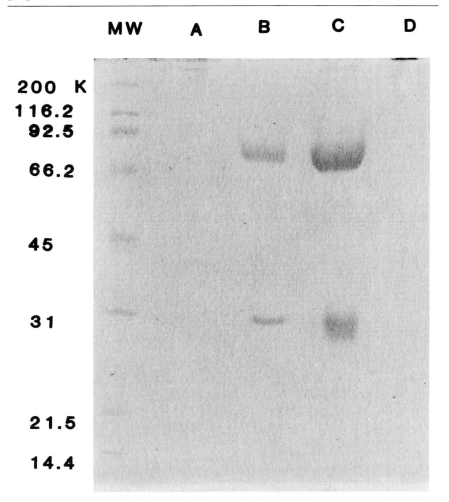

FIG. 6. SDS–PAGE of affinity-purified LHRB-3. Affinity-purified LHRB-3 was applied on a 10% polyacrylamide gel before (A) and after (B) reduction. Polyclonal IgM was co-electrophoresed before (D) and after (C) reduction. Molecular weight standards (MW) were also included.

outlines detailed by Rosen et al.[31] Sorbitol and agarose were used at 10% (w/v) and 0.8% (w/v), respectively, for the preparation of the gel. A pH gradient of 3.5 to 10 was established with the ampholine mixture. The samples applied (20 μl) were at a concentration of 1 mg/ml in PBS. The

[31] A. Rosen, E. K. Kristina, and A. Pierre, J. Immunol. **28**, 1 (1979).

IEF experiments were performed at 10°. The focusing was complete in 60 min, after which the pH gradient was determined and refocused for 10 min. The gels were fixed for 5 min in fixing solution (17.3 g sulfosalicylic acid, 57.5 g TCA, 150 ml ethanol, in a final volume of 500 ml with distilled water), washed two times for 10 min in ethanol, pressed, and dried. The gels were stained with 0.05% (w/v) Coomassie blue R-250 in 35% (v/v) ethanol and 10% (v/v) acetic acid in distilled water. Destaining was performed two times for 10 min in 35% (v/v) ethanol and 10% (v/v) acetic acid.

When affinity-purified monoclonal Ig were subjected to isoelectric focusing, LHRB-1 and LHRB-2 focused around pH 8.5 and 8.0, respectively, indicating that this particular monoclonal IgG_1 has a higher isoelectric point than the monoclonal IgG_2 derived in this study. LHRB-3 focused around an isoelectric point of pH 5.5.

Determination of Chromosome Numbers in LHRB Hybridomas

Hybridoma cells at metaphase were prepared according to the method described by Moorhead et al.,[32] with slight modifications. The $LHRB_x$ hybridoma cells, SP2/0 cells, and LPS-stimulated bovine PBLs were cultured in RDGS (1 × 10^6 cells/10 ml) containing 0.2 μg/ml colcemid (GIBCO)[11] for 4 hr at 37° in 90% air/10% CO_2. The cells were harvested by centrifugation at 400 g for 10 min and resuspended in 10 ml of 0.075 M KCl and incubated at 37° for 10 min. Following this hypotonic treatment, the cells were fixed and washed three times with fresh, cold acetic acid–alcohol (3 : 1, methanol : glacial acetic acid) and resuspended in 1 ml of acetic acid–alcohol. The cell suspension was immediately dropped from a height of approximately 10 in. onto clean glass microscope slides. The slides were then tilted to a vertical position and allowed to air dry at room temperature overnight. The slides were stained with Wright's stain, and individual cell spreads were photographed in a Leitz photomicroscope. The chromosomes were counted, from six different cell spreads, for each cell line and the average taken.

The chromosome numbers of the hybridomas secreting LHRB-1, LHRB-2, and LHRB-3, SP2/0, and bovine B lymphocytes obtained from metaphase cell preparations are given in Table VI. All hybridomas had more chromosomes than either of the parents. Since both the SP2/0 and bovine lymphocytes have telocentric chromosomes, it is not possible to determine the parental origin of the chromosomes in the hybridomas without conducting a formal karyotypic analysis.

[32] P. S. Moorhead, P. C. Nowel, W. J. Mellman, D. M. Battips, and D. A. Hungerford, *Exp. Cell Res.* **20,** 613 (1960).

TABLE VI
CHROMOSOME NUMBER OF BOVINE × MURINE
HYBRIDOMAS

Cell lines	Chromosome number ± SD
SP2/0	59 ± 3
LHRB-1 hybridoma	66 ± 9
LHRB-2 hybridoma	65 ± 7
LHRB-3 hybridoma	68 ± 5
Bovine lymphocytes	60

However, these hybridomas have continued to secrete their respective bovine Ig isotype for over 3 years, which indicates that at least the bovine genes encoding the Ig heavy and light chains are retained by the hybridomas, if not the entire chromosome bearing these genes. Also, the genes coding for the bovine cell surface antigens should be present in the hybridomas secreting LHRB-1 and LHRB-3, since these hybridomas were rejected by normal BALB/c mice when injected subcutaneously.

Production of DNP-Specific Hybridomas

Coupling of DNP to Protein Carriers for Immunization

Twenty microliters of 1 M dinitrofluorobenzene (DNFB) was mixed with 10 ml of either BSA or ovalbumin (OVA) (50 mg/ml) and agitated slowly for 2 hr in the dark. At the end of 2 hr, the mixture was dialyzed two times against PBS (4 liters) for 48 hr with PBS, to remove the DNFB.

Immunization of Calves against DNP

A 4-month-old male Holstein Friesian calf was primed by intramuscular injections of 3 ml of DNP–OVA (2 mg/3 ml) emulsified 1 : 1 in Freund's complete adjuvant, given at multiple sites. One month later a booster injection of 10 ml DNP–OVA (1 mg/10 ml PBS) was administered by slow intravenous injection. Three days after the booster, the calf was sacrificed and the spleen and a mesenteric lymph node were removed.

Production of Hybrids

A cell suspension was prepared from both spleen and lymph node and each fused with SP2/0 cells as previously described. These fusions resulted in 14 and 13 cloned hybridomas, respectively. The culture supernatants from these clones were screened for bovine antibody against DNP by an indirect solid-phase radioimmunoassay (ispRIA) based on the procedure of Rosenthal *et al.*[33] DNP–BSA was coated on PVC plates by adding 20 μl of a 25 μg/ml DNP–BSA solution in PBS per well. After 1 hr incubation at room temperature the PVC plates were washed three times with PBS–BSA. Twenty microliters of culture supernatants was added to the wells, and the plates were incubated for 1 hr and washed three times with PBS–BSA. Culture supernatant from SP2/0 served as the negative control. ^{125}I-labeled guinea pig antibody to bovine Ig light chains (20 μl was added to detect bovine antibody to DNP. After 1 hr incubation, the plates were washed and the wells were counted in the gamma counter. The counts per minute are proportional to the bovine antibody to DNP.

One of these clones secreted bovine antibody to DNP. This clone continued to secrete anti-DNP antibodies when transferred to a 24-well tissue culture plate and expanded for cloning. However, it was subsequently lost in culture. Nevertheless, these results demonstrate the feasibility of employing bovine × murine interspecific fusion for the production of bovine monoclonal antibodies of predefined specificity.

Large-Scale Production, Preservation, and Application of Bovine × Murine Hybridomas

The three LHRB hybridomas were grown in mass culture and 5×10^6 cells in 0.3 ml of PBS were injected subcutaneously into 3- to 4-month-old female nude BALB/c mice in the region of the groin, where they gave rise to Ig-secreting tumors. The mice were tail bled when the tumors became palpable. The plasma from these mice were tested for the presence of bovine Ig by comparing with plasma from normal mice in a cRIA.

The tumors were removed under sterile conditions, minced, and a 5×10^6 cells/ml suspension prepared. A fraction of the cell suspension was used to inoculate a second group of 3- to 4-month old normal BALB/c mice and the rest of the tumor was frozen in freezing media (70% PBS, 20% fetal calf serum, and 10% dimethyl sulfoxide) in liquid nitrogen. The LHRB-2-secreting tumor, when subsequently repassaged, gave rise to tumors in normal BALB/c mice, whereas the LHRB-1-secreting tumor was rejected by normal mice. LHRB-3-secreting cells when injected subcutaneously into normal BALB/c mice also were rejected. LHRB-2-secreting hybridomas could possibly have lost the bovine chromosome or genes coding for the histocompatibility antigens.

These hybridomas have continued to secrete their respective bovine

[33] J. D. Rosenthal, K. Hayashi, and A. L. Notkious, *Appl. Microbiol.* **25**, 567 (1973).

Ig isotype for over 3 years, which indicates that at least the bovine genes encoding the Ig heavy and light chains are retained by the hybridomas, if not the entire chromosome bearing these genes. Also, the genes coding for the bovine cell surface antigens should be present in the hybridomas secreting LHRB-1 and LHRB-3, since these hybridomas were rejected by normal BALB/c mice when injected subcutaneously.

Continuous cultures of bovine × murine hybridomas will supply material that will open areas of investigation of the bovine immune system heretofore inaccessible. These hybridomas will provide monoclonal bovine Ig for (1) serological standards, (2) production of polyclonal and monoclonal antisera to bovine Ig isotypes, (3) sequencing studies, (4) serological and structural studies of bovine Ig isotypes and allotypes, and (5) defining bovine Ig classes and subclasses (IgA, IgM, IgG_1, IgG_{2a}, IgG_{2b}, and possibly IgE and IgD if it exists in the bovine species). Also, these hybridomas will provide mRNA for the production of cDNA probes for the cloning of bovine Ig genes and for the determination of the organization of Ig genes in the bovine genome.

Even though the bovine × murine hybridoma secreting bovine antibodies to DNP was subsequently lost in culture, it demonstrates the feasibility of deriving bovine × murine hybridomas producing bovine antibodies "tailored" to specific purposes. For example, situations may arise in which there is a requirement for monoclonal reagents which carry out isotype-associated specific effector functions, i.e., (1) that do or do not fix complement, (2) that do or do not bind Fc receptors on certain kinds of cells, or (3) that have long or short serum half-lives. Construction of bovine × murine interspecific hybridomas will be the method of choice for the derivation of such "tailored" antibodies in the bovine.

Addendum

Further experimentation has produced bovine mouse hybrids specific for *Streptococcus agalactiae*.[34] The procedure was the same as described above except for the following:

Immunization

A multiparous Holstein was immunized by injecting heat-killed (56°, 30 min) *S. agalactiae* (5×10^8) iv and 5×10^8 sc in and around each quarter of the udder.

---

[34] R. A. Goldsby, B. Hague, F. A. Ponce de Leon, M. Sevoian, S. Srikumaran, and A. J. Guidry, *Vet. Immunol. Immunopathol.* (submitted).

Preparation of Bovine Lymph Node Cells for Fusion

Mesenteric and supramammary lymph nodes were harvested 4 days after immunization. Following removal of the surrounding fat, lymph nodes were sterilized by immersion in 95% ethanol for 1 min and then transferred to cold (4°) PBS. Scissors were used to first cut the nodes into several 2- to 3-cm cubes (approximately 30 g) which were then minced with scissors for 30 sec in 200 ml of cold PBS. The tissue was allowed to settle and the supernatant, containing the cells, was decanted and held on ice. The mincing operation was repeated five times, and the supernatants pooled and poured through sterile cheesecloth to remove bits of tissue and fat. The cold suspension was spun at 1000 g for 5 min at room temperature. The supernatant was discarded and the cell pellet was immediately suspended in 200 ml of cold PBS and centrifuged at 1000 g for 5 min. The washed cell pellet was resuspended in 100 ml of cold PBS and an aliquot counted. Yields of 5×10^9 to 1×10^{10} cells were routinely obtained. In our experience the rapid mincing and washing in cold PBS and maintaining a cold processing environment were critical to avoid clumping. An aliquot of these cells were fused with SP2/0 and an aliquot saved for LPS stimulation prior to fusion.

In Vitro Stimulation of Lymph Node Cells with LPS

Washed lymph node cells from the above preparation were suspended in RDG to contain 3×10^6 cells/ml and distributed in 1-ml aliquots to the chambers of 24-well dishes (Costar[35]). One-milliliter aliquots of LPS (*Escherichia coli* 0111:B4, Difco[36]) solution, at a concentration of 50 μg/ml of growth media, were added to all but four wells containing the cell suspension. These four wells, which served as unstimulated controls, received 1 ml of RDG. The dishes were incubated at 37° in a humidified atmosphere containing 93% air and 7% CO_2. Blast colonies were apparent within 48 hr. LPS cultures were harvested for fusion 5–6 days following the initiation of culture.

Assay of Bovine Antibodies Specific for Bacterial Pathogens

Supernatants from hybridomas secreting bovine Ig were screened against *Staphylococcus aureus, S. agalactiae, E. coli,* BALB/c red blood cells (BRBC), DNP–BSA, phosphorylcholine coupled to BSA (PC–BSA), and BSA. BRBC, BSA, PC–BSA, and DNP–BSA were included in the panel as controls to identify those members of the collection which

[35] Costar, Cambridge, Massachusetts.
[36] Difco, Detroit, Michigan.

secreted antibodies which tended to bind nonspecifically to irrelevant cell surfaces, to irrelevant proteins coating microtiter wells, or to the microtiter wells themselves, using a radioimmunoassay.

To assay for antibody activity to the bacteria, 24-hr cultures of the bacteria were suspended in PBS so that the absorbance at 750 nm (A_{750}) was 0.6. Fifty microliters of this suspension was placed in each of the 96 wells of a PVC microtiter plate. The plate was centrifuged at 900 g for 10 min at 4° and the supernatant fluid was removed by gently flicking the plate. The wells were then filled with 0.25% glutaraldehyde in PBS (200 μl/well) and incubated at 4° for 15 min. After incubation the glutaraldehyde was removed by flicking the plate, which was then washed three times with PBS. The wells were then filled with the blocking solution (PBS containing 1% casein, 0.2% bovine serum albumin, and 0.2% sodium azide). After overnight incubation at 4°, the blocking solution was removed and the plate washed three times with PBS.

The procedure for binding BRBC to PVC microtiter plates was similar to the above except that 1×10^6 BRBC/ml were used and the glutaraldehyde treatment was eliminated.

BSA, PC–BSA, and DNP–BSA were coated to microtiter plates by adding 20 μl of the antigen (100 μg/ml in PBS) to each well and incubating for 1 hr at room temperature in a humidity chamber. The plates were then washed three times with PBS.

Culture supernatants were tested for the presence of bovine antibodies by adding one drop of the sample to appropriately labeled wells and incubating for 1 hr at room temperature in a humidified chamber. The plate was then washed three times with PBS–BSA and 20 μl of ^{125}I-labeled DAS-9 (20,000 cpm; a mouse × mouse monoclonal antibody to bovine Ig light chains) was added to each well. After 1 hr incubation and three PBS–BSA washes, the wells were cut and counted for radioactivity. Growth media which had no contact with the cells served as negative controls. Culture supernatants giving counts per minute more than twice the negative controls were judged as positive.

The fusion of bovine lymph node cells from an immunized donor with SP2/0 yielded 277 hybrids, 22 of which were shown to secrete bovine Ig. Assay of the hybrids resulting from the fusion of LPS-stimulated bovine lymph node cells from the immunized donor showed that 160 of 171 hybrids tested were positive for Ig secretion. Two of the hybridomas were positive for *S. agalactiae* and were passaged and continue to secrete Ig specific for *S. agalactiae*.

[22] Serum-Free Medium for the Growth of NS-1 Mouse Myeloma Cells and the Isolation of NS-1 Hybridomas

By Tomoyuki Kawamoto, J. Denry Sato, Don B. McClure, and Gordon H. Sato

Since the production of hybridomas relies heavily on *in vitro* cell culture techniques, we have become interested in using serum-free cell culture to understand the growth requirements of myeloma cells and their hybridoma derivatives. We are taking this approach in hope that this knowledge will contribute to more efficient and reproducible isolation of hybridoma cell lines. Progress in the development of serum-free media for myeloma cells and their hybridomas should be particularly useful for *in vitro* immunization techniques, for the initial growth and cloning of nascent hybridomas when the variable effects of serum are most evident, and for the production of monoclonal antibodies through large-scale culture of hybridomas.

Here we describe the serum-free medium, designated KSLM medium, which was developed for NS-1-Ag4-1[1] (NS-1) mouse myeloma cells. We also demonstrate that KSLM medium is at least as effective as a screened batch of fetal calf serum in supporting the growth of nascent hybridomas. In addition we use as a hybridoma parent cell line a subclone of NS-1, NS-1-503, which was selected for its ability to survive and grow in lipid-free KSLM medium. At the time this research was started several serum-free media had been used to grow established rodent hybridoma cell lines,[2-4] however, none of these media were able to support the growth of NS-1 or its parent cell line, P3-X63-Ag8.[5] Furthermore, two of the media[2,3] were unable to sustain the growth of newly formed hybridomas unless supplemented with fetal calf serum (T. Kawamoto and J. D. Sato, unpublished results); CITTL medium,[4] which was originally developed for T lymphoma cells,[6] was not tested.

Since NS-1 cells appeared to have more stringent growth requirements than NS-1 hybridomas, we decided to investigate first the requirements of

[1] G. Köhler, S. C. Howe, and C. Milstein, *Eur. J. Immunol.* **6**, 511 (1976).
[2] T. C. Chang, Z. Steplewski, and H. Koprowski, *J. Immunol. Methods* **39**, 369 (1980).
[3] H. Murakami, H. Masui, G. H. Sato, N. Sueoka, T. P. Chow, and T. Kano-Sueoka, *Proc. Natl. Acad. Sci. U.S.A.* **79**, 1159 (1982).
[4] F. J. Darfler and P. A. Insel, *Exp. Cell Res.* **138**, 287 (1982).
[5] G. Köhler and C. Milstein, *Nature (London)* **256**, 495 (1975).
[6] F. J. Darfler, H. Murakami, and P. A. Insel, *Proc. Natl. Acad. Sci. U.S.A.* **77**, 5993 (1980).

NS-1 cells in serum-free culture conditions and then to test the resulting medium for its ability to support the growth of NS-1 hybridomas from the time of fusion. As demonstrated below, NS-1 cells have an absolute lipid requirement which can be met by human low-density lipoprotein (LDL); this LDL requirement is not shared by NS-1 hybridomas. The growth of both NS-1 cells and NS-1 hybridomas is enhanced by oleic acid provided in the form of a BSA–fatty acid complex; this effect is most evident at low cell densities. We have recently further defined the lipid requirement of NS-1 cells as a requirement for cholesterol,[7] which is a major component of LDL.[8]

Cell Culture Media

Serum-Supplemented RDF Medium

NS-1 cells were initially maintained in RDF nutrient medium supplemented with 10% fetal calf serum (FCS) (Reheis; batch T48006). RDF medium consisted of a 2 : 1 : 1 mixture (by volume) of RPMI 1640 (GIBCO; 430-1800), Dulbecco's modified Eagle's medium (DME) (GIBCO; 430-2100), and Ham's F-12 medium (GIBCO; 430-1700) to which was added 2 mM L-glutamine, 0.01% sodium pyruvate, 15 mM HEPES, 2.2 g sodium bicarbonate, 40 mg penicillin, 8 mg ampicillin, and 90 mg streptomycin per liter. The medium was prepared with water purified by deionization and reverse osmosis (Millipore), and it was adjusted to pH 7.6 and sterilized by filtration through a 0.2-μm filter. NS-1 cells were grown at 37° in a humid atmosphere of 7.5% CO_2.

Serum-Free KSLM Medium

KSLM medium consisted of RDF medium supplemented with 10 μg crystalline bovine insulin/ml (Sigma), 10 μg human transferrin/ml (Sigma; Fe^{3+} free), 10 μM 2-aminoethanol (Sigma), 10 μM 2-mercaptoethanol (Sigma), 1 nM sodium selenite (Difco), 2 μg human LDL/ml (density, 1.019–1.063 g/ml) (Meloy Laboratories), and 4 μg oleic acid/ml (Sigma) complexed in a 2 : 1 molar ratio with crystalline fatty acid–free bovine serum albumin (FAF–BSA) (Miles). The FAF–BSA–oleic acid complex was prepared by adding dropwise 20 μl of oleic acid (20 mg/ml in ethanol) per 1 ml of sterile FAF–BSA solution (50 mg/ml in PBS or RDF, pH 7.4) with gentle shaking at 20°. The complex was shaken overnight at 4° and stored protected from light. Each supplement except LDL was prepared as a 100× stock solution, and all supplements were stored at 4°.

---

[7] J. D. Sato, T. Kawamoto, D. B. McClure, and G. H. Sato, *Mol. Biol. Med.* **2**, 121 (1984).
[8] J. L. Goldstein and M. S. Brown, *Annu. Rev. Biochem.* **46**, 897 (1977).

Selection of NS-1-503 Cells

NS-1 cells maintained in RDF + 10% FCS medium were unable to survive the transition to lipid-free KSLM medium unless FCS was included at concentrations of 0.5 to 1%. The cells were therefore passaged continuously in lipid-free KSLM medium supplemented with 1% FCS. After more than 6 months in 1% FCS, a small proportion of the NS-1 cells were able to survive in lipid-free KSLM medium when plated at 1×10^4 cells/0.1 ml per microtest well. A clonal cell line, NS-1-503, was isolated by limiting dilution from the surviving cells. These cells were resistant to 8-azaguanine and were HAT sensitive.

Production and Screening of Hybridomas

The production of the hybridomas used here has been reported previously[9,10] and so will not be described in detail. Hybridomas were generated by fusing NS-1 or NS-1-503 cells with spleen cells from BALB/c mice immunized with fixed A431 human epidermoid carcinoma cells.[11] The fusion method used was that of Galfré et al.[12] Hybridomas were screened for A431 antibodies by an indirect radioimmunoassay[9] or by the inhibition of binding of radiolabeled ligand to fixed A431 cells.[10]

Growth of Myeloma Cells

NS-1 Cells in KSLM Medium

Since NS-1 cells passaged in serum-supplemented medium were unable to survive in lipid-free KSLM medium, several lipoproteins and BSA-bound saturated and unsaturated fatty acids were individually tested for growth-promoting activity. Only human LDL at 10 μg/ml and human high-density lipoprotein (HDL) at 100 μg/ml were able to support NS-1 growth in lipid-free KSLM. None of the BSA-bound fatty acids, including oleic acid and linoleic acid, were adequate for survival and growth. BSA–oleic acid was subsequently found to stimulate NS-1 growth in medium containing suboptimal concentrations of LDL. Figure 1 shows the growth

---

[9] T. Kawamoto, J. D. Sato, A. Le, D. B. McClure, and G. H. Sato, *Anal. Biochem.* **130**, 445 (1983).

[10] J. D. Sato, T. Kawamoto, A. Le, J. Mendelsohn, J. Polikoff, and G. H. Sato, *Mol. Biol. Med.* **1**, 511 (1983).

[11] R. N. Fabricant, J. E. De Larco, and G. Todaro, *Proc. Natl. Acad. Sci. U.S.A.* **74**, 565 (1977).

[12] G. Galfré, S. C. Howe, C. Milstein, G. W. Butcher, and J. C. Howard, *Nature (London)* **266**, 550 (1977).

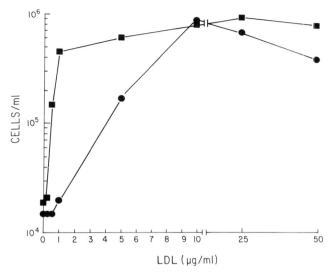

FIG. 1. Effect of LDL on the growth of NS-1 myeloma cells. NS-1 cells maintained in RDF + 10% FCS were plated at 1 × 10⁴ cells/ml in lipid-free KSLM medium supplemented with increasing concentrations of LDL with (■) or without (●) oleic acid. Cells in duplicate wells were counted on day 6. (From Ref. 9.)

response of NS-1 cells to increasing concentrations of LDL in the presence and absence of 4 μg/ml oleic acid. LDL at 10 μg/ml elicited a 100-fold increase in cell number; a similar degree of growth was observed with 1–2 μg/ml LDL in the presence of oleic acid. Based on these results, KSLM medium was made to include 2 μg LDL/ml and 4 μg oleic acid/ml. Modified versions of KSLM medium which contain altered supplement concentrations or in which LDL has been replaced by BSA–cholesterol have been described recently.[7,13] Figure 2 compares the growth of NS-1 cells in KSLM medium and RDF + 10% FCS. In both media NS-1 cells proliferated with doubling times of 22 hr and attained maximum densities of 1.5 × 10⁶ cells/ml. In control cultures the myeloma cells did not survive in lipid-free KSLM medium. These experiments demonstrate that NS-1 cells maintained in 10% FCS have an absolute requirement for LDL, or some of its constituents, when transferred to serum-free medium. Since LDL at sufficiently high concentrations can eliminate the stimulatory effect of oleic acid on NS-1 growth (Fig. 1), LDL probably serves as an alternative source of fatty acid.[8]

[13] J. D. Sato and T. Kawamoto, submitted for publication.

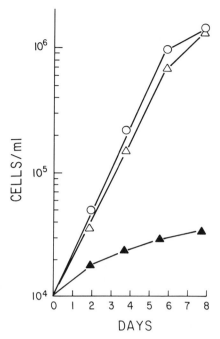

FIG. 2. Growth of NS-1 myeloma cells. NS-1 cells maintained in RDF + 10% FCS were plated at 1×10^4 cells/ml in complete KSLM medium ($\triangle$), lipid-free KSLM ($\blacktriangle$), or RDF + 10% FCS ($\bigcirc$). Cells in duplicate cultures were counted on the indicated days. (From Ref. 9.)

NS-1-503 Cells in Lipid-Free KSLM Medium

In parallel with the development of KSLM medium, we selected an NS-1 subclone, NS-1-503, on the basis of its ability to grow in lipid-free KSLM medium (see above). The growth rates of NS-1-503 in lipid-free KSLM, complete KSLM, and RDF + 10% FCS are compared in Fig. 3. The cells exhibited a slightly longer lag phase in lipid-free KSLM medium, but during logarithmic growth NS-1-503 cells proliferated equally well in all three media with a doubling time of 18.5 hr. In each medium the maximum cell density was approximately 1.3×10^6 cells/well.

Growth of Nascent Hybridomas

NS-1 Hybridomas in Complete and Lipid-Free KSLM Medium

To determine whether KSLM medium would support the growth of newly formed NS-1 hybridomas, the products of an NS-1 × spleen cell

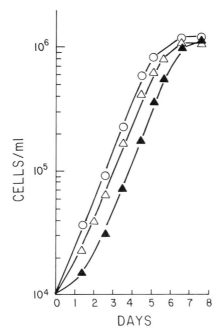

Fig. 3. Growth of NS-1-503 myeloma cells. NS-1-503 cells maintained in lipid-free KSLM were plated at 1×10^4 cells/ml in complete KSLM (△), lipid-free KSLM (▲), or RDF + 10% FCS (○). Cells in duplicate cultures were counted on the indicated days. (From Ref. 9.)

fusion were plated in KSLM medium or RDF + 10% FCS. After 2 weeks the wells were scored for hybridoma colonies, and the medium from positive wells was tested for antibodies to whole A431 cells (Table I). The number of wells containing hybridoma colonies was nearly identical for KSLM and RDF + 10% FCS. In each case approximately 50% of the wells contained one or two colonies, and similar numbers of wells contained A431 antibodies.

Since established hybridoma cell lines had been reported to grow in lipid-free media,[2,3] we examined the effects of LDL and oleic acid on the growth of newly formed NS-1 hybridomas by deleting the lipid supplements from KSLM medium (Table II). In each case microtest wells that were positive for hybridomas contained one or two colonies and approximately 20% of these wells had A431 antibodies. In the absence of LDL the percentage of wells with hybridomas increased from 50 to 70%. The omission of oleic acid from the medium resulted in a marked decrease, to 10%, in the percentage of wells with hybridoma colonies. The omission of

TABLE I
MYELOMA × SPLEEN CELL FUSION IN KSLM MEDIUM AND RDF + 10% FCS[a]

Parent myeloma	Condition	Positive wells (%)	Colonies/well	A431 antibody (% of positive wells)
NS-1	KSLM	54	1–2	25
	KSLM + 10% FCS	51	1–2	33
NS-1-503	KSLM	85	5–10	60
	RDF + 10% FCS	75	5–10	57

[a] Myeloma cells were grown in the appropriate medium (RDF + 10% FCS or KSLM medium) for 3 days prior to fusion. The cells were washed with RDF nutrient medium, and 2×10^7 myeloma cells were fused with a 10-fold excess of spleen cells from immunized mice. Fusion products were resuspended in 70 ml of RDF + 10% FCS or KSLM supplemented with HAT and were plated in 96-well microtest plates. Two weeks after fusion, wells with hybridomas were counted and assayed for A431 antibodies. (From Ref. 9.)

both LDL and oleic acid had the same effect on hybridoma survival and growth as omitting oleic acid alone. These results indicate that nascent NS-1 hybridomas do not require LDL for growth and that LDL may in fact be deleterious to newly formed hybridomas. In addition it appears

TABLE II
EFFECT OF OLEIC ACID AND LDL ON MYELOMA × SPLEEN CELL FUSION
IN KSLM MEDIUM[a]

Parent myeloma	Deletion from KSLM	Positive wells (%)	Colonies/well	A431 antibody (% of positive wells)
NS-1	None	52	1–2	22
	LDL	69	1–2	23
	Oleic acid	11	1–2	17
	LDL + oleic acid	9	1–2	33
NS-1-503	None	92	5–10	69
	LDL	98	5–10	92
	Oleic acid	94	2–3	50
	LDL + oleic acid	100	2–3	91

[a] NS-1 or NS-1-503 cells were fused in independent experiments with spleen cells from immunized mice. The fusion products were divided among 10-ml aliquots of the following HAT-supplemented media: KSLM (none), LDL-free KSLM (LDL), KSLM minus oleic acid (oleic acid), or lipid-free KSLM (LDL + oleic acid). Each cell suspension was plated in one 96-well microtest plate. Two weeks after fusion hybridoma colonies were counted and supernatants were assayed for A431 antibodies. (From Ref. 9.)

that some nascent NS-1 hybridomas are able to grow without any exogenous lipid; however, oleic acid markedly increases the survival and outgrowth of new NS-1 hybridomas.

NS-1-503 Hybridomas in Complete and Lipid-Free KSLM Medium

NS-1-503 cells passaged in lipid-free KSLM were fused with spleen cells from the same splenocyte preparation used in an NS-1 fusion (Table I), and the fusion products were plated in complete KSLM medium or in RDF + 10% FCS. After 2 weeks 85% of the wells with KSLM medium contained hybridomas, and a slightly lower percentage of the wells with RDF + 10% FCS medium were positive for hybridomas. Thus, both nascent NS-1-503 hybridomas and NS-1 hybridomas grew equally well in complete KSLM medium and serum-supplemented medium. It is interesting that in the NS-1-503 fusion wells positive for hybridomas contained about five times as many colonies as did positive wells in the NS-1 fusion. Also, the fusion with NS-1-503 cells resulted in a 1.6-fold increase in the number of wells with hybridomas. These results suggest that NS-1-503 cells fuse two to eight times more efficiently than NS-1 cells. This difference in fusion efficiencies may directly reflect differences in plasma membrane lipid compositions resulting from endogenous lipid synthesis or uptake of exogenous lipid.[14]

As NS-1-503 was selected for growth in lipid-free KSLM medium, we tested the effects of LDL and oleic acid on the growth of newly formed NS-1-503 hybridomas (Table II). Under all culture conditions more than 90% of the wells contained hybridomas. The deletion of LDL, oleic acid, or both supplements caused a modest increase in the percentage of wells with hybridomas. However, the omission of oleic acid resulted in a 2- to 3-fold reduction in the number of colonies per positive well. These results indicate that a large proportion of nascent NS-1-503 hybridomas are capable of growth in the absence of lipid but that oleic acid increases the proportion of surviving hybridomas. LDL seems to be slightly deleterious to new NS-1-503 hybridomas.

Growth of Established Hybridoma Cell Lines

Because nascent NS-1 and NS-1-503 hybridomas were able to grow in the absence of LDL (Table II), we examined the growth of two hybridoma cell lines in LDL-free KSLM medium. Hybridoma 528 is an NS-1 derivative[10] whereas hybridoma 225 was obtained from an NS-1-503 fusion.[10] When plated at a density of 2×10^4 cells/ml, both hybridomas were able

---

[14] L. L. Stoll and A. A. Spector, *In Vitro* **20,** 732 (1984).

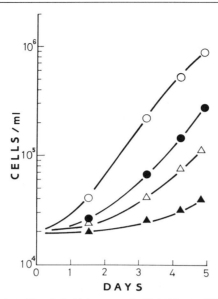

FIG. 4. Effect of oleic acid on hybridoma growth. Hybridomas 528 (●, ○) and 225 (▲, △) were plated at 2×10^4 cells/ml in lipid-free KSLM medium (closed symbols) or in KSLM medium minus LDL (open symbols). Cells in duplicate cultures were counted on the indicated days.

to grow in lipid-free KSLM, but both cell lines exhibited increased growth rates in medium supplemented with oleic acid (Fig. 4). Thus, as with nascent hybridomas, oleic acid enhanced the survival and growth of hybridoma cell lines regardless of the origin of the parent myeloma cells. In addition to the lipid composition of the culture medium, the rate of hybridoma growth was influenced by cell density. Both 528 and 225 cells exhibited progressively lower initial growth rates and longer lag phases as plating cell densities were decreased from 5×10^4 to 3×10^3 cells/ml (not shown).

In our experience most if not all NS-1 and NS-1-503 hybridoma lines, whether isolated in serum-free medium or not, were able to survive and grow in LDL-free KSLM medium without appreciable cell death as long as a minimum cell density was maintained. This minimum density must be determined for each hybridoma line; however, a density of 1×10^4 cells/ml was usually satisfactory. Hybridomas can be cloned in LDL-free KSLM medium using normal spleen cell feeder layers, but under the more stringent growth conditions involved in cloning, decreased cell viability may become an important factor for a given cell line. If cell viability is a

TABLE III
ANTIBODY SECRETION IN LIPID-FREE KSLM MEDIUM[a]

Hybridoma	Medium	Antibody (pg/hr per cell)
528	KSLM without lipid	1.1
	KSLM without LDL	1.2
	RDF + 10% FCS	1.2
225	KSLM without lipid	1.7
	KSLM without LDL	2.0

[a] Hybridoma cells (4 × 10[6]) in each of 10 100-mm plates were incubated in the indicated media for 24 hr at 37° in 7.5% CO_2. Conditioned media were collected by low-speed centrifugation and passed over a column of protein A–agarose. Antibody concentrations were measured by absorbance at 280 nm.

problem at clonal densities it can be circumvented by using fetal calf serum or horse serum to increase the proportion of surviving clones. Cloned hybridomas can later be weaned from the serum supplement at higher cell densities.

Antibody Secretion in Serum-Free Medium

Antibody secretion by 528 and 225 cells was examined in LDL-free and lipid-free KSLM medium (Table III). Immunoglobulin was recovered from culture medium by protein A–agarose chromatography[15] and quantified. Both hybridomas secreted antibodies equally well in the LDL-free and lipid-free media. The rate of antibody secretion by 528 cells also remained unchanged in FCS-supplemented medium.

Comments

KSLM medium[16] consists of a basal nutrient medium (RDF) supplemented with insulin, transferrin, 2-aminoethanol, selenium, 2-mercaptoethanol, LDL, and BSA–oleic acid. BSA and transferrin along with soybean lipid were used by Iscove and Melchers[17] to study the growth and maturation of lipopolysaccharide-reactive mouse lymphocytes in serum-

[15] P. L. Ey, S. J. Prowse, and C. R. Jenkin, *Immunochemistry* **15**, 429 (1978).
[16] A modified version of KSLM medium is available from Hana Media, Inc., Berkeley, California, 94710.
[17] N. N. Iscove and F. Melchers, *J. Exp. Med.* **147**, 923 (1978).

free medium. Murakami *et al.*[3] were the first to use insulin, transferrin, ethanolamine, and selenium (ITES) to grow hybridoma cell lines, but the usefulness of this serum-free medium was highly dependent on the growth characteristics of each cell line. Mendelsohn *et al.*[18] later showed that ITES-supplemented medium did not support optimal growth of mitogen-stimulated normal human lymphocytes. We have retained the ITES supplements in KSLM medium and added 2-mercaptoethanol and lipids. Of these supplements insulin, transferrin, and LDL are the most important for the growth of NS-1 cells. LDL satisfies an absolute lipid requirement of these cells, but we have recently shown that LDL can be replaced by cholesterol complexed with BSA.[7] Oleic acid as a sole source of lipid is not sufficient to support NS-1 survival and growth, but in complete KSLM it enhances the growth rate of NS-1 cells. The effects of oleic acid on cell growth are most apparent at low cell densities. Iscove and colleagues have used lipids such as phosphatidylcholine, oleic acid, linoleic acid, and cholesterol to maintain mouse B lymphocytes[17] and mouse erythroid precursor cells,[19] but with the exception of cholesterol the effects of individual lipid species were not examined. Cholesterol was found to stimulate CFU-E colony formation, but it was not required by normal mitogen-stimulated B cells. By contrast, we have found that NS-1 myeloma cells, and the sibling X63-Ag8.653 cell line, require LDL or BSA–cholesterol for survival and growth in serum-free culture conditions. The use of 2-mercaptoethanol[20] increases the survival of NS-1 cells at clonal densities, and it stimulates antibody production by NS-1 hybridomas (unpublished results). Selenium and 2-aminoethanol, which was required by MPC-11 hybridomas,[3] are not essential for NS-1 growth but are included in KSLM because they have slight stimulatory effects.

Although originally developed for NS-1 cells, KSLM medium also supports the growth of nascent NS-1 hybridomas and established hybridoma lines. An unexpected result of these studies is that NS-1 hybridomas, unlike NS-1 cells, do not require LDL, or cholesterol, for growth. In fact LDL appears to be somewhat deleterious to newly formed NS-1 hybridomas. It may be possible to exploit this difference in growth requirements by using LDL-free, cholesterol-free medium in place of HAT medium to select NS-1 hybridomas. We have found that KSLM medium can also be used to maintain a variety of mouse and human lymphoid cell lines. The cells tested included Sp2/0-Ag14 mouse myeloma cells,[7] X63-Ag8.653 mouse myeloma cells,[13] IM-9 human B lymphocytes, UC-729-6

[18] J. Mendelsohn, A. Caviles, Jr., and J. Castagnola, *Cold Spring Harbor Conf. Cell Proliferation* **9**, 679 (1982).

[19] N. N. Iscove, L. J. Guilbert, and C. Weyman, *Exp. Cell Res.* **126**, 121 (1980).

[20] R. E. Click, L. Benck, and B. J. Alter, *Cell. Immunol.* **3**, 155 (1972).

human lymphoblastoid cells, 8226 human myeloma cells, GM1500 human myeloma cells, WIL-2 human lymphoblastoid cells, and WIL-2 hybridomas.

Finally, it is worth noting that the requirements of NS-1 cells and NS-1 hybridomas for optimal growth appear to be relatively simple in comparison to the requirements of normal B lymphocytes, which respond to a number of T cell- and possibly B cell-derived growth and differentiation factors.[21,22] A reduced dependence on external growth regulators is characteristic of transformed cells, perhaps because they have acquired the ability to produce their own growth factors[23,24]; nevertheless, transformed cells remain responsive to exogenous growth factors. Whether any of the known lymphokines in purified form will enhance the survival of myelomas or hybridomas is an intriguing and unanswered question. One area in which purified lymphokines may prove to be extremely useful is in augmenting the immune response of mouse or human lymphocytes during *in vitro* immunization. Medium conditioned by EL-4 thymoma cells was used recently to generate hybridomas through *in vitro* immunization,[25] but the effects of specific lymphokines remain to be clarified.

Acknowledgments

We thank Anh Dao Le for technical assistance. This research was supported by NIH grants to G.H.S. J.D.S. is the recipient of an NIH postdoctoral fellowship from the Institute of General Medical Sciences.

[21] M. Howard and W. E. Paul, *Annu. Rev. Immunol.* **1,** 307 (1983).
[22] M. Howard, K. Nakanishi, and W. E. Paul, *Immunol. Rev.* **78,** 185 (1984).
[23] P. L. Kaplan and B. Ozanne, *Cell* **33,** 931 (1983).
[24] D. B. McClure, *Cell* **32,** 999 (1983).
[25] M. Ma, S.-J. Wu, M. Howard, and A. B. Borkovec, *In Vitro* **20,** 739 (1984).

[23] Serum-Free Medium for Hybridoma and Parental Myeloma Cell Cultivation

By JAN KOVÁŘ and FRANTIŠEK FRANĚK

Many cell lines including hybridomas and parental myelomas can grow in serum-free media supplemented with hormones, transferrin, lipids, trace elements, and other factors. Several laboratories have reported cultivation of hybridomas in serum-free chemically defined media developed for this purpose.[1-5] Iscove's medium[6] was the first serum-free medium successfully used for hybridoma cultivation.[7] SFH (serum-free hybridoma) medium developed in our laboratory[5] is characterized by the largest set of supplements which are known to support hybridoma growth under serum-free conditions.

Cultivation of animal cells in defined serum-free media has several advantages. Serum-free media facilitate studies which require absence of serum proteins and endogenous serum substances, such as hormones or natural antibodies. Replacement of ill-defined serum by a limited number of defined substances is advantageous, especially in studies of control of cell proliferation and differentiation. The economy of serum-free media represents an additional advantage, particularly in the case of large-scale cultivation of cells. Hybridoma cultivation in serum-free media also enables relatively easy purification of monoclonal antibodies or, in some cases, direct application without further purification.

Composition of SFH Medium

SFH medium was developed by testing individual substances which could support mouse hybridoma growth under serum-free conditions. The results showed that transferrin, insulin, ethanolamine, linoleic acid, ascorbic acid, hydrocortisone, and certain trace element compounds stimulated hybridoma growth. On the other hand, many substances tested had no growth-supporting effect (e.g., triiodothyronine, testosterone, putrescine, 2-mercaptoethanol, α-tocopherol, retinal).

2-Mercaptoethanol is a common component of media for hybridoma cultivation. However, in our experience 2-mercaptoethanol does not exert any growth-supporting effect on stabilized hybridomas under serum-free conditions or in serum-supplemented medium.

Cholesterol or dipalmitoyl lecithin applied without linoleic acid, but with fatty acid-free albumin as a binding protein, exerted a significant growth-stimulating effect under serum-free conditions. The optimum concentration of cholesterol was ~1 μg/ml and of lecithin ~3 μg/ml. However, linoleic acid alone could be used as a substitute for these lipids.

[1] T. H. Chang, Z. Steplewski, and H. Koprowski, *J. Immunol. Methods* **39**, 369 (1980).
[2] F. J. Darfler and P. A. Insel, *Exp. Cell Res.* **138**, 287 (1982).
[3] H. Murakami, H. Masui, G. H. Sato, N. Sueoka, T. P. Chow, and T. Kano-Sueoka, *Proc. Natl. Acad. Sci. U.S.A.* **79**, 1158 (1982).
[4] T. Kawamoto, J. D. Sato, A. Le, D. B. McClure, and G. H. Sato, *Anal. Biochem.* **130**, 445 (1983).
[5] J. Kovář and F. Franěk, *Immunol. Lett.* **7**, 339 (1984).
[6] N. N. Iscove and F. Melchers, *J. Exp. Med.* **147**, 923 (1978).
[7] J. Andersson and F. Melchers, *Curr. Top. Microbiol. Immunol.* **81**, 130 (1978).

TABLE I
SUPPLEMENTS TO THE BASIC MEDIUM USED IN
SFH MEDIUM

Substance	Concentration in the medium
Transferrin	5 μg/ml
Insulin	10 μg/ml
Ethanolamine	20 μM
Linoleic acid	5 μg/ml
Albumin (fatty acid free)	1 mg/ml
Ascorbic acid	3 μg/ml
Hydrocortisone	2 ng/ml
Trace element compounds	
$CdSO_4 \cdot 8/3H_2O$	50 nM
$CoCl_2 \cdot 6H_2O$	10 nM
$CuSO_4 \cdot 5H_2O$	10 nM
$(NH_4)_6Mo_7O_{24} \cdot 4H_2O$	0.5 nM
$MnCl_2 \cdot 4H_2O$	0.5 nM
$NiSO_4 \cdot 6H_2O$	0.25 nM
Na_2SeO_3	40 nM
Na_2SiO_3	200 nM
$SnCl_2 \cdot 2H_2O$	0.25 nM
NH_4VO_3	2.5 nM
$ZnSO_4 \cdot 7H_2O$	1000 nM

SFH medium consists of basic medium and supplements. The basic medium is prepared from RPMI 1640. Supplements (Table I) represent optimized concentrations of transferrin, insulin, ethanolamine, linoleic acid, fatty acid-free albumin, ascorbic acid, hydrocortisone, and also compounds of 11 trace elements (Cd, Co, Cu, Mo, Mn, Ni, Se, Si, Sn, V, Zn). Fatty acid-free albumin is used as a binding protein for linoleic acid. Eight of the trace elements employed are those used by Hutchings and Sato[8] to which compounds of Co, Cu, and Zn are added. Addition of an iron compound was found to be unnecessary, due to inclusion of iron-saturated transferrin in the medium.

Basic Medium

RPMI 1640 medium containing additional L-glutamine (300 μg/ml), Na pyruvate (110 μg/ml), HEPES (15 mM), penicillin (100 IU/ml), streptomycin (100 μg/ml), and gentamicin (40 μg/ml) is used as a basic medium.

[8] S. E. Hutchings and G. H. Sato, *Proc. Natl. Acad. Sci. U.S.A.* **75,** 901 (1978).

To prepare fresh basic medium 100 ml RPMI 1640 of standard quality is supplemented with 1 ml of L-glutamine solution (30 mg/ml), 1 ml of Na pyruvate solution (11 mg/ml), 1 ml of antibiotic solution (10^4 IU of penicillin, 10 mg of streptomycin, and 4 mg of gentamicin per ml), and 1 ml of HEPES solution (1.5 M). Basic medium is stored at 4° for no longer than 10 days.

Solutions of L-glutamine, Na pyruvate, and antibiotics are prepared in distilled water (tissue culture quality). HEPES dissolved in distilled water (tissue culture quality) is adjusted to pH 7.2 by addition of 1 M NaOH. Solutions are sterilized by filtration through a 0.22-μm Millipore filter (Bedford, MA).

Basic medium prepared from a mixture (1 : 1) of Dulbecco's modified MEM (DMEM) and Ham's F-12 medium was also tested. This basic medium is also suitable for preparation of SFH medium. In some cases use of the mixture of DMEM and F-12 results in a significantly faster growth of hybridomas in SFH medium.

Supplements

Transferrin. Pig transferrin prepared from pig serum according to Kovář and Franěk[9] was found to be suitable for cultivation of mouse hybridomas in SFH medium. Many authors used human transferrin in their serum-free media because of its commercial availability. Although the species origin of transferrin may influence the value of the lowest concentration of the optimum plateau, it does not seem crucial.

The optimum concentration of transferrin that stimulates growth of various hybridomas in SFH medium is about 5–10 μg/ml (Fig. 1). It should be kept in mind that transferrin at concentrations higher than the optimum was found to be effective and without evident toxicity,[6] perhaps because the concentration of transferrin in body fluids is ~3 mg/ml. In other words, a broad optimum plateau is a characteristic feature of the transferrin effect.

The growth-supporting effect of transferrin is significant; i.e., the number of cells grown with transferrin, even at a concentration of

[9] J. Kovář and F. Franěk, *Folia Biol.* (*Prague*) **31**, 167 (1985).

FIG. 1. Effect of transferrin, insulin, ethanolamine, linoleic acid, ascorbic acid, and hydrocortisone at concentrations near the optimum on growth of hybridomas in SFH medium. Curves represent the effect of transferrin, insulin, ethanolamine, and ascorbic acid on growth of hybridoma PTF-02 and the effect of linoleic acid and hydrocortisone on growth of hybridoma T3-03. Cells were grown 3 days from an inoculum of 60 × 10^3 cells per well containing 1 ml of medium. Each point represents mean ± SEM.

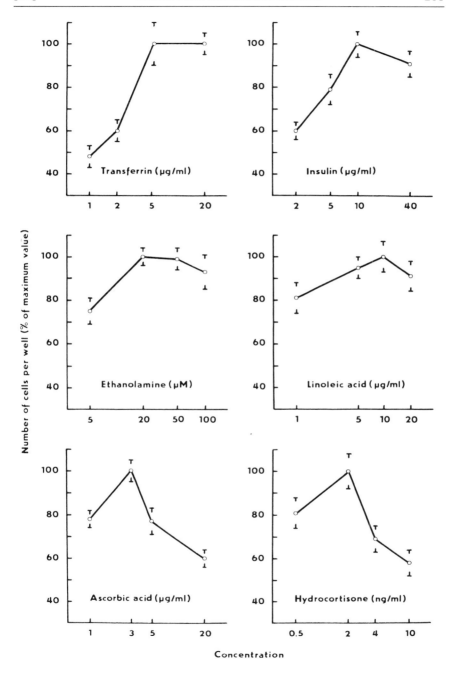

0.1 μg/ml, is significantly higher than that obtained without transferrin. Concentrations of 0.5 μg/ml and higher are significantly stimulatory; i.e., the number of cells grown with transferrin increases over that of the inoculum.

Transferrin is essential for the survival of hybridoma cells under serum-free conditions. Omission of transferrin from SFH medium results in total inhibition of hybridoma growth and cell death (Fig. 2). The rate of decay of the culture after removal of transferrin depends on the hybridoma. The effect is more pronounced in the case of fast-growing hybridomas derived from myeloma FO than with slower growing hybridomas derived from myeloma X63-Ag8.653.

Transferrin action is closely related to mechanisms controlling hybridoma proliferation.[9] Therefore, we assume that transferrin acts as a hybridoma growth factor.

Insulin. Crystalline bovine insulin of standard quality (28 IU/mg, zinc content 0.5%) is used. We assume that the species origin of insulin is not an important factor. The growth-stimulating effect of porcine insulin was found to be very similar to that of bovine insulin.

The optimum concentration of insulin for stimulating growth of hybridomas in SFH medium is about 10 μg/ml (Fig. 1). The stimulating effect of higher concentrations was the same or less.

Both insulin and transferrin are common components of serum-free media for cultivation of various cell lines including hybridomas. As shown previously,[5] hybridoma growth under serum-free conditions depends strictly on the presence of transferrin, whereas insulin is not strictly required. For example, hybridomas derived from myeloma X63-Ag8.653 do not grow without insulin, while fast-growing hybridomas derived from myeloma FO grow well without it (Fig. 2).

Insulin action may be based on mimicking insulin-like growth factors.[10] If this is the case, an excess of insulin is necessary to compensate for lower affinity of insulin to receptors for these insulin-like substances. Thus effective concentrations of insulin are much higher than physiological concentrations in body fluids.

Ethanolamine. Ethanolamine (2-aminoethanol) was shown to be essential for hybridoma growth under serum-free conditions by Murakami and co-workers.[3] For preparation of SFH medium, ethanolamine (pure) of standard quality is used. Liquid ethanolamine is of the same quality as crystalline ethanolamine hydrochloride (research grade) with regard to the growth-supporting effect and toxicity at concentrations higher than the optimum.

[10] D. Barnes and G. Sato, *Anal. Biochem.* **102**, 255 (1980).

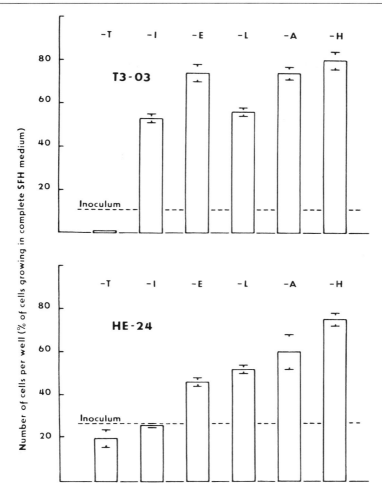

FIG. 2. Effect of omission of transferrin (−T), insulin (−I), ethanolamine (−E), linoleic acid (−L), ascorbic acid (−A), and hydrocortisone (−H) on growth of two hybridomas in SFH medium. Hybridoma T3-03 was derived from myeloma FO and hybridoma HE-24 from myeloma X63-Ag8.653. Cells were grown 3 days from an inoculum of 60×10^3 cells per well containing 1 ml of medium. Dashed lines represent number of cells of the inoculum. Columns lower than the level of dashed lines show that cells do not grow and die. Each column represents mean ± SEM.

Ethanolamine concentrations of 20–50 μM were found to be optimal for growth of hybridomas in SFH medium (Fig. 1). At higher concentrations the growth-stimulating effect decreases slowly, probably due to increasing toxicity. Omission of ethanolamine results in markedly decreased growth of hybridomas derived from myeloma X63-Ag8.653, whereas growth of hybridomas derived from FO is not so strongly affected (Fig. 2).

Another amine with known cell growth-supporting activity,[10] putrescine, is ineffective.[3,5]

Linoleic Acid and Albumin. Linoleic acid (analytical grade) of standard quality is used. Essentially fatty acid-free (less than 0.005%) bovine albumin prepared from fraction V(Sigma, St. Louis, MO) is employed as a carrier.

Fatty acid-free albumin alone at a concentration of 1 mg/ml has no effect on hybridoma growth under serum-free conditions. However, higher concentrations exert an increasing inhibitory effect, probably due to increasing toxicity. Albumin at a concentration of 1 mg/ml is used, due to insufficient capacity of lower concentrations to bind the required levels of linoleic acid.

The optimum concentration of linoleic acid (applied with 1 mg/ml of albumin) for stimulating hybridoma growth in SFH medium is about 10 μg/ml (Fig. 1). However, at concentrations higher than 20 μg/ml the stimulatory effect decreases sharply, due to toxicity. A strong inhibitory effect is observed at concentrations about 5-fold higher than the optimum. Thus in some cases, the inhibitory levels are very close to the optimum stimulatory concentration. On the other hand, omission of linoleic acid from SFH medium inhibits growth of hybridomas markedly (Fig. 2).

It should be kept in mind that a certain ratio of linoleic acid and fatty acid-free albumin concentrations should not be exceeded because the toxic effect of the fatty acid could appear. This critical ratio is about 1 : 100 (w/w).

Ascorbic Acid. It was shown previously[5] that ascorbic acid supported hybridoma growth under serum-free conditions. Ascorbic acid (pharmaceutical grade) is used as a component of SFH medium.

The range of effective growth-stimulating concentrations, with an optimum concentration of ~3 μg/ml (Fig. 1), is relatively narrow. However, omission of ascorbic acid significantly decreases growth of hybridomas (Fig. 2).

The growth-supporting effect of ascorbic acid may be connected with its antioxidant activity, which results in protection of cells from toxic effects of peroxides.

Hydrocortisone. Hydrocortisone (11β,17α,21-trihydroxypregn-4-ene-3,20-dione) was also found to support hybridoma growth under serum-free conditions.[5] For preparation of SFH medium, hydrocortisone 21-hemisuccinate (sodium salt, pharmaceutical grade) is used.

Hydrocortisone exerts the growth-stimulating effect over a relatively narrow range of concentrations with the optimum at about 2 ng/ml (Fig. 1). The effect of hydrocortisone omission on hybridoma growth is less, though still significant, than the effect of omitting other supplements tested (Fig. 2).

Trace Elements. All used compounds of trace elements are of analytical grade. Compounds of selenium (Na_2SeO_3) and also manganese ($MnCl_2$) exert a significant growth-supporting effect on hybridomas. The optimum concentration of selenium is 30–60 nM. At higher concentrations the stimulatory effect decreases gradually. Omission of selenium affects hybridoma growth in SFH medium significantly. The number of cells grown over 3 days of cultivation without selenium is only 60–70% of cells growing with selenium.

In the case of manganese, the optimum concentration is about 0.5 nM. At higher concentrations the stimulatory effect decreases, but toxicity does not appear, even at a concentration 100-fold higher than the optimum. Omission of manganese leads to decreased hybridoma growth. The number of cells growing 3 days without manganese represents about 80% of cells growing with manganese.

Selenium compounds are widely used as components of serum-free media for cultivation of many types of cells. In contrast, the stimulatory effect of manganese on hybridoma growth in serum-free medium was discovered only recently.[5] The nature of this effect is unknown. The other trace elements used in SFH medium do not exert any significant growth-stimulating effect. Compounds of Cr, Ti, B, I, and F also were tested, but they displayed no effect.

Modifications

Two modifications of complete SFH medium may also be employed. One modification does not contain ascorbic acid and hydrocortisone and enables short-term or long-term cultivation of all hybridomas which can grow in complete SFH medium. Growth of all hybridomas tested was slower than in complete SFH medium. However, the growth is sufficient, especially with rapidly proliferating hybridomas. For example, hybridoma T3-03 adapted to growth in SFH medium displays, during exponential growth, a doubling time of about 12 hr in complete SFH medium and about 14 hr in the modification without ascorbic acid and hydrocortisone.

The other modification lacks linoleic acid and albumin and is suitable for experiments requiring absence of these substances, especially albumin. Growth of hybridomas is slower, due to omission of the fatty acid, but the rate of growth is sufficient in the case of rapidly proliferating hybridomas. This modification also enables successful freezing and thawing of hybridoma cells, but is not suitable for cloning, which requires the presence of albumin.

Preparation of SFH Medium

Stock solution of transferrin (5 mg/ml) is prepared in phosphate-buffered saline (pH 7.4). Stock solution of insulin (10 mg/ml) is prepared in distilled water (tissue culture quality), adjusted to pH 2.5 by addition of HCl.[1] Stock solutions of ethanolamine (20 mM), ascorbic acid (3 mg/ml), hydrocortisone (2 μg/ml), and trace element compounds (concentrations 10^4 times higher than final concentrations in the medium) are prepared in distilled water (tissue culture quality). These solutions are sterilized by filtration through a 0.22-μm Millipore filter. Stock solution of linoleic acid (5 mg/ml) is prepared in 96% ethanol, which is nontoxic for hybridoma cells at a concentration of 0.1% (v/v).

Stock composite solution of supplements is prepared as follows: 1 ml of stock solution of linoleic acid is added to 93 ml of basic medium and mixed thoroughly. Fatty acid-free albumin (1 g) is added and dissolved without stirring. The solution is sterilized by filtration through a Millipore filter. Stock solutions of transferrin (1 ml), insulin (1 ml), ethanolamine (1 ml), ascorbic acid (1 ml), hydrocortisone (1 ml), and trace element compounds (100 μl each) are added to the sterilized solution of albumin with linoleic acid and mixed thoroughly. A fresh solution of ascorbic acid is always used. Vials containing appropriate amounts (10 ml for preparation of 100 ml of SFH medium) of stock composite solution of supplements are stored frozen at $-20°$.

To prepare 100 ml of SFH medium, 90 ml of basic medium is mixed with 10 ml of thawed stock solution of supplements. It is recommended that fresh SFH medium be prepared daily. If stored at 4°, SFH medium should not be kept longer than 5 days.

Hybridoma and Myeloma Cultivation in SFH Medium

Manipulations with cells cultivated in serum-free medium are not entirely the same as in the case of cells held in serum-supplemented medium. Serum-free culture is more sensitive to environmental changes (e.g., changes in pH due to changes in CO_2 concentration or evaporation of the medium due to insufficient humidity). It is recommended that hybridoma cells cultivated in SFH medium be passaged every 2–3 days to avoid rapid cell degeneration and death.

TABLE II
DOUBLING TIMES OF MYELOMAS DURING
EXPONENTIAL GROWTH IN SFH MEDIUM

Adaptation[a]	Myeloma	Doubling time[b] (hr)
Nonadapted	FO	23.1 ± 2.2
Nonadapted	Sp2/0-Ag14	34.4 ± 1.6
Nonadapted	X63-Ag8.653	N
Adapted	FO	16.2 ± 3.2[c]
Adapted	Sp2/0-Ag14	32.6 ± 5.3

[a] Myeloma nonadapted or adapted to growth in SFH medium.
[b] Mean value of doubling time ± SEM (N, cells do not proliferate).
[c] Growth in modification of SFH medium without linoleic acid and albumin.

It is also necessary to distinguish between cultivation of cells not adapted to growth in SFH medium and adapted cells. Nonadapted cells are cells just transferred from serum-supplemented medium into serum-free medium, with one washing cycle in basic medium. Adaptation takes approximately five passages (12 days). Adapted cells grow significantly faster than nonadapted ones (Table II and Table III).

As discussed below, use of SFH medium enables high-efficiency cloning of suitable hybridomas and successful freezing and thawing of hybridoma cells.

Growth of Nonadapted Cells

Various nonadapted parental myelomas behave differently when cultivated in SFH medium. Myelomas Sp2/O-Ag14 and particularly FO grow well, whereas myeloma X63-Ag8.653 does not grow at all (Table II). Similar differences appear when comparing growth of nonadapted hybridomas derived from these myelomas. The best growing hybridomas in SFH medium are derived from FO and the worst from X63-Ag8.653 (Table III).

The fastest growing nonadapted hybridomas display a doubling time of about 14 hr during exponential growth. Slow-growing hybridomas derived from X63-Ag8.653 have a doubling time of about 30 hr. Some of the hybridomas derived from myeloma X63-Ag8.653 grow very slowly or do not grow in SFH medium, e.g., hybridomas PTF-01 and TU-01. Hybri-

TABLE III
Doubling Times of Hybridomas during Exponential Growth in SFH Medium

Adaptation[a]	Hybridoma	Parental myeloma	Doubling time[b] (hr)
Nonadapted	PLV-01[c]	FO	17.5 ± 1.3
Nonadapted	PLV-02[c]	FO	14.1 ± 1.2
Nonadapted	PLV-04[c]	FO	18.5 ± 1.8
Nonadapted	T3-03[d]	FO	14.1 ± 1.4
Nonadapted	MEM-12[e]	Sp2/0-Ag14	22.4 ± 2.8
Nonadapted	PLV-20[c]	X63-Ag8.653	24.6 ± 3.3
Nonadapted	HE-24[f]	X63-Ag8.653	32.2 ± 3.2
Nonadapted	TU-01[g]	X63-Ag8.653	N
Nonadapted	PTF-01[h]	X63-Ag8.653	N
Nonadapted	PTF-02[h]	X63-Ag8.653	33.6 ± 1.4
Nonadapted	PGG-02[i]	X63-Ag8.653	31.5 ± 3.7[j]
Nonadapted	PGG-05[i]	X63-Ag8.653	D
Adapted	PLV-01[c]	FO	17.0 ± 1.4
Adapted	T3-03[d]	FO	11.6 ± 0.6
Adapted	T3-03[d]	FO	13.5 ± 0.2[k]
Adapted	HE-24[f]	X63-Ag8.653	18.1 ± 0.4[j]
Adapted	PTF-02[h]	X63-Ag8.653	32.9 ± 1.5[j]

[a] Hybridoma nonadapted or adapted to growth in SFH medium.

[b] Mean value of doubling time ± SEM (N, cells do not proliferate or proliferate very slowly; D, cells die).

[c] Hybridoma producing monoclonal antibodies against potato leaf-roll virus. (J. Kovář, F. Franěk, M. Čech, M. Filigarová, and R. Zelenka, unpublished results, 1984.)

[d] Hybridoma producing monoclonal antibodies against triiodothyronine. (J. Kovář, J. Nedvídková, F. Franěk, and V. Felt, unpublished results, 1983.)

[e] Hybridoma producing monoclonal antibodies against human HLA-DR antigens. (I. Hilgert, V. Hořejší, and H. Krištofová, unpublished results, 1984.)

[f] Hybridoma producing monoclonal antibodies against human erythrocyte blood group antigen A. [M. Němec, V. Viklický, J. Bártek, D. Dřímalová, and J. Vaňák, Czechoslovak Patent No. 229 995 (1984).]

[g] Hybridoma producing monoclonal antibodies against pig brain tubulin. [V. Viklický, P. Dráber, J. Hašek, and J. Bártek, *Cell Biol. Int. Rep.* **6**, 725 (1982).]

[h] Hybridoma producing monoclonal antibodies against pig transferrin. [J. Bártek, V. Viklický, F. Franěk, P. Angelisová, P. Dráber, T. Jarošíková, M. Němec, and H. Verlová, *Immunol. Lett.* **4**, 231 (1982).]

[i] Hybridoma producing monoclonal antibodies against pig IgG. [M. Němec, F. Franěk, and V. Viklický, Czechoslovak Patents No. 228 856 and No. 228 858 (1984).]

[j] Growth in modification of SFH medium without ascorbic acid and hydrocortisone.

[k] Growth in modification of SFH medium without linoleic acid and albumin.

doma PGG-05 does not grow at all and dies within 3 days of cultivation (Table III).

It should be kept in mind that successful cultivation of nonadapted hybridomas in serum-free medium depends strongly on the condition of the cells used for seeding. The maximum cell density reached by nonadapted hybridomas in SFH medium is about 600×10^3 to 800×10^3 cells/ml in the case of hybridomas derived from FO and about 400×10^3 cells/ml in the case of hybridomas derived from X63-Ag8.653.

Growth of Adapted Cells

The fastest growing nonadapted parental myeloma, FO, is also the fastest growing adapted myeloma (Table II). As in the case of nonadapted cells, the best growing adapted hybridomas are derived from myeloma FO. Adapted hybridomas derived from X63-Ag8.653 grow more slowly (Table III).

The doubling time during the exponential growth phase of the fastest proliferating hybridoma adapted to SFH medium is about 12 hr (Table III). It should be kept in mind that successful growth of nonadapted hybridomas in SFH medium does not imply successful adaptation to long-term cultivation in the medium. An example is hybridoma PGG-02. This hybridoma grew nonadapted in SFH medium (Table III), but numerous attempts at long-term cultivation were unsuccessful. Cells died within two or three passages.

Adapted hybridomas derived from FO can grow in SFH medium up to a maximum cell density of about 800×10^3 to 1000×10^3 cells/ml. Adapted hybridomas derived from X63-Ag8.653 reach maximum cell density of about 600×10^3 cells/ml.

Once hybridoma cells are adapted, they can be propagated in SFH medium as long-term cultures without any special care. Hybridoma T3-03 was cultivated in complete SFH medium as well as in the modification lacking linoleic acid and albumin for more than 30 passages without any change of growth characteristics. Similarly, myeloma FO was propagated in SFH medium for about 30 passages.

We found that some adapted hybridoma cells did not require all the growth-supporting supplements necessary for nonadapted cells. Nonadapted hybridoma T3-03 required all the growth-stimulating supplements present in SFH medium (Fig. 2). On the other hand, the same hybridoma adapted to the modification of SFH medium lacking linoleic acid and albumin required only transferrin and ascorbic acid. In the case of this adapted hybridoma, insulin even exerted an inhibitory effect at concentrations near the concentration used in SFH medium (Fig. 3).

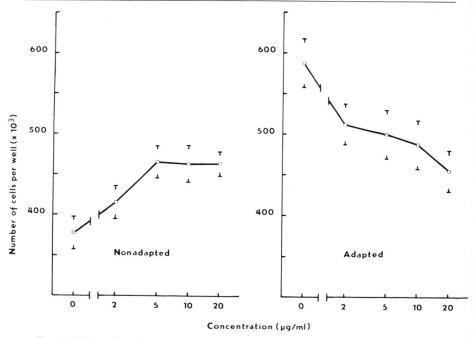

FIG. 3. Effect of insulin at concentrations near the concentration used in SFH medium (5 μg/ml) on growth of nonadapted hybridoma T3-03 in the modification of SFH medium lacking linoleic acid and albumin. Nonadapted hybridoma represents cells just transferred from serum-supplemented medium into the serum-free medium and adapted hybridoma represents cells after adaptation in the same modification of SFH medium (approximately five passages). Cells were grown 3 days from an inoculum of 60×10^3 cells per well containing 1 ml of medium. Each point represents mean $\pm$ SEM.

We also found that the change of specific growth requirements of hybridomas by adaptation to SFH medium was reversible. The adapted hybridoma T3-03, mentioned above, if readapted to serum-supplemented medium and used as nonadapted cells, again required all the growth-stimulating SFH medium supplements.

Cloning

Cloning in serum-free medium enables one to obtain producing clones of hybridomas completely adapted to growth under serum-free conditions. Fast-growing hybridomas, particularly those derived from myeloma FO, are appropriate for cloning in SFH medium.

Modified Bishop's method[11] of cloning in wells of a Terasaki plate is employed. Cloning medium contains one part of conditioned SFH medium (medium from a 3-day culture of hybridoma which we intend to clone) and five parts of fresh SFH medium. It is recommended that exponentially growing cells be used for cloning.

Cells are resuspended in the cloning medium at a concentration of 60 cells/ml. The suspension is seeded into wells (20 μl/well), after 4 hr the plate is viewed under the microscope, and wells with one cell only are labeled. The plate is held motionless in a humidified atmosphere (petri dish with distilled water). After 7 days, the first grown clones are transferred into larger wells containing 200 μl of fresh SFH medium. Clones suitable for transferring cover more than one-half of the bottom of a Terasaki plate well.

Cloning of hybridoma PLV-01 (previously nonadapted to growth in SFH medium) in SFH medium showed that 53% of single cells in the wells yielded growing clones. In the case of hybridoma PLV-01 adapted to growth in SFH medium, 83% efficiency was achieved.

Freezing

Storing frozen hybridoma cells adapted to growth in SFH medium is more advantageous than repeated adaptation of the cells, because adaptation is a time-consuming procedure. Hybridoma cells can be frozen and thawed in SFH medium supplemented with a cryoprotective agent.

A two-step freezing method[12] is used. A suspension of approximately 3×10^6 cells in 1 ml of SFH medium with 5% DMSO (dimethyl sulfoxide) per glass vial is allowed to stand for 10 min, then frozen in a $-25°$ bath within 10 min. Vials are then transferred directly into liquid nitrogen.

Quick thawing in a hot (60–80°) bath is necessary. The thawed suspension is diluted with fresh medium. Cells are then harvested by low-speed centrifugation. Harvested cells are resuspended in fresh SFH medium and seeded (cells from one vial per plastic dish with 6 ml of medium). Changing the medium on the following day(s) is recommended.

Monoclonal Antibody Production in SFH Medium

Efficient antibody production by hybridomas grown in SFH medium is very important, because only hybridomas producing monoclonal antibodies in sufficient concentrations are suitable for practical use.

[11] C. E. Bishop, *J. Immunol. Methods* **46**, 47 (1981).
[12] J. Pěknicová and V. Landa, *Folia Biol. (Prague)* **31**, 340 (1985).

Production of monoclonal antibodies against triiodothyronine produced by hybridoma T3-03 was tested by radioimmunoassay (RIA). An aliquot of SFH medium from a 3-day culture ($698 \times 10^3 \pm 24 \times 10^3$ cells/ml) of adapted hybridoma T3-03 bound $10,100 \pm 200$ cpm in the RIA. In the case of the same hybridoma cultivated in medium supplemented with 10% bovine serum, the result was $11,100 \pm 100$ cpm (3-day culture, $886 \times 10^3 \pm 36 \times 10^3$ cells/ml). Similar results were obtained with clone PLV-01.2 of hybridoma PLV-01 in an enzyme immunoassay for detection of monoclonal antibodies against potato leaf-roll virus. The cells were obtained by cloning adapted hybridoma PLV-01 in SFH medium.

Our experience with numerous hybridomas has demonstrated that cells adapted to grow in SFH medium do not cease to produce monoclonal antibodies. The concentration of monoclonal antibodies achieved in culture medium depends on the hybridoma cell density and on the length of time of cultivation. Thus lower production of monoclonal antibodies in SFH medium reflects lower cell density (e.g., hybridomas derived from myeloma X63-Ag8.653).

Concluding Remarks

Growth of nonadapted hybridoma cells in SFH medium is significantly slower than growth of an adapted hybridoma. Therefore, to evaluate hybridoma growth parameters in SFH medium based on the growth of nonadapted cells is not quite correct. It is necessary to take this fact into account when the growth of a hybridoma in SFH medium is compared with growth in serum-supplemented medium.

Growth efficiency of hybridomas in SFH medium is, to a high degree, determined by parental myelomas. This fact may be crucial when choosing a parental myeloma with the aim of cultivating hybridomas in serum-free medium. From this point of view, myeloma FO is more suitable than myeloma X63-Ag8.653. Hybridomas derived from various myelomas also differ as to dependence of their growth on individual components of SFH medium.

Finally, it should be emphasized that none of the serum-free media developed for hybridoma cultivation are suitable for cultivation of all hybridomas or myelomas. This fact can be explained by assuming the existence of one or more hitherto uncharacterized growth and/or nutrient factors essential for some hybridomas.

[24] Endothelial Cell Growth Supplements for Promoting the Growth of Monoclonal Antibody-Producing Hybridoma Cells

By JANET H. RANSOM

The clonal growth of hybridoma cells is greatly enhanced by the addition of a variety of growth factors. Mouse peritoneal, thymocyte, or spleen cell feeders are the most commonly used growth-promoting conditions for hybridomas.[1-4] Microbial contamination, however, can be encountered when using freshly dissociated cells from animals. Soluble growth supplements can abrogate contamination problems and can be quality controlled for their growth-supporting effects. Astaldi *et al.*[5] showed that human endothelial cell culture supernatants (HECS) were even more effective than feeder cells in supporting the clonal growth of hybridomas. The limitation of HECS is the lack of available human umbilical cords from which to prepare the endothelial cells. We have found that a commercially available endothelial cell growth supplement (ECGS, Collaborative Research, Lexington, MA) similar to HECS was superior to feeder cells as a growth factor for hybridomas.[6] ECGS is an extract of bovine hypothalamus standardized for promoting the growth of human endothelial cells.[7,8] Our experience using ECGS in place of feeder cells for supporting the clonal growth of hamster fetal cells prompted us to test it with hybridomas.[9,10] The purpose of this report is to outline in detail the methods we found successful in utilizing ECGS as a growth factor for antibody-producing hybridomas.

Preparation before Fusion

1. Sp2/0-AG14 mouse myeloma cells[11] are subpassaged twice weekly at a density of 2×10^5 cells/ml RPMI 1640 with 10% fetal bovine serum

[1] G. Köhler and C. Milstein, *Eur. J. Immunol.* **6**, 511 (1976).
[2] G. J. Hämmerling, H. Lemke, U. Näurling, C. Höhmann, R. Wallich, and K. Rajewsky, *Curr. Top. Microbiol. Immunol.* **81**, 100 (1978).
[3] W. Lernhardt, J. Andersen, A. Coutinho, and F. Melchers, *Cell Res.* **111**, 309 (1978).
[4] S. Fazekas de St. Groth and D. Scheidegger, *J. Immunol. Methods* **35**, 1 (1980).
[5] G. C. B. Astaldi, M. C. Janssen, P. M. Lansdorp, C. Willems, W. P. Zeijlemaker, and F. Oosterhof, *J. Immunol.* **125**, 1411 (1980).
[6] C. Pintus, J. H. Ransom, and C. H. Evans, *J. Immunol. Methods* **61**, 195 (1983).
[7] T. Maciag, *Proc. Natl. Acad. Sci. U.S.A.* **76**, 5674 (1979).
[8] J. Folkman and C. Haudenschild, *Nature (London)* **288**, 551 (1980).
[9] C. H. Evans and J. A. DiPaolo, *J. Natl. Cancer Inst.* **68**, 127 (1982).
[10] J. H. Ransom, C. H. Evans, and J. A. DiPaolo, *J. Natl. Cancer Inst.* **69**, 741 (1982).
[11] M. Shulman, C. D. Wilde, and G. Köhler, *Nature (London)* **276**, 269 (1978).

(FBS). Once a month the cells should be subpassaged in medium containing 20 μg 8-azaguanine/ml for two subpassages. At least 3 days prior to fusion, cells should be passaged in medium without 8-azaguanine.

2. Prepare 100× stock solutions containing 1×10^{-2} M hypoxanthine, 4×10^{-5} M aminopterin, and 1.5×10^{-3} M thymidine (HAT), and store frozen. Prepare HAT selection medium on the day of the fusion to obtain a 1× working solution in Dulbecco's modified Eagle's minimum essential medium with 10% FBS, L-glutamine, and gentamicin. Different lots of FBS should be tested for the ability to support the clonal growth of the myeloma cells and selected for optimal cloning efficiency. Sp2/0 cells should also be tested for aminopterin sensitivity in HAT before fusion.

3. BALB/c mice are immunized with soluble antigen or cell membranes by sc inoculation at 2-week intervals with antigen mixed initially with complete Freund's adjuvant and then with incomplete adjuvant.[6] Three days prior to fusion the antigen is administered intravenously.

4. To prepare medium on the day of the fusion reconstitute a 15-mg vial of ECGS with 3 ml of HAT medium. The lyophilized ECGS dissolves readily and is supplied in a sterile package. We have stored lyophilized ECGS for over a year at $-30°$ without observing any loss of activity. ECGS after reconstitution is best stored frozen and used within 2 weeks. Dilute 1 ml of the reconstituted ECGS with 100 ml of HAT medium for a final concentration of 50 μg ECGS/ml HAT medium.

Fusion

The fusion was performed essentially as described by Herzenberg et al.[12] (1) Splenic lymphocytes are added to myelomas at a ratio of 10 lymphocytes per myeloma cell and centrifuged. (2) One milliliter of polyethylene glycol (M_r 1000, 50% w/v) is added dropwise over 5 min to the pelleted cells, which are gently agitated between additions. The cells are then suspended in 10 ml of HAT, centrifuged, and washed once. (3) The cells are resuspended in a volume of HAT medium containing ECGS based on the initial lymphocyte count such that a concentration of 10^5 lymphocytes/ml is obtained. Cells, 200 μl per well, are plated in 96-well tissue culture cluster plates and the plates incubated at 37° in a humidified 95% air/5% CO_2 chamber. After 1 week approximately half of the medium per well is aspirated with a sterile Pasteur pipet and 100 μl of HAT–ECGS is added. Hybridoma colonies are visible at 1 week and can usually be tested for antibody production between 2 and 4 weeks after the fusion.

[12] L. A. Herzenberg, L. A. Herzenberg, and C. Milstein, in "Handbook of Experimental Immunology" (D. M. Weir, ed.), p. 25.1. Blackwell, Oxford, 1978.

Results Obtained with ECGS

We found in a series of three fusions, in which we divided the cells into two groups, one plated on BALB/c resident peritoneal feeder cells and the other with ECGS, that in all cases there were more colonies when ECGS was used as the feeder system (ranging from 1.5- to 7.4-fold more colonies).[6] One unique feature of the ECGS is that a larger number of cells with a fibroblast morphology appear when the fused cells are plated in ECGS compared to plating on peritoneal feeder cells. We know that ECGS is an excellent growth factor for hamster fetal fibroblasts and therefore may cause the splenic connective tissue cells to grow. This increase in the splenic adherent cells may act as a growth-enhancing effect. We have observed that the majority of hybridoma colonies that appear grow on top of the adherent cells as if the colony is loosely attached. The ECGS effect, however, is probably not solely due to its effect on adherent spleen cells because ECGS also enhances the colony formation of hybridomas during single-cell cloning procedures. Thus ECGS can be used as a clonal growth factor immediately after the fusion as well as during limiting dilution clonal selection.

Conclusions

ECGS acts as a clonal growth factor for murine antibody-producing hybridomas. The advantages of ECGS over feeder cells are that sterility can be assured and that a larger number of hybridoma colonies develop after fusion. The advantages of ECGS over HECS is that it is readily available, highly stable, and standardized from lot to lot.

[25] Feeder Effect of Enriched Human Monocytes on Human Hybridoma, Myeloma, and Lymphoma Cell Lines

By THOMAS BRODIN, LENNART OLSSON, and HANS OLOV SJÖGREN

In mouse × mouse, mouse × rat, and rat × rat hybridoma systems,[1,2] the use of feeder cells early after fusion and in cloning steps is established as an important factor for improving hybrid cell growth. Mouse or rat thymocytes, spleen cells, and peritoneal macrophages and irradiated 3T3

[1] S. Fazekas de St. Groth and D. Scheidegger, *J. Immunol. Methods* **35**, 1 (1980).
[2] R. Nilsson, T. Brodin, and H. O. Sjögren, *J. Immunol. Methods* **55**, 179 (1982).

cells have been routinely used in the mouse and rat systems.[3] The development of human × human hybridoma technology has met with difficulties both in finding a malignant cell line as fusion partner that will give a high yield of Ig-producing hybrids and in the principal and technical problem of optimal antigen stimulation of human B lymphocytes *in vivo* or *in vitro*.[4] In this chapter we want to emphasize also the importance of using a feeder layer for human lymphoid cell lines and describe the methods used for large-scale preparation of monocyte feeder cells of human origin.

Methodology

Preparation of Human Monocytes

Heparinized blood or buffy coats from healthy donors were used as a source of PMC (peripheral blood mononuclear cells). Autologous plasma was saved for pretreatment of gelatin columns (see below), as the adherence of monocytes to the gelatin beads is probably partly mediated through fibronectin coating the collagen surface of the bead. Gelatin beads were prepared as described[5] but are also available commercially (Geli-Bead Microcarriers, KC Biological, KA). The use of gelatin bead columns for separation of PMC subpopulations has been described.[6]

Procedure. (1) Buffy coats or heparinized blood was mixed with an equal volume of phosphate (10 mM)-buffered saline (0.15 M) with 50 IE preservative-free heparin/ml (Novo, Copenhagen, Denmark), layered on top of a cushion of Ficoll 400–diatrizoate sodium (density 1.077 g/ml, Ficoll-Hypaque, Pharmacia Fine Chemicals, Uppsala), and centrifuged at 400 g for 30 min. (2) The cells at the interface were aspirated, washed twice in PBS–heparin (more than two times the volume of the aspirate) by centrifugation at 300 g for 10 min, and finally resuspended in 3 ml of RPMI 1640 medium with 10% autologous plasma and 50 IE heparin/ml (R10–hep). (3) Gelatin beads were autoclaved at 120° for 15 min in Ca- and Mg-free PBS, washed in PBS, and sedimented in a 10-ml sterile disposable plastic syringe attached to an outlet control. (4) Twenty milliliters of PBS followed by 6 ml R10–hep were passed through the column at a flow rate of 2 ml/min.

[3] P. J. Lachmann, R. G. Oldroyd, C. Milstein, and B. W. Wright, *Immunology* **41,** 503 (1980).

[4] L. Olsson, H. Kronström, A. Cambon-De Mouzon, C. Honsik, T. Brodin, and B. Jakobsen, *J. Immunol. Methods* **61,** 17 (1983).

[5] L. Nilsson and K. Mosbach, *FEBS Lett.* **118,** 145 (1980).

[6] H. O. Sjögren, K. Nilsson, P. Malmström, and B. Axelsson, *J. Immunol. Methods* **56,** 285 (1983).

(5) The mononuclear cell suspension (10^8–4×10^8 cells/ml) in 3 ml R10–hep was loaded on the column and filtrated at 1.5–2.0 ml/min with a total of 15 ml R10–hep. Nonadherent cells washed out this way were almost entirely free of monocytes.[6] Loosely attached cells were detached by adding 5 ml R10–hep and gently stirring the beads with a Pasteur pipet, followed by washing with 20 ml R10–hep. (6) Adherent cells were eluted by adding 6 ml of PBS containing 50 mM EDTA and 10 IE heparin/ml, incubating the column for 15 min at room temperature, and then resuspending the beads by pipetting while adding another 9 ml PBS–EDTA. (7) The eluted fraction was washed twice in culture medium: RPMI 1640 with 5% fetal calf serum (FCS), 4 mM L-glutamin, 1 mM sodium pyruvate, 15 mM NaHCO$_3$, and 10 mM HEPES. The monocyte content and yield in this fraction were 70 ± 5 and 71 ± 20%, respectively.[6]

Recently a technique was developed that selectively eluted large adherent lymphocytes in a preceding step, thus increasing the purity of monocytes to above 80%. After step 5, R10–hep supplemented with 10% dimethyl sulfoxide (DMSO) was added in a volume of 20 ml at a flow rate of 1.5–2.0 ml/min. Cells remaining detached in the column were washed out with 3 ml of PBS containing EDTA. Adherent cells were subsequently eluted as described in step 6.

Eluted monocytes either were used immediately in cell fusion or cloning experiments or were frozen in culture medium with 20% FCS and 10% DMSO. Eluted cells, 2×10^7 in one freezing vial with 1.4 ml medium, were frozen to $-70°$ in an automated graded freezing device (Planer Products, Great Britain) and then stored in liquid nitrogen. Thawing of cells was rapid according to standard techniques with gradual dilution of the DMSO on ice. A typical yield of monocytes after thawing was about 50%.[7]

Preparation of Thymocytes

Thymocytes were prepared from 4- to 6-week-old BALB/c mice according to methods described in another volume in this series.[8]

Preparation of Mouse and Rat Peritoneal Cells

Two- to three-month-old BALB/c mice and Wistar/Furth rats were used. Ca- and Mg-free PBS was instilled intraperitoneally, the abdomen was gently massaged for 1 min, and the buffer was aspirated. This flushing was not repeated nor was any irritating agent used to produce more cells in the lavage. Peritoneal cells from two or more animals were always

---

[7] T. Brodin, L. Olsson, and H. O. Sjögren, *J. Immunol. Methods* **60**, 1 (1983).

[8] R. P. Siraganian, P. C. Fox, and E. H. Berenstein, this series, Vol. 92, p. 17.

pooled. The typical yield was $1-2 \times 10^6$ nucleated cells from a mouse and $5-10 \times 10^6$ cells from a rat.

Production of a Human × Human Hybridoma Cell Line

The cell fusion, culture, and characterization of a human antibody-producing hybrid cell line have been described previously.[4,7] Briefly, 10^7 PMC from a blood group A-positive healthy blood donor were fused with 10^7 SKO-007 human myeloma cells using polyethylene glycol. This donor had a significant agglutination serum titer against blood group B. After fusion, cells were seeded in 96-well plates with or without a feeder layer of human monocytes (see next section). Hybrids were selected in HAT medium and were tested after 3–5 weeks for production of human Ig and antibodies binding to B-active glycoproteins in ELISA techniques. One hybrid showing production of antibodies reactive in these tests was selected for cloning experiments.

Cloning by Limiting Dilution

Procedure. (1) One day before seeding the tumor cells, 96-well plates (Falcon, Oxnard, CA or Nunc, Denmark) were prepared with feeder cells. Fifty thousand cells of the freshly prepared or a frozen and thawed preparation of human monocytes or mouse or rat peritoneal cells were seeded per well in 50 μl culture medium with 20% FCS. (2) Thymocytes used as feeder cells were freshly prepared and the cells (6×10^5/well) were seeded together with the tumor cells. (3) SKO-007 cells, hybridoma cells derived from this line, and cells from RH-L4, a HAT-sensitive lymphoma cell line also used for cell fusions,[9] were seeded at a concentration of 1 or 10 cells/well in a final volume of 0.2 ml culture medium per well. The cultures were inspected microscopically and refed by replacing half of the medium once a week. Clones (more than half the well area covered by cells) were counted by microscopy 3–5 weeks after seeding.

The table[7] demonstrates the effect of feeder cells on the outgrowth of clones in two experiments (18 different combinations of tumor and feeder cells in each experiment). Human monocytes and mouse thymocytes both dramatically increased cloning efficiencies compared to growth without feeder cells (a 100- to 1000-fold higher concentration of tumor cells had to be used to get any growth of clones without a feeder layer). Although initial growth of clones was seen with mouse and rat peritoneal cells as feeder layer, the growth ceased after about 2 weeks. At that time large adherent cells that seemed to phagocytize the tumor cells appeared.

[9] L. Olsson and H. S. Kaplan, this series, Vol. 92, p. 3.

CLONING EFFICIENCY IN LIQUID MEDIUM[a]

| Feeder cell type | Tumor cell type and cells/well | | | | | |
| | Human hybridoma | | SKO-007 | | RH-L4 | |
	1	10	1	10	1	10
None	<1	<1	<1	<1	<1	<1
Human monocytes	6, 50	94, 94	6, 69	100, 100	44, 87	87, 100
BALB/c thymocytes	2, 37	87, 87	13, 37	100, 100	21, 63	94, 94
BALB/c peritoneal macrophages	<1	<1	<1	<1	<1	<1
W/F peritoneal macrophages	<1	<1	<1	<1	<1	<1

[a] Data represent frequency (%) of wells with clones of total number of wells (16 to 48) seeded with 1 or 10 tumor cells/well. Results are from two experiments.

Cloning in Semisolid Medium

Procedure. (1) Twenty-four-well plates (Nunc, Denmark) were seeded with human monocytes or mouse peritoneal cells (10^5/well in 0.5 ml culture medium) 1 day before seeding the tumor cells. (2) The medium was aspirated and the tumor cells (10^2/well) were seeded in 1.0 ml of 0.3% agar (Nobel, Difco) in RPMI 1640 with 15% FCS. When thymocytes were used (10^6/well), they were mixed with the tumor cells. The batch of agar used was screened to rule out inhibitory effects on cell growth.

Without feeder cells no growth of clones (clusters of >50 cells were recognized as growing clones) was seen when inspected 2 weeks after seeding. In contrast, both monocytes/macrophages and thymocytes improved the conditions for clonal growth of the three tumor cell lines. The frequency of clones growing thus reached 5–16% of the number seeded.

The dependence on feeder cells for clonal growth might differ not only between different malignant cell lines and their corresponding hybrids but also between individual clones within a population. It has recently been shown that treatment of the RH-L4 lymphoma cell line with 5-azacytidine generates clones with the stable expression of high clonogenicity without the dependence on feeder cells.[10] Although the mechanism of this action is not fully understood, it is known that 5-azacytidine treatment leads to

[10] L. Olsson, *Med. Oncol. Tumor Pharmacother.* **1** (4), 235 (1984).

activation of genes by reduction of the level of methylated cytosine in the DNA. Thus, growth factors required for clonal growth appear to be produced by the tumor cells themselves. The growth-stimulatory effect of the supernatants from these clones on other malignant cell lines and on normal B cells *in vitro* is currently being tested. However, supernatants of mass cultures of the parental cell lines or media conditioned by the various feeder cells have been tested and do not improve cloning efficiencies for these three lines. It should also be mentioned that hybridomas derived from other malignant fusion partners, especially B lymphoblastoid cell lines, might not require feeder cells either after fusion or in the cloning step. It has in fact been recommended not to use feeder cells for particular cell lines.[11]

Conclusions

Although mouse thymocytes work as well as the human monocyte preparations as feeder cells for the lymphoid cell lines, there are at least four reasons we consider of principal and practical importance to choose the human feeder cell in the human × human hybridoma system. First, if the products of human antibody-producing cell lines are to be administered to patients for diagnostic or therapeutic purposes, it will be important to try to avoid contamination with material from animal cells during the different stages of culture of these cells. The reasons for this are of course to avoid sensitization of patients to animal antigens and the theoretical risk of infections with possibly xenotropic viruses, especially tumor viruses. Second, during the early stages of hybrid outgrowth there is massive cell death due to the effect of selective media. Subsequently there is a need for a cell with phagocytic capacity to remove dead cells and debris to avoid toxic effects on the hybrid cells. Third, during the relatively long time period for outgrowth of the primary hybrids and clones we regularly notice the problem of overgrowth of cultures by adherent cells, including fibroblasts originating from the thymocyte preparation. Although preincubation of thymocytes in petri dishes to remove adherent cells diminishes this risk, it is not possible in our hands to remove it completely. The fourth reason is also practical in nature. The rather simple procedure of preparing a large number of monocytes by the column technique and the possibility to store frozen aliquots render this a more attractive alternative than the use of thymocytes, which we have not been able to recover after thawing.

[11] M. C. Glassy, H. H. Handley, H. Hagiwara, and I. Royston, *Proc. Natl. Acad. Sci. U.S.A.* **80,** 6327 (1983).

[26] Removal of Bovine Immunoglobulin from Serum in Hybridoma Culture Media Using Protein A

By P. A. UNDERWOOD

Rationale

Most monoclonal antibodies are produced under culture conditions which result in contamination with nonspecific immunoglobulins (Ig). In tissue culture, addition of serum to the culture medium results in contamination with Ig (usually bovine) at a level comparable with the monoclonal antibody itself, even if fetal serum is used.[1] Table I shows the content of protein A-binding Ig (PAIg) in different commercial batches of fetal bovine serum. If used as a 10% medium supplement, the range of concentrations is very close to that observed for monoclonal antibodies (10–100 µg/ml; values from Ref. 2). There is also considerable variation between bottles within a batch. When hybridomas are grown as ascites in mice or rats, very high titers of monoclonal antibody are produced but nonspecific Ig can account for up to 10% of the total Ig.[3] In some circumstances the specificity of the contaminating antibody can interfere with the monoclonal antibody.[4] If the monoclonal antibody is to be labeled for assay procedures, colabeling of the nonspecific fraction can result in high backgrounds, poor sensitivity, and impaired specificity.

It is therefore desirable to remove such contaminating antibodies from the monoclonal preparation. Antibodies from different classes can be separated from each other by standard methods, but contaminating Ig of the same class as the monoclonal antibody will copurify with it. For monoclonal antibodies representing the more common classes (IgG and IgM), this poses a problem. Table II demonstrates the copurification of bovine Ig and monoclonal antibodies on protein A–Sepharose. Monoclonal antibody in ascites fluids can be separated from such contamination only by affinity chromatography with specific antigen, which represents expensive use of antigen and may result in physical damage of the monoclonal antibody.

[1] P. A. Underwood, J. F. Kelly, D. F. Harman, and H. MacMillan, *J. Immunol. Methods* **60**, 33 (1983).
[2] J. W. Goding, V. T. Oi, P. P. Jones, and L. A. Herzenberg, *in* "Cells of Immunoglobulin Synthesis" (B. Pernis and H. J. Vogel, eds.), p. 309. Academic Press, New York, 1979.
[3] P. A. Underwood, unpublished observations (1984).
[4] H. C. Gooi and T. Feizi, *Biochem. Biophys. Res. Commun.* **106**, 539 (1982).

TABLE I

CONTENT OF PAIg IN COMMERCIAL BATCHES OF
FETAL BOVINE SERUM[a]

Batch	Bottle	Ig (mg/ml)[b]
1	1	0.06
	2	0.13
	3	0.26
	4	0.04
2	1	0.22
	2	0.23
3	1	0.15
	2	0.03
	3	0.14
	4	0.10

[a] From Underwood et al.,[1] with permission of the publishers.

[b] Protein concentrations measured from the pool of immunoglobulin (Ig) eluted from protein A–Sepharose after repeated passages of unbound material. Entries are means of two estimations.

TABLE II

CONTAMINATION OF BOVINE IMMUNOGLOBULIN IN HYBRIDOMA CULTURE
SUPERNATANTS BEFORE AND AFTER PURIFICATION ON PROTEIN A–SEPHAROSE[a]

Monoclonal antibody	Total PAIg in culture fluid (μg/ml)	Bovine PAIg in culture fluid (μg/ml)	Contamination by bovine PAIg (% of total)	Contamination by bovine PAIg after purification on protein A–Sepharose (% of total)
A71	58.62	26.0	44.3	13.0
A195	51.02	26.0	50.9	21.7
A158	52.10	26.0	49.9	22.7
A119	35.75	26.0	72.7	50.5
A124	54.00	26.0	48.1	31.5
A200	57.00	26.0	45.6	30.1

[a] Spent tissue culture medium (40 ml) was passed through a 5-ml column of protein A–Sepharose. Bound Ig was eluted with a pH gradient. (Adapted from Underwood et al.,[1] with permission of the publishers. Full experimental details are given in this reference.)

In tissue culture, hybridomas can be grown in chemically defined serum-free medium. Each hybridoma clone, however, may have its own unique combination of type and concentration of growth factors required and no universal completely defined additive has yet been described. Some commercially available "serum-reduced" additives still contain concentrations of Ig comparable to those secreted by hybridomas.[5] Apparatus separating the growing hybridomas from nondialyzable serum components in the medium tends to be expensive, and the microporous membrane components generally have a limited lifetime.

Immunoglobulin can be removed from serum by affinity chromatography on protein A before the serum is added to the medium, or by affinity chromatography on anti-immunoglobulin directed to the serum species, either before the serum is used, or from the culture medium after growth of the hybridoma. Of these two methods the former is the most practicable. Protein A is readily available coupled to Sepharose and can be reused indefinitely. The monoclonal antibody can be subsequently concentrated and purified by the same technique. This means, however, that the method can only be used to remove potential contaminating immunoglobulins when the hybridoma to be cultured is of a type which binds to protein A (all classes of IgG[6]). This constitutes the bulk of monoclonal antibodies produced from repeatedly immunized animals. In cases in which monoclonal antibodies of class M are generated (from unprimed animals or from *in vitro* antigenic stimulation), this method cannot be used. Since many useful monoclonal antibodies are of the G class, stripping serum of PAIg is a valuable precursor to hybridoma production.

Materials

Protein A–Sepharose (Pharmacia, South Seas), 15 g dry gel and 1.5 g dry gel.

Buffered sterile saline, pH 8.6. Earles balanced salt solution (GIBCO) is adjusted to pH 8.6 with sterile 1 N NaOH. Penicillin and streptomycin (Glaxo) are added immediately before use at 6 and 10 μg/ml, respectively.

Cleaning buffer, pH 3.0, 0.5 N Gly–HCl: 3.7 g glycine; 0.08 g NaN$_3$; 1 N HCl to pH 3.0; double-distilled water to 100 ml.

Washing buffer, pH 8.6, 0.05 N Tris–HCl: 6.06 g Tris; 8.5 g NaCl; 0.8 g NaN$_3$; 1 N HCl to pH 8.6; double-distilled water to 1 liter.

Eluting buffer, pH 3.0, 0.05 N Gly–HCl: 3.7 g glycine; 8.5 g NaCl; 0.8 g NaN$_3$; 1 N HCl to pH 3.0; double-distilled water to 1 liter.

[5] P. A. Underwood, unpublished observations (1984).
[6] I. Seppälä, H. Sarvas, F. Peterfy, and O. Mäkelä, *Scand. J. Immunol.* **14**, 335 (1981).

Serum: fetal bovine serum (Commonwealth Serum Laboratories, Parkville, Victoria; Flow Laboratories, NSW), in 400- or 500-ml bottles.

Autoclavable bottles and tubing

Peristaltic pump

Three-way connectors (Pharmaseal, CA)

Preparation of Affinity Columns

The two aliquots of dry protein A–Sepharose were allowed to swell separately in washing buffer. They were then washed in several changes of cleaning buffer, followed by several changes of washing buffer. They were used to prepare 50- and 5-ml chromatography columns, respectively. The large column was stored at 4° and the small column at room temperature, both in washing buffer.

Test of Serum Batches

Individual bottles of serum were thawed. A 10-ml aliquot was removed and 0.1 ml 1 N NaOH was added to it. This sample was pumped through the small protein A column at a flow rate of 0.5 ml/min, and was followed by 6 ml of washing buffer. Bound Ig was eluted with 10 ml of eluting buffer and the column washed with 10 ml of washing buffer. Fractions of 0.5 ml were collected. Those comprising the eluted peak were pooled and neutralized with 1 M Tris, and the protein content estimated by the method of Lowry et al.,[7] using bovine serum albumin as standard. From this, the original concentration of PAIg in the serum was calculated (70% of the total PAIg is extracted on one passage through the column[1]). If the concentration was less than 20 μg/ml (2 μg/ml when used as 10% supplement to medium), the remainder of the bottle was heated at 56° for 30 min and then stored frozen for use in tissue culture without further treatment. Bottles containing concentrations higher than 20 μg/ml were stripped of PAIg as follows.

Serum Treatment

One-hundredth volume of sterile 1 N NaOH was added to the bottle of 400–500 ml of serum. Penicillin and streptomycin were added as for buffered sterile saline. The serum was allowed to stand overnight at 4° to allow formation of slow-developing precipitates which otherwise clogged

[7] D. H. Lowry, N. J. Rosebrough, A. L. Farr, and R. J. Randall, *J. Biol. Chem.* **193**, 265 (1951).

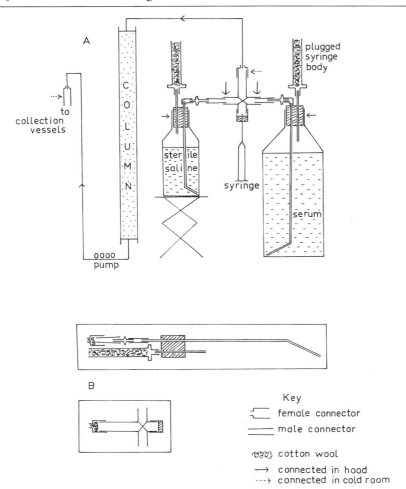

FIG. 1. Apparatus for stripping serum of PAIg. (A) Assembly of apparatus showing arrangement of input vessels. In addition, at the left, two collection vessels are linked to the column outflow via a three-way connector in an identical arrangement to the input vessels. (B) Packaging of tubes and connectors for autoclaving.

the protein A–Sepharose column. These were removed by centrifugation at 16,000 g.

The large column was assembled in a cold room at 4° as shown in Fig. 1. Air was removed from the input lines using a syringe and needle inserted through the rubber seal on the three-way connector. The column was prewashed with 30 ml buffered sterile saline, followed by the serum.

Flow rate was 0.4 ml/min. When serum started to exit the column the outflow was switched from a waste vessel to a collection vessel via a second three-way connector. The serum was followed with a wash of 50 ml buffered sterile saline. When all the serum had been collected, the outflow was switched back to the waste vessel. Thus, the whole procedure was performed without breaking any of the sterile connections. The saline wash was followed by elution of the column with 30 ml elution buffer and final wash of 80 ml wash buffer. When the eluate reached the waste vessel (visible by color change in the buffered saline), the two collection vessels were disconnected from the column and transported to a sterile laminar air flow cabinet. The serum was resterilized through a 0.22-μm pore filter. A 10-ml aliquot was processed on the small column as before to check for removal of Ig. The remainder was neutralized with 1 N HCl, treated at 56° for 30 min, and then stored at $-20°$ in suitable aliquots. From the time of disconnection of the collection vessels from the large column, azide was present throughout the system and sterile conditions were no longer required. The column was stored in wash buffer at 4°.

Comments

The efficiency of removal of immunoglobulin from serum is directly dependent on the concentration of protein A in the column, contact time, and the affinity constant of the binding reaction.[1] With bovine PAIg, approximately 80% of the input is actually bound on one passage through the large column.[1] This is good enough for most batches of fetal bovine serum to reduce the Ig contamination to acceptable levels. The slow flow rate ensures that the serum is in contact with protein A for long enough (2 hr) for maximal binding to take place. If smaller columns are used to strip smaller quantities of serum, the flow rate should be reduced accordingly so that contact time in the column is still 2 hr.

The large protein A–Sepharose column described above was used over an 18-month period to remove immunoglobulin from 30 liters of serum. Periodically the column became compacted and disassembly was required. Following thorough washing and repacking with minimal replacement of lost Sepharose (<20% over this period), the column showed no deterioration of binding capability.

[27] A Single-Step Technique for Selecting and Cloning Hybridomas for Monoclonal Antibody Production

By JOHN M. DAVIS

The technique described here, which involves the simultaneous selection and cloning of hybridomas in semisolid medium immediately after fusion, was devised in order to overcome the problems of clonal competition in a complex mixture of hybrids, and to maximize the number of discrete hybridomas which could be isolated from a single fusion. It also has certain other advantages over many of the liquid culture techniques for hybridoma isolation, including the elimination of problems due to fibroblast growth and a great reduction in the amount of recloning of hybrids which is necessary. These advantages have resulted in its use to generate monoclonal antibodies against a wide range of different antigens from both animals[1–6] and plants.[7]

Introduction

When spleen cells are fused with azaguanine-resistant myeloma cells and then selected for growth using the HAT selection system,[8,9] the cells which survive are hybrids of the myeloma cells with cells of the B cell lineage. (There is no evidence that myeloma × T-cell heterokaryons form viable hybrids in this system.[10,11]) Most of these hybrids will initially express the immunoglobulin specificity of the spleen-derived cells, but due to rapid chromosome loss the proportion of hybrids which still express this phenotype after 2–3 weeks in culture is reduced (in fusions employing mouse myelomas) to around 50%.[11] Furthermore, there is a widely observed tendency for the hybrids which have lost immunoglobu-

[1] H.-K. Hochkeppel, U. Menge, and J. Collins, *Eur. J. Biochem.* **118**, 437 (1981).

[2] H.-K. Hochkeppel and M. de Ley, *Nature (London)* **296**, 258 (1982).

[3] J. M. Davis, A.-M. Kubler, and J.-F. Conscience, *Exp. Hematol.* **11**, 332 (1983).

[4] G. Huber and A. Matus, *J. Cell Biol.* **98**, 777 (1984).

[5] C.-Y. G. Lee, E. Wong, and A. C. Menge, *Fertil. Steril.* **41**, 131 (1984).

[6] C.-Y. G. Lee, E. Wong, D. E. Richter, and A. C. Menge, *J. Reprod. Immunol.* **6**, 227 (1984).

[7] M.-M. Cordonnier, C. Smith, H. Greppin, and L. H. Pratt, *Planta* **158**, 369 (1983).

[8] W. Szybalski, E. H. Szybalski, and E. H. Ragni, *Natl. Cancer Inst. Monogr.* **7**, 75 (1962).

[9] J. W. Littlefield, *Science* **145**, 709 (1964).

[10] G. Köhler, T. Pearson, and C. Milstein, *Somatic Cell Genet.* **3**, 303 (1977).

[11] M. R. Clark and C. Milstein, *Somatic Cell Genet.* **7**, 657 (1981).

METHODS IN ENZYMOLOGY, VOL. 121

lin expression to overgrow those which have retained it.[12-15] In liquid culture techniques, in which hybrids are grown in a limited number of culture wells each usually containing more than one hybrid—and in some cases up to 100 different hybrids[13]—there is a great danger of losing interesting specificities due to overgrowth by these nonproducers. Clonal competition between different immunoglobulin-producing hybrids can also result in loss of potentially interesting hybridomas. Attempts to overcome such problems by plating fusions in a large number of wells result in a decrease in the efficiency of hybrid growth, even in the presence of suitable feeder cells.[16]

The system described here overcomes many of these problems. Immediately after fusion, the cell mixture containing the nascent hybrids is suspended (along with feeder cells) in a semisolid medium, the make-up of which has been optimized in order to support growth of the maximum number of hybrids.[17] This suspension is then plated out into a limited number of petri dishes. Over a period of 1–4 weeks the hybrids grow into discrete colonies, spatially localized by the semisolid nature of the medium. These can then be removed for growth in liquid medium and tested for antibody activity.

This system does not overcome the problem of initial instability in immunoglobulin production, and individual clones in which nonproducer variants occur and outgrow the producers will be detected simply as nonproducers. However, because such nonproducer cells cannot contaminate other colonies, being unable to move through the semisolid medium, the problem of the overgrowth of other producer clones by these nonproducers is eliminated. Similarly, there is no danger of overgrowth of one producer clone by another. Furthermore, large numbers of clones can be directly isolated from the plates with none of the problems of decreased growth efficiency seen when limiting dilution techniques are employed.[16]

Reagents and Cells

Tissue Culture Medium. Iscove's modified Dulbecco's medium (IMDM) (430-2200, GIBCO, Paisley, Scotland) has been found to be the

[12] H. Lemke, G. J. Hämmerling, and U. Hämmerling, *Immunol. Rev.* **47,** 175 (1979).
[13] G. Galfré, G. W. Butcher, J. C. Howard, C. D. Wilde, and C. Milstein, *Transplant. Proc.* **12,** 371 (1980).
[14] J. W. Goding, *J. Immunol. Methods* **39,** 285 (1980).
[15] S. Fazekas de St. Groth and D. Scheidegger, *J. Immunol. Methods* **35,** 1 (1980).
[16] A. L. de Blas, M. V. Ratnaparkhi, and J. E. Mosimann, *J. Immunol. Methods* **45,** 109 (1981).
[17] J. M. Davis, J. E. Pennington, A.-M. Kubler, and J.-F. Conscience, *J. Immunol. Methods* **50,** 161 (1982).

best medium to use in the postfusion cloning step,[17] and because it is easiest for practical reasons to standardize on one medium, IMDM is used throughout. This should be prepared from the powder precisely according to the manufacturer's instructions, and with all additives (NaHCO₃, 2-mercaptoethanol, penicillin, streptomycin). It is particularly important to add the correct amount of $NaHCO_3$, and not to adjust the pH. Correct buffering is obtained when used in an atmosphere of 5% CO_2 in air.

Fetal Calf Serum. Fetal calf serum (FCS) is used throughout as it gives the best results when preparing hybrids.[17,18] Also, it has a low immunoglobulin content, so it generally does not interfere with assays for monoclonal antibodies. Batches of fetal calf serum should be tested for their ability to support cell growth, and the best selected for use. A suitable testing procedure has been described by Galfré and Milstein.[18]

50% Polyethylene Glycol (PEG). The agent used to fuse the myeloma and spleen cells is a 50% solution of Merck polyethylene glycol 4000 (for gas chromatography, Merck, Darmstadt, West Germany) in serum-free IMDM. Aliquots (5 g) of PEG are sterilized by autoclaving in glass universal tubes. Prior to use the PEG is melted in a boiling water bath, transferred to a 56° water bath, and allowed to equilibrate, whereupon 5 ml of warmed, filter-sterilized, serum-free IMDM is added and the solution immediately mixed on a vortex mixer and allowed to cool. It is not necessary to adjust the pH. This solution can be stored at 4° for at least 4 weeks.

Comment: The use of Merck PEG 4000 is strongly recommended. Not only is it an extremely efficient fusing agent[15] but in my experience every batch retains this property. This eliminates the tiresome necessity to test batches for their fusing activity, which is absolutely essential when using PEG from certain other manufacturers. Moreover, the high fusing efficiency is obtained without the addition of DMSO, which has been found necessary when using PEG from some other sources.[19] Neither addition of DMSO nor substitution of phosphate-buffered saline for the IMDM has been found to improve the fusing properties of the solution described above.[20]

HAT Stock Solution (100×). Hypoxanthine (136 mg), aminopterin (1.91 mg), and thymidine (38.9 mg) (all from Sigma, Poole, England) are added to 90 ml distilled water along with a few grains of phenol red. A few drops of 5 *M* NaOH are added to make the solution slightly alkaline. This

[18] G. Galfré and C. Milstein, this series, Vol. 73, p. 3.
[19] T. H. Norwood, C. J. Zeigler, and G. M. Martin, *Somatic Cell Genet.* **2,** 263 (1976).
[20] J. M. Davis and J. E. Pennington, unpublished results (1980).

suspension is stirred on a magnetic stirrer until the solid has completely dissolved. Heating to 50° may assist the process, and if the solid still refuses to dissolve the addition of a few more drops of NaOH may be necessary. When all components are dissolved, the volume is adjusted to 100 ml and the solution filter sterilized. This solution can be stored indefinitely in small aliquots at −20°. Prior to use, thaw in a 56° water bath to ensure all components are in solution.

Double-Strength IMDM. This is made up exactly as if making 1 liter of normal medium, except that the initial mixing and dissolving is performed using 450 ml of distilled water and the volume is finally adjusted to 500 ml. No adjustment should be made to the pH. The medium is sterilized by filtration and should preferably be used fresh. It can be stored in aliquots at −20° for long periods, but if a precipitate is observed the medium should be discarded and a fresh batch prepared.

Methylcellulose Stock Solution. The 2% (w/v) methylcellulose stock solution is prepared in a wide-mouthed conical flask containing a large stirrer bar and capped with aluminum foil. This equipment should be prepared in advance and sterilized by hot air or by autoclaving. If the latter technique is used only a minimal amount of water should be retained in the flask after sterilization; otherwise the concentration and osmolarity of the methylcellulose solution will be adversely affected.

The flask complete with stirrer bar and cap is weighed and 100 ml of glass-distilled water added. This is boiled gently over a Bunsen burner for 5 min. The foil cap is then removed and 4 g of methylcellulose powder (Methocel MC, Premium 4000cP from Dow Chemical Co., Midland, MI, or Methocel MC 4000cP from Fluka A.G., Buchs, Switzerland) is added carefully, such that all of it falls on the surface of the water and none of it touches the walls of the flask. The flask is then recapped and the contents heated until they just start to boil. When this is achieved, the Bunsen burner is removed and the flask swirled *gently* to help mixing until the opaque white suspension has ceased to boil. The contents of the flask are then brought back just to the boil, and the procedure repeated. Five minutes after the contents first started to boil, the flask is removed from the heat and plunged into an ice–water slurry, in which it is swirled continuously until all the contents of the flask have become viscous. This is accompanied by a partial clearing, such that the solution is now translucent. Sterile double-strength IMDM (100 ml) is added, and mixed initially by swirling until the entire contents of the flask are mobile. The flask is then transferred to a magnetic stirrer and stirred at 4° for 1 hr. Lost water is then replaced by weighing the flask and adding sterile water until the total weight is equal to 204.5 g plus the original weight of the flask, stirrer, and cap. Stirring is continued at 4° overnight, after which the methylcellulose is dispensed (by careful pouring) into 100-ml sterile bottles. These may be stored at −20° and will keep for up to 6 months.

Comment: This is not a difficult procedure, but it *must* be performed with care as there are a number of pitfalls into which the unwary will fall:

1. All boiling must be gentle and for no more than the time stated. Although these times are short, they have always proved sufficient to ensure sterility. Prolonged or violent boiling will result in excessive loss of water. The result of this will be a thick, lumpy methylcellulose solution which will be useless, as it will not form a homogeneous solution despite subsequent replacement of the water and days of stirring. All methylcellulose solutions should be checked for the absence of lumps prior to storage.

2. It is important that the methylcellulose powder is added directly to the water and none of it falls on the walls of the flask. Any attempt to tip or agitate the flask in order to wash deposits off the walls into the bulk of the solution will only leave further deposits on the glass. This will result in a weak and dirty solution, as such deposits, which dry out on the hot walls of the flask, never subsequently hydrate properly. For the same reason, the subsequent swirling of the methylcellulose *must* be performed gently.

3. After addition of the methylcellulose powder, the boiling step must not only be performed gently and only for the time stated, but the flask must never be left unattended while being heated. The solution froths extremely easily and even a few seconds of too much heat will result at best in deposits left all over the walls of the flask, and at worst with complete loss of the solution. Even if this is avoided, excessive boiling will result in partial hydrolysis of the methylcellulose, leading to the formation of a solution of decreased viscosity.

4. The long period of stirring at 4° may not always be necessary in order to obtain a homogeneous solution, but is important in order to ensure the maximum hydration of the methylcellulose. This in turn ensures maximum viscosity of the solution. There is, however, always some transparent cellulose debris remaining, the amount varying between different batches of methylcellulose. This can only be seen under the microscope and does not affect the cultures (but may be removed by centrifugation at 15,000 g for 3 hr under sterile conditions if required).

Lipopolysaccharide. LPS-W from *Escherichia coli* 0111 B4 (code 3122-25 Bacto: Difco Laboratories, Detroit, MI) is prepared as a 5 mg/ml stock solution in serum-free IMDM, and stored in aliquots at −20°.

Solution A. This should be prepared freshly immediately before use. It consists of 53.3% (v/v) FCS, 2.66% (v/v) HAT stock solution, and 133 μg LPS/ml in IMDM.

Thymus Cells

Thymuses from a number of animals are placed in a 10-cm diameter petri dish with 10 ml of IMDM (with or without serum). They are then cut into small pieces with a pair of sterile scissors and the whole suspension transferred to a 15-ml conical centrifuge tube with cap. This is placed on a vortex mixer for 10–15 sec and then allowed to stand for 3–5 min to allow large debris and cell clumps to settle out. The cell suspension is aspirated, and the cells pelleted by centrifugation at 300 g for 10 min prior to resuspension in a small volume of solution A. After counting, a proportion of this suspension is further diluted in solution A to give the required volume of cells at a concentration of 8×10^6 cells/ml.

Comment: I have always used thymus cells obtained from DBA/2 mice. However, Andersson and Melchers have successfully used xenogeneic thymocytes to support the growth of hybridomas in liquid cultures,[21] and thus the choice of thymocyte donor may be unimportant.

Spleen Cells

The spleen from a suitably immunized mouse or rat is placed on a sterile piece of stainless-steel mesh (about 5×3 cm, mesh count 8.0/cm) in a 10-cm petri dish with 10 ml IMDM. Using the plunger from a 5 or 10-ml syringe, the organ is rubbed back and forth over the grid, freeing the spleen pulp and leaving the capsule which will not pass through the mesh. The grid and capsule are discarded, and the cells pipetted up and down a few times to disperse large clumps. They are then transferred to a tube in which they are allowed to stand for 3–5 min in order to allow large debris and cell clumps to settle. The cell suspension is aspirated, and after counting is ready for use.

Comments: If more readily available, a stainless-steel tea strainer may be used in place of the wire grid and can, of course, be reused. Whichever is used, it is wrapped in aluminum foil and autoclaved prior to use.

The spleen of an adult mouse will yield in the region of 1×10^8 nucleated cells, whereas that of an adult rat will yield nearer 5×10^8. I have never made any attempt to remove red cells from the spleen cell suspension prior to fusing and find no convincing reason to do so.

Myeloma Cells: Choice of Cell Line

A number of mouse and rat myelomas suitable for fusion with spleen cells for the production of monoclonal antibody-secreting hybridomas are

---

[21] J. Andersson and F. Melchers, *Curr. Top. Microbiol. Immunol.* **81**, 130 (1978).

SUITABLE PARENTAL MYELOMA LINES[a]

Name	Species	Strain	Derived from	Immunoglobulin expression	Hybridoma morphology in methylcellulose
P3-X63-Ag8[b]	Mouse	BALB/c	MOPC 21[c]	γ_1 and κ	Not tested
P3-X63-Ag8.653[d]	Mouse	BALB/c	P3-X63-Ag8	None	Compact
NSI/1Ag4.1[e]	Mouse	BALB/c	P3-X63-Ag8	Intracellular κ[f]	Compact
NSO[g]	Mouse	BALB/c	NSI/1Ag4.1	None	Compact
SP2/0[h]	Mouse	BALB/c	P3-X63-Ag8	None	Compact
FO[i]	Mouse	BALB/c	SP2/0	None	Compact
210-RCY3-Ag1.2.3[j]	Rat	Lou	R210	κ	Less compact[k]
YB2/0[l]	Rat	(Lou × AO)F$_1$	YB2/3a[m]	None	Not tested

[a] This is not a comprehensive list, and only includes lines generally available.
[b] Köhler and Milstein.[30]
[c] K. Horibata and A. W. Harris, *Exp. Cell Res.* **60**, 61 (1970).
[d] J. F. Kearney, A. Radbruch, B. Leisegang, and K. Rajewsky, *J. Immunol.* **123**, 1548 (1979).
[e] G. Köhler, C. S. Howe, and C. Milstein, *Eur. J. Immunol.* **6**, 292 (1976).
[f] The myeloma κ chains may be secreted in hybridomas (reference in footnote *e*).
[g] Clark and Milstein.[11]
[h] M. Schulman, C. D. Wilde, and G. Köhler, *Nature (London)* **276**, 269 (1978).
[i] Fazekas de St. Groth and Scheidegger.[15]
[j] G. Galfré, C. Milstein, and B. Wright, *Nature (London)* **277**, 131 (1979).
[k] See text.
[l] J. V. Kilmartin, B. Wright, and C. Milstein, *J. Cell Biol.* **93**, 576 (1982).
[m] P. J. Lachmann, R. G. Oldroyd, C. Milstein, and B. W. Wright, *Immunology* **41**, 503 (1980).

now available (see table above). All of these are resistant to 8-azaguanine and are therefore suitable for use in conjunction with the HAT hybrid selection system.

Six of the eight cell lines in the table have been tested for their behavior when fused and cloned in the methylcellulose system described here.[17,22] All six behaved satisfactorily and formed hybrids which grew as distinct colonies in the methylcellulose. The morphology of the colonies was compact (i.e., with neighboring cells touching each other and the whole colony being roughly spherical with well-defined boundaries) except for those formed using the rat cell line 210-RCY3-Ag1.2.3. These colonies were slightly more diffuse, as the cells appeared to have a limited ability to move through the methylcellulose. Greater care is thus required when picking these colonies in order to avoid cross-contamination.

The choice of which myeloma to use for a particular application will depend on three factors:

[22] J. M. Davis, unpublished results (1982).

1. *The species of animal from which the spleen will be taken.* It is generally better to use a myeloma derived from the same species as the spleen cells. This not only makes the production of large quantities of antibody in ascites form much simpler, but the proportion of hybrids which secrete spleen cell-derived immunoglobulin tends to be higher in intraspecies rather than interspecies fusions.[11] However, other factors may override these considerations (see below).

2. *The nature of the antibody required.* In hybridomas there is coexpression of the spleen cell-derived immunoglobulin chains, along with any that the myeloma may produce, and these associate randomly[23,24] to form the final immunoglobulin molecule. Thus in the situation in which a myeloma is used which makes both heavy and light chains, a derived hybridoma with an interesting monoclonal IgG antibody activity will in fact secrete 10 different distinguishable immunoglobulin molecules (not in equimolar proportions) of which only one is the bivalent spleen cell-derived form. Even if the myeloma used secretes only its own light chain (and no heavy chain), three different immunoglobulins are formed, of which again only one is the bivalent spleen cell-derived form. These considerations have led to the development and widespread use of myelomas which do not produce any immunoglobulins of their own, and which thus only secrete the spleen cell-derived immunoglobulin. These myelomas are ideal for most applications. However, recent work has suggested important applications of monoclonal antibodies in which the use of an immunoglobulin light chain-producing myeloma is essential.[25] In this case monovalent monoclonal IgG molecules were used, i.e., those having two heavy chains and one light chain derived from the spleen cell, along with one myeloma light chain. The use of these antibodies, which were directed against cell surface antigens, was shown to eliminate the antigenic modulation which was seen in the presence of the bivalent antibody, as well as considerably increasing the level of complement-dependent cell lysis. This system does, however, necessitate fractionation of the secreted hybridoma antibodies.

3. *The fusion efficiency of the myeloma and the stability of the hybrids obtained.* All the myelomas in the table are reported to be efficient at fusion with spleen cells, and to yield stable hybrids. However, these characteristics seem to vary, for the same cell line, between different

---

[23] Spleen and myeloma immunoglobulin chains may not associate entirely randomly in quantitative terms.[24] Association of heavy chains only occurs if they are of the same immunoglobulin class; e.g., a γ_1 will associate with a γ_{2a} but not with a μ.[18]

[24] C. Milstein and A. C. Cuello, *Nature (London)* **305**, 537 (1983).

[25] S. P. Cobbold and H. Waldmann, *Nature (London)* **308**, 461 (1984).

laboratories. This may be due to any number of factors including the exact fusion technique employed and the culture history of the cell line. The best policy is to obtain several lines (if possible) which appear suitable for the purpose by the criteria above, and try fusions using each.

The fusion efficiency may also depend on the ratio of spleen cells to myeloma cells employed in the fusion. For mouse myelomas, a spleen to myeloma cell ratio of 10 : 1 has been widely used and yielded good results. In the case of rat myelomas, however, a ratio of 10 : 6 may be more effective.[18]

Myeloma Cells: Growth

All of the cell lines in the table grow well in IMDM + 10% FCS. For optimum results the cells should be maintained in exponential growth phase for several days prior to fusion. The fusion efficiency of rat myelomas may be increased if they are grown in spinner cultures for extended periods before use.[18]

Fusion, Cloning, and Picking of Colonies

Myeloma cells (1×10^7) are placed in a 50-ml conical centrifuge tube, and the tube is filled with serum-free IMDM and centrifuged at 200 g for 10 min. The supernatant is aspirated, the cells resuspended in a small volume of serum-free IMDM, and 1×10^8 spleen cells added. Again the tube is filled with serum-free IMDM and centrifuged as before. After aspiration of the supernatant, the pellet is loosened by gently flicking the tube, which is then held in one hand such that the bottom end is immersed in the 37° water bath, while the cap can be removed when required with the thumb and forefinger. Warmed PEG solution (0.7 ml) is then added dropwise to the pellet over a period of 60 sec, with constant agitation of the tube. After a further 90 sec of agitation the tube is removed from the water bath, and 15 ml of warm serum-free IMDM added dropwise over a period of 2–3 min, again with constant agitation. It is important that the medium is added very slowly at first (one or two drops at a time initially), then gradually increasing the rate of addition.

After centrifugation at 200 g for 10 min and removal of the supernatant, the cells are resuspended by gentle vortexing in 15 ml of solution A plus thymus cells. Warm 2% methylcellulose stock solution (25 ml) is then removed from its bottle using a sterile syringe without a needle and added to the cell suspension. This is mixed initially by inverting the tube several times, followed by gentle vortexing for a few seconds.

Aliquots (1 ml) of this suspension are placed in 35-mm bacteriological petri dishes using a syringe fitted with an 18- or 19-gauge needle. Each plate is tipped to distribute the suspension over the whole surface, and two such dishes (with lids) are placed inside a 100-mm diameter petri dish along with an open 35-mm dish containing distilled water.[26] These are then placed in a humidified 37° incubator containing an atmosphere of 5% CO_2 in air. The dishes may be safely left undisturbed for 9 days before they are first examined. [Each of the 40 1-ml aliquots into which the fusion is dispensed contains IMDM, HAT, 20% (v/v) FCS, 1.25% (w/v) methyl-cellulose, 50 μg LPS, 3×10^6 thymus cells, 2.5×10^6 spleen cells, and 2.5×10^5 myeloma cells.] On day 9, and at 2- to 3-day intervals thereafter, the plates are examined for the presence of colonies visible to the naked eye. If present, these are examined using an inverted microscope to check for the following features:

1. That the "colony" is not in fact a clump of cell debris.
2. That the cells in the colony are at least as large as the myeloma cells used in the fusion. (Very occasionally a lymphocyte colony may be found, but the cells in such a colony are much smaller than myeloma cells.)
3. That the colony is of a suitable size for picking, i.e., that it is at least 0.5 mm in diameter. Smaller colonies should be left to grow up to this size; otherwise they may have difficulty establishing themselves in liquid culture, due to overdilution. However, it is also advisable not to leave colonies until they are very large (more than about 1–1.25 mm diameter) as many of the cells in such colonies may be found to be dead, presumably due to an insufficient supply of nutrients to the central parts of the colony.
4. That there are no other colonies within about 1.5 mm. If there are, there is a danger of contamination of one colony with cells from the other on picking. Single colonies have a morphology which under the microscope appears very close to circular. Any colony which is markedly elliptical is probably two overlapping colonies.

The positions of colonies suitable for picking are marked on the underside of the petri dish using a felt tip pen. Those not suitable are indicated with a different mark. Colonies are removed from the methylcellulose using either a Pasteur pipet, or a capillary pipet (5 or 10 μl) connected via a trap to a mouth tube. (Viewing of the colonies during this procedure is aided by use of a magnifying glass or dissecting microscope.) The picked colonies are ejected into a small volume (maximum 1 ml) of IMDM + 20% FCS + HAT in a well of a 24- or 48-well tissue culture plate or a 35-mm diameter tissue culture dish (96-well plates are not recommended as the

---

[26] This ensures maximum humidity in the atmosphere of the large petri dish, and thus prevents any possible drying of the methylcellulose cultures.

colonies tend to outgrow the wells too fast). To ensure efficient transfer of the cells and aid disaggregation of the colony, it is advisable to suck medium into and out of the pipet several times. Picked colonies and methylcellulose plates are then returned to the incubator.

Comment: The fusion technique described above may, if desired, be replaced by an alternative technique.[27,28] However, much trouble has been taken to optimize the subsequent steps of plating, growth, and picking[17] and should be closely adhered to. The process of marking the position of colonies not only assists the picking but ensures that colonies appearing later in the same place are not picked again, as they will almost certainly have grown from residual cells left behind when the original colony was picked. A suitable color code should be devised so that colonies to be picked can be distinguished from those already picked once, and those which are not suitable. I have always used red for unsuitable colonies, plus a different color each time the plates are examined, for colonies to be picked.

Screening

In the experience of both myself[17] and others[7] about 60–70% of the picked clones grow to the stage at which supernatants can be tested for antibody activity, and almost all grow indefinitely thereafter. Screening is usually performed when the cells are at a concentration of $5 \times 10^5 - 1 \times 10^6$ cells/ml and have turned the medium orange or yellow (although occasional hybridomas grow to high density without noticeably changing the color of the medium). The method employed for screening the supernatants will depend very much on the nature of the antigen source to be used and the application for which the antibodies are required and is outside the scope of this chapter. However, the method ideally should be both fast and capable of handling large numbers of samples in order that decisions can be made quickly as to whether clones should be kept and frozen, or discarded. In this way the tissue culture load can be minimized. One factor acts to spread the screening load, however; that is, that each individual hybrid has its own particular growth rate and this may vary between semisolid and liquid culture conditions. Thus, not only do different hybrids grow up at different rates so that they are ready for picking at different times, but those picked on the same day will not all be ready for screening at the same time. This enables one to screen many more clones in total than the screening assay can handle at one time. As an example, I

[27] M. L. Gefter, D. H. Margulies, and M. D. Scharff, *Somatic Cell Genet.* **3**, 231 (1977).
[28] K. A. O'Malley and R. L. Davidson, *Somatic Cell Genet.* **3**, 441 (1977).

picked 600 colonies from one fusion, 62% of which grew to the stage of screening (= 372 hybrids). These were all screened without difficulty using a method that could handle only 24 samples per day.[29]

A number of factors limit the number of hybrids which can be screened from one fusion:

1. *The number of growing hybrids which are actually formed in the fusion.* This can vary greatly, independent of the technique used, and this fact has been widely observed in many different laboratories.[15,30-34] In my hands, and using the technique described here, the yield of hybrids has varied from 0 to 3000 in fusions using 10^8 rat spleen cells and 10^7 P3-X63-Ag8.653 myeloma cells.[17,22] The undefined variable appears to lie somewhere in the actual fusion step itself. Using a pool of myeloma cells (those mentioned above) along with a spleen cell suspension from a single rat, I have performed four fusions using the same PEG solution and within minutes of each other and plated them out in the same media. Two yielded no hybrids, while the other two yielded 600 and 800 hybrids each.[35] Although this experiment was performed before the plating technique was optimized[17] (i.e., with 12.5% FCS instead of 20% and without LPS or thymus cells) and although the present technique has increased both the number of successful fusions and the average number of hybrids obtained per fusion,[17] unsuccessful fusions still occur, and it is always worth considering doing more than one at a time.

2. *The total number of screening assays which can be performed.* This is only usually a problem in cases in which the supply of antigen (or other reagent) is limited.

3. *The rate at which screening can be performed.* This is a function of the assay chosen, and bears on point 4.

4. *The number of clones which can actually be picked and subsequently handled in terms of tissue culture.* Picking, the subsequent tissue culture, and screening are the most labor-intensive parts of the procedure. The faster screening can be performed, the less tissue culture is involved and thus the more clones that can be picked.

[29] J. M. Davis and A.-M. Kubler, unpublished results (1981).
[30] G. Köhler and C. Milstein, *Nature (London)* **256**, 495 (1975).
[31] G. Köhler and C. Milstein, *Eur. J. Immunol.* **6**, 511 (1976).
[32] G. Köhler, *in* "Immunological Methods" (I. Lefkovits and B. Pernis, eds.), p. 391. Academic Press, New York, 1979.
[33] A. R. Bellve and S. B. Moss, *Biol. Reprod.* **28**, 1 (1983).
[34] S. P. Kwan, D. E. Yelton, and M. D. Scharff, *Genet. Eng.* **2**, 31 (1980).
[35] J. M. Davis, unpublished results (1980).

One strategy which can be used to increase the number of hybrids that can be screened when factor 2 and/or 3 above is limiting is prescreening of pooled supernatants. In this system the initial screening assay would be performed on pools of supernatants each made up from those of, say, five individual clones. The constituent members of positively reacting pools would then be screened individually. This approach should only be used (a) if a sufficiently sensitive assay is available that will pick up one positive component diluted by other constituents of the pool and (b) if the number of positively reacting clones is thought to be a small proportion of the total to be screened. If either of these conditions is not met, then this approach is a waste of time and materials.

Another approach which might be taken in order to increase the number of clones that can be screened from a single fusion is to freeze (in aliquots) a proportion of the fused spleen cell/myeloma cell suspension. These could then be thawed at a later date and plated, after removal of the freezing medium, as if the cells were from a fresh fusion. Harwell et al.[36] have published a suitable technique for this purpose, although as this requires short-term (24–72 hr) bulk culture before freezing it would no longer be possible to guarantee that every colony obtained has arisen from a separate fusion event. While this approach could prove useful, particularly in cases in which antigen for immunization is in short supply, it is offered only as a suggestion as I have never attempted it.

After Screening

Once a hybridoma of possible interest has been identified, a stock of cells should be frozen in liquid nitrogen as soon as possible. This minimizes the chance of losing the cell line for any reason, e.g., due to contamination during culture.

Cells may continue to be grown in medium containing HAT (in which case continued growth depends on retention of the spleen cell-derived X chromosome), or may be transferred to normal medium. In the latter case the cells must first be grown in medium supplemented with hypoxanthine and thymidine but without aminopterin. After perhaps a week or two this medium may be replaced by the normal medium. Cells transferred straight from HAT-containing medium to normal medium will die, presumably due to the lingering effects of aminopterin.

Should an established hybridoma need recloning at any time, the tech-

[36] L. W. Harwell, M. Bolognino, J. M. Bidlack, R. J. Knapp, and E. M. Lord, *J. Immunol. Methods* **66**, 59 (1984).

nique described above for cloning the hybrids formed in the fusion may also be used (without HAT if desired) for recloning.

Discussion

The technique described above has a number of advantages over conventional liquid culture techniques:

1. Clonal competition is eliminated. This means that one can isolate many potentially interesting hybridomas which might, in other systems, have been lost due to overgrowth by faster growing (e.g., nonproducer) clones.

2. A very large number of different hybrids can be isolated from a single fusion.

3. Almost every colony picked will be a clone. This has been dealt with elsewhere,[17] but briefly stated, the probability of two colonies overlapping in a 35-mm diameter plate containing colonies each 0.75 mm in diameter is 4%. The probability of picking such colonies is small, as the morphology is characteristic unless the overlapping colonies are absolutely concentric. Furthermore, the data obtained in dilution experiments[17] are consistent with each colony arising from a single cell.

4. Because cloning is performed immediately after fusion, each clone obtained will have arisen from a different fusion event. This is unlike the situation in which cloning is performed after an initial growth period, when multiple identical daughter clones may be generated.

5. Because essentially every colony picked is a clone, routine recloning is eliminated. In an occasional cell line, during prolonged culture, recloning has proved necessary.[17] However this is inevitable in any system in which chromosome loss cannot be completely eliminated.

6. Time is saved not only by minimizing recloning (and the associated retesting) but also by eliminating the necessity to constantly tend and feed the newly fused cells. Once the fusion has been plated out it is unnecessary even to look at it for the first 9 days.

7. The problem of overgrowth of hybridomas by fibroblasts is eliminated. The combination of methylcellulose with the use of non-tissue culture petri dishes means that they simply do not grow. This has proved to be a decisive reason to use this technique.[1,2]

There are however, disadvantages:

1. The screening load is large, and quick decisions must be made whether to keep hybrids or discard them.

2. The picking and subsequent culture of the hybrids is time-consuming. This must be balanced against the time saved prior to picking (point 5 above).

Methods by which these disadvantages can be minimized have already been outlined.

The decision whether to use this technique must be made by balancing the advantages and disadvantages mentioned above, along with those inherent in whatever alternative technique is being considered. I would like to suggest that this technique is most suitable for use when both a *mouse* myeloma is to be fused and where a *large* number of different clones are required, e.g., when attempting to define individual antigens present in a crude immunizing preparation. It is less appropriate for use when a pure antigen is available and only a limited number of hybrids are required. In this case, much time can be saved using a liquid culture technique with a fusion plated into a limited number of culture wells unless, of course, other factors such as the prevention of fibroblast growth override in importance.

The use of rat myelomas requires further careful consideration of the best postfusion technique to employ. Hybridomas formed from these cells are far more stable with regard to immunoglobulin secretion than those formed from mouse myelomas, and 90–99% of hybrids formed in rat × rat fusions secrete spleen cell-derived immunoglobulin at 2–3 weeks after culture (cf. 50% for mouse myeloma hybrids).[11] Thus overgrowth by nonproducers is seldom, if ever, observed, and distribution of a fusion into 96 culture wells, followed by subsequent freezing of stocks from each well, alleviates the pressure for rapid screening. Furthermore, the same wells can be screened numerous times with different assays, even years after the fusion.[37] Although the possibility of clonal competition still exists in this system, in practice it does not seem to cause any problems.

One alternative strategy for hybridoma isolation, which I have not so far mentioned, is that of Sharon *et al.*[38] This is similar in principle to the methylcellulose technique described here but instead uses agar, and has the advantage that colonies can be screened while still in the plate (e.g., by transferral of antibody to a nitrocellulose sheet) and thus only hybridomas of interest are picked. The great disadvantage which I have found[17,35] is that, using agar or agarose, only a fraction of the number of hybrids which can be obtained using methylcellulose will grow in these systems;

[37] M. Clark, S. Cobbold, G. Hale, and H. Waldmann, *Immunol. Today* **4,** 100 (1983).
[38] J. Sharon, S. L. Morrison, and E. A. Kabat, *Proc. Natl. Acad. Sci. U.S.A.* **76,** 1420 (1979).

and this comparison was carried out before the methylcellulose technique had been optimized (i.e., with no LPS or thymus cells, and only 12.5% FCS).

Conclusion

The technique described here is ideal for the isolation of large numbers of independent hybridomas from a single mouse myeloma × mouse or rat spleen cell fusion. It may also be useful for other sorts of fusions for hybridoma production, and for the recloning of existing hybrids.

[28] Cloning of Murine Hybridoma Cells in Ultra-Low Gelation Temperature Agarose

By Curt I. Civin and M. L. Banquerigo

Lymphocyte hybridoma production is now highly standardized and automated.[1-3] However, the need to rigorously clone hybridomas remains a tedious part of the procedure that may be rate limiting. Monoclonal antibody-producing hybridomas must be cloned both to eliminate unwanted contaminating cells (e.g., non-immunoglobulin-secreting cells) and to select for clonal stability and high-level antibody secretion. Cloning in liquid suspension culture is slow and requires large quantities of incubator space, culture, medium, and single-use supplies, unless expensive cell sorting devices are used.[4] An alternative, cloning in semisolid agarose medium,[1,5] requires that care be taken to avoid thermal injury to cells, premature gelation of the agarose during procedures at room temperature, and cytotoxicity of the cells due to impurities in the agarose. Furthermore, colonies selected from semisolid agarose may be difficult to disperse to a viable single-cell suspension for subsequent growth in liquid medium.

[1] R. H. Kennett, T. J. McKearn, and K. B. Bechtol, "Monoclonal Antibodies." Plenum, New York, 1980.
[2] G. Köhler and C. Milstein, *Nature (London)* **256**, 495 (1975).
[3] S. Fazekas de St. Groth and D. Sheidegger, *J. Immunol. Methods* **35**, 1 (1980).
[4] D. R. Parks, V. M. Bryant, V. T. Oi, and L. A. Herzenberg, *Proc. Natl. Acad. Sci. U.S.A.* **76**, 1962 (1979).
[5] R. Cotton, D. Secher, and C. Milstein, *Eur. J. Immunol.* **3**, 135 (1973).

We describe a rapid, high-yield hybridoma cloning method which takes advantage of highly purified ultra-low gelation temperature agarose.[6]

Methods

Reagents

Solution A: 3% FMC Sea Prep 15/45 Agarose. Weigh 0.6 g agarose into a 100-ml glass bottle. Add 20 ml glass-distilled water. Sterilize by autoclaving (with cap loose). Tighten cap and store bottle indefinitely in (warmest part of) 37° incubator or water bath. (If larger volumes are prepared and stored long-term, there may be some gelation at the bottom of the bottle. If this happens, the bottle can be reboiled prior to use.)

Solution B: 1× Cloning Medium. RPMI 1640 (or DMEM or Iscove's medium) containing 10% fetal bovine serum (from a lot screened for support of hybridoma growth at limiting dilution) and 2 mM L-glutamine ± antibiotics (e.g., 100 μg gentamicin/ml). Note: If the hybridoma is being cloned directly from HAT or HT medium, fresh (less than 1 week old) HT medium should be used as the 1× cloning medium.

Solution C: 2× Cloning Medium. Double-strength (prepared from powdered concentrate) RPMI 1640 (or DMEM or Iscove's) containing 20% screened fetal bovine serum and 4 mM L-glutamine ± antibiotics. Note: Simple 2× medium can be filter sterilized and stored at 22°. Store at 4° after addition of serum, glutamine, etc.

Cloning Procedure. (1) For best results, assure that the hybridoma culture to be cloned is highly viable (by inverted phase microscopy and by counting an aliquot mixed with an equal volume of 0.2% trypan blue dye). If there are >10% dead cells, it is preferable to pass or feed the bulk culture and observe it daily until it is highly viable and growing vigorously. (If this is impossible due to concern of overgrowth by a contaminating clone, proceed and hope for the best!) (2) Estimate viable count of hybridoma cell suspension to be cloned (trypan blue dye exclusion, hemacytometer). (3) Suspend 5 × 10⁵ viable hybridoma cells in 0.5 ml of 1× cloning medium (solution B) in a 5-ml tissue culture tube (e.g., Falcon No. 2054). (4) Make serial 10-fold dilutions (150 μl cell suspension serially into tubes containing 1.35 ml 1× cloning medium) to obtain tubes containing 10⁵, 10⁴, 10³, and 10² hybridoma cells per tube. (Prepare duplicate tubes at each dilution.)

[6] C. I. Civin and M. L. Banquerigo, *J. Immunol. Methods* **61**, 1 (1983).

(5) Mix 9 ml of (37°) 2× cloning medium (solution C) with 9 ml of (37°) 3% agarose (solution A) to obtain solution D (isotonic). (6) Add 2 ml of solution D (step 5 above) to each tube containing 10^5, 10^4, 10^3, or 10^2 hybridoma cells (step 4 above). Mix well by pipetting. (7) Refrigerate (4°) tubes for 45 min to allow agarose to gel (longer if agarose is not gelled). (8) Incubate tubes in a humid 37°, 5–10% CO_2 incubator.

(9) Macroscopic (up to almost 1 mm diameter) clones will appear within 10–21 days. One of the dilutions (usually the 10^2 cells/tube) almost always will have 5–20 clones/tube and will be easy to pick. (10) Clones can be picked in a laminar flow hood using gentle aspiration with a sterile 9-in. Pasteur pipet and a rubber bulb. Successful aspiration of a single clone is visually obvious in the barrel of the pipet. Transfer the clone to a 5- or 10-ml tissue culture tube (e.g., Falcon No. 2057) or to a well of a 24-well plate containing 1–2 ml (37°) 1× cloning medium or HT medium. Pipet up and down gently to disperse "ball" of cloned cells. Note: Use a fresh pipet for each clone picked. Routinely, at least 20 clones are picked. (11) Incubate cloned cultures (37°, 5–10% CO_2). (12) When suspension cultures begin to become acidic (usually, 90% of the cultures grow within 10–21 days), supernates can be removed and tested for antibody production.

Notes

If >90% of these clones are positive for the antibody in question, it is reasonable to assume that the initial culture was already monoclonal.

Routinely, important hybridomas are cloned twice, or at least once beyond the stage at which >90% of clones are positive for the desired antibody, to assure monoclonality.

The vast majority of murine hybridomas can be successfully cloned by this simple method. However, it may be impossible to clone poorly viably cultures (cf. procedure step 1). If this must be done, it may be beneficial to try (1) use of murine peritoneal macrophages as "feeder cells" in the tubes, and/or (2) cloning at 10^6 and 10^7 cells per cloning tube, in addition to 10^5–10^2 cells per tube.

Results

We have reported a detailed illustration of the use of this methodology.[6] Figure 1 shows clone tubes from a SP2/0-Ag14[7] × human granulocyte-immunized CB_6F_1/J spleen IgM(κ)-producing murine hybridoma.[6]

[7] M. Shulman, C. D. Wilde, and G. Kohler, *Nature (London)* **276,** 269 (1978).

FIG. 1. A set of four cloning tubes was photographed 20 days after cloning. Initially, 10^2 viable hybridoma cells were placed in the first (leftmost) tube, 10^3 in the second tube, 10^4 in the third tube, and 10^5 in the fourth (rightmost) tube. On day 20, clones were picked from the tubes which had been started with 10^2 and 10^3 cells, and grown in liquid culture. All liquid cultures grew and produced antibody. (Adapted from Ref. 6, with publisher's permission.)

As can be seen from Fig. 1 and the table (given the difficulty in obtaining accurate counts of clones in tubes), the number of clones obtained is directly proportional to the numbers of cells initially plated.

Conclusions

We have subsequently used this methodology to subclone scores of murine hybridomas, and have had excellent results in over 90% of cases. Although cloning efficiency varies from hybridoma to hybridoma, rapidly proliferating, highly viable hybridomas tend to clone at high dilution. Our present routine is to plate newly fused hybridomas initially in microwells at near-limiting dilution concentrations.[3,8] After screening to identify de-

[8] C. I. Civin, L. C. Strauss, C. Brovall, M. J. Fackler, J. F. Schwartz, and J. H. Shaper, *J. Immunol.* **133,** 157 (1984).

NUMBERS OF HYBRIDOMA COLONIES
IN CLONING TUBES[a]

Hybridoma designation	Macroscopic colonies per tube[b] for various cloning tube dilutions (cells/cloning tube)			
	10^5	10^4	10^3	10^2
33/7[c]	TNTC[d]	TNTC	77	10
33/8[c]	TNTC	TNTC	54	22
33/50	TNTC	37	9	0
33/59	TNTC	112	36	6
33/66[c]	TNTC	TNTC	64	9
33/75	TNTC	TNTC	32	8
33/91	TNTC	TNTC	28	5

[a] From Ref. 6, with publisher's permission.
[b] Values represent estimates of macroscopic colonies per cloning tube.
[c] Hybridomas successfully cloned only on the second attempt. The values shown derive from that attempt.
[d] Too numerous to count.

sired antibody-secreting hybridomas, we "expand" the positive hybridomas to macrocultures, then passage them two to three times before attempting to clone them. (Exceptions are made when we try to "rescue" poorly proliferating hybridomas with diminishing antibody production, but this has a less than 50% chance of success.)

When cloning hybridomas, we are able to keep the ultra-low gelation temperature agarose for at least several minutes at room temperature, and cells are never exposed to toxic temperatures above 37°. It is not necessary to place a water bath in the laminar flow hood (this potential source of contamination is avoided). Furthermore, the agarose stock solution can be stored indefinitely in the 37° incubator without gelation. Finally, time and effort spent cloning are reduced by avoiding the bothersome manipulations which are necessary to avoid gelation of conventional agarose. Several hybridomas can be cloned in an hour. Growing clones are easily picked from the tubes, more easily than from petri dishes, and over 50 clones can be plucked from these tubes in an hour. The colonies are easily dispersed by trituration during the process of transfer to liquid culture, due to the low gel strength of the purified agarose, and the cells grow well in liquid culture. We routinely subclone a valuable hybridoma twice, each time selecting the subclone producing the highest titer of (desired) antibody in a given time. These cloned hybridomas are usually stable long-term, and they produce antibody of a single isotype and light chain composition, as verified by immunoassay.[6]

Acknowledgments

Supported in part by NIH Grants CA32318, CA06973, Grant 1418 from the Council for Tobacco Research U.S.A., Inc., Grant BSI-029 from the Blood Systems, and the Heart of Variety Fund. Curt I. Civin is a Scholar of the Leukemia Society of America.

[29] A Simple Method for Cloning Hybridomas in 20-μl Hanging Drops

By MARVIN B. RITTENBERG, ABIGAIL BUENAFE, and McKAY BROWN

We have developed a simple and convenient hanging drop microculture system for cloning mouse hybridoma cells.[1] Using this method it is easy to ascertain that limiting dilution conditions have been achieved through microscopic verification of a single cell resting on the meniscus of a hanging drop. Since visual inspection accurately establishes the frequency of negative wells (1% error), it is possible to establish unambiguously pure cultures with only two clonings. The cloning efficiency of the drop culture method is approximately 21% for the first and 60% for the second cloning, based on isolation of different hybridomas representing all murine immunoglobulin isotypes except IgD and IgE.

Mice. Adult female BALB/c mice were obtained from Fred Hutchinson Cancer Research Laboratory, Seattle, WA. CBA/N mice were obtained from Dominion Laboratories, Dublin, VA. (CBA/N × BALB/c)F₁ mice were bred in our laboratories.

Antigens and Immunization. Phosphocholine–keyhole limpet hemocyanin (PC–KLH) was prepared[2] and used to immunize mice in order to produce anti-PC hybridomas as described previously.[3] Hybridomas to the organophosphorus compound soman (methylphosphonofluoridic 1,2,2-trimethylpropyl ester) were prepared with cells from mice immunized as above with soman–KLH; soman–KLH and soman–bovine serum albumin (soman–BSA) were prepared by diazotization.[4]

---

[1] E. B. Bell, M. Brown, and M. B. Rittenberg, *J. Immunol. Methods* **62,** 137 (1983).

[2] B. Chesebro and H. Metzger, *Biochemistry* **11,** 766 (1972).

[3] S. P. Chang, R. M. Perlmutter, M. Brown, C. H. Heusser, L. Hood, and M. B. Rittenberg, *J. Immunol.* **132,** 1550 (1984).

[4] K. W. Hunter, D. E. Lenz, A. A. Brimfield, and J. A. Naylor, *FEBS Lett.* **149,** 147 (1982).

Antibody Assays. Antibody assays were performed using an isotype-specific enzyme-linked immunosorbent assay (ELISA) as described previously for anti-PC antibodies.[5,6] Anti-soman antibodies were detected as described in the anti-PC ELISA but using soman–BSA to coat the plates.[5]

Cell Fusions. Fusions were performed with either Sp2/0-Ag14 (SP2/0)[7] or FO[8] cells, both of which were obtained from the American Type Culture Collection, Rockville, MD. The fusion protocols were those described by Oi and Herzenberg[9] for SP2/0 and by Fazekas de St. Groth and Scheidegger for FO.[8]

Cloning of Hybridomas

Fused cells are cultured in 96-well microculture plates (Falcon Plastics, Oxnard, CA) using 10^6 cells per well (SP2/0 fusions) or 5×10^5 cells per well (FO fusions) in RPMI 1640 supplemented with sodium pyruvate (1 mM), nonessential amino acids (0.1 mM), gentamicin (50 μg/ml), and 20% fetal calf serum (Hyclone, Logan, UT). Cultures are maintained in HAT selective medium for 14 days after fusion.[9] Cultures of FO-fused cells also contain 2×10^3 normal peritoneal cells as feeders.[8] The supernatants are screened for antibody production between days 10 and 14 of culture. ELISA-positive wells that have achieved confluent growth are used for cloning.

One day prior to cloning, the cultures are fed with medium containing 30% fetal calf serum. An increase in serum concentration from 20 to 30% in the cloning medium was found to increase cloning efficiency in three-quarters of the cell lines compared, but different batches of serum seemed to be equally effective at 30% concentration (Table I). The following day the cells are harvested from the wells and viability determined by trypan blue dye exclusion. Cells are diluted in medium containing 30% serum and dispensed into Terasaki plates (Nunc, GIBCO Laboratories; Lux, Flow Laboratories, Rockville, MD; or Robbins Scientific, Mt. View, CA) at 1 and/or 5 or 10 viable cells per 20-μl drop, using either a Tridak dispenser (Bellco Glass, Vineland, NJ) or a Hamilton repeating dispenser fitted with a 1-ml syringe and 21-gauge needle. If HAT medium is being used at the time of cloning, then HT[9] is included in the cloning medium. Plating at 5 or 10 viable cells per drop provides assurance of growth from wells that

[5] S. P. Chang, M. Brown, and M. B. Rittenberg, *J. Immunol.* **128,** 702 (1982).
[6] S. P. Chang, M. Brown, and M. B. Rittenberg, *J. Immunol.* **129,** 1559 (1982).
[7] M. Schulman, C. D. Wilde, and G. Köhler, *Nature (London)* **276,** 269 (1978).
[8] S. Fazekas de St. Groth and D. Scheidegger, *J. Immunol. Methods* **35,** 1 (1980).
[9] V. I. Oi and L. A. Herzenberg, *in* "Selected Methods in Cellular Immunology" (B. B. Mishell and S. M. Shiigi, eds.), p. 351. Freeman, San Francisco, California, 1980.

TABLE I

EFFECT OF SERUM CONCENTRATION ON CLONING EFFICIENCY OF
HYBRIDOMA CELLS IN HANGING DROP CULTURES

	20% FCS		30% FCS	
Cell line[a]	Growth/ single cell[b]	Cloning efficiency	Growth/ single cell[b]	Cloning efficiency
PC-G1-1	12/27	0.44	12/29	0.41
PC-G1-2	6/29	0.21	8/24	0.33
PC-M-2	10/21	0.48	14/22	0.64
PC-M-1	5/21	0.24	11/21	0.52
PC-G3-2, serum lot[c]				
1			8/15	0.53
2			13/24	0.54
3			11/19	0.58

[a] Hybridoma cell lines secreting anti-phosphocholine antibody.
[b] The number of wells that formed clones per number of wells that were initially scored as containing a single cell.
[c] Serum lots 1, 2, and 3 were Hyclone lots 100294, 100408, and 100411, respectively.

may contain few antibody-producing cells but means that limiting dilution conditions will not be obtained at this stage. As shown in Table II, the cloning efficiency increases from 21 to 60% between the first and second cloning in drop cultures. Occasionally, drops originally scored as cell free were found subsequently to contain colonies; the frequency of this occurrence ranged from 0.7 to 1.0% (Table II). We have found that some cells from fusions grew poorly when first placed in drop culture. Such cells require adaptation to hanging drop culture, and plating at the higher cell number makes this possible; however, since other cells adapt readily to the hanging drops, simultaneous plating at 1 cell per drop can save one step and approximately 2 weeks of culture time. We have also noticed that the lowest plating efficiencies have generally been obtained by novices. It is our impression that with the small volumes used, speed in handling and dispensing the cells is critical to high plating efficiencies.

Once the cells have been dispensed, the lids are replaced and the plates are inverted and placed in a 100×15-mm square petri dish (Lab Tek No 4021, Miles Laboratories, Naperville, IL) humidified with a 75×75-mm sterile gauze sponge soaked with 10 ml sterile saline containing 2.5 μg Fungizone/ml (GIBCO Laboratories) and 50 μg gentamicin/ml (Schering Corp., Kenilworth, NJ). For convenience our cultures are

TABLE II

CLONING EFFICIENCY OF HYBRIDOMAS AT FIRST OR SECOND CLONING BY THE HANGING
DROP METHOD

Hybridoma[a]	Heavy chain isotype	First cloning		Second cloning	
		Growth/ single cell[b]	Cloning efficiency	Growth/ single cell	Cloning efficiency
PC-G1-4	γ_1	6/19	0.31	28/44	0.63
PC-G1-5	γ_1	5/19	0.26	14/17	0.82
PC-G1-6	γ_1	5/25	0.20	20/30	0.67
PC-G1-7	γ_1	3/19	0.16	12/23	0.52
PC-A-1	α	5/20	0.25	9/21	0.43
PC-M-11	μ	4/18	0.22	22/22	1.00
SO-M1-1	μ	2/9	0.22	9/25	0.36
SO-G1-1	γ_1	6/20	0.30	15/18	0.83
SO-G2a-1	γ_{2a}	2/18	0.11	14/29	0.48
SO-G2a-2	γ_{2a}	3/15	0.20	8/19	0.42
SO-G2b-1	γ_{2b}	6/18	0.33	10/17	0.59
SO-G3-1	γ_3	2/26	0.08	9/17	0.53
SO-G3-2	γ_3	1/17	0.06	11/18	0.61
SO-G3-3	γ_3	3/18	0.17	7/16	0.44
		Mean	0.21 ± 0.08		0.60 ± 0.18

[a] Hybridoma lettering designates antibody specificity: PC, anti-phosphocholine; SO, anti-soman (methylphosphonofluoridic 1,2,2-trimethylpropyl ester).

[b] The number of wells that formed clones per number of wells that were initially scored as containing a single cell. The mean cloning efficiencies for the first and second clonings of these 14 cell lines are shown ± standard deviation. A total of 304 negative wells were scored in the first cloning and 324 in the second cloning; the percentage of error was 0.7 and 1.0%, respectively, based on the number of negative wells that subsequently showed growth.

placed in a humidified, airtight gas box (C.B.S. Scientific, Del Mar, CA) equilibrated with 10% CO_2, 7% O_2, 83% N_2; however, any humidified CO_2 incubator should suffice. The cultures are allowed to stand undisturbed for 2 hr at 37° to allow cells to settle onto the meniscus. The Terasaki plates are then removed from the petri dishes and examined at 32× on an inverted microscope. The number of cells present in each drop is recorded, and the plates returned to the humidified petri dishes for incubation in the gas boxes for approximately 11 days, at which time they are scored for growth.

Clones arising from one cell are removed when approximately one-third to one-half of the meniscus is covered by cells. The cells can be recovered either from the meniscus of the drop hanging beneath the plate by keeping it inverted during collection or by turning the plate over and harvesting from the top. Either sterile microcap capillary tubes fitted with a rubber bulb (Drummond Scientific, Broomall, PA) or a sterile plastic-tipped pipet (Pipetman P20, Rainin Instruments, Woburn, MA) can be used to transfer cells and medium to the wells of a Terasaki monoclonal cluster plate (Costar No. 3560, Costar, Cambridge, MA) containing 50 μl of culture medium (20% fetal calf serum) per well; the new plates are allowed to stand in equilibrated gas boxes overnight at 37° to allow the cells to settle. The supernatants can then be removed for testing at any time, but the cells are allowed to grow for 3–4 days before recloning by the hanging drop procedure described above. The cells remaining in the cluster plates can be frozen *in situ*[10] or expanded and frozen in vials as a safety precaution.

Remarks

Cloning of hybridoma cells by hanging drop is a simple and convenient method that requires fewer cells than the traditional limiting dilution procedure and no feeder layer.[9] As described previously, this method can also be used to study *in vitro* antibody synthesis by small numbers of murine[1] or human lymphocytes (F. Makowski and M. B. Rittenberg, unpublished). Because the cells are allowed to settle onto the meniscus of a small drop of medium, the field required for microscopic inspection is limited and can be scanned with minimal focus adjustment. Direct visualization of single cells for cloning was employed previously in noninverted cultures[10]; however, the use of hanging drops permits easy recovery of clones that might otherwise adhere to the culture dish surface, a property of hybridoma cells fused with SP2/0 or FO. Cloning efficiencies are usually high, ranging from 6 to 31% for the first cloning and 36 to 100% for the second. We have also used this method for cloning rat basophil leukemia cells (T. Hall, unpublished). Other types of cells that are not anchorage dependent should clone equally well by the hanging drop technique.

Acknowledgments

We thank Dr. E. B. Bell, who first established this method in our laboratory for studying antibody synthesis. This work was supported in part by NIH Grant AI 14985, ACS Grant IM172, and by US Army Medical Research and Development Command Contract DAMD 17-83C-3246.

[10] K. W. Choi and A. D. Bloom, *Nature (London)* **227**, 171 (1970).

[30] Clonal Isolation of Hybridomas by Manual Single-Cell Isolation

By Albert Boeyé

It ain't necessarily so.[1]

Hybridomas Are Not Necessarily Monoclonal, nor Their Antibodies Homogeneous

The original method of Köhler and Milstein[2] for the production of monoclonal antibodies can be divided into six stages: (1) immunization of an animal and collection of its spleen cells; (2) fusion of these splenocytes with myeloma cells to yield hybrids; (3) selection of the hybrids in HAT medium; (4) screening of the hybrids for the production of a desired antibody; (5) recloning of hybridomas; and (6) further cultivation of those hybridomas *in vitro* or as ascites cells. As thousands of hybridoma antibodies were produced by this method in the last years, the monoclonality of the hybridomas and the molecular homogeneity of the antibodies were seldom questioned. It was generally assumed that (1) spleen cells always produced a single kind of antibody molecules, and (2) the viable hybrids were derived from a single lymphocyte parent.

The first assumption is that single lymphocytes cannot produce multiple antibodies. When animals were immunized with two unrelated antigens, lymphocytes producing antibodies against both were either found[3–5] or not.[6,7] Even though bispecific lymphocytes are now generally considered unimportant in the overall picture of the immune response, it is hard to estimate how frequently such cells will enter the fusion process. The use of a single immunogen does not preclude the synthesis of multiple antibodies, directed against the same or different epitopes, by a single cell. Moreover, the antigen may undergo *in vivo* transformations generating new epitopes. A case in point is poliovirus. Upon heat treatment at 56°, native poliovirus undergoes a conversion from N to H antigen (N and

---

[1] I. Gershwin, in "Porgy and Bess" (music by G. Gershwin) (1935).

[2] G. Köhler and C. Milstein, *Nature (London)* **256**, 495 (1975).

[3] G. Attardi, M. Cohn, K. Horibata, and E. S. Lennox, *J. Immunol.* **92**, 335 (1964).

[4] J. Couderc, C. Bleux, and P. Liacopoulos, *Immunology* **29**, 665 (1975).

[5] J. Couderc, C. Bleux, M. Ventura, and P. Liacopoulos, *J. Immunol.* **123**, 173 (1979).

[6] O. Mäkelä, *Cold Spring Harbor Symp. Quant. Biol.* **32**, 423 (1967).

[7] I. Green, P. Vassalli, V. Nussenzweig, and B. Benacerraf, *J. Exp. Med.* **125**, 511 (1967).

H stand for native and heated, respectively[8]). Animals immunized with pure N antigen will develop not only neutralizing antibodies directed against N antigen, but also nonneutralizing anti-H antibodies,[9] presumably as a result of partial *in vivo* conversion of N to H. This duality is observed not only with conventional antibodies, but also with hybridoma antibodies. For instance, when hybridomas were constructed with spleen cells of mice immunized with N antigen, some antibodies turned out to be specific for N and others for H antigen.[10]

The second assumption is that all stable hybrids arise by fusion of only one lymphocyte with a myeloma cell. Although multiple fusion has not been demonstrated directly, it proved possible to construct multiple hybrids by fusing preexisting hybridoma cells with a second set of spleen cells. The resulting hybridomas were genetically stable and each produced two sets of unrelated antibodies.[11,12]

Another reason why a hybridoma may be secreting two kinds of antibodies is that clonal isolation may not have been achieved owing to inadequate methods (see next section). As a result, the population remains oligoclonal with each monoclonal subpopulation secreting its own species of antibodies.

If all pitfalls have been avoided thus far, the antibodies may still develop molecular heterogeneity due to class switching.[13]

Finally, ascitic fluids will contain not only antibodies secreted by the hybridoma cells, but also admixtures of the animal's own immunoglobulins. Depending on the type of work, these may be more or less of a nuisance, but one should remember that ascitic fluids or immunoglobulins purified from this source do not qualify as monospecific antibody preparations.

Procedures of Clonal Isolation

Hybridomas are usually recloned either by the soft agar method[14] or by limiting dilution.[15] The soft agar method does not ensure monoclonal-

[8] K. Hummeler and V. V. Hamparian, *J. Immunol.* **81**, 499 (1958).
[9] P. D. Minor, G. C. Schild, J. M. Wood, and C. N. Dandawate, *J. Gen. Virol.* **51**, 147 (1980).
[10] P. Brioen, R. J. Sijens, R. Vrijsen, B. Rombaut, A. A. M. Thomas, A. Jackers, and A. Boeyé, *Arch. Virol.* **74**, 325 (1982).
[11] C. Milstein and A. C. Cuello, *Nature (London)* **305**, 537 (1983).
[12] L. Wang, C. S. Hexter, and M. Inbar, *in* "Cell Fusion: Gene Transfer and Transformation" (R. F. Beers and E. G. Bassett, eds.), p. 315. Raven Press, New York, 1984.
[13] C. E. Müller and K. Rajewsky, *J. Immunol.* **131**, 877 (1983).
[14] I. Macpherson and L. Montagnier, *Virology* **23**, 291 (1964).
[15] D. Osoba, *J. Exp. Med.* **129**, 141 (1969).

ity as there is no way to tell whether a given colony originated from one or more cells. In the limiting dilution method, a diluted cell suspension is dispensed into a number of wells, and these are observed for growth. On the assumption that all cells are (1) viable, (2) dispersed singly, and (3) distributed at random among the wells, the fraction of unpopulated wells can be equated to the zero term of a Poisson distribution. The chance of having failed clonal isolation is then computed as the probability that any given, populated well received more than one cell. However, the value of this calculation rests on the three assumptions made above, and these are seldom if ever verified. For instance, if the viability of isolated cells is enhanced by the presence of other hybridoma cells, calculations based on the Poisson distribution will grossly overestimate the probability of having achieved clonal isolation. In the extreme case, growth may be absolutely dependent on complementation between two types of cells, and clonal isolation therefore impossible.[16]

The uncertainties of the limiting dilution and soft agar methods for clonal isolation can be avoided by direct isolation of single cells. The task of picking single cultured cells requires neither sophisticated equipment nor special skills. Table I[17–21] lists a number of studies in which cells were isolated by micromanipulation for various purposes. The survey shows that two methods were used. Either a cell was drawn into a micropipet under microscopic control, or droplets from a diluted cell suspension were examined microscopically and those containing exactly one cell selected. The latter method, which requires no micromanipulation, is exemplified in the following procedure, which was developed in the author's laboratory.[21]

Materials and Methods

Microscope: binocular, inverted microscope with a simple, fixed stage, brightfield illumination, 10× eyepieces, and a 10× or 20× objective.
Laminar air flow cabinet: all work with uncovered petri dishes and microtitration plates must be done in a laminar air flow cabinet.
Glassware: a Bürker cell counting chamber, disposable 1-ml syringes fitted with a fine needle (e.g., Plastipak U-40 INSULIN, needle 13 × 0.38 mm), graduated 1-ml glass pipets, plastic tissue culture petri dishes (e.g., Greiner 60 × 15-mm dishes).

[16] F. Bach, *Immunol. Today* **4,** 243 (1983).
[17] A. Lwoff, R. Dulbecco, M. Vogt, and M. Lwoff, *Virology* **1,** 128 (1955).
[18] P. Wildy and M. Stoker, *Nature (London)* **181,** 1407 (1958).
[19] A. J. Cunningham and S. A. Fordham, *Nature (London)* **250,** 669 (1974).
[20] D. Zagury, D. A. Morgan, and M. Fauchard, *Biomedicine* **33,** 272 (1980).
[21] R. J. Sijens, A. A. M. Thomas, A. Jackers, and A. Boeyé, *Hybridoma* **2,** 231 (1983).

TABLE I
A Survey of Cell Isolation Techniques

| Cell type | Object of study | Technique of single-cell isolation | | Percentage of cells that yielded a progeny | Ref. |
		Apparatus	Cells transferred to		
HeLa	Poliovirus release by single cells	Micromanip-ulator[a]	Microdrops in oil	N.D.[b]	17
HeLa	Multiplication of single cells	Micropipet hand held[a]	Microdrops in oil	33	18
Lymph node cells	Specific Ab production of single cells	Micromanip-ulator[c]	Microdrops in oil	N.D.	3, 6
PFC[d]	Variation in PFC progeny	Micropipet, hand held[a]	Wells in polyacryl-amide raft	10	19
PFC	Cloning of bispe-cific B cells	Micromanip-ulator[a]	Wells in polyacryl-amide raft	18–23	5
T cells	Cytotoxic activity of clones	Micropipet[a]	Microplate wells	30–50	20
Hybridoma cells	Recloning of hybridoma	Syringe[c]	Microplate wells	31	21

[a] Aspiration of single cells under microscopic control.

[b] Not determined.

[c] Aspiration of droplets, followed by microscopic examination and selection of those containing exactly one cell.

[d] Plaque-forming cells, i.e., central cells of hemolytic plaques.

Culture medium: Dulbecco's modified Eagle's medium (GIBCO) supplemented with 15% newborn calf serum (GIBCO).

Hybridoma: the hybridoma to be recloned should be available as an actively growing culture containing as few dead cells and cell debris as possible.

Macrophage cultures: a microplate with 2- to 4-day-old macrophage cultures in 50 μl culture medium. Per hybridoma to be recloned, about a dozen cultures are required.

Procedure

The aim of operations 1 and 2 is to dispense droplets containing an average of one cell each; hence, the required cell density (see 1) depends on the volume of the droplets, which must be determined in advance, e.g., by weighing.

(1) Determine the number of cells per milliliter in the hybridoma culture using a Bürker cell counting chamber, and dilute an aliquot in culture medium to a final density of $10^2–10^3$ cells/ml as required. (2) Using a 1-ml syringe, deposit about 30 separate droplets of a diameter of 2 mm onto the bottom of a petri dish. Flatten the droplets with the needle tip to 4–5 mm for easier microscopic observation. (3) Replace cover on the petri dish and examine each droplet using an inverted microscope. Each droplet is scanned by moving the petri dish manually. Mark the droplets that contain exactly one cell. (4) Using a new syringe each time, add 50 μl of culture medium to each of the marked droplets, and transfer to a 50-μl macrophage culture.

Comment: operations 2–4 must be carried out rapidly to prevent drying out. Until sufficient practice has been acquired, it may be advisable to handle fewer than 30 droplets at a time, repeating operations 2–4 as necessary. With practice, these operations can be completed in 30 min.

(5) Examine wells for growth after 5 days. About 3 out of 10 isolated cells are expected to yield a clone.

This recloning method was applied to a number of hybridomas whose antibodies recognized two different poliovirus-related antigens. Table II[22,23] illustrates two such cases. (1) The antibodies produced by hybridoma 39-3f1 recognized both N and H antigen. After it was established by separate exhaustion (see Fig. 1) that the anti-N and anti-H specificities belonged to distinct populations of antibody molecules, the hybridomas were recloned by manual single-cell picking. The antibodies thereafter still recognized N, but not H antigen. (2) Hybridoma 42-1c9 secreted antibodies recognizing both N antigen and the isolated poliovirus capsid protein VP3. Again, it was established that the two specificities involved different antibody populations,[21] and the hybridoma was recloned manually. The new set of antibodies still reacted with the isolated capsid protein VP3, but not with N antigen.

Although there is no formal proof that the two sets of antibodies produced by each of the original hybridomas were secreted by different cell subpopulations, this would appear to be the least contrived explanation of the findings, since in both cases the dual antibody production was terminated by direct recloning, and there was no evidence for hybrid antibody molecules.[11] It may be emphasized that the dual antibody production had persisted through three attempts at clonal isolation by limiting dilution.

[22] R. Vrijsen, B. Rombaut, and A. Boeyé, *J. Immunol. Methods* **59**, 217 (1983).
[23] H. Towbin, T. Staehelin, and J. Gordon, *Proc. Natl. Acad. Sci. U.S.A.* **76**, 4350 (1979).

TABLE II
EFFECT OF MANUAL SINGLE-CELL ISOLATION ON ANTIBODY PRODUCTION
OF TWO HYBRIDOMAS[a]

Hybridoma	LD[b]	Subsequent single cell isolation[c]	Protein A-aided immunoprecipitation[d]		Capsid polypeptides bound in immunoreplica[e]	Neutralization titer[f]
			N	H		
39-3f1	3	–	3.2	4.6	—	3.0
	3	+	3.8	<0	—	3.0
42-1c9[g]	3	–	2.4	<0	VP3	2.5
	3	+	<0	<0	VP3	<0

[a] From Sijens et al.[21]
[b] Number of clonal reisolations by limiting dilution (LD).
[c] See text for method.
[d] Negative logarithm of ascitic fluid dilution causing 50% of antigen to precipitate. For method, see Vrijsen et al.[22]
[e] Blotting performed essentially as described in Towbin et al.[23]
[f] Negative logarithm of ascitic fluid dilution causing 50% plaque reduction of 100 PFU inoculum of poliovirus.
[g] This hybridoma was obtained after immunization of mice with a reconstituted mixture of capsid proteins VP1, VP2, and VP3.

How to Recognize That a Hybridoma Produces a Mixture of Antibodies

The Basic Method: Exhaustion by Excess Antigen

When an antibody preparation recognizes two different antigens Ag1 and Ag2, the two specificities may be associated with one or several sets of immunoglobulin molecules. In the former case, absorption with excess Ag1 or Ag2 will remove the anti-Ag1 *and* anti-Ag2 activities (simultaneous exhaustion). In the latter case, the antibodies directed against Ag2 will subsist after absorption with Ag1, and vice versa (separate exhaustion). Both the simultaneous and separate exhaustion are exemplified in Fig. 1.[24] The hybridomas 39-3f1 and C3 each secreted antibodies recognizing both the N and H antigens of poliovirus. With hybridoma 39-3f1, absorption with an excess of N antigen failed to remove any of the anti-H antibodies, and vice versa, thus showing that the anti-N and anti-H specificities were associated with separate sets of antibody molecules (Fig.

[24] B. Blondel, O. Akacem, R. Crainic, P. Couillin, and F. Horodniceanu, *Virology* **126,** 707 (1983).

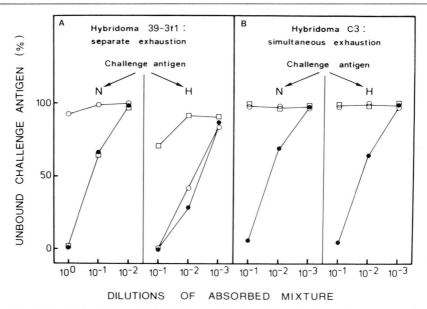

FIG. 1. Analysis of bispecific hybridoma antibodies: effect of exhaustion by one antigen on the antibodies directed against the second antigen. Fifty-microliter portions of diluted (1 : 100) ascitic fluid were incubated for 1 hr without added antigen (●), or with a great excess (100 μg) of native (N antigen, ○) or heated poliovirus (H antigen, □). The three mixtures were then serially diluted 10-fold. Each dilution was tested by protein A-aided immunoprecipitation[22] for its ability to bind 0.3 μg of radiolabeled challenge N or H antigen. The radioactivity of the supernatant was measured to determine the amount of unbound antigen. (A) Hybridoma 39-3f1: see Table II (first line). (Redrawn from Brioen *et al.*[10] with permission.) (B) Hybridoma C3[24]: unpublished results by P. Brioen. Ascitic fluids were kindly provided by B. Blondel.

1A). The opposite result was obtained with hybridoma C3 (Fig. 1B). In this case, all the antibodies were removed by an excess of either N or H antigen, thus showing that the two specificities were associated with one and the same set of immunoglobulin molecules.

The exhaustion method was applied to the study of cross-reactions between the three serotypes of poliovirus.[25] The simultaneous exhaustion of the antibodies recognizing homotypic H antigen, heterotypic H antigen, and the isolated VP1 capsid polypeptide of poliovirus proved that the three specificities were associated with a single set of molecules and therefore genuine cross-reactions.

[25] R. Vrijsen, B. Rombaut, and A. Boeyé, *J. Virol.* **49**, 1002 (1984).

A third example of the application of the exhaustion method concerns a set of hybridoma antibodies directed against the Thy1.2 alloantigen of mouse thymocytes. These antibodies were found to induce complement lysis of target cells bearing the Thy1.2 marker.[26] A feeble reaction with Thy1.1 cells was also noted and originally ascribed to low-affinity cross-reaction. This interpretation was challenged after it was found that repeated absorptions with formalin-fixed Thy1.1 thymocytes completely removed the anti-Thy1.1 activity without concomitant reduction of the anti-Thy1.2 titer.[27] Furthermore, the antibodies absorbed to Thy1.1 cells were eluted at pH 4.0 and titrated against Thy1.1 and Thy1.2 target cells. The anti-Thy1.1 titer of the eluate was $10^{3.0}$ and the anti-Thy1.2 titer only $10^{1.8}$. When these titers are compared with of the preabsorption titers in the original ascitic fluids (anti-Thy1.1 $10^{1.8}$; anti-Thy1.2 $10^{5.0}$), it becomes evident that the anti-Thy1.1 antibodies were concentrated by the absorption–elution procedure.

Occasional Differences among Hybridoma Antibodies of Different Specificities

Thermal Stability. In the work just discussed,[27] it was observed that the anti-Thy1.2 activity was rapidly lost at 56°, whereas the anti-Thy1.1 activity was unaffected, thus confirming that the Thy1.1 and Thy1.2 specificities belonged to different sets of Ig molecules.

Sedimentation Velocity. Hybridoma 36-5d10, generated in the author's laboratory, secreted poliovirus antibodies which scored as IgM in the Ouchterlony test, and which were specific for N antigen in the immunoprecipitation test. As expected from the isotype, the bulk of the antibody was found to sediment in the 17 S region, and this fast-sedimenting antibody was exclusively N specific (Fig. 2). However, a minor fraction (about 0.1%) of the anti-N activity sedimented as 7 S material, and this antibody also recognized H antigen. Thus, the hybridoma produced two sets of antibody molecules of different sedimentation coefficients and specificities.

Conclusion

The methods described in this chapter may help to decide whether the antibodies secreted by a hybridoma belong to one or several sets of immunoglobulin molecules. When the antibodies recognize different anti-

[26] A. Marshak-Rothstein, P. Fink, T. Gridley, D. H. Raulet, M. J. Bevan, and M. L. Gefter, *J. Immunol.* **122**, 2491 (1979).

[27] E. Kubota, H. Ishikawa, and K. Saito, *J. Immunol.* **127**, 1498 (1981).

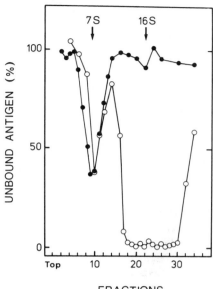

FRACTIONS

FIG. 2. Sucrose gradient centrifugation of the antibodies from a single hybridoma: sedimentation profile of the anti-N and anti-H activities. Ascitic fluids containing the antibodies of hybridoma 36-5d10 were collected and the immunoglobulins purified by ammonium sulfate precipitation. After dialysis, a sample was centrifuged for 18 hr at 90,000 g in a 15–30% sucrose gradient. Fifty fractions were collected and tested by protein A-aided immunoprecipitation for the presence of antibodies directed against N or H challenge antigen. The method involved the following steps: (1) incubation of the sample with ^{3}H-labeled N(ative) (○) or H(eated) (●) poliovirus; (2) addition of rabbit anti-mouse Ig antibodies to mediate the binding of the immune complexes to the staphylococci, to which IgM immunoglobulins do not bind directly; (3) addition of protein A-bearing staphylococci; (4) removal by centrifugation of the organisms and the immune complexes attached to them; and (5) determination of the input radioactivity remaining in the supernatants. The arrows indicate the location of radiolabeled IgG (7 S) and of β-galactosidase activity (16 S) in simultaneously run control tubes. (Unpublished results by A. A. M. Thomas and A. D'Hulst.)

gens, the exhaustion method should give the answer. However, when the antibodies all recognize the same antigen, it may be much harder to verify their molecular homogeneity *a posteriori*. The best insurance against antibody mixtures is a really monoclonal hybridoma, and this requires a good recloning method. As was pointed out, there is no need to rely on statistics (limiting dilution) or sheer luck (soft agar). The direct isolation of hybridoma cells is safe and easy to perform.

[31] Semiautomated Plaque Method for the Detection of Antibody-Forming Cell Clones

By BEVERLEY L. PIKE

In vitro limiting dilution analysis provides an elegant means of assessing the functional potential of a population of cells in terms of the number of precursors within that population which are competent to respond under defined conditions to form clones of effector cells. One of its major drawbacks is that large numbers of replicate cultures need to be assayed for the presence or absence of clones, and as a consequence the procedure is both extremely time-consuming and labor intensive. Simple, semiautomated assay procedures which enable the rapid detection of clones without any loss in sensitivity from previously used methods are therefore essential.

In our laboratory, limiting dilution analysis is used as a standard tool for the assessment of the potential of a given cell population to form clones containing antibody-forming cells (AFC) under a variety of experimental conditions. Antibody formation is assessed at the cellular level by the presence of AFC, which are detected using one of a variety of the modifications of the Jerne hemolytic plaque technique.[1-4] As limiting dilution analysis is generally performed in 96-well microculture trays, we have modified in the "*in situ*" microtray hemolytic plaque method described by Kappler,[3] which allows detection of hemolytic plaque-forming cells (PFC) in the wells of flat-bottomed 96-well microculture trays. The method as outlined below is simple, robust, and provides a rapid and inexpensive approach to the assay of large numbers of replicate cultures for AFC clones without any loss in sensitivity[4] from the previously used liquid monolayer slide method of Cunningham and Szenberg.[2] It allows simple detection of directly hemolytic antigen-specific AFC clones and also of all clones secreting immunoglobulin per se, regardless of specificity, as detected using the protein A reverse plaque assay.[5] The procedure is semiautomatable, which provides a considerable advantage when large numbers of trays need to be processed.

[1] N. K. Jerne and A. A. Nordin, *Science* **140**, 405 (1963).
[2] A. J. Cunningham and A. Szenberg, *Immunology* **14**, 599 (1968).
[3] J. W. Kappler, *J. Immunol.* **112**, 1271 (1974).
[4] B. L. Pike, G. Jennings, and K. Shortman, *J. Immunol. Methods* **52**, 25 (1982).
[5] E. Gronowicz, A. Coutinho, and F. Melchers, *Eur. J. Immunol.* **6**, 588 (1976).

Detection of Anti-Hapten AFC Clones

The hemolytic plaque assay as first described by Jerne and Nordin[1] allowed the enumeration of cells secreting antibody to erythrocyte antigens. Spleen cells from mice immunized with sheep red blood cells (SRC) were suspended in agar medium containing SRC. On the addition of complement, clear zones of lysis (plaques) appeared around cells which were secreting IgM antibody reactive against the SRC. The scope of the method has been extended to detect cells secreting IgM antibody to a variety of antigens, by the attachment of defined antigens such as haptens polysaccharides, polypeptides, and proteins to the surface of the target erythrocyte. The variety of methods used for attachment of antigens to the SRC are described in detail elsewhere.[6] The method as used by us is described below. Antibodies of immunoglobulin classes other than IgM can be detected by the addition of immunoglobulin class-specific antisera in the assay procedure.[6] We have made extensive use of a variety of haptens as antigens in our studies on directly hemolytic IgM-secreting AFC clone development *in vitro*.

Equipment

Flat-bottomed, rigid, polystyrene 96-well microtiter trays. Choose a brand which has the least slope in the vertical walls of the wells as this minimizes the peripheralization of the SRC around the rim of the well and also provides better optical quality. Most brands of plates as now available meet this criteria. Plates from Falcon Plastics, Oxnard, CA; Disposable Products, Australia; Linbro, Conn.; Costar, Mass., have been found to be satisfactory. New plates are essential as the cleanliness of the surface of the bottom of the well is extremely important with respect to the quality of the SRC lawn that is formed in the plaque assay.

Multichannel pipettor, 8 channel or 12 channel, with volume capacity of 50–200 μl (Titertek, Flow Laboratories, Finland) or preferably a 96-well replicator. We presently use a 96-well replicator made in our workshop but commercially available replicators with the required volume capacities are available (e.g., Dynatech Laboratories, or Costar, MA).

Reservoir for fluid for multichannel pipettor or replicator

Disposable tips for multichannel pipettor (Titertek)

Mechanical plate shaker (Titertek, Flow Laboratories, Finland, Cooke, USA)

---

[6] D. Dresser, *in* "Handbook of Experimental Immunology" (E. M. Weir, ed.), Vol. 2, Chapter 28. Blackwell, Oxford, 1978.

Microtiter tray carriers for centrifugation (Cooke Microtiter System, Dynatech Laboratories)

Centrifuge with capacity for centrifugation of microtiter trays (Damon I.E.C. PR6000)

37° incubator

Dissecting microscope

Reagents

Phosphate-buffered saline (PBS), pH 7.2, 0.02 M sodium phosphate solution (2.85 g $Na_2HPO_4 \cdot 2H_2O$, 0.625 g $NaH_2PO_4 \cdot 2H_2O$ per liter) containing either 8.7 g NaCl/liter (0.15 M) (mouse tonicity, MT-PBS) or 7.0 g NaCl/liter (0.12 M) (human tonicity, HT-PBS)

Balanced salt solution (BSS). We use Eagle's minimal essential medium (GIBCO, Grand Island, NY), buffered with 20 mM HEPES (Calbiochem, Los Angeles) (HEM).

Sheep red blood cells (SRC), collected and stored in Alsever's solution for a period of at least 1–2 weeks

Haptenated $(Fab')_2$ fragments of the IgG fraction from a hyperimmune rabbit anti-SRC serum (see below)

SRC-absorbed complement (see below)

Anti-foam Emulsion (Sigma Chemicals, No. A5758)

Preparation of Haptenated SRC

We use the principle of immunological coupling as described by Strausbach et al.[7] to couple haptens to the surface of the SRC. Briefly, $(Fab')_2$ fragments of the IgG fraction from a hyperimmune rabbit anti-SRC serum are conjugated with haptens by the standard procedures. The haptenated $(Fab')_2$ is then reacted with SRC. A major advantage of haptenated $(Fab')_2$-coupled SRC is that the target SRC exhibit the same sensitivity to lysis from batch to batch, one preparation of haptenated $(Fab')_2$ lasting over a long period. A further practical advantage is that $(Fab')_2$-coupled SRC can be stored for up to 2 weeks before use without any detrimental effects, providing they were prepared and stored under sterile conditions. We have not made extensive use of directly haptenated SRC,[6,8–10] but these may be used if care is taken not to use SRC which are too heavily haptenated, as these tend to lyse nonspecifically during the assay.

[7] P. Strausbach, A. Sulica, and D. Givol, *Nature (London)* **220**, 927 (1970).

[8] M. B. Rittenberg and K. L. Pratt, *Proc. Soc. Exp. Biol. Med.* **132**, 575 (1969).

[9] V. J. Pasenan and O. Mäkelä, *Immunology* **16**, 399 (1969).

[10] T. Ramos and G. Moller, *Scand. J. Immunol.* **8**, 1 (1978).

Preparation of Haptenated (Fab')₂ Fragments

(Fab')₂ fragments are prepared from the IgG fraction from a hyperimmune rabbit anti-SRC serum. High-titer commercial preparations of either the antiserum or the (Fab')₂ fragments are acceptable. We prepare our own by immunizing a rabbit by the intravenous administration of 0.5 ml of 5% (v/v) washed SRC three to four times at 2-week intervals. Bleed the rabbit 10 days after the last boost and collect serum from blood. The IgG is isolated from the serum as using a protein A–Sepharose CL-4B column (Pharmacia, Uppsala, Sweden) as described by Goding.[11] Equilibrate a 10-ml column with MT-PBS, and run 8–10 ml of serum through the column. Wash column with MT-PBS, and then elute the IgG with 0.58% glacial acetic acid in 0.15 M NaCl. Adjust the eluted IgG to pH 4.5 and then digest in the presence of 2% pepsin (Calbiochem, B grade, porcine stomach mucosa) for at least 20 hr at 37°. Dialyze the digested IgG for 24 hr against MT-PBS, then pass it over a protein A–Sepharose column, and collect the (Fab')₂ fragments in the runthrough. (The Fc fragments bind to the column and are eluted with 0.58% glacial acetic acid in 0.15 M NaCl.) Concentrate the (Fab')₂ using an Amicon hollow-filter system (molecular weight cutoff 10,000) and dialyze for 24 hr against MT-PBS. Store in aliquots at −70° until use. Determine the protein concentration by spectrophotometry.

Hapten Conjugation of (Fab')₂

The standard procedures for haptenation of proteins are used. The optimal substitution ratio of hapten to protein has to be determined for each hapten. We have found substitution ratios of 15–17 mol of hapten per mole of (Fab')₂ to provide maximal plaque development for the haptens fluorescein (FLU), 4-hydroxy-3-iodo-5-nitrophenylacetic acid (NIP), 2,4-dinitrophenyl- (DNP), or 2,4,6-trinitrophenyl- (TNP) sulfonic acid. Lower substitution ratios result in a lower hapten density on the erythrocyte surface, and fewer clones may be detected, presumably only those which are secreting higher avidity antibody. Overhaptenation of the (Fab')₂ can result in a significant lowering of its anti-SRC binding capacity for virtually no gain in sensitivity in the plaque assay. As a guide for preparation of NIP and FLU conjugates, our general procedures are as follows. NIP is conjugated to (Fab')₂ by the method of Brownestone et al.[12] React 1 mg of NIP–azide (Institute of Drug Technology, Melbourne,

[11] J. W. Goding, *J. Immunol. Methods* **13**, 215 (1976).
[12] A. Brownestone, N. A. Mitchison, and R. Pitt-Rivers, *Immunology* **10**, 465 (1966).

Australia) dissolved in dimethyl sulfoxide (DMSO) with 5 mg of (Fab')$_2$ in 5 ml of 0.2 M sodium carbonate buffer (8.6 g Na$_2$CO$_3$, 17.2 g NaHCO$_3$ per liter, pH 9.2) at room temperature for 2 hr with constant stirring, followed by extensive dialysis against MT-PBS. This procedure gives a conjugate with an average of 15–17 mol NIP per mole of (Fab')$_2$ as determined by spectrophotometry. FLU–(Fab')$_2$ is prepared by reaction of fluorescein isothiocyanate (FITC) (Molecular Probes, Plano, TX) dissolved in DMSO[11] with (Fab')$_2$ essentially as described above. Reaction of 1 mg of FITC with 3 mg of (Fab')$_2$ in 3 ml of 0.2 M sodium carbonate buffer (pH 9.2) has resulted in FLU–(Fab')$_2$ conjugates with substitution ratios of 15–19. Store haptenated (Fab')$_2$ in aliquots at $-70°$ until use.

Procedure for Coupling of Haptenated (Fab')$_2$ to SRC

Each batch of haptenated (Fab')$_2$ needs to be titrated to determine the amount to be added to the SRC to allow optimal plaque development without causing either agglutination or lysis on storage. This is achieved by making SRC and testing for plaque development using spleen cells from immunized mice as a source of AFC. The procedure for testing reagents is outlined below. Assessment is made on the criteria of both plaque number and plaque quality (plaque clarity and plaque size). In general, these criteria are met at approximately the same (Fab')$_2$ concentration. The amount used must be a subagglutinating concentration, and a hemagglutination titration can provide some guide to the upper limits of the titration. Most of our batches are optimal at a final concentration of around 1 : 500. This is of course dependent upon the titer of antibody. Suboptimal concentrations give lower numbers of plaques and the plaques are generally diffuse and difficult to score.

(1) Wash SRC which have been stored for at least 1–2 weeks in Alsever's solution four times with HT-PBS by centrifugation at 800 g for 10 min, taking care to remove the buffy coat between washes. (2) Resuspend SRC to 10% (v/v) in HT-PBS. (3) Add the predetermined optimal quality of haptenated (Fab')$_2$ to the SRC suspension and mix well. (4) Hold at 37° in a water bath for 30 min and mix gently each 10 min. (5) Wash three times with HT-PBS and resuspend to 20% (v/v) after the final wash. (6) Store at 4° for up to 2 weeks prior to use. Hapten-coupled SRC must be washed three times in PBS just prior to use.

Each batch of SRC should be tested prior to use for plaque development. We routinely test all new batches against the previous batch for plaque number and plaque quality, using spleen cells from immunized mice as a source of AFC (see "Procedure for Optimization of Reagents for Plaque Assay").

Complement

We use fresh guinea pig serum as a source of complement (Commonwealth Serum Laboratories, Australia) and absorb large quantities at a time. Frozen guinea pig serum or lyophilized guinea pig serum can be used, although we have found the titer to be somewhat lower than fresh serum. Rarely, some batches have been found to be lytic despite absorption with SRC prior to use and such batches are discarded.

(1) Wash SRC five times with HT-PBS by centrifugation (10,000 g for 10 min), taking special care to remove the buffy coat by aspiration through a Pasteur pipet after each wash. Keep SRC at 4° throughout. (2) Resuspend packed SRC to 30% (v/v) in guinea pig serum after the last wash. Mix gently to avoid frothing and leave on ice for 30 min. (3) Centrifuge at 10,000 g for 10 min, retain supernatant (complement) and add fresh packed SRC to 30% (v/v) as before. Mix gently and leave on ice for 30 min. (4) Centrifuge, retain and pool supernatants, then aliquot in small volumes (0.5–1.0 ml), and store at −70° until use. Complement should be thawed only once and then discarded, as it loses activity on freezing and thawing. Each batch of complement should be titrated to find its optimal concentration in the assay system. Most of the batches that we prepare are used at a final concentration of 10–15% (v/v) when used for the revelation of directly hemolytic IgM anti-hapten AFC clones and at 2–3% (v/v) for the revelation of all immunoglobulin secreting clones in the protein A reverse plaque assay (procedure is outlined below).

Procedure for Assay for Anti-Hapten AFC Clones

All manipulations except the final incubation step are performed at room temperature. All reagents should also be at room temperature when used to avoid the formation of tiny gas bubbles during the final incubation step. The procedure is shown diagrammatically in Fig. 1.

Plaque revelation mix: 0.4 ml 20% haptenated SRC, 1.0 ml SRC-absorbed complement. (Complement is added at the predetermined optimal concentration.) HEM or BSS added to give a final volume of 10 ml. The plaque revelation mix should be used within 30 min of making and should be well mixed immediately prior to dispensing into the wells to ensure an even distribution of SRC.

(1) Remove supernatant from culture wells by a single sharp flick on inverting the tray. (2) Immediately blot the upper surface of the tray and replace the medium with 0.05 ml of plaque revelation mix using either a multichannel pipettor or a 96-well replicator. Care should be taken to avoid the formation of bubbles as their presence can give rise to difficulty

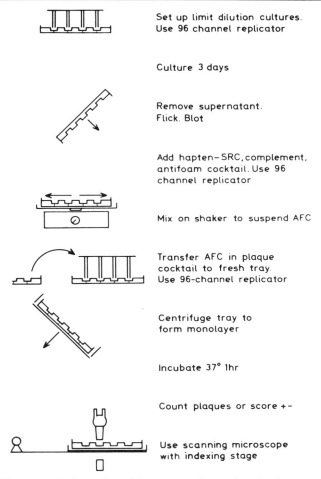

Set up limit dilution cultures.
Use 96 channel replicator

Culture 3 days

Remove supernatant.
Flick. Blot

Add hapten–SRC,complement,
antifoam cocktail.Use 96
channel replicator

Mix on shaker to suspend AFC

Transfer AFC in plaque
cocktail to fresh tray.
Use 96-channel replicator

Centrifuge tray to
form monolayer

Incubate 37° 1hr

Count plaques or score +–

Use scanning microscope
with indexing stage

FIG. 1. Diagrammatic illustration of the automated procedure for the assay of microcultures for AFC clones. Taken from Pike et al.[4]

in scoring plaques. Bubbles can be easily scored as plaques by the untrained observer. The addition of anti-foam reagent to the plaque revelation mix (1 drop of 0.5% Sigma Anti-foam Emulsion to 10 ml of mix), although not essential, can alleviate bubble formation. (3) Mix contents of wells thoroughly using a mechanical plate shaker and then transfer to a new tray using either a multichannel pipettor or 96-well replicator. After transfer, shake plates on mechanical shaker to ensure even dispersion of cells in the wells. Tips of multichannel pipettor or 96-well replicator should be rinsed between transfers to ensure that no carryover of PFC occurs between wells. (4) Centrifuge trays at 400 g for 5 min with a minimum of delay. The centrifuge should be used without the brake activated to ensure minimal disruption to the SRC layer at the bottom of the well. (5) Remove plates from centrifuge and leave in a horizontal position at 37° for 1–1.5 hr for the development of the directly hemolytic IgM antihapten plates. Particular care should be taken when handling the trays after this centrifugation step to ensure that the SRC layer is not disrupted. (6) Score wells as positive or negative using a dissecting microscope at 10× magnification. The number of PFC per well can be enumerated if desired. Scoring becomes inaccurate when more than 40–60 PFC are present in a well. A scanning stage[13] can be most useful in locating positive wells.

Further Comments

Most of the critical factors which influence the successful reproducibility of this assay are outlined in the procedure above. Others are as follows: (1) The total volume of liquid in the wells for plaque revelation should not exceed 0.05 ml. Larger volumes result in impairment of optical visualization of the AFC in the readout stage. (2) The number of target SRC added should be adjusted so that there is a monolayer at the bottom of the well at the end of the incubation stage. Too many SRC can result in small plaques, too few in the inability to discriminate plaques. (3) It is essential that care be taken to ensure that the SRC are evenly distributed on the bottom of the well. Mechanical disruption and bubble formation can make scoring difficult and may result in false positives. (4) As with all assay procedures, care with standardization and optimization of reagents is an important factor in the reproducibility and reliability of the assay. (5) Any free polystyrene pieces in the wells of the assay plates should be removed by firmly tapping the empty plate (inverted) prior to use. These can prevent the formation of an even SRC layer and give rise to plaque-like entities.

Detection of AFC Clones Using the Protein A Reverse Plaque Assay

Immunoglobulin-secreting clones (ISC), that is, clones which are secreting immunoglobulin per se, regardless of specificity, are detectable using the protein A reverse plaque assay of Gronowicz *et al.*[5] This method

---

[13] W. Darling, O. Justin, and K. Shortman, *J. Immunol. Methods* **51,** 38 (1982).

uses protein A-coated SRC (PA-SRC) as target cells and a developing anti-murine immunoglobulin antibody (anti-Ig) is included in the plaque revelation mixture. The anti-Ig antibody should be of the IgG class, as the method depends on it binding to the protein A by its Fc portion. In the majority of cases a polyvalent anti-Ig serum is used, although the use of immunoglobulin class-specific antibody allows the class of secreted antibody to be determined.[6] Immunoglobulin secreted by the AFC is then bound by the anti-Ig antibody (its antigen) and on addition of complement, lysis of the SRC is effected. A major application of this method has been to assess activation of AFC precursors into AFC clone formation using polyclonal B-cell activators rather than antigen as the stimulus.

Materials. As above for the anti-hapten plaques.

Reagents

HEM or BSS for washing and transfer of microcultures (as before) 0.15 *M* NaCl solution (normal saline, NS)

Phosphate-buffered saline, MT-PBS, and HT-PBS (as before)

Washed SRC as a 50% solution in NS. SRC used should have been stored for at least 2 weeks in Alsever's solution prior to use. SRC are washed five times in NS, with special care taken to remove the buffy coat after each centrifugation step.

SRC-absorbed complement (as before)

Rabbit anti-murine immunoglobulin antibody. This can be a commercial preparation. We prepare our own by subcutaneous administration of 1 mg of protein A–Sepharose purified (for method see above) murine antibody from ascites fluid, emulsified in 1 ml of complete Freund's adjuvant to a rabbit. Boost rabbit at 2-week intervals with 1 mg of antibody in incomplete Freund's adjuvant about three to five times, and then bleed 10 days after final boost. Collect serum and store in aliquots at −70°. Titrate antibody in the protein A reverse plaque assay, using spleen cells from immunized mice as a source of ISC (see below). Most of our batches are optimal at a final concentration of 1 : 200 in the assay mix.

Lyophilized staphylococcal protein A (Pharmacia, Uppsala, Sweden) reconstituted to 1 mg/ml in 0.15 *M* NaCl (NS). The solution is stored in 0.3-ml aliquots at −20° until use.

Chromic chloride solution: a 0.1% $CrCl_3$ solution prepared as described by Parish and Hayward.[14] Dissolve 100 mg of $CrCl_3 \cdot 6H_2O$ (B.D.H. Chemicals, Poole, England) in 100 ml of NS and adjust to pH 5 by the

[14] C. R. Parish and J. A. Hayward, *Proc. R. Soc. London, Ser. B* **187,** 47 (1974).

addition of 1 M NaOH. Age solution by storage at room temperature protected from light for at least 6 months before use. Adjust to pH 5 at weekly intervals for the first month. Titrate solution to determine the optimal concentration for coupling the protein A to the SRC. This is done by preparing batches of protein A-coupled SRC and testing. The optimal concentration for most of our batches has varied between a 1 : 40 to a 1 : 80 dilution of the 0.1% solution.[15]

Preparation of Protein A-Coupled SRC (PA-SRC)

Protein A is coupled to the surface of the erythrocyte by the use of chromic chloride as a coupling agent.[15–17] It is important that there is no contamination of any of the reagents with phosphate ions as these inactivate the coupling reaction. (1) Add 0.3 ml of protein A solution (0.3 mg) to 1 ml of 50% (v/v) washed SRC in NS and mix well. (2) Add 1.4 ml of 0.1% $CrCl_3$ solution (diluted to the predetermined optimal concentration in NS) in a dropwise fashion with continuous gentle shaking. This is best achieved by continuous, gentle vortexing of the tube during the procedure. (3) Allow to stand at room temperature for 15 min. (4) Wash SRC in 10 ml of NS by centrifugation at 800 g. (5) Wash twice more with HT-PBS and reconstitute to 20% (v/v). Some hemolysis is generally observed in these washing steps. This indicates that efficient coupling has occurred. (6) Store at 4° until use. Wash cells in HT-PBS just prior to use and reconstitute to 20% (v/v). PA-SRC can be stored for up to 1 week prior to use. This storage time varies with each batch.

Procedure for Assay for ISC Clones

The procedure for the assay for ISC clones is essentially as described above for anti-hapten AFC clones with the exception that extra washing steps are essential to remove antibody that has accumulated in the supernatant fluid during the culture period. In this assay, accumulated antibody can effect a general lysis of the PA-SRC lawn and thus prevent discrimination of plaques.

Plaque revelation mix: 0.4 ml 20% PA-SRC, 0.2 ml SRC-absorbed complement, the developing antisera, and HEM added to give final volume of 10 ml. The volume of SRC-absorbed complement is determined by titration for each batch of complement; we have generally found most batches to be optimal at 2–3% (v/v). The developing antisera is a rabbit

[15] G. F. Burns and B. L. Pike, *J. Immunol. Methods* **41,** 269 (1981).
[16] E. R. Gold and H. H. Fudenberg, *J. Immunol.* **99,** 859 (1967).
[17] J. W. Goding, *J. Immunol. Methods* **10,** 61 (1976).

anti-murine immunoglobulin antibody to be used at the optimal concentration as determined by prior titration.

The plaque revelation mix should be dispensed into the wells immediately after preparation to avoid agglutination before centrifugation in the wells to form the SRC layer at the bottom of the well. This is crucial to the success of this plaque method as performed in microtrays. Agglutination of the PA-SRC layer can make discrimination of AFC extremely difficult.

(1) After flicking tray to remove culture supernatant, add BSS or HEM to the wells for transfer to assay tray. A volume of either 0.05 or 0.20 ml may be used, as the next procedure is to wash the cells twice by centrifugation in 0.20 ml of medium. (2) Replace medium with 0.05 ml of freshly made plaque revelation mix after the second wash, mix contents of wells using mechanical shaker, and centrifuge at 400 g for 5 min without delay. (3) Leave trays at 37° for 4–5 hr to allow plaque development. (4) Score wells as positive or negative as described above for anti-hapten plaques.

Further Comments

Comments listed above for the assay for anti-hapten AFC clones apply to this assay procedure as well. The protein A reverse plaque assay is technically more difficult than that used for detection of directly hemolytic IgM anti-hapten AFC clones. However, with careful attention to determination of optimal concentration of reagents and with heed to the technical points outlined above which contribute to the successful reproducibility of this assay procedure, the method works well.

Procedure for Optimization of Reagents for Plaque Assay

The assay procedure is essentially as described above with the exception that spleen cells from immunized mice are used as a source of AFC, and the variation of the reagents is in the plaque revelation mix.

(1) Make plaque revelation mixtures as required. For example, the haptenated SRC or the complement dilution may be varied in the anti-hapten AFC assay or the complement dilution and/or the anti-Ig sera dilution in the protein A reverse plaque assay. (2) Dilute spleen cell suspension so that 0.025 ml contains about 30–50 AFC in optimized assay. (3) Dispense the required number of 0.025-ml replicates of AFC containing spleen cell suspension into the assay plate. We generally do four replicates per group. (4) Add the plaque revelation mix to the respective wells. (5) Mix the contents of the wells on the plate shaker, centrifuge at 400 g, and leave at 37° as described above. (6) Score wells for plaque number. Assess quality of plaques with respect to size and clarity. Assess quality of SRC layer, with particular note being taken of nonspecific lysis.

Acknowledgments

This work was supported by the National Health and Medical Research Council, Canberra, Australia; by Grant Number AI-03958 from the National Institute of Allergy and Infectious Diseases, U.S. Public Health Service; and by the generosity of a number of private donors to The Walter and Eliza Hall Institute of Medical Research.

[32] Production of Monoclonal Antibodies by Agarose-Entrapped Hybridoma Cells

By K. NILSSON, W. SCHEIRER, H. W. D. KATINGER, and K. MOSBACH

Mouse ascites culture is currently the most commonly used system for generation of monoclonal antibodies because it gives a much better yield than *in vitro* cultivation of hybridoma cells. However, this *in vivo* production is limited when scaling up, by the need for large numbers of animals. The contamination of ascites preparations by proteins of the host animal is another disadvantage, and in addition, human hybrids cannot be grown in ascites at all. On the other hand, the *in vitro* cultivation of hybridoma cell lines gives low antibody concentrations, only 1–10% of the levels normally reached in ascites fluid, and only a few cell lines have been grown in large scale. The reason for these disappointing results may be the extreme fragility of hybrid cells and/or the inadequate supply of nutrients and oxygen. It is likely, though, that large-scale operations using both suspension cultures as well as hollow-fiber microcarriers or ceramic systems will increase in importance.

We have tried an alternate scheme to overcome some of the problems mentioned above by entrapment of cells in a matrix such as agarose. The matrix protects the cells from mechanical stress, and makes the preparations suitable for continuous operation in that the produced antibodies are excreted into the medium, thereby eliminating the need for separation of product from the cells.

Preparation of Extracted Paraffin Oil

Paraffin oil[1] (100 ml) is extracted four times with PBS[2] (100 ml) in a separating funnel (500 ml). After the final extraction the mixture is al-

[1] Merck No. 7162 or BDH No. 29436.

[2] K. Nilsson, W. Scheirer, O. W. Merten, L. Östberg, E. Liehl, H. W. D. Katinger, and K. Mosbach, *Nature (London)* **302,** 629 (1983).

lowed to stand for 30 min to allow complete phase separation. The collected paraffin oil is either sterilized by heating for 2 hr at 160°, or autoclaved in closed bottles at 120° for 30 min.

Each lot of paraffin oil should be tested for toxicity. This may be done, for instance, by comparing the growth curves of the cell line of interest in the presence or absence of paraffin oil (5%, v/v). If the extraction procedure does not remove all traces of toxic compounds paraffin oil from different manufacturers should be tested.

Agarose Preparation

Two types of agarose are suitable for the entrapment of animal cells. Sigma type VII and FMC Sea Plaque both have a dynamic gelling temperature of 28°, and Sigma type I or FMC SeaKem LE have dynamic gelling temperatures of 36°. As the dynamic gelling temperatures are determined when a solution is cooled at fixed rate, and are about 10° lower than the static gelling temperatures, one has to thermostat the different agarose solutions to about 37 and 45°, respectively. The lower gelling temperature is obtained through a chemical modification of the agarose, which makes the polymer less porous and decreases its mechanical strength.

Procedure. The required amount of agarose is mixed with PBS and autoclaved (it is not necessary to dissolve the polymer before steriliza-

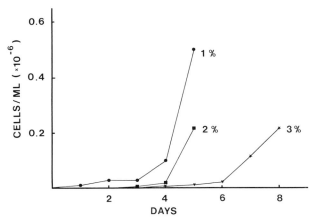

FIG. 1. Influence of agarose concentration on cell growth. Hybridoma cells (mouse–mouse against ovalbumin) were entrapped in agarose (Sigma type VII) of different concentrations at a cell concentration of 1.0 million cells/ml beads. Beads with entrapped cells (10 ml) were cultivated in a 50-ml spinner bottle with 50 ml medium, and 50% of the medium was replaced on days 3, 5, and 7. The number of free cells in the medium were counted in a Burker chamber each day. (●) 1%; (■) 2%; (★) 3% (w/v) agarose.

tion). After sterilization it can be stored at room temperature. Before use it is remelted by heating to 70° and thermostatted to either 37 or 45°, depending on the type being used.

Notes: The concentration of agarose is dependent on the type and the desired mechanical strength of the beads. For low temperature gelling agarose a final strength of at least 1% (w/v) should be used. The polymeric network will have an influence on cell growth, and therefore at higher agarose concentrations growth will be more restricted (Fig. 1). High temperature gelling agarose at 0.5% (w/v) will provide enough mechanical stability for small-scale culture. The most convenient way to immobilize cells is to prepare the agarose solution at twice the final concentration and mix it with an equal volume of suspended cells. Due to the viscosity of agarose solutions at high concentrations this is not practical for concentrations higher than 5% (low gelling temperature) or 4% (high gelling temperature). However, as the agarose solution is made up in PBS, it is possible to centrifuge down the required amount of cells and redisperse them directly into the agarose solution.

Entrapment in Agarose Beads[2,3]

General Procedure. The preparation of agarose beads from high or low gelling temperature agarose differs only in the mixing step: for low gelling temperature agarose, the paraffin oil, agarose solution, and cell suspension are all thermostatted to 37°, whereas for high gelling temperature agarose, the paraffin oil and cell suspension are thermostatted to 37° and the agarose solution is thermostatted to 45°.

After mixing the cell suspension and agarose, the mixture is dispersed in the paraffin oil and, when the desired bead size is reached, the dispersion is cooled to at least 10° below the gelling temperature. Medium[4] is added, and after sedimentation of the beads the oil phase and most of the washing medium are aspirated. The beads are further washed with medium until they are essentially free from oil.

Small-Scale Procedure. The cell suspension (5 ml) is mixed with agarose (5 ml, 2% w/v) and poured into a beaker (100 ml) containing paraffin oil (20 ml). The mixture is dispersed with a magnetic stirrer, and when the desired bead size is obtained (100–300 μm), the beaker is cooled in an ice bath. After solidification, medium is added (30 ml) and the beads are allowed to sediment into the medium. They are further washed with several portions of medium until essentially free from oil.

---

[3] All experiments described in this chapter were carried out with low temperature gelling agarose (Sigma type VII).

[4] The culture medium for entrapped cells is the same as in the normal cultivation.

Notes. (1) The whole procedure is carried out in a sterile hood. (2) Sedimentation of the beads can be speeded up by gentle centrifugation. (3) In the washing steps media can be replaced by PBS.

Medium-Size Procedure. The cell suspension (50 ml) is mixed with agarose (50 ml, 2% w/v) and poured into a round-bottomed glass centrifuge tube (250 ml) containing paraffin oil (100 ml). The liquids are emulsified at room temperature, with a Vibromixer E1 fitted with a vibrator plate (P1, 54 mm diameter), to the desired bead size. The mixing vessel is cooled in an ice bath for 5 min and 50 ml growth medium is added. After 10 min at room temperature the tube is centrifuged at 1200 g for 10 min. The oil phase is removed by suction and approximately 100 ml growth medium is added. After mixing with the vibrator plate, the suspension is centrifuged again and the remaining oil removed.

Note: If volumes larger than 100 ml of beads are needed the process may be repeated several times. The method is convenient for batches of beads up to 1000 ml, but if larger volumes are needed the method must be modified, either by using larger mixing vessels, or by making the dispersion directly in a reactor equipped with a stirring device, and thereby carrying out the whole procedure in the cultivating vessel.

Cell Concentration

With the entrapment method one has the possibility to obtain a wide variety of cell concentrations. There are actually two types of cell concentration that have to be considered: (1) the total cell concentration, i.e., the total number of cells divided by the total volume used, and (2) the concentration of cells per volume of beads. As the usual amount of beads is 10% (v/v), the cell concentration inside the beads will be 10 times higher than the total cell concentration. Entrapped cells will experience those small molecules provided by the medium at a concentration equal to the total cell concentration; however, molecules produced by the cells themselves will accumulate inside the beads and the cells will experience them at substantially higher concentrations than those seen in the medium. This may be advantageous if the cells produce a stimulator; but, if an inhibitory substance is produced by the cells, entrapment will have a negative influence on performance. This effect can be counteracted by increased mixing in the cultivating vessel and/or a more frequent exchange of media, thereby making the concentration gradient for the substance steeper.

The method described here makes it possible to entrap cells at a low concentration and after a growth phase reach a high cell density, this will reduce the amount of cells needed for the inoculum. On the other hand it is also possible to entrap cells at an extremely high density and obtain a

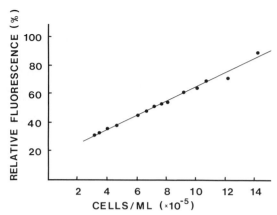

FIG. 2. Correlation between concentration of free cells (mouse–mouse hybridoma) and relative fluorescence after staining with mithramycin.

high catalytic activity per reactor volume. Cells have been entrapped in agarose at concentrations between 0.1 and 20 million cells/ml beads. As the entrapped cells have the same nutritional demands as free cells, one has to consider the extreme cell densities which can be reached when supplying medium and oxygen.

Monitoring of Cell Growth

Direct microscopic observation for monitoring of cell growth is impossible due to the high concentration of cells inside the beads. Attempts to free the cells from the beads result in partial destruction. Indirect measurement of cell concentrations must therefore be applied. A suitable method is to determine the amount of DNA and correlate it to cell concentration. This is conveniently done with the antibiotic mithramycin, which binds to double-stranded DNA and fluoresces in direct proportion to the DNA present.[5]

Procedure. A 4-ml sample of suspended beads is centrifuged, and after decanting of the supernatant, 4 ml mithramycin solution is added (2.5 mg mithramycin in 250 ml PBS containing 15 mM MgCl$_2$). The sample is cooled in an ice bath and sonicated (70 W, microtip) for 30 sec to ensure destruction of the beads. The fluorescence is then measured directly (excitation wavelength 450 nm, emission wavelength 550 nm).[6]

[5] B. T. Hill and S. Whatley, *FEBS Lett.* **56**, 20 (1975).
[6] G. Himmler, G. Palfi, H. W. D. Katinger, and W. Scheirer, *Dev. Biol. Stand.* **60**, 291 (1985).

Calibration is performed by estimation by the same method of a suspension of free cells of known concentration. In this way a calibration curve is obtained (see Fig. 2). Residues of phenol red in the tissue culture media and polymeric material do not interfere. The useful range of the estimation is between 0.05 to 2 million cells/ml. The linear regression coefficient has been found to be 0.98.

Reactor Design

For small-scale preparations (up to 50 ml of beads in 500 ml of medium), it is usually not necessary to provide an external source of oxygen. The most convenient way to cultivate these entrapped cells is by using spinner flasks or roller bottles (see table), in which the pH is controlled

PRODUCTION OF MONOCLONAL ANTIBODIES BY
AGAROSE-ENTRAPPED CELLS

Day	IgG[a] (reciprocal dilution)	IgM[b] (μg/ml)
1	256	7.4
2	512	6.0
3	256	6.3
4	512	6.0
5	512	6.7
6	n.d.[c]	6.7
7	256	6.7

[a] Monoclonal antibody (IgG) against herpes simplex type 2 glycoprotein was produced by a mouse–mouse hybridoma (LSP 21), which was entrapped in 2.5% (w/v) agarose at a concentration of 6.2 million cells/ml beads. Beads with entrapped cells (20 ml) were cultivated in 100 ml medium in a 250-ml spinner bottle, and 50% of the medium was replaced daily. Figures show IgG concentration in the harvested medium.

[b] Monoclonal antibody (IgM) against human urokinase was produced by a mouse–mouse hybridoma (2T2 E8) which was entrapped in 1.0% (w/v) agarose at a cell concentration of 5.6 million cells/ml beads. Beads with entrapped cells (120 ml) were cultivated in a roller bottle with 400 ml medium. The medium was replaced daily. Figures show IgM concentration in the harvested medium.

[c] n.d., Not determined.

with a mixture of 5% CO_2 and 95% air. Medium can easily be perfused by equipping the outlet tube with a sintered-glass filter. For a larger scale the most convenient reactor is the draft tube fermenter (Fig. 3), in which the beads are circulated by an axial marine-type impeller. Oxygenation is performed by direct titration with pure oxygen by gentle sparging. In addition, surface aeration can supply some oxygen and remove metabolic

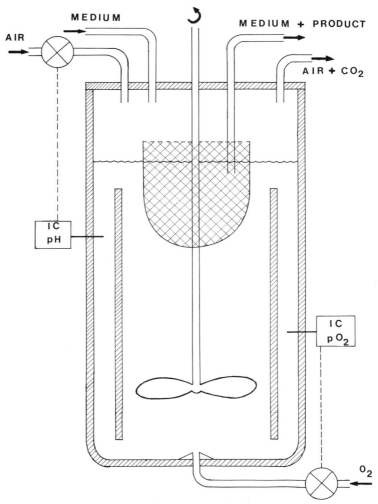

FIG. 3. Draft tube fermenter fitted with rotating basket for continuous perfusion with medium. Control circuits for oxygen and pH are shown.

CO_2 from the suspension to keep the pH in an appropriate range. Perfusion is performed by fitting a basket of stainless-steel mesh to the impeller shaft, thus making it possible to remove the medium from the inside of this basket without removing the beads.

Growth Control

If the cells are entrapped in low concentrations of agarose, the cell growth will be almost unaffected, and therefore, after a few days a large number of free cells will appear in the medium. To avoid problems associated with free cells (need for centrifugation, clogging of filters, etc.), it is thus necessary to control the cell growth inside the beads. This can be done in several ways: (1) Use of higher concentrations of agarose, as seen in Fig. 1. The cell growth can be slowed considerably by using a final agarose concentration of 3% (w/v). (2) Reduction of the temperature. As seen in Fig. 4, cell growth is reduced if the culturing temperature is

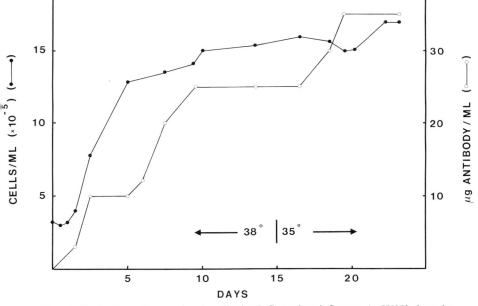

FIG. 4. Production of monoclonal antibody (IgG) against influenza A, H3N2, by a human–mouse hybridoma. Cells were entrapped in 1.0% (w/v) agarose at a concentration of 3.3 million cells/ml beads. One liter of beads was cultivated in 10 liters of medium in a draft tube fermenter (shown in Fig. 3). Perfusion rate was 3.6 liters/day. At day 15 the cultivation temperature was lowered from 38 to 35°. (●) Cell concentration per total volume (determined by mithramycin staining); (○) μg human IgG/ml.

decreased from 38 to 35°. In this case the reduction in temperature also results in increased product formation. The optimal temperature has to be determined for each cell line. The goal is to find a temperature at which the reduction in cell number (caused, for instance, by proteolytic enzymes) is balanced by net growth. This will provide a production of antibodies at a constant high level. (3) Reduction of the fetal calf serum concentration. Cell growth is also retarded if the concentration is decreased from the normally used 5 or 10% to 0.5 or 1%. This obviously may make product purification easier.

Conclusions

We have presented here methods for the entrapment of animal cells in beaded polymers which easily can be carried out in a normal laboratory without specialized equipment. These agarose-entrapped cells have been used for production of monoclonal antibodies (see table and Fig. 4). The method has been used both on a small scale (50 ml reactor volume) and on a large scale (10 liters reactor volume).

The use of this method is of course not limited to hybridoma cells. Other cell lines which have been entrapped are Chinese hamster ovary cells (genetically modified to produce human interferon) and lymphoblastoid cells (producing interleukin 2). Experimental details, as well as entrapment matrices for anchorage-dependent cells, will be described in a forthcoming volume of this series.[7]

[7] K. Nilsson, W. Scheirer, H. W. D. Katinger, and K. Mosbach, this series, in press.

[33] Automated Production of Monoclonal Antibodies in a Cytostat

By S. FAZEKAS DE ST.GROTH

A conventional tissue culture flask of 75-cm^2 growth area will support, at most, 4×10^7 hybridoma cells and may thus maximally yield around 1 mg of monoclonal antibody. Average, practical yields are about an order of magnitude lower. By using larger bottles, hollow-fiber systems, or suspension cultures with or without microcarrier beads, the number of cells per culture unit can be increased up to 10-fold, thus considerably reducing the labor per unit. But each of these systems is self-terminating as the cells will eventually multiply beyond their concentration limit, degenerate, and die.

Cytostatic culture overcomes this problem by skimming off extra growth, and collecting the cells and their products in the same operation. The process can be fully automated and kept running for indefinite periods. Cytostats of 500- to 1000-ml capacity will yield the equivalent of 50–100 tissue culture bottles each day. Production at levels higher than that cannot be achieved by simply scaling up the apparatus to be described: suspension, gas exchange, prevention of foaming, etc., present difficulties as yet unsolved, even at the pilot scale.

Principles

A cytostat maintains cells in exponential growth at a fixed concentration and in a fixed volume.[1] The constancy of concentration is achieved by exactly matching the growth of the cells by the input of fresh medium, while the volume is fixed by an overflow arrangement.

Exponential growth depends only on the specific doubling time (τ) of the cells, whose concentration changes at the rate $dc/dt = kc$, where the rate constant $k = \ln 2/\tau$.

The basic cytostatic equation is thus

$$dc/dt = kc - (m/v)c = 0 \tag{1}$$

where v is the volume of the culture, and m, the medium input per unit time. The value of m defines, of course, also the rate of overflow.

If a fraction, $1 - \alpha$, of the cells dies per unit time (or, what is formally equivalent, fails to divide), we have

$$dc^+/dt = \alpha k c^+ - (m^+/v)c^+ = 0 \tag{2}$$

for live cells (symbolized by c^+) and, by adjusting the flow of medium to $m^+ = \alpha k v$, the concentration of live cells will remain constant.

Dead cells will accumulate at the rate of

$$dc^-/dt = (1 - \alpha)kc^+ - (m^+/v)c^- \tag{3}$$

and will also reach a fixed concentration, as seen by integrating Eq. (3):

$$c_t^- = c_0^- e^{-\alpha kt} + (1 - e^{-\alpha kt}) \frac{1 - \alpha}{\alpha} c^+ \xrightarrow[t \to \infty]{} \frac{1 - \alpha}{\alpha} c^+ \tag{4}$$

[1] J. Monod, *Ann. Inst. Pasteur (Paris)* **79**, 390 (1950).

The exponential factor $\exp(-\alpha kt) = \exp[-(\ln 2)t/\tau]$ in terms of the doubling time, and rapidly approaches zero as $(1/2)^{t/\tau}$ becomes negligible after three to four divisions.

At an arbitrary rate of input, m, of fresh medium the concentration of live cells will change from c_0^+ to c_t^+ over the interval t, as given by the solution of Eq. (2):

$$\ln(c_t^+/c_0^+) = (\alpha k - m/v)t \tag{5}$$

The concentration of cells is stabilized (i.e., $c_0^+ = c_t^+$) at the input of m^+ ml medium/min, and Eq. (5) becomes

$$\ln 1 = 0 = (\alpha k - m^+/v)t$$

and hence

$$\alpha k = m^+/v \tag{5a}$$

Substituting into Eq. (5) we have

$$\ln(c_t^+/c_0^+) = (m^+/v - m/v)t$$

and after rearranging

$$m^+ = m + (v/t)\ln(c_t^+/c_0^+) \tag{6}$$

Thus by determining the concentration of live cells, say, 24 hr apart, the correct cytostatic input m^+ can be defined. The doubling time, obtained by substituting in Eq. (5a), is

$$\tau = v(\ln 2)/m^+ \tag{7}$$

The yield (overflow) of the cytostat over an interval t is

$$y = m^+c^+t \tag{8}$$

live cells and their product, together with $y(1 - \alpha)/\alpha$ dead cells. During a single doubling time, the yield is

$$y_{(\tau)} = m^+c^+\tau = m^+c^+\,\frac{v\ln 2}{m^+} = 0.693\,vc^+ \tag{8a}$$

or somewhat more than two-thirds of the contents of the cytostat.

Apparatus

Figure 1, reproduced from the original publication,[2] is a schematic drawing of the cytostat; it has since gone through some minor improvements over its 5 years of use.

[2] S. Fazekas de St.Groth, *J. Immunol. Methods* **57,** 121 (1983).

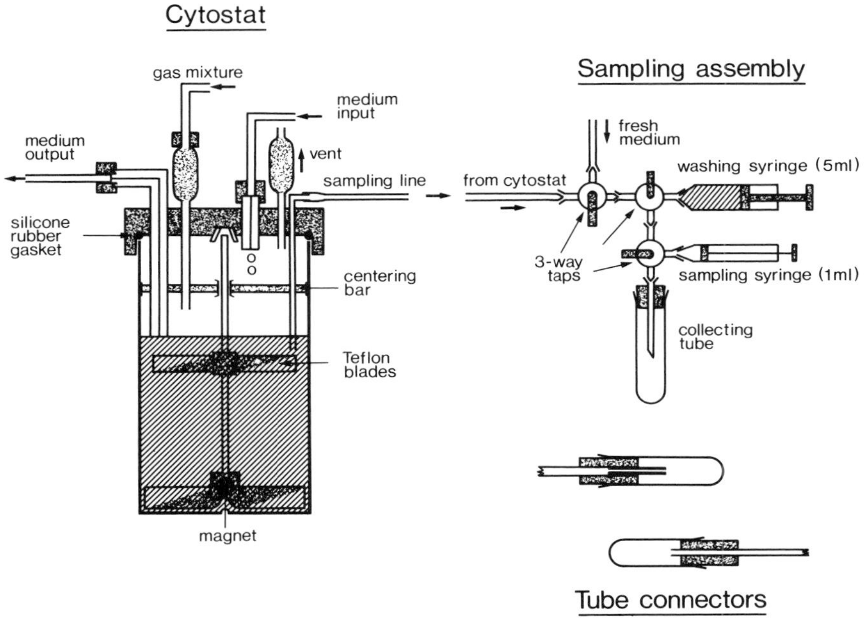

FIG. 1. Diagram of cytostat and accessories. (From Fazekas de St.Groth.[2])

The *culture vessel* is a borosilicate glass jar, 160 mm tall and of 80 mm internal diameter, with a 3-mm-high central nipple to serve as pivot for the stirring blades. The lid, made of stainless steel, is fitted with a silicone rubber ring matching the rim of the jar. It seals effectively by its own weight (600 g). Four ports, each 6.5 mm diameter, take the input and output tubes for medium and gas supply. They are fitted with silicone rubber rings and ring bolts to keep the tubes in place. Through a fifth hole, 2 mm diameter, a stainless-steel sampling tube may be inserted.

The Teflon *stirring blades* are mounted on a 6-mm-diameter glass rod. The lower blade (75 × 20 × 1.5 mm) carries a Teflon-coated magnet (60 × 6 mm) in its housing, and is set 1–2 mm above the bottom of the jar. The upper blade (75 × 10 × 1.5 mm), movable along the shaft, is set about 5 mm below the eventual fluid level, i.e., the orifice of the output tube. The upper and lower blades are arranged at right angles to each other, and each is made into a propeller by bending the two halves of the blade 15–20° to the vertical. Their action results in regular convection and uniform distribution of cells even at stirring rates as low as 10 rpm.

The *input and output tubes* are of borosilicate glass (6 mm o.d., 4 mm i.d.) with 30-mm horizontal arms above the lid, and vertical arms of 30 mm for the gas inlet and outlet tubes, 50 mm for the medium inlet tube, and 90 mm for the medium outlet tube. The latter can thus be inserted at various depths, setting the cytostatic volume between 400 and 750 ml. The horizontal arms of the gas inlet and outlet tubes are pinched and plugged with cotton wool.

The *sampling tube* (stainless steel, 1.8 mm o.d., 1.0 mm i.d.) has a 20-mm horizontal arm and a 100-mm vertical arm, and can be inserted to reach or clear the level of medium.

The *flexible connections* between the cytostat, pump, collection vessel, medium, and gas supply are silicone rubber tubes (3.0 mm o.d., 1.3 mm i.d.). Their ends are sleeved through a 25-mm piece of tubing (6 mm o.d., 3 mm i.d.), with a short stainless-steel tube (20 mm, 1.5 mm o.d.) inserted into one of the matching ends. The sleeves serve both as handles when joining a pair of tubes, and also hold the small protector tubes (45 mm, 6 mm o.d. test tubes) during sterilization and storage (see Fig. 1).

The *sampling device* is made up of three three-way taps and two syringes (see Fig. 1). This arrangement allows the sequence of (1) flushing the sampling tube by drawing about 2.5 ml medium into the 5-ml syringe; (2) taking and delivering about 0.5 ml through the 1-ml syringe; (3) emptying the large syringe and backflushing the sampling line with about 3 ml of fresh medium.

Pump and pump tubing. As the volume of the cultures is maintained through the overflow (output) tube and not by a fixed side arm, a two-channel peristaltic pump operates the cytostat. The input tube is of 1.0 mm internal and 3.0 mm outside diameter, while the output tube is of 1.5 mm i.d. and 3.5 mm o.d., both of silicone rubber. The tubes are color coded to prevent false connections. This arrangement will maintain a constant level at whatever speed the pump is set. Peristaltic pumps with clip-on modules have the great advantage that all sterile tube connections can be made safely, under a laminar flow hood. We are using Ismatec IP-4 pumps[3] which have the added advantage of an overriding maximum flow switch; i.e., the long feeding lines from the medium reservoir can be filled within seconds.

Stirring bank. Most magnetic stirrers used in the laboratory are designed to generate turbulence and cannot be set to the low speeds optimal for suspension cultures. Stirring banks promoted for suspension cultures can be set to low speeds, but have other disadvantages.[2] The magnetic stirrer built at the Institute's instrument shop is of 800 × 140 mm surface dimension, to accommodate six water-jacketed cytostats in a row. The linear arrangement is convenient as it allows connections of minimal

---

[3] Ismatec Labtechnic, Limmatstrasse 107/109, 8031 Zurich, Switzerland.

length, by placing a pump behind and a collecting vessel in front of each cytostat, such as could not be achieved on a conventional square grid. The height of the stirring bank is 200 mm; i.e., manifolds of required slope for delivery and return of thermostatted water can be permanently mounted on its rear face, together with the lines supplying the preheated, humidified gas mixture. The six magnets are belt driven, and isolated from the motor (1/60 HP, operating through an 80 : 1 gearbox) and the regulating device (a small variable transformer). The rotational speed of the magnets can be set between 10 and 120 rpm.[4]

Assembly. The cytostats are conveniently mounted on a trolley with a shelf size to accommodate the stirring bank (i.e., a number of cytostats in a row), with their individual pumps placed at a corresponding height behind them and a row of collecting bottles in front. (The trolley illustrated in Fig. 2 is 900 mm long and 500 mm deep.) The lower shelf will take a small refrigerator (capable of holding two 5000-ml conical flasks) and a circulating water bath (capable of maintaining 37° in the heating jackets). The upper shelf has to be screened from light—we use black curtains; otherwise the cells suffer and the medium deteriorates.[5-8]

Media

Saline: 80 g NaCl, 4.0 g KCl, 17.7 g $Na_2HPO_4 \cdot 2H_2O$, 6.9 g $NaH_2PO_4 \cdot H_2O$, 20 g glucose, 0.1 g phenol red, and H_2O to 1000 ml. This 10× stock can be stored at 4°. For use it is diluted 10-fold, the pH adjusted to 7.2, and the solution autoclaved at 115° for 15 min.

EDTA–saline: 10 ml of 10× saline stock, 0.035 g Na_2EDTA, and H_2O to 100 ml. Autoclave at 115° for 15 min.

R: RPMI 1640 (GIBCO 430-1800), to which is added before use 2% 0.1 *M* glutamine, 2% 0.1 *M* pyruvate, and 0.05% 0.1 *M* 2-mercaptoethanol.

I: 246 ml 2× DMEM (GIBCO 430-2100), 200 ml H_2O, 15 ml 1 *M* HEPES (pH 7.3), 30 ml 5% $NaHCO_3$, 12 ml 0.1 *M* glutamine, 12 ml 0.1 *M* pyruvate, 0.5 ml 0.028% Na_2SeO_3, and 0.3 ml 0.1 *M* 2-mercaptoethanol.

[4] The only commercially available cytostat I know of, Model CS-100 (Techne Inc., 3700 Brunswick Pike, Princeton, NJ 08540), has a more elegant solution for these problems. It makes use of the Thomson effect and keeps the cells in suspension by a floating stirrer, thus eliminating the need for a stirring bank altogether.

[5] R. J. Wang, J. D. Stoien, and F. Landa, *Nature (London)* **247**, 43 (1974).

[6] J. D. Stoien and R. J. Wang, *Proc. Natl. Acad. Sci. U.S.A.* **71**, 3961 (1974).

[7] R. J. Wang, *In Vitro* **12**, 19 (1976).

[8] R. J. Wang and B. T. Nixon, *In Vitro* **14**, 715 (1978).

Fig. 2. Working assembly of six cytostats. The top shelf of the trolley holds the pumps, the water-jacketed cytostats on the stirring bank, and the collection vessels. Left on the bottom shelf is the circulating water bath, with the humidifier in front of it. The refrigerator on the right holds two 5-liter containers of fresh medium.

N: newborn calf serum (GIBCO 021-6010); the percentage in the medium is indicated by a subscript.

A: 4.8 ml amino acid stock (0.9 g alanine, 0.78 g asparagine, 1.08 g aspartic acid, 1.44 g proline, 360 ml H_2O) + 0.05 ml vitamin stock (5 mg vitamin B_{12}, 5 mg biotin, 0.01 ml 1 M HCl, 20 ml H_2O) + 2.4 ml cystine stock (0.7 g cystine, 25 ml 1 M HCl, 75 ml H_2O) + 3.0 ml 20% bovine serum albumin (Armour) + 0.75 ml transferrin stock [2.25 g human transferrin (Sigma), 5 mg $FeCl_3 \cdot 6H_2O$, 50 ml 2× DMEM, 1.0 ml 1 M HEPES, 47 ml H_2O] + 5 ml lipid stock (0.24 g soybean lipids– Astec FLVP, 0.017 g cholesterol, 3.0 ml 20% bovine serum albumin, 50 ml 2× DMEM, 1.0 ml 1 M HEPES, 47 ml H_2O, sonically dispersed and passed through a Nalgene filter of 0.45-μm pore size).

Mixture A represents the additives required for Iscove's serum-free medium, symbolized by IA in contradistinction to IN_{10}, Iscove's medium with 10% newborn calf serum. The formulation differs somewhat from previous descriptions,[9-12] which differ among themselves.

Media to supply the cytostats are made up in 5000-ml lots and filtered directly into 5000-ml vacuum flasks, by passing them through Selas candles (Type FPS 126). The flasks are gassed with a mixture of 10% CO_2, 7% O_2, and 83% N_2, then fitted with the syphoning closure and stored at 4° in the dark. Of course, storage bottles of any shape or size may be used, but sterile filtration directly into the storage vessel eliminates an extra transfer and thus an extra chance of contamination.

Characteristics of Cytostatic Culture

The *growth rate* of most cell lines is somewhat slower in suspension cultures than in stationary cultures. Antibody-producing hybridomas are no exception (Fig. 3). Comparative tests on 10 hybridomas[2] gave an average of 15% increase in doubling time, but with a wide scatter. Since then we have had a few cell lines that multiplied only half as fast as in stationary culture.

The multiplication rate depends on several factors (medium, aeration, agitation, etc.) that can be optimized, but the overriding component is inherent in the cell line and has to be defined for each. This can be readily done over the period between starting up the cultures and reaching the cytostatic volume.

[9] L. J. Guilbert and N. N. Iscove, *Nature (London)* **363,** 594 (1976).
[10] N. N. Iscove and F. Melchers, *J. Exp. Med.* **147,** 923 (1978).
[11] N. N. Iscove, L. J. Guilbert, and C. Weyman, *Exp. Cell Res.* **126,** 121 (1980).
[12] M. H. Schreier and R. Tees, *in* "Immunological Methods" (I. Lefkovits and B. Pernis, eds.), Vol. 2, p. 263. Academic Press, New York, 1981.

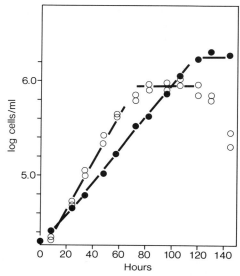

Fig. 3. Growth of a hybridoma in stationary (○) and suspension (●) culture. Cultures of the cell line N-527 were set up from a common stock of 2×10^4 cells/ml in RN_{10} and were sampled twice daily.

Limiting density is that concentration of cells at which exponential growth ceases. When this limit is passed, the number of dead cells keeps increasing and eventually the culture dies (see Fig. 3). As with growth rates, several factors influence the limiting density value, the most important being a cellular property. This property varies from cell line to cell line and is independent of the doubling time.

Unlike the growth rate, which is reduced in suspension cultures, the limiting density is invariably higher. Among the 83 different hybridomas we have grown in the cytostat there was not a single one that did not reach higher concentrations than in stationary culture, and some rose above their stationary density limit by a factor of 8. The average difference was 230% in favor of suspension cultures.

Definition of the density limit is the prime requisite for successful cytostatic runs, for two reasons: first, because exponential growth, i.e., staying below the density limit, is a sine qua non of the process and, second, because operating as close to the density limit as possible is the measure of efficiency. Density limits for each cell line have to be established, and that can be done during the first few days after initiating the cultures, by the simple rule of thumb to be given below.

Special Requirements. Parenchymal tissues or stable lines derived from them usually require special media and special treatment of the glassware to avoid attachment of the cells. We tested these (siliconized glassware, MEMS or Joklik's medium) but found them unnecessary; indeed, media of low Ca-ion content were even deleterious. Cell lines of myeloid origin, as are all hybridomas, apparently do not require special conditions for growth in suspension. In fact, only 2 out of the 83 lines we tested did not begin to grow immediately when transferred from stationary culture to the cytostat, and even those two were readily adapted after a lag of a day and slower replication over the next few days.

The only special requirement for cytostatic growth is the exclusion of light. As demonstrated by Wang and collaborators,[5–8] several components of tissue culture media are photosensitive and, especially in combination, generate toxic substances (mostly peroxides) on exposure to light. The range includes ultraviolet and most of the visible spectrum, so that the only sound solution is to keep the cultures in the dark.

Media. Since transfer to suspension culture presents no problems, any standard medium used in stationary cultures will also serve in the cytostat. But, with an eye on purifying and concentrating the yield, we prefer serum-free media. My personal experience covers only Iscove's medium and its simplified forms in some depth, but in cursory comparisons with other published formulations it proved to be equal to or better than most. It will be taken here as paradigmatic of serum-free media.

Of the 83 hybridoma lines grown in the cytostat 3 could not be adapted to grow in serum-free medium at all, and another 5 had very low density limits. Each of these lines multiplied satisfactorily and reached density limits above 10^6 cells/ml after adding 1% fetal or newborn calf serum to Iscove's medium. That, of course, is no longer serum-free medium, and it should be expected therefore that about 1 in 10 hybridomas require conventional tissue culture media, with perhaps reduced serum content, for cytostatic growth.

Aeration. Aeration has been tested in respect to both composition of the gas mixture and the rate of supply.[2] Mixtures of CO_2 (5–10%), O_2 (7–10%) in N_2 were equally satisfactory. It is essential to humidify the gas mixture as otherwise, at the rate of optimal supply, it will take up water within the cytostat and inspissate the medium. Prewarming is advisable, for the same reason.

The rate of supply, both for standard and serum-free media, was optimal at and above 10 cm^3/min for 500-ml cultures. We routinely set the gas flow between 20 and 30 cm^3/min, and use a mixture of 10% CO_2, 7% O_2, and 83% N_2, passed through a reducing and a metering valve. Such an arrangement, relying on surface exchange, is satisfactory for cytostatic volumes up to 1500 ml. Signs of inadequacy (increase in the fraction of dead cells) become apparent already at volumes of 2000 ml.

Stirring. Hybridomas, with specific gravities close to that of the medium, are easy to keep in suspension. In the apparatus described a rate of 10 rpm of the large stirring blades will achieve this. For uniform density and visible convection from top to bottom, about 20–30 rpm is needed, and this is the rate of stirring we use routinely. At higher rates, above 100 rpm (which are the minima for most laboratory magnetic stirrers), many hybridoma lines are damaged by the shearing forces. In the sample we tested (admittedly small) about a third of them showed reduced growth rate and accumulation of dead cells at stirring rates above 60 rpm.

Yield. By comparing the output of monoclonal antibodies under various experimental conditions, it was found that the yield depended only on the number of cells in culture.[2] This was an unexpected finding and therefore carefully checked in further tests, by influencing in various ways the growth rate and general well-being of the cells.

Cultures expand at lower rates and reach lower ceiling concentrations in the incomplete synthetic media (left panel of Fig. 4), but the yield of

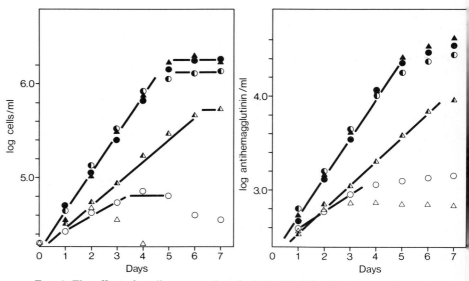

FIG. 4. The effect of media on growth and yield of N-527 cells in suspension culture. Cultures were set up at a cell density of 2×10^4/ml and sampled daily. The left panel shows the density of cells; the right panel the concentration of monoclonal antibodies, assayed as antihemagglutinin. Media: (●) RN_{10}; (▲) IN_{10}; (◐) IA; (△) IA minus nonessential amino acids and vitamins; (○) IA minus lipids; (△) IA minus transferrin.

monoclonal antibodies per cell remains constant even under quite inadequate conditions (right panel of Fig. 4). The constancy of output was proved for seven cell lines tested in depth, and we found no obvious exception to it among all the other hybridomas grown to date.

The strict correlation between cell number and yield points up the irrelevance of doubling time and the importance of the density limit for cytostatic production of monoclonal antibodies. If cells can be maintained in exponential growth at high concentrations, the yield will also be high, irrespective of whether the cells are growing fast or not. In fact, a slower rate of growth at a given cell density is entirely advantageous as it leads to the same quantity of antibody recovered in a smaller volume, i.e., more cheaply and with less bulk for the subsequent isolation of the antibodies.

Yields of particular lines vary over a 100-fold or more. Our highest producing hybridoma, with an output of 8000 antibody molecules/sec, yields 100 mg monoclonal antibody per day in a 500-ml cytostat. Many others barely reach the 1 mg/day level. The average yield, with cells secreting about 1000 molecules/sec, is 10–20 mg antibody/day. There is no proven method of increasing the rate of antibody production characteristic of a hybridoma line, despite numerous attempts.

Permanence. Our standard cytostatic runs aimed at producing monoclonal antibodies equivalent to 1000 ml of hyperimmune serum, i.e., about 100 mg of immunoglobulin. The average hybridoma produces this amount in a week after reaching the cytostatic level, or in about 10 days after setting up the run. But there is a wide scatter among hybridomas. The extreme example we had was a line with a doubling time of 52 hr in serum-free medium and a secretion rate of 75 antibody molecules/sec. It took 2 weeks to reach the overflow level and then another 4 months to produce the required quantity of antibodies. The culture remained in exponential growth over the whole period and the fraction of dead cells never rose above 5%. Judging by this behavior, there seems to be no limit to the permanence of cytostatic cultures. Judging by the behavior of some of the faster replicating lines which grew severalfold beyond the so-called Hayflick limit, hybridomas are not bound by the rules believed to be governing the expansion of cellular clones *in vivo*.

The limitations to cytostatic culture come from another direction. A common risk attending long-term cultures is the loss of particular functions through random mutation. Hybridomas, being polyploid, can even lose whole chromosomes and survive. Indeed, chromosome-loss mutants frequently have shorter doubling times than their parents and will outgrow them in time. If the loss involves either of the chromosomes carrying the expressed globulin genes, the culture will gradually cease producing antibodies. We had several instances of this (some possibly because the starting cultures were not monoclonal), and in each case a new culture set up with recloned seed resulted in continued, satisfactory antibody production.

Loss of production or overgrowth by mutants is less frequent in lines that have been in culture for weeks, presumably because they have already undergone most of the nonlethal mutations. Such so-called stable lines are best suited for cytostatic growth. The other class of choice is hybridomas of short doubling time, as these are less likely to be overgrown by their mutants.

Practice

Seed Culture. If there is a choice, cloned lines of fast-growing hybridomas are preferred for cytostatic work.

Assuming that the seed is about 10^6 cells stored in liquid N_2, a single 75-cm^2 culture bottle can be set up with 10 ml of the same medium in which the cells were grown before freezing. If the culture bottle has been preincubated for a day with serum-containing medium, most of the live cells in the primary inoculum will adhere overnight, and the dead cells can be removed the next day and replaced by fresh medium. The cultures are fed every second day by replacing spent medium with gradually increasing volumes (up to 24 ml) of fresh medium.

If the cytostat is to be run on serum-free medium, a two-stage adaptation can start on the second day. First, the cells are given an equal mixture of their habitual medium and Iscove's made up with the same kind and quantity of serum, say, $RN_{10} + IN_{10}$. Most cell lines will continue to grow in this mixture and may receive pure IN_{10} on the next feeding. If they do not grow as well in the mixture, the transition should be made gradually, with daily increments over 3–4 days. The second stage starts when the cells have reached one-quarter confluence (about 8×10^6 cells/bottle). Then they are fed with an equal mixture of IN_{10} and IA. Again, most cell lines will keep growing in this, and these receive then pure serum-free medium, IA, at next feeding. A minority of hybridomas will slow down or stop dividing altogether, and it is then the experimenter's choice whether to persevere with the adaptation or opt for cytostatic culture in serum-containing media.

When the initial culture has reached one-half or three-quarters confluence (by now 50–60 ml medium) it is ready for transfer into the cytostat.

Starting Up. First the peripheral equipment is put in running order: the water bath switched on and allowed to reach 37° (the line to the heating jackets is still clamped), the gas line connected to the medium supply bottle and to the manifold serving the cytostats (the individual lines to the cytostats still clamped), the gas flow set (20 ml/min for each cytostat and 80 ml/min for the medium bottle, i.e., to 200 ml/min for six cytostats), and the magnetic stirrer switched on. Then the medium input lines are fitted into their peristaltic pumps, and the medium supply line attached to the storage bottle. The latter is an aseptic operation and we use a small butane gas burner for flaming the connector link (see Fig. 1).

The next few steps are performed under a laminar flow hood. First the output tubes of the cytostats are connected to the wider bore pump tubes. Then the starting cell suspension is prepared. Both trypsinization and mechanical flushing can considerably damage the cells. Any damage is avoided by the following treatment: transfer 50 ml of the culture supernatant to a sterile bottle or centrifuge tube; this will be used as conditioned medium for the cytostat. Suck off the remaining spent medium and replace by 10 ml EDTA–saline. Incubate culture bottles at 37° for 5–10 min, with occasional shaking. By the end of this period the cells will have detached from the plastic; the process can be made complete by gentle flushing with an L pipet (Pasteur pipet with the last 5 mm of its tip bent at right angles). Transfer the cell suspension to a 15-ml centrifuge tube, add 0.10 ml of a sterile 0.2 M CaCl$_2$ solution (to bind the EDTA), and centrifuge for 10 min at 200 g. Discard the supernate, take up the pellet, and disperse in the 50 ml of conditioned medium.

The lid of the cytostat jar is slightly lifted, the starting suspension is poured in, the lid replaced, and the culture vessel is ready for connection to its supply lines. This is done in the following order. Place culture vessel in its heating jacket, open the thermostatted water supply, and adjust to correct rate of flow. Connect the gas inlet to gas supply manifold, and open the gas line serving the cytostat. Aseptically connect the medium supply (small-bore pump tube) to the cytostat and switch on the pump at maximum setting, allow about 50 ml of fresh medium to be pumped in, and then set pump to minimum supply (not more than 0.05 ml/min). The cytostats are thus starting at a cell density of about 2×10^5/ml.

Setting of Optimal Density. Over the first few days, while the medium input is kept at a minimum, the cultures are sampled daily. By using an exclusion dye, positive or negative, the number of live and dead cells is determined and recorded, together with v, the volume of the culture, and m, the input of medium in milliliters per minute. Most hybridomas will have less than 5% dead cells during exponential growth, but we had also one rat–mouse hybrid which regularly produced about 25% nonviable cells at each division. At any rate, the fraction of dead cells will remain constant until the density limit is reached which, for an average hybridoma, should be well above 10^6 cells/ml. The first sign of having reached the limit is the increase in dead cells. We follow the simple rule that when the fraction of dead cells has risen by 10% (i.e., usually from 2 to 12% or, in the exceptional case, from 25 to 35%), the volume of the culture is rapidly doubled by letting the pump run at maximum speed for as long as necessary. The concentration thus set, i.e., half of the last count and about 25–50% below the density limit, is then to be maintained over the rest of the culture period.

Adjustment of the Cytostatic Input. By the time the optimal density is set there is enough information for roughly calculating m^+, the cytostatic input. But final setting, by use of Eq. (6), should be made only once the final volume is reached.

If cytostats are run at a predetermined volume, say 600 ml, and counts made at regular intervals, say every 24 hr (1440 min), Eq. (6) can be tabulated in a convenient form, giving the increment needed for attaining the correct input. For the above constants the equation would read: increment $= (m^+ - m) = (600/1440) \ln(c_t^+/c_0^+)$, and produce the following simple tabulation:

Ratio of concentrations 24 hr apart

0.6	0.7	0.8	0.9	1.0	1.1	1.2	1.3	1.4	1.5	1.6
−0.21	−0.15	−0.09	−0.04	0.0	0.04	0.08	0.11	0.14	0.17	0.20

Increment of input (ml/min)

Thus, for instance, if the concentration has risen in 24 hr from 1.85×10^6 to 2.4×10^6/ml, the ratio is $2.4/1.85 = 1.30$, and hence the input has to be increased by 0.11 ml/min. If the readings were in the opposite order, i.e., the concentration falling, the ratio $1.85/2.4 = 0.77$ would indicate that the input of medium has to be decreased by about 0.11 ml/min (by interpolation between the ratios 0.7 and 0.8, i.e., between the corresponding increments of −0.15 and −0.09).

Collection and Processing of Output. Originally[2] the overflow of the cytostat was passed over a cell trap and then directly through an affinity column, so that pure antibody could be eluted every day or two. This esthetically pleasing arrangement had several practical shortcomings. First, the cell trap, repeatedly redesigned, could not be made to function for more than a few days before either clogging up or leaking. (This only confirms the adage that if a man invents a better cell trap the world will beat a path to his door.) Another flaw was the need to wash, elute, and regenerate several small columns each day, making a farce of automation.

Over the past 2 years we have been using a simpler method that proved entirely satisfactory. The output of the cytostats is collected in 1- or 2-liter bottles which contain 10 or 20 ml, respectively, of 8% NaN_3 as a bactericidal agent. The bottles are stored in the cold, and by the time 5–10 liters have accumulated the cells have settled and at least 90% of the clear supernatant can be sucked off. The residues are pooled and cleared in a single centrifugal run. For the next step, concentration, we use the Amicon hollow-fiber system and, by running it at low back pressure, can reduce 10 liters to about 100 ml without loss of antibody activity. If the cytostat has been run on serum-free medium, the concentrate contains only the monoclonal antibodies minimally contaminated by cellular debris. For complete purification the concentrate can then be passed through an affinity column. For this purpose we use a mixture of medium-affinity monoclonal antibodies directed against each of the isotypes of mouse immunoglobulin.

Shutoff. The medium supply line is disconnected and the pumps switched to maximum rate to clear the output lines. The water bath, gas supply, and the refrigerator are turned off. The culture jars are removed from their jackets and the cell suspension poured out, to be processed after settling in the cold.

Before sterilization and preparation for the next run the equipment must be cleaned. Flushing all tubing with hot water and then distilled water is usually sufficient, and it is not necessary to disassemble the lid attachments for this purpose. The culture vessels and medium reservoirs are cleaned by the usual procedure for tissue culture glassware. The clean components are then reassembled and sterilized and are ready for the next run.

[34] The Effect of Pristane on Ascites Tumor Formation and Monoclonal Antibody Production

By Nicholas J. Hoogenraad and Christopher J. Wraight

Large quantities of mouse monoclonal antibodies can be produced by propagating hybridomas as ascites tumors in histocompatible mice after pretreating them with pristane (2,6,10,14-tetramethylpentadecane, Aldrich). Since a mouse can yield 5–15 ml of fluid containing 5–15 mg/ml antibody it is possible to produce ~100 mg of monoclonal antibody in a single mouse.[1] The practice of preconditioning the peritoneal cavity with

[1] N. Hoogenraad, T. Helman, and J. Hoogenraad, *J. Immunol. Methods* **61**, 317 (1983).

pristane in order to obtain a high percentage of tumors stems from the observation that mineral oils induce plasmacytomas when injected intra-peritoneally into mice.[2,3] A branch-chain alkane, pristane was shown to be the plasmacytogenic component in mineral oil,[4] and it acts by severely depressing the normal immunological function of the animal.[5] Once mice have been preconditioned with pristane, plasmacytogenicity can be trans-ferred to other mice by transferring cells from the peritoneal cavity of treated mice.[6] The induction of plasmacytomas is dose dependent, and multiple injections with 0.5 ml of pristane gives a higher percentage of mice with tumors than single injections with 0.5 ml or larger volumes of pristane.[7,8] In order to produce ascites tumors from hybridomas, how-ever, a single injection of pristane has proved to be adequate. Monoclonal antibodies are routinely produced in BALB/c mice by injecting 0.5 ml of pristane intraperitoneally followed sometime later (e.g., 1–2 weeks) with 5×10^5 to 5×10^6 hybridoma cells.[9] In this chapter, we suggest proce-dures to optimize the production of monoclonal antibodies from ascites tumors with respect to the preinjection with pristane.

Production of Hybridomas

Two hybridomas were used in this study, one producing IgM against a rat liver enzyme and another producing IgG$_1$ against a hapten. Mono-clonal antibodies were prepared against carbamoyl-phosphate synthase (carbon dioxide : ammonia ligase, EC 6.3.4.16) by immunizing mice with the enzyme after purifying it to homogeneity from rat liver.[10] The spleen cells of immunized mice were later fused with NS-1 cells and hybridomas were produced by the method of Galfré et al.[11] The cloned hybridoma line used, C1/F10, produces IgM specific for carbamoyl-phosphate synthase.[1] Monoclonal antibodies were also produced against 2′–5′ linked oli-goisoadenylate coupled to hydrazide derivatives of bovine serum al-bumin.[12] A cloned line, B3/C6, was obtained which produces IgG$_1$ specific for oligomers containing 2′–5′ linked adenylates.

[2] M. Potter and C. L. Robertson, *J. Natl. Cancer Inst. (U.S.)* **25**, 847 (1960).
[3] M. Potter and C. Boyce, *Nature (London)* **193**, 1086 (1962).
[4] P. N. Anderson and M. Potter, *Nature (London)* **222**, 994 (1969).
[5] Y. R. Freund and P. B. Blair, *J. Immunol.* **129**, 2826 (1982).
[6] M. Platica, C. Bojko, and V. P. Hollander, *Cancer Res.* **40**, 579 (1980).
[7] M. Potter, J. G. Pumphrey, and J. L. Walters, *J. Natl. Cancer Inst. (U.S.)* **49**, 305 (1972).
[8] M. Potter and J. S. Wax, *J. Natl. Cancer Inst.* **71**, 319 (1983).
[9] P. Parham, this series, Vol. 92, p. 110.
[10] P. McIntyre and N. Hoogenraad, *FEBS Lett.* **135**, 65 (1981).
[11] G. Galfré, S. C. Howe, C. Milstein, G. W. Butcher, and J. C. Howard, *Nature (London)* **266**, 550 (1977).
[12] C. L. Hersh, T. R. Reid, R. Friedman, and G. R. Stark, *J. Biol. Chem.* **259**, 1727 (1984).

Production of Ascites Tumors

BALB/c mice were maintained on a 12-hr light/dark cycle and 1-month-old mice were randomly arranged into groups of six. In experiments to determine the optimum interval between injection of pristane and injection of hybridomas, a single 0.5-ml intraperitoneal injection of pristane was given 1, 10, 20, 30, and 60 days prior to injection of 5×10^5 of C1/F10 hybridoma cells. A control group was injected with hybridomas but not with pristane. In experiments to determine the optimum dose of pristane, mice were injected intraperitoneally with a single injection of 0, 0.05, 0.1, 0.2, or 0.5 ml of pristane 10 days before the injection of 10^6 B3/C6 hybridoma cells.

Mice were inspected visually for the appearance of ascites tumors, which were then drained once every 2 days from the onset of tumor formation until death. Tumors were drained by insertion of a 20-gauge needle into the abdomen. The fluid is made cell free by centrifugation at 400 g for 10 min. The supernatant fractions were stored at $-15°$ until all collections were finished.

Variations of Ascites Fluid Collection

A proportion of mice develop solid tumors from which only a small amount of fluid can be drained. Antibodies can be obtained from these mice by killing the mouse, injecting normal saline into the peritoneal cavity, and then draining the fluid after mixing the saline with peritoneal contents. This method may also be used as an alternative to frequent draining of fluid from mice. Mice with advanced tumors are killed by cervical dislocation, saline is injected into the peritoneal cavity, and a single collection of fluid is obtained. Tumors may be propagated by injecting ascites cells into mice preconditioned with pristane. Cells obtained from tumors are more virulent than hybridomas obtained from tissue culture; consequently mice bearing tumors produced from tumor cells die sooner and thus less ascites fluid can normally be collected from these mice. By the same token, propagation of hybridomas as ascites tumors is an effective way of increasing the vigor of cell lines which are difficult to establish in cell culture. Cells from ascites tumors may be frozen in 90% fetal calf serum and 10% dimethyl sulfoxide.

Quantitation of Monoclonal Antibodies Produced

IgM. Thawed ascites fluid was filtered through glass wool to remove aggregated lipid and the filtrate was made 50% with respect to ammonium sulfate by the dropwise addition of saturated ammonium sulfate while stirring. After 30 min at 4°, the precipitated immunoglobulin fraction was collected by centrifugation at 10,000 g for 20 min. The pellet was redissolved in a volume of PBS one-tenth that of the volume of the original ascites fluid. IgM was further purified by dialysis against distilled water at 4° and by redissolving the precipitated IgM in 1.8% NaCl.

IgG₁. The ammonium sulfate-fractionated immunoglobulin fraction was dialyzed against PBS and further purified by passage through a DEAE-cellulose column preequilibrated with 10 mM Tris–HCl (pH 8.2). IgG$_1$ was eluted with a 0 to 0.2 M NaCl gradient.[13] The IgG$_1$ produced was unusual in that it bound tightly to *Staphylococcus* protein A. The antibody could thus be purified by passing through a protein A column preequilibrated with PBS. After washing the column with PBS until the absorbance at 280 nm returned to zero, the monoclonal IgG$_1$ was eluted with 0.05 M glycine–HCl (pH 2.5). The eluted immunoglobulin was immediately removed from low pH buffer by adding an equal volume of saturated ammonium sulfate and after collection of the precipitate by centrifugation at 10,000 g for 20 min, the pellet was dissolved in PBS as described above. The purified immunoglobulins were stored at 4° in 0.05% sodium azide.

Optimum Interval between Injecting Pristane and Injecting Hybridomas

The important variables when deciding upon the treatment of mice with pristane are the effect of this treatment on percentage of mice developing tumors, volume of ascites fluid produced, concentration of antibody in ascites fluid, and time for tumors to form.

Table I summarizes the effects on ascites formation and monoclonal antibody production of varying the time between priming with pristane and injecting hybridomas. A preinjection time of 10 days was optimum with respect to time for tumors to form; the first tumors were detected within 10 days and all mice had tumors 12 days after injection of hybridomas. Whereas a preinjection time of 20 days gave almost identical results (10 days for first mouse to develop tumors and 14 days for last mouse), a preinjection time of 30 days gave far more variable results, since the first tumor did not appear until 22 days and the last tumor appeared on day 56. In both the 10- and 20-day preinjection groups, 100% of the mice developed tumors. The volume of ascites fluid collected was variable. Thus, some mice developed solid granulomatous tumors from which little fluid could be drained, while the fluid collected from other mice varied from a clear ascites liquid to a bloody fluid. The volume of ascites fluid collected

[13] J. W. Goding, "Monoclonal Antibodies: Principles and Practice," p. 105. Academic Press, London, 1984.

TABLE I
EFFECT OF PREINJECTION OF MICE WITH PRISTANE ON ASCITES TUMOR FORMATION[a,b]

Interval from preinjection (days)	Time for appearance of tumors (days)		Mice developing tumors (%)	Volume of ascites fluid collected (ml)	Antibody produced	
	First	Last			(mg/ml)	(total mg)
0	17	17	50	12	0.58	7.0
1	25	33	50	34	0.37	12.6
10	10	12	100	37	11.16	412.8
20	10	14	100	32	7.14	228.6
30	22	56	83	55	6.30	346.8
60	14	15	100	22[a]	7.44[c]	163.8[c]

[a] Reproduced from Hoogenraad et al.[1] with permission of the authors and publisher.

[b] Groups of six mice were preinjected intraperitoneally with 0.5 ml pristane for the periods of time shown, before injection of 0.5×10^6 hybridoma cells (C1/F10).

[c] Two mice developed spontaneous tumors before hybridoma cells were injected. These are not included in the data shown. Following injection of hybridomas into these mice, 38 ml of ascites fluid was collected, having 3.12 mg/ml monoclonal IgM against CPSase.

from mice preinjected with pristane 10 days and 20 days before injection of hybridomas was similar (37 and 32 ml, respectively), but the concentration of IgM purified from the fluid was much higher in the 10-day group (11.2 mg/ml) compared with the 20-day group (7.1 mg/ml). The volume of fluid collected from mice preinjected for 30 days was the greatest of all groups investigated but the concentration of monoclonal antibody in ascites fluid was only 6.3 mg/ml. The results suggest that it is an advantage to preinject mice with pristane 10 days before injection of hybridomas with respect to both the quantity of monoclonal antibody produced and the convenience in having all mice develop tumors over a narrow period of time.

Optimum Quantity of Pristane to Use

When 0.5 ml of pristane is used to prime the peritoneal cavity for tumor formation, it is often found that the ascites fluid is initially oily, particularly if mice develop tumors within 2 weeks of injecting hybridomas. We varied the dose of pristane used to prime tumor formation to determine whether doses smaller than 0.5 ml could be used. Table II summarizes the results for mice pre-injected with varying amounts of

TABLE II
EFFECT OF DOSE OF PRISTANE ON ASCITES
FLUID PRODUCTION[a]

Dose of pristane (ml)	Mice developing tumors (%)	Volume of ascites fluid collected (ml)
0	33	0.6
0.05	67	18.4
0.1	100	57.9
0.2	100	47.8
0.5	100	58.3

[a] Groups of six mice were preinjected with varying amounts of pristane as shown, 10 days prior to injection of 10^6 hybridoma cells (B3/C6).

pristane 10 days before the injection of 10^6 hybridoma cells producing IgG_1 (B3/C6). These results show that 0.1 ml pristane is no less effective than 0.5 ml pristane in priming the peritoneal cavity for ascites tumor formation and there was also no difference in the time taken for mice to develop tumors. Only two-thirds of mice developed tumors when preinjected with 0.05 ml pristane and one-third of mice developed tumors upon injection of hybridomas without prior priming with pristane. When no pristane was used, the tumors formed were solid and very little fluid could be drained from the peritoneal cavity.

Variability in Ascites Tumor Formation

Some hybridoma lines predominantly produce solid tumors and other lines are difficult to establish as tumors. Some of these difficulties result from prolonged propagation of the hybridomas in culture. For example, the hybridoma which produces antibodies against 2-5A, B3/C6, produced only solid tumors after being maintained in culture for 6 months and another hybridoma after cloning by limiting dilution became nontumorigenic. These problems are caused by instability of hybridomas and can best be avoided by freezing sufficient ampules of cells so that the original clones can be used for ascites production. Conversely, if a hybridoma initially produces solid tumors, it is possible to select for ascites-forming cells by propagating any liquid which can be drained from the peritoneal cavity in mice primed with pristane. Ascites-forming hybridomas may subsequently be cultured in vitro and frozen for long-term storage in liquid nitrogen.

Summary

Preinjection of mice 10 days before intraperitoneal injections of hybridomas gives optimum development of ascites tumors with respect to the rate at which tumors form, percentage of mice developing tumors, volume of ascites fluid produced, and concentration of monoclonal antibody in ascites fluid. The dose of pristane injected has little or no effect on ascites formation down to 0.1 ml of pristane.

[35] Production of Ascites and Rescue of Hybridomas by Intrasplenic Inoculation

By PAMELA L. WITTE and ROSALIE BER

The usual course of acquiring large amounts of hybridoma-derived antibodies is to clone initial fusion products and then to expand the cells until large numbers are available for massive liquid culture or intraperitoneal inoculation into mice to induce antibody-laden ascites production. For vigorous growth of the hybridoma cells and ample ascites production, recipient mice are commonly "primed" with the hydrocarbon pristane, injected into the peritoneal cavity weeks before the hybridomas are inoculated. Pristane-priming appears to elicit a milieu within the peritoneal cavity capable of enhancing and perhaps necessary for plasmacytoma (or hybridoma) tumor growth.[1,2]

Ber and Lanir[3] found that in unprimed animals, the minimal number of plasmacytoma cells capable of producing tumors is much lower when the cells are inoculated by the intrasplenic route compared to subcutaneous, intrathymic, and peritoneal inoculation routes. Thus, the unprimed splenic milieu may well provide the microenvironment initiated by pristane in the peritoneum. Moreover, the tumors produced by intrasplenic inoculation are accompanied by marked ascites.

We have extended these observations to hybridomas.[4] Because far fewer cells are required to generate ascites, the intrasplenic route of inoculation affords several advantages over intraperitoneal injection into pristane-primed mice (Table I).

[1] M. Potter, J. G. Pumphrey, and J. L. Walters, *J. Natl. Cancer Inst. (U.S.)* **49**, 305 (1972).
[2] M. Cancro and M. Potter, *J. Exp. Med.* **144**, 1554 (1976).
[3] R. Ber and N. Lanir, *J. Natl. Cancer Inst.* **72**, 403 (1984).
[4] P. L. Witte and R. Ber, *J. Natl. Cancer Inst.* **70**, 575 (1983).

TABLE I
ADVANTAGES OF ASCITES PRODUCTION BY INTRASPLENIC INOCULATION

Time and expense required to grow large numbers of hybridoma cells for ip-derived ascites
production are reduced

The need for few cells limits tissue culture time and therefore acts as a safeguard against loss
of the clone

Single hybridoma colonies can be directed immediately into ascites production

In vivo growth can be established directly from frozen samples, thus eliminating reestablishment in culture

The splenic milieu can be used to "clean up" contaminated cultures

Antibody-secreting hybridoma cells in the ascitic fluid can be readily reestablished *in vitro*

Materials

BALB/c mice, 8 to 12 weeks of age

Surgical instruments (soaked in 70% ethanol and drained on sterile
gauze): toothed forceps, scissors, blunt curved forceps, hemostat

Chloral hydrate (36 g/liter)

Dissecting board, pins, rubber bands

Silk suture

Hybridoma cells (preferably in log phase growth), suspended in serum-
free balanced salt solution at 10^5 or 10^6 viable cells/ml: used here are
hybridomas from BALB/c splenocytes fused with the SP2/0-Ag14
plasmacytoma line.

Syringe, 0.5-ml glass or 1.0-ml plastic

Needles, 27 or 30 gauge

Complete hybridoma medium: used here is Dulbecco's modified Eagle's medium plus 15% fetal calf serum, 1% penicillin/streptomycin,
1% L-glutamine (200 mM stock), and 1% sodium pyruvate (100 mM
stock).

Procedures

Intrasplenic Inoculation of Cells. Mice are injected ip with chloral
hydrate at 0.1 ml/10 g body weight. Each anesthetized mouse is immobilized on a surgical board. The abdomen is swabbed with 70% ethanol. A
midline abdominal incision is made of approximately 5–10 mm to expose
the spleen. By gently pulling the omentum with blunt, curved forceps, the
spleen is positioned so that only a small portion of the splenic tail is
exposed through the slit.

The hybridoma cells are inoculated in a total volume of 0.1 ml into the
splenic pulp. The needle tip is directed toward the tail of the spleen and

placed about midway into the pulp. Care should be taken not to puncture through the organ, and a correctly injected inoculum should form a small "blister" of the splenic capsule. No bleeding should occur at the site of injection.

The entire incision is closed with one to three silk sutures. Wound clips can be used but sutures are preferred as healing is more rapid and less likely to allow tumor formation around the incision site. The mice are kept warm (under a bright lamp) until they revive from the anesthesia; subsequently, they are maintained on the usual food and water regimen. We have not found it necessary to include antibiotics in the water. The mice should be observed the next day to be sure that the sutures are intact.

Ascites is harvested by puncturing the lower abdomen with a 20-gauge needle and allowing the fluid to drain into a centrifuge tube. The fluid is centrifuged at 1000 g; the supernatant is collected, titered for activity, and stored at $-70°$.

Dose of Cell Inoculum. Ber and Lanir[3] found that 10^4, but not 10^3, BALB/c plasmacytoma 4T00.1 cells inoculated intrasplenically consistently develop omental tumors and ascites. Similarly, about 80% of the hybridoma lines we have analyzed develop ascites when as few as 10^4 cells are injected into recipient spleens (Table II), and with 10^4 or 10^5 cells, positive growth seems more dependent on the individual hybridoma line than on the number of cells in the inoculum.[4] Thus, in general, 10^4 viable cells is the minimal dose required for both tumor growth and ascites production.

TABLE II

INCREASED INCIDENCE OF ASCITES FORMATION BY INTRASPLENIC INJECTION OF A PLASMACYTOMA OR HYBRIDOMAS

Source of inoculum	Route[a]	No. of cells	No. of takes
Plasmacytoma 4T00.1[b]	ip	10^5	0/4
	is	10^3	1/4
		10^4	4/4
		10^5	5/5
BALB/c × SP2/0 hybridomas	ip	10^4	0/6
		10^5	2/7
	is	10^3	0/3
		10^4	15/19
		10^5	20/25

[a] Recipient mice were unprimed in all cases.

[b] Data adapted from Ref. 3.

Patterns of Hybridoma Growth after Intrasplenic Inoculation. Intrasplenic inoculation of hybridomas, as well as plasmacytomas, yields a palpable abdominal mass in addition to ascites. Autopsy of intrasplenically inoculated mice developing ascites reveals solid tumor growth predominantly within the mesentery without gross infiltration of the spleen and with no evidence of metastasis to the liver.

The time course of growth and ascitic fluid yield are highly dependent on the individual hybridoma clone, as we consistently observe with intraperitoneal inoculation into pristane-primed mice. The ascitic fluid from the developing tumors is easily harvested 3–6 weeks after intrasplenic inoculation (Table III). Two to seven milliliters of ascites can be harvested from each mouse.

Reestablishment of Ascites-Derived Hybridomas in Vitro. The ascitic fluid is a rich source of antibody-secreting hybridoma cells, which can be readily reestablished *in vitro*. For this purpose the ascites is tapped with a 20-gauge needle and 5-ml syringe. Care is taken to maintain sterility. Cells suspended in the ascitic fluid are centrifuged at 200 g for 10 min and resuspended in complete DMEM. The cell concentration is adjusted to 1– 5×10^5 viable nucleated cells/ml, and 10 ml of the cell suspension is incubated under usual conditions for hybridomas (37°, 8% CO_2). Within 48 hr the hybridoma cells overgrow the other peritoneal exudate cells and can be transferred and maintained again as a cell line. In our experience, supernatants from the explanted hybridoma cells continued to contain antibody over several passages. We have found that the ability to explant hybridomas in the ascites is especially valuable in overcoming some problems that are often encountered in the production of hybridomas and their antibody products.

Special Applications of the Intrasplenic Inoculation Technique

The low number of cells needed for ascites production can be harvested from a single hybridoma colony, thus shortening the time required for growing sufficient cells for intraperitoneal inoculation and alleviating the crisis period that often occurs when the cells are transferred to larger volumes. As few as 10^4 cells from one colony (one well) grown at limiting dilution is suitable for this purpose.

Reestablishing antibody-secreting hybridoma clones from liquid nitrogen storage is a frequently encountered problem. Intrasplenic inoculation of freshly thawed hybridoma cells consistently resulted in ascites formation (even those cell lines that were difficult to reestablish *in vitro*). Cells frozen at approximately 10^6/vial are quickly thawed and washed in 10 ml

TABLE III
TIME REQUIRED FOR ASCITES GENERATION AFTER INTRASPLENIC
INOCULATION OF HYBRIDOMAS

No. of cells inoculated	Percentage of hybridomas that developed ascites at various intervals from inoculation to first ascites harvest			
	<3 weeks	3–4 weeks	4–5 weeks	>5 weeks
10^4	8	75	17	0
10^5	44	22	0	33

of complete DMEM (warmed to 37°). The cell pellet is resuspended in 0.1 ml of medium without serum and immediately injected into the spleen of a recipient mouse. Within 3–4 weeks ascites develops. The hybridoma cells can be retrieved and explanted *in vitro* from the resulting ascitic fluid.

Occasionally, we have "saved" *in vitro* yeast- and fungus-contaminated cultures from the hybridoma cells in the ascitic fluid, and we suggest that the intrasplenic inoculation route may be useful in the rescue of valuable hybridomas.

Conclusions

Intrasplenic inoculation of small numbers of antibody-producing hybridoma cells into unprimed BALB/c mice results in high-titered ascites. The method is particularly valuable if tissue culture facilities are limited or when the hybridoma cells have reached certain critical or unstable periods. Although the splenic environment does not appear to overtly influence the secretory capability of the hybridoma cell (i.e., a nonsecreting cell does not regain that ability), the splenic milieu does appear to enhance tumorigenicity and may better aid in reviving the health and stability of hybridoma cells.

Acknowledgments

We thank Dr. J. Wayne Streilein for providing support and facilities for several of the studies reported here. This work was in part supported by Cancer Immunology Training Grant CA-09082 from the National Cancer Institute.

[36] Growth of Rat–Mouse Hybridomas in Nude Mice and Nude Rats

By Dhirendra N. Misra, Saad A. Noeman, Heinz W. Kunz, and Thomas J. Gill III

The hybridoma technology, introduced by Köhler and Milstein,[1] using hybridization of antibody-producing lymphocytes from immunized animals with plasmacytoma cells not only has made possible production of antibodies which are homogeneous with respect to determinant specificity, immunoglobulin class, and affinity, but it has also made the antibody source almost permanent. Monoclonal antibodies are now having a revolutionary impact on the biological and medical sciences; they allow the detection, purification, and analysis of virtually any biological structure and they are valuable reagents for diagnostic and therapeutic use.

One drawback of the hybridoma technology is that the antibody concentration in the culture supernatant of the hybrid clones is low, usually of the order of 10 μg/ml,[2] although concentrations as high as 10–50 times this value have been reported.[3,4] In our laboratory, we have produced a large number of monoclonal antibodies against rat major histocompatibility complex (MHC) class I antigens. They were selected by their strong hemagglutination activities, and their concentration in the spent culture medium ranged from 100 to 400 μg/ml.[5] Primary selection of the antibody-producing clones by techniques such as hemagglutination requires antibodies of high affinity and concentrations for positive reactions, and may select only the clones producing such antibodies; hence, many clones producing useful antibodies at low concentrations may remain undetected or unusable. Some of these antibodies can be detected by other methodologies, e.g., cytotoxicity, radioimmunoassay (RIA), or enzyme-linked immunosorbent assay (ELISA), and they can be used as analytical reagents if their concentration can be increased.

Two different approaches have been tried to improve the concentration of monoclonal antibody reagents. First, improved culture conditions for the hybridoma cells can be used for bulk production of culture supernatants.[2] The supernatants can then be concentrated at least 10-fold by

[1] G. Köhler and C. Milstein, *Nature (London)* **256**, 495 (1975).
[2] G. Galfré and C. Milstein, this series, Vol. 73, p. 3.
[3] P. Dráber, J. Zikán, and M. Vojtisková, *J. Immunogenet.* **7**, 455 (1980).
[4] P. Parham, C. J. Barnstable, and W. F. Bodmer, *J. Immunol.* **123**, 342 (1979).
[5] D. N. Misra, S. A. Noeman, H. W. Kunz, and T. J. Gill, III, *J. Immunol.* **128**, 1651 (1982).

precipitation with $(NH_4)_2SO_4$ (50% final concentration).[2] The antibody concentration can also be increased by lyophilization after partial or complete purification by gel filtration, ion-exchange chromatography, or affinity chromatography.[6,7] Second, Köhler and Milstein[1,8] suggested in their first reports on the hybridoma technology that suitable animals with subcutaneous or ascites tumors, produced by implantation of the antibody-producing hybridoma cells, be used to get monoclonal antibodies at high concentrations from their sera or ascites.

Growth of Hybridomas in Animals: Specific Requirements

The *in vivo* course of amplification of antibody concentration, however, is subject to some specific requirements. The animals that are to be used for tumor growth should be histocompatible with the antibody-producing hybridoma clones that are to be injected. For example, Köhler and Milstein[8] immunized BALB/c mice with sheep RBC. The antibody-producing lymphocytes were then fused with P3-X63 Ag8 myeloma which originated in BALB/c mice, and the antibody-producing hybridomas could be injected into BALB/c mice for tumor production. When the primary immunization must be made in a different strain of mice, then the hybridomas from the splenic cells of this mouse and the myeloma of BALB/c origin can be injected in animals of the F_1 generation from the cross of this strain and BALB/c. Ivanyi,[9] for example, could not immunize BALB/c mice against the human pituitary protein hormone hPRL (prolactin), but AB/H mice responded well to this antigen. The hybridomas from the fusion of splenic cells from the AB/H mice with P3-NS1/1-Ag4-1 myeloma cells, which originated in BALB/c, were then implanted in (BALB/c × AB/H)F_1 animals for *in vivo* production of monoclonal antibodies.

Animals with partial or total histocompatibility mismatching can sometimes be used for growth of hybridomas after immunosuppression by X-ray irradiation and/or by injection of immunosuppressive agents such as antilymphocyte globulin or drugs such as methotrexate or cyclophosphamide. Even completely histocompatible animals often require mild immunosuppressive treatments for successful and rapid growth of implanted tumors, probably because of somatic drift of tumor antigens.

[6] J. W. Goding, *J. Immunol. Methods* **39**, 285 (1980).
[7] P. Parham, this series, Vol. 92, p. 110.
[8] G. Köhler and C. Milstein, *Eur. J. Immunol.* **6**, 511 (1976).
[9] J. Ivanyi, *in* "Monoclonal Hybridoma Antibodies: Techniques and Applications" (J. G. R. Hurrell, ed.), p. 59. CRC Press, Boca Raton, Florida, 1982.

The problems for generation of high-titer antibodies by *in vivo* growth of interspecies hybridomas are more critical than those for intraspecies hybridomas. Even in syngeneic combination, large doses of cells are required to initiate tumor growth, probably because of minor histocompatibility differences between putatively syngeneic mice from different sources. Also, there are differences between different hybridomas in terms of their ability to grow in syngeneic mice, indicating involvement of other factors. Immunosuppression may decrease longevity of animals substantially and thus hamper growth of hybridomas and the collection of large amounts of antibodies over a long period of time. Another alternative for generation of high-titer monoclonal antibodies from interspecies hybridomas is *in vivo* growth of hybridomas in genetically immunodeficient (nude) animals.

Nude Mice and Nude Rats

The discovery of a hairless mouse mutant, briefly mentioned by Isaacson and Cattanach[10] in 1962, was first described in detail by Flanagan[11] in 1966. The genetics of the mutation confirmed that the lack of hair was determined by a recessive autosomal gene to which Flanagan gave the name nude and the symbol *nu*. The importance of this mutant animal in biomedical research was recognized when Pantelouris[12] in 1968 reported that, except for a small rudiment, no thymus could be found in any of the homozygotes. It is interesting to note that the discovery of this mutant and the immediate observation that it lacked a thymus took place at a critical phase in the development of immunology when the dichotomy of the immune response system and the role of the thymus in immune response were firmly established. The thymus turned out to be a primary organ in the immune response, and the contribution of the thymus and the cells processed by it (T lymphocytes) to graft rejection was clearly established by the mid-1960s. The nude mutant thus provided a natural model for the study of thymus function in place of artificially thymectomized animals. Soon after the discovery of thymic aplasia in nude mice, Rygaard and Povlsen[13] reported successful transplantation of human malignant tumors into these animals. These observations started a new era in oncological research by providing a natural *in vivo* model for the study of neoplasms. Growth of antibody-producing, interspecies hybridomas in

[10] J. H. Isaacson and B. M. Cattanach, *Mouse Newsl.* **27**, 31 (1962).
[11] S. P. Flanagan, *Genet. Res.* **8**, 295 (1966).
[12] E. M. Pantelouris, *Nature (London)* **217**, 370 (1968).
[13] J. Rygaard and C. O. Povlsen, *Acta Pathol. Microbiol. Scand.* **77**, 758 (1969).

nude animals to increase the concentrations of monoclonal antibodies can be considered the third important application of nude animals.

A second nude mutation, which occurred in AKR mice maintained at the Jackson Laboratory, was reported by Shultz et al.[14] and was designated as nu^{str} (nude-streaker). These animals also are athymic and they accept xenografts. Eventually, different congeneic strains were established in which the nude gene(s) was placed on different genetic background.[15]

The nude mutation occurred in the rat also, and according to Festing[16] its advent preceded that of the nude mouse. This mutation was first seen in outbred hooded rats at the Rowett Research Institute in 1953, and Festing et al.[17] formally described this mutant as an autosomal recessive with full penetrance of the nude characteristic and assigned the gene symbol rnu to it. Histologically, the nude rats are similar to the nude mice. The adult rnu/rnu rats, like the nude mice, are hairless and athymic, and their lymph nodes, Peyer's patches, and spleen display lymphoid depletion in the thymus-dependent areas.[16,18–21] In addition, their splenic lymphocytes do not respond to T-cell mitogens, and there is enhanced susceptibility to a number of infectious diseases.[19,20] There are, however, some distinct differences between the nude rats and the nude mice. First, the nude rats show greater resistance than the nude mice to intercurrent infection. Secondly, there is conflicting evidence of the ability of the nude rat to accept xenografts and sustain their progressive growth.[22–24] This

[14] L. D. Shultz, H.-J. Heiniger, and E. M. Eicher, 48th Annu. Rep. Jackson Lab. p. 75 (1977).

[15] C. T. Hansen, in "The Use of Athymic (Nude) Mice in Cancer Research" (D. P. Houchens and A. A. Ovejera, eds.), p. 11. Fischer, Stuttgart, 1978.

[16] M. F. W. Festing, in "Immunological Defects in Laboratory Animals" (M. E. Gerschwin and B. Merchant, eds.), Vol. 1, p. 267. Plenum, New York, 1981.

[17] M. F. W. Festing, D. May, T. A. Connors, D. Lovell, and S. Sparrow, Nature (London) 274, 365 (1978).

[18] J. G. Vos, J. M. Berkvens, and B. C. Kruijt, Clin. Immunol. Immunopathol. 15, 213 (1980).

[19] J. G. Vos, J. G. Kreefetenberg, B. C. Kruijt, W. Kruizinga, and P. Steerenberg, Clin. Immunol. Immunopathol. 15, 229 (1980).

[20] C. G. Brooks, P. J. Webb, R. A. Robbins, G. Robinson, R. W. Baldwin, and M. F. W. Festing, Eur. J. Immunol. 10, 58 (1980).

[21] S. Fossum, M. E. Smith, E. B. Bell, and W. L. Ford, Scand. J. Immunol. 12, 421 (1982).

[22] M. F. W. Festing, in "Thymusaplastic Nude Mice and Rats in Clinical Oncology" (H. P. Fortmeyer and H. Schmidt-Matthiesen, eds.), p. 15. Fischer, Stuttgart, 1981.

[23] R. Korsgaard, C.-J. Lindén, R. Willén, H. Willén, G. Svensson, and B. G. Simonsson, Int. J. Cancer 32, 793 (1983).

[24] C. Partridge, J. Boden, J. C. M. Lewis, F. Searle, and K. D. Bagshawe, Lab. Anim. 18, 261 (1984).

latter difference is of acute concern for our present study, and it will be elaborated on in a subsequent section.

A second nude mutation, the New Zealand nude (*nznu*), was discovered in 1976 in a colony of outbred albino rats maintained at the Victoria University of Wellington, New Zealand.[25] These animals appear to be different in some respects from the Rowett nude, and they may have a more profound and more uniform depletion of T-cell function.[26]

Growth of Hybridomas in Animals: General Considerations

Mode of Transplantation of Hybridomas

In general, tumors may be implanted in animals as solid blocks (2–3 mm in diameter), a mince of tumor tissue, or isolated tumor or hybridoma cells. The preferred site of implantation is the subcutaneous (sc) space, but tumor growth can be induced by intraperitoneal (ip), intramuscular, or intracranial inoculation or by implantation under the kidney capsule. Some important factors controlling the successful tumor growth are tumor type, tissue of origin, implantation site and technique, and humoral and nutritional status of the recipient animals. Two different methods have been used for implantation of hybridoma cells for *in vivo* production of monoclonal antibodies.[2]

Solid Tumors. Hybridoma cells from vigorously growing cultures are inoculated subcutaneously in the back of histocompatible animals. Solid tumors grow in several weeks. The sera from such animals contain monoclonal antibodies in high (5–25 mg/ml) concentrations. Solid blocks or cell suspensions from freshly excised tumors from these animals can be used to implant in new animals for further production of monoclonal antibodies.

Ascitic Tumors. This is a two-step procedure: induction of ascites in animals followed by ip implantation of hybridomas. The production of ascites in immunized mice was first demonstrated by Munoz.[27] Following this work, a number of investigators demonstrated production of ascites fluids containing antibodies in the peritoneal cavities of mice[28,29] and

[25] M. V. Berridge, R. Moore, B. F. Heslop, and L. J. McNeilage, *Rat Newsl.* **4,** 23 (1978).

[26] M. V. Berridge, N. O'Kech, L. J. McNeilage, B. F. Heslop, and R. Moore, *Transplantation* **27,** 410 (1979).

[27] J. Munoz, *Proc. Soc. Exp. Biol. Med.* **95,** 757 (1958).

[28] R. Liebermann, N. Mantel, and W. Humphrey, *Proc. Soc. Exp. Biol. Med.* **107,** 163 (1961).

[29] A. Tung, S.-T. Ju, S. Kato, and A. Nisonoff, *J. Immunol.* **116,** 676 (1976).

rats.[30,31] Various high- and low-viscosity mineral oils or homogeneous mineral oil, pristane,[32] Freund's adjuvant,[29-31] or antigen–antibody complexes[33] can be used for induction of ascites. In the early studies, the ascites-inducing reagents were administered in immunized or unimmunized animals after mixing with antigens, and the resulting ascites fluids contained antibodies at least at the same or higher concentrations than in the serum of the immunized animal. However, ascites can be induced in unimmunized animals by injecting the reagents without mixing with the antigens.[29] Also, it has been reported that implanted tumors grow faster in mice which have been treated previously with mineral oil[34] or pristane.[35] Both observations have been useful for *in vivo* production of monoclonal antibodies. A single or a number of ip injections of ascites-producing reagents are given to the animals prior to inoculation of the hybridoma cells.[2,36] The ascites fluids collected from these animals 1–2 weeks later and every 1–3 days thereafter usually contain antibody at a very high concentration.

Number of Cells per Inoculum Required to Initiate Tumor Growth

The number of cells per inoculum for normal or immunodeficient animals may be an important factor for successful growth of hybridoma tumors. These figures will depend on the nature of hybridomas, recipient animals, and mode of tumor production. Galfré and Milstein[2] suggested implantation of $2-6 \times 10^6$ cells/mouse, and more than $4-12 \times 10^6$ cells/rat to induce a solid tumor, and 10^7 cells/mouse for an ascites tumor in histocompatible animals. Parham[7] used from as few as 5×10^5 to 1×10^7 hybridoma cells/mouse for production of ascites monoclonal antibodies. Kwan *et al*.[36] suggested injection of 2 to 3×10^7 cells/mouse, immunosuppressed by 600 rad for quicker generation of ascites, since such animals die sooner. It is generally believed that even in a syngeneic combination, large doses of cells (10^6 to 10^7) are required to initiate hybridoma tumor growth in mice.[37]

[30] J. Olson, D. Dawson, and G. Leslie, *Fed. Proc., Fed. Am. Soc. Exp. Biol.* **36**, 1198 (1977).
[31] E. G. Douglas, Y. Hamada, and T. J. McKearn, *J. Immuol. Methods* **26**, 69 (1979).
[32] P. N. Anderson and M. Potter, *Nature (London)* **222**, 994 (1969).
[33] S. A. Noeman, D. N. Misra, R. J. Yankes, H. W. Kunz, and T. J. Gill III, *J. Immunol. Methods* **55**, 319 (1982).
[34] M. L. Kripke and D. W. Weiss, *Int. J. Cancer* **6**, 422 (1970).
[35] M. Potter, J. G. Pumphrey, and J. L. Walters, *J. Natl. Cancer Inst. (U.S.)* **49**, 305 (1972).
[36] S.-P. Kwan, D. E. Yelton, and M. D. Scharff, *Genet. Eng.* **2**, 31 (1980).
[37] H. Zola and D. Brooks, *in* "Monoclonal Hybridoma Antibodies: Techniques and Applications" (J. G. Hurrell, ed.), p. 3. CRC Press, Boca Raton, Florida, 1982.

Studies in nude mice on the factors affecting the initiation of tumor growth indicate that there is a threshold for the number of cells required and that this threshold is a function of the specific cell injected.[38] Injection of even 100 cells of some tumors may initiate tumor growth, whereas injection of fewer than 10^3 and 10^4 cells from some other tumors may fail to initiate growth.

General Methodology

The methodology for growing interspecies or intraspecies hybridomas in normal mice and rats has been described by several investigators.[2,37,39,40] Young adult animals are generally used. For syngeneic combination, the animals are used as they are or they are lightly irradiated with 350–600 rad.[36,40] For histoincompatible animals, Galfré and Milstein[2] suggested irradiation with 500 rad and/or injection of cyclophosphamide, 0.5 mg/20 g animal weight, 24 hr before implantation of the hybridoma cells. For more rigorous immunosuppression, McKearn[39] suggested injection of animals with antilymphocyte serum (40–50 μl/mouse and 0.25–1.0 ml/rat) 3–4 days prior to hybridoma inoculation, irradiation with 600–800 rads on the day of hybridoma inoculation, and injection of syngeneic bone marrow (1–2 $\times$ 10^7 cells/animal) 6–8 hr later.

Hybridoma cells are collected from vigorously growing cultures, and they are centrifuged and resuspended in the original tissue culture medium with a reduced concentration (5%) of fetal calf serum (FCS), which normally ranges from 10 to 20% in regular medium. The cell concentration is adjusted to 1–3 $\times$ 10^7 cells/ml.

For the growth of solid tumors, the animals are inoculated subcutaneously between the scapulae with the hybridoma cells (5 $\times$ 10^6 to 1 $\times$ 10^7 cells/mouse and 1–2 $\times$ 10^7 cells/rat). Progressive growth of tumors can be seen at the location of inoculation by visual inspection of the animals every 2–3 days. Successful tumor growth can be seen within 2 weeks.[39] The animals are then test-bled and their sera tested for the presence of antibodies. The sera from such animals containing a high concentration of antibodies can be collected a number of times.[39] Cell suspensions from these solid tumors can be used to inoculate more animals for both solid tumors and ascites tumors.[2]

For ascites tumors, the recipient animals are first adapted for ascites

[38] S. Shin and V. H. Freedman, *Proc. Int. Workshop Nude Mice, 2nd, 1976* p. 337 (1977).

[39] T. J. McKearn, *in* "Monoclonal Antibodies. Hybridomas: A New Dimension in Biological Analyses" (R. H. Kennett, T. J. McKearn, and K. B. Bechtol, eds.), p. 403. Plenum, New York, 1980.

[40] J. W. Goding, *J. Immunol. Methods* **39,** 285 (1980).

by injecting an ascites-inducing reagent. Pristane has been the reagent of choice for the production of hybridoma tumors, although other reagents are also capable of inducing ascites, as mentioned before. Usually the animals are inoculated ip with pristane (0.5 ml/mouse and 1.0 ml/rat), and they are rested for 1–9 weeks[2,39] before ip injection of hybridoma cells in amounts similar to those used for solid tumors. Kwan et al.[36] used two 0.2-ml pristane injections in mice at 7-day interval and the hybridoma cells were injected a day after the second injection. The pristane-treated animals develop ascites within 2 weeks of hybridoma inoculation, and the ascitic fluids can be removed by inserting a hypodermic needle (size 18, 19, or 20) into the abdominal cavity close to the area of inoculation and letting the fluids drip into a container. The ascites can be drained from the animals a number of times before the tumors kill the animals eventually. Galfré and Milstein[2] mentioned that the ascites collected by the first tap did not usually contain antibodies in high titers, and that the ascites could be collected every 1–3 days for 10 times without sacrificing the animals.

The hybridoma tumors grown in a single animal can be implanted in a number of new animals to increase production of monoclonal antibodies. However, the virulence of the tumors increases with increased passage, resulting in death of animals before usable quantities of ascites fluids can be collected. Parham[7] suggested rejection of tumor cells after three passages and use of freshly cultured hybridoma cells for further inoculation. He also mentioned that since the ascites fluids contain about 10^8 tumor cells/ml and an average of 10 ml ascites fluids can routinely be obtained per mouse, liter quantities of ascites fluids can be generated by starting with 10^7 to 10^8 cultured hybridoma cells.

The total yield of ascites fluids can be 10–20 ml/mouse and 60–100 ml/rat.[39] The sera from these animals contain the same level of antibody as the ascites, typically in the range of 5–25 mg/ml for IgG antibodies, but much lower for IgM antibodies.[40] The ascites fluids can be collected in heparin, centrifuged for clarification, and frozen for future use.[7] Alternatively, the fluids are allowed to coagulate overnight and clarified by centrifugation.[33]

Growth of Rat–Mouse Hybridomas in Nude Mice and Nude Rats: Specific Examples

In the following sections we describe some results of our experiments[33] on the production of monoclonal antibodies in vivo in nude mice and nude rats by implanting in the animals some rat–mouse hybridomas secreting monoclonal antibodies to class I antigens coded by the major histocompatibility complex (MHC) of the rat (RT1).

Animals

Rats of various inbred strains and nude rats (*rnu/rnu*) from our colony at the University of Pittsburgh School of Medicine (Department of Pathology) were used. The origin of the athymic rats was the breeding nucleus at the MRC Laboratory Animal Centre, Carlshalton, United Kingdom. Homozygous and heterozygous animals were produced by mating *rnu/rnu* males with +/*rnu* females. The nude mice (BALBc/*nu/nu,* 6 weeks old) were purchased from GIBCO Animal Resource Laboratory, Madison, WI. The animals were kept under strict hygienic isolation.

Production of Rat–Mouse Hybridomas Secreting Monoclonal Antibodies to MHC Class I Antigens of the Rat (RT1)

Köhler and Milstein[1] used a variant (P3-X63 Ag8) of the HAT-sensitive myeloma cell line originally derived from the BALB/c myeloma MOPC-21[41] for their first demonstration of the hybridoma technique. This line, although frequently used for fusion, was not advantageous, since the hybridomas derived from the fusions with these cells continue to produce the IgG_1 of the myeloma parent, and this immunoglobulin is cross-reactive with anti-rat Ig reagents. We tried several other myeloma lines,[42] and a variant, P3-X63 Ag8.653, of the original line which does not synthesize any immunoglobulin was found most suitable.

WF strain rats were immunized with two split-thickness skin grafts from DA donors at an interval of 3 weeks and then injected ip with 1×10^7 splenic lymphocytes 3 weeks after the second graft. Cell fusions were performed using splenic lymphocytes from the immunized animals 3 days after they were finally injected intravenously with lymphocytes. The methodology of fusion was essentially that described by Galfré *et al.,*[43] but polyethylene glycol (PEG) 4000 (BDH Chemical Ltd., Poole, England) was used as the fusing reagent instead of PEG 1500. PEG 4000 had been proposed as a better fusion reagent than PEG 1500,[44] and, since it comes as flakes, it is easier to handle than PEG 1500, which is a very viscous liquid. Since rat red blood cells (RBC) express class I MHC antigens, the myeloma supernatants were assayed by hemagglutination as described in the next section. The cells from the positive cultures were cloned and recloned by the limiting dilution technique using irradiated (2000 rad)

[41] K. Horibata and K. W. Harris, *Exp. Cell Res.* **60,** 61 (1970).

[42] D. N. Misra, S. Noeman, S., H. W. Kunz, and T. J. Gill, III, *Transplant. Proc.* **13,** 1347 (1981).

[43] G. Galfré, S. C. Howe, C. Milstein, G. W. Butcher, and J. C. Howard, *Nature (London)* **266,** 550 (1977).

[44] S. Fazekas de St.Groth and D. Scheidegger, *J. Immunol. Methods* **35,** 1 (1980).

thymocytes ($1-2 \times 10^5$ cells per 0.2-ml well) from WF (recipient) rats as the feeder layer. Many clones were generated, and five hybridomas, 3-1-3(B-1), 3-3-56(A-24), 3-3-60(C-14), 3-5-118(A-2), and 2-1-155(G-4), producing useful monoclonal antibodies to rat MHC class I antigens were studied in detail.

The monoclonal antibodies secreted by all five hybridomas (*3, 56, 60, 118,* and *155*) were both hemagglutinating and cytotoxic, and they reacted with three different rat MHC (RT1) class I antigens.[45] Four of the hybridomas, *3, 56, 60,* and *118,* produced IgG_{2b} antibodies, and *155* produced an IgM antibody. The amounts of antibodies secreted by these hybridomas in the tissue culture fluids were more than 100 $\mu g/ml$. Two of the IgG hybridomas, *60* and *118,* had an average antibody concentration of 150 and 400 $\mu g/ml$ in their culture fluids, respectively, and were chosen for propagation in nude mice and nude rats.

Specific Hemagglutination Assay for Monoclonal Antibodies

Since rat RBC express MHC class I antigens, the hemagglutination technique was the main serological assay method for these studies. A modification of the original method,[46] which includes addition of normal rat serum to the RBC suspension, is described here because it has been very useful for the assay of the monoclonal antibodies (MAb) which otherwise adhere to glass surfaces quite strongly, making the quantitation of the hemagglutination titers difficult.[47]

Materials

HEPES–saline buffer (20 mM HEPES + 0.15 N NaCl, pH 7.2)
Ficoll (Pharmacia Fine Chemicals, Piscataway, NJ), 5% in HEPES–saline
Antibody (antisera, hybridoma culture supernatants or ascites and sera from animals bearing hybridoma tumors)
RBC from DA rats
Procedure. (1) One milliliter of blood was collected in 0.2 ml ACD solution (GIBCO, Grand Islands, NY), and the RBC were washed four times with HEPES–saline. (2) Forty microliters of packed RBC was added to a solution containing 9.9 ml HEPES–saline and 0.1 ml normal serum from DA rats (donor animals). (3) Ficoll (0.1 ml/tube) was added to 12 round-bottomed 3.0-ml-capacity glass tubes. (4) One hundred microliters of the antibody was added to the first tube, and the antibody was

[45] D. N. Misra, H. W. Kunz, and T. J. Gill III, *J. Immunogenet.* **10,** 379 (1983).
[46] H. W. Kunz and T. J. Gill III, *J. Immunogenet.* **1,** 413 (1974).
[47] H. W. Kunz, T. J. Gill III, and D. N. Misra, *J. Immunol.* **128,** 402 (1982).

serially diluted 2-fold by transfer of 0.1 ml of mixture to the successive tubes. (5) One hundred microliters of the RBC suspension was added to each tube, and the samples were incubated at 22° for 1 hr and then centrifuged for 1 min at 700 rpm at the incubation temperature. (6) An inverted microscope was used to observe the hemagglutination, which was scored as 0 (no agglutination), ± (questionable agglutination), + (clear agglutination), ++ (agglutination with clumping), and +++ (agglutination with heavy clumping).

Growth of Hybridomas in Nude Mice

Materials

Nude (*nu*/*nu*) BALB/c mice
Rat–mouse hybridoma *118*, 1 × 10⁷ cells/ml DMEM (Dulbecco's modified Eagle's medium, GIBCO, Grand Islands, NY) containing 5% FCS (fetal calf serum)
Pristane (2,6,10,14-tetramethylpentadecane, Aldrich Chemical Co., Milwaukee, WI)

Solid Tumors. Mice were injected with 1.0 ml of the hybridoma cells subcutaneously in the back region, between the scapulae. The subcutaneous tumors became palpable 2 weeks after injection. They grew progressively to a large nodular mass (2–3 cm in diameter) in the anatomic plane below the dermis and above the muscular aponeurosis. The tumor was completely encapsulated by stroma and did not metastasize or infiltrate the surrounding tissue, and the overlying skin was not ulcerated (Fig. 1A). Histologically, the rat–mouse hybridomas in culture were polymorphous with strongly basophilic cytoplasm and a round nucleus (Fig. 2A), and the hybridomas grown in the nude mice showed similar histological features (Fig. 2B). The sera collected from these animals after 4 weeks of inoculation had an average hemmaglutination titer of 4096 (Table I) and an antibody concentration of approximately 10 mg/ml.

Ascites Tumors. (1) The mice were injected ip with 0.5 ml pristane. (2) After 2–4 weeks, each animal was injected ip with 1.0 ml cell suspension. (3) The animals were checked every 3 days for ascites formation. (4) The ascites fluids were collected by tapping the mice during the fourth week after the hybridoma inoculation. The tapping was done by inserting a 1½-in. 18-gauge hypodermic needle into the abdominal cavity close to the site of inoculation. The needle was attached to a 1-ml syringe which was inserted in a 50-ml tube. The fluid was allowed to drip by gravity. The sera of the animals were collected the same day as the ascites. (5) The ascites fluids were allowed to coagulate overnight at 4°, were clarified by centrifugation at 3000 rpm for 30 min, and were tested for antibody reactivity.

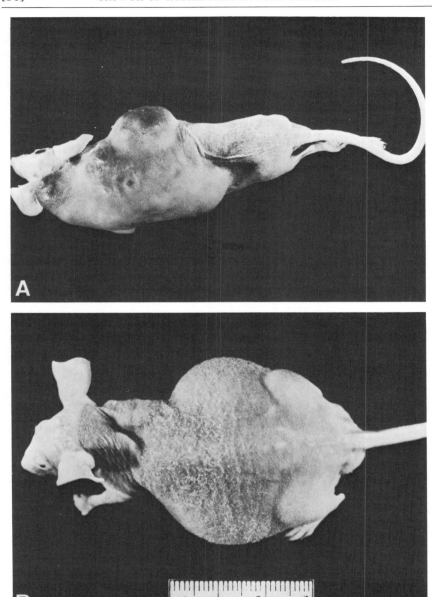

FIG. 1. (A) A nude mouse, inoculated subcutaneously with the rat–mouse hybridoma *118*. This photograph was taken 5 weeks after the injection. (B) A nude mouse showing marked abdominal distention due to ascites accumulation 30 days after ip injection of the rat–mouse hybridoma *118*.

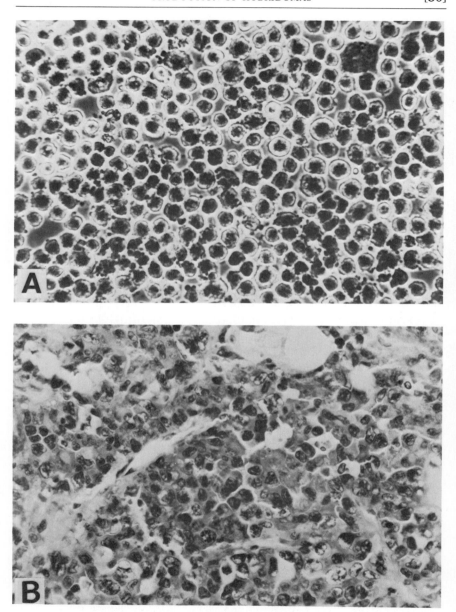

FIG. 2. (A) Photomicrograph of the rat–mouse hybridoma *118* in culture. (B) Section of the tumor induced by sc injection of the cultured rat–mouse hybridoma *118* in a nude mouse after one passage. The tumors showed neoplastic cells with histological features similar to those of the original hybridoma cells.

TABLE I
HEMAGGLUTINATION REACTIVITY OF DIFFERENT SAMPLES AGAINST RBC FROM
DA RATS

| | Hemagglutination | |
Sample	Titer	Strength[a]
Culture supernatant of hybridoma 60	128	+ +
Culture supernatant of hybridoma 118	128–256	+ + to + + +
Ascites or sera from nude mice after ip inoculation and growth of hybridoma 118	2048–4096	+ +
Sera from nude mice after sc inoculation and growth of hybridoma 118	4096	+ +
Sera from normal nude mice	0	0

[a] Range: 0 to + + +.

Figure 1B shows a nude mouse 30 days after intraperitoneal inoculation with the hybridoma cells. Ascites formation could be detected in these animals 10 days after hybridoma inoculation, and 2–7 ml of ascites fluid could be collected. Hemagglutination titers of 2048–4096 were obtained, as opposed to titers of 128–256 for the culture supernatants from the hybridoma 118 (Table I). The amounts of antibody in the ascites, as measured by quantitative precipitation, were 10–15 mg/ml.[5]

Growth of Hybridomas in Nude Rats

Solid Tumors. Several nude rats were implanted subcutaneously with hybridoma 118 (2×10^7 cells/animal), but they did not show any tumor growth during 60 days of observation. Therefore, we tried several methods to induce ascites in the nude rats followed by implantation of the hybridomas in order to produce ascites tumors, and the results are described in the following sections.

Ascites Tumors. Several methods for the induction of ascites tumors were tried, and the results are summarized in Table II.

COMPLETE FREUND'S ADJUVANT (CFA). Four groups of nude rats each containing five animals were injected ip with 9 parts of CFA (Difco Laboratories, Detroit, MI) mixed with 1 part of 0.15 M NaCl until a uniform emulsion was formed.[29] Each group received five injections of 0.5, 1.0, 2.0, or 5 ml of the emulsion; 2 weeks elapsed between the first two injections, and the remaining injections were given weekly. No accumulation of ascites fluid was observed in any of these animals, and autopsy showed very pronounced adhesions in the peritoneal cavity.

PARAFFIN OIL. Two groups of nude rats, each containing three animals, were injected ip with 10 or 20 ml paraffin oil (Fisher Scientific Co.,

TABLE II

PRODUCTION OF ASCITES TUMORS IN NUDE RATS

Treatment (and day)	Ascites induction Substance	Ascites induction Volume in ml (and day injected)	Hybridoma[a] (day injected)	Tumor growth[b] (no./total)	Ascites appearance [week (and no./total)]	Hemagglutination titer Ascites	Hemagglutination titer Serum
None	CFA[c]	0.5–5 (1)	None		None (0/20)	0	0
None	Paraffin oil	10–20 (1)	30	6/6	None (0/6)	0	0[e]
None	Pristane	0.5–10 (1)	30 or 90	18/18	9–15 (18/18)		0[e]
None	Ag–Ab complex[d]		40	5/5	5–13 (3/5)	4096	2048–4096
Irradiation with 250 or 500 rad (30)	Pristane	5 (1)	31	8/8	6 (8/8)		
Splenectomy (1)	Pristane	5 (4)	35	6/6	None (0/6)	2048–4096	2048–4096

[a] Hybridomas 60 or 118, 2 × 10⁷ cells/animal.

[b] Determined after autopsy.

[c] Complete Freund's adjuvant.

[d] Antigen–antibody complexes formed from reaction between 2.5 × 10⁸ DA rat RBC and 1 ml culture supernatant from hybridoma 118 containing anti-DA antibody, in 2.5 ml 0.9% NaCl, injected ip into each animal.

[e] Only one animal showed low antibody titers (256–512) in ascites and serum.

Pittsburgh, PA). On day 30, the animals were injected intraperitoneally with 2×20^7 hybridoma cells (*60* or *118*), but no visible ascites could be detected even on day 120. The animals showed growth of tumors in nodular patches on the mesentery and infiltration in the peritoneal cavity. The sera of these animals did not contain any antibody.

PRISTANE. Three different groups of nude rats were injected ip with pristane for ascites production. The first group (three animals) received 0.5 ml pristane on day 1, 3 ml on day 7, 10 ml on day 14, and 10 ml on day 52. The second and third groups (six and nine animals) received only one injection of 5 or 10 ml pristane, respectively. The hybridoma cells (2×10^7 cells/animal) were injected ip on day 90 (the first and the third group of animals) or on day 30 (second group of animals).

All these animals produced ascites which could be detected in 9–15 weeks. None of the animals, however, showed any antibody in their ascites or serum, except only one animal from group one, which had a low titer of antibody in its serum (titer 256) and ascites fluid (titer 512). There was heavy growth of the tumors in all animals; the peritoneal membranes were heavily infiltrated with the tumors; and the mesentery showed tumors in a nodular, patchy distribution. The tumors showed a network of small vessels, scattered lymphoid cells, and fibroblasts, and the cells were morphologically the same as the cultured hybridomas.

ANTIGEN–ANTIBODY COMPLEXES. (1) RBC from 1 ml of blood from a DA rat (donor strain) were washed three times in HEPES–saline buffer (20 mM HEPES + 0.15 M NaCl, pH 7.4) and suspended in 1 ml of the same buffer. (2) One milliliter of supernatant from hybridoma *118* containing anti-DA MAb was then mixed with 50–100 μl of the RBC suspension (2–2.5×10^8 cells), and the mixture was incubated at 22° for 30 min. (3) The cell–antibody complex was then washed twice with 0.9% NaCl, resuspended in 2.5 ml of 0.9% NaCl, and injected ip into a nude rat. (4) Two groups of rats were injected similarly with the antigen–antibody complexes. The first group (three animals) was injected without previous treatment. The second group (two animals) was primed with pristane (0.5 ml on day 1, 0.5 ml on day 37, and 3 ml on day 45) and then injected with antigen–antibody complexes on day 70. (5) The first group of animals was injected ip with the hybridoma *118* (2×10^7 cells/animal) on day 40, and the second group was injected with the same hybridoma on day 90.

Two animals from the first group showed ascites formation in the fifth week, and one animal of the second group showed ascites formation in the thirteenth week. Sera and ascites fluids were collected on day 30 after the injection of hybridomas. All five animals showed tumor growth, but only one animal (from the second group) showed a low titer of antibody in the serum (titer 256) and in the ascites (titer 512).

Effect of Irradiation and Splenectomy on the Growth of Rat–Mouse Hybridomas in Nude Rats and Production of Ascites Monoclonal Antibodies

The results of the previous sections showed that nude rats injected with CFA or paraffin oil did not develop ascites, but they did when primed with pristane or antigen–antibody complexes or both. These animals showed heavy growth of tumors in the peritoneum when they were injected with hybridoma cells, but they did not produce antibodies. Several possibilities were checked:

a. The hybridomas grown in nude rats did not synthesize antibody. In order to check this possibility, tumor cells were isolated from the peritoneum of nude rats showing ascites production and growth of tumors, and they were stained with fluorescinated rabbit anti-rat Ig antiserum. Examination of the cells by fluorescence microscopy showed heavy staining of the cytoplasm, indicating production of the antibody by the cells.[33]

b. The antibody was formed and secreted, but it was absorbed by the cells of nude rats. The nude rats used in this study were segregating for the *RT1^c* and *RT1^u* haplotypes. They would not absorb the anti-*RT1^a* monoclonal antibody produced by the implanted hybridoma, since this antibody does not cross-react with the *RT1^c* or *RT1^u* haplotypes.[5] In order to test this point further, the MAb *118* was injected ip into several nude rats (3–5 ml/animal), and blood was collected 8 hr later. The sera tested against DA rat showed strong reactivity without significant loss of titer, indicating the absence of any cross-reactivity of the MAb with antigens in the nude rats.

c. The hybridomas synthesized antibody, but could not secrete it. The growth of hybridomas and their ability to secrete the antibody were tested in irradiated nude rats in order to test this hypothesis. (1) Two groups of nude rats each containing four animals were primed with pristane (5 ml/animal) ip and rested for 30 days. (2) The two groups were given whole-body γ-irradiation of 250 and 500 rad, respectively. (3) One day thereafter, the animals were injected ip with *60* or *118* cells (2×10^7 cells/animal).

All animals developed ascites 10–15 days after inoculation of the hybridoma cells. On day 60, the ascites and the sera were collected. Autopsy of the animals showed massive growth of tumors in the peritoneum, and both the ascites and the sera from all animals had very high titers (4096) of antibodies. The results suggest that some suppressor mechanism is preventing the hybridoma cells from secreting the antibodies and that this mechanism is destroyed by irradiation.

d. Suppressor cells or their soluble factors prevented secretion of antibodies. Normal rats contain a large number of suppressor cells in their spleen[48]; hence, three different types of experiments were conducted to test this possibility in nude rats.

1. *Splenectomy*. Spleens were removed from 6 nude rats, and they were allowed to rest for 3 days. The animals were primed ip with pristane (5 ml/animal) on the fourth day. On day 35, two of the animals were injected ip with hybridoma *60*, and the other 4 animals received hybridoma *118* in a similar way (2 × 10⁷ cells/animal).

The animals did not show any visible ascites, even on day 90 when their sera were collected. All animals showed tumor growth in the peritoneum, and the sera of the animals showed antibody of high titers (2048–4096).

2. *In vitro culture of hybridomas with sera from nude rats*. Cells from hybridoma *118* (5 × 10⁶ cells/culture) were cultured in DME medium supplemented with 15% serum from nude rats, from nude rats that had peritoneal tumors following inoculation with hybridoma *118* but without any antibody in the ascites or serum, or from a normal PVG rat which had the same haplotype (*RT1 ᶜ*) as the nude rats. Supernatants were collected from each culture on different days and tested for antibody reactivity against DA rat RBC. The results (Table III) showed that the secretion of antibody by the hybridoma was not inhibited either by the normal nude rat serum or by the serum from hybridoma-bearing nude rats. However, there was some inhibition of antibody production by normal rat serum. The results suggest that there are no soluble inhibitors in the sera of the nude rats that block antibody secretion by the hybridomas.

3. *In vitro culture of the hybridomas in the presence of splenic cells from nude rats*. Cells from hybridoma *118* (2 × 10⁶ cell/culture) were cocultured with 2 × 10⁷ splenic cells from PVG rats, normal nude rats, or nude rats bearing tumors from inoculation of hybridoma *118*. The results (Table IV) showed that splenic cells from both nude rats and normal rats inhibited antibody secretion by the hybridoma.

Evaluation of the Results

The results of the experiments described in the previous sections show that congenitally athymic nude mice inoculated with the rat–mouse hybridomas either ip or sc develop progressive tumors having histological features similar to the original hybridomas. The hybridomas growing in the nude mice secrete antibodies which can be obtained from both the ascites and the sera. The titers and concentrations of these monoclonal antibodies are much higher than those of the antibodies obtained from the

[48] H. Folch and B. H. Waksman, *Cell. Immunol.* **9,** 12 (1973).

TABLE III

HEMAGGLUTINATION REACTIVITY OF SUPERNATANTS COLLECTED ON DIFFERENT DAYS
FROM CULTURES OF HYBRIDOMA *118* WITH DIFFERENT SERA

Type of serum in the culture[a]	Hemagglutination reactivity[b] with DA rat RBC													
	Day 0		Day 1		Day 2		Day 3		Day 4		Day 5		Day 6	
	T	S	T	S	T	S	T	S	T	S	T	S	T	S
Fetal calf serum	0	0	32	++	64	++	64	++	64	+++	128	+++	128	+++
Normal rat serum	0	0	0	0	0	0	0	0	0	0	0	0	32	++
Nude rat serum	0	0	8	±	16	±	16	±	32	+	64	++	64	++
Serum from a nude rat with growing hybridoma tumors[c]	0	0	8	±	16	+	16	+	32	+	64	++	64	++

[a] Hybridoma *118* cells (2×10^6 cells/culture) were cultured in 10 ml DMEM supplemented with all essential components and 15% of the different sera shown in this column.

[b] Reactivity: T, titer; S, strength.

[c] Serum obtained from an animal which was previously primed with pristane and injected ip with hybridoma *118*. The animal showed tumor growth, but its serum did not have any antibody activity.

TABLE IV

Hemagglutination Reactivity of Supernatants Collected on Different Days from Cocultures of Hybridoma *118* with Splenic Lymphocytes from Different Sources

Origin of culture supernatants[a]	Hemagglutination reactivity[b] with DA red blood cells												
	Day 0		Day 1		Day 2		Day 3		Day 4		Day 5		Day 6	
	T	S	T	S	T	S	T	S	T	S	T	S	T	S
Hybridoma *118*	0	0	16	+	32	++	32	++	64	++	64	++	128	+++
Hybridoma *118* + PVG rat lymphocytes	0	0	0	0	0	0	0	++	0	0	16	±	32	++
Hybridoma *118* + nude rat lymphocytes	0	0	0	0	0	0	0	0	0	0	8	±	16	++
Hybridoma *118* + lymphocytes from a nude rat with growing hybridoma tumors[c]	0	0	0	0	0	0	0	0	0	0	0	0	16	+

[a] Hybridoma *118* cells (2 × 10^6 cells/culture) alone or mixed with splenic lymphocytes (2 × 10^7 cells) from different sources, shown in this column, were cultured in 10 ml DMEM supplemented with all essential components and 15% fetal calf serum.

[b] Reactivity: T, titer; S, strength.

[c] Lymphocytes were obtained from a nude rat which was previously primed with pristane and injected ip with hybridoma *118*. The rat showed tumor growth, but its serum was devoid of antibody activity.

tissue culture supernatants. Thus, nude mice can be successfully used for *in vivo* amplification of concentrations of monoclonal antibodies produced by rat–mouse hybridomas.

Our work indicates that the rat–mouse hybridomas, implanted subcutaneously in nude rats, do not grow as tumors. In contrast to our observation, Kluskens *et al.*[49] implanted subcutaneously four rat–mouse hybridomas, secreting monoclonal antibodies to rat or human antigens, into congenitally athymic nude rats and observed development of palpable tumors in all rats in 9–22 days after inoculation. The sera collected from the tumor-bearing rats had antibody titers 32- to 128-fold higher than the titers in the respective tissue culture supernatants. The reason for this disagreement is not known, since many of the details of these experiments as to the source of the nude rats, their age, and the myeloma line used for production of the hybridomas have not been reported. Salomon *et al.*[50] reported results on three hybridomas implanted subcutaneously in nude mice and Rowett nude rats. While a human–mouse hybridoma and a Chinese hamster–mouse hybridoma grew in both nude mice and rats, a mouse–mouse hybridoma did not grow in the rat. These results show that these nude rats are capable of controlling growth of interspecies hybridomas, and in this respect they differ from nude mice.

As mentioned before, histologically both nude mice and rats are similar. Both accept skin allografts and xenografts readily.[22,51] But although both nude mice and nude rats possess a mechanism(s) for controlling tumor growth,[52,53] a very high incidence of tumor regression occurs in the rat compared to the mouse.[51,52] Festing[16] reviewed the experience of many investigators for growing different tumors in nude rats and showed that while a wide range of different tumors could grow in the nude rats, a large number were rejected. Progressive tumor growth in the nude rats has, however, only been observed in a few cases[23,52,53] and in some cases xenografts have been rejected altogether.[24,54]

The mechanism(s) of rejection of xenografts by nude animals is not fully understood. Various mechanisms have been implicated: (1) residual

[49] L. F. Kluskens, J. Ely, P. J. Dawson, M. J. Colston, and A. H. Fieldsteel, *Fed. Proc., Fed. Am. Soc. Exp. Biol.* **40**, 818 (1981).

[50] J.-C. Salomon, N. Lynch, J. Prin, V. Lascaux, and A. Galinha, in "Immunodeficient Animals for Cancer Research" (S. Sparrow, ed.), p. 105. Oxford Univ. Press, London and New York, 1980.

[51] J. Rygaard, in "The Nude Mouse in Experimental and Clinical Research" (J. Fogh and B. C. Giovanella, eds.), p. 95. Academic Press, New York, 1978.

[52] M. J. Colston, A. H. Fieldsteel, and P. J. Dawson, *J. Natl. Cancer Inst.* **66**, 843 (1981).

[53] P. J. Dawson, L. F. Kluskens, M. J. Colston, and A. H. Fieldsteel, *Cancer* **50**, 1151 (1982).

[54] H. J. Hedrich and K. Wonigeit, *Z. Versuchstierkol.* **24**, 38 (1982).

population of T cells,[22] development of some spontaneous T-cell function in privileged organ sites,[55,56] and progressive appearance of T-cell function in aging nudes[57]; (2) an antibody-mediated phenomenon[58]; and (3) cell-mediated "cytostasis" by increased population of natural killer (NK) and other cells found in nude mice and rats.[59,60] The prerequisite role of the thymus for T-cell competence has also been questioned.[61] However, immunological mechanisms other than those mediated by the T cells have been thought to be of importance for xenograft regression in nude rats,[19] and our experiments give some support to this assumption. For example, the hybridomas could grow and secrete antibodies in the nude rats that were irradiated or when their spleens were removed (Table II).

Natural killer cells might play an important role in controlling tumor growth in nude animals. It is possible that the natural killer cells kill the hybridomas when they are implanted subcutaneously and allow the growth of ip-implanted hybridomas but prevent their functional development leading to secretion of the antibody. This presumption is supported by our results. First, the monoclonal antibodies did not cross-react with antigens carried by the nude rats, as shown by absorption studies. Second, there was no suppressor factor(s) in the sera of the nude rats to suppress the antibody formation by hybridomas grown in them (Table III). Third, when the splenic cells from nude rats were incubated *in vitro* with the hybridoma cells, the latter stopped secreting antibodies for a few days and then resumed (Table IV). Abbas[62] summarized different regulatory stimuli which modulate the function and growth of myeloma cells *in vivo* and *in vitro,* and thymocytes and different T cells are listed among the agents which cause reduced tumor growth and suppression of antibody secretion. Although the presence of a small number of functional T cells in nude animals has not been ruled out yet, as mentioned before, it is entirely possible that the natural killer cells represent another such agent. Natural killer cell activity in nude rats is age dependent, with greatest activity in rats 8–10 weeks old.[60] Transplantability of human tumors to

[55] H. Ishikawa and K. Saito, *J. Exp. Med.* **151,** 965 (1981).

[56] E. J. Jenkinson, W. van Ewijk, and J. J. T. Owen, *J. Exp. Med.* **153,** 280 (1981).

[57] J. R. Klein and M. J. Bevan, *J. Immunol.* **130,** 1780 (1983).

[58] R. A. P. Koene, P. G. G. Gerlag, J. J. Jansen, J. F. H. Hagemann, and P. G. A. B. Wijdeveld, *Nature (London)* **251,** 69 (1974).

[59] R. B. Herberman, *in* "The Nude Mouse in Experimental and Clinical Research" (J. Fogh and B. C. Giovanella, eds.), p. 35. Academic Press, New York, 1978.

[60] W. H. De Jong, P. A. Steerenberg, P. S. Ursem, A. D. M. E. Osterhaus, J. G. Vos, and E. J. Ruitenberg, *Clin. Immunol. Immunopathol.* **17,** 163 (1980).

[61] H.-M. Dosch, D. White, and C. Grant, *J. Immunol.* **134,** 336 (1985).

[62] A. K. Abbas, *Immunol. Rev.* **48,** 245 (1979).

nude rats is also age dependent, with greatest success in younger animals.[24] Our results, therefore, lend strong support for the assumption that natural killer cells control growth and antibody secretion by hybridomas in nude rats.

Nature of the Monoclonal Antibodies Produced in Vivo

The combined sera or ascites from mice implanted with antibody-producing hybridomas contain between 5 and 20 mg antibody/ml[63] as opposed to between 10 and 100 μg antibody/ml in the hybridoma culture supernatant. However, the antibody-containing culture supernatants contain no other proteins except those from the tissue culture media and cell debris. Sera from the hybridoma-bearing animals contain all of the serum proteins besides the antibody, whereas in the ascites from these animals, the major protein will be the antibody.

Our studies show concentrations between 5 and 15 mg hybridoma antibody/ml, from hybridomas grown in nude mice or in irradiated nude rats, in both sera and ascites fluids. The degree of contamination of these antibodies with other proteins can be easily detected by sodium dodecyl sulfate–polyacrylamide gel electrophoresis (SDS–PAGE). Figure 3 is a 12.5% SDS–PAGE gel prepared by the method of Porzio and Pearson,[64] separating the antibodies from hybridoma *118* after reduction by boiling in sample buffer for 5 min in the presence of 1% DTT (dithiothreitol, Sigma Chemical Co., St. Louis, MO). The IgG$_{2b}$ MAb *118* from tissue culture supernatant was affinity purified on a column containing CNBr-activated Sepharose 4B (Pharmacia Fine Chemicals, Piscataway, NJ) coupled to goat anti-rat IgG antibody, and it is used for reference. The heavy and light chains of the antibody are the major prominent components in the ascites fluid, and they are also detectable in serum and in tissue culture supernatant when compared with normal ascites, normal serum, and tissue culture medium, respectively. The serum from the nude rat showed a few differences in composition, compared with normal rat serum. These differences may reflect the differences in immunoglobulin classes between nude rats and normal rats: in both nude mice and nude rats the total globulin content is within the normal range, but it differs from normal animals substantially in terms of immunoglobulin subclasses.[65,66]

The monoclonal antibody in the tissue culture medium is contaminated with fetal bovine serum proteins and also with any immunoglobulin

[63] C. Milstein and E. Lennox, *Curr. Top. Dev. Biol.* **14,** 1 (1980).
[64] M. A. Porzio and A. M. Pearson, *Biochim. Biophys. Acta* **490,** 27 (1977).
[65] A. L. Luzzati and E. B. Jacobson, *Eur. J. Immunol.* **2,** 473 (1972).
[66] H. Bazin, B. Platteau, R. Pauwels, and A. Capron, *Ann. Immunol. (Paris)* **131c,** 31 (1980).

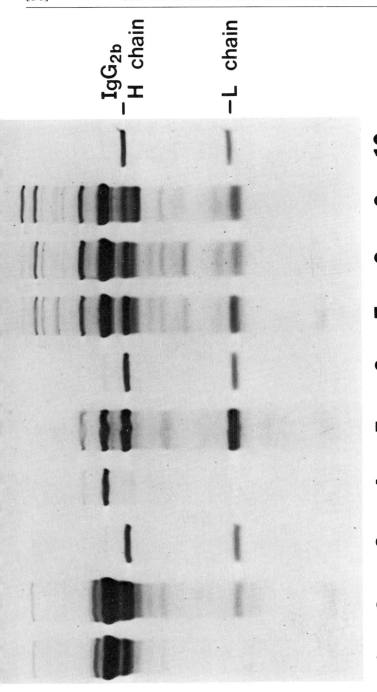

FIG. 3. SDS–PAGE profiles of sera and ascites from normal and nude rats. Gels 3, 6, and 10: Affinity-purified MAb *118* from the culture supernatant of hybridoma *118* (10 μg/gel). The heavy (H) and the light (L) chains of this IgG$_{2b}$ monoclonal antibody are marked for reference. Gel 1: supernatant of hybridoma *118* (10 μg/gel). The heavy (H) and the light (L) chains of this IgG$_{2b}$ monoclonal antibody are marked for reference. Gel 1: Ascites from a pristane-primed nude rat (3.5 μl). Gel 2: Supernatant from culture of hybridoma *118* growing in DMEM with 15% FCS (15 μl). Gel 4: Ascites from a pristane-primed nude rat (3.5 μl). Gels 5 and 7: Ascites (3.5 μl) and serum (1.25 μl), respectively, from a nude rat bearing hybridoma *118* after irradiation and induction of ascites by pristane priming. Gels 8 and 9: Serum from a normal nude rat and a normal WF strain rat, respectively (1.25 μl/gel).

produced by the myeloma used for hybridoma production if it is of secretory type. The monoclonal antibody in the serum of nude animals is contaminated heavily with serum proteins. These monoclonals can be purified only by affinity chromatography using specific antibodies to the monoclonal immunoglobulins. The monoclonal antibody is the major protein in the ascites fluid, although it is contaminated with albumin and to some extent, with other serum proteins of the nude animals. Significant purification of these monoclonals can be achieved by gel filtration or ion-exchange chromatography.[6,7] Unpurified or partially purified monoclonal antibodies from all three sources can be used for affinity purification of the specific antigens. However, it is safer to use purified monoclonal antibodies for detection of specific antigens by indirect binding studies using a radiolabeled or fluoresceinated second antibody.

Conclusions

The congenitally athymic rats have several advantages over the athymic mice. Under conventional conditions, the life expectancy of nude mice is short (about 25 weeks) since they are very susceptible to infection, although in a germ-free or specific pathogen-free environment they live as long as normal mice. The average adult mouse weighs only 20–25 g, and tumors growing in athymic mice seldom weigh more than 20–25 g. The quantity of serum obtainable from each mouse is about 1.0 ml, and the maximal amount of ascites fluid from each tapping is 10 ml. On the other hand, the nude rats apparently possess greater resistance to intercurrent infection than the nude mice, and they often live more than 1 year even under ordinary laboratory conditions.[17] An average adult nude rat weighs 300 g or more, and in excess of 5 ml of serum and 50 ml of ascites fluid can be collected from each rat. Besides, surgical procedures, serial blood or ascites sampling, etc. can be performed easily in rats.

The rat–mouse hybridomas produced by using myelomas from BALB/c origin can be grown in nude mice both as solid tumors and in ascites form. No immunosuppressive treatments of the nude animals are necessary for progressive growth of these tumors. Both the sera and the ascites of the mice bearing ascites tumors and the sera of the mice bearing subcutaneous solid tumors contain monoclonal antibody at concentrations in excess of 10-fold the concentration in hybridoma culture supernatants. Thus, nude mice are usable for the growth of interspecies hybridomas and for the amplification of monoclonal antibody concentrations.

The Rowett strain nude rats support the growth of rat–mouse hybridomas only in the ascites form, but untreated they do not allow the secretion of monoclonal antibodies into the ascites fluid. Low-dose radiation (250 rad/animal), however, improves ascites formation and tumor growth, and allows the secretion of monoclonal antibodies in very high concentrations. Growth of subcutaneous solid tumors after irradiation of the animals has not been tested, but these tumors might also grow like the ascites tumors and secrete monoclonal antibody into the serum. A useful strategy would be to establish the rat–mouse hybridoma tumors in nude mice or nude rats and then to transfer the tumor cells from tumor tissue or from peritoneum of these animals into lightly irradiated nude rats for massive production of monoclonal antibodies. An identical strategy was suggested by Hämmerling et al.[67] for the use of nude rats for in vivo monoclonal antibody production. The report by these authors also suggests that life of the animals bearing intraperitoneal hybridoma tumors can be prolonged by replacing the ascites fluids that are collected with equivalent volumes of physiological saline every time the animals are tapped.

A recent report by Hirsch et al.[68] suggests another possible way for the production of monoclonal antibodies in nude rats when the hybridomas fail to grow in these animals after subcutaneous or intraperitoneal immunization. A number of rat–rat hybridomas which failed to grow in histocompatible or rnu/rnu rats after subcutaneous or intraperitoneal inoculation proliferated mainly in the liver 3–7 weeks after they were injected intravenously through tail vein. When histocompatible animals were inoculated with liver homogenate of these animals, they showed ready growth of hybridoma cells within 1–2 weeks of inoculation, giving rise to subcutaneous or ascites tumors. The sera or ascites of these animals contained the expected monoclonal antibodies. The authors suggested that homing in the liver might have caused the cells to acquire some new properties which enabled them to grow when implanted subcutaneously or intraperitoneally and also to secrete the desired monoclonal antibodies.

Acknowledgment

Work in the authors' laboratory was supported by Grants CA 18659, HD 08662, and HD 09880 from the National Institutes of Health and by grants from the Beaver County Cancer Society and the Tim Caracio Memorial Cancer Fund.

[67] G. J. Hämmerling, U. Hämmerling, and J. F. Kearney, eds., "Monoclonal Antibodies and T-Cell Hybridomas: Perspectives and Technical Advances," p. 563. Elsevier/North-Holland Biomedical Press, Amsterdam, 1981.

[68] F. Hirsch, B. Vendeville, L. DeClercq, H. Bazin, and P. Druet, J. Immunol. Methods 78, 103 (1985).

[37] Poisson Statistical Analysis of Repetitive Subcloning by
the Limiting Dilution Technique as a Way of Assessing
Hybridoma Monoclonality

By HILARY A. COLLER and BARRY S. COLLER

It is essential that the monoclonality of hybridoma-derived antibodies
be assured before one draws conclusions about their functional significance. Presumptive evidence can be obtained by subclass (and light
chain) typing and electrophoretic behavior, but the former suffers from
there being only a limited number of possibilities and the latter from the
difficulty of distinguishing between microheterogeneity of a truly monoclonal antibody and the presence of more than one antibody. Cloning in
soft agar theoretically permits the selection of a single clone, but cells that
grow well in liquid culture may not grow as well in soft agar. New cell
sorter technology has permitted the development of instruments that are
capable of placing a single cell in a given well,[1] but access to such equipment is not widespread. Thus, many laboratories still rely upon subcloning by the technique of limiting dilution[2,3] for increasing the probability of
monoclonality. The statistics for analyzing a single subcloning by application of the Poisson distribution have been described in great detail[2,3];
however, in hybridoma studies it is customary to subclone at least twice
and the statistics for repetitive subclonings were not readily available at
the time we published our earlier study.[4]

We experimentally verified the appropriateness of the Poisson distribution for analyzing the subcloning technique by using a model system
wherein small ion-exchange beads (representing individual cells) were
pipetted into microtiter plates much as one would under experimental
conditions. In fact, there was excellent agreement between the predicted
and actual distribution of wells containing different numbers of beads.[4] It
should be stressed, however, that the Poisson equation assumes a random distribution of elements in the suspension being sampled (which we
were able to ensure in our model system by vigorous stirring of the

[1] D. R. Parks, V. M. Bryan, V. T. Oi, and L. A. Herzenberg, *Proc. Natl. Acad. Sci. U.S.A.*
76, 1962 (1979).
[2] I. Lefkovits and H. Waldmann, "Limiting Dilution Analysis of Cells in the Immune System." Cambridge Univ. Press, London and New York, 1979.
[3] I. Lefkovits, *in* "Immunological Methods" (I. Lefkovits and B. Pernis, eds.), Vol. 1, p.
356. Academic Press, New York, 1979.
[4] H. A. Coller and B. S. Coller, *Hybridoma* **2,** 89 (1983).

METHODS IN ENZYMOLOGY, VOL. 121

beads). Thus, it is important that the cell suspension be thoroughly mixed before performing limiting dilution subcloning. Moreover, in our model system we did not have to consider any cooperative effects between the beads as may potentially exist between hybridoma cells. Theoretically, the use of feeder cells (or perhaps conditioned medium) during subcloning could minimize such cooperative effects by providing a minimum density of cells (or cell products) in each well. Although the foregoing considerations must be kept in mind, we believe that analysis of limiting dilution subcloning by the Poisson distribution does permit a reasonable estimation of the likelihood of monoclonality. Below, we offer a derivation of the equations for repetitive subcloning and a simple table for determining the 95 and 99% confidence limits for monoclonality based upon the total number of wells showing growth.

The Poisson probability

$$P(r) = (\mu^r/r!)e^{-\mu}$$

can be derived from the more general binomial probability.

$$P(r) = \frac{c!}{r!(c-r)!} \left(\frac{1}{w}\right)^r \left(1 - \frac{1}{w}\right)^{c-r}$$

where $P(r)$ is the probability that a particular well contains exactly r cells (with the condition that r is either 0 or a positive integer), c is the total number of cells distributed, w is the total number of wells, and μ is the mean number of cells per well (c/w). If c and w are large, then the binomial probability approaches the Poisson probability.[2]

Although one does not empirically know the mean number of cells per well, this can be calculated from determining the percentage of wells showing no growth (0 viable cells/well), applying the Poisson distribution equation for $r = 0$ [$P(0) = e^{-\mu}$], and solving for μ. Once μ is determined, the frequency of wells containing 1, 2, 3, 4, . . . cells can be calculated.

From these data, it is then possible to determine the fraction of wells showing growth that are monoclonal (that is, they contained only a single viable cell at the time of plating) by the equation

$$\frac{P(1)}{P(1) + P(2) + P(3) + \cdots} = \frac{P(1)}{1 - P(0)} = \frac{S \quad \text{(single)}}{R \quad \text{(responding, growing)}}$$

As the value S/R approaches 1.0, the likelihood that any given well is monoclonal approaches 100%.

Table I gives the S/R values for various percentages of wells showing growth. It should be noted that even when just 50% of the wells show growth, and the mean number of cells per well is 0.69, the S/R value is

TABLE I
CORRELATION BETWEEN THE PERCENTAGES OF WELLS SHOWING GROWTH, THE MEAN
NUMBER OF CELLS PER WELL, AND THE FRACTION OF WELLS SHOWING GROWTH THAT
CONTAIN ONE OR MORE CELLS PER WELL

Wells showing growth (%)	Mean no. cells/well	S/R^a	$2/R^b$	$3/R$	$4/R$	$5/R$
1	0.01	0.995	0.004			
5	0.05	0.975	0.024			
10	0.10	0.950	0.047	0.001		
15	0.16	0.922	0.073	0.003		
20	0.22	0.894	0.099	0.007		
25	0.29	0.861	0.124	0.012		
30	0.35	0.835	0.146	0.017	0.001	
35	0.43	0.800	0.172	0.024	0.002	
40	0.51	0.766	0.195	0.033	0.004	
45	0.61	0.725	0.221	0.044	0.006	
50	0.69	0.694	0.239	0.055	0.009	0.001
55	0.80	0.652	0.261	0.069	0.013	0.002
60	0.91	0.613	0.278	0.084	0.019	0.003
65	1.05	0.565	0.296	0.103	0.027	0.005
70	1.20	0.517	0.310	0.124	0.037	0.008
75	1.39	0.461	0.320	0.148	0.051	0.014
80	1.61	0.402	0.329	0.179	0.069	0.022

[a] The fraction of wells showing growth that contain only a single cell per well.
[b] The fraction of wells showing growth that contain two (three, four, five) cells per well.

only 69.4%, indicating that the cells growing in almost one-third of the wells will not be monoclonal.

If sufficient certainty about monoclonality is not achieved in the first subcloning, the cells from a single well can be subcloned a second time. The statistical analysis of the likelihood of monoclonality becomes somewhat more complex. First, after determining the percentage of wells in the second subcloning (plate 2) that did not show growth, the S/R (the likelihood of a well in plate 2 having received only a single viable cell) for plate 2 can be calculated as was done for plate 1. However, even if a well in plate 2 received more than one cell, it still may be monoclonal. Consider the possibilities of a well in plate 2 receiving two cells: (1) if the well chosen in plate 1 for subcloning was itself monoclonal, then the well in plate 2 will also be monoclonal; (2) if the well chosen from plate 1 contained two different types of cells, the two cells in plate 2 have 1 chance in 2 of being monoclonal; (3) if the well chosen from plate 1 contained three different types of cells, there is a 1 in 3 chance that the well in plate 2 with two cells is monoclonal. This same pattern continues as the number of cells in the chosen well in plate 1 increases.

In the case in which a well in plate 2 receives three cells at the time of subcloning, (1) if the well chosen in plate 1 was monoclonal, then the well in plate 2 will also be monoclonal; (2) if the well chosen in plate 1 contained two cells, there is a 1 in 4 chance that the well in plate 2 containing three cells will receive three identical cells and thus be monoclonal; (3) if the well in plate 1 contained three different cells, there is a 1 in 9 chance that a well in plate 2 received three identical cells, etc. For each case it can be shown that the likelihood of monoclonality in a well in plate 2 containing more than one cell at the time of subcloning is given by the equation $C_2/C_2{}^{C_1} = 1/C_2{}^{C_1 - 1}$ where C_2 is the number of different cells in the well in plate 2 and C_1 is the number of different cells in the well in plate 1.

The final form of the equation for two repetitive subclonings will be

$$P(1) = y + x(1 - y) + \frac{Aa}{2} + \frac{Ab}{3} + \frac{Ac}{4} + \cdots$$
$$+ \frac{Ba}{4} + \frac{Bb}{9} + \frac{Bc}{16}$$
$$+ \frac{Ca}{8} + \frac{Cb}{27} + \frac{Cc}{64}$$
$$+ \frac{Da}{16}$$

where $P(1)$ is the probability that a given well in plate 2 contains only a single clone and

$y = S/R$ for the second subcloning

$x = S/R$ for the first subcloning

$A = \dfrac{\text{fraction of wells in second subcloning containing two cells } [F_2(2)]}{\text{fraction of wells in second subcloning showing any growth } (R_2)}$

$B = \dfrac{\text{fraction of wells in second subcloning containing three cells } [F_2(3)]}{R_2}$

$C = \dfrac{F_2(4)}{R_2}$,   etc.

$a = \dfrac{\text{fraction of wells in first subcloning containing two cells } [F_1(2)]}{\text{fraction of wells in first subcloning showing any growth } (R_1)}$

$b = \dfrac{F_1(3)}{R_1}$

$c = \dfrac{F_1(4)}{R_1}$,   etc.

TABLE II
PROBABILITY OF MONOCLONALITY OF CELLS
SUBCLONED TWICE

Percentage of wells showing growth in first subcloning	Maximum % of wells that can show growth in second subcloning and still achieve $P(1)$ of	
	0.95	0.99
5	—	75
10	—	49
15	93	36
20	86	30
25	74	20
30	66	18
35	60	15
40	53	12
45	45	10
50	43	9
55	38	8
60	35	7
65	32	6
70	29	5
75	27	4
80	24	4
85	21	3

The first part of the expression (y) takes into account the likelihood of monoclonality based solely on the second subcloning; the second part $x(1 - y)$ takes into account the increased probability of monoclonality in the second subcloning based upon the probability of monoclonality in the first subcloning; the complex third part of the equation takes into account the increased likelihood of monoclonality in the second subcloning derived from the above analysis of multicelled wells. It should be noted that our equation assumes that wells in the first plate that contain more than one cell type have equal numbers of each cell type. Should one cell type predominate over another, the likelihood of multicelled wells in the second plate being monoclonal would increase. In that sense, the equation should be considered a "worst case" analysis that provides the minimal probability of monoclonality.

A sample is given below:

On the first subcloning 70% of the wells show growth. From Table I, the mean number of cells per well is 1.2 and $(S/R)(x) = 0.517$.

On the second subcloning 25% of the wells show growth. From Table I, the mean number of cells per well is 0.29 and $(S/R)(y) = 0.861$.

$$A = 0.123 \qquad a = 0.310$$
$$B = 0.012 \qquad b = 0.124$$
$$c = 0.037$$

$$P(1) = y + x(1 - y) + \frac{Aa}{2} + \frac{Ab}{3} + \cdots$$

(consideration of additional multicelled wells would not add significantly to the final probability)

$$P(1) = 0.861 + 0.072 + 0.019 + 0.005 = 0.957$$

It can be seen that the first two parts of the expression make the major contribution to the final probability and thus the simplified expression $P(1) = y + x(1 - y)$ will give a minimal estimate that will be within a few percentage points of the final probability. It can also be used to estimate (actually slightly underestimate) the probability of monoclonality for additional subclonings if y is the S/R for the last subcloning performed and x is the $P(1)$ for all the previous subclonings.

Finally, Table II, based on the full equation for $P(1)$, was developed to assist the investigator in the simple and rapid determination of $P(1)$ for two repetitive subclonings. Based upon the percentage of wells showing any growth in the first subcloning, it indicates the maximum number of wells that can show growth in the second subcloning and still achieve a $P(1)$ of 0.95 or 0.99.

Acknowledgment

The work reported here was supported by Grant 19278 from the National Heart, Lung, and Blood Institute.

[38] A Method for Freezing Hybridoma Clones in 96-Well Microculture Plates

By David E. Wells and William F. Bibb

The production of monoclonal antibodies consists of four phases: (1) immunization, (2) fusion, (3) rapid identification of antibody-secreting cells, and (4) cloning and expansion of cells producing relevant antibody. The immunization and fusion phases are the least demanding, requiring a minimum investment in time and materials. The third phase is critical. It can be relatively simple or complex and demanding. Regardless of the difficulties one may encounter in this phase, identification of cells producing useful antibodies must be completed as rapidly as possible.[1,2] The length of time necessary to identify relevant clones, however, depends on (1) the number of clones generated, (2) the number of antigens used in screening cell supernatants, and (3) the number and or types of screening assays used. If one must search through the hundreds of thousands of cells which can be generated from one or more fusion experiments for a few cells meeting specific criteria (production of antibodies specific for a species- or genus-specific antigen, a subgroup-specific antigen, a tumor-specific antigen, a disease-specific antigen, or cells producing antibodies with unique specificities and functions), then extensive and often time-consuming testing, involving multiple and sometimes complex assays, has to be performed with each supernatant to identify cells producing useful antibodies. The laboratorian cannot indulge in the luxury of delaying the selection of cells for cloning while thorough evaluations of the hybridoma supernatants are being made. To delay cloning could result in the loss of cells secreting coveted antibodies due to overgrowth by irrelevant, non-antibody-secreting cells. Laboratories with limited resources can easily be overburdened and often are able to clone only a small fraction of the total antibody-producing cells identified and discard or expand (frequently in mixed culture) the remaining clones. Incomplete characterization of cell supernatants should be avoided, if at all possible, because it can result in the cloning and expansion of hybridomas of dubious value and the loss of rare, possibly valuable hybrids. The workload expands exponentially as the cloning and expansion phase progresses. What may have begun as a reasonable workload can easily multiply beyond manageability. Again, decisions have to be made rapidly as to which clones to reclone and which ones to discard or expand. Resources may restrict the number of subclones kept and characterized. Cryopreservation of the initial hybridomas generated in a fusion or their subclones in 96-well microculture plates enables researchers to cope more successfully with some of the technical limitations of hybridoma production referred to above.

The method for freezing hybridomas in 96-well microculture plates described in this chapter is one we have found to be useful in our laboratories. We routinely select hybridomas from 10–30 wells for cloning and expansion on the basis of full or partial characterization of culture super-

[1] J. W. Goding, *J. Immunol. Methods* **39**, 285 (1980).
[2] S. P. Kwan, D. E. Yelton, and M. D. Scharff, *Genet.* **2**, 31 (1980).

natants, and freeze the remaining hybridomas for future characterization and possible needs. The supernatant fluids aspirated from clones before freezing are evaluated as time permits. Recovery of our mouse hybridomas from freezer storage has consistently been between 95 and 100%. Similar methods for freezing newly formed hybridomas in batch culture and in 96-well microculture plates have been described.[3-6]

Methodology

General Comments

In microculture good cell culture techniques must be used to ensure 95–100% recovery of hybridomas from frozen storage. All manipulations must be done asceptically in a laminar flow cabinet. Successful freezing and recovery of hybridoma clones ultimately depends on the following five variables: (1) the metabolic and nutritional state of the cells at the time of freezing, (2) the freezing medium, (3) the freezing procedure, (4) the storage temperature, and (5) the recovery process.

The Cells. Cells should be healthy and in the logarithmic phase of growth before any attempt at cryopreservation is made. Healthy and actively growing mouse–mouse hybridoma cells (clones) derived from the fusion of immune mouse lymphoblasts with mouse myeloma and hybridoma cell lines X63-Ag8.653[7] and Sp2/0-Ag14,[8] respectively, are easily identified microscopically (100× magnification) by the rather smooth appearance of the cell membrane and by the presence of numerous large dividing cells. When examined by phase-contrast microscopy, viable cells are luminous and translucent and possess a dense central region which emits an orangish hue. Compared with healthy cells, unhealthy or dying cells are frequently smaller, have irregular or broken cell membranes, and have dark grainy cytoplasms.

Cells stressed by deprivation of nutrients as might occur in confluent wells or by prolonged exposure to severely acidic or alkaline cultural conditions usually can regain their vigor and be cryopreserved successfully if they are fed 2 or 3 consecutive days before freezing.

Although clones covering 1–100% of a well's surface are recoverable

[3] D. E. Wells and P. J. Price, *J. Immunol. Methods* **59,** 49 (1983).

[4] L. De Leij, S. Poppema, and T. H. The, *J. Immunol. Methods* **62,** 69 (1983).

[5] L. W. Harwell, M. Bolognino, J. M. Bidlack, R. J. Knapp, and E. M. Lord, *J. Immunol. Methods* **66,** 59 (1984).

[6] R. Patel and J. C. Brown, *J. Immunol Methods* **71,** 211 (1984).

[7] J. F. Kearney, A. Radbruch, and K. Rajawsky, *J. Immunol.* **123,** 1548 (1979).

[8] M. Shulman, C. D. Wilde, and G. Kohler, *Nature (London)* **276,** 269 (1978).

from freezer storage, we consider clones covering 15–50% of a well a good size for freezing.

The Freezing Medium. We use two freezing media. One of these is Dulbecco's modified Eagle's medium (DME) with 4.5 mg glucose/ml (GIBCO Laboratories, Buffalo, NY),[9] supplemented with 20% fetal bovine serum (FBS), $5 \times 10^{-5} M$ 2-mercaptoethanol, 584 mg glutamine/liter, 110 mg sodium pyruvate/ml, antibiotics (100 units penicillin G, sodium; 50 μg streptomycin sulfate; and 2 μg amphotericin B per milliliter), and 6% (v/v) dimethylsulfoxide (DMSO).

The other is Hy-Clone FBS (Sterile Systems, Logan, UT) supplemented with 8% (v/v) DMSO. Both work well. Generally, the cell culture medium used to cultivate cells can be used in conjunction with DMSO (5–10%) as the freezing medium. The freezing media may also contain hypoxanthine (H) $10^{-4} M$, aminopterin (A) $4 \times 10^{-7} M$, thymidine (T) $1.6 \times 10^{-5} M$ (HAT) or HT.

It has been suggested that HEPES buffer in the presence of DMSO may be toxic for cells.[10] However, we have found that there is no significant reduction in the percentage of clones recovered if 15 mM HEPES is added to the freezing medium. Although we do not normally incorporate HEPES buffer in our freezing or growth medium, its use permits better pH control of cultures when they are outside the CO_2 incubator.

The Freezing Procedure. Although some hearty cell lines can be frozen rapidly,[11] we have always attempted to slow the rate of freezing by inserting the microculture plates in size 4 or 5 insulated Jiffy shipping bags (Jiffy Packaging Company, High Point, NC) before placing the plates in a −80° mechanical freezer. We do not know if hybridoma clones would survive a more rapid freeze in an uninsulated plate. Harwell *et al.*,[5] however, reported freezing hybridomas in the vapor phase (−150 to −180°) of a liquid nitrogen freezer. Their work suggests that microcultures may survive a rapid freezing process.

When freezing clones in 96-well microculture plates they should be frozen in 50 μl of freezing medium. Freezing in larger volumes will lead to an increase in the time necessary to thaw cultures and may result in cell damage and death.

The Storage Temperature. Hybridomas frozen in 96-well microculture plates can be stored for 1–6 months at −70 to −80°.[3,6] If cells are to be

---

[9] Use of trade names and commercial sources is for identification only and does not constitute endorsement by the Public Health Service or the U.S. Department of Health and Human Services.

[10] R. H. Kennett, this series, Vol. 58, p. 356.

[11] D. Gray and S. H. Golub, this series, Vol. 108, p. 365.

stored for more extended periods we recommend that they be stored in the vapor phase of a liquid nitrogen freezer.

The Recovery Process. Upon removal from frozen storage, cells should be thawed as *rapidly* as possible, and the DMSO-containing medium aspirated and replaced with the same growth medium used before freezing. Peritoneal macrophage feeder cells must be used to consistently recover 95–100% of the frozen clones. Recovery of frozen clones may vary from 67 to 100% when feeder cells are not used.

The Cryopreservation Procedure

(1) All manipulations are done at room temperature (22°). (2) Developing clones that have not been stressed by lack of nutrients or by prolonged exposure to harmful acidic or alkaline cultural conditions are prepared for freezing the day before they are to be frozen by complete removal and saving of culture fluids and refeeding the cells with the appropriate growth medium. Refeeding unhealthy clones for 1–3 consecutive days before freezing may restore their viability and enable them to survive cryopreservation.

The next three steps should be completed as rapidly as possible. (3) All of the growth medium is aspirated from the wells of plates to be frozen using single or multichannel pipetting devices, or Pasteur pipetes. The tip(s) of the aspirating apparatus used is placed in a corner of a well and the fluid sucked out. If one does not need additional supernatant fluids for subsequent testing and if one is not overly concerned about the cross-mixing of hybridomas, a Pasteur pipet connected to a vacuum via a collection flask can be used to rapidly aspirate all wells of a plate. (4) Cold (4°) freezing medium is added to all wells containing cells to be frozen in aliquots of 50 μl (approximately one drop from a 10-ml disposable serologic pipet). Volumes of freezing medium larger than 50 μl are not recommended for use with this procedure. (5) The plate(s) is then immediately wrapped in plastic wrap, placed inside a sealed size 4 or 5 insulated Jiffy shipping bag, and frozen by transfer to a -70 to $-80°$ freezer. After 16–24 hr, the plate(s) can be transferred to the vapor phase of a liquid nitrogen freezer for extended storage.

Recovery of Hybridoma Clones from Frozen Storage

(1) Media in wells containing frozen clones should be thawed rapidly (whenever possible, within 5 min after removal from freezer storage) by the addition of 0.3 ml of prewarmed (37–41°) growth medium (pH 6.8–7.8) to all wells of the plate(s). (2) The plate(s) is then incubated at 37° in a 15% CO_2 environment until the contents of the wells have thawed, usually 1–5

min. The incubation period should be as short as possible. (3) The medium is aspirated from all wells and replaced with 200 μl of growth medium (37°) containing approximately $1-4 \times 10^4$ peritoneal macrophage feeder cells. Feeder cells are essential for recovery of 95–100% of the frozen clones. (4) The plate(s) is then incubated in a CO_2 incubator (15% CO_2) at 37°, 95% relative humidity. (5) Viable clones (cells) can be observed by phase-contrast microscopy immediately or the next day. (6) After 3–5 days, viable clones can be tested for production of antibodies, cloned, or expanded.

Discussion

Some newly formed antibody-producing hybridomas are genetically unstable and may cease to produce or secrete antibody due to chromosome loss. Cloned hybridomas of any age are also susceptible to spontaneous loss of antibody production. We were therefore concerned about freezing nascent hybridomas before they were expanded or cloned. However, our experience and that of others[4] suggest that freezing newly formed hybridomas does not increase genetic instability. Clones producing antibody before they are frozen usually continue to produce antibody upon reconstitution from freezer storage.

The method we describe for freezing and recovering antibody-producing hybridomas in 96-well microculture plates is simple and rapid, requires a minimum number of manipulations, and eliminates the necessity of expanding cells prior to freezing. Hybridomas generated in the initial culture plates or in subsequent cloning plates that cover 1–100% of the surface of a well can be frozen and recovered. Investigators adopting this method can (1) thoroughly evaluate cell supernatants before selecting cells for cloning, (2) preserve possibly valuable hybridomas not initially selected for cloning, (3) distribute workloads to more manageable levels, (4) provide time, if required, to modify or refine the screening assay(s), and (5) preserve numerous subclones of important clones with minimum effort.

Our experience with this freezing method has been limited to mouse–mouse hybridomas. Investigators working with other types of hybridomas, such as interspecies hybridomas (mouse–human, etc.) or human–human, are encouraged to first demonstrate the survival of established hybrids of similar origin or parental cell lines when frozen as small clones before they use this method on their valuable hybridomas.

Acknowledgments

We are grateful to Roger McKinney for reviewing the manuscript and Debbie Hooper for typing it.

Section II

Monoclonal Antibodies

A. Screening Assays for Monoclonal Antibodies
Articles 39 through 55

B. Purification of Monoclonal Antibodies and Preparation
of Antibody Fragments
Articles 56 through 65

[39] Multivalent Antibody Radioimmunoassay (MARIA) for Screening Specific Antibody Secretion by Lymphocyte Hybridoma Cultures

By J. GHEUENS and D. E. McFARLIN

Many different types of assays are being used to screen lymphocyte hybridoma cultures for specific antibody secretion. Most commonly, the culture supernatants to be tested are first reacted with solid-phase antigen. Subsequently, the presence of specific antibody bound to the antigen is assessed using a labeled anti-immunoglobulin reagent. Many variations exist on this theme. The substance to which antigen is bound can be, for example, polyvinyl chloride beads, cups, or plates, nitrocellulose filters, microcrystalline cellulose, or polydextrans. Sometimes the antigen is available in a form such as a tissue section or microorganism which can be used directly as a solid phase. The anti-immunoglobulin reagent can be labeled with radioactive isotope, enzyme, or fluorochrome, depending on the detection system one prefers. Apart from technical factors, such as appropriate antigen reactivity, labeling of the anti-immunoglobulin, and standardization of the detection procedure, the success of such assays is highly dependent on the quality of the anti-immunoglobulin reagent. To provide the broadest screening capabilities, this needs to have sufficient reactivity to detect hybridoma-secreted immunoglobulin of any class, subclass, and type. In addition, the anti-immunoglobulin reagent should not cross-react with the antigen. This requires considerable precautions when monoclonal antibodies are produced against immunoglobulins, in particular when monoclonal antiidiotypic antibodies are made.

These considerations are not limited to screening procedures for monoclonal antibodies. They also apply to methods designed to detect serum autoantiidiotypic antibodies. Such methods are of increasing importance as the concept of the immune system as a functioning idiotype–antiidiotype network gains experimental support and becomes of clinical interest.

The assay described here makes use only of solid-phase antigen and soluble labeled antigen to detect specific antibody, and therefore offers an alternative to the use of an anti-immunoglobulin reagent. Its principle is based on the multivalency of antibodies. Supernatant of the culture to be tested is first incubated with solid-phase antigen. In a second step, labeled soluble antigen is added. If specific antibody was present in the sample, labeled antigen will be bound to the solid phase. Because of its principle,

Copyright © 1986 by Academic Press, Inc.

this method was termed multivalent antibody radioimmunoassay (MARIA).[1]

Material and Methods

Cellulose-Coupled Antigen

Cellulose Activation with Cyanogen Bromide (CNBr). This procedure[2] is done entirely in a chemical fume hood. First, 25 g CNBr is dissolved in 1 liter of distilled water. This is done at room temperature, by magnetic stirring, in a glass Erlenmeyer flask with glass or aluminum foil-covered rubber stopper. Subsequently, the CNBr solution is transferred to a glass beaker in which a pH electrode is placed. Next, 25 g of microcrystalline cellulose (as used in thin-layer chromatography, e.g., Merck Art. 2330 or Baker TLC) is added to the CNBr solution, which is stirred magnetically. Immediately, 1 N sodium hydroxide is added dropwise to the mixture so that the pH is maintained between 10.5 and 11.0. After 6 min, the mixture is transferred to a Büchner filter on a side-arm flask under vacuum, and washed with 2.5 liters of ice-cold distilled water, 250 ml 50% acetone p.a., 250 ml 75% acetone p.a., and 250 ml acetone p.a. The CNBr-activated cellulose is then left to dry overnight at room temperature. It is then stored frozen at $-20°$.

Antigen for Coupling to CNBr-Activated Cellulose. The antigen is dissolved in 0.1 M sodium bicarbonate. When immunoglobulin is used as antigen, it can first be precipitated from serum or hybridoma ascites with 18% sodium sulfate. After one wash with 18% sodium sulfate, the precipitate can then be dissolved directly in 0.1 M sodium bicarbonate, and used for coupling.

Preparation of Cellulose–CNBr-Coupled Antigen. All incubations and washes are done at room temperature by end-over-end rotation, followed by centrifugation of the suspension at 2200 g for 10 min and aspiration of the supernatant. A plastic 15 ml tube with cap is used. Typically, 1 g of CNBr-activated cellulose is incubated with 1.5 mg of antigen in 5 ml 0.1 M sodium bicarbonate. After 24 hr the cellulose is washed twice for 20 min with 0.5 M sodium bicarbonate. Next, 10 ml sodium acetate buffer (pH 4.0) is added to the cellulose. The suspension is gently stirred with a spatula until CO_2 formation is no longer apparent and then incubated for an additional 60 min. This is followed by a second incubation in 10 ml

[1] J. Gheuens and D. E. McFarlin, *J. Immunol. Methods* **47**, 183 (1981).
[2] M. Noppe, A. Lowenthal, D. Karcher, and J. Gheuens, *J. Immunol. Methods* **27**, 75 (1979).

0.1 M sodium acetate (pH 4.0) for 16 hr. Subsequently, the cellulose is washed twice for 20 min in 0.05 M sodium phosphate buffer (pH 7.5) with 0.05% (w/v) sodium azide, 0.5% (w/v) bovine serum albumin, and 0.5% (v/v) Tween 20 (BSA buffer). The cellulose is then suspended to 10 ml in BSA buffer (10% cellulose suspension) and stored frozen in aliquots until further use.

Adsorption of Antigen to Plastic Plates

Antigen is diluted in a 0.015 M Na$_2$CO$_3$–0.035 M NaHCO$_3$ solution. The optimal concentration of antigen has to be established for each application, but generally lies between 5 and 50 μg/ml. Fifty microliters of this antigen solution is applied in each well of polyvinyl chloride flat-bottomed 96-well plates (Falcon 3912). The plates are covered and stored overnight at 4°. The next day the antigen solution is removed from the wells. The plates are washed three times with 0.1 M sodium phosphate buffer (pH 7.4) containing 0.15 M sodium chloride and 2% fetal calf serum (PBS with 2% FCS). Next, the plates are incubated with PBS with 2% FCS for 2 hr at room temperature.

Radiolabeling of Antigen

A modification of the chloramine-T method is used.[3] In brief, 5 μg of purified antigen in 50 μl 0.4 M sodium phosphate buffer (pH 7.4) is added to 1 mCi Na^{125}I (10 μl). Next, 20 μl of a 2 mg chloramine-T/ml solution is added. After 60 sec, the reaction is stopped by adding 40 μl of a 2 mg sodium metabisulfite/ml solution. The labeled antigen is then separated from free iodine by gel filtration on a Sephadex G-75 column (bed volume 5 ml), equilibrated in 0.01 M veronal-buffered saline (pH 7.8) containing 10% fetal calf serum. The iodination efficiency is between 20 and 35%.

Assay Procedure

In this section, the general procedures for doing the assay are described. Optimization of assay conditions is described in the next section, in which actual examples are given.

Using Cellulose-Coupled Antigen. Clear, round-bottomed capped polystyrene tubes (12 × 75 mm) (Markson R-5541 or Multilab BR.005.13) are used. BSA buffer is used as diluent throughout the procedure. All incubations are done at room temperature by end-over-end rotation. Washes are done by adding 3 ml of BSA buffer to each of the tubes,

---

[3] E. S. Mingioli, W. Strober, W. W. Tourtelotte, J. M. Whitaker, and D. E. McFarlin, *Neurology* **28**, 991 (1978).

followed by centrifugation at 2200 g for 10 min and by aspiration of the supernatant.

For the assay, the sample to be tested (200 μl) is first incubated with 500 μl of a 1 : 150 dilution of cellulose–CNBr-bound antigen (0.07% cellulose suspension) for 16–24 hr. After one wash, 500 μl of labeled antigen (75,000 cpm) is added to each tube and incubated for 16 hr. Afterwards, the cellulose-bound antigen is washed once again, and counted for 1 min in a gamma counter.

Using Antigen-Coated Plates. PBS with 2% FCS is used as diluent. All incubations are done on a rocking platform at room temperature. Washes are most conveniently done by spraying the plates with PBS with 2% FCS, followed by aspiration of the fluid from the wells and drying the top of the plates with paper towel.

For the assay, the PBS with 2% FCS is aspirated from the wells of the antigen-coated plates. The sample to be tested (50 μl) is then applied to the well. After 4 hr of incubation, the wells are aspirated and washed three times. Next, 50 μl of labeled antigen (35,000 cpm) is added to each well. After 2 hr of incubation, the labeled antigen is removed, and the plates are washed three times. The wells are cut from the plate with a hot-wire and counted for 1 min in a gamma counter.

Examples

Screening Assay for Detection of Monoclonal Antiidiotypic Antibody by Lymphocyte Hybridoma Cultures

The antigen in this case was a BALB/c monoclonal antibody to measles virus hemagglutinin (HA), termed C2.[4] The MARIA was developed and optimized using syngeneic antiidiotypic antisera, raised in BALB/c mice by immunization with a keyhole limpet hemocyanin conjugate of the monoclonal C2 antibody.[5] The MARIA was used as screening assay for the detection of monoclonal antiidiotypic antibody.[1]

First, cellulose–CNBr-coupled C2 (C2–cellulose), and ^{125}I-labeled C2 were prepared as described above. Next, the optimal dilution of solid-phase antigen was established. This was done by incubating serial dilutions of C2–cellulose for 16 hr with normal BALB/c or syngeneic anti-C2 antisera, diluted 1 : 500. After one wash, the C2–cellulose was incubated

[4] D. E. McFarlin, W. J. Bellini, E. S. Mingioli, T. N. Behar, and A. Trudgett, *J. Gen. Virol.* **48,** 425 (1980).
[5] J. Gheuens, D. E. McFarlin, K. W. Rammohan, and W. J. Bellini, *Infect. Immun.* **34,** 200 (1981).

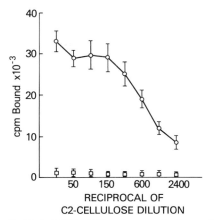

FIG. 1. Binding of radiolabeled C2 to different concentrations of C2–cellulose, by syngeneic anti-C2 serum, 1 : 500 (○), and normal BALB/c serum, 1 : 500 (□). At a 1 : 150 dilution
of C2–cellulose, the ratio of specific binding to nonspecific binding was optimal. Results are
the mean ± SEM of duplicate determinations.

with ^{125}I-labeled C2 (75,000 cpm) for another 16 hr. It was then washed
again, and counted. The results (Fig. 1) indicated that a 1 : 150 dilution of
the 10% C2–cellulose suspension was optimal for further studies, as
higher dilutions lowered the binding capacity, and lower dilutions did not
increase it. Subsequently, optimal incubation times were determined. To
do this, assays were performed using a 1 : 150 dilution of C2–cellulose,
and identical serum samples and amounts of radiolabeled C2 as in the
preceding experiment. In one set of such assays, the first incubation time
was varied from 4 to 48 hr, while the second incubation time was constant
at 16 hr. In another set of assays, the first incubation time was 16 hr,
whereas the second incubation time was varied from 4 to 48 hr. The
results showed (Fig. 2) that the optimal time for the first incubation was
between 16 and 24 hr, and that nonspecific binding increased when the
second incubation was 24 hr or longer (Fig. 3). It was also shown that
substantial but suboptimal specific binding was obtained with both incubation periods as short as 4 hr. In subsequent assays, a first incubation of
16–24 hr was used, and a second incubation of 16 hr. It was then determined that tissue culture medium supplemented with 7.5% fetal calf serum and 7.5% γ-globulin-free horse serum, and the BALB/c IgM
myeloma protein TEPC183 did not increase nonspecific binding in the
test.
     The assay was used successfully to screen lymphocyte hybridoma
cultures for antibody secretion to C2. These cultures had been established

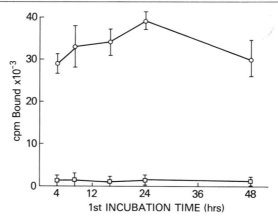

FIG. 2. Effect on the assay of varying the duration of the first incubation. A 1 : 150 dilution of C2–cellulose is used. Syngeneic anti-C2 serum, 1 : 500 (○), and normal BALB/c serum, 1 : 500 (□), were used as sample. The second incubation time was 16 hr. Substantial but suboptimal binding occurred with a first incubation time of 4 hr. Incubation for over 24 hr resulted in lower specific binding. Results are mean ± SEM of duplicate determinations.

after fusion of spleen cells from a BALB/c mouse, immunized with C2 hybridoma product, and P3/NS1/1-Ag4-1 myeloma cells. Syngeneic anti-C2 serum, diluted 1 : 1000, was used as positive control. The level of nonspecific binding was established using culture medium. A hybridoma

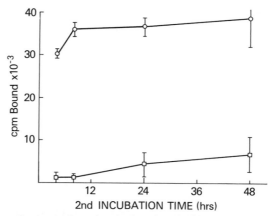

FIG. 3. Effect on the assay of varying the duration of the second incubation. C2–cellulose dilution and samples were as in Fig. 2. The first incubation time was 16 hr. With a second incubation time of 24 hr, nonspecific binding was increased. Results are mean ± SEM of duplicate determinations.

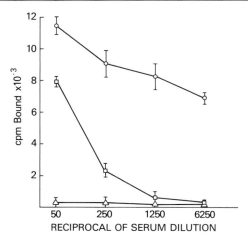

FIG. 4. MARIA to detect antibody to human IgG. Rabbit antiserum to this IgG (○), commercially available rabbit anti-human IgG (□), and normal rabbit serum (△) were used as samples. Results are mean ± SEM of duplicate determinations.

supernatant was considered positive when the radioactivity bound by it was greater than the level of nonspecific binding plus two standard deviations. Using this criterion five hybridomas were selected; three secreted monoclonal antiidiotypic antibody to the C2 anti-HA antibody, and two secreted monoclonal antibody specific for the idiotype of the P3X63 myeloma protein, which was also present in the C2 hybridoma product.[1,6]

MARIA for Detection of Antibody to Immunoglobulin G

The antigen in this example was IgG purified from serum of a patient with subacute sclerosing panencephalitis. This IgG was used to coat polyvinyl chloride plates and an aliquot was radioiodinated as described in the previous section. Two different anti-IgG sera were used as samples to develop the assay. One was raised in a rabbit against the IgG that was used in the MARIA. The other was a commercial rabbit anti-human IgG serum. Normal rabbit serum was used as control.

Of the several IgG concentrations that were used for coating the plates, 20 μg/ml gave the best results with the procedure described in the previous section. At this concentration, levels of nonspecific binding with normal rabbit serum were minimal, whereas specific binding obtained using different dilutions of the anti-IgG sera as samples was high (Fig. 4).

[6] J. Gheuens and D. E. McFarlin, *Eur. J. Immunol.* **12**, 701 (1982).

Discussion

The examples given illustrate that this type of assay is a reliable alternative procedure for detection of specific antibody secretion by lymphocyte hybridoma cultures. There are two instances in which an assay of this type offers significant advantages over the more commonly used ones, in which a labeled anti-immunoglobulin reagent is used to detect specific antibody. First, in the detection of monoclonal antibodies to immunoglobulins, the potential problem of cross-reaction between the labeled anti-immunoglobulin reagent and the antigen is eliminated. Second, the assay can be useful in some instances when only limited amounts of pure antigen are available. It is not uncommon that relatively large amounts of a crude antigen preparation, but only limited amounts of pure antigen, are available. If that is the case, the crude antigen preparation can be used for immunization and for preparation of a solid phase, whereas a small amount of pure antigen can be labeled and be used in the second incubation. Thus, specificity of the screening assay can be assured with only microgram quantities of pure antigen available. The major limitation of the MARIA is that it obviously can only be applied in instances in which antigen can be made available in a solid-phase as well as a labeled soluble form.

There are different relative advantages of cellulose–CNBr-coupled antigen, or polyvinyl chloride-coupled antigen as solid phase (table). Though somewhat more complex to prepare, both cyanogen bromide-activated cellulose and cellulose-coupled antigen can be stored frozen in concentrated suspensions for several months without losing their activity. This offers an advantage over coated plates. On the other hand, the washes required during the procedure are more easily performed and require fewer manipulations when antigen-coated plates rather than cellulose-coupled antigen are used. Sensitivity appears to be similar with use of cellulose-coupled antigen and antigen-coated plates. The useful range

COMPARISON OF CELLULOSE-COUPLED ANTIGEN
AND ANTIGEN-COATED PLATES[a]

	Cellulose	Plates
Storage	+	−
Washes	−	+
Sensitivity	=	=
Range	+	−

[a] Symbols: +, superior; −, inferior; =, equivalent.

of this assay appears to be greater when solid-phase antigen, rather than antigen-coated plates, are used.

Like any other radioimmunoassay, the MARIA requires the necessary precautions in storing and handling radioactive isotope and radioactive biologicals and proper disposal of solid and liquid radioactive waste.

[40] A Rapid Technique Using Radiolabeled Soluble Antigen to Screen Hybridoma Culture Supernatants

By K. F. MILLER, D. J. BOLT, and R. A. GOLDSBY

Production of specific monoclonal antibodies requires the screening of large numbers of hybridomas in order to identify those which secrete immunoglobulin with the desired specificity. Screening has commonly been done with an indirect solid-phase immunoassay.

With the solid-phase screen, the antigen is placed in the wells of microtiter plates where it binds to the plastic surface. The wells are washed to remove nonbound antigen and filled with supernatants from hybridoma cultures. Antibody from hybridoma cultures that bind to the immobilized antigen are identified with the aid of a second, polyclonal, antiserum. This second antibody attaches to the hybridoma-derived mouse immunoglobulins that have bound to the antigen immobilized on the microtiter plate. The second antibody–hybridoma antibody complex is detected by either radioactivity[1] or an enzyme[2] on the second antibody.

Although solid-phase screens require relatively large amounts of antigen, a more serious disadvantage may occur when the screen is for monoclonal antibody to be used for detecting antigens in solution, such as in radioimmunoassays. Some monoclonal antibodies may be so specific that they do not recognize antigen immobilized on plastic and antigen in solution equally.

To maximize the chances of detecting a useful monoclonal antibody for solution phase uses, a solution-phase screen was devised.[3] Hybridoma culture supernatants were incubated with nanogram quantities of radiolabeled antigen. Hybridoma antibody capable of binding antigen in solution

[1] J. D. Rosenthal, K. Hayashi, and A. L. Notkins, *Appl. Microbiol.* **25,** 567 (1973).
[2] R. M. Kennett, *in* "Monoclonal Antibodies" (R. M. Kennett, T. J. McKearn, and K. B. Bechtol, eds.), p. 376. Plenum, New York, 1980.
[3] K. F. Miller, D. J. Bolt, and R. A. Goldsby, *J. Immunol. Methods* **59,** 277 (1983).

was detected with the aid of polyclonal antibody to mouse immunoglobulin that was coupled to Sepharose beads. Radioactivity associated with the Sepharose beads was thus dependent on the presence of hybridoma immunoglobulin that possessed the ability to bind the radiolabeled antigen in solution.

Procedures

Preparation of Screening Immunoadsorbent. A commercial preparation (Pharmacia) of freeze-dried cyanogen bromide-activated Sepharose 4B was swollen in 2 mM HCl for 15 min. The gel was then washed once in a 0.1 M NaHCO$_3$ buffer (pH 8.3, with 0.5 M NaCl). Mouse immunoglobulin dissolved in the NaHCO$_3$ buffer was added to the swollen gel at a concentration of 5–6 mg/g of dry gel and mixed gently for 2 hr at room temperature. The protein solution was removed and replaced with 0.2 M glycine in NaHCO$_3$ buffer to block any remaining active groups. After incubation overnight at 4° the gel was washed six times, alternating the NaHCO$_3$ buffer and an acetate buffer (0.1 M, pH 4.0 with 0.5 M NaCl). The gel was washed twice with PBS and used as the affinity reagent to purify sheep antibodies to mouse immunoglobulin. Polyclonal antibodies to mouse myeloma proteins were obtained by ammonium sulfate precipitation of immunized sheep serum. The precipitate was redissolved in PBS and applied to the mouse Ig–Sepharose column. The column was washed and the specifically bound sheep antibodies were then eluted by lowering the pH to 3. This fraction was neutralized and coupled to cyanogen bromide-activated Sepharose as before and served as the specific sheep anti-mouse immunoglobulin screening immunoadsorbent.

Radioiodination of Antigen. Iodogen was dissolved in chloroform to make a 20 μg/ml working stock. This can be stored in the dark for several months. The radioiodination vial was prepared by adding 50 μl (1 μg) of Iodogen working stock to a 1-ml glass vial and removing the chloroform by drying under a stream of N$_2$. Ten micrograms of antigen in a 1-ml glass vial was dissolved in 35 μl of 0.5 M NaPO$_4$ (pH 7.4). The dissolved antigen was transferred to the radioiodination vial and quickly sealed with a septum cap before the addition of radioactivity. Five hundred μCi ^{125}I was added to the radioiodination vial with a Hamilton syringe and gently mixed for 10 min with a vortex mixer fitted with a rubber stopper to hold the radioiodination vial. The reaction was stopped with the addition of 0.2 ml 0.5 M NaPO$_4$ containing 5 μg of sodium metabisulfite and transferred to an anion-exchange column (Bio-Rad AG 2 × 8) to remove the nonprotein bound radioactivity. The protein-bound radioactivity was eluted by the addition of 2.5 ml 1% BSA–PBS. A Geiger Muller survey meter can be used to estimate the incorporation of radioactivity into protein by readings made at a uniform distance (e.g., 10 cm) from the anion-exchange column, which represents the non-protein-bound radioactivity and the column effluent plus the rinsed radioiodination vial, which represents the protein-bound radioactivity. Percentage incorporation should range from 50 to 80%. The amount of radioactivity needed to radioiodinate antigens with smaller molecular weight will be proportionately greater to maintain a similar molar ratio of radioactivity to antigen.

Screening Protocol. The screening immunoadsorbent was used at a dilution corresponding to 20–30 ml per gram of dry Sepharose 4B. One drop (50 μl) of this suspension in phosphate-buffered saline with 0.1% bovine serum albumin (PBS–BSA) was added to each well of a 96-well poly(vinyl chloride) microtiter plate. The wells were then filled with PBS–BSA, centrifuged at 800 g for 5 min, and the liquid removed by gentle inversion of the plate. One drop of radioiodinated antigen (10,000–20,000 cpm/well) and one drop of culture supernatants or dilutions of mouse sera were then added. The plates were mixed briefly on a Cooke Microtiter Mixer and incubated at room temperature for 2–4 hr. The wells were washed two to four times with 0.2 ml PBS–BSA and centrifuged at 800 g for 3 min. The liquid was removed, and one to two drops of hot agarose (1%) were added to hold the beads in the bottoms of the wells. The plates were then cut apart with a hot wire device (D. Lee Co., Sunnyvale, CA) and each well counted in a gamma counter.

Alternatively, the screening procedure was carried out in 12 × 75-mm glass tubes. The procedure was the same except that at the end of the incubation period, 2 ml of PBS–BSA was added and liquid was removed by aspiration after centrifugation.

Indirect Solid-Phase Radioimmunoassay. For purposes of comparison, supernatants and sera were also tested in an indirect solid-phase immunoassay system. In each well of a 96-well microtiter plate, one drop (50 μl) of a solution of the test antigen (100 μg/ml) was incubated overnight at 4°. Prior to addition of test supernatants, the antigen was removed and plates washed as before, once with 1% BSA in PBS and three times with PBS–BSA. After 1 hr at room temperature, the supernatants were removed, plates were washed three times with PBS–BSA, and radioiodinated sheep antibody to mouse immunoglobulin was added (15,000–20,000 cpm/well). Incubation was continued for an additional hour; the plates were then washed three times with PBS–BSA, dried, cut apart, and counted as before.

Results

We have used the solution-phase screening test with thousands of hybridoma supernatants. It has proved to be a useful and reliable tool.

The results of screening selected supernatants and sera for antibodies to bovine follicle-stimulating hormone using both the immunoadsorbent screening system (Fig. 1) and the solid-phase systems (Fig. 2) are shown. The results are expressed relative to the counts bound by culture medium or normal mouse serum for culture supernatants or sera from tumor-bearing mice, respectively. Samples that bound more than twice the background level were defined as positive. For the group shown, two supernatants were clearly positive in both systems. In addition, a third supernatant gave a positive response only in the solid-phase system. Of the sera, two were positive in the solid-phase system, but not the solution system, while a third serum was only positive in the solution system. Examination of the clones which were positive only in the solid-phase system indicated that the cells did secrete immunoglobulin but that the binding was not specific for FSH. These are examples of clones that secreted something that appeared to bind to antigen-coated plastic but not to antigen in solution.

Several attempts were made to reduce the nonspecific binding of antibody to plastic in the solid-phase assay. However, using a different protein (ovalbumin) or a different concentration of BSA (5-fold less or 5-fold greater) did not alter the results.

This solution-phase screening test, like the traditional solid-phase screen, has the characteristics of speed (2 hr) and large sample-handling

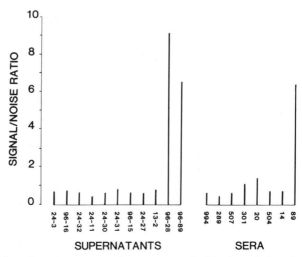

FIG. 1. Selected supernatants and sera screened with the solution-phase technique. Signal/noise ratio is counts bound by test substance divided by counts bound by negative control.

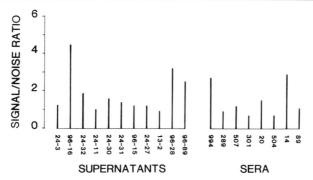

Fig. 2. Selected supernatants and sera screened with the solid-phase technique. Signal/noise ratio is counts bound by test substance divided by counts bound by negative control.

capacity. However, there are several advantages of the solution screening test not shared by the solid-phase screen. The first is less chance for false positives or negatives due to sticking of substances to the plates. This problem has been encountered at times in the solid-phase system when immunoglobulin concentrations were high. Certain immunoglobulin sticks nonspecifically to the plate and is therefore detected by the labeled sheep antibody to mouse immunoglobulin. Solid-phase screening will also yield false negative results if the antigenic determinant is obscured or altered when the antigen is coated to the plastic plate. A second major advantage of the solution-phase screen is in the conservation of rare or valuable antigens. In the solid-phase system, nearly 500 μg of antigen was needed to coat a single plate. However, in the solution phase system we describe, 5 μg or less of antigen can be radioiodinated and used for screening thousands of samples. A third advantage is the inherent selection of antibodies with high affinity because of the small amounts of antigen used in screening. The fourth advantage is the generally higher signal to noise ratio of the solution-phase system.

In summary, a rapid screening technique has been described for detecting antibody specific for a soluble antigen. This method can easily be adapted to other soluble antigens and should prove useful for rapidly screening large numbers of hybridoma culture supernatants.

[41] Culture-Well Solid-Phase ^{3}H-RIA for the Isotype-Specific Measurement of Antibody from Mouse and Human Antibody-Secreting Cells

By PATRICIA K. A. MONGINI and CLARE BLESSINGER

Antibody-producing cells (APC) from *in vivo* lymphatic tissue or from *in vitro* cultures of lymphoid cells have often been measured with the plaque-forming cell (PFC) assay.[1] This assay permits the quantitation and actual visualization of individual cells secreting antibody to a given antigen and has contributed significantly to the analysis of questions in cellular immunology. However, attempts to apply this assay to every experimental situation has revealed some of its inherent limitations. Thus, not every antigen can be effectively coupled to the red blood cells (RBC) which are used as indicators, and in cases where coupling is achieved, the antigen-coupled RBC can be unstable. The PFC assay is also limited in the ease with which cells that secrete antibody of isotypes other than IgM can be detected. Because IgG and IgA antibody are relatively inefficient at causing the lysis of antigen-coupled RBC, isotype-specific developing sera are necessary.[1] Since extensive APC analyses require considerable amounts of these antisera, the study of certain isotypic responses is often not very feasible. Isotype-specific assays of human antibody-producing cells are particularly compromised by the scarcity of good subclass developing sera.

The above problems encountered with the PFC assay have encouraged the use of solid-phase ^{125}I-RIAs and enzyme-linked immunosorbent assays (ELISA) for the detection of soluble-antibody in the supernatants of *in vitro* cultured cells.[2-5] These assays are widely used for the assay of antibody in hybridoma cell cultures. The advantages of these solid-phase assays have been the ease with which they can be performed, the ability of most antigens to bind to poly(vinyl chloride) (PVC) microtiter wells used for detection of antibody in the assay, the requirement for considerably lower amounts of isotype-specific antibody to produce probes which

---

[1] C. Henry, *in* "Selected Methods in Cellular Immunology" (B. B. Mishell and S. M. Shiigi, eds.) p. 69. Freeman, San Francisco, California, 1980.

[2] N. R. Klinman, *J. Exp. Med.* **136**, 241 (1972).

[3] T. T. Tsu and L. A. Herzenberg, *in* "Selected Methods in Cellular Immunology" (B. B. Mishell and S. M. Shiigi, eds.), p. 373. Freeman, San Francisco, California, 1980.

[4] E. Engvall and P. Perlman, *Immunochemistry* **8**, 871 (1971).

[5] J. F. Kearney, A. Radbruch, B. Liesegang, and K. Rajewsky, *J. Immunol.* **123**, 1548 (1979).

quantitate the secreted antibody, and the ability to quantitate antibody responses in a less subjective fashion.

The culture-well assay system for detection of APC described here is a modification of solid-phase assays for antibody in culture supernatant. While it shares the above-discussed advantages of these assays, it appears to be slightly more sensitive at detecting antibody from APC.[6] In addition, it obviates certain undesirable aspects of the assays which measure antibody in culture supernatant, i.e., the inability to directly measure antibody secretion from APC taken from *in vivo* lymphoid tissue, and the diminished ability to detect *in vitro* antigen-induced antibody because of competing soluble antigen in the culture supernatant.

The culture-well assay described here uses ³H-labeled anti-Ig antibody probes. These endow this assay with a sensitivity that is not always achievable with radioiodinated or enzyme-conjugated anti-Ig probes.

Principle

The culture-well solid-phase RIA measures antibody produced from APC at the peak in their antibody-producing potential, as does the plaque-forming cell assay. The assay involves incubating washed APC for short-periods ($\leq$24 hr) on antigen-coated, flexible, flat-bottomed, PVC culture wells. Secreted antibody which binds to the culture wells is subsequently detected with ³H-radiolabeled anti-Ig antibody probes. A schematic of the steps involved in the culture-well RIA is illustrated in Fig. 1.

Procedure for Culture-Well RIA

(1) Nonsterile, flat-bottomed, flexible PVC microtiter plates (Dynatech Laboratories, Alexandria, VA) are aseptically removed from their packing box and washed twice with sterile saline. This involves flooding the wells and discarding the saline by quickly inverting the plate and flicking out remaining fluid. It should be noted that although the flexible plates available are in nonsterile form, the combination of aseptic technique, sterile saline wash, and the inclusion of gentamicin in the subsequent assay culture medium have prevented detectable bacterial growth during the culture phase of the assay.

(2) After washing, the plates are immediately covered with a sterile plastic lid (Falcon Microtest II) available from Falcon Plastics, Cockeysville, MD, and placed in a hood.

(3) Wells to be used for cell culture are precoated with antigen (or anti-Ig antibody) to create a solid-phase ligand for secreted Ig. The anti-

[6] P. K. A. Mongini and E. Heber-Katz, *J. Immunol. Methods* **49**, 39 (1982).

Wells coated with antigen or anti–light chain Ab

Cells added to washed wells

Short–term incubation at 37°, 5% CO_2

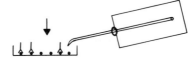

Cells washed from culture wells

^{3}H–anti–Ig antibody added

Cpm ^{3}H–Ab bound counted

FIG. 1. Schematic of steps in short-term, culture-well, solid-phase ^{3}H-RIA for secreted Ig.

gen or anti-Ig antibody should be in pure form for maximal sensitivity of the assay. A sterile solution of ligand, 50 μl, in phosphate-buffered saline (PBS) (pH 7.4) is added to each well and incubated for 1 hr at room temperature. The concentration of the ligand solution used for coating wells depends upon the species used. We have found that a 10 μg/ml concentration of TNP_{15}–BSA can optimally coat assay wells while maximal coating of Ig proteins does not occur unless concentrations of 50–100 μg/ml are used. After the 1-hr incubation, antigen-coated plates can be frozen at -20 or -70° to eliminate the antigen-coating step on the day of the assay.

(4) Antigen-coated wells are washed free of soluble antigen by flooding the plate with sterile saline or PBS. The washing procedure is repeated four times. To avoid denaturation of the bound ligand at this stage in the assay, the wells are never allowed to dry. The next step should be initiated as soon as possible.

(5) Next, nonspecific sites are blocked. After allowing ligand to bind nonspecifically to the PVC wells, steps must be taken to prevent further nonspecific binding of secreted Ig or the ³H-anti-Ig probes. With one exception, this can usually be achieved when APC are transferred to the wells in culture medium containing 15% fetal calf serum (FCS). The high protein concentration in FCS results in the effective blocking of most remaining sites on the PVC wells. However, the FCS-mediated blocking does not appear to be very efficient at saturating sites to which secreted IgM can nonspecifically bind. Whether the increased "stickiness" of IgM, in contrast to IgG or IgA, for PVC wells is due to its polymeric nature or due to its charge characteristics is not known. The nonspecific binding of secreted IgM to PVC culture wells can be somewhat reduced by introducing a deliberate blocking step between the ligand-coating step and the step in which APC are transferred to the culture wells. The blocking step is used only when specific IgM antibody is to be measured and involves incubating 100 μl of a 10% BSA solution for 30 min in each well previously coated with ligand.

(6) Single-cell suspensions of washed APC from *in vitro* culture or *in vivo* lymphoid tissue are transferred to the washed, ligand-coated culture wells (100 μl of cell suspension per well). We routinely use RPMI 1640 + 15% FCS + 2 mM L-glutamine + 50 μg gentamicin/ml as the culture medium. A number of different cell concentrations are cultured to assure that the secreted antibody is titratable and does not saturate the ligand on the wells. Triplicates are generally made of each cell concentration to provide statistics for each point in the binding curve generated when cell number is plotted against bound counts per minute. The addition of filler cells to maintain some critical cell density during the secretion phase of the assay does not appear necessary. Our experience has indicated that the presence of thymocyte filler cells does not improve the secretory potential of small numbers of hybridoma cells during this short-term culture.

(7) Negative controls for background are routinely included. These consist of (a) specific ligand-coated wells which contain culture medium but no APC and (b) irrelevant ligand-coated wells which contain various concentrations of the APC. The former control wells monitor the nonspecific binding of the ³H-anti-Ig probe and the latter control wells measure the degree of nonspecific binding exhibited by the secreted immunoglobulins.

(8) To provide a means for evaluating the sensitivity of the assay, an Ig standard is routinely incorporated. This involves titrating various concentrations of soluble antibody in culture medium onto a series of ligand-coated culture wells and allowing this antibody to incubate on the wells for the duration of the APC culture.

(9) Upon transfer of APC to ligand-coated wells, the cells are incubated for 3–24 hr. Incubation is carried out under the usual conditions for cell culture, i.e., in a humidified, 5% CO_2–air atmosphere at 37°.

(10) After incubation, the cells and supernatant are discarded by washing the culture wells four times with a squirt bottle filled with PBS. At this point in the assay, aseptic technique is no longer required.

(11) The amount of secreted Ig bound to the ligand-coated culture wells is quantitated by the addition of a ^{3}H-labeled anti-Ig antibody in PBS + 1% BSA + 0.1% sodium azide. Generally 30,000 cpm of ^{3}H-labeled probe in 50 μl is added to each well. Incubation for 2 hr at 37°, 3 hr at room temperature, or overnight at 4° achieves maximum or near-maximum binding.

(12) The ^{3}H-labeled antibody and the first PBS wash are removed with a proper aspirator flask apparatus. The wells are subsequently washed with running tap water (13×) in a sink.

(13) Dried wells are separated from the plate by an appropriate well-cutting device. The individual wells are placed in scintillation vials (4-ml capacity), 2 ml of emulsifier-type scintillation fluid for aqueous samples is added, and the amount of ^{3}H-labeled probe bound to each well is counted in a beta scintillation counter. To enable evaluation of the percentage of added ^{3}H-labeled antibody probe bound to each well, a 50-μl aliquot of the ^{3}H-labeled probe is directly counted in the scintillation fluid.

^{3}H-Labeled Anti-Ig Antibodies

A factor important in the sensitivity, reproducibility, and flexibility of the culture-well RIA described in this chapter is the use of ^{3}H-labeled antibodies for measuring secreted Ig. The long half-life of ^{3}H (12.26 years) and the mild reductive methylation reaction used for labeling endow ^{3}H-labeled antibodies with long-term stability, high specific activity, and low backgrounds. Tack and Wilder have previously described the method for labeling proteins with tritium.[7] The HCHO and NaB^{3}H$_4$ mediated chemical reaction involves substitutions at amino groups of usually abundant lysyl residues. Since the reductive methylation reaction does not affect the net charge of the lysyl side chain, the conformational stability of the proteins is maintained. Thus, although ^{3}H-labeled proteins can exhibit specific activities comparable to proteins labeled with ^{125}I, they, in contrast to iodinated proteins, exhibit minimal or no loss in biological or immunological activity and little background "stickiness."[7]

We have used this technique to label over 30 affinity-purified antibodies to human or mouse Ig determinants.[6,8,9] These include purified anti-

[7] B. F. Tack and R. L. Wilder, this series, Vol. 73, p. 138.
[8] P. K. A. Mongini, K. E. Stein, and W. E. Paul, *J. Exp. Med.* **153**, 1 (1981).
[9] P. K. A. Mongini, unpublished results.

bodies from sera and purified hybridoma antibodies. Specific activities of the labeled proteins have ranged from 0.5×10^6 to 2.6×10^6 cpm per microgram of labeled protein. Aliquots of the labeled antibodies, in a solution of 2% BSA + 0.1% azide, are stored in liquid nitrogen. For active use, labeled antibodies are routinely stored at 4° for up to 6 months.

Liquid nitrogen is preferable for the long-term storage of molecules labeled to high specific activity with ³H because the rapid freezing process at this temperature (−196°) minimizes self-decomposition.[10] ³H-labeled compounds frozen at −20 to −40° have accelerated self-decomposition, because at these temperatures the molecules are frozen slowly and tend to cluster as a result of the more rapid freezing of pure solvent around the edge of the sample.[10] Since tritium β radiation energy is virtually completely absorbed within the environs of the ³H species, the higher concentrations of labeled proteins in the cluster can lead to greater radiation-induced self-decomposition with time. Liquid nitrogen obviates this problem by freezing the solution before the solute molecules can cluster.

Labeled antibodies which have been preserved in liquid nitrogen have been found to be remarkably stable. Figure 2 shows a comparison of the binding curves generated when an ³H-labeled goat anti-mouse IgG₁ antibody and a ³H-labeled goat anti-mouse IgG₂ᵦ antibody were tested in their ability to detect nanogram per milliliter concentrations of IgG₁ and IgG₂ᵦ anti-TNP antibody soon after labeling or after 4 years of storage in liquid nitrogen. After this interval, the labeled antibodies have 80% of their original ³H activity remaining. Although background "stickiness" to wells with no mouse antibody appeared to have slightly increased (30–40 cpm in 1980 versus 75–200 cpm in 1984), the sensitivity of ³H-labeled anti-mouse isotype antibodies did not change substantially during the 4-year span. The ³H-labeled goat anti-mouse anti-IgG₁ and anti-IgG₂ᵦ were still capable of detecting mouse Ig at <1 ng/ml concentration.

Similar sensitivity in detection of human Ig has recently been achieved by ³H-labeling several murine hybridoma antibodies to human Ig classes (see Fig. 3). It should be noted that our experience with a number of ³H-labeled monoclonal antibodies has indicated that monoclonal antibodies exhibit a greater variability in their sensitivity for their Ig substrates than do different preparations of ³H-labeled polyclonal antibodies from sera.[9] This variability does not appear to be due to major differences in the efficiency with which each monoclonal antibody can be labeled, in that specific activities of all labeled antibody preparations are similar. Rather, the lower efficiency of Ig detection by some ³H-labeled antibodies appears

[10] E. A. Evans, in "Self-decomposition of Radiochemicals: Principles, Control, Observations and Effects," Rev. No. 16, p. 22. Radiochemical Centre Ltd., Amersham, England, 1976.

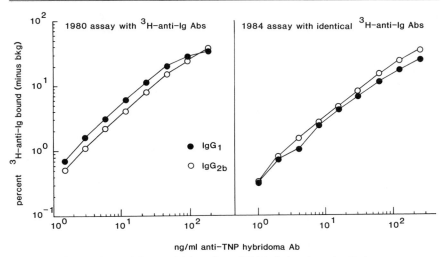

FIG. 2. Comparison of the sensitivity of two ³H-labeled anti-murine Ig isotype reagents when tested immediately after labeling or after 4 years of storage in liquid nitrogen. In each assay, various concentrations of purified IgG₁ or IgG₂ᵦ anti-TNP hybridoma antibody were incubated for 3 hr on PVC wells precoated with TNP₁₅–BSA. The bound anti-TNP antibody was measured by the addition of 28,000–30,000 cpm of ³H-labeled goat anti-mouse IgG₁ or ³H-labeled goat anti-mouse IgG₂ᵦ to each well. After 4 years, the specific activity (cpm/µg) of the ³H-labeled antibody preparations used had diminished by 20%.

to reflect affinity differences which are inherent to the monoclonal antibodies.

The ³H-labeled probes necessitate the use of scintillation fluid for measurement of β emissions. This is disadvantageous in that it constitutes an added expenditure and involves an added step in the assay for well-bound Ig. We feel the long-term stability, high sensitivity, low background, and relatively low biohazard characteristics of ³H-labeled probes, however, outweigh these disadvantages.

Antigen-Coated Culture Wells

Flat-bottomed, flexible, PVC microtiter plates are used for the short-term culture-well RIA. Wells are precoated with antigen (or anti-Ig antibody) to create a solid-phase ligand for antibody secreted from APC. Antigens which have been used to coat wells for the culture-well RIA include trinitrophenyl–bovine serum albumin (TNP–BSA), dansyl-β-alanylglycylglycyl-BSA (dansyl–AGG–BSA), phosphorylcholine–BSA (PC–BSA), various human immunoglobulins, and PR8 influenza virus.[6,8,9] Since numerous examples of other antigens which can bind to solid-phase

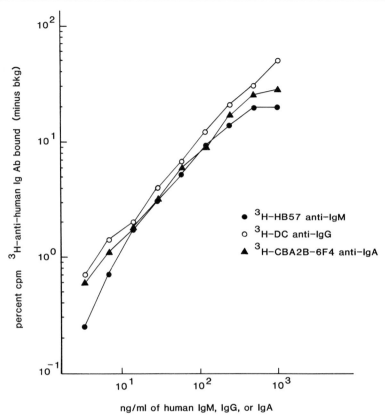

ng/ml of human IgM, IgG, or IgA

FIG. 3. Sensitivity of solid-phase RIA with ³H-labeled murine hybridoma antibodies against human IgM, human IgG, and human IgA. PVC wells were coated with 20 μg of purified anti-human κ light chain hybridoma antibody per milliliter. Various concentrations of purified IgM κ, IgG₁ κ or IgA₁ κ human myeloma proteins were incubated for 3 hr on the anti-κ coated wells. The bound human Ig was measured by the addition of 21,300 cpm of ³H-HB57 anti-IgM (specific activity = 2.1 × 10⁶ cpm/μg), 25,000 cpm of ³H-DC anti-IgG (specific activity = 2.1 × 10⁶ cpm/μg), or 26,800 cpm of ³H-CBA2B-6F4 anti-IgA (specific activity = 1.3 × 10⁶ cpm/μg) to each well. The ³H-anti-IgG and the ³H-anti-IgA reagents recognize epitopes common to all IgG subclasses or both IgA subclasses, respectively.

plantics have been reported,[7,11,12] it is likely that this assay can be utilized to detect APC directed to a variety of other antigens including polysaccharides and single-stranded DNA molecules.

[11] K. E. Stein, D. A. Zopf, B. M. Johnson, C. B. Miller, and W. E. Paul, *J. Immunol.* **128**, 1350 (1982).
[12] E. B. Steinberg, T. J. Santoro, T. M. Chused, P. A. Smathers, and A. D. Steinberg, *J. Immunol.* **131**, 2789 (1983).

Figure 4 shows the ability of wells coated with TNP–BSA, phosphorylcholine–BSA, human IgA$_1$, or human IgA$_2$ to bind antigen-specific antibody secreted from various myeloma and hybridoma cell lines. It should be noted that very little if any of the secreted antibody from as many as 2×10^3 APC binds to wells coated with irrelevant ligands, including ligands that display comparable charges. For example, antibodies

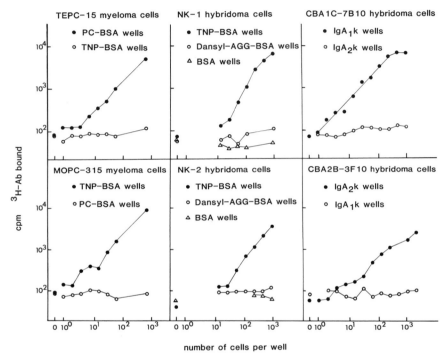

Fig. 4. Use of the culture-well RIA for antigen-specific detection of antibody secreted from murine myeloma or hybridoma cells. Various numbers of cells were cultured for 24 hr on PVC wells coated with various proteins. The tested myeloma and hybridoma cells included those secreting antibody of the following murine isotype and binding specificity: TEPC-15 myeloma cells from ascites (IgA isotype with anti-phosphorylcholine specificity); MOPC-315 myeloma cells from ascites (IgA isotype with anti-TNP specificity); NK-1 hybridoma cells from ascites (IgG$_1$ isotype with anti-TNP specificity); NK-2 hybridoma cells from ascites (IgG$_{2b}$ isotype with anti-TNP specificity); CBA1C-7B10 *in vitro*-passaged hybridoma cells (IgG$_1$ isotype with anti-human IgA$_1$ specificity), and CBA2B-3F10 *in vitro*-passaged hybridoma cells (IgG$_{2b}$ isotype with anti-human IgA$_2$ specificity). The amount of secreted antibody which bound to the wells was measured by the addition of 30,000–80,000 cpm of an appropriate ^{3}H-labeled anti-mouse isotype reagent. ^{3}H-labeled goat anti-mouse IgA was used to detect antibody from TEPC-15 and MOPC-315 cells. ^{3}H-labeled goat anti-mouse IgG$_1$ was used to detect antibody from NK-1, CBA1C-7B10, and CBA2B-3F10 cells. ^{3}H-labeled goat-anti-mouse IgG$_{2b}$ was used to detect antibody from NK-2 cells.

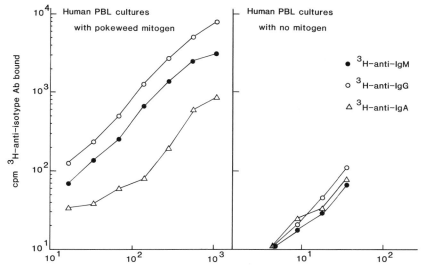

FIG. 5. Secretion of IgM, IgG, and IgA antibody from various numbers of pokeweed mitogen-induced human plaque-forming cells in culture wells coated with anti-light chain antibody. Human peripheral blood lymphocytes (PBL) cultured for 7 days with pokeweed mitogen were found to have 5500 plaque-forming cells per 10⁶ cultured cells by the reverse PFC assay with staphylococcal protein A-coated red blood cells[1]; human PBL cultured without mitogen were found to have 180 PFC per 10⁶ cultured cells. The cultured PBL were diluted so as to place a range of 5–1100 PFC in each of the culture wells precoated with 20 μg/ml of a 1 : 1 mixture of anti-human κ light chain and anti-human λ light chain monoclonal antibodies. After 24 hr of incubation, the cells were washed away and ³H-labeled human Ig class-specific hybridoma antibodies (see Fig. 3) were used to assay the amount of secreted IgM, IgG, and IgA bound to the culture wells.

secreted from two anti-TNP hybridoma lines, NK-1 and NK-2, fail to bind to wells coated with dansyl–AGG–BSA despite the fact that dansyl–AGG–BSA and TNP–BSA have similar charges at physiological pH.[13]

The culture-well RIA can also be used to quantitate APC independent of their antigen specificity. To accomplish this, the culture wells are coated with purified anti-Ig antibodies. As an example, when detection of all Ig from cells producing IgM, IgG, or IgA classes of antibody in pokeweed mitogen-stimulated human lymphocyte cultures was desired, culture wells were coated with 20 μg/ml of a 1 : 1 mixture of purified anti-human κ light chain and anti-human λ light chain hybridoma antibodies. After APC were incubated on these wells, the amount of bound IgM, IgG, or IgA antibody was measured with ³H-labeled isotype-specific probes (see Fig. 5).

[13] J. Inman, personal communication.

Antibody-Producing Cells

The culture-well RIA can quantitate antibody from any antibody-producing cell if the antigen to which the antibody is directed can be absorbed to PVC wells. This assay has been used to measure Ig secretion from myeloma and hybridoma cells passaged in ascitic form or in *in vitro* culture (Fig. 4). In addition, it has been used to measure antibody secreted by antigen-specific plasma cells from *in vivo* lymphatic tissue (Table I) or from *in vitro* mitogen- or antigen-induced lymphocyte cultures (Figs. 5 and 6). The assay appears capable of detecting antibody from at least 5–10 antibody-secreting cells. This threshold of sensitivity has been established by measuring antibody secreted from various numbers of hybridoma or myeloma cells (Fig. 4) or by measuring antibody secreted from cell populations containing various numbers of mitogen- or antigen-activated plaque-forming cells (Figs. 5 and 6).

We have attempted to determine whether the assay's threshold of detection of APC is compatible with the estimated secretion rate of antibody-producing cells,[14–16] and the known sensitivity of the ^{3}H-anti-Ig probes used. It has been estimated that a single APC secretes 1000–4000 molecules of antibody per cell per second.[14–16] At the more conservative rate, one APC should, in a 24-hr culture period, secrete 0.022 ng into 200 μl of culture supernatant (a concentration of 0.11 ng/ml); 10 APC should generate a concentration of approximately 1 ng/ml. Given that the threshold sensitivity, i.e., the antibody concentration required to give significant binding above background, for our ^{3}H-anti-Ig reagents ranges from 0.1 to 1 ng/ml, we would anticipate that the assay should be capable of detecting from 1 to 10 APC. This is indeed compatible with our empirically derived sensitivity of at least 5–10 APC.

In the culture-well assay, steps must be taken to assure that the antibody detected reflects the secretion of antibody from the APC population placed in the antigen-coated culture well and not a carryover of antibody from serum or culture supernatant. Thus, the cells should be washed with medium several times before being placed in culture. In the case of *in vitro* antigen-stimulated cultures, this washing procedure also precludes the carryover of soluble antigen which may interfere with the sensitivity of the assay.

[14] N. R. Klinman and G. Aschinazi, *J. Immunol.* **106,** 1338 (1971).
[15] J. L. Fahey and I. Finegold, *Cold Spring Harbor Symp. Quant. Biol.* **32,** 283 (1967).
[16] J. Weyer and A.-E. Bussard, *Ann. Immunol. (Paris)* **125C,** 947 (1974).

TABLE I

QUANTITATION OF ANTI-TNP ANTIBODY OF VARIOUS ISOTYPES SECRETED BY
ANTIBODY-PRODUCING CELLS FROM *in Vivo* IMMUNIZED MOUSE SPLEEN

Donor of spleen cells[a]	Percentage of anti-isotype antibody bound to wells				
	IgM	IgG$_1$	IgG$_{2a}$	IgG$_{2b}$	IgG$_3$
Nonimmune *nu/nu* mouse	1.23	0.01	0.05	0.01	0.01
nu/nu mice immunized 9	17.87	5.00	0.79	1.29	13.52
days previously with TNP–	± 6.95	± 0.97	± 0.19	± 0.69	± 4.71
Ficoll[b]					

[a] Cells were incubated on culture wells coated with TNP$_{15}$–BSA (2.5 × 10⁵ cells per assay well) for 24 hr. ³H-labeled goat anti-mouse isotype antibody was used to measure the amount of anti-TNP antibody bound to the assay wells.

[b] Values represent mean ± SEM of spleen cells from three individual mice.

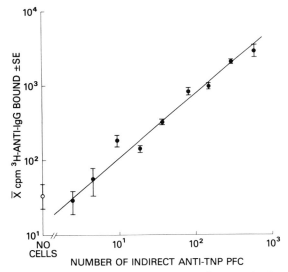

FIG. 6. Secretion of IgG anti-TNP antibody in TNP–BSA-coated culture wells by various numbers of IgG anti-TNP plaque-forming cells. Spleen cells taken from CBA/Ca mice 7 days after TNP–*Brucella abortus* immunization were found to have 297 indirect PFC per 10⁶ spleen cells. Spleen cells were diluted so as to place a range of approximately 2–594 PFC in each 100-μl culture. The spleen cells were incubated for 24 hr in TNP–BSA-precoated microtiter wells. For assay of IgG antibody secreted, 75 μl of a cocktail of ³H-anti-IgG$_1$ + ³H-anti-IgG$_{2a}$ + ³H-anti-IgG$_{2b}$ (144,000 cpm/75 μl) was added. (From Mongini and Heber-Katz.[6])

The culture-well assay has been used to measure human IgM APC in cultures in which soluble anti-IgM antibody was being tested for ability to block the induction of IgM APC by polyclonal activating agents such as pokeweed mitogen and Nocardia.[17] In these types of experiments also, the thorough washing of the cultured cells is important to preclude the transfer of soluble anti-IgM into the assay culture. The soluble anti-IgM could potentially interfere at two levels in this assay for APC: (1) by blocking the ability of the ^{3}H-labeled anti-IgM probe to detect the secreted IgM and possibly (2) by inhibiting the secretion of IgM antibody from APC in the assay wells. It should be clear that, in experiments of this latter nature, these two factors make the culture-well assay preferable to the culture supernatant assay for detecting IgM APC.

Kinetics of APC Secretion in Culture-Well Assay

The choice of the appropriate incubation period for APC secretion on ligand-coated wells is dependent upon the number of APC in the cell suspension to be assayed. Longer incubation periods will increase the sensitivity with which the assay can detect few APC. However, if a large number of APC are present, longer incubation times will also increase the chance that the secreted antibody will saturate the ligand sites on the well. These phenomena are illustrated in Fig. 7. The data are taken from an experiment in which the amount of antibody secreted from various numbers of CBA1C-7B10 murine hybridoma cells was measured after various culture intervals. The antibody from this hybridoma has specificity for human IgA_1. The experiment shows that although antibody from approximately 10 hybridoma cells could be detected after as little as 3 hr of incubation, a substantially greater amount of antibody from this number of cells was detected when the culture period was extended to 24 hr. In contrast, when 560 hybridoma cells were cultured, the amount of antibody detected from a 24-hr incubation was only slightly more than that detected from a 3-hr incubation. The plateau in antibody detected when increasing numbers of APC are cultured is due to saturation of well-bound ligand.

When various concentrations of purified soluble monoclonal antibody from the CBA1C-7B10 hybridoma are titrated onto antigen-coated wells, a plateau in binding is reached at an antibody concentration of 250 ng/ml. From the fact that 160 cultured hybridoma cells secreted enough antibody to saturate the antigen-coated culture wells in 18 hr, one can very roughly approximate the secretion rate of the hybridoma cells at 7000 molecules

[17] S. M. Rudich and P. Mongini, unpublished results.

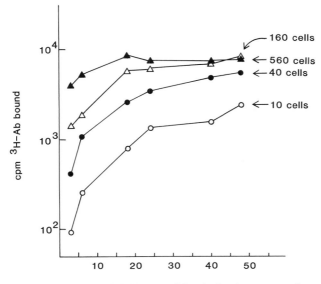

FIG. 7. Kinetics of antibody secretion by CBA1C-7B10 anti-human IgA₁ hybridoma cells as measured by culture-well RIA. Various numbers of CBA1C-7B10 hybridoma cells were cultured on PVC wells precoated with 80 μg purified human IgA₁ myeloma protein/ml. After various intervals, the cells were washed away and the amount of bound hybridoma antibody measured by adding 26,000 cpm of ³H-labeled goat antimouse IgG₁.

per cell per second. This figure is compatible with the calculated secretion rate of myeloma APC.[16]

In cases in which the number of APC in the cell suspension tested is unknown, we routinely extend the secretion phase of the assay to 24 hr. However, because the presence of an excess of APC can result in saturation of the solid-phase ligand with Ig, we test various concentrations of cells in the culture-well RIA. This assures that the antibody detected will quantitatively reflect the amount of antibody secreted from a given number of cells.

It should be noted that although one can use standard curves made from analysis of the binding of purified soluble antibody in a solid-phase RIA to *approximate* the amount of antibody secreted by cells in the culture-well RIA, the antibody-binding efficiency in the two assays appears to be slightly different.[6] Our past experience has indicated that the culture-well RIA has an approximately 2-fold greater sensitivity at detecting secreted antibody than the solid-phase RIA for antibody in culture supernatant.[6] This may be attributed to the presence of an antibody concentration gradient in the culture-well assay in which the antibody concentration in the immediate mileau of the APCs on the well surface is higher than the antibody concentration in the supernatant at equilibrium.

Conclusions

The culture-well, solid-phase RIA described here has a number of advantages which make it a superior assay for APC in a number of experimental systems. Table II has a summary of the advantages and disadvantages of the culture-well assay for APC compared to the PFC assay for APC or the assay for APC-secreted antibody in *in vitro* culture supernatants. In addition to the advantages listed in Table II, the culture-well RIA

TABLE II

ADVANTAGES AND DISADVANTAGES OF THE CULTURE-WELL ^{3}H-RIA FOR DETECTION OF
APC COMPARED TO OTHER ANTIBODY ASSAYS

	Advantages	Disadvantages
Compared to PFC assay	Culture-well RIA can measure secreted antibody to virtually any antigen Culture-well RIA avoids repeated conjugation and testing of RBC indicators Culture-well RIA is less subjective Culture-well RIA can more easily and more quantitatively assess antibody responses of the individual Ig classes and subclasses	Culture-well RIA cannot visualize and quantitate individual APC and thus cannot distinguish between many APC secreting little antibody or a few APC secreting much antibody
Compared to assay for APC-secreted antibody in culture supernatants	Culture-well RIA can detect secreted antibody without the interference of soluble antigen (or anti-Ig ligand) in culture supernatant Culture-well assay has an approximately 2-fold greater sensitivity in the detection of antibody from APC Culture-well assay can directly assay APC taken from *in vivo* lymphoid tissue	Culture-well assay must measure APC at the peak in their secretory potential, unlike assay of antibody in culture supernatant, which measures cumulative antibody production Culture-well assay discards APC after the secretion phase of the assay

we describe utilizes ^{3}H-labeled anti-Ig probes. These probes exhibit long-term stability with little or no denaturation after labeling. Thus, the use of these probes can eliminate the hazards and inconvenience associated with frequent ^{125}I labeling or enzyme conjugation procedures. The high sensitivity of these probes allows the assay to detect the presence of at least 5–10 APC.

[42] The Spaghetti Overlay Procedure

By W. Steven Adair

Several procedures have been developed over the past few years for the identification of specific members of complex mixtures of polypeptides or peptides resolved by one-[1] or two-dimensional[2] SDS–polyacrylamide gel electrophoresis (SDS–PAGE). Many probes have been employed, including antibodies,[3-8] lectins,[4,7,9-12] hormones,[13-16] ligands,[17,18] and living cells.[19] In many cases it is useful to screen resolved components with several different probes simultaneously. The use of mono-

[1] U. K. Laemmli, *Nature (London)* **227**, 680 (1970).
[2] P. Z. O'Farrell, H. M. Goodman, and P. H. O'Farrell, *Cell* **12**, 1133 (1977).
[3] W. E. Stumph, S. C. R. Elgin, and L. Hood, *J. Immunol.* **113**, 1752 (1974).
[4] K. Burridge, *Proc. Natl. Acad. Sci. U.S.A.* **73**, 4457 (1976).
[5] K. Olden and K. M. Yamada, *Anal. Biochem.* **78**, 483 (1977).
[6] W. S. Adair, D. Jurivich, and U. W. Goodenough, *J. Cell Biol.* **79**, 281 (1978).
[7] K. Burridge, this series, Vol. 50, p. 54.
[8] W. S. Adair, *Anal. Biochem.* **125**, 299 (1982).
[9] J. W. Gurd and W. H. Evans, *Can. J. Biochem.* **54**, 477 (1976).
[10] N. A. Guzman, R. A. Berg, and D. J. Prokop, *Biochem. Biophys. Res. Commun.* **73**, 279 (1976).
[11] J. A. P. Rostas, P. T. Kelly, and C. W. Cotman, *Anal. Biochem.* **80**, 366 (1977).
[12] B. Monk, W. S. Adair, R. Cohen, and U. W. Goodenough, *Planta* **158**, 517 (1983).
[13] J. Massagne, B. J. Guillette, M. P. Czech, C. J. Morgan, and R. A. Bradshaw, *J. Biol. Chem.* **256**, 9419 (1981).
[14] S. Paglin and J. D. Jamieson, *Proc. Natl. Acad. Sci. U.S.A.* **79**, 3739 (1982).
[15] P. F. Pilch and M. P. Czech, *J. Biol. Chem.* **255**, 1722 (1980).
[16] J. P. Yip, C. W. T. Yeung, and M. L. Moule, *Biochemistry* **19**, 70 (1980).
[17] J. R. Glenney and K. Weber, *J. Biol. Chem.* **225**, 10551 (1980).
[18] R. K. Carlin, D. J. Grab, and P. Siekevitz, *J. Cell Biol.* **89**, 449 (1981).
[19] E. G. Hayman, E. Engvall, E. A'Hearn, D. Barnes, M. Pierschbacher, and E. Ruoslahti, *J. Cell Biol.* **95**, 20 (1982).

clonal antibody libraries for epitope mapping,[20-22] for example, is a powerful approach to dissecting the structural organization of polypeptides. For such analyses, a preparative gel (or transfer) is usually sliced into lanes which are reacted individually with each probe, a process which can be cumbersome and make precise alignment of closely migrating species problematic. An alternative approach, the spaghetti overlay,[8] has been developed to simplify the screening of multiple probes without the necessity of slicing gels. With this procedure, probes are dissolved in low melting temperature agarose and drawn into capillary tubes. After setting, the agarose strips are placed on the surface of a prepared gel. Lanes are created by the probes themselves. Antigen–antibody complexes are visualized by autoradiography as discrete spots which can be easily aligned with stained side strips. In this chapter, the spaghetti overlay technique is described in detail for use in immunoautoradiographic screening procedures employing polyclonal or monoclonal antibodies. Methods for performing multiple overlays on microgels and nitrocellulose transfers are presented together with a general outline of the relative merits of each approach and limitations of the overlay procedure itself. While the methods detailed here have been developed specifically for antibody overlay, they can obviously be adapted for use with other probes as well.

Buffers and Solutions

Buffer A: 25 mM sodium phosphate, 0.15 M NaCl, 0.02% NaN$_3$, pH 7.0
Buffer B: 125 mM sodium borate, 0.15 M NaCl, pH 8.2
Fix solutions: 25% isopropanol/10% acetic acid (fix 1); 2% glutaraldehyde in buffer A (fix 2)
Wash buffer: buffer A + 0.1% Tween-20
Quench solution: 1% bovine hemoglobin, 0.1% Tween-20, in buffer A
SDS–Polyacrylamide Gel Electrophoresis (SDS–PAGE). The use of micro slab gels[23] allows short run times, rapid fixation, equilibration, and washing, as well as conservation of sample. Gels (0.5 mm thick) are cast eight at a time in a Plexiglas chamber, using lantern glass slides (8.2 × 10.2 cm) for gel plates, the exact gel specifications (concentration, gradient, etc.) depending on the specific application. When several antibodies are reacted with a common antigen mixture, a stacking gel is omitted; lanes are created by the antibody overlays themselves. When several

[20] M. Dziadek, H. Richter, M. Schachner, and R. Timpl, *FEBS Lett.* **155,** 321 (1983).
[21] D. A. Winkelmann, S. Lowey, and J. L. Press, *Cell* **34,** 295 (1983).
[22] D. P. Kiehart, D. A. Kaiser, and T. D. Pollard, *J. Cell Biol.* **99,** 1002 (1984).
[23] P. T. Matsudaira and D. R. Burgess, *Anal. Biochem.* **87,** 386 (1978).

antigen mixtures are probed on the same gel, a 3% stacker and comb are employed. Gels are run at a constant voltage of 150 V for approximately 1.5 hr using a discontinuous buffer system.[1] Following fixation (45 min, fix 1) gels are equilibrated in buffer A, then incubated for 1 hr in the quench solution. For certain applications (e.g., electrodestaining), a second fixation (fix 2) precedes equilibration and quenching. For orientation, the bottom right corner of the gel is clipped off diagonally. Reference strips are cut from each side and stained for protein by silver stain[24] or for carbohydrate by the periodic acid–Schiff (PAS) method.[20] Prior to overlay, excess solution is removed by Pasteur pipet from the surface of the gel, which is supported on the glass plate.

Preparation of Labeled Probes

In Vitro Labeling (Iodination). Antibodies and protein A are labeled using the Iodogen procedure.[25] A 50-μl aliquot of methylene chloride containing 2 μg Iodogen (Pierce) is added to a glass test tube (12 × 75 mm) and the methylene chloride evaporated off in a 37° water bath with rotation of the tube. To the dried film is added 200 μl buffer B containing 35–50 μg protein, 250 μCi carrier-free Na[125]I (Amersham), and 0.5 μg KI. The reaction is allowed to proceed on ice for 5 min with gentle agitation. The labeling solution is then removed and rapidly desalted over a bed of Biogel P6-DG[26] as follows. The bottom of a 1.5-ml microfuge tube is pierced with a 25-gauge needle and a small plug of glass wool placed in the bottom. A settled bed of 1.3 ml BioGel P6-DG (Bio-Rad) in buffer A is poured and allowed to drain dry. The tube is then suspended in a 12 × 75-mm polypropylene tube and spun for 1 min in a clinical centrifuge at 200 g. The flow-through buffer is discarded and the labeling solution added to the dried bed. The tube is then respun for 1 min at the same speed. Labeled protein is recovered in the bottom of the polypropylene tube while unreacted iodine is retained in the BioGel matrix. Residual iodine is removed by dialysis against buffer A after addition of carrier protein (hemoglobin) to 1%. Aliquots are stored at −70°.

In Vivo Labeling. Monoclonal antibodies are labeled *in vivo* with [35S]methionine following the procedure of Haas and Kennett.[27] A sterile

[24] J. H. Morrissey, *Anal. Biochem.* **117**, 307 (1981).
[25] P. J. Fraker and J. C. Speck, Jr., *Biochem. Biophys. Res. Commun.* **80**, 849 (1978).
[26] G. P. Tuszynski, L. Knight, J. R. Piperno, and P. N. Walsh, *Anal. Biochem.* **106**, 118 (1980).
[27] J. B. Haas and R. H. Kennett, *in* "Monoclonal Antibodies" (R. H. Kennett, T. J. McKearn, and K. B. Bechtol, eds.), Plenum, New York, 1980.

suspension of 1×10^6 log phase hybridoma cells is washed once with methionine-deficient medium and resuspended in 2.5 ml medium containing 10% dialyzed horse serum, 5% dialyzed fetal bovine serum, 30 mg glutamine/ml, and 50–100 μCi [^{35}S]methionine. Cells are incubated for 18–24 hr at 37° in a 5% CO_2 incubator. The supernatant is removed, rapidly desalted as above, dialyzed against buffer A, and stored at −70° in aliquots.

Overlay Procedures

Prior to the overlay, the gel and its glass support are placed on a reference plate which is constructed of transparent Plexiglas and has grooves spaced at 3.5-mm intervals. This entire ensemble rests on a light box. Grooves in the reference plate serve as guides for the application of spaghetti strips in evenly spaced lanes.

Spaghetti strips are formed by mixing equal aliquots (35 μl) of either antibody (0.5–5 μg in buffer A) or spent hybridoma medium with liquified low melting temperature agarose (2% in buffer A, 0.2% Tween-20), then drawing the mixture into a 50-μl glass capillary tube (Corning), and allowing it to set (1–2 min). To facilitate removal of the agarose strips during overlay, the capillary tubes are precoated with 0.05% Photo-flo 200 (Eastman-Kodak). When a large number of antibodies are to be screened at one time, a Plexiglas plate containing labeled grooves is used to hold the capillary tubes in order horizontally until overlays are performed.

After all spaghetti strips have set, each is gently applied to the surface of the gel by gentle blowing through a mouth adapter. When all strips are in place, excess agarose is trimmed from the top and bottom ends of each and the overlay placed in a humidified box for 12–24 hr at 4°. Following the primary incubation, spaghetti strips are washed from the surface of the gel with a gentle stream of buffer A, and excess antibody removed by washing (2–3 hr in wash buffer with several changes). The gel is then reacted with a radiolabeled second probe.

The labeled probe, either a second antibody or protein A, is used at 5×10^5 dpm/ml (in quench buffer) and incubation of the gel in this solution carried out at 25° for 2–3 hr. When a second antibody is employed, lower backgrounds are usually obtained with F(ab')$_2$ fragments. After the secondary incubation, the gel is washed extensively until counts in the wash solution reach background levels (usually 4–5 hr). The gel is then dried and placed in contact with preflashed XAR film (Kodak) and Cronex intensifying screens, for 12–48 hr at −70°. For orientation, radioactive ink spots are applied to a corner of the dried gel prior to autoradiography. The developed autoradiogram is placed on the reference plate and compared with stained side strips of the gel.

Variations of the Overlay

One-Step Overlay. Several steps can be eliminated by combining primary and secondary incubations. This can be accomplished by using either labeled primary antibody or a conjugate of secondary antibody with ^{125}I-labeled protein A (2 : 1 molar ratio). Primary antibody can be labeled *in vitro* by iodination or *in vivo* metabolically. While more time-consuming, metabolic labeling is generally preferred for monoclonal antibodies, since iodination can affect the binding properties of antibodies even when performed under relatively gentle conditions. The use of antibody–protein A conjugates takes advantage of the fact that protein A binds to the Fc fragment of immunoglobulins, leaving the antigen-combining sites free. This approach is limited, however, to certain IgG antibodies (e.g., rabbit) which are bound by protein A with relatively high affinity. Mouse IgGs show a wide variability in this regard and are less suitable for this method.

Electrodestain. This procedure can be used in conjunction with one-step overlays as an alternative to postincubation washing of the gel. Gels are fixed in glutaraldehyde (fix 2) prior to equilibration, quenching, and overlay. After the overlay, they are placed in contact with a sheet of wet DE-81 paper and electroblotted[24] for 1 hr using a 12-V battery charger as a power source. Other (more expensive) power sources can obviously be substituted but a battery charger does a very adequate job. After blotting, unreacted probe is bound to the DE-81 paper for convenient disposal, while the gel is ready for drying and autoradiography. Although the antibodies examined to date using this electrodestain procedure have remained sufficiently complexed with antigen for detection, antibodies with low binding affinities could be lost using this method.

Transfer Overlays. While original overlay procedures were performed on gels, most workers now routinely transfer electrophoresed components to a solid substrate, such as nitrocellulose or Zeta-bind, prior to incubation with probes (see Ref. 28 for an excellent recent review). Spaghetti overlays have been successfully performed on nitrocellulose transfers using the protocol outlined in Fig. 1.[29] The major advantages and disadvantages of each approach are summarized in the table.

[28] J. M. Gershoni and G. E. Palade, *Anal. Biochem.* **131,** 1 (1983).
[29] K. Hancock and V. C. W. Tsang, *Anal. Biochem.* **133,** 157 (1983).

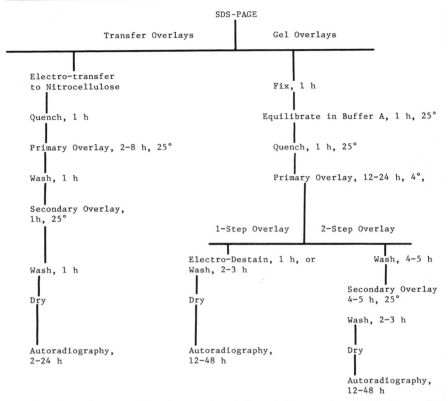

FIG. 1. Steps for spaghetti overlay on gels and nitrocellulose transfers. Incubation, wash, and autoradiographic exposure times are approximate. Actual times will vary in practice with the concentration of primary antibody and the specific activities of labeled probes. For orientation, gel slices are stained as described in the text; strips of nitrocellulose are stained with india ink.[29]

Concluding Remarks

The procedures outlined above have been used successfully for confirming the specificity of polyclonal and monoclonal antibodies, for screening of hybridomas supernatants prior to cloning, and for domain-mapping procedures employing peptide digests. Other potential applications include lectin and ligand screening, probing for receptors (e.g., hormone or growth factors), and other protein–protein interactions. The primary limitation is the conservation of binding functions following electrophoresis under denaturing conditions. In practice, however, this has not turned out to be as much a problem as one might expect.

COMPARISON OF GEL AND TRANSFER OVERLAYS

	Advantages	Disadvantages
Gel overlays	Polypeptides are probed in an unbiased fashion; particularly important for very high and very low molecular weight components Conformationally dependent epitopes often retained to a greater degree	More time-consuming; longer incubation and washing times Lower sensitivity Gels are more fragile than paper Gels cannot be reused for multiple reactions
Transfer overlays	More sensitive; less material required Faster Multiple reactions possible	Polypeptides often not sampled equally. High molecular weight polypeptides transfer inefficiently or not at all, while low molecular weight components can be lost. Also, some polypeptides bind weakly or not at all to nitrocellulose Reactivities to some antibodies can be lost due to the denaturing affects of adsorption

Acknowledgments

The application of the spaghetti overlay technique to nitrocellulose transfers was developed in collaboration with Dr. Jerry Bryant, Washington University Biology Department. This work was supported by NIH Grants GM-26117 and GM-26150, awarded to Dr. Ursula Goodenough.

[43] Solution-Phase RIA and Solid-Phase EIA Using Avidin–Biotin Systems for Analysis of Monoclonal Antibody Epitopes and Affinity Constants

By JOHN E. SHIVELY, CHRISTOPH WAGENER, and BRIAN R. CLARK

A monoclonal antibody (MAb) should recognize a single epitope on the antigen used for immunization. Although this generalization can be complicated by the occurrence of multiple identical or cross-reactive epitopes, or the presence of overlapping epitopes, it is a good starting point for epitope analysis. One of the initial problems in selecting a suitable MAb for antigen screening is a determination of which epitope(s) is recognized by each MAb. This chapter describes two types of immunoassays which can be used to perform epitope analysis and one immunoassay to determine the affinity constant (K_{aff}) associated with a MAb and its antigen. K_{aff} can be calculated from a solution-phase RIA which utilizes the avidin–biotin complex to remove the antibody–antigen complex from free antibody or antigen. Since this system makes use of the high affinity of the avidin–biotin interaction (10^{-15} M), it avoids the complications often encountered using second antibodies at high primary antibody concentrations or chemical precipitants. One of the assays for performing epitope analysis is a solid-phase radioimmunoassay (RIA) which does not use avidin–biotin, and the other is a solid-phase enzyme immunoassay (EIA) involving the use of avidin–biotin–peroxidase conjugates. Either assay gives equivalent results for epitope analysis. The determination of K_{aff} should be performed by the biotin–avidin solution-phase RIA to avoid "solid-phase" effects. Either type of assay can be used as a routine screening procedure for the antigen once a MAb is selected.

The principle of the epitope assay is that enzyme- or radioisotope-labeled MAb 1 will compete for the same binding site on an antigen as unlabeled MAb 1 or any other MAb with the same or overlapping specificity. An alternate inhibition assay involves immobilizing MAb 1, and allowing the test MAb (MAb 2) to incubate first with the antigen and then with immobilized MAb 1. The determination of affinity constants also involves a competitive assay. The labeled antigen competes with unlabeled antigen for MAb binding. All three assays include steps which either separate bound from free MAb or bound from free antigen.

General Procedures

Monoclonal Antibodies. The production of monoclonal anti-carcinoembryonic antigen (CEA) antibodies is described in detail by Wagener et al.[1] MAbs produced by immunizations with purified CEA are given the "CEA." designation and those obtained with the colon carcinoma cell line T84 as immunogen (currently known as HC84S) are given the "T84." designation. CEA was purified according to Coligan et al.,[2] and the T84 cell line was obtained from Murakami and Masui.[3]

Preparation of IgG. The IgG fraction of a MAb is best purified from ascites fluid. We have used the protein A affinity chromatography of Ey

[1] C. Wagener, Y. H. J. Yang, F. G. Crawford, and J. E. Shively, *J. Immunol.* **130**, 2308 (1983).
[2] J. E. Coligan, J. T. Lautenschleger, M. L. Egan, and C. W. Todd, *Immunochemistry* **9**, 377 (1972).
[3] H. Murakami and H. Masui, *Proc. Natl. Acad. Sci. U.S.A.* **77**, 3464 (1980).

et al.[4] An alternate method involves sequential ammonium sulfate precipitation and DEAE–cellulose chromatography.[5] IgG may also be purified from culture supernatants, but the concentration is at least 10-fold lower than the ascites fluid. The purified IgG can be dialyzed against water or a low ionic strength buffer (0.001 M sodium phosphate, pH 7.0), lyophilized, and stored at $-20°$. The $A_{280\ nm}$ of a 10 mg/ml solution of mouse IgG is 14.[6]

Epitope Analysis Using a Solid-Phase RIA

Materials

PBS: 0.05 M sodium phosphate buffer (pH 7.0) containing 0.15 M NaCl and 0.1% NaN_3

PBS–BSA: PBS containing 1% (w/v) bovine serum albumin (Sigma)

Microtiter plates: polyvinyl, 96-well (Costar)

Preparation of Radiolabeled MAb. Purified IgG MAb is ^{125}I-labeled by the chloramine-T procedure of Hunter and Greenwood[7] or any other appropriate method. The specific activity should be at least 10^4 cpm/ng MAb.

RIA Protocol. A constant volume (50 μl) of ^{125}I-labeled MAb is added to 100 μl of serial 2-fold dilutions of unlabeled MAb. An aliquot (50 μl) is added to each well of a 96-well poly(vinyl chloride) microtiter dish previously coated with antigen. [In this case 100 μl of CEA, 20 μg/ml, in 0.2 M sodium carbonate buffer (pH 9.3) is incubated in each well for 12 hr at room temperature; the CEA coating solution may be reused one to two times before discarding.] Nonspecific binding is blocked by incubating antigen-coated wells with PBS–BSA for 2 hr at 37° followed by rinsing with PBS five times. A possible range of MAb could be from 0.5–1100 ng per microtiter plate well. The amount of label per well should be at least 20,000 cpm (up to 100,000 cpm/well). In the example given here, six MAbs (MAbs 1–6) are tested. In one experiment, radiolabeled MAb 1 is diluted with an unlabeled MAb (MAbs 1–6) and then incubated with the antigen-coated wells. In a second experiment, radiolabeled MAb 2 is diluted with an unlabeled MAb and then incubated with the antigen-coated wells. Experiments 3–6 are arranged in a similar manner. In each of the experiments the incubation of MAb with antigen-coated plates is

[4] P. L. Ey, S. J. Prouse, and C. R. Jenkin, *Immunochemistry* **15**, 429 (1978).

[5] J. S. Garvey, W. E. Cremer, and D. H. Sussdorf, *in* "Methods in Immunology," 3rd ed. p. 218. Benjamin, Reading, Massachusetts, 1977.

[6] H. N. Eisen, E. S. Simms, and M. Potter, *Biochemistry* **7**, 4126 (1968).

[7] W. M. Hunter and F. C. Greenwood, *Nature (London)* **194**, 495 (1962).

for 2–3 hr at 37°. The plates are washed five times with PBS and the wells are excised and counted in a gamma scintillation counter. Controls include wells not coated with antigen, incubations with no MAb, and incubations with normal mouse serum. Backgrounds of 200–300 cpm per well are acceptable.

RIA Results. Four examples of the results for the epitope screening of six MAbs against CEA by this procedure are shown in Fig. 1. As can be seen each MAb is capable of inhibiting its own binding to CEA. In addition, MAb 5 (CEA.281 H6) is partly inhibited by MAb 1 and completely inhibited by MAb 6. It was concluded that MAbs 5 and 6 recognized the same epitope, and that MAbs 1 and 5 recognized overlapping epitopes. MAb 4 is weakly inhibited by MAb 1.

The strategy for screening a large number of potentially interesting culture supernatants is the following. First, test each for antigen binding and select those hybridomas which secrete antigen-binding MAb. Second, pick two or three at random, grow the cells in ascites, purify the IgG, and

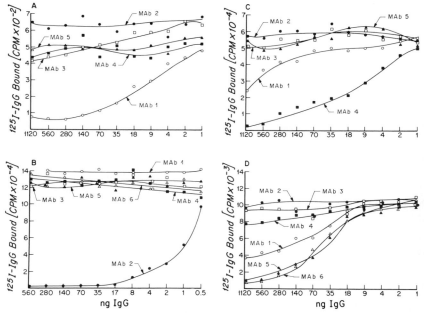

FIG. 1. Epitope analysis using a solid-phase RIA. The wells of a microtiter plate were coated with CEA as described in the text and incubated with a radiolabeled MAb and decreasing dilutions of unlabeled MAb (ng IgG). (A) Radiolabeled MAb 1; (B) radiolabeled MAb 2; (C) radiolabeled MAb 4; (D) radiolabeled MAb 5. (○) MAb 1; (●) MAb 2; (□) MAb 3; (■) MAb 4; (▲) MAb 5; (△) MAb 6.

radiolabel. Third, perform the competitive inhibition assay with the radiolabeled MAb and culture fluid from every hybridoma secreting antigen-specific MAb. Any MAb which completely inhibits the binding of a radiolabeled MAb is not further screened since it recognizes the same epitope. Fourth, repeat step two with several of the remaining MAbs. After several iterations only MAbs recognizing unique epitopes will remain.

With this assay it is important that the radiolabeled MAb is prepared from purified IgG. The radiolabeled purified MAb may be tested against any solution of the other MAbs including ascites fluid, culture fluid supernatants, or purified IgG.

Epitiope Specificity Using Biotinylated MAb in an EIA

Materials

PBS: 0.05 M sodium phosphate (pH 7.2) containing 0.15 M NaCl and 0.1% NaN$_3$

Na$_2$CO$_3$, 0.2 M (pH 9.3–9.4)

PBS–BSA: PBS containing 1% (w/v) bovine serum albumin (Sigma)

PBR (phosphate buffer–rabbit serum): 0.2 M phosphate (pH 6.5) containing 20% (v/v) normal rabbit serum

ABC: avidin–biotin–peroxidase complex (Sigma) diluted 1 : 100 in PBR

3 M HCl: dilute 260 ml conc. HCl in 1 liter of distilled H$_2$O

Substrate-1: 6 mM H$_2$O$_2$ (freshly prepared) and 40 mM o-phenylenediamine (Sigma) in citrate buffer

6 mM H$_2$O$_2$: dilute 68 μl of 30% H$_2$O$_2$ (w/v) in 100 ml of distilled H$_2$O

Citrate: 0.1 M sodium citrate (pH 5.0)

NSB: N-hydroxysuccinimidobiotin (Sigma)

DMF: dimethylformamide (J. T. Baker) distilled from ninhydrin

Preparation of Biotin-Labeled MAb. A modification of the method of Clark and Todd[8] is employed. An equal volume of MAb (70 mg/ml in PBS, 0.1 ml) is added to a freshly prepared solution of NSB (1 mg/ml, 0.1 ml). The NSB (2.0 mg) is added to 0.5 ml of DMF, stirred 5 min, and diluted to 2.0 ml with 1.5 ml of water. The NSB solution is immediately added to the MAb dropwise with constant stirring, allowed to react 2 hr at room temperature, diluted to 1 ml with PBS, and dialyzed versus against three to four changes of PBS. The degree of biotinylation can be changed by increasing or decreasing the amount of NSB by a factor of 2–3 if desired. Aliquots of the biotinylated MAb are stored at $-20°$ until used.

[8] B. R. Clark and C. W. Todd, *Anal. Biochem.* **121,** 257 (1982).

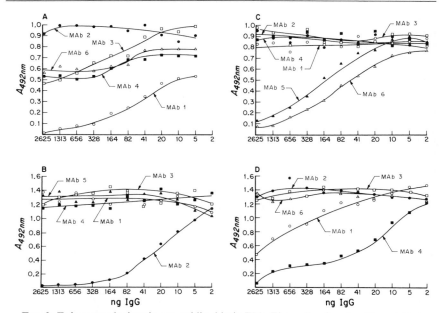

FIG. 2. Epitope analysis using an avidin–biotin EIA. The wells of a microtiter plate were coated with CEA and incubated with a biotinylated MAb and decreasing dilutions of unlabeled MAb. The bound biotinylated MAb was detected with an avidin–biotin–peroxidase conjugate. (A) Biotinylated MAb 1; (B) biotinylated MAb 2; (C) biotinylated MAb 5; (D) biotinylated MAb 4. See Fig. 1 for explanation of symbols.

EIA Protocol. The protocol is similar to that described by Wagener *et al.*[9] The wells of a 96-well polyvinyl microtiter plate are coated with antigen as described above. A constant amount (50 μl; see below) of biotinylated MAb is added to 50 μl of serial 2-fold dilutions of unlabeled test MAb in PBS–BSA. Aliquots (50 μl) are added to the wells and the plate is incubated for 2 hr at 37° and washed three times with PBS. The wells are washed once with PBR and then incubated with ABC conjugate (100 μl of conjugate diluted 1 : 100 in PBR) for 2 hr at 37°, washed five times with citrate buffer (0.1 *M*, pH 5.0), and incubated with 100 μl of substrate for 30 min at room temperature in the dark. The reaction is stopped with 100 μl of 3 *M* HCl and the absorbance is read at 492 nm. The dilution of the biotinylated antibody was chosen to give a maximum A_{492} value of 0.8–1.5 in the absence of unlabeled MAb. Controls include wells not coated with antigen, incubations with no MAb, and incubations with

[9] C. Wagener, U. Fenger, B. R. Clark, and J. E. Shively, *J. Immunol. Methods* **68**, 269 (1984).

normal mouse serum. Nonspecific binding should not exceed 0.05 absorbance units.

EIA Results. Sample results for epitope analysis of four MAbs are shown in Fig. 2. The results are equivalent to those shown in Fig. 1 for the solid-phase RIA. The biotinylated MAbs may be compared also with polyclonal antibodies. This analysis is shown in Fig. 3A for five of the MAbs, each of a unique epitope specificity, versus a rabbit polyclonal antibody raised against CEA. It can be seen that the polyclonal antibody is able to inhibit the binding of each MAb to CEA, thus indicating that it recognizes each of the epitopes. It can also be asked if the polyclonal antibody recognizes any additional epitopes. This experiment involves biotinylation of the rabbit anti-CEA IgG fraction and an inhibition experiment performed with a combination of all five MAbs. The results shown in Fig. 3B indicate that inhibition is limited to 50–60%. These results are

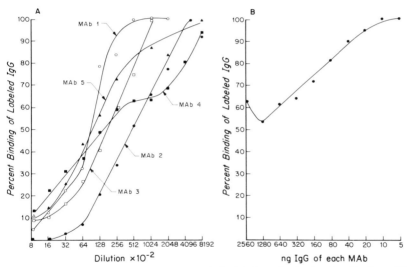

FIG. 3. (A) Competition of biotinylated MAb for binding of polyclonal antibody to CEA. Microtiter wells coated with CEA were incubated with biotinylated MAbs and increasing dilutions of a polyclonal rabbit anti-CEA antiserum. The bound biotinylated MAb was detected using an avidin–biotin–peroxidase conjugate. Binding is expressed as percentage material measured at $A_{492\,nm}$ in the presence of rabbit CEA antiserum compared to percentage material measured at $A_{492\,nm}$ at infinite antiserum dilution (i.e., in the absence of rabbit CEA antiserum) (100% binding). The symbols are explained in Fig. 1. (B) Competition of biotinylated polyclonal antibody for the binding of five MAbs to CEA. Microtiter wells coated with CEA were incubated with biotinylated polyclonal rabbit anti-CEA antiserum and decreasing dilutions of a combination of five MAbs. The percentage binding is given as in Fig. 3A.

consistent with the conclusion that the rabbit polyclonal antibody recognizes additional antigenic determinants in CEA. Although we have not performed the equivalent test with the original mouse antisera, this approach is useful if one wants to determine whether all possible epitopes are represented in a panel of MAbs. This type of analysis may be useful to determine the antibody repertoire for a given species or to compare the response across species for a given antigen.

Epitope Specificity Using a Biotinylated Antigen in an EIA

Materials

PBS: 0.01 M sodium phosphate buffer (pH 7.4) containing 0.15 M NaCl
PBS–Tween: PBS plus 0.05% (v/v) Tween 20 (Sigma)
Reaction buffer: 0.02 M sodium phosphate (pH 6.8)
Coating buffer: 0.01 M sodium phosphate (pH 7.4) containing 150 mM NaCl and 0.1% NaN$_3$
ABC: avidin–biotin–peroxidase complex (Miles-Yeda) diluted 1 : 500 in PBS–Tween
Substrate-2: 1 mg/ml of 5-aminosalicyclic acid (Sigma) in preheated (56°) reaction buffer; add 5 mg active charcoal per 100 ml, and filter; add 100 μl of freshly prepared 1% H$_2$O$_2$ per 10 ml of above
1% H$_2$O$_2$: dilute 30% H$_2$O$_2$ 1 : 30 in distilled water
3 M NaOH: dissolve 12 g of NaOH in 100 ml of distilled water
NSB: N-hydroxysuccinimidobiotin (Sigma)
DMF: Dimethylformamide, distilled from ninhydrin

Preparation of Biotinylated Antigen. CEA (0.5 mg in 0.1 ml of PBS) is treated with an equal volume of freshly prepared aqueous NSB (1 mg/ml, 0.1 ml). The NSB preparation, reaction conditions, and dialysis are described under "Preparation of Biotin-Labeled MAb."

EIA Protocol. The wells of a 96-well polystyrene microtiter plate (Costar) are coated with MAb (5 μg MAb/ml in coating buffer) for 2 hr at 37° and then overnight (8–12 hr) at 4°. Biotinylated CEA (50 μl of 1.0 μg/ml) is added to a separate tube containing 50 μl of the test MAb dilution (0.5–1000 ng of IgG is a good range), and the tubes containing the biotinylated CEA–MAb mixture are incubated overnight at 37°. The plates are washed three times with PBS, incubated for 1 hr at room temperature with 150 μl of BSA–PBS to block nonspecific binding, and washed three times with PBS. The biotinylated CEA–MAb mixture (100 μl) is added to the wells and incubated for 90 min at room temperature. The plates are washed five times with PBS–Tween, treated with 100 μl of ABC (1 : 500 dilution), incubated for 2 hr at room temperature, and washed as follows: (1) rinse once with PBS; (2) fill wells to top with PBS, wait 5 min, discard, and repeat two times; (3) rinse wells with distilled water three times. The wells are incubated with 200 μl of substrate-2 for 15 min and the reaction is stopped with 100 μl of 3 M NaOH. Absorbance is read at 450 nm. The usual controls are run. Nonspecific binding should be <0.01 absorbance units.

The inhibition analysis of five MAbs versus two MAbs coated on microtiter wells is shown in Fig. 4. The binding of biotinylated CEA to wells coated with MAb 2 is not inhibited by MAbs 1, 3, 4, or 5 (Fig. 4A). The binding of biotinylated CEA to MAb 4 is slightly inhibited by MAb 2 and significantly inhibited by MAb 1, a result equivalent to that obtained with the procedure in Fig. 1.

A possible objection to an immunoassay requiring the labeling of an antigen or antibody is that the labeling process may affect the binding. In solid-phase assays, a further objection is that either an antigen or an antibody bound to a solid phase may undergo a conformation change affecting binding. By reversing the roles of antigen and antibody in the

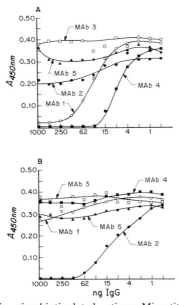

FIG. 4. Epitope analysis using biotinylated antigen. Microtiter wells coated with MAb IgG were incubated with biotinylated CEA and decreasing dilutions of MAbs. The bound biotinylated CEA was detected with the avidin–biotin–peroxidase conjugate. (A) Plates coated with MAb 1; (B) plates coated with MAb 2. The symbols are explained in Fig. 1.

two tests described above it is possible to probe the effect of both parameters on the formation of the antigen–antibody complex.

Determination of K_{aff} Using a Solution-Phase, Avidin–Biotin RIA

Materials

PBS: 0.05 M sodium phosphate buffer (pH 7.0) containing 0.15 M sodium chloride and 0.1% NaN_3

Avidin–PEG: avidin (Sigma) 0.1 mg/ml in PBS containing 5% (w/v) PEG 6000 (Sigma)

Preparation of ^{125}I-Labeled Antigen. See "Epitope Analysis Using a Solid-Phase RIA."

Preparation of Biotinylated MAb and Carrier Protein. Biotinylated MAb is prepared as described under "Epitope Specificity Using Biotinylated MAb in an EIA." Either normal rabbit or goat serum can be used to prepare biotinylated carrier protein. After dialysis against PBS, carrier serum (2 ml) is treated with 2 ml of freshly made aqueous NSB, prepared by dissolving 20 mg NSB in 0.5 ml of DMF and diluting to 2.0 ml with 1.5 ml of distilled water. The reaction conditions, dialysis, and storage are as described under "Preparation of Biotin-Labeled MAb." For use in the assay, the biotinylated carrier serum is diluted 1:800 in normal goat or rabbit serum diluted 1:40 in PBS.

RIA Overview. The procedure is similar to that described by Clark and Todd[8] and Wagener *et al.*[10] Determination of K_{aff} is performed in two steps. First, binding curves for each MAb are determined. A constant amount of radiolabeled antigen (0.5 ng of ^{125}I-CEA) is titered against serial 2-fold dilutions of MAb. The concentration of MAb IgG yielding half-maximal binding is determined. This concentration is used in the second step. The second step is a competitive inhibition RIA involving the addition of increasing amounts of unlabeled antigen (0.5–100 ng of CEA) which competes with a fixed amount of MAb (determined in stage one) for the binding of a constant amount of radiolabeled antigen (0.5 ng of ^{125}I-CEA).

Each RIA requires the separation of free from bound radiolabeled antigen. This is accomplished by precipitation of the biotinylated MAb with avidin. Since only a minute amount of MAb is present, the precipitation is driven to completion by adding a carrier biotinylated protein. Biotinylated rabbit or goat serum is chosen as carrier because mouse serum is rather expensive.

[10] C. Wagener, B. R. Clark, K. J. Rickard, and J. E. Shively, *J. Immunol.* **130**, 2302 (1983).

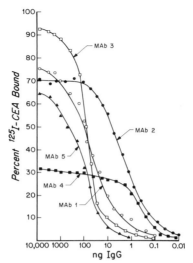

FIG. 5. Binding curves for radiolabeled antigen to MAb in a solution-phase, avidin–biotin-based RIA. Radiolabeled CEA was titered with decreasing dilutions of biotinylated MAbs. The biotinylated MAb and MAb complex were precipitated with avidin in the presence of 5% PEG. Symbols are explained in Fig. 1.

Binding RIA Protocol. The RIA is performed in 400-μl polypropylene tubes (BioRad) which can be tightly capped and centrifuged in a Beckman microfuge. Serial 2-fold dilutions of biotinylated MAb (50 μl; 0.01–1000 ng) in biotinylated carrier serum (1 : 800 dilution in normal rabbit or goat serum diluted 1 : 40 in PBS) are incubated with 200 μl of PBS containing 6.5% PEG 6000 (Sigma) and 72 mM EDTA and with 10 μl of ^{125}I-CEA (0.5 ng in PBS; ~10^4 cpm) for 18 hr at 37°. The ^{125}I-CEA cocktail may include [57]Co as a volume marker if desired.[8,11] Biotinylated MAb and biotinylated MAb–antigen complex are coprecipitated with biotinylated carrier proteins by addition of 10 μl of avidin (1.0 mg/ml in PBS containing 5% PEG 6000) for 1 hr at room temperature. The tubes are centrifuged, the supernatants are removed, and the precipitates are counted.

The binding curves for MAbs 1–5 are shown in Fig. 5. It should be noted that each MAb has its own unique maximum percentage binding and concentration of IgG at the 50% inhibition point. The plateau region for maximum binding for each MAb is found and used to estimate the maximum percentage binding. The IgG concentration at one-half this value is used for the competitive inhibition studies. The amounts of IgG at

[11] M. L. Egan, C. W. Todd, and W. S. Knight, *Immunochemistry* **14**, 611 (1977).

50% inhibition for each of the MAbs in Fig. 5 are MAb 1, 27 ng; MAb 2, 1 ng; MAb 3, 97 ng; MAb 4, 1 ng; and MAb 5, 172 ng. The concentration is calculated from these values (in nanograms) divided by the assay volume (260 μl).

The explanation(s) for less than 100% binding of radiolabeled antigen includes the partial destruction or damage of the antigen by the labeling process and/or the heterogeneity of the antigen. It is assumed that the MAb is homogeneous. This phenomenon is commonplace for MAbs and is only partly understood. Since there is a good agreement between relative maximum percentage binding of MAbs to CEA obtained by the RIA and EIA, it can be argued that the K_{aff} determined by RIA is truly representative of the binding of the MAb to all the molecules of CEA that it can bind. In spite of this apparent heterogeneity, the homogeneity of the antigen binding site was demonstrated for each MAb (see next section).

Competitive Inhibition Assay Protocol. The assay tubes, centrifugation protocol, and reagents are the same as in the previous section. To each assay tube (in duplicate) is added 10 μl of ^{125}I-labeled CEA (0.5 ng in PBS), 50 μl of biotinylated MAb at the dilution calculated for 50% maximum binding (see Fig. 5; the dilution is performed in a 1 : 800 dilution of biotinylated goat serum in normal goat or rabbit serum diluted 1 : 40 in PBS), and 200 μl of a CEA inhibitor solution (0.5–100 ng in PBS with 6.5% PEG). The tubes are incubated, precipitated with 10 μl avidin (1.0 mg/ml in PBS with 5% PEG), and counted as before.

The inhibition curves for MAbs 1–5 are shown in Fig. 6. The calculation of K_{aff} according to a modification[8] of the method of Müller[12] for MAb 1 is

$$K_{aff} = 1/(I_t - T_t)(1 - 1.5b + 0.5b^2)$$

where I_t is the inhibitor concentration at 50% inhibition of tracer binding; T_t, the total tracer concentration; b, the fraction of tracer bound in absence of inhibitor; I_t = ng/(260,000 nl)(180,000), i.e., moles unlabeled CEA per liter (CEA, MW 180,000); T_t = 0.5 ng/(260,000 nl)(180,000), i.e., moles labeled CEA per liter; and b = 0.4 for MAb 1. Thus,

$$K_{aff} = 3.7 \times 10^9 \, M^{-1} \quad \text{for MAb 1}$$

The affinity constants of MAbs 1–5 are shown in the table.[12] For comparison the affinity constant range of a polyclonal goat anti-CEA antibody is also given. The K_{aff} values of MAbs 1, 2, and 4 are sufficiently high to warrant their use in an immunoassay for CEA. The final choice of

[12] R. Müller, *J. Immunol. Methods* **34**, 345 (1980).

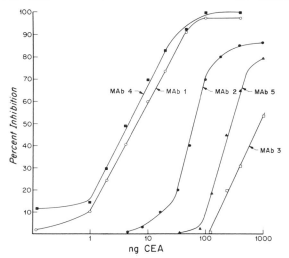

FIG. 6. Inhibition curves for calculating affinity constants of five MAbs. A constant amount of radiolabeled CEA and biotinylated MAb was incubated with increasing amounts of unlabeled CEA. The biotinylated MAb and MAb complex were precipitated with avidin in the presence of 5% PEG. The amount of MAb was calculated from the 50% binding point in Fig. 5. (○) MAb 1, 20.5 ng IgG per tube; (●) MAb 2, 1.4 ng IgG per tube; (□) MAb 3, 96.9 ng IgG per tube; (■) MAb 4, 0.9 ng IgG per tube; (▲) MAb 5, 171.6 ng IgG per tube.

the optimum MAb is also dependent, however, on the required epitope specificity. A discussion of this topic and the problem of cross-reacting antigens is given by Wagener *et al.*[1,9]

A demonstration of the homogeneity of the antibody–antigen combining sites can be achieved by double-reciprocal plots of bound versus free antigen. Examples of this plot for MAbs 1, 2, and 4 are shown in Fig. 7. Since the plots are linear, both sites are considered homogeneous.

AFFINITY CONSTANTS OF MONOCLONAL
ANTI-CEA ANTIBODIES[a]

MAb	Affinity constants (M^{-1})
1 CEA.66-E3	3.7×10^9
2 T841.1-E3	1.8×10^{10}
3 CEA.41C-12.1-D8	1.0×10^8
4 T84.66-A3.1-H11	2.6×10^{10}
5 CEA.281-H6	3.8×10^8
Polyclonal (goat)	0.7×10^{11}–1.4×10^{11}

[a] Calculated by the method of Müller.[12]

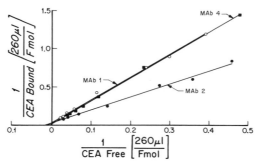

FIG. 7. Reciprocal plots of bound versus free antigen for three MAbs. Increasing amounts of radiolabeled CEA were added to a constant amount of biotinylated MAb. (●) MAb 2, 2.7 ng IgG per tube; (○) MAb 1, 6.6 ng IgG per tube; (■) MAb 4, 3.7 ng IgG per tube.

Acknowledgments

This research was supported by a grant from the National Large Bowel Program, NCI Grant CA37808. We wish to thank Frances Crawford and Karen Rickard for their expert technical assistance, and Dr. Y. H. Joy Yang for production of the monoclonal antibodies. Special thanks are given to Dr. Chas. W. Todd for his encouragement on this project.

[44] A Simple Method for Ranking the Affinities of Monoclonal Antibodies

By Veronica van Heyningen

The affinity of a monoclonal antibody for its antigen is an important parameter in determining its usefulness. Among the numerous applications for monoclonal antibodies, immunoassay and immunohistochemistry require high-affinity antibodies so that complexes of antigen and antibody are not easily disrupted. On the other hand, immunoaffinity purification is best achieved with low-affinity antibodies bound to a solid-phase support so that antigen can be specifically adsorbed and then released under chemically mild conditions without damage to either antigen or antibody, and the column can be reused.

Many established methods for the measurement of affinity constants are complex and subject to considerable experimental error. Antibody affinity for a given antigen can, however, be estimated or ranked[1] by performing a simple dilution analysis at an early stage after initial screening of monoclonal fusion products for specific antigen recognition. Because only low- and high-affinity antibodies are usually sought in a fusion, many of intermediate affinity can be discarded at an early stage and efforts to grow suitable hybridomas can be concentrated on potentially useful clones.

Principle

Antibody molecules bind specific antigens. The strength of this binding is described as the affinity of the antibody for antigen, and it can be quantitated by a variety of methods which attempt to measure the components at equilibrium in the following type of idealized reaction:

$$Ab + Ag \rightleftharpoons AbAg$$

In such systems the affinity constant K is defined as

$$K = [AbAg]/[Ab][Ag]$$

in which case K will have the units of liters per mole. The higher the numerical value of K the greater the affinity of the antibody.

In some methods of affinity measurement the constant derived is the reciprocal of K ($1/K$) which therefore has the units of moles per liter and is analogous to the Michaelis constant of enzyme kinetics. In this case, the smaller the value the higher the affinity.

By analogy with Michaelis–Menten kinetics it can be shown that the affinity of an antibody for its antigen can be estimated if bound and free antigen can be measured when a fixed trace amount of antigen is allowed to bind to serial dilutions of antibody.[1] The antibody concentration at half-maximal antigen binding is a measure of affinity. The smaller the amount of specific immunoglobulin required to bind 50% of the available antigen, the higher the affinity of the antibody for the antigen. Although this theory oversimplifies the true situation, results are at least as good as with other methods.

Thus, if antibody dilution analysis is carried out for a series of monoclonal antibodies directed to the same antigen and the percentage of bound antigen is plotted against the decreasing antibody concentrations for each antibody, then the order of the affinities of the different antibod-

---

[1] V. van Heyningen, D. J. H. Brock, and S. van Heyningen, *J. Immunol. Methods* **62**, 147 (1983).

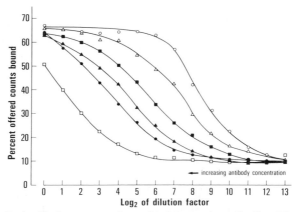

FIG. 1. Antibody dilutions curves for anti-α-fetoprotein antibodies. The percentage of labeled antigen bound is plotted against the antibody doubling dilution on a log scale. (□) AFP22.4; (●) AFP21.1; (▲) AFP21.2; (■) AFP490; (△) AFP384; (○) AFP144. The order of affinities is read off at 50% maximal antigen binding (see discussion under "General Comments"), i.e., at about 32% offered counts bound in this case, from the left (for low affinity) to the right (for high affinity).

ies can simply be read off the plot at half-maximal antigen binding from left to right for low to high affinity (Figs. 1 and 2).

General Comments

Antibodies

This simple affinity ranking technique is valid only for monoclonal antibodies which bind to a single antigenic species in the antigen source used for dilution analysis. In principle, the *specific* immunoglobulin (Ig) concentration of the monoclonal antibody must be known. This means that dilution analysis can only be carried out with hybridoma culture supernatants, or with carefully purified ascites Ig, since in ascites there are many irrelevant antibodies in addition to the specific monoclonal one. (For methods of purification from ascites see Ey *et al.*[2] and Parham.[3] In practice, when culture supernatants from confluent monoclonal hybridomas are used the variations in Ig concentration are small (less than 10-fold[4]) compared with the affinity constant differences between low-affin-

[2] P. L. Ey, S. J. Prowse, and C. R. Jenkin, *Immunochemistry* **15,** 429 (1978).
[3] P. Parham, this series, Vol. 92, p. 110.
[4] G. Galfré and C. Milstein, this series, Vol. 73, p. 3.

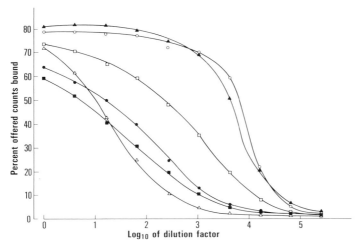

FIG. 2. Antibody dilution curves for anti-thyroid-stimulating hormone antibodies. Data are plotted as in Fig. 1, except that here 4-fold serial dilutions were made. (△) TSH258; (■) TSH88; (●) TSH286; (□) TSH323; (○) TSH42; (▲) TSH301 (cross-reacts with other pituitary hormones.

ity ($K \approx 10^6$–10^7) and high-affinity ($K \approx 10^9$–10^{12}) antibodies. Thus quantitation of monoclonal immunoglobulins with its attendant difficulties is not essential for successful affinity ranking so long as culture supernatants are used in dilution analysis. The problems of measuring monoclonal antibody concentrations accurately are discussed briefly later.

Antigens

Antibody dilution analysis in its simplest form is carried out using trace amounts of labeled purified antigen and some means of separating bound antigen from unbound. However, if a suitable labeled second antibody is available (for criteria of suitability, see below), unlabeled purified or even unpurified antigen can be used in an indirect binding assay in which trace amounts of antigen are bound to microtiter plates. Dilutions of antibody then bind to the antigen and specifically bound antibody is quantitated with labeled second antibody.

When the antigen of interest is a cell surface molecule studied *in situ* there are additional complications of topology and antigenic mobility.[5] Further problems are introduced if the antigen is part of a cross-reacting

[5] D. W. Mason and A. F. Williams, *Biochem. J.* **187,** 1 (1980).

family of gene products, as in the case of histocompatibility antigens. The antibodies usually have different affinities for each gene product, all of which are present together on the cell surface. Affinity ranking by antibody dilution analysis is not a valid technique in these circumstances.

When purified labeled antigens are used for antibody dilution analysis, the maximal (or plateau) antigen binding level is unlikely to be 100% because all labeled antigen preparations contain some labeled impurities which will not bind to the antibody. These impurities include contaminating molecules not removed in the course of purification, antigen molecules whose specific binding site(s) have been destroyed during labeling, and some label which is not attached to antigen molecules. Conversely, not all individual antibodies will achieve the plateau binding observed for those of high affinity because the lower affinity antibodies require a correspondingly higher specific immunoglobulin concentration to bind all the available antigen. This immunoglobulin concentration is not always achieved in culture supernatants, or sometimes even in ascites Ig preparations. The 50% of maximal binding is the same potentially achievable level for all the antibodies (e.g., at 32% of offered counts bound, in Fig. 1, and at 40% of offered counts bound, in Fig. 2).

Antibody Dilution Analysis with Labeled Antigen

In our laboratory we have used this technique to select suitable monoclonal antibodies for immunopurification and for immunoassay of antigens such as human α-fetoprotein (AFP) and human thyroid-stimulating hormone (TSH) which are available in purified form and can be efficiently labeled with radioiodine (^{125}I).

Reagents

Diluent. For AFP: 0.05 M potassium phosphate (pH 7.5); for TSH: 0.25 M Tris–HCl (pH 8.5) both with 2% horse serum and 1% Tween 20 added.

Monoclonal antibody: supernatant from confluent cultures. The minimum volume required for assay in duplicate is 0.5 ml. This is easily achieved when early clones are growing in 2-ml wells before the first freezing away in liquid nitrogen. Serial 2- or 4-fold dilutions are made in diluent to a final dilution factor of 10^4–10^5. Neat supernatant from an irrelevant hybridoma is used as negative control.

^{125}I-labeled antigen. Stock solution is diluted in diluent so that 50 μl will contain 2–10 $\times$ 10^4 cpm, with the specific activity at 20–60 μCi/μg protein.

Solid-phase anti-mouse immunoglobulin antibody. High-titer second antibody bound to Sepharose or other support is readily available commercially or can be made by standard techniques.[3,6] This component must be added in excess (determined by previous titration), suspended in 50–100 μl diluent.

Procedure. (1) One hundred microliters of appropriately diluted monoclonal antibody is dispensed in duplicate into polystyrene tubes of about 4-ml capacity. (2) Diluted labeled antigen, 50 μl, is added. The covered tubes are incubated for 2 hr at room temperature. (3) Solid-phase second antibody, 50–100 μl, is added and the tubes shaken for 2 hr. (4) Then 3 ml of diluent is added, and the tubes are centrifuged, decanted, and washed with another 3 ml of diluent. (5) The final sedimented solid phase is counted in a gamma counter.

An alternative washing procedure for solid-phase bound complexes is the sucrose layering technique of Wright and Hunter.[7] This was used for the TSH assays.

An alternative to the use of solid-phase second antibody in separating Ig-bound antigen from free antigen is the use of polyethylene glycol (PEG).[8] This method was used routinely for the AFP assays. Steps 1 and 2 in the procedure above were unchanged, but the separation of Ig-bound antigen was effected simply by the addition of 1 ml 13% PEG 6000 in 0.05 *M* phosphate buffer (pH 7.5). The precipitate was separated by centrifugation and counted as above. Although identical results were obtained with the AFP system using PEG precipitation and solid-phase second antibody, the PEG technique is not as widely applicable as the second antibody method, as each system needs to be optimized individually for PEG concentration.

Results. Figure 1 shows antibody dilution curves for a series of different anti-AFP monoclonal antibodies. Figure 2 shows a similar dilution analysis for anti-TSH antibodies. In each case the percentage of labeled antigen which bound to each antibody dilution was plotted against the antibody dilution factor. From these simple plots the relative affinities of each series of antibodies can be read off. The highest affinity antibodies can be diluted most before antigen binding drops to less than 50% of plateau levels. Thus for the anti-AFP antibodies in Fig. 1 the order of

[6] J. F. Wright and W. M. Hunter, *J. Immunol. Methods* **48**, 311 (1982).

[7] J. F. Wright and W. M. Hunter, *in* "Immunoassays for Clinical Chemistry" (W. M. Hunter and J. E. T. Corrie, eds), p. 170. Churchill-Livingstone, Edinburgh and London, 1983.

[8] T. Chard, this series, Vol. 70A, p. 280.

affinities is AFP144 > 384 > 490 > 21.2 > 21.1 > 22.4. For the anti-TSH antibodies (Fig. 2), the order is TSH301 > 42 > 323 > 286 > 88 > 258.

Problems. As different hybridoma culture supernatants will contain different molar amounts of immunoglobulins, the x axes are not strictly superimposable in terms of antibody concentration. Therefore, it could be argued that the approximate affinity constants at 50% antigen binding cannot always be read off with confidence. However, as shown below, antibodies at the high and low ends of the affinity scale can almost always be pinpointed.

Monoclonal Immunoglobulin Quantitation

The Ig concentration has been measured for the anti-AFP antibodies by an immunoradiometric assay (IRMA). Accurate measurement of different monoclonal immunoglobulins is a tricky problem. Different immunoglobulins may be of a different class or subclass and may have a different number of determinants reacting with most available anti-Ig antisera. The choice of immunoglobulin standards is difficult for the same reason. Most commercially available polyclonal second antibodies will contain a large proportion of molecules reacting with immunoglobulin class- and subclass-specific regions.[9] Only antisera which react specifically with the Fab region of Ig molecules, or with bound light chain subunits, are suitable for accurate quantitation of hybridoma antibodies. Monoclonal reagents which react equally with one site present on all Ig molecules would also be suitable.[9]

Reagents

Diluent: 0.25 M Tris–HCl (pH 8.5) with 2% horse serum and 1% Tween 20.

[125]I-labeled rabbit anti-mouse light chain: specific activity 3 μCi/μg, diluted in diluent to 2×10^5 cpm in 50 μl. This antibody was the gift of Dr. A. F. Williams. It was raised against an IgA mouse myeloma protein and affinity purified on solid-phase mouse IgG myeloma protein. It should therefore recognize predominantly the bound light chain portion common to IgA and IgG.

Standards: purified mouse monoclonal IgG$_1$[10] at concentrations from 40 to 0.1 μg/ml at serial doubling dilutions in diluent.

Samples: 4-fold serial dilutions of hybridoma culture supernatants in diluent.

[9] T. A. Springer, this series, Vol. 92, p. 147.
[10] W. M. Hunter, J. G. Bennie, D. J. H. Brock, and V. van Heyningen, *J. Immunol. Methods* **50,** 133 (1982).

Solid-phase anti-mouse immunoglobulin antibody: This can be the same
as that used for antibody dilution analysis, but here it will work as the
solid-phase side of an IRMA assay in which the antigen analyte happens to be an Ig molecule. This reagent must be in excess.

Procedure. (1) Fifty microliters of diluted standard or sample is incubated with 50 μl of ^{125}I-labeled rabbit antibody in covered 4-ml tubes for 2
hr at room temperature. (2) Solid-phase second antibody, 50–100 μl, is
added, and the tubes shaken for 2 hr. (3) Then, 3 ml of diluent is added,
and the tubes are centrifuged, decanted, and washed with another 3 ml of
diluent. (4) The final sedimented solid phase is counted in a gamma
counter.

Results

The number of counts in each tube is plotted against the Ig concentration of the standards. The sample values, which should fall on a parallel
curve, are read off.

Figure 3 shows the dilution analysis of the anti-AFP antibodies in Fig. 1
replotted with Ig concentration on the *x* axis. The immunoglobulin concentration is shown as the molar concentration of half-Ig molecules in
order to fulfill the condition for 1 : 1 protein–ligand binding stipulated for
the simple theory above. The order of affinities is still very similar to that
seen in Fig. 1. Only AFP490 and AFP21.2 change places as 490 produces
a higher concentration of lower affinity antibody than 21.2. The order now

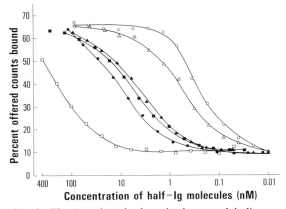

FIG. 3. The data in Fig. 1 replotted when the immunoglobulin concentration of the
hybridoma supernatants has been measured and converted into molar concentrations of
half-Ig molecules. Apart from the single changeover for AFP21.2 and AFP490, the order of
affinities is unchanged. Symbols as for Fig. 1.

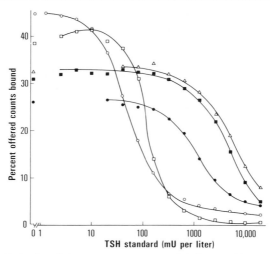

FIG. 4. Unoptimized radioimmunoassay curves for the specific anti-TSH antibodies shown in Fig. 2. In each case 50 μl of ^{125}I-TSH (at 4 ng/ml and containing 20,000 cpm) was competed with appropriate dilutions of a standard unlabeled TSH preparation. The symbols are as for Fig. 2. The higher the affinity of the antibody, the lower the TSH concentrations it can detect in RIA, i.e., the greater its sensitivity.

is AFP144 > 384 > 21.2 > 490 > 21.1 > 22.4. This order is exactly that deduced from the range of antigen concentrations that each antibody is capable of covering in a classical radioimmunoassay (RIA).[1] The value for $1/K$ which can be read off Fig. 3 for AFP144 is about 3×10^{-10} mol/liter, so that K is approximately 3×10^9 liters/mol. This is a likely value for a fairly high affinity antibody, usable in immunoassay of biological levels of AFP. AFP21.1 turned out to be most suitable for affinity purification of antigen.[11] The affinity of AFP22.4 was too low to retain antigen efficiently.

In the case of the anti-TSH monoclonal antibodies Ig quantitation was not done, but the range covered in rough, unoptimized RIA assays carried out with each antibody is in exactly the same order (Fig. 4) as that deduced from the simple dilution analysis (Fig. 2). It should be noted that the higher the affinity of an antibody the smaller the amount of antigen which it can detect. Adrion[12] has shown that the affinity constant of antibody for antigen can be calculated from RIA data. This has been done

[11] V. van Heyningen, L. Barron, D. J. H. Brock, D. Crichton, and S. Lawrie, *J. Immunol. Methods* **50,** 123 (1982).

[12] R. F. Adrion, *Clin. Chem.* (*Winston-Salem, N.C.*) **28,** 717 (1982).

AFFINITY CONSTANTS CALCULATED FROM
RIA CURVES[a]

TSH clone number	K (liters/mol)
42	3×10^{10}
323	1×10^{10}
286	7×10^{8}
258	2×10^{8}
88	2×10^{8}

[a] From Ref. 12.

from the curves in Fig. 4 for the anti-TSH antibodies. The values for K are shown in the table.

The anti-TSH antibodies were produced with a view to using two on opposite sides of a two-site IRMA assay. High-affinity antibodies were selected by dilution analysis alone at a very early stage after initial screening. The chosen antibodies were then subjected to strict specificity tests and to epitope analysis to ensure that the two antibodies finally used will bind simultaneously to the antigen molecule. We also had to check that the antibodies chosen could be easily labeled (in our case with iodine, but enzyme or biotin labeling are increasingly used), or bound to solid-phase carrier without loss of binding affinity or specificity. Thus, it is useful to select several antibodies in the appropriate affinity range soon after initial screening, so that if any fail to meet the criteria outlined above, other candidates are available. Nevertheless, in a prolific fusion which may produce as many as a hundred different hybridomas which bind antigen, a large number having intermediate affinities can be discarded. Efforts at maintaining and characterizing hybridomas can then be concentrated on a dozen high-affinity ones and two or three low-affinity ones.

[45] The Hazards of Mycoplasma Contamination in the Screening of Hybridoma Supernatants for Effects on [3H]Thymidine Incorporation

By JAMES P. JAKWAY

In recent years, monoclonal antibodies have been very useful in advancing our understanding of lymphocyte biology. Antibodies that affect a specific lymphocyte function can be used to identify and/or isolate molecules (either lymphocyte cell surface antigens or soluble mediators) involved in that function. One can either test established monoclonal antibodies or screen new hybridoma supernatants for their effects on a given lymphocyte response. However, when testing monoclonal antibodies in a functional assay, it is essential to show that any activity observed is due to antibody and not to a contaminant in the hybridoma supernatant.

Various species of mycoplasma are known to inhibit and/or nonspecifically stimulate lymphocyte proliferation. Mycoplasma are also common contaminants of tissue culture. Therefore, when testing an established monoclonal antibody or screening new hybridomas for their effects on lymphocyte proliferation, one must be certain that the observed effects are due to antibody and not to contaminating mycoplasma.

In this chapter, I will discuss the various mechanisms by which mycoplasma inhibit or stimulate the proliferation of lymphocytes. I will also discuss methods for removing the inhibitory or stimulatory activities from antibody preparations. Procedures for the detection of mycoplasma contamination in cell cultures have been addressed elsewhere.[1] Methods for clearing cultures of mycoplasma contamination, a notoriously difficult task, will not be discussed.

Mycoplasma inhibit lymphocyte proliferation by consuming essential media components. The nonfermenting mycoplasma species, including *Mycoplasma arthritidis, M. hominis, M. orale,* and *M. salivarium,* utilize arginine as an energy source.[2] These species, through arginine deiminase,[3] quickly deplete the culture medium of this essential amino acid, resulting in lymphocyte starvation.[4-6] Other species, including *Acholeplasma laidlawii, M. arginini, M. hyorhinis, M. pulmonis,* and *M. neurolyticum,* consume thymidine.[7-9] Lymphocytes can continue to grow in the presence of these species by synthesizing their own thymidine. However, since they are making thymidine, they do not take up and incorporate into DNA the [³H]thymidine which is added to culture to measure proliferation.

[1] G. J. McGarrity, this series, Vol. 58, p. 18.
[2] R. T. Schimke and M. F. Barile, *J. Bacteriol.* **86,** 195 (1963).
[3] R. T. Schimke and M. F. Barile, *Exp. Cell Res.* **30,** 593 (1963).
[4] R. Copperman and H. E. Morton, *Proc. Soc. Exp. Biol. Med.* **123,** 790 (1966).
[5] M. F. Barile and B. G. Leventhal, *Nature (London)* **219,** 751 (1968).
[6] M. S. Simberkoff, G. J. Thorbecke, and L. Thomas, *J. Exp. Med.* **129,** 1163 (1969).
[7] M. T. Hakala, J. F. Holland, and J. S. Horoszewicz, *Biochem. Biophys. Res. Commun.* **11,** 466 (1963).
[8] E. M. Levine, L. Thomas, D. McGregor, L. Hayflick, and H. Eagle, *Proc. Natl. Acad. Sci. U.S.A.* **60,** 583 (1968).
[9] D. M. Callewaert, J. Kaplan, W. D. Peterson, Jr., and J. J. Lightbody, *J. Immunol.* **115,** 1662 (1975).

MYCOPLASMA SPECIES THAT STIMULATE LYMPHOCYTE PROLIFERATION

Mycoplasma species	Lymphocyte subpopulation stimulated	Species stimulated[a]	Heat stability[b]	Ref.[c]
Acholeplasma laidlawii	B and T	Mouse, human, not rat	Stable	1–3
Mycoplasma arthritidis	B and T	Mouse, human, rat	Membrane stable	1, 4, 5
			Soluble labile	6
M. canis	N.T.[d]	Mouse	Stable	1
M. fermentans	N.T.	Mouse, not rat	Stable	1, 3
M. gallisepticum	N.T.	Mouse	Stable	1
M. neurolyticum	B	Mouse, rat	Labile	3, 7
M. pneumoniae	B	Mouse, human, not rat	Stable	1, 3, 8, 9
M. pulmonis	B and T	Mouse, rat	Labile	1, 10, 11
M. synoviae	N.T.	Mouse	Stable	1
Spiroplasma citri	N.T.	Mouse	Stable	1

[a] Other species not tested.
[b] 56°, 30 min.
[c] Key to references: 1, B. C. Cole, K. E. Aldridge, and J. R. Ward, *Infect. Immun.* **18**, 393 (1977); 2, H. Kirchner, H. Brunner, and H. Ruhl, *Clin. Exp. Immunol.* **29**, 176 (1977); 3, Y. Naot, J. G. Tully, and H. Ginsburg, *Infect. Immun.* **18**, 310 (1977); 4, K. E. Aldridge, B. C. Cole, and J. R. Ward, *Infect. Immun.* **18**, 377 (1977); 5, R. A. Daynes, J. M. Novak, and B. C. Cole, *J. Immunol.* **129**, 936 (1982); 6, B. C. Cole, G. J. Sullivan, R. A. Daynes, I. A. Sayed, and J. R. Ward, *J. Immunol.* **128**, 2013 (1982); 7, Y. Naot and H. Ginsburg, *Immunology* **34**, 715 (1978); 8, G. Biberfeld and E. Gronowicz, *Nature (London)* **261**, 238 (1976); 9, G. Biberfeld, *Scand. J. Immunol.* **6**, 1145 (1977); 10, H. Ginsburg and J. Nicolet, *Nature (London) New Biol.* **246**, 143 (1973); 11, Y. Naot, S. Merchav, E. Ben-David, and H. Ginsburg, *Immunology* **36**, 399 (1979).
[d] Not tested.

Many species of mycoplasma have been reported to stimulate lymphocyte proliferation (table). Different species of mycoplasma stimulate (1) different lymphocyte subpopulations, and (2) lymphocytes from different species. The mechanism by which mycoplasma stimulate lymphocyte proliferation is unknown.

It is very difficult to clear a culture of a mycoplasma infection. In contrast, removing the mycoplasma lymphocyte inhibitory and stimulatory activities from antibody preparations can, in many instances, be quite simple. This is done by subjecting antibody preparations to procedures that destroy the mycoplasma activities but not antibody activity.

The consumption of thymidine by mycoplasma is a property of viable organisms. Mycoplasma are rapidly killed by heating at 56°.[10] The arginine deiminase activity of mycoplasma is also heat labile.[5] Because antibodies are unaffected by heating at 56°, heating hybridoma supernatants at 56° for 30 min will eliminate the inhibitory activities of any contaminating mycoplasma while leaving antibody activity intact. This approach can be used on supernatants from established hybridoma lines. It can also be used in the initial hybridoma screen by aliquoting the supernatants to be screened into microtiter plates and then heating the microtiter plates before adding cells and other culture components. In this laboratory, all hybridoma supernatants are routinely heated at 56° for 30 min, regardless of whether a mycoplasma contamination is suspected.

The lymphocyte-stimulating activity of some species of mycoplasma is heat labile (table) and can be removed by heating at 56° for 30 min. Unfortunately, the stimulatory activity of many species is heat stable. The biochemical nature of this heat-stable activity has not been well studied. However, in one species of mycoplasma stimulatory activity was found both in the membrane fraction and released into the culture medium in a soluble form. While the membrane-associated activity was heat stable, the soluble activity was destroyed by heating.[11]

If this proves to be a general finding for all mycoplasma species, the lymphocyte-stimulating activity can be removed by a two-step procedure. Bacteria and membrane fragments could first be removed by high-speed centrifugation ($50,000\ g$, 1 hr). The few remaining bacteria and the soluble stimulatory activity could then be destroyed by heating at 56° for 30 min. Since it would be unwieldly to centrifuge a large number of supernatants in a hybridoma screening assay, this procedure is only applicable to treating preparations of established monoclonal antibodies.

[10] N. F. Freiis, *Acta Vet. Scand.* **15**, 288 (1974).
[11] B. C. Cole, G. J. Sullivan, R. A. Daynes, I. A. Sayed, and J. R. Ward, *J. Immunol.* **128**, 2013 (1982).

[46] The Dot Immunobinding Assay

By Richard Hawkes

Nitrocellulose paper has been widely used as a support for solid-phase immunoassay, most notably for proteins electrophoretically blotted from polyacrylamide.[1] More recently, a dot immunobinding assay has been

[1] H. Towbin, T. Staehelin, and J. Gordon, *Proc. Natl. Acad. Sci. U.S.A.* **76**, 4350 (1979).

described[2] in which the antigen is directly applied to the nitrocellulose filter as a dot. The assay is both simple and reliable and presents a number of attractive advantages over conventional immunoassays. First, because the dot permits the color reaction to be viewed against a white background, it is often possible to detect positive responses not apparent by conventional ELISA. Second, the assay is extremely sparing of antigen, often a crucial consideration, and a spot of 0.5 μl of solution (average diameter 0.3 mm) is easily recognizable. Third, it is possible to use the dot immunobinding assay with a roster of different antigens, thereby simultaneously detecting and characterizing antibodies of interest. On the other hand, a conventional ELISA, where possible, is probably more appropriate for quantitative studies, even though scanning densitometry of dot assays can provide useful quantitative information. The procedure described below is based on our original description with various modifications and additions as noted. The antigen is applied as a discrete dot to a nitrocellulose filter. Once nonspecific binding sites are blocked, the dot is incubated in the putative antibody-containing solution. Antibody binding is detected with a second, species-specific antibody conjugated to horseradish peroxidase. The assay also can be used to detect the binding of other ligands, such as lectins.[3]

Procedure

Step 1. To prepare the filter for dotting, a rectangular grid is drawn onto the nitrocellulose sheet (e.g., Schleicher and Schuell; 0.22-μm average pore size) using pencil and ruler, such that an individual grid element will fit into the well of a 96-well microtiter plate (i.e., less than 4 mm per side). It is important to use pure nitrocellulose since some combination filters have a low binding capacity for proteins. Nitrocellulose sheets are also available with a 3 $\times$ 3-mm grid already printed (Millipore). These sheets can be cut into individual test strips after dotting. As an alternative, a filtration manifold can be used[4] (e.g., Bethesda Research Laboratories) which effectively divides a single sheet of nitrocellulose into 96 individual reaction wells, avoids the need to cut the filter into pieces, and makes subsequent storage more straightforward. In all cases, the filter should be washed for 5 min by gentle shaking in a bath of distilled water and then air-dried before use.

Step 2. Antigen is applied as a small drop to each square of the filter. Dotting may begin as soon as the filter is dry; dotting onto a wet filter

[2] R. Hawkes, E. Niday, and J. Gordon, *Anal. Biochem.* **119,** 142 (1982).
[3] R. Hawkes, *Anal. Biochem.* **123,** 143 (1982).
[4] F. C. Bennett and L. Y. Yeoman, *J. Immunol. Methods* **61,** 201 (1983).

results in unacceptable spreading of the antigen. Various micropipetting devices have been successfully used to apply antigens to the filter. For qualitative studies, we use a 20-μl sampling pipet. For quantitative work, a 5-μl Hamilton syringe is appropriate. The appropriate concentration will vary from antigen to antigen. For complex antigenic mixtures, such as membrane fractions, concentrations in the range of 0.1–1.0 mg/ml are suitable. When purified antigens are being used, this concentration can be reduced accordingly. The dot volume can vary between 0.1 and 2 μl. If the antigen is too dilute, successive dots can be applied to the same site, provided that the filter is allowed to dry each time; a hair dryer can be used to speed up the process.

A wide range of different antigens have been successfully applied to nitrocellulose in this way including proteins, synthetic polypeptides, nucleic acids (binding is enhanced by baking at 80° for 1 hr), glycoproteins, glycoplipids, membrane fractions, nuclear fractions, viruses, yeast, protozoa, and fibroblasts. Aldehyde-fixed cells will also bind satisfactorily. Many smaller molecules do not bind well to nitrocellulose and a postfixation step may be valuable [e.g., 15 min in 10% acetic acid/25% isopropyl alcohol (v/v) in water[5] or overnight in glutaraldehyde vapor followed by 15 min in 0.05% $NaBH_4$ in TBS (50 mM Tris–HCl, pH 7.4, 200 mM NaCl)], or activated supports may be used which permit covalent bonding between antigen and sample (e.g., diazobenzyloxymethyl paper[6]). For a wide range of antigens, these filters may be stored dry in the dark for up to a year without deterioration. We have observed that detergents such as Triton X-100, NP-40, sodium deoxycholate, and sodium dodecyl sulfate all interfere with protein binding to the filter and thus should be avoided although specific detergent combinations may be acceptable.[5]

Protein binding to the filter can be confirmed using Ponceau S, which colors the dots pink (0.2% solution in 3% trichloroacetic acid, 3% sulfosalicylic acid; available as a 10× concentrate from Sigma). Staining is removed by washing the filter in buffer and does not appear to interfere with subsequent antibody binding. It is often useful to include both positive and negative control dots such as some irrelevant proteins (negative) and various dilutions of mouse serum (positive).

After the dot has been allowed to dry, the filter should be washed for 10 min in TBS and then cut into individual test squares. We prefer to use a scalpel and ruler to cut the filter into individual strips and then scissors to separate the squares. The filter is friable and should be cut when thor-

[5] R. Jahn, W. Schiebler, and P. Greengard, *Proc. Natl. Acad. Sci. U.S.A.* **81,** 1684 (1984).
[6] J. C. Alwine, D. J. Kemp, B. A. Parker, J. Reiser, J. Renart, G. R. Stark, and G. M. Wahl, this series, Vol. 68, p. 220.

oughly wet; a pad of wet filter paper makes cutting easier. Others have used cork borers[7] or special cutting tools[8] to obtain individual test filters. When an array of antigens are to be tested, it is convenient to keep them together on a single strip and perform the incubations accordingly.

Step 3. It is necessary to block nonspecific antibody-binding sites on the filter. We currently use 10% normal horse serum in TBS, but a variety of other reagents can be used equally well. The filters are blocked by incubation for 15–30 min at room temperature under constant shaking. This results in blocking of both the filter and the plastic walls of the incubation well.

Step 4. The primary incubation is started by removing the blocking solution and adding the test antibody. If the 2-fold dilution is unimportant, the test antibody may be added directly to the blocking solution. The volume of supernatant necessary varies with the size of the incubation well; 150 μl/well is more than enough in a 96-well tray. The incubation is performed under continuous agitation at room temperature. A 2-hr primary incubation is usually sufficient, although overnight incubation may substantially increase the sensitivity. If the incubation is allowed to continue overnight, precautions should be taken to avoid excessive evaporation. We have found that 0.05% NP-40, 0.2% Triton X-100, or 0.3% Tween-20 in the incubation medium significantly reduces nonspecific binding in some cases. However, others have reported elution of polypeptide antigens from the filter in the presence of detergents[9] so they should be used with caution.

Step 5. After the primary incubation the antibody solution is removed by aspiration and the filters washed for 30 min in several changes of TBS. If a filtration manifold has been used, the filter may be removed at this stage and treated as a single unit for subsequent washes and incubations (taking care to clip one corner to establish the correct orientation). There is a risk under these conditions that antibody bound to one dot may dissociate and reattach to another, thereby producing false positive reactions. This is especially true for low-affinity antibodies, and we have observed it from time to time.

Step 6. After washing, the filters should be reblocked as described in step 3 and then incubated for 2 hr in an appropriate peroxidase-conjugated second antibody solution. Where the primary monoclonal antibody was raised in mouse, the second antibody is usually a peroxidase-linked goat or rabbit anti-mouse Ig (e.g., DAKO Inc.). The dilution will vary from

---

[7] A. Esen, J. M. Conroy, and S. Z. Wang, *Anal. Biochem.* **132,** 462 (1983).
[8] G. Weinbrenner, *J. Immunol. Methods* **61,** 321 (1983).
[9] L. Lin and U. H. Kamamatsu, *Anal. Biochem.* **128,** 302 (1983).

supplier to supplier but between 1/100 and 1/1000 in blocking solution is about right. Radioiodinated protein A or second antibody have also been used to detect antibody binding.[5,10-12] If a chain type-specific peroxidase-conjugated second antibody is used, the dot immunobinding assay becomes both antigen-specific and antibody-type specific. In this way it is possible to choose, say, only IgG antibodies when immunocytochemical uses are plannned. When reduced sensitivity is acceptable, for example during the subcloning of a strongly reactive antibody, it is possible to save time by combining the first and second antibody incubations (i.e., steps 4 and 6; B. Riederer, personal communication).

Step 7. Repeat the washing (step 5).

Step 8. Bound antibody can be revealed with a variety of chromogens. We find that 4-chloro-1-naphthol is the most sensitive and gives the lowest background staining. The 4-chloro-1-naphthol is prepared as a 3 mg/ml stock solution in methanol. It can be stored at 4° in a dark bottle for several weeks and should be discarded if yellowing or precipitation is apparent. To prepare the working solution, the 4-chloro-1-naphthol stock is diluted with 5 volumes of TBS and hydrogen peroxide is added to give a final concentration of 0.01% (v/v). The working solution should be used immediately. Positive primary antibodies will give a blue spot after 15 min. We have also tested 3,3'-diaminobenzidine and o-dianisidine. In our hands they give no increase in sensitivity and higher background staining, and furthermore both are suspected to be carcinogenic. Some proteins are themselves pseudoperoxidases (e.g., hemoglobins, cytochromes) and can give spurious positive reactions. This activity can be eliminated by incubation in 3% H_2O_2 in TBS for 10 min followed by incubation with 3% periodic acid in TBS (10 min) and 0.05% $NaBH_4$ in TBS (1 min). Alternatively, the assay can be restructured to use alkaline phosphatase-conjugated second antibodies and β-naphthyl phosphate and a diazotized amine as substrate[13]; the sensitivity of this latter method appears to be similar to that with horseradish peroxidase but a direct comparison has not been reported. After staining, the reacted filters should be washed in distilled water and air-dried. Once dry they should be kept in the dark.

Quantitation. The staining can be converted into a quantitative estimate of antibody binding by densitometric scanning.[2] The filter can be rendered transparent, if necessary, in a glycerol–water mixture. If diaminobenzidine has been used as chromogen, toluene can also be used.

[10] P. Herbrink, F. J. VanBussel, and S. O. Warnaar, *J. Immunol. Methods* **48**, 293 (1982).

[11] J. W. Davis, J. M. Angel, and J. M. Bower, *J. Immunol. Methods* **67**, 271 (1984).

[12] J. Huet, A. Sentenac, and P. Fromageot, *J. Biol. Chem.* **257**, 2613 (1982).

[13] B. M. Turner, *J. Immunol. Methods* **63**, 1 (1983).

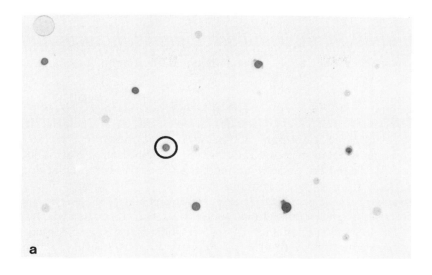

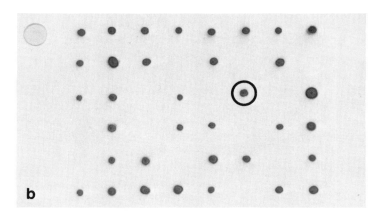

FIG. 1. (a) A dot immunobinding assay for monoclonal anti-synaptosomal plasma membrane antibodies. Synaptosomal plasma membrane preparation, at 0.4 mg/ml, was dotted (0.5 µl/dot) using a filtration manifold (Bethesda Research Laboratories) as template. The filter was blocked in the template and then 100 µl of culture supernatant was added to each well. The culture supernatants were taken from mouse hybridomas growing in Iscove's medium plus 15% fetal calf serum in 2-ml culture wells. Just before testing, the culture media had begun to turn yellow and cells covered 25–50% of the bottom surface of the well. After a 4-hr incubation the wells were washed individually and then the filter removed and washed *en bloc*. Antibody binding was detected as described in the text using rabbit anti-mouse immunoglobulin conjugated to horseradish peroxidase and 4-chloro-1-naphthol as chromogen. Culture well G10 is circled. (b) Subcloning of antibody G10 from the experiment described in Fig. 1A. The cell hybridomas from well G10 were plated at 0.2 cells/well over a feeder layer of mouse splenocytes. Five hundred wells were seeded and colonies grew in 56 wells. Forty-eight wells were tested as described in Fig. 1A and 35 wells assayed strongly positive. One of these (no. 22, circled) was chosen for expansion and further testing.

For quantitative applications it is important to include positive controls, such as a titration series of mouse immunoglobulins, among the dots to be tested.

Results

An example of a dot immunobinding assay is shown in Fig. 1a. The antigen was isolated neonatal rat cerebellar synaptosomal plasma membranes (SPM) and the putative antibodies were derived from hybridomas constructed from a mouse immunized with SPM. The dotting, blocking, and first incubation were performed in a filtration manifold, and the subsequent stages were conducted in an open tray. Anti-SPM antibodies were identified in 17 wells. In Fig. 1b we see the results of subcloning the hybridoma from well G10 at 0.2 cells/well. In all, 48 wells containing hybridomas were tested and 35 of them assayed strongly positive.

In Fig. 2, the distribution of the MAb G10/22 immunoreactivity was tested against cerebellar homogenates from rats of various ages from newborn to adult. It can be seen that MAb G10/22 seems to be develop-

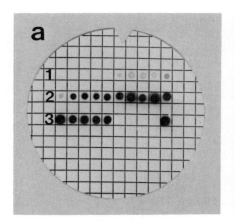 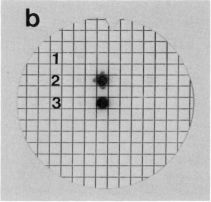

FIG. 2. (a) The development of MAb G10/22 immunoreactivity in rat cerebellum. Homogenates of rat cerebellum were dotted onto a nitrocellulose disk with a preprinted grid (0.5 mg protein/ml, 0.5 μl/dot). Homogenates were taken from animals ranging from the day of birth (P0) to postnatal day 40 (P40). Row 1 is samples P0–P9 at daily intervals, row 2 is P10–P19, row 3 is P20, P22, P25, P30, P40, and, at the right, adult (25 weeks). The total array was then tested against MAb G10/22. There is no immunoreactivity at birth and the MAb G10/22 antigen appears during the second postnatal week. (b) The chain type specificity of MAb G10/22. Rabbit anti-mouse chain-specific antibodies (Nordic) were dotted onto nitrocellulose (1 μl/dot; antibodies diluted 1/30 in 10% normal horse serum). Row 1: anti-μ; row 2: anti-γ_1, anti-γ_{2a}, anti-γ_{2b}, anti-γ_3; row 3: anti-λ, anti-κ. The MAb G10/22 reacts with the anti-γ_{2a} heavy chain and the anti-κ light chain antibodies.

mentally regulated in rat cerebellum, reaching mature levels of expression between days 8 and 15 postnatally. Similar dot arrays can be used to determine the species specificity and the organ specificity of the antibody.[14]

Finally, in Fig. 2b, the chain type of the MAb G10/22 antibody has been determined using a series of chain-specific antibodies (Nordic) on the dot. It can be seen that MAb G10/22 is an IgG with a γ_{2a} heavy chain and a κ light chain.

[14] R. Hawkes, E. Niday, and A. Matus, *Cell* **28**, 253 (1982).

[47] Detection of Antibody-Secreting Hybridomas with Diazobenzyloxymethyl Paper

By Geneviève Motta and Daniel Locker

The availability of a rapid, specific, and sensitive assay is an important condition for obtaining monoclonal antibodies. In the case of soluble antigens a number of immunoassays have been developed which involve the fixation of antigen or antibody to a solid phase, and direct or indirect detection of the antigen–antibody complex. When screening for antibody-secreting hybridomas, a large number of culture supernatants must be tested, and the immunoassays are often performed in plastic 96-well plates, coated with one of the reagents, usually the antigen.[1] In the case of enzyme-linked immunosorbent assays (ELISA) this may require a large amount of pure antigen when thousands of hybrid cultures have to be screened for a rare hybridoma. We describe in this chapter an immuno-binding assay on diazobenzyloxymethyl (DBM) paper which requires only ~1 μg antigen and 1 μl of each culture supernatant and allows the screening of hundreds of culture supernatants in the same day.

DBM paper was originally developed by Alwine *et al.*[2] for transferring ribonucleic acids after gel electrophoresis and was later applied by Renart *et al.*[3] to the transfer and immunological identification of proteins fractionated by gel electrophoresis. We have adapted the method for the rapid screening of hundreds of postfusion supernatants. As the detection only

[1] See this series, Vol. 92(E), and this volume.
[2] J. C. Alwine, D. J. Kemp, and G. R. Stark, *Proc. Natl. Acad. Sci. U.S.A.* **74**, 5350 (1977).
[3] J. Renart, J. Reiser, and G. R. Stark, *Proc. Natl. Acad. Sci. U.S.A.* **76**, 3116 (1979).

depends on the antigen–antibody interaction, it is highly specific and is independent of the type of immunoglobulin produced by the hybridoma.

Other authors have developed immunobinding assays involving the immobilization of antigen or antibody on alternative supports such as nitrocellulose[4,5] or diazophenylthioether paper.[6] Compared with nitrocellulose, DBM paper presents the advantages of a better resistance upon handling and lower cost, as it may be easily synthesized in the laboratory.

Since the original publication of our method,[7] we have further developed the conditions for the application of the test and we have modified our procedure for the synthesis of DBM paper according to the improved method published by Christophe et al.[8]

Assay Method

Principle. Small amounts of hybrid culture supernatants are spotted onto DBM paper. During incubation, the proteins and antibodies present are immobilized through reaction with the diazonium groups. After saturation of the excess diazonium sites, the paper is incubated with ^{125}I-radiolabeled antigen. After extensive washing the fixation of antigen is detected by autoradiography or quantified by a gamma counter.

Procedure. DBM paper is produced through activation of aminobenzyloxymethyl (ABM) paper available from various commercial sources. For instance, the ABM-1015 paper (from Schleicher and Schuell[9]) compared with the paper synthesized in our laboratory gave similar results in various immunoassays.

Alternatively, ABM and DBM papers may be easily synthesized according to procedures published in the literature; and a combination of the methods described by Christophe et al.[8] for the synthesis of ABM paper and by Alwine et al.[2] for the activation of ABM to DBM paper has been developed. Briefly, the various steps are as follows. Cut pieces of Whatman 450 or Schleicher and Schuell 589-WH filter paper of the appropriate size (usually 10 × 14 cm for screening 96 hybrid supernatants). Prepare a

---

[4] J. Sharon, S. L. Morrison, and E. A. Kabat, *Proc. Natl. Acad. Sci. U.S.A.* **76**, 1420 (1979).

[5] E. Smith, K. Roberts, G. W. Butcher, and G. Galfré, *Anal. Biochem.* **138**, 119 (1984).

[6] J. Reiser and J. Wardale, *Eur. J. Biochem.* **114**, 569 (1981).

[7] D. Locker and G. Motta, *J. Immunol. Methods* **59**, 269 (1983).

[8] D. Christophe, H. Brocas, and G. Vassart, *Anal. Biochem.* **120**, 259 (1982).

[9] Schleicher and Schuell, Keene, NH 03431, U.S.A. Distributed in France by Cera-Labo, 143 Avenue Jean Jaurès, 93307 Aubervilliers Cedex.

solution of NBPC[10] in DMF[11] by heating at 40° in a water bath ~612 mg of NBPC and ~2.6 ml of DMF for each 10 × 14-cm paper. Heating is performed in a stoppered vial until the suspension becomes turbid. Immerse the paper into this solution and immediately place it in an oven at 130–135° for 30 min. After cooling, wash the paper twice with 100 ml acetone and twice with 200 ml water. Immerse the paper in a freshly prepared solution of 20 g sodium dithionite in 200 ml of 50 mM sodium hydroxide and agitate for 2 hr at room temperature. Then wash the paper four times with ~200 ml water and twice with ~100 ml acetone and dry it at 37° for 10 min. This ABM paper is then stored at −20° in air-free sealed plastic bags. Under these conditions it may be stored for several months without any loss of activity.

The activation of ABM to DBM paper for hybridoma screening includes the following steps. With a soft pencil draw on the ABM paper a grid of 12 × 8 squares (1 × 1 cm each) corresponding to the 96 wells of a microtitration plate. Soak the paper in a solution precooled at 4°, containing 80 ml 1.8 M HCl, 40 ml water, and 3.2 ml of a freshly prepared solution of NaNO$_2$ (10 mg/ml water), and incubate 30 min at 4°. Wash five times (5 min each) in precooled water and twice (10 min) in precooled 0.1 M phosphate buffer (pH 7.5) at 4°.

The activated DBM paper is then air-dried and should be used for transfer of supernatants as soon as possible (although it retains some activity if stored at 4° for 1 or 2 days).

Detection of Antibody-Producing Clones. To each square of the DBM paper, 1 μl of each hybrid well supernatant to be tested is spotted. For qualitative tests, any type of micropipet (1–20 μl) is suitable. The paper is then incubated in a humidified incubator at room temperature for 2 hr to allow for covalent fixation of proteins (and monoclonal antibodies if they are present). The excess of diazonium groups is then saturated by incubation in a 1% (w/v) solution of bovine serum albumin in 1 M glycine for 2 hr at 37°. The paper is then immersed in a solution of ^{125}I-labeled antigen in 0.1 M phosphate buffer (from 3,000,000 to 5,000,000 cpm in 100 ml) for 3 hr at 4°. The unfixed radioactive material is eliminated by setting the paper under running tap water overnight. The paper is then air-dried and used for autoradiography with X-rays film (Kodak or Fuji) and Cronex

[10] NBPC: *N*-(3-nitrobenzyloxymethyl) pyridinium from BDH Biochemicals, Poole, United Kingdom.

[11] DMF: *N,N*-dimethylformamide for spectroscopic use (Uvasol) from Merck, Darmstadt, West Germany.

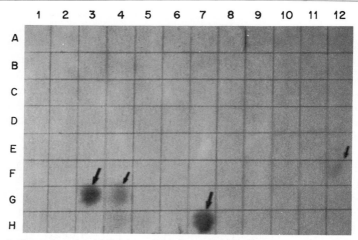

FIG. 1. Demonstration of the detection of positive hybridoma supernatants against Aa6 scorpion hemocyanin subunit. From each of 96 supernatants 1 μl was spotted on DBM paper and incubated with ^{125}I-radiolabeled Aa6 subunit as described in the text. After 2 days of exposure at $-80°$ with intensifying screens, two strongly positive (wide arrows) and two weakly positive (thin arrows) hybridomas are detectable on the film after development.

Lightning Plus intensifying screens at $-70°$, according to Laskey and Mills[12] for 2–4 days.

Alternatively when a rapid result is required, the paper can be cut into squares and each square counted in a gamma counter. This method is also suitable for either titration of ascites or any conventional antisera (see below).

Applications and Discussion

Detection of Monoclonal Antibodies. The method has been applied to the screening of hybrid supernatants obtained after fusion of the myeloma cell line Sp2/0/Ag14[13] with spleen cells of mice immunized against various subunits of the hemocyanin of the scorpion, *Androctonus australis,* purified and characterized in the laboratory of J. Lamy[14] (Faculté de Pharmacie, Tours, France). The method used for fusion and selection of hybrid clones was an adaptation of that of Gefter *et al.*[15] and screening of

[12] R. A. Laskey and A. D. Mills, *FEBS Lett.* **82,** 314 (1977).
[13] M. Shulman, C. D. Wilde, and G. Köhler, *Nature (London)* **273,** 666 (1978).
[14] J. Lamy, J. Lamy, J. Bonaventura, and C. Bonaventura, *Biochemistry* **19,** 3033 (1980).
[15] M. Gefter, D. M. Margulies, and M. D. Scharf, *Somatic Cell Genet.* **3,** 231 (1977).

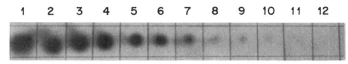

FIG. 2. Titration of antiserum with DBM paper assay. Twofold serial dilutions, starting at 1/10, of anti-Aa6 rabbit antiserum were spotted on DBM paper, which was then treated as described in Fig. 1. The last positive well (11) corresponds to the 1/10,240 dilution.

the supernatants was performed according to the method described: 1 μl from each supernatant was applied onto DBM paper and the papers were incubated at room temperature for 2 hr. After blocking the unreacted diazonium groups in the bovine serum albumin solution, the papers were immersed in 100 ml phosphate buffer containing 1 μg of the antigen radiolabeled with ^{125}I by the chloramine-T method to a total activity of about 5,000,000 cpm. Figure 1 gives an example of the autoradiogram obtained after screening 96 supernatants of a fusion involving spleen cells immunized against the hemocyanin Aa6 subunit; G_3 and H_7 wells show a strong positive reaction and G_4 and F_{12} a weak reaction.

Positive primary clones are then repeatedly subcloned by limiting dilution until they are stable and passaged into nude mice to produce ascites fluid. The detection of positive subclones and the titration of the ascites are performed by the same method. In each series of tests, we always include two spots of a dilution of the serum of mice immunized for fusion as a positive control, and two spots of the culture supernatant of the original myeloma cell line as a negative control.

Monoclonal antibodies obtained by this method proved to be highly positive in other immunological tests such as ELISA and immunoelectron microscopy, and directed against a single epitope of the immunizing antigen.[16] The specificity of the assay was also demonstrated; antibodies directed against the Aa6 subunit did not react on DBM paper with radiolabeled Aa2 subunit or with other unrelated radiolabeled antigens.

Sensitivity of the Assay. The sensitivity of the assay has been tested by titration of a polyclonal rabbit antiserum directed against subunit Aa6. The autoradiogram obtained is presented in Fig. 2. It shows that 1 μl of a 1/10,240 dilution of the antiserum still gives a positive reaction with radiolabeled Aa6. The table further indicates a good correlation between the intensity of the radioactive spot and the number of counts detected when the squares of paper corresponding to each spot are counted in a gamma

[16] J. Lamy, J. Lamy, P. Billiald, P. Y. Sizaret, G. Cavé, J. Frank, and G. Motta, *Biochemistry* **24**, 5532 (1985).

CORRELATION BETWEEN ^{125}I COUNTS AND
ANTIBODY CONCENTRATION[a]

Antiserum dilution	cpm[b]	Antiserum dilution	cpm[b]
1/10	3,339	1/640	502
1/20	2,125	1/1,280	177
1/40	2,032	1/2,560	103
1/80	1,476	1/5,120	77
1/160	1,057	1/10,240	53
1/320	881	1/20,480	54

[a] Squares of DBM paper obtained from the experiment described in Fig. 2 were cut and counted in a MR 252 Kontron gamma counter.
[b] A background of 850 cpm obtained by counting the same surface area of DBM paper treated with 1 μl of the myeloma cell line culture supernatant was subtracted from all values.

counter. The sensitivity depends in part on the intensity of labeling of the antigen and on the length of exposure of the autoradiogram. The exposure time can be increased when the radiolabeled antigen has been stored for some time. It is possible to use the same solution of radioactive antigen for about 1 month, but precautions are to be taken in order to prevent bacterial and fungal contamination. Indeed, we have observed in some cases that old solutions may lead to nonspecific fixation of the label on all the supernatant spots. This has been ascribed to radiolysis of the antigen following contamination. Preservation of the antigen solution in the presence of antibiotics or frozen at −20° avoids the problem.

Other Applications of the DBM Assay. Although developed originally for hybrid supernatant testing, the method is suitable for various types of immunological tests as it requires only small amounts of antigen and antibody. We have used it for class and subclass determination of the monoclonal antibody by spotting the culture supernatant on DBM and incubating it with ^{125}I-labeled anti-IgM, anti-IgG$_1$, anti-IgG$_{2a}$, anti-IgG$_{2b}$, or anti-IgG$_3$ reagents.

Another possibility is to test the same supernatant against various radiolabeled fractions of the same antigen in order to detect fine specificity. For instance, we immunized mice against whole scorpion hemocyanin, which is easy to prepare, and tested the hybrid postfusion supernatants against the eight different radiolabeled hemocyanin subunits. It is also possible to label the hybridoma culture and to fix the antigen onto the DBM paper first.

Other applications may include competition experiments, detection of cross reactions, and characterization of conformation-specific antibodies.

Whatever the type of immunological problem studied, the DBM assay presents the main advantages of requiring minute amounts of antigen and antibody and of allowing the detection of any type of immunoglobulin. Furthermore, its sensitivity, specificity, and rapidity prove it to be a very useful tool for screening hybridomas directed against various antigenic determinants of complex molecules.

Acknowledgments

Part of this work was supported by a CNRS Grant ATP 3948. We thank Pr. J. Lamy for providing the scorpion hemocyanin and subunits as well as the rabbit anti-Aa6 serum. We are also grateful to Mrs. M. C. Gonzalez for her expert technical assistance.

[48] The Use of Alkaline Phosphatase-Conjugated Anti-Immunoglobulin with Immunoblots for Determining the Specificity of Monoclonal Antibodies to Protein Mixtures

By PETER L. EY and LEONIE K. ASHMAN

Since their initial description by Köhler and Milstein,[1] monoclonal antibodies (MAbs) have been utilized in a wide variety of fields.[2] These highly specific reagents are especially useful in identifying individual components within complex mixtures of antigens.[3-6] Precipitin reactions cannot be used with most MAbs, since many antigen molecules possess only a single determinant of each type.[7] This quality of antigens does not affect the utility of solid-phase assays, however, and the need to determine the specificity of MAbs raised against complex mixtures of protein antigens has led to the development of two-dimensional solid-phase immunoassay

[1] G. Köhler and C. Milstein, *Nature (London)* **256,** 495 (1975).
[2] J. W. Goding, *J. Immunol. Methods* **39,** 285 (1980).
[3] R. Hawkes, E. Niday, and J. Gordon, *Anal. Biochem.* **119,** 142 (1982).
[4] C. G. O'Connor and L. K. Ashman, *J. Immunol. Methods* **54,** 267 (1982).
[5] B. M. Turner, *J. Immunol. Methods* **63,** 1 (1983).
[6] P. J. Talbot, R. L. Knobler, and M. J. Buchmeier, *J. Immunol. Methods* **73,** 177 (1984).
[7] G. A. Molinaro and W. C. Eby, *Mol. Immunol.* **21,** 181 (1984).

systems for proteins electrophoretically blotted ("electroblotted") from polyacrylamide gels onto nitrocellulose or other suitable supports.[8-10] This procedure, based on the transfer of DNA fragments from agarose gels originally described by Southern[11,12] and first adapted to proteins by Towbin et al.,[8] has been termed "immunoblotting."

The method employed most frequently to resolve protein components prior to electroblotting (i.e., prior to transfer) has involved separation of the reduced polypeptides by electrophoresis on polyacrylamide gels (PAGE) in the presence of sodium dodecyl sulfate (SDS).[9,10] Unfortunately, the antigenic determinants of many proteins can be irreversibly altered upon reduction and denaturation.[6,13] Samples containing labile antigens may be subjected to isoelectric focusing or electrophoresis in the absence of SDS (thus allowing antigens to remain in their native state) or in SDS but without reduction. Samples may also be applied directly as "spots" to nitrocellulose sheets ("dot blotting"), and the adsorbed proteins can be tested for the presence of a given antigen.[3,6,10] This is done for both "spots" and "blots" by incubating the nitrocellulose filter, to which the proteins are bound, with selected MAbs or antisera. The presence of bound antibodies is then tested using radiolabeled or enzyme-labeled probes, e.g., ^{125}I-labeled protein A,[14,15] or peroxidase-labeled antibodies specific for the primary antibody.[3] These are detected by autoradiography or histochemically. Both methods exhibit high sensitivity, in the order of 10^{-8} to 10^{-12} g of bound antibody. However, enzyme-labeled probes are rapidly becoming the reagents of choice, principally for their convenience of use, stability, and nonhazardous nature. The enzymes most commonly employed for this purpose are horseradish peroxidase (donor: H_2O_2 oxidoreductase, EC 1.11.1.7), alkaline phosphatase (orthophosphoric monoester phosphohydrolase, EC 3.1.3.1), glucose oxidase (β-D-glucose: O_2 oxidoreductase, EC 1.1.3.4), and β-galactosidase (β-D-galactoside galactohydrolase, EC 3.2.1.23). Based on our experience with peroxidase and alkaline phosphatase (AP) in enzyme-linked immunoassays, we prefer to use AP-conjugated antibodies. These can be prepared more reliably, they tend to be more stable (particularly in dilute solutions), and they continue to produce color for a considerably longer period of time during incubation with substrate solutions.

[8] H. Towbin, T. Staehelin, and J. Gordon, Proc. Natl. Acad. Sci. U.S.A. 76, 4350 (1979).
[9] V. C. W. Tsang, J. M. Peralta, and A. R. Simons, this series, Vol. 92, p. 377.
[10] J. M. Gershoni and G. E. Palade, Anal. Biochem. 131, 1 (1983).
[11] E. M. Southern, J. Mol. Biol. 98, 503 (1975).
[12] N. Arnheim and E. M. Southern, Cell 11, 363 (1977).
[13] R. Thorpe, C. R. Bird, and M. Spitz, J. Immunol. Methods 73, 259 (1984).
[14] W. N. Burnette, Anal. Biochem. 112, 195 (1981).
[15] J. F. Erickson, L. N. Minier, and R. S. Lasher, J. Immunol. Methods 51, 241 (1982).

The histochemical stains used to develop AP-labeled bands on nitrocellulose blots have been based on the reaction of diazotized amine dyes, e.g., Fast Red TR[4,16,17] or Fast Blue salts[5,18] with α-naphthol, formed by the enzymatic hydrolysis of α-naphthyl phosphate. The stain produced by Fast Red TR is pale and difficult to photograph,[4] unlike the darker stain produced with Fast Blue salts, or that produced from o-dianisidine[8] or 4-chloronaphthol[3,19] by peroxidase. Moreover, the diazotized dyes suffer the disadvantage that they cannot be used at the conditions of alkaline pH suited to optimal AP activity (pH 9.5–9.8). These problems are circumvented by the use of 5-bromo-4-chloro-3-indolyl phosphate (BCIP), which upon hydrolysis by AP at pH 9.5 forms insoluble indigo dyes which undergo a further redox reaction in the presence of nitroblue tetrazolium to additionally produce the insoluble formazan dye.[20] This reaction proceeds rapidly at pH 9.5, leading to the deposition of a highly insoluble blue-black stain. Its use for staining DNA and RNA blots has recently been described by Leary *et al.*[21] and for protein blots by Blake *et al.*[22] We have investigated the use of this staining system on protein blots incubated with MAbs and AP-labeled antibodies, and find it to be far superior to the stains previously used for this purpose.

Enzyme–Antibody Conjugates

Most of the conjugates used are made by coupling AP or peroxidase to affinity-purified antibodies (prepared in our laboratory) according to established techniques.[23] Commercially available peroxidase conjugates, e.g., from Bio-Rad, are also used. We shall describe only the method for coupling AP.

Preparation of AP-Conjugated Antibody. (1) Mix 1.0 mg of calf intestinal alkaline phosphatase (Sigma, type VII-S) with 1.0 mg of antibody. (2) Dialyze 48 hr at 4° against 2 liters of 13 mM sodium phosphate, 0.15 M NaCl, 0.5 mM MgCl$_2$, 1×10^{-6} M ZnCl$_2$, pH 7.4 (Mg,Zn–PBS). Change at 12 and 24 hr. (3) Remove, rinse bag with 0.5–1.0 ml of Mg,Zn–PBS and add to dialyzed sample. (4) Add 0.11 volumes of 0.25% glutaraldehyde

---

[16] M. Druguet and M. B. Pepys, *Clin. Exp. Immunol.* **29,** 162 (1977).

[17] D. E. Stage and S. Avrameas, *J. Immunol. Methods* **10,** 105 (1976).

[18] D. Y. Mason and R. Sammons, *J. Clin. Pathol.* **31,** 454 (1978).

[19] "Bio-Rad Immun-blot (GAR-HRP) Assay Kit." Bio-Rad Laboratories, Richmond, California, 1983.

[20] J. McGadey, *Histochemie* **23,** 180 (1970).

[21] J. J. Leary, D. J. Brigati, and D. C. Ward, *Proc. Natl. Acad. Sci. U.S.A.* **80,** 4045 (1983).

[22] M. S. Blake, K. H. Johnston, G. J. Russell-Jones, and E. C. Gotschlich, *Anal. Biochem.* **136,** 175 (1984).

[23] S. Avrameas, T. Ternynck, and J.-L. Guesdon, *Scand. J. Immunol.* **8,** Suppl. 7, 7 (1978).

(electron microscope grade), which has been freshly prepared in 0.15 M sodium phosphate (pH 7.4). (5) Mix, seal, and incubate in dark at room temperature for 3 hr, with occasional mixing. (6) Add 0.2 ml of 1 M glycine (pH 7–8) to stop the reaction. Leave 1 hr. (7) Dialyze at 4° overnight against 2 liters of Mg,Zn–PBS plus 0.05% sodium azide. (8) Remove contents from bag. Add 0.1 volume of bovine serum albumin (Cohn Fraction V; 20 mg/ml in 0.15 M NaCl). (9) Dilute to 12.5 ml with 12.5 mM triethanolamine–Cl, 0.15 M NaCl, 1 mM MgCl$_2$, 2.5 × 10^{-7} M ZnCl$_2$, 15 mM NaN$_3$, 0.2 mg bovine albumin/ml, pH 7.6 (AP diluent), then mix with 12.5 ml of A.R. grade glycerol. Dispense into 4- to 5-ml aliquots. Store at 4°.

The stock conjugates are stable for several years at 4°. A working 1 : 20 stock is made by dilution in AP diluent. A dilution of 1 : 500 (relative to the main stock) in diluent is normally used for immunoblotting. This contains 80 ng antibody/ml.

Polyacrylamide Gel Electrophoresis (PAGE)

Samples are analyzed by electrophoresis at room temperature on 1.2-mm-thick, 10 × 16-cm polyacrylamide gel slabs in the presence of SDS using a discontinuous buffer system.[24] This technique is comprehensively described elsewhere[9,25] and as the exact conditions for resolving components depend on individual requirements, we shall not describe this method in any detail. We use a 3% stacking gel, with either fixed-strength resolving gels ranging in concentration from 7 to 13% (depending on the size of particular polypeptides of interest, and whether or not reducing conditions are used) or 5–15% gradient gels. Samples are mixed with an equal volume of 20 mM Tris–HCl, 2 mM EDTA, 20% glycerol, 0.004% bromophenol blue, 4% SDS, pH 8.0 ± 10% 2-mercaptoethanol, and heated at 100° for 3–4 min prior to application. A mixture comprising at least two to three reference proteins (e.g., transferrin, bovine albumin, IgG, aldolase, carbonic anhydrase, or trypsin inhibitor) is always included.

Detection of Polypeptide Bands in Gels. Polypeptide bands are visualized in gel slabs after staining with Coomassie Blue G-250.[26] The method is rapid and sensitive, detecting as little as 0.1 μg of polypeptide within a

[24] B. Lugtenberg, J. Meijers, R. Peters, P. van der Hoek, and L. van Alphen, *FEBS Lett.* **58,** 254 (1975).

[25] B. D. Hames and R. Rickwood, eds., "Gel Electrophoresis of Proteins: A Practical Approach." IRL Press, Oxford, 1981.

[26] A. H. Reisner, P. Nemes, and C. Bucholtz, *Anal. Biochem.* **64,** 509 (1975).

single band. It is useful to stain gels after the transfer step, to determine how efficiently various bands have been transferred. All steps require the gel to be kept at room temperature in constant gentle motion with a rotary (or side-to-side) shaker.

Procedure. (1) Separate main gel from stacking gel and immerse it in 75 ml of 25% trichloroacetic acid for 30–60 min. (2) Rinse with 50–100 ml of distilled water for 1 min. (3) Immerse in 100 ml of 0.06% Coomassie Blue G-250 (in 3.5% perchloric acid) for 6–18 hr (or 3 hr at 56°). (4) Destain in several 200-ml aliquots of 5% acetic acid, changed one to two times hourly. (5) Photograph (or photocopy) and store gel in sealed plastic bag.

Electrotransfer ("Protein Blotting")

The principles of protein blotting, including factors affecting transfer efficiency, are discussed in detail elsewhere.[9,10] We use a homemade Perspex transfer cell (15 × 16 cm square × 14 cm deep) similar to those available commercially. The gel filter assembly is similar to that described by Towbin *et al.*[8]

Transfer Buffer: 25 mM Tris, 192 mM glycine (pH 8.3)–methanol, 4 : 1 v/v). The inclusion of SDS (0.1%) in the transfer buffer may enhance the transfer of larger polypeptides from SDS gels.[10,15]

Procedure. (1) Place the polyacrylamide gel slab on one of the Scotch-Brite pads of the transfer cell, with the gel face up. (2) Soak a 10 × 13-cm sheet of nitrocellulose (0.45 μm; Schleider & Schüll, West Germany) in transfer buffer. (3) Wet the gel surface with 10 ml of transfer buffer. Carefully lay the wet nitrocellulose sheet directly onto the gel surface, ensuring that no air bubbles are trapped between gel and the sheet. (4) Overlay the nitrocellulose with a piece of Whatman 3MM filter paper soaked in buffer. Take care to eliminate air bubbles. (5) Place the second Scotch-Brite pad over the filter paper. It is useful to label this pad, e.g., with a cut corner, to ensure correct orientation for the transfer. (6) Place perforated plastic support frames on either side of the "sandwich," secure with rubber bands, and carefully lower the entire assembly into the transfer buffer in the transfer cell. The nitrocellulose side must face the anode. (7) Electrophoretic transfer of polypeptide bands from gels containing SDS is performed at 4° at 60–80 V dc. Most bands of $M_r \leq 50,000$–100,000 will be transferred within 4–6 hr, but larger molecules may require 12–18 hr. The current required to maintain voltage is usually 150–200 mA. (8) After transfer, the nitrocellulose sheet is marked with a pencil or fine ball-point pen to identify the gel perimeter and its orientation. It is then separated from the gel.

Staining Transferred Proteins

Proteins/polypeptides bound to the nitrocellulose may be stained directly with Amido Black (0.1% in methanol : glacial acetic acid : water, 45 : 10 : 45, vol %).[27] Destain for no more than 5 min with methanol : acetic acid : water, 90 : 2 : 8 (vol %), then wash in distilled water.

Detection of Transferred Antigens

Following electrotransfer or dot blotting, the residual binding sites on the nitrocellulose must be blocked in order to prevent nonspecific uptake of antibodies. Once this is done, the nitrocellulose sheet, or selected sections of it, are incubated with one or more (mouse) MAbs, washed, and then incubated with an AP–antibody conjugate directed against (mouse) immunoglobulin. Alternatively, the blot may be incubated directly with the appropriately diluted AP-conjugated MAb, if this is available. After washing away unbound conjugate, the strips are incubated in substrate solution to develop the bands or spots. The stain used here is modified from that described originally by McGadey[20] and more recently by Leary et al.[21] and Blake et al.[22]

Solutions and Reagents

TBS: Tris-buffered saline; 25 mM Tris–Cl, 0.15 M NaCl (pH 7.5)

TTBS: TBS plus 0.05% Tween-20 (polyoxyethylene sorbitan monolaurate, from Sigma)

Blocking medium: TTBS containing 0.1% NaN$_3$ and either 1% (w/v) bovine albumin (BSA; Cohn Fraction V)[8] or 1% (w/v) nonfat dry milk powder ("Blotto").[28] Other quenching agents may be used, e.g., gelatin,[29] or heat-inactivated normal serum,[3] providing they do not interfere with the assay. Detergents other than Tween-20 should not be used, as there is evidence that they may displace adsorbed proteins from the nitrocellulose.[29]

Substrate solution

Solution A: Nitroblue tetrazolium (Sigma, Grade III), 0.33 mg/ml in 0.1 M Tris–Cl, 25 mM diethanolamine, 0.1 M NaCl, 2 mM MgCl$_2$, 1 × 10^{-6} M ZnCl$_2$ (pH 9.55)

Solution B: Phenazine methosulfate (Sigma), 2 mg/ml in distilled water

---

[27] W. Schaffner and C. Weissmann, *Anal. Biochem.* **56,** 502 (1973).

[28] D. A. Johnson, J. W. Gautsch, J. R. Sportsman, and J. H. Elder, *Gene Anal. Technol.* **1,** 3 (1984).

[29] W. Lin and H. Kasamatsu, *Anal. Biochem.* **128,** 302 (1983).

Solution C: 5-Bromo-4-chloro-3-indolyl phosphate (BCIP; Sigma), 40 mg/ml in anhydrous dimethylformamide

Preparation: To each milliliter of solution A, add with rapid mixing 6.7 μl of solution B and 3.4 μl of solution C, immediately before use. Solutions A and B must be freshly prepared. Solution C is stable for 3–4 weeks at 4°.

Procedure. (1) Immerse the nitrocellulose in BSA–TTBS or TTBS–Blotto. Incubate at 37° for 30–60 min, or at 4° overnight. (2) Wash once with TTBS (5 min). (3) Cut the nitrocellulose into vertical strips corresponding to selected sample lanes. (4) Incubate each strip for 1 hr at room temperature with (a dilution of) MAb or hybridoma culture fluid (0.15 ml/cm²). (5) Wash three or four times in TTBS (5–10 min per wash). Drain thoroughly. (6) Overlay with a freshly diluted solution of the appropriate AP–antibody conjugate (0.1 ml/cm²). Incubate for 1 hr at room temperature. (7) Wash two or three times in TTBS supplemented with 0.1 mM MgCl$_2$ and 4×10^{-7} M ZnCl$_2$ (5–10 min per wash). (8) Overlay with 0.1 ml of substrate solution/cm². Incubate in the dark at 37° for 20–60 min. (9) When sufficient color has developed, rinse strips thoroughly in distilled water and dry. Store in the dark.

Application Notes

Blocking Solutions. The blocking efficacy of various solutions was assessed by their ability to prevent the subsequent binding of mouse IgG$_1$. Replicate strips spotted with IgG$_1$ (20, 10, 5, . . . ng) were each immersed for 30 min at room temperature in a different blocking solution, rinsed twice in TTBS, then incubated together in a 25 μg/ml solution of IgG$_1$ for 1 hr at 37°. Following washing and exposure to AP-conjugated rabbit anti-mouse Fcγ_1 antibodies, the strips were stained to assess background color and spot sensitivity. Control strips, "blocked" in TBS only, exhibited intense background staining and the spots could not be seen. Faint background staining was observed using TBS plus 0.1% Tween-20, 0.1% Triton X-100, 0.1% milk powder, or 1% normal rabbit serum. Complete blocking (no detectable background) was achieved using TBS/0.05% Tween-20 (TTBS) plus 0.1, 1, or 3% BSA, 10% rabbit serum, or 1% milk powder. There was no difference between these solutions in the sensitivity of dot staining. We therefore use TTBS plus either 1% BSA or 1% milk powder as routine blocking solutions.

Substrate Solution. Various parameters were studied to determine the conditions yielding maximum assay sensitivity.

1. Phenazine Methosulfate. The addition of this electron carrier to the substrate solution of Leary *et al.*[21] was found to increase the staining rate and the final color intensity.

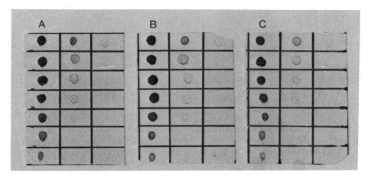

Fig. 1. Influence of different substrate buffers on the color intensity and sensitivity of AP dot blots. Serial 2-fold dilutions of AP were made from 40, 1.0, and 0.1 μg/ml in TBS plus 1 mM MgCl$_2$, 2.5×10^{-7} M ZnCl$_2$, and 5 μg BSA/ml. Two-microliter aliquots of each dilution were spotted onto replicate nitrocellulose filters. These were immediately incubated for 2 hr at room temperature in BCIP staining solutions which differed only in buffer composition: 0.1 M Tris–Cl, pH 9.5 (A); 0.1 M diethanolamine–Cl, pH 9.5 (B); 0.1 M sodium carbonate/bicarbonate, pH 9.5 (C). The vertical columns represent each dilution series, the top dot (left to right) containing 80, 2, and 0.2 ng of enzyme, respectively.

2. Buffer Composition. AP activity is influenced markedly by certain buffers, particularly diethanolamine.[30] Unfortunately, high concentrations of diethanolamine (0.5–1 M) which activate AP about 10-fold caused the stain to decompose within several minutes. Solutions of Tris–Cl, diethanolamine–Cl, and sodium carbonate/bicarbonate (each 0.1 M, pH 9.5) were therefore compared as substrate buffers. It can be seen from Fig. 1 that there was only a slight difference in the staining efficiency of each solution. The sensitivity using direct enzyme spotting was about 6 pg of AP in diethanolamine or Tris, and about 12–25 pg in carbonate. In order to maximize sensitivity, a substrate buffer consisting of 0.1 M Tris, 0.025 M diethanolamine (pH 9.55) and containing MgCl$_2$ and ZnCl$_2$[30] was adopted for routine use.

3. Conjugate Dilution. Figure 2 depicts how staining is affected by varying the conjugate concentration. There is a rapid loss of sensitivity using dilutions beyond 1 : 500 of the conjugate stock. Each new conjugate should be tested at various dilutions on dot blots to select an appropriate working dilution.

4. Comparison of BCIP and Fast Red Stains. It can be seen from Fig. 3 that the BCIP staining method yields a more intense and darker stain than that obtained from Fast Red TR/naphthyl phosphate.[4] The difference

[30] P. L. Ey and E. Ferber, *Biochim. Biophys. Acta* **480,** 403 (1977).

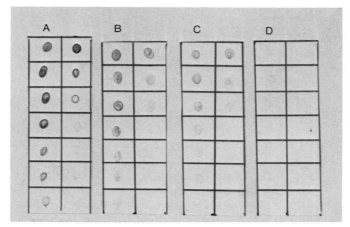

FIG. 2. Effect of conjugate concentration on the staining intensity and sensitivity of dot blots. Serial 2-fold dilutions of the MOPC-21 mouse IgG$_1$ myeloma protein were made from 10 μg/ml and 1 μg/ml in TBS plus 5 μg/ml BSA. Two-microliter aliquots of each dilution were spotted onto replicate nitrocellulose filters. These were blocked in TTBS–Blotto, then incubated for 1 hr with AP-labeled anti-mouse Fcγ_1 antibody at the indicated dilutions of the stock conjugate as follows: (A) 1/500; (B) 1/1000; (C) 1/1500; and (D) 1/2000. The top dots on each panel contained 20 ng (left column) and 2 ng (right column) of IgG$_1$ antigen.

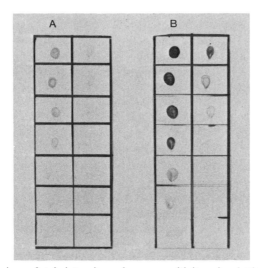

FIG. 3. Comparison of stain intensity and assay sensitivity using dot blots developed with α-naphthyl phosphate/Fast Red TR (A) and the BCIP stain (B). Two-microliter aliquots of MOPC-21 mouse IgG$_1$ solutions, diluted serially in 2-fold steps from 10 μg/ml and 1 μg/ml, were spotted onto replicate nitrocellulose strips. These were blocked and incubated with a 1 : 500 dilution of AP-labeled anti-mouse Fcγ_1 antibody (cf. Fig. 2). The strips were then developed at 37° for 30 min in either 0.2 mg/ml naphthyl phosphate AS-MX plus 3 mg Fast Red TR salt/ml in 0.1 M Tris–Cl (pH 8.2 or pH 9.5), or BCIP staining solution (pH 9.5). Panel A ("Fast Red") was incubated at pH 8.2. At pH 9.5, this stain produced an unacceptably high background color.

in sensitivity of these two stains is also evident. As little as 0.1–0.2 ng of IgG antigen can be detected by the dot blot assay described here.

  5. Substrate Concentration. Dilutions of the BCIP substrate solution were tested for their capacity to stain dot blots of enzyme. The results shown in Fig. 4 indicate that the stain can be diluted in buffer up to 1:3 before staining intensity begins to be affected.

  Use of MAbs to Detect Antigens in Complex Samples. Figure 5 illustrates the specificity with which antigens can be identified on immunoblots using culture supernatants from various hybridoma lines. In this experiment, a complex bacterial cytoplasmic extract was subjected to SDS–PAGE and the resolved bands were electroblotted onto nitrocellulose. Although a large number of polypeptide bands was present on the blot, each culture supernatant detected only one or two antigenic components. These appeared to be different for each supernatant, indicating that distinct antigens were being detected. Background staining was negligible. Blots incubated with supernatants of hybridomas raised against unrelated antigens (e.g., erythrocytes, lane 1) were completely blank, demonstrating the high specificity of the technique. The bands shown in Fig. 5 were obtained with different MAb isotypes using an anti-mouse $F(ab')_2$ conjugate which detected all mouse immunoglobulins. The use of isotype-

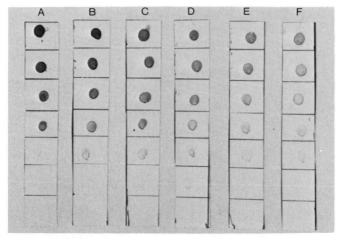

FIG. 4. Effect of BCIP stain concentration on color intensity. Two-microliter aliquots of AP (100, 50, 25, 12.5, . . . ng/ml in TBS–Mg,Zn–BSA; Fig. 1) were spotted onto replicate strips of nitrocellulose. These were immediately incubated at 37° for 1 hr with 0.1 ml/cm² of neat BCIP staining solution (A), or with the indicated dilutions of stain [(B) 1/2; (C) 1/3; (D) 1/4; (E) 1/6; and (F) 1/8] in pH 9.55 stain (solution A) buffer. The top spot of each strip contained 0.2 ng of enzyme.

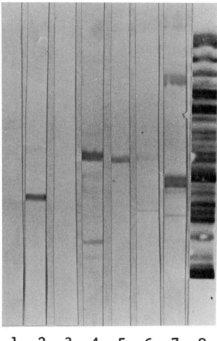

1 2 3 4 5 6 7 8

FIG. 5. Detection of antigenic polypeptides with various mouse MAbs on a blot of *Salmonella enteritidis* 11RX cytoplasmic proteins[4] separated under reducing conditions by SDS–PAGE on a 10% gel. After transfer, one strip was stained for protein with Amido black (lane 8). The remaining strips (1–7) were blocked with TTBS–Blotto, then incubated with different hybridoma culture supernatants (diluted 1 : 2 in TTBS), followed by AP-labeled rabbit antibody specific for murine F(ab′)$_2$ fragments. Each strip contained the equivalent of 40 μg of bacterial protein. Strip 1 was incubated with an anti-human erythrocyte IgG$_1$ as a specificity control. The other strips (2–7) were incubated with anti-*S. enteritidis* supernatants: 2, Sal-2 IgG$_1$ (monoclonal); 3, Sal-5 IgG$_{2a}$ (monoclonal) recognizing a labile antigen; 4, Sal-6 IgG$_{2a}$ (monoclonal); 5, Sal-4 IgG$_{2b}$ (monoclonal); 6, Sal-3 IgM (monoclonal); 7, uncharacterized clone.

specific conjugates yielded bands only with supernatants containing the corresponding class of antibody.

Sensitivity. The high sensitivity of the BCIP stain has been mentioned above from dot-blotting experiments, e.g., 6 pg of AP stained directly, or approximately 100 pg of mouse IgG$_1$ stained after incubation with AP-conjugated anti-mouse immunoglobulin. Figure 6 shows the result of incubating blots of *Salmonella enteritidis* antigens in solutions containing known concentrations of three purified IgG MAbs. A strongly stained

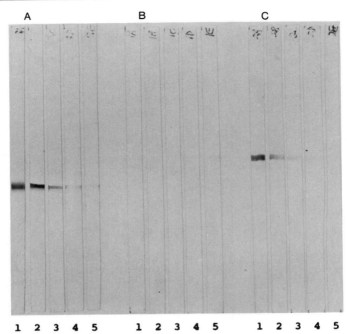

FIG. 6. Titration of purified MAbs (A) Sal-2 IgG_1, (B) Sal-5 IgG_{2a}, and (C) Sal-4 IgG_{2b} to assess the sensitivity of the BCIP immunoblot staining technique. Each nitrocellulose strip contained the equivalent of 40 μg of *S. enteritidis* protein separated by SDS–PAGE on a 10% gel under reducing conditions (*cf.* Fig. 5). After blocking, each strip was incubated with a different dilution of purified MAb (0.15 ml/cm²), and then with AP-labeled anti-mouse F(ab')₂ antibody. The MAb concentrations used were 10 μg/ml (1), 1 μg/ml (2), 0.1 μg/ml (3), 0.01 μg/ml (4), and 0.001 μg/ml (5). Sal-5 recognizes a labile antigen which is destroyed by SDS/reduction.

band was evident using Sal-2 IgG_1 at concentrations as low as 0.1 μg/ml, but the band could still be detected using Sal-2 at 1 ng/ml. A different antigenic polypeptide recognized by Sal-4 IgG_{2b} could be detected using Sal-4 down to 0.1 μg/ml. The concentration of antibody required to stain an antigenic component may be expected to vary between one MAb and another, due to differences in binding affinity and epitope stability. Sensitivity may be increased by using conjugates prepared from polymerized AP.[21]

Lability of Antigenic Determinants. Loss of antigenicity may be a problem in staining blots made from gels on which denatured antigens have been resolved.[6,13,14] This problem is evident in Figs. 5 and 6, where Sal-5 IgG_{2a} failed to label any of the denatured bacterial components present on the blots. This MAb reacts strongly with an antigen present in the undenatured extract. Information on antigen lability may be obtained by comparing samples, denatured to varying degrees, with the untreated preparation on dot blots.

Endogenous AP Activity. Blots made from antigen preparations which have been reduced and/or denatured in SDS will exhibit no background whatsoever. However, endogenous AP activity may sometimes be a problem if attempts are made to analyze samples rich in AP, e.g., certain eukaryotic cell membranes, without prior denaturation. In such cases, much of the endogenous AP activity can be destroyed by incubating the blots overnight at room temperature or 37° in a solution containing 0.1 M EDTA.

Acknowledgments

This work was supported by grants from the Anti-Cancer Foundation of the Universities of South Australia, and the National Health and Medical Research Council of Australia (NHMRC). L. K. Ashman is Senior Research Fellow of the Rotary Peter Nelson Leukaemia Research Fund and P. L. Ey is a Research Fellow of the NHMRC. We thank Neal Shead and Silvana Niutta for skilled technical assistance.

[49] Slide Immunoenzymatic Assay (SIA) in Hybridoma Technology

By EVERLY CONWAY DE MACARIO, ALBERTO J. L. MACARIO, and ROBERT J. JOVELL

The slide immunoenzymatic assay (SIA) has proved useful for different purposes in a variety of antigen–antibody systems.[1] In this chapter, we will focus on the uses of SIA in hybridoma technology, with generation of monoclonal antibodies against bacteria as an illustrative example. We will concentrate on monoclonal antibodies directed toward antigens in the bacterial envelope, which are important for identification (diagnosis) and classification, and are detectable on the surface of whole bacteria. This topic restriction is based on these arguments: (1) we have accumulated considerable experience with SIA in the study of the superficial

---

[1] E. Conway de Macario, A. J. L. Macario, and R. J. Jovell, *J. Immunol. Methods* **59,** 39 (1983).

antigenic mosaics of methanogenic bacteria with monoclonal antibodies[2]; and (2) some characteristics of SIA make it particularly useful for studying microbes, of which bacteria may be used as prototypes for the purpose of describing the assay.

Modifications of the procedures to adapt them for studying other microbes (e.g., protozoa and fungi), mammalian cells (e.g., lymphocytes and tumor cells), and nonparticulate antigens (e.g., enzymes, immunoglobulins, drugs, hormones, and tumor antigens) will be obvious in most instances. However, we will make remarks in various places to draw attention to SIA variations we have already tested in studying a range of different antigens with monoclonal antibodies.

The Assay

SIA[3] (patent pending) is based on the principles of the enzyme-linked immunosorbent assay (ELISA).[4,5] In its most basic form, SIA is carried out on a glass slide with one of its surfaces coated with an ultrathin layer of a hydrophobic substance except for one or more circles, or circular reaction areas (circle and reaction area will be used interchangeably throughout this chapter). Several variations of the basic design are possible, and some have already been tested. A few of the latter will be mentioned here.

A fundamental feature of SIA is that reagents are applied and allowed to interact on a small, flat, circular reaction area surrounded by a hydrophobic surface, thus allowing volumes of 10 μl or less to remain drop shaped on the reaction area (Fig. 1). This geometry allows rapid contact of the reagents in the drop with a reagent anchored on the circle, i.e., the solid phase, and avoids contact of reagents with other surfaces such as vertical (or semivertical) walls such as those of test tubes or wells of microtiter plates.[6] These characteristics of SIA are most likely the reason why incubation times of reagent interaction can be kept much shorter than is possible with other methods, and background values and false positives due to reagents sticking to surfaces other than antigen are negligible. This enhances the specificity and sensitivity of SIA. False positives are rare, and false negatives due to a positive reaction being submerged into background values virtually do not occur. Exceptions can be ex-

---

[2] A. J. L. Macario and E. Conway de Macario, *in* "Monoclonal Antibodies Against Bacteria" (A. J. L. Macario and E. Conway de Macario, eds.), Vol. II, p. 213. Academic Press, Orlando, Florida (in press).

[3] E. Conway de Macario, A. J. L. Macario, and O. Kandler, *J. Immunol.* **128,** 1670 (1982).

[4] E. Engvall and P. Perlmann, *Immunochemistry* **8,** 871 (1971).

[5] Y. D. Carlier, D. Bout, and A. Capron, *Bull. Inst. Pasteur (Paris)* **79,** 313 (1981).

[6] E. Conway de Macario, R. J. Jovell, and A. J. L. Macario, *BioTechniques* **3,** 138 (1985).

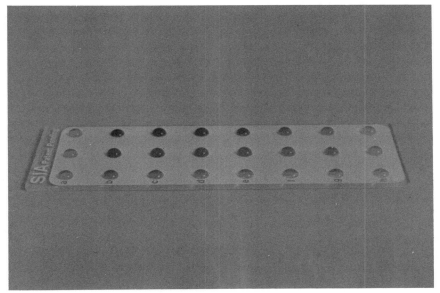

FIG. 1. An SIA slide showing the drops of enzyme substrate solutions, to illustrate determination of antibacterial antibodies in microculture supernatants from a cloning plate. The same series of samples were assayed in the three rows of circles, with second antibody labeled with peroxidase (top row), alkaline phosphatase (middle row), and β-D-galactosidase (bottom row). Substrates were o-phenylenediamine, p-nitrophenyl phosphate disodium, and 4-methylumbelliferyl-β-D-galactoside, respectively. Whereas antigen (bacteria heat-fixed onto the circles) was the same in all circles, culture supernatants were replaced in the first and last circle of each row by used medium from a nonproducer myeloma line and from a hybridoma producing antibodies against another bacterial species (negative controls).

pected, however. We, for example, have occasionally come across a monoclonal antibody which sticks to glass more strongly than most. In these cases, coating the circles with inert molecules, i.e., molecules unable to react with any of the reagents used in the assay, notably the antibodies, solves the problem.

Other practical advantages of SIA attributable to its geometry are that it requires only 10 μl or less of sample and reagent (thus saving sample and reducing costs), and allows microscopic examination. The absence of vertical or semivertical walls eliminates the physical obstacle which otherwise prevents bringing a microscopic objective of very short focal distance (e.g., 100× objectives) close to the reaction area, an obstacle which is present in other reaction vessels (e.g., test tubes and wells of microtiter plates). Therefore, it is possible with SIA to examine particulate antigens on the circle not only with low magnification (e.g., 50×) but also with the greatest magnification allowed by standard microscopes (e.g., 1200×) with bright light illumination or phase-contrast optics. This opens a series of technical possibilities in the study of microbes by SIA with monoclonal antibodies. The SIA constellation is a battery of tests that can be performed in a single SIA slide, including SIA, immunofluorescence, gram staining, and other cytochemical methods, all amenable to microscopic examination.[6] The SIA constellation provides immunological, morphological, topological, and chemical data on microbes in the reaction areas, whether as pure populations or mixtures. Elucidation of the latter is greatly helped by the SIA constellation, as we shall discuss later in this chapter.

Another practical advantage derived from microscopic examination of the reaction area is that antigen, e.g., bacteria, can be monitored visually throughout the SIA procedure. At the beginning when bacteria are being applied onto the reaction areas, it is possible with the SIA slides to establish if (1) the quantity of bacteria is adequate in all circles; (2) the morphology of the bacteria corresponds to the expected strains, indicating a single population or a mixture, or showing contamination with unwanted microorganisms; and (3) the distribution of the bacteria on the circles is even or in clumps, and is comparable in all circles.

Also, during the performance of the assay, microscopic examination of the reaction areas helps to monitor and determine any loss of antigen due to washing. This was uncommon in our experience with heat-fixed methanogenic bacteria, but some other species may require other fixation procedures to enhance their anchorage to the circles. Stability of antigen anchorage must be checked every time a new microbe is used, and for this purpose SIA is very convenient.

After the assay has been performed, microscopic examination of the reaction areas may be instrumental in reevaluating reactions. When peroxidase-labeled second antibody is used, crystals are formed whose size and abundance roughly correlate with reaction intensity.[7] A semiquantitative estimation of reaction intensity can be done by comparing different circles, microscopically, any time after the assay was carried out. Thus SIA slides permit retrospective evaluation of results, which is useful, at times, for comparison with a more recent test.

Reproducibility of SIA results is good (Table I). A cautionary note is pertinent, however. The quality, purity, and specificity of reagents from

[7] E. Conway de Macario, A. J. L. Macario, and M. J. Wolin, *J. Bacteriol.* **149,** 320 (1982).

TABLE I
REPRODUCIBILITY OF SIA RESULTS[a]

| Antigen | Monoclonal antibody | Reaction type (min)[b] | | |
		Fast (10)	Average (30)	Slow (45)
Methanosarcina strain R1M3 (whole bacteria)	31A	0.405 ± 0.034[c] (0.450–0.350)	0.400 ± 0.037 (0.490–0.320)	0.218 ± 0.022 (0.250–0.180)
Glycan strands (*Methanobacterium thermoautotrophicum*)	91B	n.d.[d]	0.168 ± 0.014 (0.190–0.150)	0.218 ± 0.016 (0.250–0.200)

[a] Reproduced from Conway de Macario *et al.*,[1] by permission.

[b] Minutes after addition of substrate solution (for peroxidase). Three different antibody dilutions were assayed for R1M3 and two for the glycan strands (nonparticulate antigen extracted from the cell wall of *M. thermoautotrophicum*) to reproduce common types of reactions: strong (fast), average, and weak (slow).

[c] Data represent SIA spectrophotometric values at OD = 450 nm. Values given are the arithmetic mean ± SD (and the range). $n = 15$.

[d] Not done.

commercial suppliers, notably second antibodies labeled with enzymes, must always be checked to ensure that the product obtained is as pure as required. This quality control of all reagents must be performed routinely. Sometimes additional purification procedures are necessary to upgrade reagents to a satisfactory level.

Procedure

The basic procedure from which all SIA variations derive involves the following major steps: anchoring antigen onto the circle; adding antibody (i.e., the sample in which antibody is to be measured) (10 μl or less); incubating for 15 min in a humid atmosphere; removing antibody solution; washing; allowing slide to dry; adding second (revealing) antibody labeled with an enzyme (10 μl); incubating, removing second antibody solution, and washing as above; allowing slide to dry; adding 10 μl of enzyme substrate solution; watching appearance of yellow color and measuring absorbance at 5 and 15 min; allowing slides to dry for crystal formation; and storing slides. Technical details, reagents, and variations are described under Protocol I.

Protocol I. SIA for Antibacterial Antibodies in Supernatants of Hybridoma Cultures

1. Use SIA slides (Cel-Line Associates, Newfield, NJ) with three rows of eight circles, 3 mm in diameter, with distribution pattern compatible with instrumental automation. *Variations.* SIA slides with 30 circles 2 mm in diameter may be used for rapid screening of many samples without instrumental reading of absorbance; reactions are read with the naked eye.

2. Apply 5 μl of bacterial suspension as a drop on each circle and allow to dry. Flame back of slide quickly three times (2–3 sec in all) with a Bunsen burner. Adjust bacterial concentration to obtain coverage of 40–50% of circle after drying. Suspending solution is phosphate-buffered saline (PBS). *Variations.* Bacteria may be fresh or formalinized. Heating may be avoided. Other fixatives may be used: methanol, ethanol, acetone, Buin's, etc. Circle coating may be necessary [10 μl of coating solution, i.e., tissue culture medium with 10% γ-globulin-free horse serum and 5% calf serum (CM), or 1% bovine serum albumin (BSA, Sigma, St. Louis, MO); allow to dry; wash salt crystals with distilled water, adding it dropwise, five drops per circle; allow to dry]. Slides with bacteria can be prepared weeks or months before use. Each slide may bear more than one bacterial strain (antigen), usually a different one for each row of circles for multiple testing of supernatants for determination of the specificity spectra of hybridoma products.

3. Check quantity, distribution, and morphology of bacteria in circles with microscope. This checking may be repeated after each of the following steps when new antigens are tested for the first time.

4. Apply 10 μl of culture supernatant/circle; incubate 15 min in humid chamber at 23°; remove by flipping the slide briskly; wash by dropwise addition of PBS and then distilled water, five drops of each per circle; allow to dry. *Variations.* Incubation at 37° increases the sensitivity of the SIA in some instances. Satisfactory results are also obtained with 5 μl of supernatant.

5. Apply 10 μl of second (revealing) antibody labeled with peroxidase (diluted 1 : 1000 in CM); incubate, remove, and wash as above (step 4). Allow to dry. *Variations.* Second antibody labeled with alkaline phosphatase or β-D-galactosidase may be used[6,8] (see Table II).

6. Apply 10 μl of substrate solution, prepared immediately before use by adding 1 μl of 30% H_2O_2 to 10 ml of o-phenylenediamine (OPD) solution (Sigma). OPD solution: 1 mg OPD in 1 ml of buffer (0.1 M citric acid

[8] E. Conway de Macario, A. J. L. Macario, and R. J. Jovell, *J. Immunol. Methods* **68**, 311 (1984).

TABLE II
DIRECT DETECTION OF MONOCLONAL IgG IN MOUSE ASCITIC FLUID BY SIA[a]

Ascitic fluid dilution (reciprocal × 2)[c]	Reaction intensity[b]		
	Peroxidase (OD)	Alkaline phosphatase (OD)	β-D-Galactosidase (rfu)[d]
10^2	1.96	1.15	4000
10^3	1.97	0.95	2690
10^4	1.16	0.45	961
10^5	0.20	0.06[e]	79[e]
10^6	0.12[e]	0.01	42

[a] Reproduced from Conway de Macario et al.,[6] by permission.

[b] Readings were done with a vertical-beam spectrophotometer for peroxidase and alkaline phosphatase or with a microfluorometer for β-D-galactosidase. Negative controls included bovine serum albumin dilutions instead of ascitic fluid, or omission of enzyme-labeled antibodies, and the other standard SIA controls (see text).

[c] Ten microliters of ascitic fluid with IgG monoclonal antibody against *Methanogenium cariaci* was allowed to dry on the circles, and then anti-mouse IgG antibodies labeled with different enzymes were applied to complete the procedure (see Protocol I, steps 5 through 8).

[d] Relative fluorescence units (see text).

[e] These results are the last in each column still positive, i.e., the limit is ≥ 0.05 for peroxidase and alkaline phosphatase and ≥ 40 rfu for β-D-galactosidase (these limits were established on the basis that negative controls read at most 0.02, or 20 rfu, respectively).

in H_2O, pH 4.5, adjusted with NaOH). The OPD solution can be prepared beforehand and stored frozen for a week at most. *Variations*. For alkaline phosphatase substrate (spectrophotometry, $OD_{410\,nm}$),[6,8] dissolve 1 mg p-nitrophenyl phosphate disodium (PNPP) "Sigma 104" (Sigma) in 1 ml buffer: [0.05 M Na_2CO_3, pH 9.8 (J. T. Baker Chemical Co., Phillipsburg, NJ) and 0.001 M $MgCl_2$ (Sigma). For 1 liter add 5.3 g Na_2CO_3 and 0.2 g $MgCl_2 \cdot 6\,H_2O$; bring to 900 ml with H_2O. Adjust pH to 9.8 with HCl and bring to 1 liter with H_2O.] The substrate solution may be prepared beforehand and stored frozen for a week at most.

For β-D-galactosidase substrate (spectrophotometry, $OD_{410\,nm}$),[6,8] dissolve 0.03 M o-nitrophenyl-β-D-galactopyranoside (ONPG) (o-nitrophenyl-β-D-galactoside; Sigma) in buffer B, and freeze in aliquots until needed. Thaw and dilute 1 : 10 (to achieve 0.003 M) in fresh BME solution immediately before use. Buffer B (pH 7.1): 73 ml 0.2 M CH_3COOH (Fisher Scientific Co., Fairlawn, NJ) + 20 ml 1 M Tris + 200 ml 0.1 M

$MgCl_2$; bring to 1400 ml with H_2O. BME solution: 0.025 M 2-mercapto-ethanol (Sigma) in buffer B.

For β-D-galactosidase substrate to use in SIA fluorometry (OD: emission, 450 nm, and excitation, 365 nm),[6] dissolve 0.1 mg 4-methylumbelliferyl-β-D-galactoside (MUB) (American Qualex International, La Mirada, CA) in 1 ml buffer [0.01 M Na_2HPO_4 (J. T. Baker) 1000 ml + 0.01 M $NaH_2PO_4 \cdot H_2O$ (J. T. Baker) 135 ml; pH 7.8]. Dissolve MUB in buffer, rock 30 min, and use. Protect from light at all times.

7. Keep slides with drops of substrate solution on circles in humid chamber at 23°. Watch appearance of yellow color. Read $OD_{450\ nm}$ with vertical-beam spectrophotometer (e.g., Mini Reader II, Dynatech Instruments, Alexandria, VA) using the SIA-slide Carrier (patent pending) at 5 and 15 min. *Variations.* Rapid screening of many supernatants to discriminate antibody-producing hybridomas from nonproducers does not require instrumental readings.[3] Visual identification of "positive" circles is readily done since negative controls do not show visible yellow color. If a vertical-beam spectrophotometer is not available, readings may be done in a conventional, horizontal-beam spectrophotometer (e.g., Gilford Model 250) using a Microsample Holder and Carrier (patent pending). If SIA fluorometry is used, readings are done in a microfluorometer (MicroFluor fluorescence reader, Dynatech) using the SIA-slide Carrier. In this case, results are expressed as "relative fluorescence units" (rfu) (MicroFluor Reagent Sample Pack, American Qualex International). Visual inspection of the reaction can be done using an Ultraviolet Fluorescence Analysis Cabinet (Model CX-20, Spectronics Corp., Westbury, NY).[6] Special studies may require incubation with enzyme substrate solution at 37°.

8. Allow to dry, and store slides. Brown crystals formed on circles are a permanent record of the reactions (see text).

A second basic procedure involves anchoring the antibody onto the circle first (rather than antigen)[6]; adding 10 μl or less of the sample containing antigen; incubating in a humid atmosphere; removing antigen solution and washing as above; and following as described in the preceding basic procedure (Protocol I). Technical details and variations are described under Protocol II.

Protocol II. SIA for Antigens Released by Bacteria into Their Fluid Milieu

1. Use SIA slides as in Protocol I.
2. Apply 10 μl of biotinylated monoclonal antibody against the antigen of interest onto a circle. Incubate, remove, and wash as in Protocol I,

step 4. Two or more circles may be coated with two or more antibody dilutions. *Variation.* Purified antibody from an antiserum may substitute for the monoclonal antibody.

3. Apply 5 μl of the solution containing the antigen under investigation. Incubate, remove, and wash as above. *Variations.* Incubation at 37° for 30 min may increase sensitivity. The fluid sample in which antigen is to be detected may be clarified by centrifugation for 5 min at 15,000 g in a microfuge (Beckman Instruments, Berkeley, CA). More than one antibody may be used, one per row of circles.

4. Apply 10 μl of the same monoclonal antibody (although not biotinylated) used in step 2, at a selected concentration. Incubate, remove, and wash as above.

The antibody concentration is chosen beforehand. A series of 2-fold dilutions (in CM) of the antibody solution (purified antibody dissolved in CM, or ascitic fluid, or culture medium) is assayed with a reference antigen (usually the immunizing bacterial strain) by SIA (using peroxidase). A dilution is chosen which gives an $OD_{450\,nm}$ of 0.200–0.300, 30 min after the addition of enzyme substrate (see Protocol I, step 6). This working (W) dilution is determined for every monoclonal antibody to be utilized, since it provides the basis for calibrating the antigen–antibody curve for comparative analysis of antibodies and antigens.[3,9]

5. Continue as in Protocol I, steps 5 through 8. If the monoclonal antibody is available labeled with peroxidase, step 5 (Protocol I) is omitted. Other enzyme labels may be used instead of peroxidase, as described in Protocol I.

Variations

Versatility is a salient feature of SIA.[6] Much of this versatility is due to SIA's geometry and to the slide's properties and modularity. These lend great flexibility to the assay: one, a few, or many samples can be assayed simultaneously with one or more antigens; readings can be done with the naked eye or instrumentally by moving the slide by hand or with an automated device; other reactions, in addition to SIA, can be performed (the SIA constellation).

The basic SIA design described in the preceding section can be altered to suit different situations (e.g., in the laboratory or in the field)[2,6] involving a variety of antigen–antibody systems, and to take into account the need and means of the user. In hybridoma technology, SIA has proved useful in practically any procedure in which it is necessary to detect, or

[9] E. Conway de Macario, A. J. L. Macario, M. C. Magariños, H. König, and O. Kandler, *Proc. Natl. Acad. Sci. U.S.A.* **80**, 6346 (1983).

quantify, monoclonal antibodies against bacteria and other antigens, and to study these antigens.[2,3,9,10] SIA is most convenient for rapid surveys to obtain yes or no answers with minute sample volumes in short times (e.g., less than 1 hr). Major components of SIA that have been modified and tested are briefly discussed as follows.

Slide. The slide used routinely in our laboratory (see Protocol I) is made of quality glass for immunofluorescence, of the size (25 × 75 mm) and shape (Fig. 1) suitable for (1) microscopic examination in a standard microscope with a standard platform and holder; and (2) automated readings with standard vertical-beam spectrophotometers or microfluorometers using the SIA-slide Carrier.[6] Up to four of these slides can be accommodated in the SIA-slide Carrier, with their circles (24 per slide, 96 in all) distributed like the wells of a microtiter plate, allowing automated readings of one or more slides, depending on the needs of the user.

Slides of other sizes and shapes may also be used. We have designed one slide for use in conventional, horizontal-beam spectrophotometers (Microsample Holder and Carrier). This device is useful in laboratories that do not possess and cannot afford a vertical-beam spectrophotometer, or do not need it because they process only a small number of samples that can be handled without the full automation provided by this instrument.

The slide circles may be smaller than those in a standard slide (Protocol I). Circles 2 mm in diameter (of which 30 can fit on one slide of standard dimensions and shape such as the one in Fig. 1 have proved excellent for rapid screening of many microculture supernatants when it was imperative to save antigen (bacteria were scarce, or when only a few tenths of a microgram of a nonparticulate antigen such as an enzyme was available in purified form). These small-circle slides are not suitable for instrumental reading; the drop of enzyme substrate is too small for accurate OD determination with standard instruments.

The distribution pattern of circles on the slide surface may also vary. Our standard slides have the circles in a pattern matching that of the wells of standard microtiter plates. Slides made for reading in a conventional horizontal-beam spectrophotometer have the circles distributed in patterns that match that of the cuvettes normally used in these instruments. The circles on the Microsample Holder are located precisely to intersect the light beam when in position for reading.

Although our standard slides are made of glass, plastic substitutes can be used when, for example, the antigen under study can be anchored more readily to plastic than to glass.

---

[10] E. Conway de Macario, H. König, A. J. L. Macario, and O. Kandler, *J. Immunol.* **132,** 883 (1984).

Enzyme Labels. Second antibodies labeled with alkaline phosphatase or β-D-galactosidase instead of peroxidase can be utilized.[6,8] The choice of enzyme label depends on several factors concerned with the antigen–antibody system, availability of reagents, and needs and means of the user. Peroxidase is the least costly and, in our studies, has yielded as good or better results in terms of sensitivity compared to the other two enzymes (Table II). However, alkaline phosphatase may be preferred when time-enhanced sensitivity is sought and absorbance readings after 2 hr become necessary to disclose small differences between samples or to unveil minimal reactions; or when the antigen contains endogenous peroxidase. The use of peroxidase has the additional advantage of crystal formation which, as discussed above, constitutes a permanent record of the reactions for future reexamination.

The three enzymes allow readings with the naked eye as well as instrumental measurements of absorbance. However, the yellow color given by peroxidase with *o*-phenylenediamine as substrate on slides with a white surface is the most convenient for visual readings.

β-D-Galactosidase is the label we used for SIA fluorometry with 4-methylumbelliferyl-β-D-galactoside as substrate.[6] Visual readings were done with an Ultraviolet Fluorescence Analysis Cabinet, and instrumental, automated readings were done with a MicroFluor fluorescence reader in conjunction with our SIA-slide Carrier (see *Protocol I,* step 7).

Applications

SIA was extensively applied to measure antibodies and antigens in hybridoma technology aimed at the study of bacteria (see subsections below).[2,3,9,10] Antibody measurements on several types of samples obtained at various stages during generation and expansion of hybridomas were done with bacteria directly anchored onto the SIA slide circles.

If the antigenic determinant of interest does not withstand fixation by heat or other means, indirect methods for anchoring the antigen to the circles are available. One of these methods involves the use of antibodies (mono- or polyclonal from antisera) against the molecule that bears the antigenic determinant of interest. Typically, we raised an antiserum against the bacterial strain bearing the determinant we wanted to study with monoclonal antibodies. The antiserum was then used to anchor partially purified antigen onto the reaction area (see Protocol II). Slides were prepared to screen supernatants from hybridoma microcultures in search of antibodies that would react with the unfixed determinant. This allowed isolation of monoclonal antibodies that reacted with the immunizing bacterial strain only if it was fresh, i.e., unfixed, as opposed to other antibodies that reacted with fresh as well as fixed whole bacteria. The latter antibodies were detected using fixed bacteria on the SIA slide circles from the outset, i.e., from the time of the initial screenings.

The use of antibodies to anchor the antigen to the circles is less harsh in the sense that it may not denature some determinants as compared with fixation. However, anchoring the antigen by means of antibody might alter antigenicity of the anchored molecule by comparison with the same native molecule free in solution, or *in vivo*. For example, if the determinant in question is complex, resulting from a quaternary structure, allosteric interactions with the anchoring antibody could alter the determinant beyond recognition. Also, the anchoring antibodies may cover the determinant of interest by directly binding to it, or by steric hindrance if they bind to a nearby determinant.

These and other problems, sometimes of unclear mechanism, represent a serious obstacle to the detection of monoclonal antibodies against certain antigens. As a rule, however, it is possible to proceed with the generation of monoclonal antibodies which are extremely useful for studying bacteria and many other antigens.[11] For example, in the case of bacteria, when the immediate objective is to elucidate their antigenic mosaics, generation of a panel of monoclonal antibodies is the first step. A series of experimental conditions are set which are feasible and even simple to achieve concerning availability of antigen and amenability to testing by SIA, and a panel of monoclonal antibodies is generated. The antigenic mosaic of the immunizing strain is examined and its dissection into components (determinants) begins. Important information is rapidly gathered to guide preparation of other antibody panels, and the purification and characterization of antigens. This approach includes, as a preliminary step, determination of antigenic relationships of the immunizing strains with other strains and species of interest by means of antisera.[2,12]

SIA slides are then prepared with a panel of bacteria for screening hybridomas and determining their specificity spectra from the outset. Typically, the immunizing strain, a cross-reactive strain, and a distant reference species (weakly cross-reactive, or non-cross-reactive) are anchored on to the circles in the top, middle, and bottom rows, respectively. Fifty microliters of used medium is collected from every hybridoma microculture (initial, master culture plates and subsequent cloning plates) showing cell growth. Aliquots of 10 μl from each supernatant are deposited in three circles, one in each row forming a column. A fourth 10-μl aliquot is deposited in a circle of another slide without bacteria, to test the antibody's affinity for glass and help to disclose rare false positives. This

[11] A. J. L. Macario and E. Conway de Macario, *Surv. Synth. Pathol. Res.* **3,** 119 (1984).
[12] E. Conway de Macario and A. J. L. Macario, *Am. Soc. Microbiol. News* **49,** 1 (1983).

multiple testing allows identification from the outset of antibodies differing in specificity spectrum and is useful for assembling multispecific panels. Panels of monoclonal antibodies recognizing different determinants are helpful in rapidly dissecting antigenic mosaics; their resolution power is greater than a single antibody, or a panel of antibodies of undefined or perhaps identical specificity spectra.[2] Therefore, every effort must be made from the beginning to avoid saving and expanding hybridomas of apparently identical specificity.

Multiple testing with SIA slides containing various bacteria is repeated during the course of expansion and recloning of the initially selected hybridomas to monitor stability of specificity spectra since changes in the latter do occur. Only after several weeks of cell line stability in terms of growth and specificity spectrum do we expand the hybridoma in mice for collecting ascitic fluids. Antibody titration of these fluids is done by SIA using only one bacterial species, which is the immunizing one when the antibody is known to react with it, or the cross-reactive strain for antibodies that react only with it (heteroclitic antibodies).[2,9,10] Subsequent antibody and antigen studies are done by SIA, or SIA constellation, or using these procedures along with others. More detailed lists of SIA applications in hybridoma technology for antibody measurements and study of antigens follow.

Uses of SIA in the Measurement and Characterization of Antibacterial Monoclonal Antibodies

1. Measuring antibody in mouse sera to establish (a) whether a mouse responded to immunization, and (b) the time course of serum antibody titers to decide when after immunization spleens should be excised for fusion.

2. Screening of hybridoma microculture (master plates) supernatants to (a) identify antibody producers, and (b) discriminate between producers that react with the immunizing strain only, with the cross-reactive (reference) strain only, or with both.

3. Screening of clone microculture (cloning plates) supernatants to achieve the same as in point 2, above.

4. Monitoring antibody production levels and the specificity spectrum (see in point 2b, above) throughout clone expansion procedures, i.e., in supernatants of 1-ml, 5-ml, and 15-ml cultures, which are established in this sequence for freezing the hybrid cells, and inoculating mice to generate ascitic fluids.

5. Surveying ascitic fluids from individual mice before pooling, and measuring antibody titers in the pools. This is done immediately after

pooling, at different times during storage, and after lyophilization and reconstitution to determine stability of the antibody molecules.

6. Titrating antibodies in ascitic fluid or culture medium before starting antibody purification, and in the fractions obtained at successive purification steps. SIA has been useful in directly monitoring antibody in 10-μl aliquots of fractions obtained by protein A–Sepharose and DEAE–Affi-Gel Blue chromatography, HPLC, ammonium sulfate precipitation–dialyses–concentration, etc.[2,9,10] In some cases SIA fractions must be adjusted to appropriate ionic strength and pH, or concentrated, prior to assaying, although these preparative steps are by no means a requirement for rapid sample screening.

7. Measuring antibodies in ascitic fluid, culture medium, or other solutions after absorption with whole bacteria or insolubilized antigen, or after precipitation (or coprecipitation) of antibody–antigen complexes, or after incubation with soluble antigen or haptens of known structure in inhibition-blocking experiments, to establish how much antibody remains unbound to antigen or hapten.[2,9,10,13] In this context, SIA has been instrumental in determining the fine (molecular) specificity of monoclonal antibodies, and corroborating the specificity spectrum determined by direct binding methods. In the case of absorption with whole bacteria and subsequent elution for antibody purification, a combination of SIA with an immunoenzymatic assay in suspension (IAS) is extremely useful in monitoring antibodies free in the fluid phase and bound to the bacteria, throughout the procedure.[2,3]

8. Determining immunoglobulin class, subclass, and light chain type of monoclonal antibodies.[7,13]

9. Correlating antibody measurements using antigen anchored to a solid phase (i.e., SIA slide's circle) with results obtained by other tests in which antigen is in solution (or in suspension) in a liquid or semisolid phase, or with methods that reveal the anatomic distribution of the antigen recognized by the antibodies. Comparison of results obtained by SIA with those of other methods help to differentiate one antibody from the other in a panel, to dissect the antigenic mosaic of the species strain examined, and to study the chemical nature and functional role of the determinants involved (see also next section).

Uses of SIA in the Study of Bacterial Antigens

1. Antigen purification. Monitoring of antigen contained in a series of products or fractions obtained during purification procedures can be done

---

[13] E. Conway de Macario, A. J. L. Macario, and A. Pastini, *Archiv. Microbiol.* **142**, 311 (1985).

using only 10 μl.[2] The antigen is anchored to the circle and then a monoclonal antibody recognizing the antigen is reacted with the sample (see Protocol I). Alternately, the antibody can be anchored first (see Protocol II), but this is done only when one wants to avoid changes of antigenicity due to drying or fixation.

2. Antigen localization and identification. For example, monitoring presence of the antigenic determinant recognized by a monoclonal antibody in the components of a cell wall extract resolved by SDS–PAGE.[10] Elution from the gel must be done without destruction of the determinant for this SIA application. It is always worth trying because it requires only minute amounts of eluate, particularly if SIA slides with circles smaller than the standard 3 mm in diameter are used to reduce the area over which the antigen will spread.

3. Epitope mapping. Determining whether two monoclonal antibodies against the same bacterial strain recognize the same determinant (or different ones that are close to each other) or different determinants far apart on the bacterial envelope (or fraction therefrom). Competitive inhibition experiments using mixtures of the two antibodies or one antibody after the other[11,14] can be carried out by SIA with the relevant antigen anchored onto the circles.

4. Measurement and comparison of antigenicity. Measuring and comparing the antigenicities of two bacterial strains (or antigens purified from them) with one monoclonal antibody. Two procedures have been tested. (a) The antibody is titrated with one of the two antigens by assaying a series of 2-fold dilutions against a constant dose of antigen. A W dilution is thus identified (see Protocol II, step 4) and is subsequently used to assay against the same dose of the other antigen. All conditions being equal, a difference in SIA results can be taken to indicate a difference in antigenicity between the two antigens. Either they both possess the determinant recognized by the monoclonal antibody but in different numbers, or the determinant recognized by the antibody is different in the two antigens but sufficiently similar to give a cross-reaction, or a combination of both situations. Whatever the underlying cause, comparison of antigenicities is useful to differentiate closely related bacterial strains, and to discriminate between antibodies when they give identical reaction with one strain. (b) The antibody is titrated with both antigens at the same dose. Two or more titration curves may be obtained with two or more antigen doses. A comparison of the titration curves given by the two antigens will tell whether they differ in antigenicity. While this procedure

[14] B. Friguet, L. Djavadi-Ohaniance, J. Pages, A. Bussard, and M. Goldberg, *J. Immunol. Methods* **60,** 351 (1983).

is very informative, it requires considerably more work, and more importantly, larger quantities of the antigens, than procedure (a). Therefore, method (a) is preferred if SIA is to be used, since it takes advantage of one of the salient features of this assay, i.e., its requirement for only minute quantities of antigen. It is the method of choice when one of the antigens under examination is scarce or very costly.

5. Antigen detection. Monitoring the presence of antigens released by bacteria in the fluid phase of bacterial cultures and suspensions, biological fluids (blood, pathologic exudates, etc.), anaerobic digestors, and other ecologic niches. Direct (see point 1, above) and indirect (see Protocol II) methods can be applied.

6. Elucidation of complex microbial communities. Identifying bacterial species or strains in mixtures of microbes with panels of monoclonal antibodies. The SIA constellation is applied to correlate SIA results with immunofluorescence and gram staining data and with the morphological characteristics of the immunofluorescence reactions. These data are also studied in parallel with the morphology of the reactive and nonreactive microbes using standard bright light and phase-contrast optics. Thus, a complete picture is obtained of the bacteria that react with the monoclonal antibodies as well as information on those that do not react.

Conclusions

SIA is a simple laboratory tool useful in hybridoma technology, especially for rapid determination of antibody at every stage from initial screening of microculture supernatants to characterization of the final product. SIA is also convenient for monitoring antigen in a variety of specimens, e.g., throughout purification procedures using monoclonal antibodies. The method is ideal for obtaining yes or no answers with samples as small as 5 μl in less than1 hr and is, therefore, very helpful when antibody, antigen, or both are scarce or very costly. Versatility is another feature of SIA, mostly due to its geometry and the modularity of the slide on which it is carried out. As stated before, one, few, or many samples can be tested simultaneously; reaction readings can be done with the naked eye as well as with spectrophotometers and microfluorometers, manually or with automated devices; particulate and nonparticulate antigens can be assayed. Microscopic examination of the reaction areas in which antigen may be anchored, even with short-focal-distance highpower objectives, makes SIA suitable for studying microbes, e.g., bacteria. The SIA constellation is a battery of tests that can be run on a single SIA slide, including SIA, immunofluorescence, and gram staining, to provide immunological, morphological, topological, and cytochemical information on one or more microbes in the sample. This approach simplifies analysis of complex microbial communities with the use of monoclonal antibodies.

Acknowledgments

This work was supported in part by Grants DE-FG02-84ER 13197 from the U.S. Department of Energy, and RG 261.82 from the North Atlantic Treaty Organization (NATO).

[50] Use of Mouse and Human Monoclonal Antibodies in Enzyme Immunofiltration

By MARK C GLASSY and PATRICK H. CLEVELAND

The antigen–antibody interaction has inspired a plethora of assays capable of analyzing this reaction, which suggests that no single method has satisfied the needs of the majority of investigators. Irrespective of the assay used, there are several underlying principles which determine the utility of the assay, such as method of antigen immobilization, speed, simplicity, accuracy, and sensitivity. The combination of nonisotopic enzyme immunoassays (EIA[1]) with monoclonal antibody (MAb) technology[2] has provided the means whereby the antigen–antibody reaction can be qualitated and quantitated with easy and simple methodology. Since many laboratories produce large numbers of MAbs, emphasis must be placed on rapid and facile assays to identify the MAbs of choice. In this chapter we discuss the utility and versatility of the enzyme immunofiltration assays (EIFA) used in our laboratories to determine mouse and human MAb class, concentration, and specificity.

Immunofiltration was first described in 1979[3] as a gentle and rapid method of immobilizing cell-associated antigens without changing their antigenicity (Fig. 1). Subsequently, it was shown that the extensive surface area present in the filter material could be used to rapidly adsorb and immobilize large amounts of soluble antigens or capture antibodies.[4]

[1] E. Engvall and P. Pearlman, *Immunochemistry* **8**, 871 (1971).

[2] G. Köhler and C. Milstein, *Nature (London)* **256**, 495 (1975).

[3] P. H. Cleveland, D. Richman, M. N. Oxman, M. C. Wickman, P. S. Binder, and D. M. Worthen, *J. Immunol. Methods* **29**, 369 (1979).

[4] P. H. Cleveland, M. G. Wickham, M. H. Goldbaum, A. Ryan, and D. M. Worthen, *J. Immunoassay* **2**, 117 (1981).

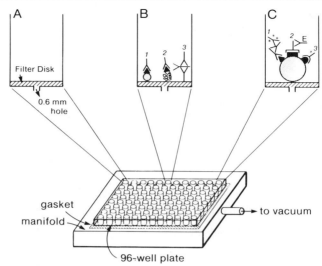

Fig. 1. Enzyme immunofiltration manifold and plate. A specially designed 96-well plate[3] sits on top of a vacuum manifold. (A) The filter disk in each well serves as the solid support for the incubation chamber and the liquid phase is evacuated through the 0.6-mm hole in the bottom. (B) Three types of antigens amenable to EIFA analysis: (1) cell bound or particulate; (2) soluble, such as a protein; and (3) antigens (such as MAbs themselves) captured by immobilized antibody. (C) Options in immunoassay protocols with monoclonal antibodies reactive with a cell-bound antigen. The three types of assays used in conjunction with MAbs are (1) amplification, such as an additional avidin–biotin or an anti-peroxidase step to greatly boost the signal-to-noise ratio; (2) the indirect type of EIFA, which uses an Ig class-specific affinity-purified antiserum conjugated to an enzyme (see Ref. 13), such as horseradish peroxidase; and (3) the direct type, in which an enzyme or some other type of chromophore or fluorophore is directly conjugated to the test MAb.

Later, the technology of enzyme-conjugated antisera was applied to immunofiltration,[5] followed by incorporating MAb technology[5–8] to exploit the specificity and precision of these antibodies with the ease, speed, and antigen immobilization advantages of the EIFA. The EIFA we describe here is well suited for, though not limited to, the screening of both mouse and human hybridoma supernatants in a rapid, simple, and sensitive man-

[5] D. Richman, P. H. Cleveland, and M. N. Oxman, *J. Med. Virol.* **9,** 299 (1982).

[6] P. H. Cleveland, D. R. Disharoon, and D. D. Richman, *Invest. Ophthalmol. Visual Sci.* **24,** 192 (1983).

[7] H. Handley, M. C. Glassy, P. H. Cleveland, and I. Royston, *J. Immunol. Methods* **54,** 291 (1982).

[8] M. C. Glassy, H. Handley, P. H. Cleveland, and I. Royston, *J. Immunol. Methods* **58,** 119 (1983).

ner for the detection of MAbs themselves and to detect their binding to either soluble, particulate, or cellular antigens. The conventional EIFA[6-8] can be completed within 2 hr. However, a subsequent modification of our EIFA into an enzyme immunofiltration staining assay (EIFSA) has been developed which can be completed within 10 min,[9] and is capable of detecting one positive cell.

Principles of Immunofiltration

In concept and principle the EIFA is elegantly simple and nearly identical to conventional EIAs. Our EIFA exploits the physical nature of antigen–antibody interactions by the ease with which the fluid phase is separated from the solid phase in a filter system. Furthermore, the assays may be performed in either direct or indirect manners. In the direct EIFA, an enzyme is covalently conjugated to the MAb itself for detecting reactivity to its antigen, whereas in the indirect EIFA, an enzyme-conjugated Ig class-specific antiglobulin or staphylococcal protein A (SPA) is used to react with the test MAb already bound to its antigen. This is summarized in Fig. 1. In addition, a modification[10] of the indirect assay method using the avidin–biotin system of coupling enzyme to antigen allows for amplification of the signal (color) to noise (background) ratio. Moreover, a variety of different enzymes (horseradish peroxidase, alkaline phosphatase, β-galactosidase, and β-D-glucose oxidase) and both fluorogenic and chromogenic substrates may be used, each of which may have special utility to a specific investigational need. EIFA has the added feature that it takes advantage of the principle of liquid surface tension to provide an incubation chamber that acts as both a solid-phase reaction site and a filtration device. This is accomplished by utilizing a 96-well plate[3] modified with a small capillary-type hole in the bottom of each well. The surface tension forces of the liquid prevent incubation fluids from leaking out until a vacuum is applied. Over each hole is placed a filter which acts as the reaction surface (see Fig. 1). These filters are available in either glass fiber, cotton lentil, nitrocellulose, or polycarbonate form. Each type of filter differs from the others in the size of the particles retained on the surface area, flow rate, and amount of nonspecifically bound protein; all types serve as a solid-phase incubation chamber until a vacuum is applied uniformly across the bottom of the plate. Application of a gelatin-supplemented phosphate-buffered saline (see below) to each well completes the vacuum-facilitated wash step.

[9] D. D. Richman, P. H. Cleveland, D. C. Redfield, M. N. Oxman, and G. M. Wahl, *J. Infect. Dis.* **149**, 298 (1984).
[10] P. H. Cleveland, unpublished observations.

Buffers

The buffers used in our EIFA protocols and their formulations are outlined in detail in Table I. In this format, investigators wishing to adopt our EIFA procedures may make the necessary buffers by mixing the specified amounts of indicated reagents and adjusting each to its appropriate pH.

The carbonate buffer is used to attach an antibody or soluble antigen to its solid-phase support. Gelatin buffer is used for washing. Nearly all incubations and secondary reagent dilutions are made with fetal calf serum (FCS) buffer to reduce nonspecific binding of antibody or enzyme to the filter material. o-Phenylenediamine (OPD), diluted in citrate buffer with hydrogen peroxide, is the substrate we use for the horseradish peroxidase enzyme.

Assay Procedure

Our EIFA utilized to identify the type, concentration, and specificity of MAbs requires modified microtiter plates available through V & P

TABLE I
EIA BUFFER FORMULATIONS[a]

Reagent	Phosphate-buffered saline	Gelatin buffer	Fetal calf serum buffer	Citrate buffer	Carbonate buffer	o-Phenylene diamine buffer
NaCl	8.00	8.00	8.00			
Na_2HPO_4	1.14	1.14	1.14	14.18		14.18
KCl	0.20	0.20	0.20			
KH_2PO_4	0.20	0.20	0.20			
Na_2CO_3					1.59	
$NaHCO_3$					2.93	
H_2O_2						60 ng/ml
Citric acid				9.34		9.34
Swine skin gelatin, type 1		3.00	3.00			
Thimersol		0.10	0.10			
Bovine serum albumin			10.0			
Fetal calf serum			10% (v/v)			
o-Phenylene-diamine						400 μg/ml
pH (final)	7.4	7.4	7.4	5.0	9.3	5.0
Reference	19	7	7	5	5	8

[a] Unless otherwise indicated, all amounts are in grams per liter.

Scientific[11] or Millipore.[12] The bottom of each well of the former (see Refs. 3 and 11) contains a 0.6-mm hole covered by a filter which allows the passage of liquids, upon application of a vacuum, while immobilizing particulate material. This is diagramatically shown in Fig. 1. Both soluble and insoluble antigens can be immobilized onto the surface of the filter by vacuum drying.

A key element in the successful performance of these assays is the reduction of nonspecific binding to the filter by MAb, the enzyme-conjugated antiglobulin, or SPA. We have found that phosphate buffers containing fetal bovine serum, bovine serum albumin, and gelatin (see Table I) are essential during the conditioning and incubation steps.

All of the conventional reagents we have used in our EIFA procedures are commercially available, and the investigator is encouraged to consult Linscott's Directory of Antibody Reagents.[13] This directory lists virtually every type of reagent available for EIA's and their commercial source.

Detection of MAb Specificity

A partial list of the antigens and immunoglobulins actually studied by EIFA is presented in Table II. In all cases, the immunofiltration manifold plates have been effective in immobilizing the two major types of antigens, particulate and soluble; both are well represented in this table. Soluble antigen is immobilized onto the filters by adding 10 μl of the solution to the filters and applying the vacuum for 10 min to dry the filters. Excess antigen is eluted by incubation with FCS buffer for 15 min. When the antigen is a cell-bound macromolecule, then the cells are resuspended in FCS buffer (Table I) at 2×10^5 to 4×10^6 cells/ml. A 50-μl suspension of the cells is then added to each well of the immunofiltration manifold plate, which is incubated for 30 min at room temperature with 50 μl of the test MAb, washed three times, incubated for 30 min with 50 μl of the appropriate HRP-conjugated antisera or SPA, washed three times, and then developed by adding 50 μl of OPD and either read visually or quantitated by an EIA reader (see the flow chart in Fig. 2).

Enzyme Immunofiltration Staining Assay

The enzyme immunofiltration staining assay (EIFSA) may be performed on large particulate and cellular antigens that are immobilized on

---

[11] V & P Scientific, Inc., 4657 Huggins St., San Diego, California, 92122.

[12] Millipore Corp., 80 Ashby Road, Bedford, Massachusetts, 01730.

[13] W. D. Linscott, ed., "Linscott's Directory of Immunological and Biological Reagents," 2nd ed. Mill Valley, California, 1982–1983.

TABLE II

ANTIGENS ANALYZED BY IMMUNOFILTRATION

Microorganisms	Normal cells
Dictyostelium discoideum	Lymphocytes, HLA antigens
Treponema pallidum	Red blood cells
Escherichia coli	Vaginal cells
Staphylococcus aureus	Sperm
BCG	Kidney
Chlamydia trachomatis	Spleen
Soluble material	Hepatocytes
Bovine serum albumin	Endothelial cells
Herpes simplex virions	Epithelial cells
Influenza virions	Fibroblasts
Tetanus toxoid	Skin
Laminin	Muscle
Fibronectin	Virus-infected cells and cellular
EGF	debris
KLH	Herpes simplex virus (type 1
IgA, IgG, IgM	and 2)
IgG subclass	Varicella-zoster virus
Alkaline phosphatase	Human cytomegalovirus
Tumor cells	Influenza virus (types A and B)
Melanoma	Lassa virus
Hepatoma	Ebola virus
Leukemia	Mozambique virus
T cell lymphoma	Adenovirus (types 3, 4, 7, 7A,
B cell lymphoma	10, 13, 18, 19, and 35)
Oat cell carcinoma	Human rotavirus
Adenocarcinoma	Echo virus
Epidermoid carcinoma	Measles
Medullary thyroid carcinoma	LCM virus
Squamous cell carcinoma	Marburg virus
Immunobeads	
Anti-IgA	
Anti-IgG	
Anti-IgM	
Monoclonal antibodies	
Anti-adenovirus	
Anti-herpes simplex virus	

the filters. The assay procedure entails a minor modification of the EIFA procedure in that a different enzyme substrate (3-amino-9-ethylcarbazole) is used in place of OPD (see Fig. 3). This substrate forms an insoluble colored reaction product at the site of the enzyme, thus staining antigen-bearing cells or particulates a bright red color (see Fig. 4A). The stained cells can easily be detected with the naked eye if there are more than 1000

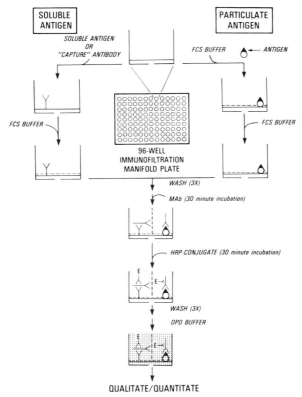

FIG. 2. Flow chart of the enzyme immunofiltration assay showing separate procedures for both soluble and particulate antigens. Results are either read visually or by an EIA reader.

on the filter and with a simple hand lens, dissecting microscope, or standard compound microscope if fewer cells are present. Because the stained cells have a characteristic morphology it is possible to detect as few as one cell per filter.[9,10]

An advantage of EIFSA has been the extremely low level of nonspecific background staining associated with it (see Fig. 4A). Consequently, we have been able to use high concentrations of biotinylated antibody (5 μg/ml) as well as enzyme-labeled avidin complexes (8 μg/ml). The ability to use such high concentrations of high-affinity reagents allows us to reduce the incubation time of antibody to 2 min and enzyme-labeled avidin to 1 min. Thus a complete assay can be performed in just 10 min

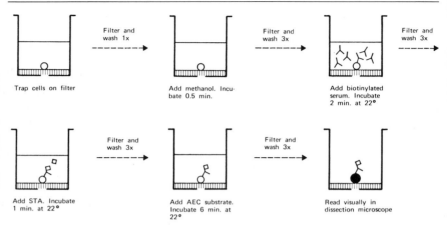

FIG. 3. Flow scheme for an enzyme-linked immunofiltration staining assay. Cells are immobilized onto the filters, washed, and incubated with the appropriate staining reagents as indicated. When completed, the cells are analyzed for reactivity with the aid of a microscope (see text). (○) HSV-infected cell; (Λ) biotinylated antibody to HSV; (□) streptavidin-horseradish peroxidase conjugate (STA).

including wash steps (a methanol incubation step to inactivate peroxidases is optional). Although we have achieved the lowest nonspecific background staining by using biotinylated primary monoclonal antibodies and avidin–horseradish peroxidase (HRP) conjugates, comparable results are obtainable with antiglobulin–HRP, SPA–HRP, or HRP conjugates of the primary antibody.[10]

FIG. 4. Photomicrographs of human cells stained by an enzyme-linked immunofiltration staining assay. (A) AEC immunostained HSV-1-infected tissue culture cells. The cells were incubated with a pool of biotinylated MAbs to common and type-specific HSV antigens and processed as described in Fig. 3. Note that the nuclear areas do not stain as intensely as the cytoplasm. ×400. (B) DAB–NiCl$_2$ immunostained HSV-1-infected tissue culture cells. The cells were processed as described in Fig. 3, except that substrate DAB–NiCl$_2$ was substituted for AEC. ×400. (C) Bluo-Gal immunostaining assay on HSV-1-infected tissue culture cell. The assay was processed as described in Fig. 3, except that streptavidin–β-galactosidase was used instead of streptavidin–horseradish peroxidase. The substrate Bluo-Gal was added and allowed to stain the cells for 60 min. ×400. (D) A serial dual staining assay in which HSV-1- and VZV-infected tissue culture cells were trapped on a filter, incubated with biotinylated antibody to HSV, followed by streptavidin–HRP, and stained with DAB–NiCl$_2$. The filter was then washed and incubated with biotinylated antibody to VZV, followed by streptavidin–HRP, and stained with AEC. Therefore, the HSV cells are stained black and the VZV cells are stained red. ×400.

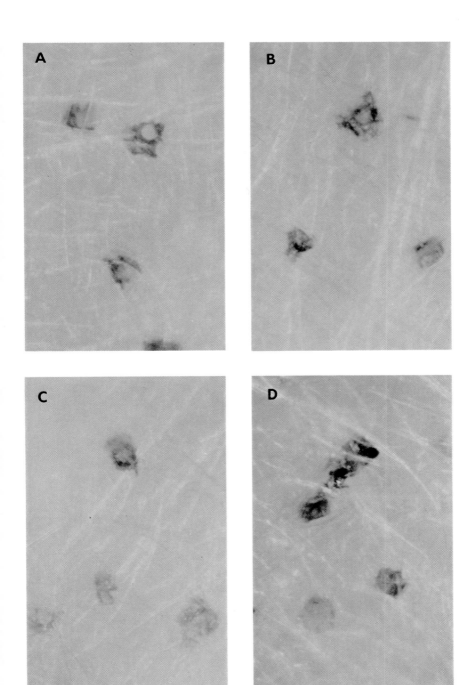

Detection of Ig Class and Concentration

Fifty microliters of an appropriate dilution of a goat anti-mouse or anti-human Ig antisera in PBS or carbonate buffer is added to each well and incubated at room temperature for 30 min. A vacuum (380 mm Hg) is then applied to the filter manifold for 10 min to dry the capture antibody to the filter material. Then, 50 μl of FBS buffer (Table I) is added to each well for the resolubilization of any unattached goat antisera. After a 15-min incubation at room temperature, all wells of the 96-well plate are washed three times under vacuum by the addition of 300 μl of gel buffer (Table I) with a repeating syringe (Cornwall) and eight-prong manifold attachment (V & P Scientific). Then, 50 μl of each test MAb hybridoma supernatant (mouse, human, or any other appropriate species) is added and allowed to bind to the capture antibody for 30 min at room temperature, and the plates are then washed three times with gel buffer. Finally, 50 μl of the appropriate dilution of HRP-conjugated goat anti-Ig (mouse, human, etc.) is then added to specified wells and incubated for 30 min at room temperature. For visualization, 50 μl of OPD (Table I) is added to each well after three washes and developed for 30 min. Since OPD is a photoactive substance it is best to develop the enzyme OPD reaction in the dark (essentially keeping the immunofiltration plate in a drawer) and to check it at the appropriate time interval.

To quantitate the MAb–antigen–enzyme reactions with micro-ELISA readers the bottom of the wells are sealed with a plate-sealing device (V & P Scientific) to prevent leakage and 250 μl of OPD substrate is added to each well and incubated in the dark. After stopping the reaction with 50 μl of 2.5 M H$_2$SO$_4$, 150 μl from each well is transferred to a half area EIA microtiter plate (Costar) and subsequently read on a micro-EIA reader. Many of the commercially available EIA readers are equipped for interfacing with a computer to perform whatever kind of data analysis the investigator requires. We have developed our own program for a Dynatech MR 580 micro-ELISA reader mated to an Apple II microcomputer and will provide it free of charge to all who send a 5-in. floppy disk and a self-addressed envelope with postage paid.

For MAb concentration determinations a titration of Ig (e.g., IgG or IgM) of known concentrations is added to some wells in lieu of the test MAb and developed as described above, to generate a standard curve. The test MAb concentrations are then obtained from this curve.

Results

One of the more attractive aspects of EIFA is that the immobilization and wash steps are very mild to intact cells. Shown in Fig. 5 is a scanning

Fig. 5. Scanning electron micrograph of human tissue culture cells immobilized onto cotton lentil filters. ×35,000.

TABLE III
TITRATION OF T101 BINDING TO FILTER-BOUND T (8402)
AND B (8392) CELLS

T101 (ng/ml)	OD$_{490}$ readings[a]		
	8402 T cells	8392 B cells	Filter only
3200	0.698 ± 0.049	0.057 ± 0.024	0.021 ± 0.021
800	0.631 ± 0.051	0.043 ± 0.020	0.027 ± 0.004
200	0.616 ± 0.045	0.030 ± 0.008	0.024 ± 0.003
100	0.534 ± 0.030	0.037 ± 0.013	0.031 ± 0.013
50	0.379 ± 0.008	0.012 ± 0.004	0.018 ± 0.012
25	0.306 ± 0.001	0.035 ± 0.001	0.018 ± 0.005
12.5	0.184 ± 0.001	0.030 ± 0.018	0.053 ± 0.012
6.2	0.123 ± 0.004	0.042 ± 0.010	0.053 ± 0.035
3.2	0.076 ± 0.002	0.052 ± 0.008	0.074 ± 0.015

[a] OD$_{490}$ readings were obtained with 1.0×10^5 cells/well by a micro-EIA reader. Numbers represent the average of six separate experiments ±SD.

electron micrograph of cultured human fibroblast cells immobilized onto cotton lentil filters. At this level of resolution there are no obvious ultrastructural alterations.

A partial list of the types of antigens and immunoglobulins studied by EIFA was presented in Table II. As stated before, immunofiltration manifold plates have been effective in immobilizing two major types of antigens, particulate or cell bound, and soluble. Examples of cell-bound antigens are those on tumor cells and/or normal cells; examples of particulate antigens are keyhole limpet hemocyanin (KLH), virus particles, cell membranes, and cell surface receptors; and soluble material usually consists of protein, such as Ig.

Several murine MAbs which recognize cell surface antigens on human T lymphocytes have been described, one of which is T101.[14] Murine MAb T101 recognizes an antigen with a molecular weight of 65,000 on all human T lymphocytes. Analysis of T101 binding to 8402 and 8392, autologous T and B lymphocyte cell lines, respectively, is shown in Table III. The amount of T101 used ranged from 3.2 μg/ml to 3.2 ng/ml. Using 2×10^5 target cells/well, this EIFA can accurately detect as little as 10 ng/ml of cell-bound murine MAbs.

[14] I. Royston, J. A. Majda, S. M. Baird, B. L. Meserve, and J. C. Griffiths, *J. Immunol.* **125**, 725 (1980).

TABLE IV
TROUBLESHOOTING USING EIFA

Problem	Cause	Solution
High nonspecific background binding	Antibody is aggregated or non-specifically bound to particulates	Prefilter or centrifuge antibody solution Do not use $(NH_4)_2SO_4$ precipitates to purify antibody prior to testing
	Antiglobulin-, SPA-, or avidin-conjugated enzyme is aggregated or nonspecifically bound to particulates	Prefilter or centrifuge reagents Prefilter or centrifuge diluent buffers
	Antibody has been dried on the filter during wash step by air being drawn through the filter	Add gelatin buffer to filters immediately after turning vacuum on
	Antiglobulin-, SPA-, or avidin-conjugated enzyme is dried on the filter during wash steps	Add gelatin buffer to filters immediately
	Concentration of antibody is too high and/or the concentration of the antiglobulin-, SPA-, or avidin-conjugated enzyme is too high	Dilute reagent more
	Waste fluid from vacuum manifold wicks back into well	Blot immediately after vacuum is turned off
	Endogenous peroxidase present in antigen preparation	Incubate with either 90% methanol, 30% H_2O_2, a mixture of methanol and H_2O_2, 20% NaN_3, or 1% formaldehyde for 2–10 min
Wells leak	Liquid on the bottom of the filter plate	Blot the bottom of the plate with tissue paper
	Surface tension forces in liquid too low	Add protein (BSA or gelatin) to incubation solution
	Incubation volumes too high	Reduce volumes to 50 μl
No specific color development	Enzyme is inactivated by impurities in deionized water used for buffers	Use glass-distilled water
	Enzyme is inactivated by NaN_3 in enzyme and/or wash buffers	Use 0.01% thimerosol as a preservative instead of NaN_3 Wash extensively to remove NaN_3
	pH of OPD citric acid buffer has changed on standing or is contaminated with bacteria	Check pH, change where appropriate
	Particulate antigen has passed through the filter	Use filter with smaller pore size, or dry antigen onto filter

In order to assist the investigator we have prepared a troubleshooting list with potential causes and solutions (see Table IV). When problems do arise, such as high background, leaky wells, or no color development, consult Table IV.

The EIFSA procedure provides a different approach to the problem of nonspecific background binding (Table IV). Nonspecific background binding has been recognized as one of the limiting factors in increasing the sensitivity of standard EIA, EIFA, and RIA procedures, as these assays are unable to discriminate between the soluble colored products produced by enzyme that is bound specifically to a high concentration of antigen and that produced by enzyme bound nonspecifically but diffusely over the entire filter or plastic wells. Both sources of enzyme contribute to the total soluble production. However, in the EIFSA the precipitation of enzyme substrate (AEC) only occurs in the presence of locally high concentrations of the enzyme. Thus only specific antigens are stained and diffusely labeled structures such as the filter are not. This simple phenomenon increases assay sensitivity about 250-fold over our previous EIFA which use OPD as a substrate (Fig. 6).

In addition to AEC, we have found two other useful HRP substrates which produce insoluble precipitates, 3′,3-diaminobenzidine tetrahydrochloride plus $NiCl_2$ (DAB–$NiCl_2$), which yields a black product (Fig. 4B) and 4-chloro-naphthol which yields a blue-black product. In addition we have examined other enzymes such as streptavidin–β-galactosidase, which gives a blue precipitate when Bluo-Gal is used as a substrate (Fig. 4C).

The ability to stain antigens with different colors makes it possible to distinguish between two or more different antigens on the same filter by performing serial assays using, for example, HSV antibody followed by

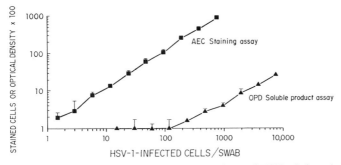

FIG. 6. Reconstruction experiment using known numbers of HSV-1-infected tissue culture cells inoculated on swabs and placed into 2 ml of viral transport media. Replicate samples were assayed by either the AEC staining assay or by our conventional EIFA which detects the conversion of a clear OPD substrate into a soluble yellow OPD reaction product.

development with AEC (red) and then, after washing, using VZV anti-body followed by development with DAB–NiCl₂ (black) (see Fig. 4D), to produce a dual-stained specimen.

The data in Fig. 7 are presented as an example of both the sensitivity of detecting and the serial titration of human IgG. To determine the Ig concentration of an unknown hybridoma supernatant by EIFA, a family of standard curves is generated for various dilutions of a goat anti-human immunoglobulin. This figure illustrates serial dilutions of a chromato-graphically purified human IgG "captured" by several dilutions of a goat anti-human polyvalent Ig antisera. As demonstrated by this figure, too high a concentration of capture antisera, while increasing sensitivity for human IgG at concentrations below 200 ng/ml, is not desired because of its limited range of quantification (a function of the limitations on the optical density reading range capability of micro-ELISA readers). Con-centrations of capture antisera too dilute do not provide any discrimina-tory capability in optical density corresponding to IgG concentration. With this particular lot of goat anti-human Ig (250 ng of Ig/well) supplied by the manufacturer, we chose a 1/40 dilution (see Fig. 7) because the linear portion of this curve covers the greatest range in concentration and optical density, allowing the greatest resolution of data. The binding effi-ciency of protein to these filters has been shown to decrease with increas-

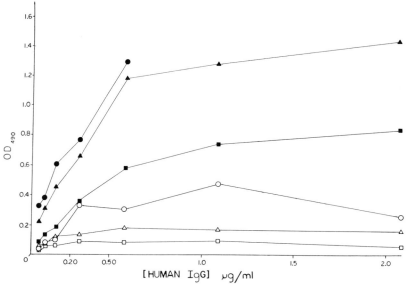

FIG. 7. A titration of human IgG against a capture antibody, affinity-purified goat anti-human IgG, diluted 1/10 (●), 1/20 (▲), 1/40 (■), 1/80 (○), 1/160 (△), and blank (□) in phosphate-buffered saline (Table I).

ing concentrations of protein.[4] Therefore, lower concentrations allow more efficient binding of capture antisera to the filter while retaining excellent sensitivity.

The sensitivity of our EIFA for human Ig is also shown in Fig. 7. By using a 1/40 dilution of "capture antibody," goat anti-human Ig, this assay can detect as little as 10 ng of human IgG/ml. Present human hybridoma cultures typically produce from 0.5 to 10 μg human Ig/ml,[15–18] significantly above the lower limits of detection.

The final process in our EIFA uses an enzyme-conjugated antibody. Like other immunological reagents, the enzyme conjugate must also be titrated to optimize resolution. In a soluble antigen assay the dilutions of the HRP-conjugated antisera are typically 1:10,000–1:20,000, whereas in the whole-cell or particulate assay the HRP-conjugated antisera is typically diluted to approximately 1:1000–1:3000. The investigator is cautioned that these values are not absolutes and that each lot from each manufacturer should be titrated to determine the optimal dilution.

The EIFA immunoreactivity of human MAbs against a panel of human cell lines is shown in Fig. 8. Here, two human IgM MAbs, termed CLNH5[15] and MHG7,[16] were reacted against a large panel of human cell types. Both human MAbs reacted with some, but not all, of the cell lines tested, indicating specificity and a discriminatory capacity of the MAbs to their target antigens. This EIFA is well suited for screening MAbs against a cell panel to analyze for specificity.

Discussion

The immunofiltration manifold plate is the workhorse of the EIFA. This specially designed 96-well plate serves as both a filtration manifold and incubation chamber. The filter serves as the solid-phase support for the antigen, facilitating the washes and simplifying incubation steps. Antigen immobilization and the use of MAbs combined with enzyme-conjugated antisera all occur within a single well of a 96-well plate. As such, this assay accomplishes two purposes in the realm of MAb technology and EIAs. The first is the determination of MAb class and concentration. It should be noted that allogeneic cross-reactivity and cross-reactivity

[15] M. C. Glassy, H. H. Handley, H. Hagiwara, and I. Royston, *Proc. Natl. Acad. Sci. U.S.A.* **80,** 6327 (1983).

[16] D. H. Lowe, H. Handley, J. Schmidt, I. Royston, and M. C. Glassy, *J. Urol.* **132,** 780 (1984).

[17] M. C. Glassy, H. H. Handley, and I. Royston, *in* "Human Hybridomas and Monoclonal Antibodies" (E. G. Engleman, S. Foung, J. Larrick, and A. Raubitschek, eds.), p. 97. Plenum, New York, 1985.

[18] S. A. Gaffar, C. D. Surh, and M. C. Glassy, *Hybridoma* (in press).

[19] R. Dulbecco and M. Vogt, *J. Exp. Med.* **99,** 167 (1954).

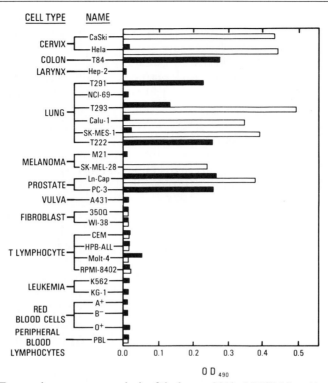

FIG. 8. Enzyme immunoassay analysis of the human MAbs MHG7 (closed bars; see Ref. 18) and CLNH5 (open bars; see Ref. 17) and their reactivity with a panel of normal and malignant human cells. Each well of the immunofiltration manifold plates contained 2×10^5 cells. A 1 : 3000 dilution of HRP-conjugated goat anti-human IgM was used to develop the MAb reactivity and, OD_{490} units were obtained from an EIA reader (model MR 600, Dynatech Laboratories).

between Ig classes have been eliminated by the use of affinity-purified reagents, most of which are commercially available (see Ref. 13). The second purpose is the determination of the specificity of the test MAbs. Large panels of either soluble or particulate antigenic material (see Table II) can be immobilized onto the filter disks to obtain both qualitative and quantitative differences in the amount of MAb bound to each cell type.

It is also important to establish that short-term drying of, and immobilization of, antigens does not significantly alter antigenic structure or density of antigenic epitopes. In our hands, the majority of the antigenic epitopes we have studied have been relatively stable.[4,7,8] Since this is a critical concern, the investigator is encouraged to analyze this using his own reagents and target antigens.

The EIFA described here has several distinct advantages over other assay systems, such as the RIA. When read visually, this EIFA takes no more than 2 hr to complete. These filter plates are more sensitive than equivalent poly(vinyl chloride) plate assays, they do not require a lengthy pretreatment of the assay plate in order to reduce nonspecific adsorption of antibody, and washes can be completed in less than 1 min without centrifugation, or poly-L-lysine or glutaraldehyde fixation which may alter epitopes. Moreover, cells are not lost or reduced as in the centrifugation–wash steps of other assays.

Acknowledgment

We would like to acknowledge the support of NIH Grants EY-0393 and CA-32047.

[51] Measurement of Monoclonal Immunoglobulin Concentrations in Hybridoma Cultures by Competitive Inhibition Enzyme Immunoassay

By KENNETH W. HUNTER, JR. and JOHN M. BOSWORTH, JR.

The selection of hybridomas most often involves a determination of specificity, and less often affinity. Still less often addressed is the secretion rate of monoclonal antibodies by particular hybridoma clones. This latter issue may be of secondary but practical importance as monoclonal antibodies are further commercialized. Although mouse monoclonal antibodies can be produced in large scale by the ascites method, human monoclonal antibody production presently relies on mass *in vitro* culture. By selecting clones that exhibit the highest rates of antibody secretion, one can substantially improve the yield per volume of culture. This chapter describes a competitive inhibition enzyme immunoassay[1] for accurately measuring the levels of immunoglobulin encountered in hybridoma cultures, the parameters that govern performance of the assay, and the advantages of the method over antigen-capture enzyme immunoassay.

Materials and Methods

Reagents. Alkaline phosphatase-conjugated goat anti-rabbit IgG and *p*-nitrophenyl phosphate were obtained from Sigma Chemical Co. (St.

[1] J. M. Bosworth, A. A. Brimfield, J. A. Naylor, and K. W. Hunter, *J. Immunol. Methods* **62**, 331 (1983).

Louis, MO). Rabbit antibodies to mouse IgG$_1$ (Lot RFC028), and the myeloma protein MOPC 21 (IgG$_1$, Lot DG071) were obtained from Litton Bionetics (Kensington, MD). Human IgG (Lot 25), goat anti-human IgG (Lot BD11-B), and alkaline phosphatase-conjugated rabbit anti-goat IgG were obtained from Kirkegaard & Perry Laboratories (Rockville, MD).

Competitive Inhibition Enzyme Immunoassay (CIEIA). The solid-phase adsorbant used in the CIEIA was a 96-well round-bottomed polystyrene microtiter plate (Dynatech Laboratories, Alexandria, VA). It should be noted that some plastic microtiter plates work very poorly in the CIEIA. The critical importance of reagent concentrations on the performance of the CIEIA will be illustrated in the experimental section. Each well of the microtiter plate is incubated with 50 μl of an optimal concentration of the immunoglobulin (Ig) to be quantified (e.g., mouse IgG$_1$), diluted in 0.1 M NaHCO$_3$ buffer (pH 9.6). The time and temperature of the incubation are not critical; we routinely use overnight incubations at 4°. The fluid phase of the competitive inhibition reaction is set up in a separate microtiter plate. We recommend washing this plate with phosphate-buffered saline containing 0.5% polyoxyethylene sorbitan monolaurate (PBS-T) to reduce adsorption of reagents to the plastic. The fluid-phase reaction consists of equal volumes (50 μl) of a known standard concentration of Ig (or your sample that contains an unknown concentration) and an antibody to that Ig. Routinely, for generating the standard curve we make serial log dilutions of Ig in the same vehicle as the test sample (e.g., culture medium), beginning at 100 μg/ml. The anti-Ig is used in a concentration that does not saturate the binding sites of an Ig-coated microwell. The mixtures are incubated for 1 hr at 4°.

The Ig-coated plates are washed by five cycles of filling and emptying all wells with cold PBS-T. Aliquots of 50 μl of the Ig–anti-Ig mixtures are transferred to the Ig-coated plates and incubated for 30 min at 4°. The Ig in the fluid phase competes with the solid-phase-bound Ig for the anti-Ig. The higher the concentration of Ig in the fluid phase the less anti-Ig will bind to the solid phase. The amount of solid-phase-bound anti-Ig is detected by an enzyme-tagged second antibody. Although reasonable results can be obtained with an enzyme-labeled first antibody, we have found that the double antibody method provides an amplified signal. After washing as described above, 50 μl of an optimal PBS-T dilution of an alkaline phosphatase-conjugated antibody to the anti-Ig is added for another 30 min at 4°. Finally, the plates are washed and 100 μl of substrate (1 mg/ml, p-nitrophenyl phosphate in 0.1 M ethanolamine buffer, pH 9.6) is added to each well. The enzymatic reaction is allowed to proceed for 30 min at room temperature, and then the colored product in each well is measured spectrophotometrically at 405 nm with a Titertek Multiscan micro-ELISA reader (Flow Laboratories, Vienna, VA). The absorbance is inversely related to the concentration of Ig in the fluid phase, and a standard curve is prepared by plotting Ig concentration versus absorbance. Each point on the standard curve represents the average absorbance of six replicates. Maximum absorbance is that obtained by incubating only vehicle with anti-Ig.

Linear regression analysis of these data usually yield correlation coefficients greater than 0.90. To determine the Ig concentration of a test sample, the mean absorbance value of the test sample (hybridoma culture supernatant) is entered as the *y* value in the regression equation of the standard curve, and the corresponding *x* value is calculated. This analysis system eliminates the subjectivity inherent in deriving data values from manually plotted standard curves, and also rectifies the small deviation from linearity seen in most standard curves.

Antigen-Capture Enzyme Immunoassay (ACEIA). The solid-phase adsorbant and washing procedure were the same as used in the CIEIA. Plates were coated overnight at 4° with 50 μl of an optimal dilution of anti-Ig in 0.1 *M* NaHCO$_3$ buffer (pH 9.6). A standard curve was generated by incubating serial log dilutions (50 μl) of Ig standard in anti-Ig-coated microtiter plates for 30 min at 4°. After washing, the "captured" Ig was sandwiched by the addition of the same anti-Ig in PBS-T for 30 min at 4°. The remainder of the ACEIA is exactly the same as that described for the CIEIA.

Optimization of the CIEIA. To illustrate the critical importance of optimization of reagent concentrations in the performance of the CIEIA, an assay of human IgG will be used. In this example, purified human IgG was adsorbed to the solid phase, and a goat anti-human IgG along with the same purified human IgG were the fluid-phase reagents. The solid-phase binding was developed with a rabbit anti-goat IgG that was tagged with alkaline phosphatase. Reaction conditions were as described in the Materials and Methods section.

In this optimization experiment, microtiter plates were coated with 10, 1, or 0.1 μg human IgG/ml. Four different concentrations of goat anti-human IgG (10, 5, 1, 0.1 μg/ml) and rabbit anti-goat IgG (10, 2, 1, 0.2 μg/ml) were also tested. The results of this optimization experiment are shown in Fig. 1. Each reagent concentration was critical to the CIEIA. As we described in an earlier paper,[1] the slope of the standard curve should be as steep as possible so that variability in absorbance values plotted arithmetically on the *y* axis will not yield unwieldly variabilities in Ig concentrations plotted logarithmically on the *x* axis. It can be seen in Fig. 1 that a human IgG coating concentration of 10 μg/ml yielded the highest absolute absorbance values, but the slopes of the curves were quite flat

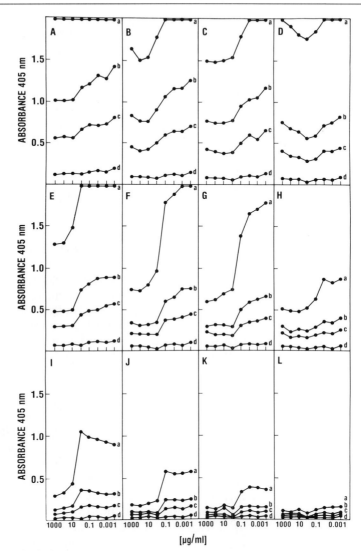

FIG. 1. Optimization of reagent concentrations for CIEIA of human IgG. The coating concentrations of human IgG were 10 μg/ml (panels A–D), 1 μg/ml (panels E–H), and 0.1 μg/ml (panels I–L). Goat anti-human IgG concentrations were 10 μg/ml (panels A, E, and I), 5 μg/ml (panels B, F, and J), 1 μg/ml (panels C, G, and K), and 0.1 μg/ml (panels D, H, and L). Rabbit anti-goat IgG concentrations were 10 μg/ml (a), 5 μg/ml (b), 2 μg/ml (c), and 0.2 μg/ml (d). Each point is the mean of six replicates.

regardless of the concentrations of the other reagents. When plates were coated with 0.1 μg/ml, the absolute absorbance values were substantially lower, and no combination of reagents produced a reasonable standard curve. At what would be considered the optimal human IgG coating concentration (1 μg/ml), standard curves with the desired characteristics were generated. However, as can easily be seen the concentrations of goat anti-human IgG (panels E–H) and rabbit anti-goat IgG (curves a–d on each panel) played a critical role. It appeared that with these particular reagents, 1 or 5 μg of goat anti-human IgG per milliliter coupled only with the highest concentration of rabbit anti-goat IgG (10 μg/ml) yielded good standard curves. These data point out the importance of optimization experiments in the development of CIEIA methods.

Comparison of CIEIA and ACEIA. Another method for quantifying immunoglobulins is ACEIA, or sandwich immunoassay. We have compared this method with CIEIA and find the latter to be superior. For example, in Fig. 2 we show standard curves obtained for mouse IgG$_1$

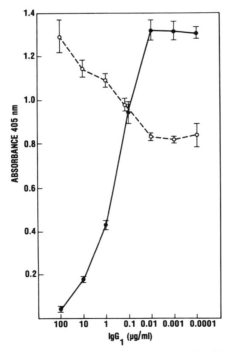

FIG. 2. Comparison of standard curves for mouse monoclonal IgG$_1$ concentrations by CIEIA (●) and ACEIA (○). Each point is the mean ± one standard deviation of six replicates.

under optimized conditions (for both CIEIA and ACEIA). In both assay modes, linear curves from approximately 100 μg/ml to 10 ng/ml were obtained. Though similar in sensitivity, the curves had very different slopes; the CIEIA curve was steeper than the ACEIA curve. Since both methods had been optimized with respect to reagent concentrations, it is likely that the difference in slope is a function of the mode of assay. This difference in slope resulted in an average standard deviation from the mean of each point on the ACEIA curve of 0.06 absorbance units, compared to only 0.02 for the CIEIA. Data from several experiments indicated excellent reproducibility in standard curves, and confirmed the larger variability associated with each point on the ACEIA curve. Together, the steeper slope and lower variability of the CIEIA curve make this assay method superior to the ACEIA. As an illustration, if the variability of IgG_1 concentrations at the point on Fig. 2 where the curves intersect (0.95 absorbance units and 0.9 μg/ml IgG_1) is assessed, the range of one standard deviation above and below the mean is 0.02–0.33 μg/ml for ACEIA, but only 0.08–0.11 μg/ml for CIEIA. Therefore, the precision with which IgG_1 concentrations can be measured is greater in the CIEIA.

Discussion

The capability of accurately measuring the rate of monoclonal antibody secretion by hybridoma cultures should facilitate the selection of clones with the greatest production potential. The concentrations of Ig found in hybridoma cultures produced in our laboratory range from 25 μg/ml to 1 ng/ml, with an average of approximately 1 μg/ml. Probably the most common method for quantifying Ig is by single radial immunodiffusion,[2,3] but this method cannot detect the low levels found in hybridoma supernatants. Other techniques which have been employed to detect Ig in cultures include immunoelectrophoresis,[4,5] hemagglutination inhibition,[6] and reverse plaquing,[7] all of which are semiquantitative. Radioimmunoassay for Ig is sensitive and quantitative, but because it requires the use of isotopes,[8,9] the enzyme-linked immunosorbent assay (ELISA) originally

[2] G. Mancini, A. O. Carbonara, and J. F. Heremans, *Immunochemistry* 2, 235 (1965).
[3] J.-P. Vaerman, this series, Vol. 73, Part B, p. 291.
[4] J. L. Fahey, I. Finegold, A. S. Rabson, and R. A. Manaker, *Science* 152, 1259, 1966.
[5] R. van Furth, H. R. E. Schuit, and W. Hijmans, *Immunology* 11, 1 (1966).
[6] F. P. Siegal and M. Siegal, *J. Immunol.* 118, 642 (1977).
[7] G. A. Molinaro and S. Dray, *Nature (London)* 248, 515 (1974).
[8] T. Hirano, T. Kuriani, T. Kishimoto, and Y. Yamamura, *J. Immunol.* 119, 1235 (1977).
[9] S. M. McLachland, B. R. Smith, and R. Hall, *J. Immunol. Methods* 21, 212 (1970).

described by Engvall and Perlmann[10] is rapidly becoming the immunoassay method of choice. The CIEIA described here is a modification of the original ELISA procedure which allows quantification of Ig down to the 10 ng/ml level.

Several practical aspects of the CIEIA require discussion. At what point in the screening of hybridomas would the CIEIA be used? Since uncloned hybridoma cultures often contain multiple clones secreting the same Ig isotype or subclass, the CIEIA would be of little value. It is best to initially screen the cultures for antibody to the desired antigen by standard methods, choosing positives for subsequent cloning. When analyzing clones, they should be screened for both specific antibody and total Ig. By determining the relative cell number (clone size, degree of confluence of the microculture), the cultures with clones secreting the most Ig can be identified. Of course the quantification can be expressed as molecules of IG secreted per cell per minute if the cells are actually counted and sampling done over time.

It is essential that the reagents employed have heavy chain specificity, particularly if more than one isotype of Ig is present in the cultures. For instance, in cultures with both IgG and IgA antibodies, in which both isotypes bear λ light chains, absolute quantification of either antibody would be impossible. Obviously the purity of the solid phase Ig would be equally essential.

The CIEIA is quantitative and reproducible, and can be performed in less than 3 hr. Its increased precision makes it more attractive than the ACEIA method. It is essential to remember that prior to employing the CIEIA in experimental studies, each reagent must be optimized for concentration with the goal of creating a standard curve that is linear and as steep as possible.

Acknowledgments

We thank Susan McLaughlin for editorial assistance, and the U.S. Army Chemical Research and Development Center for support.

[10] E. Engvall and P. Perlmann, *Immunochemistry* **8**, 871 (1971).

[52] The Detection and Characterization of Antigen-Specific Monoclonal Antibodies Using Anti-Immunoglobulin Isotype Antibodies Coupled to Red Blood Cells

By M. R. CLARK

A major requirement in attempts to derive monoclonal antibodies by cell fusion is the need for simple and rapid assays for the detection and characterization of positive cultures. In the case of rat hybrid myelomas made using the Y3/Ag1.2.3 myeloma cell line the greater stability of these hybrids[1] can be usefully exploited by altering the fusion and screening procedures[2,3] such that the uncloned hybrids are expanded in culture and frozen and the supernatants are collected for assay. Positive hybrids within mixed cultures are identified by using assays which on average detect less than one clone per well, for example, complement-mediated lysis, or indirect binding assays using isotype-restricted reagents. The positive cultures are then thawed and the cells cloned and the relevant positive clones are detected using suitably restricted assays. It is at this step that it is useful to have rapid and simple assays for the detection of specificity for antigen and for the determination of antibody isotype. Red cell-based assays offer many advantages in terms of simplicity and speed.

Some suitable systems involving the use of antigens or antibodies coupled to red blood cells for hemolytic, hemagglutination, or rosetting assays have already been described previously (see earlier volumes of Immunochemical Techniques in this series). Here three assay systems are described based on the special case in which the red cells are used as indicators for the detection of monoclonal antibodies by immunoglobulin isotype-specific antibodies. These assays are based on various systems developed by R. R. A. Coombs and collaborators.[4-8] The three assays

[1] M. R. Clark and C. Milstein, *Somatic Cell Genet.* **7,** 657 (1981).

[2] M. R. Clark, S. P. Cobbold, G. Hale, and H. Waldmann, *Immunol. Today* **4,** 100 (1983).

[3] N. M. Aqel, M. R. Clark, S. P. Cobbold, and H. Waldmann, *J. Immunol. Methods* **69,** 207 (1984).

[4] R. R. A. Coombs, *in* "Immunoassays for the 80's" (A. Voller, ed.), p. 224. MTP Press, Ltd., Lancaster, England, 1981.

[5] M. L. Scott, M. J. Thornley, and R. R. A. Coombs, *Int. Arch. Allergy Appl. Immunol.* **64,** 230 (1981).

[6] M. Kieffer, P. J. Frazier, N. W. R. Daniels, P. J. Ciclitira, and R. R. A. Coombs, *J. Immunol. Methods* **42,** 129 (1981).

[7] R. E. March, J. S. Reeback, E. J. Holborow, and R. R. A. Coombs, *J. Immunol. Methods* **42,** 137 (1981).

[8] M. P. Cranage and R. R. A. Coombs, *J. Virol. Methods* **5,** 199 (1982).

TABLE I
MONOCLONAL ANTI-IMMUNOGLOBULIN ISOTYPE ANTIBODIES USED
SUCCESSFULLY IN RED CELL-LINKED ASSAYS

Monoclonal antibody	Specificity	Ref.[a]
MAR 18.5	Rat κ light chain	a
MRC-OX 12.11	Rat κ Igk-1a light chain allotype	b
G9/1.3	Rat κ Igk-1a light chain allotype	c
RG11/15.5	Rat κ Igk-1b light chain allotype	d
RG7/1.7	Rat IgG_{2a}	d
NORIG 1.1.6	Rat IgG_{2b}	e
NORIG 7.16.2	Rat IgG_{2b}	e
NORIG 31.12.14	Rat IgG_{2c}	e
NH3/15.18.1	Human IgG_3	f

[a] Key to references: a, L. L. Lanier, G. A. Gutman, D. E. Lewis, S. T. Griswold, and N. L. Warner, *Hybridoma* **1**, 125 (1982). b, S. V. Hunt and M. H. Fowler, *Cell Tissue Kinet.* **14**, 445 (1981). c, G. A. Gutman, *Hybridoma* **1**, 133 (1982). d, T. A. Springer, A. Bhattacharya, J. T. Cardoza, and F. Sanchez-Madrid, *Hybridoma* **1**, 257 (1982). e, Obtained by fusion of the mouse myeloma line NS0/1 with BALB/c mouse spleen cells, hyperimmunized against rat anti-pertussis–pertussis immune complexes. Positive cultures were characterized by their reaction with rat monoclonal antibodies of known isotype (M. R. Clark, unpublished observations). f, D. M. Downie, D. Voak, J. Jarvis, H. Waldmann, and M. Spitz, *Biotest Bulletin* **4**, 348 (1983).

allow for the rapid isotyping of monoclonal antibodies and for the detection of monoclonal antibodies against cell surface antigens or other antigens immobilized on a solid phase, and are suitable alternatives to many assays using radiolabeled or enzyme-labelled anti-immunoglobulin isotype antibodies.[5,9] Table I lists the anti-immunoglobulin isotype monoclonal antibodies which have been used in the assays described.

Preparation of Indicator Red Blood Cells

All three of the assays make use of immunoglobulins chemically coupled to red blood cells. In the inhibition of agglutination assay the coupled immunoglobulin acts as antigen whereas in the reverse passive and hemadsorption assays the coupled immunoglobulin is itself an isotype-specific anti-immunoglobulin.

[9] M. R. Clark, S. P. Cobbold, H. Waldmann, and R. R. A. Coombs, *J. Immunol. Methods* **66**, 81 (1984).

Several factors have been found to markedly affect the sensitivity of hemagglutination reactions, and in particular, red blood cells from different species and from different blood groups within a species are not all equally sensitive.[10] The assays described have been tested using human blood group O cells. Alternatively, enzyme-treated sheep red blood cells can be used.[8] The blood should be collected into a suitable anticoagulant such as acid citrate dextrose or citrate phosphate dextrose, as used in blood transfusion packs, or the blood may be defibrinated by rotating the freshly collected blood with glass beads. The cells should then be washed into isotonic saline (0.9% sodium chloride) by centrifugation three or four times at 500 g for 10 min removing the buffy coat by aspiration.

Purification of Immunoglobulins for Coupling to Red Cells

As different proteins couple to red cells with different efficiencies it is necessary to partially purify the immunoglobulin to be coupled so as to avoid too much competition from other proteins during the coupling procedure. Suitable preparations seem to vary from one monoclonal antibody to another, but in general the immunoglobulin fraction purified by precipitation with 50% saturated ammonium sulfate from ascites or serum is sufficient. However, for some monoclonal antibodies it is necessary to purify them further, for example by ion-exchange chromatography or affinity chromatography (suitable methods are to be found in many general immunochemical textbooks as well as in other volumes of this series). The purified antibody should then be dialyzed into isotonic saline for the chromic chloride coupling reaction. The chromic chloride coupling reaction is sensitive to phosphate, so both the red cells and the antibody should be in isotonic saline.

Chromic Chloride Coupling of Immunoglobulin to Red Cells

The coupling procedure described here uses chromic chloride as the cross-linking reagent; alternative methods can be found in a previous volume of this series.[11]

Materials

From a 1% (w/v) stock solution of chromic chloride (Sigma Chemical Company Ltd., Poole, Dorset, United Kingdom, cat. no. C 1896) in

[10] R. M. Binns, S. T. Licence, B. W. Gurner, and R. R. A. Coombs, *Immunology* **47**, 717 (1982).

[11] Y. Jou, P. K. Massaferro, G. L. Mayers, and R. B. Bankert, this series, Vol. 92, p. 257.

saline, adjusted to pH 5.0 with 0.2 *M* sodium hydroxide, prepare a fresh dilution of 0.02% in saline.

Saline-washed red blood cells.

Antibody at a protein concentration of 0.1–1 mg/ml, dialyzed into saline. The optimal concentration will vary with each monoclonal antibody and the degree of purity, and needs to be determined empirically.

The coupling and wash procedures may be conveniently carried out in 30-ml plastic universal containers (Sterilin, Teddington, United Kingdom, cat. no. 128A).

Method. In a 30-ml universal container, to one volume of packed red blood cells (0.2–0.5 ml) add one volume of antibody, and then, while vortex mixing, add two volumes of the 0.02% chromic chloride solution dropwise. Continue mixing for about 10 min. At low protein concentrations it may be necessary to reduce the time to avoid the cells being over cross-linked, resulting in autoagglutination. Then wash the cells three or four times in 25 ml phosphate-buffered saline by centrifugation at 500 *g* for 10 min. The coupled cells are stable for about 2 weeks if stored in phosphate-buffered saline containing sodium azide at about 0.05% (w/v). A method has been published describing the stabilization of antibody-coupled red blood cells using glutaraldehyde, in which the cells have a considerable shelf-life but there may be a slight loss of sensitivity.[12]

Preparation of Antigen-Coated Microtiter Plates

Simple Antigen Preparations. The antigen of interest should be bound to the surface of U-well microtiter plates (e.g., Falcon plates, no. 3911, Becton Dickinson Labware). For example, purified proteins will usually coat the surface of poly(vinyl chloride) or polystyrene plates by incubating, overnight at 4°, 50 µl per well of a 1–10 µg/ml solution of the protein. The protein solution is then removed and the plates are incubated overnight at 4° with 100 µl per well of a suitable "blocking buffer" containing a high concentration of a protein which will not interfere with the assay (e.g., phosphate-buffered saline plus 5% (v/v) bovine serum and 0.05% (w/v) sodium azide). The plates can usually be prepared in large numbers and stored at this stage for several months if necessary. Alternative procedures which may be better suited to a particular antigen are described elsewhere in this series.

Fixed Whole-Cell Preparations. Cells such as normal, leukemic, or cultured cells can be fixed to flexible U-well microtiter plates as follows.

[12] M. P. Cranage, B. W. Gurner, and R. R. A. Coombs, *J. Immunol. Methods* **64**, 7 (1983).

Wash the cells and resuspend them at about 0.6 to 5×10^6 cells/ml phosphate-buffered saline. The correct concentration of cells to use depends upon the particular cell population, their morphology, and their size, and needs to be determined by trial. Plate the cell suspension out into the microtiter plates at 100 μl per well and allow the cells to settle for 1 hr at 4°. If the concentration is correct, the cells should be evenly distributed over the surface of the well without being so overcrowded that they are confluent.

The cells are fixed by immersing the plates for 5 min in a 0.25% (w/v) solution of glutaraldehyde in phosphate-buffered saline at 4°. The plates are then washed by immersion for 5 min in phosphate-buffered saline at 4°, followed by a further wash for 5 min at room temperature. Store the plates at 4° with 100 μl per well of "blocking buffer," phosphate-buffered saline containing 1% (w/v) bovine serum albumin, 0.1% (w/v) sodium azide, and 1% (v/v) heat-inactivated normal rabbit serum (to block Fc receptors).

Reverse Passive Hemagglutination Isotyping Assay

The anti-immunoglobulin isotype-coupled red blood cells can be used in both reverse passive hemagglutination and solid-phase hemadsorption assays. Reverse passive hemagglutination provides a quick method for testing whether the antibody has successfully coupled to the red cells. In addition, the assay provides a very rapid and sensitive way of determining the isotype of monoclonal antibodies. The titer of the hemagglutination reaction also indicates the concentration of the monoclonal antibody relative to a known standard. This assay can prove very useful in the monitoring of culture supernatants and column fractions during monoclonal antibody production and purification. The typical sensitivities of a number of examples of anti-isotype monoclonal antibodies coupled to human blood group O red cells are given in Table II.

Method. The assay is very simply carried out by taking each sample of interest and performing serial dilutions in a volume of 50 μl per well of U-well microtiter plates. The dilutions should be made in an isotonic buffer such as phosphate-buffered saline or perhaps cell culture medium, and it is often worthwhile having some protein present, e.g., 5% (v/v) fetal calf serum or 1% (w/v) bovine serum albumin. Next, add 50 μl per well of a 1% (v/v) suspension of the appropriate coupled red blood cells, shake the plates for a few seconds, and then allow the red cells to settle for 1 hr.

Interpretation of Results. In negative wells the red cells will settle to a tight button at the bottom of the well, whereas in a strongly positive

TABLE II
SENSITIVITY OF RED CELL-LINKED MOUSE ANTI-RAT IG
MONOCLONAL ANTIBODIES WITH DIFFERENT RAT ISOTYPES[a]

Monoclonal antibody	Maximum titer of rat Ig giving agglutination					
	IgM	IgG_1	IgG_{2a}	IgG_{2b}	IgG_{2c}	κ
MAR 18.5[b]	64000	250	250	250	250	4
MAR 18.5[c]	2000	4	4	4	4	—
RG7/1.7	—	—	>100	—	—	—
NORIG 1.1.6	—	—	—	4000	—	—
NORIG 7.16.2	—	—	—	6400	—	—
NORIG 31.12.14	—	—	—	—	>600	—

[a] Rat immunoglobulins containing κ light chains were titrated from a starting concentration of 0.1 mg/ml in reverse passive hemagglutination assays with various mouse anti-rat immunoglobulin isotype monoclonal antibodies coupled to human blood group O red cells.
[b] MAR 18.5 coupled to 0.5 mg/ml.
[c] MAR 18.5 coupled at 0.1 mg/ml.

reaction there will be an even coating of the cells over the whole surface of the well. It is possible to make subjective distinctions between intermediate reactions.

Solid-Phase Hemadsorption Assay

The following procedure is applicable to U-well microtiter plates coated with purified antigen or fixed cells prepared as described above. The assay compares very favorably with an equivalent enzyme-linked indirect binding assay[9] in sensitivity but has the advantages of fewer steps and no requirement for complicated or expensive apparatus.

Method. Flick out the blocking buffer in which the plates have been stored and wash the wells once with phosphate-buffered saline. All of the necessary wash steps can be conveniently carried out by filling the wells with buffer from a "squeeze" wash bottle, followed by flicking the liquid out into a sink. Dry the wells by tapping the inverted plates on tissue paper.

Put 50 μl of the monoclonal antibody supernatants to be assayed in each well. It is best to include replicates and a number of suitable positive and negative control supernatants in each assay plate. Incubate at room temperature for about 45 min and then flick out the supernatants. Wash the wells five times using phosphate-buffered saline containing 0.1% (w/v) bovine serum albumin, allowing the wash buffer to stand in the wells for at least 1–2 min each time.

Tap out the wash buffer from the plates and then add per well 50 μl of a 1% (v/v) suspension of red blood cells coupled with a suitable anti-immunoglobulin to detect the monoclonal antibody isotypes of interest. Allow the red cells to settle for 1 hr and then score each well for its hemadsorption pattern.

Interpretation of Results

In negative wells the red cells will settle to a tight button at the bottom of the well, whereas in a strongly positive reaction there will be an even coating of the cells over the whole surface of the well. It is possible to make subjective distinctions between intermediate reactions. The sensitivity of this assay can be increased by reshaking the red cells into suspension and then allowing them to resettle for an hour. It is likely that this increase in sensitivity is a result of some antibody being "captured" off of the surface of the plates and so that it can then participate in reverse passive hemagglutination.

Inhibition of Passive Hemagglutination

In this assay the red blood cells are coupled with immunoglobulin of an appropriate isotype to act as antigen. The red blood cells can then be agglutinated by a suitable concentration of an anti-immunoglobulin isotype antibody. This agglutination can be inhibited by the inclusion of free immunoglobulin of the same isotype. Thus monoclonal antibody-containing supernatants can be quickly characterized by the inhibition patterns with different anti-immunoglobulin isotype reagents.

Method. To carry out such an assay, first determine the titer of the hemagglutination with the anti-immunoglobulin isotype antibody. Then prepare serial dilutions of the various test monoclonal antibody supernatants (in an isotonic buffer as described above for reverse passive hemagglutination) in U-well plates, 50 μl per well. Add 25 μl per well of a dilution of the agglutinating anti-immunoglobulin isotype antibody of about four times the minimum needed to give agglutination. Finally add 50 μl per well of a 1% suspension of the immunoglobulin-coupled red blood cells, shake the plates for a few seconds, and allow the cells to settle for 1 hr.

Interpretation of Results. The results are interpreted opposite to the interpretation for reverse passive hemagglutination or solid-phase hemadsorption. A tight button indicates an inhibiting immunoglobulin of the right isotype and is therefore a positive result. No inhibiting immunoglobulin will result in complete hemagglutination, a negative result.

Problems and Considerations

The two agglutination assays described here offer different advantages and disadvantages in their use. First, the reverse passive assay requires that the anti-immunoglobulin isotype antibody is purified in sufficient quantities for the coupling procedure, typically 100–500 μg/ml packed red cells (sufficient to perform about 2000 assays), whereas only about 1–10 μg of the same antibody would be needed for a similar number of inhibition of hemagglutination assays. However the anti-immunoglobulin isotype-coupled cells are in general more sensitive and can be used in both reverse passive hemagglutination and solid-phase hemadsorption assays. The second consideration is the dependence of the systems on the valency of the "antigen"; for reverse passive hemagglutination the antigen (in this case a monoclonal antibody of unknown isotype) must be multivalent and hence be able to cross-link the anti-immunoglobulin isotype-coupled cells. Thus the degree of sensitivity is influenced by aggregation of the unknown antibody or by its isotype; for example free immunoglobulin light chain, IgG, or multimeric IgM will all have different valencies. The solid-phase hemadsorption and inhibition of hemagglutination assays are far more independent of the valency of the antigen.

In some cases it may be found that the specificity of a monoclonal antibody appears to change after it has been coupled to the red cells. Two of the antibodies mentioned in Table I show such a property. The first antibody is MAR 18.5, a mouse monoclonal antibody specific for rat immunoglobulin κ light chains. When this antibody is coupled at different concentrations, the red cells show differential agglutination with rat κ light chains in association with the isotypes IgM and IgG (see Table II). At the lower concentrations of coupling, the cells become functionally IgM (κ) specific and there is no hemagglutination with IgG (κ). However, when the assay is changed such that the MAR 18.5 is used in passive hemmagglutination of rat immunoglobulin-coupled red cells, the rat immunoglobulin isotypes are almost equal in their abilities to inhibit the agglutination (data not shown).

The second example is MRC-OX 12, a mouse monoclonal antibody which shows a preferential reaction with the rat κ Igk-1a allotype in iodine-labeled binding assays and in inhibition of passive hemagglutination assays. However, this preferential binding is not as obvious when this antibody is coupled to the red cells and reverse passive hemagglutination assays are carried out (data not shown).

These two examples illustrate why it is sometimes necessary to redefine the operational specificity of a monoclonal antibody depending upon the context of the assay. In these examples it seems likely that the observed changes in the apparent specificities is a result of differences in the effective avidity of the systems due to the problems of valency of binding outlined above.

[53] Agglutination Assay Using Protein A-Sensitized Erythrocytes for Detection of Immunoglobulin in Tissue Culture Supernatants

By DAVID MALE and GARETH PRYCE

The production of antibody-producing hybridomas invariably incorporates a step at which the colonies of hybridoma cells are tested for the production of specific antibody. However, only a proportion of fused cells produce detectable quantities of antibody, so it is possible to reduce the number of antigen-specific tests needed, by first prescreening the hybridomas, to identify those producing antibodies. This type of prescreening is valuable when the antigen-specific assays are time-consuming, or if the antigen is valuable and in short supply. It is not generally advantageous to prescreen hybridomas when the antigen-specific assay is fast and the antigen is freely available.

The method described here is a rapid single-step assay for screening tissue culture supernatants for antibody production.[1] In addition to its use in the screening of hybridomas, it may also be used to select for variants producing the highest titers of antibody, and in the general assay of immunoglobulin in any tissue culture supernatant, including mitogen- and antigen-stimulated cultures.

The assay is based on the agglutination of red blood cells sensitized with staphylococcal protein A, which binds to the Fc region of most IgG isotypes in the majority of species.[2] To increase the sensitivity of the assay an enhancing antibody is added to the protein A-sensitized cells. This enhancing antibody serves two functions. (1) It permits the cells to be agglutinated by antibodies which do not bind protein A, and therefore would not be detected by sensitized cells alone. (2) By varying the con-

---

[1] D. K. Male and G. Pryce, *Immunol. Commun.* **12**, 465 (1983).

[2] A. Johnstone and R. Thorpe, *in* "Immunochemistry in Practice," p. 210. Blackwell, Oxford, 1982.

METHODS IN ENZYMOLOGY, VOL. 121

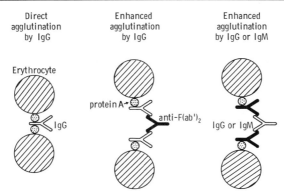

Direct
agglutination
by IgG

Enhanced
agglutination
by IgG

Enhanced
agglutination
by IgG or IgM

Erythrocyte

protein A

anti-F(ab')₂

IgG

IgG or IgM

FIG. 1. Agglutination of protein A-sensitized erythrocytes by antibody. Most IgG isotypes cause direct agglutination of the cells (left); however, this can be enhanced by the addition of anti-F(ab')₂ (center). This reagent also permits cross-linking of the cells by antibodies such as IgM which do not themselves bind to protein A (right). (Adapted from Male and Pryce,[1] courtesy of Marcel Dekker, Inc.)

centration of enhancing antibody the assay sensitivity can be set at a convenient level within the range of 1–100 ng/ml.

The overall principle of the assay is illustrated in Fig. 1. The assay may be used to detect mouse or human IgG. In the mouse, IgG_3, IgG_{2a}, and IgG_{2b} bind protein A strongly and IgG_1 relatively weakly, so these isotypes can directly agglutinate the red cells.[3] Similarly, in the human IgG_1, IgG_2, and IgG_4 bind protein A. The addition of the appropriate enhancing antibody permits detection of those isotypes such as IgM which do not bind protein A,[4] and increases the agglutination produced by those which do. Although the sensitivity for particular isotypes varies with one set of conditions, even those which agglutinate less well are still readily detected.

The method is closely related to the reverse plaque assay of Gronowicz *et al.*[5] and its recent modifications, and in experimental systems the two techniques may be used in parallel to detect both the number of antibody-producing cells and the total amount of antibody produced.

Methods and Results

Hemagglutination. To detect antibody in the tissue culture supernatants, 25 µl of sensitized erythrocytes, with or without enhancing anti-

[3] I. Seppälä, H. Sarvas, F. Peterfy, and O. Mäkelä, *Scand. J. Immunol.* **14,** 337 (1981).
[4] G. Kronvall, H. Grey, and R. Williams, *J. Immunol.* **105,** 1116 (1970).
[5] E. Gronowicz, A. Coutinho, and F. Melchers, *Eur. J. Immunol.* **6,** 588 (1976).

body, was added to 25 μl of tissue culture fluid in U-bottomed microwell plates (Gibco). The cells and supernatants were agitated and left to settle for 45 min; agglutination indicated the presence of Ig in the supernatant. To detect the immunoglobulin (Ig) quantitatively, the supernatants may be titered in doubling dilutions in phosphate-buffered saline containing 1 mg bovine serum albumin (BSA) per milliliter before the addition of the sensitized cells. It is unnecessary to titrate hybridoma supernatants when screening a fusion.

Sensitized Red Cells (Based on the Method of Fauci et al.[6]). Sheep erythrocytes were washed four times in isotonic saline and pelleted at 200 *g*. Chromic chloride coupling was used to attach staphylococcal protein A to the erythrocytes. Protein A (Pharmacia), 100 μl at a concentration of 1.25 mg/ml, was mixed with 100 μl of packed erythrocytes and 1 ml of freshly prepared $CrCl_3$ (100 μg/ml in isotonic saline) in a *glass* vessel. The mixture was incubated for 40 min at 37° with continuous gentle swirling. After incubation the cells were spun down gently (100 *g*) and washed three times in isotonic saline, before being resuspended at a concentration of 2.5 $\times$ 10^8 cells/ml in phosphate-buffered saline containing 1 mg BSA/ml. BSA is included to eliminate any tendency for the cells to agglutinate nonspecifically. For this reason it is essential that the BSA contains no immunoglobulin contaminants; Miles reagent-grade Cohn fraction V is suitable.

The preparation of the erythrocytes coupled to staphylococcal protein A (E-spA) is the most critical step of the method, since small deviations from the procedure markedly affect the efficiency of the coupling. It is also noted that some batches of $CrCl_3$ are more efficient at coupling than others. Once prepared, the sensitized cells may be stored at 4° for at least 2 weeks without loss of activity. [A bacteriostatic concentration of NaN_3 (0.05%) should be included in the buffer.] The activity of the cells may be checked by hemagglutination in the presence of normal mouse Ig (Miles Cohn fraction II). Sensitized cells are agglutinated by IgG concentrations of 0.5–2 μg/ml. This is not sufficiently sensitive by itself to detect the quantities of antibody present in most hybridoma supernatants, so an enhancing antibody is added.

Enhancing Antibody. Sheep anti-mouse F(ab′)$_2$ serum is added to the E-spA to increase the sensitivity of the assay. The system may be used to detect mouse Ig or human Ig by the addition of the appropriate enhancing serum, and the amount of serum added determines the sensitivity of the assay (Fig. 2). The appropriate amount of antiserum is determined by testing cells containing different antiserum dilutions on normal Ig (Cohn

[6] A. Fauci, G. Whalen, and C. Burch, *Cell. Immunol.* **54**, 230 (1980).

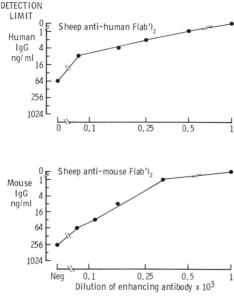

FIG. 2. The detection limit of the agglutination assay for human and mouse IgG (Cohn fraction II) using different concentrations of enhancing antibody. The dilution of enhancing antibody determines the sensitivity of the assay within a window of usable concentrations.

fraction II) titered in doubling dilutions. Suitable concentrations of antiserum usually lie between 1/1000 and 1/15,000 final dilution, incorporated in the cell suspension. Because at high serum concentrations the cells are agglutinated directly by the sheep antibody, and at low concentrations there is insufficient antibody to enhance the sensitivity, there is a window of suitable concentrations which is characteristic for each antiserum (Fig. 2). Once the appropriate concentration of antiserum is determined, this amount should be added to the E-spA immediately before use. A sensitivity of 5–20 ng Ig/ml is suitable.

Characteristics of the Assay. Normal Ig can be detected in the range of 1–250 ng of IgG/ml, but the sensitivity varies to some extent for the different Ig isotypes. This is dependent on the affinity of the protein A for different isotypes,[3] and on the enhancing serum. Using tissue culture supernatants from cloned hybridomas producing different monoclonal antibodies, it can be shown that the sensitivity of detection is $IgG_{2b} > IgM > IgG_{2a} > IgG_1$ for mouse antibodies (table). The isotype of the hybridomas used in this experiment was determined using anti-isotype sera[7] in a ra-

---

[7] G. Torrigiani, *Clin. Exp. Immunol.* **11**, 125 (1972).

AGGLUTINATION BY ISOTYPES[a]

Isotype	Allotype	Titer[b]	Concentration[c] (μg/ml)	Detection limit[d] (ng/ml)
IgM	a	12	14.7	3.6
IgG$_1$	a	9	11.5	22.4
IgG$_{2a}$	a	14	130.0	7.9
IgG$_{2b}$	a	16	61.0	0.9

[a] Reprinted from Male and Pryce,[1] courtesy of Marcel Dekker, Inc.
[b] Agglutination titer of tissue culture supernatants containing defined isotypes, expressed as reciprocal $\log_2$ of the last dilution producing complete agglutination.
[c] Antibody concentration of the supernatants, measured by laser nephelometry against a standard mouse serum.
[d] Detection limit of agglutination method for each isotype.

dioimmunoassay or immuno-double diffusion, and the level of antibody in each supernatant was determined by laser nephelometry by interpolation from reference serum Was 05 (Serotec). In this assay the sensitivity of the cells for normal mouse IgG (all isotypes) was 3 ng/ml, which lies within the range of sensitivities for the individual isotypes.

Additional Applications. The method described may be used both in the assay of hybridoma supernatants, and for more general measurement of immunoglobulin production *in vitro*. For example, Fig. 3 compares the number of antibody-producing cells detected by reverse plaque-forming cell assay[5] with the total antibody production measured by agglutination, in a culture of spleen cells stimulated with lipopolysaccharide.[8] In this system the results obtained by the two methods correlate quite closely.

Technical Notes

In the preparation of hybridoma cells, there is usually some residual antibody production by unfused spleen cells in the fusion mixture. We have found that following two changes of medium, at day 14 after fusion, there is insufficient residual antibody to interfere with the detection of that produced by active hybridomas.

It is essential that there is no immunoglobulin present in the tissue culture medium which might agglutinate the E-spA. For this reason, the assay is not suitable to detect antibody in tissue culture media which contain serum supplements with high immunoglobulin concentrations, such as normal adult serum. We have examined several batches of fetal

[8] B. Mishell and S. Shiigi, *in* "Selected Methods in Cellular Immunology," p. 156. Freeman, San Francisco, 1980.

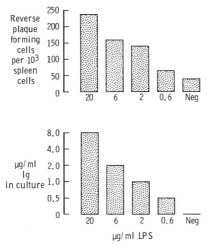

FIG. 3. Comparison of antibody-producing cells detected by reverse plaque-forming cell assay, and antibody levels detectable in the supernatant by agglutination, in tissue cultures of mouse spleen cells stimulated with 0–20 μg lipopolysaccharide (LPS) per milliliter over the course of 5 days.

calf serum, and found that there is insufficient antibody in them to cause agglutination of the cells at a 10% concentration, such as might be used in culture medium. One batch, however, did contain a detectable level of bovine Ig when used at a higher concentration. If such batches of serum are encountered, there is sufficient sensitivity available in the assay to allow for dilution of the supernatant before testing.

If the assay is to be used to select sublines of antibody-producing cells, it is worth noting that the method detects those hybridoma cultures producing the most antibody, which is dependent on both the rate of growth of the cells and the amount of antibody that each one produces. Usually it is desirable to select the most productive cultures, but if the experiment requires selection of the highest producing individual cells, then it is necessary to standardize the cultures for cell numbers.

In our experiments we have found that 50–60% of the actively growing hybridomas produce antibodies, although this varies for different fusions and with different protocols. It is thought that nonproductive hybridomas are derived either from a fusion partner lacking an active immunoglobulin gene, or because one or both of the chromosomes containing the active immunoglobulin genes have been shed.

Acknowledgments

This work was supported by grants from the Medical Research Council of Great Britain.

[54] Immunohistochemical Techniques Using Monoclonal Antibodies

By DANIEL R. CIOCCA and ROBERT J. BJERCKE

Immunohistochemical techniques are powerful tools for the screening and further characterization of monoclonal antibodies (MAbs).[1] Utilizing these techniques the researcher can visualize the specific antigen–antibody reaction on the cells or interstitium at both the light and electron microscopic level. We shall analyze briefly the specific properties of MAbs and their influence on immunohistochemistry before describing the immunohistochemical procedures.

Antibodies obtained by the hybridoma technique are homogeneous, and for this reason their properties and immunostaining characteristics can be reproduced without variability in replicates. Unlike polyclonal antisera, MAbs need not be absorbed to render them specific.[2] However, cross-reactivity may be the cause of nonspecific immunostaining using a specific MAb. The reason is that a specific MAb may recognize the same or a similar epitope present in a molecule(s) unrelated to the original antigen used to generate the MAb.[3] In addition, when MAbs are obtained from hybridoma culture supernatant containing serum or ascites fluid there are several proteins mixed with the MAb. These other protein constituents may affect the immunostaining specificity.[4,5] If necessary, a dilution curve to find the appropriate working concentration of a MAb to avoid nonspecific immunostaining should be obtained as for a polyclonal antiserum.[5,6]

Monoclonal antibodies harvested using routine procedures usually have insignificant amounts of irrelevant antibodies.[7] Therefore, by the use

---

[1] Abbreviations: MAb, monoclonal antibody; FITC, fluorescein isothiocyanate; PAP, peroxidase–anti-peroxidase complex; ABC, avidin–biotin peroxidase complex; RIA, radioimmunoassay; ELISA, enzyme-linked immunosorbent assay: DPBS, Dulbecco's phosphate-buffered saline without calcium or magnesium; BSA, bovine serum albumin.

[2] D. E. Yelton and M. D. Scharff, *Annu. Rev. Biochem.* **50**, 657 (1981).

[3] D. Lane and H. Koprowski, *Nature (London)* **296**, 200 (1982).

[4] D. M. Boorsma, A. C. Cuello, and F. W. van Leeuwen, *J. Histochem. Cytochem.* **30**, 1211 (1982).

[5] D. R. Ciocca, D. J. Adams, R. J. Bjercke, G. W. Sledge, D. P. Edwards, G. C. Chamness, and W. L. McGuire, *J. Histochem. Cytochem.* **31**, 691 (1983).

[6] P. Petruz, *J. Histochem. Cytochem.* **31**, 177 (1983).

[7] P. A. W. Edwards, *Biochem. J.* **200**, 1 (1981).

of optimally diluted MAbs, the immunostaining background is reduced. On the other hand, a monoreactive MAb binds only one antigenic epitope with the same affinity. These characteristics may be a disadvantage over using polyclonal antisera, where several antibodies with different affinities recognize multiple epitopes on the antigen. Taking this into consideration, it may be more vital to evaluate the pretreatment of the tissue under immunohistochemical study using MAbs. These characteristics explain why some MAbs give better immunostaining than polyclonal antisera whereas others may be less sensitive.[8]

One of the advantages of the hybridoma technique in immunohistology is that cloned hybridomas can produce internally labeled MAbs when radioactive ^{3}H-labeled amino acid precursors are added to the hybridoma culture medium. In this case, the MAb molecule with the incorporated radiolabeled amino acid is directly ready for radioimmunocytochemistry.[9,10] This method has been used in combination with other immunocytochemical procedures to demonstrate simultaneously two different antigen sites at the light and electron microscopic levels.[11] Recently, bispecific MAbs secreted by hybrid hybridomas have been obtained.[12] With this approach, an anti-peroxidase–anti-somatostatin antibody was produced and applied in immunocytochemistry: the sections were simultaneously incubated with the antibody and with a buffer containing horseradish peroxidase. This one-step immunocytochemical method does not require conjugation of marker molecules to the antibody and, due to its small size, the biospecific antibody may have superior penetration into the cell for use in immunoelectron microscopy. However, this method is not as sensitive as other enzyme-bridge procedures since it lacks the amplification step(s) of the indirect techniques.

Selection of the Correct Immunohistochemical Procedures

Several factors should be evaluated in advance to choose the appropriate immunohistochemical procedure. The most commonly used immunostaining methods are represented in Fig. 1. Their advantages and

[8] W. F. Hickey, V. Lee, J. Q. Trojanowski, L. J. McMillan, T. J. McKearn, J. Gonatas, and N. K. Gonatas, *J. Histochem. Cytochem.* **31**, 1126 (1983).

[9] A. C. Cuello, G. Galfré, and C. Milstein, *in* "Receptors for Neurotransmitters and Peptide Hormones" (G. Pepeu, M. J. Kuhar, and S. J. Enna, eds.), p. 349. Raven Press, New York, 1980.

[10] A. C. Cuello, C. Milstein, and J. V. Priestley, *Brain Res. Bull.* **5**, 575 (1980).

[11] A. C. Cuello, *Acta Histochem.* **28**, 9 (1983).

[12] C. Milstein and A. C. Cuello, *Nature (London)* **305**, 537 (1983).

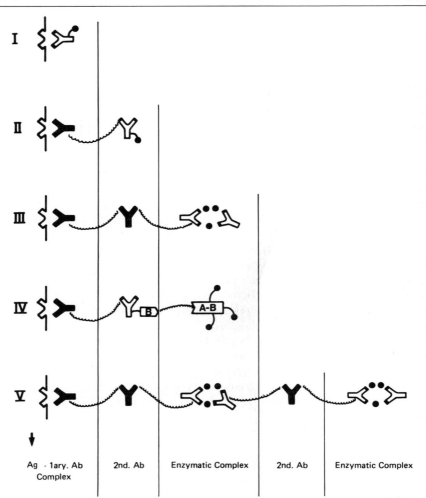

| Ag - 1ary. Ab Complex | 2nd. Ab | Enzymatic Complex | 2nd. Ab | Enzymatic Complex |

FIG. 1. Schematic representation of five immunohistochemical methods. In this example the primary antibody is a MAb. In the direct method (I), the MAb is usually conjugated (●) with a fluorescent compound, or with an enzyme, or incorporated with a radiolabeled amino acid. In the indirect method (II), the second antibody also is conjugated as above. In the PAP method (III) and in the ABC method (IV), the second antibody links the MAb to a third layer enzymatic complex. In the double PAP method (V) the second antibody and the enzymatic complex are applied twice. A, Avidin; B, biotin.

disadvantages have been reviewed.[10,13-18] Therefore, they will be considered only briefly here.

Immunoenzymatic procedures are the most popular immunohistochemical techniques, with horseradish peroxidase the most widely used enzyme bound to the primary antibody, to the second antibody, or in complexes, as with the PAP and ABC methods. Alkaline phosphatase and glucose oxidase can also be used for conjugating to antibodies. These two enzymes are alternatively used when endogenous peroxidase activity is difficult to inhibit, and when the simultaneous staining of two antigenic sites in a single slide is needed.[19,20] Theoretically, an amplification of the technique is achieved when the number of enzyme molecules attached to the antigen–antibody complex is increased. For this reason, the direct method (I of Fig. 1) is not frequently used (however, directly labeled MAbs may be useful in immunohistochemistry[21]). The indirect methods are more sensitive, especially the PAP method with its modifications: the four-layer PAP and the double PAP.[22-24] The ABC method is also very sensitive, requires the least amount of time, and gives insignificant background,[25] although it may be necessary to suppress endogenous avidin-binding activity in some tissues.[26]

These immunoenzymatic methods are mainly recommended for the study of paraffin sections and for the detection of intracellular antigens. These highly sensitive methods allow the simultaneous visualization of immunostained cells and tissue architecture with traditional counterstains. Moreover, the results are permanently recorded. They may also be well suited for membrane and interstitium antigen detection, especially if the preparation has locally dense concentrations of antigens. Disadvan-

[13] L. A. Sternberger, "Immunocytochemistry," 2nd ed. Wiley, New York, 1979.

[14] V. Bergroth, S. Reitamo, Y. T. Konttinen, and M. Lalla, *Histochemistry* **68**, 17 (1980).

[15] A. G. Farr and P. K. Nakane, *J. Immunol. Methods* **47**, 129 (1981).

[16] D. Y. Mason, M. Naiem, Z. Abdulaziz, J. R. G. Nash, K. C. Gatter, and H. Stein, *in* "Monoclonal Antibodies in Clinical Medicine" (A. J. McMichael and J. W. Fabre, eds.), p. 585. Academic Press, New York, 1982.

[17] F. T. Bosman, *Histochem. J.* **15**, 189 (1983).

[18] V. Bergroth, *Histochemistry* **77**, 177 (1983).

[19] D. Y. Mason, H. Stein, M. Naiem, and Z. Abdulaziz, *J. Cancer Res. Clin. Oncol.* **101**, 13 (1981).

[20] C. A. Clark, E. C. Downs, and F. J. Primus, *J. Histochem. Cytochem.* **30**, 27 (1982).

[21] D. M. Boorsma, *Histochemistry* **80**, 103 (1984).

[22] P. Ordronneau, P. B.-M. Lindstrom, and P. Petrusz, *J. Histochem. Cytochem.* **29**, 1397 (1981).

[23] W. W. Hancock, G. J. Becker, and R. C. Atkins, *Am. J. Clin. Pathol.* **78**, 825 (1982).

[24] W. Y. Naritoku and C. R. Taylor, *J. Histochem. Cytochem.* **30**, 253 (1982).

[25] S. M. Hsu, J. Cossman, and E. S. Jaffe, *Am. J. Clin. Pathol.* **80**, 429 (1983).

[26] G. S. Wood and R. Warnke, *J. Histochem. Cytochem.* **29**, 1196 (1981).

tages are that immunoenzymatic procedures require more steps (and time) than immunofluorescence, and that the number of antigenic sites may be reduced or even destroyed, chiefly during the fixation–embedding procedure. However, frozen sections, cytocentrifuged cells, cell smears or imprints, and cells growing on coverslips or chamber slides (all of them usually subjected to mild fixation) are well suited for enzyme cytochemistry.

Another indirect method uses colloidal gold coupled to the second antibody or to protein A, for the detection of antigens at light and electron microscopic levels.[27]

Immunofluorescence is a relatively simple, rapid, and easy alternative immunohistochemical procedure. It is best suited for the study of membrane antigens in addition to intra- and extracellular antigens, and may be applied to cells in suspension, to cells attached to glass slides or coverslips, and to frozen tissue sections. This method may be applied using the fluorescence-activated cell sorter for analysis of cell populations[28] and the simultaneous detection of two different antigens (for instance one with FITC, another with rhodamine-conjugated antibodies). The double-layer indirect method is also widely used, with variations using biotinylated antibody and fluoresceinated avidin.[29] Disadvantages of using the immunofluorescence technique are the necessity to take micrographs as soon as possible (due to loss of fluorescence intensity), the poor visualization of morphology since simultaneous traditional counterstaining is not possible, and the necessity for a fluorescence microscope.

Characteristics of the Study

The selection of the immunohistochemical procedure obviously depends on whether the intention is to monitor the production of new MAbs, as for screening new hybridomas, or if it is performed to study structural details of an antigen using a well-characterized MAb. It would also depend on the location of the antigen (cell surface, intracellular, or extracellular), and the characteristics of the immunogen (whether well-defined or unknown molecule). The available and required laboratory facilities should also be considered when planning the strategy for the study of MAbs by immunohistochemistry.

---

[27] M. De Waele, J. De Mey, M. Moeremans, M. De Brabander, and B. Van Camp, *in* "Techniques in Immunocytochemistry" (G. R. Bullock and P. Petrusz, eds.), Vol. 2, p. 1. Academic Press, New York, 1983.

[28] S. E. Zweig and E. M. Shevach, this series, Vol. 92, p. 67.

[29] J. W. Berman and R. S. Bach, *J. Immunol. Methods* **36,** 335 (1980).

The first application for using immunohistochemical methods appears in the screening of MAbs. The method(s) selected should be rapid, simple, and reproducible, allowing for testing several hybridoma supernatants simultaneously. A method that fulfills these screening requirements has been reported,[30] using an immunoperoxidase technique for labeling multiple cryostat tissue sections mounted in multitest slides. This immunohistochemical method may be used as the first screening assay[31] if the laboratory has the necessary facilities. However, most of the time the immunohistological screening has been combined with other screening methods such as the solid-phase RIA and the ELISA. The reason is that these methods allow the testing of more samples and the detection of soluble antigens. It is important to remember that by using immunohistochemistry, we can detect only antigens insolubilized on cells or tissues. Therefore, immunohistochemistry may be incorporated into the screening of MAbs in conjunction with other available methods. Figure 2 shows a diagram of the different steps at which the various screening procedures may be incorporated.

In the first and second screenings, the immunogen may be present as soluble proteins, as components of viruses, protozoan parasites, membrane fragments, or even whole cells. The MAbs that successfully pass the second screening are then analyzed by immunohistochemistry. In this manner, the number of supernatants to be tested is reduced from possibly several hundred to more manageable numbers, e.g., 30 or less. In addition, if we rely only on immunohistochemistry, we might discard MAbs against soluble antigens that can be of value in other studies, for instance, detection of tumor-associated antigen(s) in blood by RIA. Therefore, the specificity of those MAbs giving positive results by RIA or ELISA but negative results using immunohistochemistry should be further studied by the former assays. It is not possible to predict if a MAb performing well in immunochemical assays will also perform well when used in immunohistochemistry.[8] On the other hand, if the purpose of the study is to characterize MAbs useful in detecting the antigen by immunohistochemistry, this technique should be applied from the beginning of the screening.[32] In this case it might even be better to use fixed cells as immunogen[7] to obtain MAbs reacting with fixed tissues.

[30] M. Naiem, J. Gerdes, Z. Abdulaziz, C. A. Sunderland, M. J. Allington, H. Stein, and D. Y. Mason, *J. Immunol. Methods* **50,** 145 (1982).
[31] L. De Leij, S. Poppema, J. Klein Nulend, J. G. Ter Harr, E. Schwander, and T. H. The, *Eur. J. Cancer Clin. Oncol.* **20,** 123 (1984).
[32] D. Y. Mason, J. L. Cordell, and K. A. F. Pulford, *in* "Techniques in Immunocytochemistry" (G. R. Bullock and P. Petrusz, eds.), Vol. 2, p. 175. Academic Press, New York, 1983.

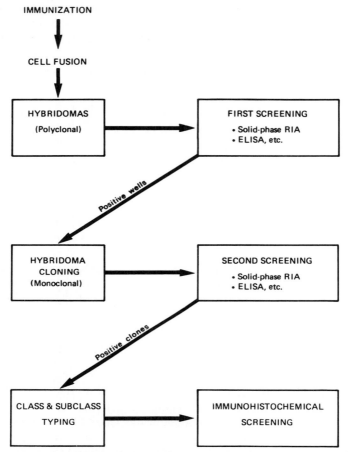

FIG. 2. Schematic representation of the strategy used for monitoring specific MAb production, incorporating immunohistochemistry in the later stages of MAb screening.

Selection of Samples for Testing

Logically, the first information to be obtained is whether or not the MAb reacts by immunohistochemistry with the cells or tissues that contain the antigen used for immunization. It is convenient and profitable to test simultaneously another unrelated cell or tissue(s) to obtain information on the specificity of the MAb. The selection of these other cells or tissues depends on the use for which the MAb has been generated. If it was raised for diagnosis, for instance to detect tumor-associated antigens,

it is useful to include the normal tissue from which the tumor cells originated. Those MAbs recognizing epitopes present on normal tissues can be
eliminated at an early stage of screening. If the MAb was raised for tumor
localization *in vivo,* organs such as liver and kidney that are involved in
metabolism should also be tested. To avoid the use of several slides, there
are tissue culture chamber slides (for cells) and multitest slides (for tissues) that can be used. An alternative is to mount on a single glass slide
several small pieces of different tissues that were embedded together in
the same paraffin block, or in the same block used for frozen sections. It
may also be useful to grow in nude mice the tumor cells containing the
antigen under study.[33] In this case unrelated mouse tissues may be simultaneously tested for MAb specificity and the effect studied of MAb dilution on the immunohistochemistry of the specimens.[5] In this way, the
same slide contains the positive control (tumor cells) and the negative
control (mouse tissues).

Preparation of the Samples for Immunohistochemistry

In one way or another, the cells or tissues will always be exposed to
different treatments that affect the antigen. At present there is no ideal
and unique treatment giving excellent structural and antigenic preservation. It is not recommended to use unfixed cells or tissues for immunohistochemistry since nonspecific staining can occur.[13] In addition, if living
cells in suspension are used, only the membrane antigens are exposed to
the antibody and when reacting with the surface antigen, several events
such as endocytosis, redistribution, and dissociation may occur.[34] Therefore, the samples should be treated with a graded degree of fixation to
determine the optimal conditions for the particular antigen under study.
We recommend some combination of immunohistochemical procedures
that offers a system capable of varying the degrees of preservation of the
antigen (Table I).

At the beginning of the screening, we prefer to use whole cells because
they expose more antigens than cross sections of cells, but this approach
depends on the availability of necessary laboratory equipment. Those
MAbs that bound to whole cells are then studied using frozen sections.
With this procedure more information regarding antigen localization and
MAb specificity can be obtained. The last step is to use paraffin sections.

---

[33] D. R. Ciocca, D. J. Adams, R. J. Bjercke, D. P. Edwards, and W. L. McGuire, *Cancer Res.* **42,** 4256 (1982).
[34] P. Biberfeld, G. Biberfeld, Z. Molnar, and A. Fagraeus, *J. Immunol. Methods* **4,** 135 (1974).

TABLE I
SCREENING OF MABS USING IMMUNOHISTOCHEMICAL PROCEDURES

Antigen localization	Step[a]	Immunohistochemical method	Cells or tissues
Surface	First	Indirect immunofluorescence	Cells in suspension or growing on chamber slides
	Second	Indirect immunofluorescence or immunoperoxidase	Frozen sections
	Third	Indirect immunoperoxidase	Paraffin sections
Intra- or extracellular	First	Indirect immunofluorescence or immunoperoxidase	Cytocentrifuged cells or frozen sections
	Second	Indirect immunoperoxidase	Paraffin sections

[a] Those MAbs staining positively in the first step can then be subsequently studied with the following steps.

It is preferred to detect MAbs reacting with paraffin sections because retrospective studies can be carried out and the cellular compartments can be revealed in more detail. Using this screening system (with different fixation procedures), we were able to detect MAbs reacting only to whole cells and frozen sections but not in paraffin sections. These antibodies were further studied using the former methods. A similar result has been obtained by other investigators, confirming that many antigens may be lost during paraffin embedding.[24,35]

Cell Samples

Single-Cell Suspensions. The cells growing in culture are harvested, resuspended (1×10^5 cells/0.2 ml of DPBS, pH 7.2, 300 mOsm), and placed in 1.5-ml micro test tubes for immunostaining. Single-cell suspensions containing neoplastic cells from pleural effusions, ascites, and solid tumors can also be used.[36] In this case tumor cells are concentrated using Ficoll-Paque (Pharmacia, NJ) gradient sedimentation.[37] The different cell types present in peripheral blood can also be isolated and concentrated by a discontinuous density gradient[38] and by counterflow centrifugation elutriation.[39] Cell samples with a viability higher than 95% (determined by

[35] P. J. Finan, R. M. Grant, C. de Mattos, F. Takei, P. J. Berry, E. S. Lennox, and N. M. Bleehen, *Br. J. Cancer* **46**, 9 (1982).

[36] D. D. von Hoff, J. Casper, E. Bradley, J. Sandbach, D. Jones, and R. Makuck, *Am. J. Med.* **70**, 1027 (1981).

[37] R. Minami, S. Yokota, and R. L. Teplitz, *Acta Cytol.* **22**, 584 (1978).

[38] A. J. Ulmer and H. D. Flad, *J. Immunol. Methods* **30**, 1 (1979).

[39] C. G. Figdor, W. S. Bont, I. Touw, J. de Roos, E. E. Roosnek, and J. E. de Vries, *Blood* **60**, 46 (1982).

trypan blue dye exclusion) are placed in the micro test tubes for immunostaining. These cells are processed for membrane immunofluorescence, although they may also be used for intracellular immunostaining, if the cell membrane is rendered permeable by adequate fixation.

Cells Growing on Chamber Slides or Coverslips. A suspension of 2×10^5 cells/0.2 ml of the corresponding culture medium is deposited in each of the eight wells of tissue culture chamber slides (Lab-Tek Prod., Miles Laboratories, Naperville, IL) and incubated for 2 days at 37°. After washing with DPBS the slides are ready for immunostaining. Several sterile coverslips can also be placed on petri dishes, and then covered and incubated with the cells. These cells may also be processed for membrane or intracellular immunostaining.

Single-cell suspensions or cells growing on chamber slides or coverslips may be incubated with the MAb (for membrane antigen detection) before fixation (at 4° to avoid capping) or they may be fixed and stored until immunostaining.[40]

Other Methods. Other methods to prepare whole cells for immunostaining use imprints and smears made in a conventional manner, and cytocentrifugation. For cytocentrifugation, the cells are resuspended in DPBS with 1% (w/v) BSA at a concentration of 5×10^6 cells/ml. Thirty microliters of cells is deposited on each slide and cytocentrifuged (500 rpm for 5 min). In both cases before immunostaining, air-dried slides are placed in the appropriate fixative for cell surface or intracellular antigen detection. The complete procedure (slide preparation, fixation, and immunostaining) may usually be performed the same day, but some investigators using imprints have stored the air-dried slides unfixed, wrapped in aluminum foil, or in sealed plastic carrier, at $-20°$ or $-70°$.[41,42]

Tissue Samples

Frozen Sections. Small pieces of fresh samples should be placed in airtight containers (labeled appropriately) with a snap cap to avoid desiccation. The container is then quickly frozen in liquid nitrogen or acetone–dry ice and stored in a freezer until required. If the tissue requires long-term storage (more than 1 month), it can be placed in a buffer (PBS containing 7% gelatin, or 5% sucrose and 0.1% sodium azide) for 12 hr before freezing, or frozen in isopentane; or it may be first fixed, washed with the above buffer, and then frozen until used. For sectioning, the

[40] W. van Ewijk, P. L. van Soest, A. Verkerk, and J. F. Jongkind, *Histochem. J.* **16,** 179 (1984).

[41] P. M. Banks, B. L. Caron, and T. W. Morgan, *Am. J. Clin. Pathol.* **79,** 438 (1983).

[42] A. K. Ghosh, A. I. Spriggs, J. Taylor-Papadimitriou, and D. Y. Mason, *J. Clin. Pathol.* **36,** 1154 (1983).

samples are embedded using mounting medium for frozen sections and cut at 6- to 8-μm thickness in a cryostat. The sections are picked up on albumin- or gelatin-coated slides at room temperature and air-dried inside the same cryostat for 15–20 min. Following fixation, the slides are immunostained. For large-scale screenings, it has been recommended to place the sections on multiwell slides and store them unfixed at $-20°$, either in or out of a vacuum chamber.[30,35,43]

Paraffin Sections. After fixation, the sample(s) is embedded in paraffin in a conventional manner. Avoid overexposure of the samples to the fixatives, to alcohols, to xylene, and to elevated temperatures during the fixation–embedding procedure in order to preserve immunoreactivity. Usually, 5- to 7-μm sections are mounted on albumin-coated slides and placed in an oven at 37° for 48 hr before immunostaining (this prevents tissue detachment). For retrospective studies, we have used paraffin-embedded blocks up to 5 years old without problems. However, it has been reported that blocks older than 10 years did not show tissue isoantigens when studied by MAbs.[44]

Fixation

The nature of the fixative can greatly influence immunoreactivity of cells and tissues studied by MAbs.[8,23,40] Table II[45-47] shows some fixation protocols commonly used.

The choice of the appropriate fixative is easier when the researcher has previous information on the immunohistological preservation of the antigen, or class of antigen, under study. But when the MAbs are generated against a new antigen, it is recommended to test several fixatives. A certain fixative may be advantageous for the study of certain antigens but not for others,[23,43] whereas special fixatives may be more appropriate for the study of a particular antigen.[48] Several other factors influence immunoreactivity of samples: dehydration, temperature, pH, and embedding. Therefore, more important than the selection of the fixative itself is the selection of the complete cell and tissue processing technique (Table I).

[43] M. A. Judd and K. J. M. Britten, *Histochem. J.* **14**, 747 (1982).
[44] C. M. Chapman, E. P. Allhoff, K. H. Proppe, and G. R. Prout, Jr., *J. Histochem. Cytochem.* **31**, 557 (1983).
[45] M. Tanaka, H. Tanaka, and E. Ishikawa, *J. Histochem. Cytochem.* **32**, 452 (1984).
[46] D. M. Knowles, R. J. Winchester, and H. G. Kunkel, *Clin. Immunol. Immunopathol.* **7**, 410 (1977).
[47] I. W. McLean and P. K. Nakane, *J. Histochem. Cytochem.* **22**, 1077 (1974).
[48] E. van Pelt-Verkuil and J. J. Emeis, *Histochemistry* **71**, 187 (1981).

TABLE II

FIXATIVES USED IN IMMUNOHISTOCHEMICAL PROCEDURES

Fixative	Preparation	Procedure[a]	Characteristics
1. Glutaraldehyde[27,40]	0.05–0.1% (v/v) in 0.1 M phosphate or cacodylate buffer, pH 7.5	The cell samples are placed in contact with the fixative for 30 min at room temperature. Frozen sections can also be used	Suitable for cell surface antigens using immunofluorescence, immunoenzymatic, or immunogold methods. Also useful for immunoelectron microscopy
2. Paraformaldehyde[23,34,40]	0.5–4% (v/v) in 0.1 M phosphate or cacodylate buffer, pH 7.5	Same as 1. Fixatives 1 and 2 may be combined	Same as 1
3. Acetone[18,30,41,43]; ethanol and methanol[18,23]	Absolute	The cell samples and frozen sections are placed in contact with the cold fixative (4°) for 5–20 min. Acetone can also be used to prepare paraffin-embedded tissue[45]	For cell surface, intra- and extracellular antigens using immunofluorescence and immunoenzymatic methods
4. Acetic acid–ethanol[46]	5% (v/v) glacial acetic acid in absolute ethanol	The slides with the air-dried cell samples are immersed in the fixative for 15 min at room temperature	For intracellular antigens using immunofluorescence and immunoperoxidase methods
5. Periodate–lysine–paraformaldehyde[23]	As described by McLean and Nakane[47]	Cells in suspension and frozen sections are placed in contact with the fixative at least 15 min at room temperature	For cell surface antigens using immunofluorescence and immunoperoxidase techniques. Also useful for immunoelectron microscopy
6. Formalin; formalin–saline; Bouin's fixative; Zamboni's fixative; etc.	As described by routine histology	The tissue if fixed by immersion or perfusion and processed for paraffin-embedding sections	Best suited for intra- and extracellular antigens using immunoenzymatic methods

[a] When fixatives 1 or 2 are used, unreacted aldehyde groups must be reduced or blocked to avoid nonspecific binding of antibodies. This is done by incubating the cell and tissue samples with 0.05–0.1 M ammonium chloride, or glycine in PBS for 45 min; or with 0.5% sodium borohydride for 10 min; or with 0.1% (w/v) BSA in PBS for 20 min. Also note that the antibodies can reach the intracellular antigens when whole cells are fixed with fixatives 3 or 4, but when other fixatives are used, further membrane permeabilization is required. This is achieved postincubation with extractives: fixative 3 or 0.5–1% (w/v) Triton X-100 in PBS for 20 min.

Immunohistochemical Methods

Immunofluorescence (Indirect Technique)

(1) The cell samples or frozen sections are incubated with 25–50 μl of undiluted supernatant from confluent hybridomas, or with optimally diluted MAb from ascites fluid. This incubation is done at 4° for 3 hr. Depending on the choice of cell preparation, the procedure varies as follows. (a) Single-cell suspensions, which are in micro test tubes, are gently vortexed every hour while they are incubated with the MAb. A microfuge is used to pellet the cells between the different steps. (b) Always use the same corner of the slide to add or remove the different reagents to the cells grown on chamber slides. This should be done carefully to avoid cell detachment. (c) When using cells grown on coverslips, the coverslips may be placed in tissue culture cluster dishes or petri dishes, with enough reagent added to cover the face containing the cells. The coverslips may also be placed cell side down over a drop of the reagent. They can be easily picked up by flotation, adding PBS. Always use the same corner to handle the coverslip and mark the face containing the cells. Incubate in a humidified chamber. (d) The central area of the slides with the cells (imprints, smears, cytocentrifuged cells) or frozen sections are encircled with a diamond pencil. This helps to visualize the area of interest during blotting and minimizes spreading of the reagents. Never allow the area containing the sample to dry. The slides are placed in humidified chambers during the incubation.

(2) Remove the primary antibody (MAb) by washing (twice, 5 min each) in phosphate-buffered saline (PBS): 0.05 M phosphate (monobasic–dibasic), 0.15 M sodium chloride, pH 7.5. If using coverslips and slides these are placed in their appropriate carriers and washed by immersion in staining jars filled with PBS. (3) If the cell samples were unfixed, incubate them with the appropriate fixative (Table II) and repeat step 2. If the cell samples are already fixed, proceed to step 4. (4) Remove (in the case of cells in suspension or grown on chamber slides) or blot (for coverslips or slides) excess PBS from the samples and incubate with the fluorescein-conjugated second (class-specific) antibody. The fluorescent antibody is usually diluted 1 : 50 to 1 : 100 in PBS (or diluted according to the manufacturer's instructions). This incubation is done at room temperature for 30 min to 1 hr in the dark. (a) Remember to resuspend single-cell suspensions immediately after adding the second antibody. (b) Slides are again placed in a humidified chamber. (5) Remove the second antibody by washing four times in PBS (as in step 2).

(6) Remove or blot excess PBS, mount, and seal. The mounting medium contains PBS–glycerol (1 : 9, v/v), pH 9 adjusted with sodium hy-

droxide. Add one drop of the mounting medium to the cell pellet in the micro test tube, resuspend the cells, transfer them to a slide, and add the coverslip. Carefully remove the chamber from the tissue culture chamber slide and blot the excess PBS before mounting. In the case of cells grown on coverslips, place a drop of the mounting medium on a slide and place the coverslip with the cell side down. In all cases, excess mounting medium is removed by carefully blotting before sealing the cover slips with fingernail polish. (7) The sealed slides can immediately be observed and photographed using the fluorescence microscope and/or stored for 2–3 weeks in a slide box, protected from the light, in a cold room.

The immunofluorescence technique can also be carried out using a biotinylated second (class-specific) antibody (step 4). In this case, the samples are washed and incubated with fluoresceinated avidin. This technique is highly sensitive because more fluorochrome is coupled to the egg white protein avidin, which has a high affinity (10^{15} M^{-1}) for the small molecular weight vitamin biotin. This technique can also be amplified by using biotinylated second antibody, followed by fluorescent-conjugated avidin, and finally incubating with a fluoresceinated anti-avidin antibody.[29]

Immunoperoxidase (Indirect Technique)

This technique may be applied to cell samples and tissue sections. Handling of the cell samples and frozen sections during the different steps of the immunoperoxidase technique is identical to the handling in the immunofluorescence procedure (indirect technique) previously described. In addition, we shall discuss the handling of paraffin sections. All the steps are carried out at room temperature. Once the staining has been initiated, do not allow the samples to dry.

(1) After etching the area around the sample with a diamond pencil, deparaffinize the sections in xylene (two changes of 10 min each) and rehydrate through a series of ethanol immersions to water. (2) If necessary, endogenous peroxidase activity can be inhibited by incubating the cell samples and tissue sections with 0.3–0.5% hydrogen peroxide in absolute methanol for 30 min (see step 1b in the PAP and ABC techniques below). (3) Wash in PBS for 20 min. (4) Block nonspecific staining with 3% normal serum in PBS, corresponding to the species from which the second antibody has been derived. Incubate for 20 min. (5) After excess serum from the area around the tissue is blotted with absorbent paper, the samples are incubated with supernatant from confluent hybridomas or with optimally diluted MAb from ascites fluid for 1–3 hr in a humidified chamber. (6) Wash in PBS for 10 min.

(7) After excess PBS is blotted, the samples are incubated with the species-specific peroxidase-conjugated second (class-specific) antibody. This is usually diluted 1 : 50 to 1 : 100 in PBS (or diluted according to the manufacturer's instructions), and incubated for 30 min to 1 hr in a humidified chamber. It is convenient to add 1% normal serum from the same species as the second antibody to the PBS as carrier protein. (8) Wash in PBS for 10 min. (9) The immunoperoxidase staining is developed by incubation of the samples with 70 mg% of 3,3'-diaminobenzidine tetrahydrochloride and 0.05% hydrogen peroxide in 0.05 M Tris buffer (pH 7.2). This solution is prepared immediately before use and handled with the necessary precaution used for carcinogenic material. The solution is filtered and incubated with the sample for 5 min. The time should be maintained constant to compare results among samples. (10) Wash in running water for 5 min. (11) The samples may be counterstained with hematoxylin. Then they are dehydrated through a graded ethanol series, followed by xylene (two changes of 10 min each), and sealed with histological mounting medium and a coverslip. Avoid inhalation of toxic xylene vapors.

Notes: (a) Step 9 arrests the reaction. At this point the samples can be left until the next day if necessary. (b) Hematoxylin counterstain helps to visualize the morphology of the samples, but excess counterstaining is a problem for visualizing contrast in black and white photomicrographs. Good visualization and photomicroscopy is obtained using a microscope with differential interference contrast optics. (c) To reduce background staining, the primary MAb can be preabsorbed with cells or tissues not containing the antigen of interest and corresponding to the species providing the immunogen.[31] (d) The second antibody may be conjugated to alkaline phosphatase instead of peroxidase. In this case, inhibition of endogenous alkaline phosphatase activity and the development of the reaction are performed using other substrate solutions.[21,42,49] In addition, to avoid use of the carcinogenic diaminobenzidine substrate for peroxidase, other substrates have been utilized.[21,50]

PAP and ABC Techniques

These techniques[13,25] can be applied to cell samples (cells growing on chamber slides or coverslips, imprints, smears, and cytocentrifuged cells) and to frozen or paraffin sections. Special instructions for handling each of these samples are described above (see indirect immunofluorescence

[49] B. Falini, I. De Solas, C. Halverson, J. W. Parker, and C. R. Taylor, *J. Histochem. Cytochem.* **30**, 21 (1982).
[50] S. Richer and R. Mir, *J. Histotechnol.* **7**, 8 (1984).

and immunoperoxidase techniques). All the steps are carried out at room temperature. Once the staining is initiated, the area containing the samples must not be allowed to dry.

(1) If necessary, endogenous peroxidase activity can be inhibited by incubating the samples with 0.3–0.5% hydrogen peroxide in absolute methanol for 30 min.[51] (a) Using the ABC technique, it may also be necessary to inhibit endogenous avidin binding activity present in some tissues.[26] This is accomplished by incubating the samples with 0.1–0.01% avidin followed by 0.01–0.001% biotin in PBS for 20 min.[26] The samples are washed in PBS for 5 min before and after each of these incubations. (b) A control sample to detect endogenous peroxidase activity may be run by omitting the primary MAb, and incubating with PBS and the substrate solution (diaminobenzidine) only. Endogenous avidin binding activity may be detected by incubating a control sample with conjugated avidin alone. In this case, preincubation with free avidin should competitively inhibit the staining.[26] To avoid the background which may be inherent with the ABC technique, the biotin–streptavidin system offers an alternative method. (2) Wash in PBS for 20 min. (3) Block nonspecific staining by incubating for 20 min with 3% normal serum in PBS, corresponding to the same species as the second antibody. (4) After blotting excess serum, the samples are incubated with supernatant from confluent hybridomas or with optimally diluted MAb from ascites fluid, for 1–3 hr in a humidified chamber. Longer incubations should be done at 4°. (5) Wash in PBS for 10 min.

(6) After blotting excess PBS, the samples are incubated with the second antibody for 30 min in a humidified chamber. (a) In the PAP technique, this class-specific antibody directed against the MAb is diluted 1 : 20 with PBS. (b) In the ABC technique, this species-specific biotinylated antibody against the primary MAb is diluted 1 : 200 with PBS. At this point it is convenient to prepare the avidin–biotin peroxidase complex (A + B), diluted 1 : 200 in PBS, since it should be mixed 30 min prior to use. (7) Wash in PBS for 10 min. (8) After blotting excess PBS, the samples are incubated with the enzymatic complex for 30 min in a humidified chamber. (a) The PAP complex is diluted 1 : 50 to 1 : 100 in PBS containing 1% normal serum from the same species providing the second antibody. (b) For the ABC method, use the A + B complex. (9) Wash in PBS for 10 min and follow steps 9, 10, and 11 described in the indirect immunoperoxidase technique.

Notes: (a) See notes a, b, and c described in the immunoperoxidase (indirect technique) section. (b) Using the ABC method, nonspecific bind-

[51] J. Burns, *Histochemistry* **43**, 291 (1975).

ing to cells rich in heparin can be prevented by preparing the ABC solution in 0.1 M carbonate buffer at pH 9.4.[52] (c) The PAP method can be amplified by repeated incubations with the second antibody and the PAP complex.[22,53] Recently, similar techniques have used PAP and alkaline phosphatase–anti-alkaline phosphatase (APAAP) complexes with hybridoma antibodies.[54–56] In addition, instead of the PAP and the APAAP complexes, the glucose oxidase–anti-glucose oxidase (GAG) complex may be used.[20] (d) When screening a large number of tissues using a specified MAb, we have immersed whole slides in glass staining jars containing optimally diluted antiserum. This method increases reproducibility and permits the use of long incubation times.[57] (e) It is also possible to detect two different antigenic sites simultaneously using the same sample, by repetition of the incubation cycles with the primary MAb, and second antibody. In this case the development of the enzymatic complex is accomplished with appropriate substrate solutions to obtain different colors.[42,49,50,57]

Controls and Validation of the Results

Frequently, MAbs are generated to define previously uncharacterized antigens. Logically, in this case, the topographic distribution of the antigen is also unknown, and for this reason, caution is recommended during the interpretation and validation of the results. One of the best controls in an immunohistochemical study is incubation of the sample(s) with the MAb preabsorbed with the purified antigen. In this case, a lack of immunostaining should be obtained. If the immunogen used to generate the MAb has well-characterized related antigenic molecules, such heterologous molecules also can be used to absorb the MAb. In this case, it is expected that the immunostaining is not abolished. When an immunoglobulin secreting myeloma cell line is employed in the fusion, supernatant from the myeloma cell culture should also be tested to show a lack of immunostaining. It is also recommended to use samples containing and lacking the antigen of interest. These positive and negative controls will indicate if the technique was performed properly. These and other essen-

[52] G. Bussolati and P. Gugliotta, *J. Histochem. Cytochem.* **31,** 1419 (1983).
[53] P. M. Lansdorp, T. H. van der Kwast, M. De Boer, and W. P. Zeijlemaker. *J. Histochem. Cytochem.* **32,** 172 (1984).
[54] D. Y. Mason, J. L. Cordell, Z. Abdulaziz, M. Naiem, and G. Bordenave, *J. Histochem. Cytochem.* **30,** 1114 (1982).
[55] A. C. Cuello, C. Milstein, B. Wright, S. Bramwell, J. V. Priestley, and J. Jarvis, *Histochemistry* **80,** 257 (1984).
[56] J. L. Cordell, B. Falini, W. N. Erber, A. K. Ghosh, Z. Abdulaziz, S. MacDonald, K. A. F. Pulford, H. Stein, and D. Y. Mason, *J. Histochem. Cytochem.* **32,** 219 (1984).
[57] M. V. Sofroniew and U. Schrell, *J. Histochem. Cytochem.* **30,** 504 (1982).

tial requirements for validation of the results have been evaluated in more detail elsewhere.[6,58]

Final Comments

It is outside of the scope of the present chapter to give detailed descriptions of all of the immunohistochemical procedures currently available. This is a rapidly growing field, with new techniques and improvements appearing frequently. We believe that most of the basic methodologies have been presented here, with special requirements cited in the literature references.

In some cases, subcellular localization of an antigen using a MAb is needed. In these cases, immunoelectron microscopy may be applied. At this level, finding an adequate balance between preservation of the antigen and of the subcellular structures is more difficult than for light microscopy. In general, the handling of the samples and the immunoelectron microscopic techniques are more cumbersome. The PAP technique is useful and can be applied in transmission microscopy before or after embedding of the tissue.[13] In our hands it has showed some limitations, also described by other authors, mainly due to poor visualization of the underlying ultrastructure. Another technique utilizes latex microspheres or erythrocytes coated with the second antibody.[59] With this technique, membrane antigens can be analyzed at light and electron microscopic levels and the cellular compartments can be well visualized by traditional staining. Internally radiolabeled MAbs are also useful to detect an antigen by light and electron microscopy.[11] This radioimmunocytochemical technique also allows good ultrastructure visualization and may be used for quantitative studies of cell surface and intracellular antigens. We have used and can recommend the colloidal gold method. It has similar advantages to the two approaches we previously mentioned; the colloidal gold is a marker for light, transmission, scanning, and freeze-etch electron microscopy.[60] The gold particles may be coupled to the MAb, to a second antibody, to avidin, or to protein A. There is increasing commercial availability of these reagents.

Acknowledgment

The authors wish to thank Dr. William L. McGuire for introducing us to hybridoma technology.

[58] G. V. Childs, *J. Histochem. Cytochem.* **31**, 168 (1983).
[59] J. Bernard, T. Ternynck, and D. Zagury, *Immunol. Lett.* **4**, 65 (1982).
[60] J. Roth, *in* "Techniques in Immunocytochemistry" (G. R. Bullock and P. Petrusz, eds.), Vol. 2, p. 217. Academic Press, New York, 1983.

[55] Method for Rapid Detection of Membrane Antigens by Immunofluorescence and Its Application to Screening Monoclonal Antibodies

By CLAUDE BOUCHEIX, PATRICIA KRIEF, JEAN-YVES PERROT, MASSOUD MIRSHAHI, and CLAUDE ROSENFELD

Immunofluorescence is widely used for the study of cell surface antigens. Compared with radioimmunoassay[1] or enzyme-linked immunosorbent assay it allows study at the single-cell level. Its use on a large scale has been hampered by the fact that it is difficult to carry out quantitative studies and a large number of tests. Centrifugation and resuspension of cells are time-consuming parts of such an assay.

In this chapter we describe a simple and rapid method of membrane immunofluorescence on living cells which allows a large number of tests to be performed, and its application for screening hybridomas.[2] Based on the results of the screening of several hybridizations for the production of monoclonal antibodies against cell-surface antigens, a strategy is proposed to optimize the yield of hybridomas of interest.

Materials and Methods

Cell Lines. REH is a human leukemic cell line derived from a common acute lymphoblastic leukemia.[3] LHN 13 is a B cell lymphoblastoid cell line induced by Epstein–Barr virus.[4] PEER is a T cell acute lymphoblastic leukemia-derived cell line kindly provided by N. Goldblum.[5]

Hybridoma Production. Mice were immunized with 2×10^7 cells at day 1 in 0.3 ml 0.15 M NaCl with an equal volume of complete Freund's adjuvant, one-third intraperitoneally and two-thirds subcutaneously. Intravenous booster injections (10^7 cells) were given on days 8 and 30, 4 days before hybridization. Three $\times 10^7$ spleen cells were fused with 5 $\times$

---

[1] J. W. Stocker and C. H. Heusser, *J. Immunol. Methods* **26**, 87 (1979).

[2] C. Boucheix, J. Y. Perrot, M. Mirshahi, A. Bernadou, and C. Rosenfeld, *J. Immunol. Methods* **57**, 145 (1983).

[3] C. Rosenfeld, A. Goutner, C. Choquet, A. M. Venuat, B. Kayibanda, J. L. Pico, and M. F. Greaves, *Nature (London)* **267**, 841 (1977).

[4] C. Rosenfeld, J. F. Doré, C. Choquet, A. M. Venuat, F. Ajuria, L. Markholev, and J. P. Wastiaux, *Transplantation* **16**, 276 (1973).

[5] S. Ravid, N. Goldblum, R. Zaizov, M. Schlesinger, T. Kertes, J. Minowada, W. Verbi, and M. Greaves, *Int. J. Cancer* **25**, 705 (1980).

10^7 NS1 myeloma cells according to the method of Köhler and Milstein[6] modified by Fazekas de St. Groth and Scheidegger,[7] and distributed in five culture microplates (Linbro). Ten to 14 days later, supernatants were transferred to test microplates to be tested (Fig. 2). Four hybridizations were performed. In two, the non-T, non-B leukemia cell line REH was used as immunogen, and in two the fresh leukemic cells of a patient with a non-T, non-B acute lymphoblastic leukemia were used. The two types of cells have similar phenotypes but the expressions of the leukocyte differentiation antigen CD10 (CALLA)[8,9] and HLA-DR[10] antigens are different. HLA-DR is strongly expressed in REH whereas CD10 has a weaker expression (C. Boucheix and J.-Y. Perrot, unpublished observation). The reverse was the case for the leukemic cells of the patient.

Preparation of Cells for Tests. Cells separated and washed from peripheral blood or washed cells from continuous cell cultures are adjusted to a concentration of 7.5×10^6/ml in Hanks' medium (Institut Pasteur) and distributed with a multichannel pipet (Dynatech) in round-bottomed microplates (Cooke microtiter system). A 200-μl aliquot of the suspension $(1.5 \times 10^5$ cells) is pipetted into each cup. The microplate is centrifuged for 5 min at 200 g. Supernatants are removed according to the sequence shown in Fig. 1, which takes less than 1 min per plate. This method allows removal of nearly all the washing medium without aspiration of the cells.

Incubation and Washing of the Cells. Microplates are covered and vigorously rubbed against a rough surface to resuspend the cells just before adding the supernatants. Supernatant (20 μl) from each well of the stock microplates is transferred with a multichannel pipet to the corresponding wells of the test microplates. After 30 min incubation at 4° in a humidified chamber, 200 μl Hanks' medium is added to each well before centrifugation of the microplates. Several washings are performed with the same method before incubation with the fluorescent anti-mouse Ig antibody (30 min, 4°, humidified chamber). The microplates are washed again and the supernatant is removed to leave about 20 μl. The cells are resuspended as previously and 1–2 μl of each suspension is transferred to individual chambers of Cooke microtiter slides. Sixteen samples are ex-

[6] G. Köhler and C. Milstein, *Nature (London)* **256,** 495 (1975).
[7] S. Fazekas de St. Groth and D. Scheidegger, *J. Immunol. Methods* **35,** 1 (1980).
[8] M. F. Greaves, G. Brown, N. T. Rapson, and T. A. Lister, *Clin. Immunol. Immunopathol.* **4,** 67 (1975).
[9] IUIS-WHO Nomenclature Subcommittee. Committee on Human Leukocyte Differentiation Antigens, *Immunol. Today* **5,** 158 (1984).
[10] G. Janossy, A. M. Goldstone, D. Cappellaro, M. F. Greaves, J. Kulenkampf, M. Pippard, and K. Welch, *Br. J. Haematol.* **37,** 391 (1977).

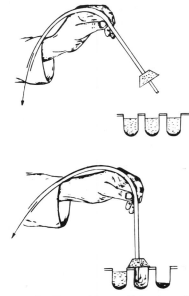

FIG. 1. Procedure for removing the washing medium. A capillary tube or Pasteur pipette is inserted into a rubber plug which maintains it in the correct position. The pipette is connected to a vacuum and plunged successively along the wall of the wells after centrifugation of the microplates. The pipette enters the well to only two-thirds of its depth, but the surface tension of the fluid during aspiration is sufficient to remove nearly all the supernatant without removing the cells. (From Boucheix *et al.*,[2] with permission from Elsevier/North-Holland Biomedical Press.)

amined on each slide using a phase-contrast microscope equipped with epifluorescence (Fig. 2).

Results

Immunofluorescence Technique

Washing. The maximum number of washings required after each incubation was three. Controls with NS1 supernatants were consistently negative.

Loss of cells. Initially, the cell concentration was evaluated with an inverted microscope. At the concentration used in these tests, REH cells form a confluent layer after centrifugation which was unchanged at the end of the experiment. Cell count controls have shown that less than 15% of the cells were lost after seven washings and two incubations.

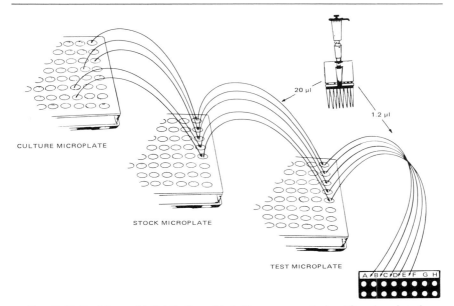

20 µl

1.2 µl

CULTURE MICROPLATE

STOCK MICROPLATE

TEST MICROPLATE

A B C D E F G H

FIG. 2. Method for rapid distribution of hybridoma supernatants. After choosing clones from the culture plates, supernatants are transferred to stock microplates in a sequential order maintained throughout the test. This allows the use of a multichannel pipette for all subsequent manipulations, i.e., incubations, washings, and transfer from stock microplates to test microplates and from the latter to microtiter slides. (From Boucheix *et al.*,[2] with permission from Elsevier/North-Holland Biomedical Press.)

Viability. With the cell lines used in this study, the viability was moderately decreased (10–15%) during the experiment.

Cross-contamination of samples. This may occur at two stages. The first is when the microplate is shaken to resuspend the cells. This can be prevented by covering the microplate with moist blotting paper inside the cover. Secondly, diffusion of cells between two chambers was sometimes observed when freshly washed Cooke microtiter slides were used. This can be prevented by reducing the volume of the sample placed in each compartment and leaving the slides to dry for 24 hr (confirmed by flow cytometry).

Reproducibility. This has been checked many times. If the same reagents were added to several wells, identical labeling was observed in all.

Volume. The volume of reagents may be reduced to about a quarter of that used in 5-ml tubes.

Cell fixation. If the test cannot be read immediately, cells may be fixed after centrifugation and removal of the supernatants by adding 200 µl of

TABLE I
RESULTS OF INITIAL SCREENING OF TWO HYBRIDIZATIONS FOR PRODUCTION OF
MONOCLONAL ANTIBODIES AGAINST REH

	Various patterns of reactivity				
REH (cALL)	+	+	+	+	−
LHN 13 (B cell line)	+	+	−	−	NT
PEER (T-ALL)	−	+	+	−	NT
Number of wells	88	46	5	4	394
(% of the total)	(16.4)	(8.6)	(0.9)	(0.7)	(73.4)

Total   143 (26.6%) ⟶ 537

PBS (Institut Merieux, Lyon, France) containing 1% formaldehyde. At 4°
the microplates can be kept for at least 1 week.

Results of Two Screening Experiments

Table I shows results of the screening of hybridizations performed
with BALB/c lymphocytes immunized against the non-T, non-B ALL cell
line REH. It can be seen that 26.6% of the wells in which cell growth was
observed contained antibodies against REH detectable by immunofluorescence; 16.4% of the positive supernatants were reactive against
REH and LHN 13 (B cell line) and not the T cell line, some of them
reacting very strongly and producing agglutination; 8.6% also reacted
with the T cell lines; 0.74% reacted only with REH. Table II shows results
with hybridomas produced against non-B, non-T fresh ALL cells. The
screening was performed with REH and LHN 13. Of the positive supernatants, 7% contained antibodies reactive against REH only and 18.9% were
also reactive against LHN 13. Several of the cell lines secreting antibodies
reactive against REH only have been cloned and a panel of antibodies
obtained which among leukemias recognize either specifically cALL,
cALL and CLL, or cALL, CLL, and some AML.[11]

Comments

The technique described has many advantages over conventional
techniques of immunofluorescence. It allows a large number of tests to be

[11] C. Boucheix, J. Y. Perrot, M. Mirshahi, F. Giannoni, M. Billard, R. Bernadou, and C.
Rosenfeld, *Leuk. Res.* **9,** 597 (1985).

TABLE II
RESULTS OF INITIAL SCREENING OF TWO
HYBRIDIZATIONS FOR PRODUCTION OF MONOCLONAL
ANTIBODIES AGAINST FRESH COMMON ACUTE
LYMPHOBLASTIC LEUKEMIA CELLS

	Various patterns of reactivity		
REH (cALL)	+	+	−
LHN 13 (B cell line)	+	−	NT
Number of wells	72	38	428
(% of the total)	(18.9)	(7)	(79.5)
Total	110 (20.4%) ⟶		538

performed (about 400 per day), and is economical for cells and reagents. If necessary, the samples may be analyzed by cytofluorography. Two points of importance remain to be discussed. First, a comparison with other methods of screening monoclonal antibodies against cell-surface antigens has been carried out in our laboratory and the results are discussed below. Second, a strategy of hybridoma production is proposed based on the results of screening by immunofluorescence.

Comparison of Immunofluorescence with Other Methods

A comparison between membrane immunofluorescence, ELISA on glutaraldehyde-fixed cells, and complement-mediated cytotoxicity was carried out (data not shown). The methodology of ELISA on fixed cells is greatly impaired by the frequent occurrence of hybridomas secreting antibodies displaying "natural antibody" properties, which are strongly reactive with intracellular antigens made accessible by the fixation procedure. This constitutes an artifact for the detection of membrane antigens. On the other hand, the low frequency of cytotoxic antibodies (between 10 and 20% in our experience) leaves membrane immunofluorescence as the best of the three methods for screening hybridoma antibodies against membrane antigens.[12] In addition, immunofluorescence permits the study of antibody binding at the single cell level; this shows the type of labeling and the approximate percentage of positive cells. Artifactual labeling

[12] J. Y. Perrot et al., in preparation.

linked to the presence of dead cells is easily recognized. No manipulation of dangerous substances is necessary. If the microscope is equipped with good phase contrast, the nature of the cells can easily be recognized by a trained observer (e.g., red blood cells, lymphocytes, blast leukemic cells, polymorphonuclear cells, and monocytes in the peripheral blood). Mixtures of cells may even be made for screening experiments (e.g., lymphoblastoid cells with peripheral blood lymphocytes, for which the diameter ratio is about 2). Quantification is of course subjective, unless the samples are analyzed by flow cytometry.

Choice of the Number of Clones per Well Based on the Expected Yield of Specific and Nonspecific Hybridomas

The mean number of clones per well is a function of the hybridization ratio and of the number of wells in which the hybridization product is distributed; the yield varies with the myeloma cell line. In fact the probability of having 2 hybridoma clones/well against the same immunogen decreases with the reduction of the clone number per well. It is of obvious importance that the first screening should be highly selective in order to discard all clones which do not correspond to the aim of the immunization, thus further reducing the number of cell cultures. It is also necessary to screen a high number of clones, since the clones of interest may occur at a very low frequency (sometimes below 1/1000). Therefore a compromise based on the expected yield of the hybridization procedure has to be found between these two constraints. In an efficient immunization protocol, approximately 15% of the hybridomas secrete antibodies against the immunogen. Figure 3 shows the respective probabilities of obtaining 1, 2, 3, or 0 clones secreting antibodies against the immunogen in the case of a 3 clones/well distribution basis. This shows that 32.5% of the wells will contain 1 specific clone, 5.7% will contain 2 specific clones, and 0.3% will contain 3 specific clones. It has to be noted that even if the wells containing more than 1 specific clone constitute a hindrance to the preliminary screening, this procedure allows a high number of clones to be screened (about 3000 if the hybridization product is distributed in 1000 wells), thus increasing the probability of detecting specific clones arising at low frequency. Another advantage of having clones growing in each well is the possibility of using devices removing the supernatants of a complete microplate simultaneously such as a replicaplater (Dynatech). On the other hand in the case of a 1 clone/3 wells distribution, the probability of obtaining more than 1 specific clone/well is extremely low, but only a low number of clones will be screened (about 300 for 1000 wells with about 50 specific for the immunogen).

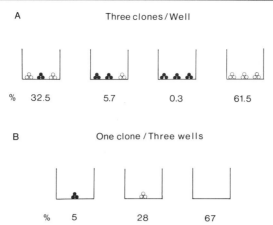

A   Three clones/Well

%   32.5   5.7   0.3   61.5

B   One clone / Three wells

%   5   28   67

Fig. 3. Two types of hybridoma distribution in microplates. Frequency of each clone combination: (A) corresponds to a 3 clones/well distribution and (B) to 1 clone/3 wells distribution. Closed circles represent a hybridoma clone specific for the immunogen and open circles represent a hybridoma clone which does not secrete antibodies against the immunogen. As discussed in the text these percentages are calculated on the basis of a yield of 15% specific clones.

In conclusion this study shows that with appropriate devices and a carefully designed strategy of hybridization which optimizes the method, membrane immunofluorescence may be a very potent tool for screening monoclonal antibodies.

[56] Purification of Mouse Monoclonal Antibodies from Ascitic Fluid by DEAE Affi-Gel Blue Chromatography

By Claudine Bruck, Jeffrey A. Drebin, Corinne Glineur, and Daniel Portetelle

The cell fusion technique of Köhler and Milstein has allowed the isolation of hybridoma cell lines which secrete monoclonal antibodies of any desired specificity. Injection of hybridoma cells into the mouse peritoneal cavity is commonly performed in order to achieve the production of large quantities of these monoclonal antibodies. Ten to 100 mg of monoclonal antibody is routinely obtained from the ascites fluid produced in a single mouse. However, monoclonal antibodies usually represent only 10% of the total protein content of the ascites fluid. The widespread use of the hybridoma technique has underlined the need for a simple and efficient method of purifying antibodies from hybridoma ascites fluid.

Affinity chromatography on protein A–Sepharose has been used widely and is suitable for the rapid purification of most monoclonal antibodies of the IgG$_{2a}$ subclass.[1,2] This chapter describes a rapid purification method which is applicable to all IgG subclasses. The DEAE Affi-Gel Blue chromatographic method described here (and previously[3]) combines ion-exchange chromatography and affinity chromatography. DEAE Affi-Gel Blue is beaded, cross-linked agarose bearing covalently linked diethylaminoethyl (DEAE) groups and the dye Cibacron Blue F3GA. The DEAE groups bind negatively charged proteins while the Cibacron Blue dye displays differential affinity for a number of proteins present in sera and ascitic fluids.

DEAE Affi-Gel Blue chromatography, in addition to being suitable for the purification of monoclonal antibodies of all IgG subclasses, offers other advantages over protein A–Sepharose chromatography: (1) elution of immunoglobulin from DEAE Affi-Gel Blue does not involve low pH or other potentially denaturing conditions and is thus suitable for the isolation of monoclonal antibodies which are sensitive to these conditions; (2) it completely removes contaminating proteases, yielding a very stable immunoglobulin preparation; (3) its cost is significantly less than protein A–Sepharose.

Materials and Methods

Treatment of Ascitic Fluids. The antibody containing ascitic fluid is centrifuged at 1000 g for 5 min to remove cells and then cleared at 100,000 g for 30 min to remove cell debris and fibrin clots. The fluid is dialyzed overnight against 100 volumes of column buffer at 4°. Column buffer is 20 mM Tris ("pH 7.2") and 25 mM NaCl for a stepwise antibody elution ("pH 7.2" is placed in quotation marks since the pH is different from 7.2 at 4°; the buffer is prepared from a 1 M Tris solution which has been adjusted to 7.2 at room temperature). For a gradient antibody elution, the dialysis buffer can contain 0 or 20 mM NaCl. A concentration of 20 mM NaCl is generally preferred, since some monoclonal antibodies precipitate in low salt. A fibrin precipitate, often observed after dialysis, is removed by centrifugation at 10,000 g for 15 min prior to the application of the dialyzed ascites to the DEAE Affi-Gel Blue column.

[1] J. W. Goding, *J. Immunol. Methods* **39,** 285 (1980).
[2] P. L. Ey, S. J. Prowse, and C. R. Jenkin, *Immunochemistry* **15,** 429 (1978).
[3] C. Bruck, D. Portetelle, C. Glineur, and A. Bollen, *J. Immunol. Methods* **53,** 313 (1982).

Conditioning of the DEAE Affi-Gel Blue Column. DEAE Affi-Gel Blue beads are provided in a hydrated form (Bio-Rad 153-7307). A ratio of 7 ml of packed beads to 1 ml of ascitic fluid has been used. This ratio can be decreased to 1 : 1 when the ascitic fluid is prepurified by an ammonium sulfate precipitation step. This is useful when antibody is purified from large amounts of ascitic fluid. The dimensions of the column are not critical. New batches of DEAE Affi-Gel Blue are prewashed with 3 bed volumes of a 0.5 M NaCl solution to elute any Cibacron Blue which is not tightly bound to the beads. The column is then equilibrated in low salt by washing with 5 bed volumes of column buffer (see "Treatment of Ascitic Fluids"). All steps are performed at 4°. This precaution is necessary to avoid monoclonal antibody cleavage by proteases which may be found in ascitic fluids. (Some ascitic fluids contain a very high level of proteases; others are virtually devoid of any protease activity.) After use, the column can be easily regenerated by washing with 3 bed volumes of 6 M guanidine hydrochloride solution followed by 10 bed volumes of 0.5 M NaCl and 5 bed volumes of column buffer.

DEAE Affi-Gel Blue Chromatography. The dialyzed ascitic fluid is applied to a preconditioned DEAE Affi-Gel Blue column. The flow rate is adjusted to 30–40 ml/hr and the fraction size is 1–2 ml. A gradient elution scheme is chosen when a purity higher than 95% is required. In this instance, the antibody is eluted with 30 column volumes of a 0–100 mM or 20–100 mM NaCl gradient.

When a large number of different ascites have to be processed, or when 90–95% purity of the monoclonal antibody is adequate, a stepwise elution of the monoclonal antibodies is more convenient. In this case, the ascitic fluid is applied to a column of 20 mM Tris buffer containing 25 mM NaCl, the column is washed with 3 bed volumes of 25 mM NaCl, and the immunoglobulin is eluted with 3 bed volumes of the same buffer containing 50 mM NaCl.

Storage of the Purified Antibodies. The fractions of the antibody peak are pooled and adjusted to 1 mg protein/ml. NaCl, 1 M, is added to bring the salt concentration to 150 mM, and 0.02% NaN$_3$ is added to avoid bacterial contamination. Long-term antibody stocks are frozen and stored. The antibody solution can be stored for more than 4 months at 4° without any detectable loss of activity.

Determination of Protease Activity in Eluted Protein. Protease activity was detected using the Bio-Rad protease detection kit.

SDS–Gel Electrophoresis. SDS–gel electrophoresis is performed on 15% SDS gels according to Laemmli (1970). Protein bands are stained with Coomassie Blue.

Protein A–Sepharose. Immunoglobulin is partially purified from ascites fluid by salt fractionation (50% saturated ammonium sulfate) and dialyzed against PBS. The antibody preparation is applied to a 5 ml protein A–Sepharose column (Pharmacia), and the column is washed with 10 column volumes of 180 mM NaCl, 20 mM Tris (pH 8.0). The bound immunoglobulin is then eluted from the column with 3.5 M MgCl$_2$, dialyzed versus normal saline and then against PBS, and stored at $-70°$.

Results

Determination of Optimal Conditions for the Purification of Mouse IgG from Ascitic Fluid

In order to determine the optimal pH value for mouse DEAE Affi-Gel Blue antibody purification, columns were run at pH 7.2 (see "Materials and Methods") and pH 8. Ascitic fluid with high levels of protease was applied to the columns and eluted stepwise with increasing NaCl concentrations. The stepwise procedure was preferred here to avoid dilution of proteases to undetectable levels. The eluted fractions were loaded on a 15% SDS gel for the evaluation of the quantity and purity of the eluted immunoglobulins and the protease contamination was determined. Elu-

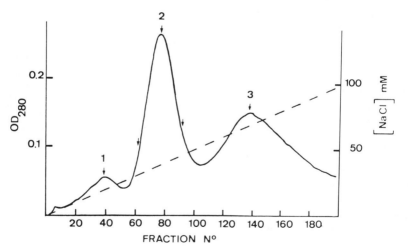

FIG. 1. Elution of monoclonal IgG$_1$ antibodies from a DEAE Affi-Gel Blue column: 1 ml of ascitic fluid dialyzed against 20 mM Tris (pH 7.2) was layered on a 7-ml DEAE Affi-Gel Blue column equilibrated with the same buffer. Elution by 200 ml of a 0–100 mM NaCl gradient was performed at a flow rate of 40 ml/hr. Fractions of 1 ml were collected. Arrows indicate fractions analyzed by SDS–PAGE. [Reproduced from *J. Immunol. Methods* **53** (1980).]

tion at pH 8 optimized the separation between the immunoglobulin and albumin peaks, but proteases and immunoglobulins were co-eluted at values between 40 and 50 mM NaCl. At pH 7.2, only immunoglobulins were eluted to the same ionic strength, whereas proteases were detached at 100 mM NaCl. Therefore, pH 7.2 was chosen for the purification of mouse IgGs.

Evaluation of Purity and Recovery

Elution by a Linear NaCl Gradient. Proteins were purified from 1 ml of ascitic fluid by a linear 1–100 mM NaCl gradient as described in "Materials and Methods." All steps were performed at 4°. The OD$_{280}$ profile of the eluate shown in Fig. 1 displays three protein peaks. Aliquots of each of the three peaks were checked for the absence of proteases and subjected to SDS–PAGE electrophoresis (Fig. 2). The nature of the proteins

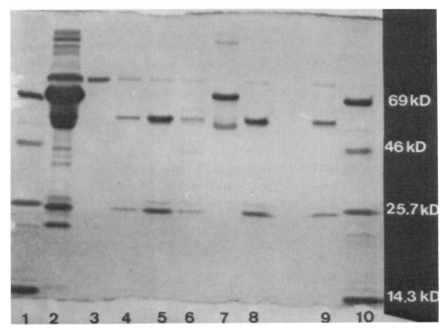

FIG. 2. SDS–PAGE analysis of DEAE Affi-Gel Blue fractions. Elution by a 0–100 mM NaCl gradient. Lanes 1 and 10, molecular weight standards; lane 2, unfractionated ascitic fluid; lane 3, first protein peak (transferrin); lane 4, beginning of Ig peak; lane 5, top of Ig peak; lane 6, end of Ig peak; lane 7, third protein peak (albumin); lane 8, pool of Ig peak middle fractions; lane 9, pool of beginning and ending Ig peak fractions. [Reproduced from *J. Immunol. Methods* **53** (1980).]

eluted was determined in immunodiffusion tests with antisera to mouse transferrin, IgG, and albumin. From those results, it was clear that the first protein peak which eluted at about 20 mM NaCl consisted of mouse transferrin, the second peak of mouse IgG, and the third peak, which consistently eluted at 70 mM NaCl, contained mouse albumin.[3] The ionic strength at which the protein peak was eluted varied among different antibodies. Each of the more than 30 antibodies (of IgG$_1$, IgG$_{2a}$, and IgG$_{2b}$ subclasses) tested have eluted between 30 and 50 mM NaCl.

The yield of purified immunoglobulins by this chromatographic method was estimated for six different ascitic fluids (six different antibodies against bovine leukemia virus envelope glycoprotein) by solid-phase radioimmunotitration of the starting material[4] and of the DEAE Affi-Gel purified Ig-containing fractions. Depending on the antibody concentration of the ascitic fluid, the yields ranged between 75 and 90% of the antibody activity contained in the crude material. The purity, as determined by SDS–PAGE analysis, was also highly dependent on the antibody content of the material applied to the column. As shown in Fig. 2, lane 8, a purity close to 100% was achieved by gradient elution when an ascitic fluid whose antibody content is 5 mg/ml is applied to the column. The recovery in this case was determined to be 84%. The contamination by transferrin increased to 10% when the Ig peak eluted at an ionic strength of 30–35 mM NaCl, or when the antibody concentration of the crude material was less than 1 mg/ml. In these particular cases, it was useful to perform an ammonium sulfate precipitation step before the DEAE Affi-Gel Blue chromatography in order to obtain a purity of greater than 90%.

Elution by Step Gradient. Elution by a NaCl gradient is inconvenient when many different antibodies are to be purified simultaneously. Based on the elution profile observed in Fig. 1, we adapted a stepwise purification system. The column was conditioned in Tris buffer containing 25 mM NaCl and the ascitic fluid (dialyzed against the same buffer) was applied to the column at 4° as described. The column was then washed extensively with the same buffer. At this ionic strength, most of the transferrin was eluted, whereas the antibodies remained bound to the column.[3] The IgGs were eluted by raising the salt concentration of the buffer to 50 mM. All the monoclonal IgGs tested so far (over 30 different antibodies with diverse antigen specificities) were eluted at the 50 mM NaCl step. The purity of the recovered antibody was consistently lower than that achieved by the gradient elution procedure. A distinct transferrin band was visible by SDS–PAGE analysis of most antibody preparations (Fig.

[4] C. Bruck, S. Mathot, D. Portetelle, C. Berte, J.-D. Franssen, P. Herion, and A. Burny, *Virology* **122,** 353 (1982).

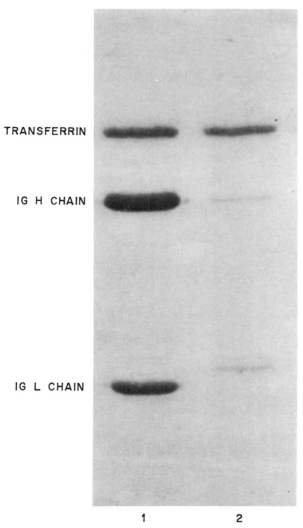

FIG. 3. This illustration shows distinct transferrin band visible by SDS–PAGE analysis. [Reproduced from *J. Immunol. Methods* **53** (1980).]

3). Antibody preparations purified from ascitic fluids with low Ig concentrations also showed traces of unidentified 31-kDa protein (Fig. 4) but were completely devoid of protease and albumin contamination on the basis of SDS–PAGE analysis. The purity of antibody preparations obtained by stepwise elution of the DEAE Affi-Gel Blue column is estimated

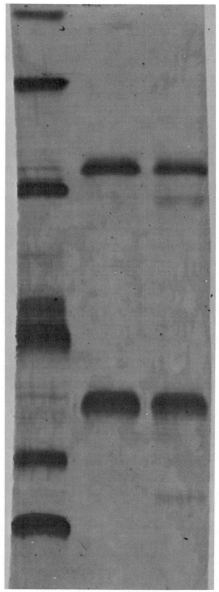

FIG. 4. Comparative SDS–PAGE analysis of monoclonal IgG$_{2a}$ antibodies obtained by DEAE Affi-Gel Blue step chromatography and protein–A Sepharose affinity chromatography. Lane 1, pool of antibody fractions obtained by stepwise elution of a DEAE Affi-Gel Blue column; lane 2, pool of antibody fractions after protein A–Sepharose; lane 3, molecular weight standards.

to lie between 85–95%, depending on the original immunoglobulin concentration in the ascitic fluid.

Comparison of Protein A–Sepharose and DEAE Affi-Gel Blue Purification of an IgG_{2a} Antibody

In this experiment, antibodies were purified from ascitic fluid containing a low concentration (0.8 mg/ml) of IgG_{2a} antibodies directed to a transformed cell surface determinant.[5] Antibodies were purified from 20 mg of ascitic fluid by the standard protein A–Sepharose procedure (see "Materials and Methods"). For DEAE Affi-Gel Blue purification, antibodies from 20 ml of ascitic fluid at 0.8 mg/ml were precipitated by ammonium sulfate, then purified on a 20-ml DEAE Affi-Gel Blue column. In the case of this low Ig concentration, ascites preconcentration of the Igs by salt fractionation was necessary to reduce the amount of Affi-Gel Blue (140 ml for uncut material to 20 ml for the ammonium sulfate precipitated material).

SDS–PAGE analysis of the IgG peaks obtained by the two methods (Fig. 4) shows that protein A–Sepharose antibody preparations reach a purity close to 100% after affinity chromatography, whereas the DEAE Affi-Gel Blue-treated material achieves a purity estimated to lie between 90 and 95%.

Stability of the Monoclonal Antibody Preparation

Stability of the purified antibody containing no detectable protease activity was assessed by comparing solid-phase radioimmunotitration curves of antibodies to bovine leukemia virus glycoprotein immediately after purification and at different time points up to 4 months of storage at 4°. For all antibody preparations tested, the deviation between the titration curves at different time points up to 4 months after purification was lower than the experimental error (3%).

Discussion

The results presented here show that monoclonal IgGs can be purified from ascitic fluid by DEAE Affi-Gel Blue in a single chromatographic step. When the column buffer is prepared from a 1 M Tris solution which has been adjusted to pH 7.2 at room temperature, mouse IgGs are consistently eluted between 30 and 50 mM NaCl, well separated from the al-

[5] J. A. Drebin, D. F. Stern, V. C. Link, R. A. Weinberg, and M. I. Greene, *Nature (London)* **312,** 545 (1984).

bumin peak which is eluted at 65 mM NaCl and the transferrin peaks which eluted at about 25 mM NaCl. At this pH, contaminating proteases are retained on the column, allowing the recovery of a stable antibody preparation from ascitic fluids which are heavily loaded with proteases. Increasing the NaCl concentration from 25 to 50 mM in a single step yields an antibody preparation that is slightly contaminated with transferrin, but whose purity (85% or more) is sufficient for most uses of monoclonal antibodies (solid-phase and liquid-phase immunotitration, fluorescent cell labeling, etc.). A linear NaCl gradient is necessary to achieve a homogeneity comparable to that obtained by protein A–Sepharose for IgG$_{2a}$ antibodies.

When antibody is purified from large volumes of ascitic fluid, or when ascitic fluids with a low antibody content (less than 1 mg/ml) are used, preconcentration of the antibody by salt fractionation allows a decrease in the size of the DEAE Affi-Gel Blue column (by 7-fold) and results in an antibody preparation of greater purity.

In conclusion, DEAE Affi-Gel Blue appears to be the method of choice for the purification of IgG monoclonal antibodies which are not of the IgG$_{2a}$ subclass and of IgG$_{2a}$ antibodies which are denatured by the conditions necessary to elute the immunoglobulin from protein A–Sepharose.

Acknowledgments

We thank Virginia McKinney and Jim Throp for excellent secretarial assistance.

C. Bruck is supported by the American Council for Tobacco Research, J. A. Drebin is supported by NIH Grant 5-T326M07753 from the Medical Scientist Training Program at Harvard Medical School, and C. Glineur is supported by the Belgian Institut pour la Recherche Scientifique dans l'Industrie et l'Agriculture.

[57] Purification and Analysis of Monoclonal Antibodies by High-Performance Liquid Chromatography

By Scott W. Burchiel

Since the development of hybridoma technology, monoclonal antibodies have found an increasing number of applications and uses. Many of these uses require highly purified and immunoreactive monoclonal antibodies in order to obtain labeled or conjugated reagents of appropriate specificity. Therefore, numerous techniques have been developed to obtain highly purified monoclonal antibodies from biologic preparations.

Techniques that can efficiently and rapidly purify monoclonal antibodies have an advantage over other techniques. For this reason high-performance liquid chromatography (HPLC) is an attractive approach to the purification and analysis of monoclonal antibodies.

HPLC separations take advantage of the same basic types of chromatography that have been used for many years in the purification of immunoglobulins, such as ion-exchange chromatography and molecular sieving. However, the advantage of HPLC over traditional methods is that it can be performed much more efficiently and quickly. In addition, the types of columns that have been used and the configurations of HPLC systems often result in an increased sensitivity for detection of immunoglobulins and impurities. The efficiency and speed of HPLC, however, must be balanced by high initial costs and column expense, depending upon the system used. Sample capacity can also be a further limitation of HPLC, especially if preparative columns are not available.

Basic Design of HPLC Systems

HPLC systems are available from numerous manufacturers that vary in design and operation. However, the components of these systems and the theory of operation are similar. In Fig. 1, a typical binary HPLC

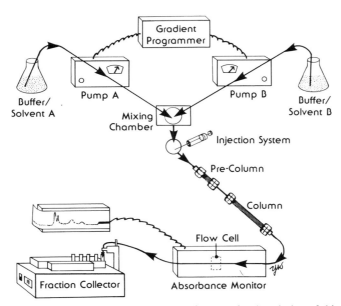

FIG. 1. Schematic of a binary HPLC system. See text for description of this system.

system is shown. Samples are generally eluted from HPLC columns using some type of a gradient system (either stepwise or linear gradients). Gradients are easily generated using a two buffer/solvent system (binary system) in which a gradient programmer controls the rate of pumping of two pumps from different reservoirs. Gradient programmers can be programmed to run various cycles for the loading and elution of samples followed by column washing and clean-up steps. In this type of system, the composition of buffer generated by the mixture of A and B can be varied, and flow rates can be adjusted. Gradient programmers can also control the composition of final buffers/solvents by metering the input into a mixing chamber through the use of solenoid valves, rather than adjusting the flow rates of pumps per se. Some protein purification columns do not require the generation of gradients and can be run isocratically (single buffer system). For example, gel permeation HPLC columns are commonly run in an isocratic mode at a constant flow rate.

An important component of an HPLC system is the buffer/solvent pump. Two basic types of pumps are available from manufacturers; the two types include reciprocating and syringe pumps. Reciprocating pumps (Beckman, Bio-Rad, ISCO, LKB, Rainin, Spectra-Physics, Varian, Waters, etc.) have been commonly used for the high-pressure applications of HPLC. A minor limitation of these types of pumps is the small pulsation that occurs during pumping, although this effect is generally substantially reduced with pressure dampening systems. Some of the components of these pumps are not completely compatible with biologic buffers, especially those buffers containing halide salts (NaCl), and must be extensively washed following operation to prevent damage to components. Some syringe types of pumps self-contain the buffers, and have been designed for compatability with halide salts (i.e., Pharmacia FPLC System). However, these systems are primarily designed for low-pressure applications (less than 1000 psi), and therefore cannot be used for most reverse-phase applications.

Other components of a typical HPLC system include a mixing chamber (can be either a high-pressure or low-pressure chamber), an injection system (commonly a loop arrangement), the precolumn (designed to remove impurities from a sample), the column (discussed below), an absorbance monitor (either fixed or variable wavelength), a recorder (strip chart that can be combined with a peak analyzer/integrator), and a fraction collector (needed if samples are to be saved). Since the initial investment in this type of instrumentation is high, most laboratories choose systems that are versatile and compatible with other assay or purification needs, combining protein and nonprotein applications.

HPLC Columns for the Purification and Analysis of Proteins

Several types of HPLC columns have been used for the purification and analysis of monoclonal antibodies and other proteins. Some of these columns are a direct extension of classical liquid chromatography separation systems, whereas other columns have been developed as an outgrowth of HPLC technology. A brief overview of the types of columns that have been applied to the purification and analysis of monoclonal antibodies is presented below. The choice of one of these types of columns will depend upon the protein to be purified and the nature of the impurities to be separated. It should be emphasized that some conditions that have been established for the purification of polyclonal antibodies do not work very well for particular monoclonal antibodies. This point illustrates the heterogeneity of immunoglobulins in general, and the fact that when dealing with a single protein, substantial variation from the norm can be observed. Thus, in the purification or analysis of monoclonal antibodies (or other cloned gene products), certain starting conditions can be followed as a guideline, but specific individual conditions must be empirically defined for each protein of interest.

Ion-Exchange HPLC Chromatography

Immunoglobulins have long been purified by liquid chromatography using ion exchangers coupled to insoluble stationary supports, such as cellulose or various types of cross-linked beads.[1,2] Depending upon the chemical nature of the ion exchanger linked to a support matrix, one can perform either anion- or cation-exchange chromatography. HPLC columns suitable for purifying proteins using either anion- or cation-exchange chromatography are available from several manufacturers. In general, immunoglobulins have been found to bind weakly to anion exchangers and moderately to cation exchangers. Therefore, either system can be used to purify or analyze monoclonal antibodies.

Anion-Exchange HPLC Chromatography

Several types of HPLC anion-exchange columns have been used for the purification/analysis of proteins by anion exchange. The column supports used thus far are either silica, coated silica, or a polymerized hydro-

[1] J. L. Fahey and E. W. Terry, *in* "Handbook of Experimental Immunology" (D. M. Weir, ed.), Vol. 1, p. 8.1. Blackwell, Oxford, 1978.
[2] J. S. Garvey, N. E. Cremer, and D. H. Sussdorf, *in* "Methods in Immunology," p. 223. Addison-Wesley, Reading, Massachusetts, 1977.

philic resin. Silica-based or -derivatized columns have been used traditionally for reverse-phase applications, and they may present some difficulties in terms of efficient protein recovery. The polymerized support systems have the advantage of being hydrophilic, allowing for the near-complete recovery of protein in an aqueous phase. While numerous companies repackage and market anion-exchange columns under their own names, many of these columns are obtained from the Toyo-Soda Company (Japan). A list of several of the anion-exchange columns that are commercially available is shown in Table I. Some of the characteristics and properties of these columns are shown in this table.

Our laboratory has experience in the use of the Mono Q (Pharmacia) and to a limited extent the DEAE-3SW (provided by Beckman) columns. We found similar elution patterns of monoclonal antibody preparations from the two columns, but we did not compare the protein recoveries directly. Two illustrations for the use of the Mono Q column in the purification of monoclonal antibodies from ascites fluid and tissue culture fluid, and examples of HPLC analysis of various antibody preparations are described below.

EXAMPLE 1: HPLC PURIFICATION OF MOUSE MONOCLONAL ANTIBODIES FROM MURINE ASCITES. The procedures described here have been found to be useful for the purification of various subclasses of mouse IgG monoclonal antibodies present in murine ascites fluid using anion-exchange HPLC chromatography. The specific conditions under which monoclonal antibodies elute from HPLC anion-exchange columns vary somewhat according to the specific antibody of interest.

Equipment and Reagents

Binary HPLC system (Beckman system used in our studies)
500-μl injection loop and injection syringe
Mono Q column and precolumn (Pharmacia) or other HPLC anion-exchange column
280-nm-wavelength absorbance monitor (8-μl flow cell)
Sample buffer A: 20 mM Tris (pH 7.7)
       buffer B: 0.5 M NaCl in 20 mM Tris (pH 7.7)
Fraction collector (time collection mode)
0.45-μm Millipore-type filter
Immune ascites fluid (see Ref. 3)

Method. (1) Obtain ascites fluid from the peritoneal cavity of pristane-primed mice injected with a syngeneic hybridoma cell line producing a

TABLE I
COMMERCIAL ANION-EXCHANGE COLUMNS FOR THE SEPARATION OF PROTEINS[a]

	TSKgel DEAE-5PW	TSKgel DEAE-3SW	Mono Q	SynChropak AX-300
Manufacturer	Toyo-Soda	Toyo-Soda	Pharmacia	SynChrome
Base material	Hydrophilic resin	Silica	Hydrophilic resin	Silica
Stable pH range	2–12	2–8	2–12	2–8
Pore size (exclusion limit for PEG)	1,000,000	30,000	500,000	150,000
Protein adsorption capacity (mg BSA/ml)	30	120	65	30
Ionic group	$-CH_2CH_2N(C_2H_5)_2$	$-CH_2CH_2N(C_2H_5)_2$	$-CH_2N^+(CH_3)_3$	$-NHCH_2CH_2^-$
pK_a	11.3	?	11.4	?
Ion-exchange capacity (meq/ml)	0.1	0.15	0.3	?
Particle size (μm)	10	10	10	10
Column size (mm i.d.)	75 × 7.5	75 × 7.5	50 × 5	300 × 4.1

[a] Data provided by Bio-Rad Laboratories, Inc.

monoclonal antibody of interest.[3] (2) Clarify ascites fluid by filtration using a 0.45-μm syringe filter (Millipore or Gelman). (3) Precipitate protein using ammonium sulfate as in method described for HPLC cation-exchange chromatography (example 4). Note: this step may be used to perform an initial enrichment of the monoclonal antibody. However, some monoclonal antibodies are denatured during ammonium sulfate precipitation. Therefore, this step should be approached with caution. If ammonium sulfate precipitation is performed, then desalting of the protein precipitate must be accomplished via dialysis or ultrafiltration before HPLC purification.

(4) Prepare HPLC system for sample injection as follows. Purge the system with buffers A and B. Equilibrate column in buffer A. Establish stable absorbance monitor baseline and set full-scale absorbance value in accordance with the amount of protein to be injected. Write or recall gradient program from memory: time 0–5 min = 100% A, time 5–25

[3] T. J. McKearn, in "Monoclonal Antibodies" (R. H. Kennett, T. J. McKearn, and K. B. Bechtol, eds.), p. 403. Plenum, New York, 1980.

min = 0–100% B linear gradient, time 25–30 = 0–100% A; flow rate equals 1 ml/min for entire run. Put system through a trial run with no sample injected to make sure that system is working and that nothing elutes from the column. Note: a change in the absorbance value will sometimes be observed at intermediate to high NaCl concentrations due to refractive index changes. (5) Inject 100–500 μl of ascites fluid into the system, and gradient program is run. (6) Collect 1-min fractions (1 ml) from the column eluate, while the absorbance detector monitors the elution profile. Note: the delay time or volume between detector and fraction collector needs to be determined.

(7) Analyze the fractions for IgG content using an ELISA.[4] (8) Determine the purity of the monoclonal antibody using SDS–polyacrylamide gel electrophoresis (SDS–PAGE) via the method of Laemmli.[5] (9) Separate potential impurities using a gel permeation column, as described later in this chapter. Note: this step is often not needed. (10) Test the immunoreactivity of the purified monoclonal antibody in an immunoassay. (This should be the assay for which the purified antibody is ultimately intended, or assays that approximate its final use.)

Results. A typical chromatogram obtained using murine ascites fluid separated using a Mono Q column is shown in Fig. 2. This particular immune ascites was obtained from BALB/c mice injected with 10^7 NS.7 murine hybridoma cells that make a mouse IgG₃ reactive with sheep erythrocytes.[6] The monoclonal antibody was found to elute in fractions 9–12, as determined using ELISA and SDS–PAGE (reduced 7.5% gel). Since the monoclonal antibody contained significant amounts of transferrin (especially in fractions 11 and 12), the antibody was further purified from this contaminant using HPLC gel permeation chromatography.[4] The resultant antibody was found to be highly purified and retained its immunoreactivity. In our hands, protein yields from the Mono Q column vary from 81.5 to 93.6%, depending upon the preparation studied. The manufacturer claims somewhat better protein recoveries than this using optimum conditions.

EXAMPLE 2: PURIFICATION OF RAT MONOCLONAL ANTIBODIES FROM SERUM-FREE TISSUE CULTURE MEDIA. Despite the larger monoclonal antibody yields that can be obtained using hybridomas grown in peritoneal ascites, numerous groups continue to produce their monoclonal antibodies in tissue culture. This is due to several factors, including the lack

[4] S. W. Burchiel, J. R. Billman, and T. R. Alber, *J. Immunol. Methods* **69,** 33 (1984).
[5] U. K. Laemmli, *Nature (London)* **227,** 680 (1970).
[6] Hybridoma donated to the American Type Culture Collection by Dr. W. C. Raschke, La Jolla Cancer Research Foundation, La Jolla, California.

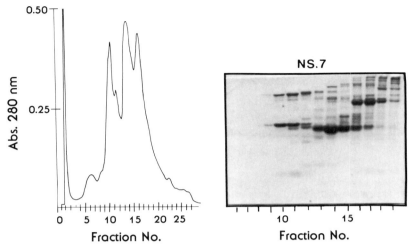

FIG. 2. HPLC separation of murine monoclonal antibody NS.7 using a Mono Q column (Pharmacia). Elution profile was obtained using a binary gradient system. At time 0, 500 μl of clarified neat ascites fluid containing the NS.7 antibody (IgG$_3$) anti-SRBC) was injected into the system. During the time period of 0–5 min, 20 mM Tris (pH 7.7) was pumped through the system. Then during the 5- to 25-min period a linear NaCl gradient (0–0.5 M NaCl) was established in the 20 mM Tris (pH 7.7) buffer. A final wash with the Tris buffer alone occurred during minutes 25–27. An SDS–polyacrylamide gel (7.5% gel) was used to analyze the proteins eluted in the various fractions. The NS.7 antibody was found to be present in fractions 9–12.

of growth of some cell lines in ascites (due to histocompatability and other problems), the desire to not have the monoclonal antibody preparation contaminated with endogenous immunoglobulins present in the ascitic fluid, or to retain the ability to manipulate the antibody's synthesis *in vitro* (i.e., perform biosynthetic labeling or other procedures).

One of the main problems associated with the production of monoclonal antibodies *in vitro* is that the hybridoma cell lines require serum for growth. Therefore, large amounts (milligram quantities) of serum protein components must be separated from small amounts (microgram quantities) of monoclonal antibody, which can be a difficult task. Our approach has been to produce monoclonal antibodies in serum-free media, and then to purify the monoclonal antibody from minor serum contaminants using HPLC. The example below illustrates our method.

Equipment and Reagents

Binary HPLC system (Beckman system used in our studies)
500-μl injection loop and injection syringe

Mono Q column and precolumn (Pharmacia) or other HPLC anion-exchange column

280-nm-wavelength absorbance monitor (8-μl flow cell)

Sample buffer A: 20 mM Tris (pH 7.7)

      buffer B: 0.5 M NaCl in 20 mM Tris (pH 7.7)

Fraction collector (time collection mode)

0.45-μm Millipore-type filter

Method. A. Preparation of Monoclonal Antibodies in Serum-Free Media. (1) Grow hybridoma cell line of interest in complete media (normal growth media plus serum) to a cell concentration of approximately 10^6 cells/ml. (2) Harvest cells aseptically via centrifugation at 600 g for 15 min at room temperature and resuspend cells to their original cell concentration (approximately 10^6 cells/ml) in RPMI 1640 supplemented with glutamine, nonessential amino acids, sodium pyruvate, and penicillin–streptomycin (serum-free media). Note: cells do not necessarily continue to proliferate in this media, but they continue to produce monoclonal antibody at approximately the same rate as in serum-containing media; other enriched media have also been successfully used including Iscove's modified MEM and alpha-MEM. (3) Incubate cells for 48 hr at 37° in 5% CO_2.

(4) Obtain spent tissue culture fluid from 48-hr culture supernatant via centrifugation of cells at 600 g for 15 min (the $A_{280\,nm}$ value is typically in the range of 0.2 to 0.5, depending on the antibody secretion rate of the hybridoma). (5) Concentrate immune tissue culture fluid (spent tissue culture fluid containing the monoclonal antibody of interest) via ultrafiltration (Amicon PM30 filtration membrane or CH-4 hollow-fiber system with H1-P100 cartridge for large volumes) to an $A_{280\,nm}$ value of 3.0 to 5.0. Dialyze the protein sample against 20 mM Tris (pH 7.7). Dialysis and concentration can be achieved simultaneously for small sample volumes using an Amicon 8MC system. Note: the final concentration of protein should be determined by the amount of sample capacity of the column and the solubility of the monoclonal antibody preparation in the low ionic strength Tris buffer.

B. Anion-Exchange Purification of Rat Monoclonal Antibodies from Immune Tissue Culture Fluid. (1) Inject 100–500 μl of immune tissue culture fluid onto the Mono Q column, and then start the elution program described in Example 1 at a constant flow rate of 1 ml/min. (2) Collect 1-min fractions using a fraction collector. (3) Analyze the collected fractions for purity using SDS–PAGE. (4) Examine the purified monoclonal antibodies for immunoreactivity using an immunoassay. In the case of Example 2, the rat H-12 antibody (anti-mouse Thy 1.2) is examined for immunoreactivity using quantitative immunofluorescence and a fluorescence-activated cell sorter (Becton-Dickinson FACS III).

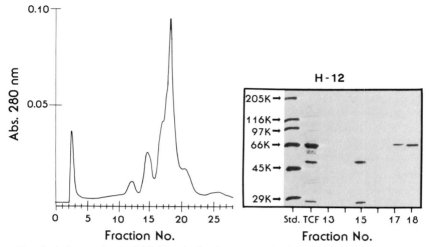

FIG. 3. Anion-exchange HPLC analysis of rat monoclonal anti-mouse Thy 1.2 obtained from serum-free tissue culture fluid. A sample (500 μl) was analyzed using a Pharmacia Mono Q column as in Fig. 2. A 5–18% gradient SDS–polyacrylamide reducing gel was used to analyze fractions. The H-12 antibody was found to elute in fraction 15. Neat serum-free tissue culture fluid (TCF) obtained following growth of the H-12 hybridoma was found to contain mostly the antibody plus albumin that was carried over from the growth of the cells in fetal bovine serum.

Results. The elution profile of concentrated tissue culture fluid containing the rat IgG_1 H-12 monoclonal antibody[7] is shown in Fig. 3. Three major peaks of protein were detected via the absorbance monitor. The second peak of activity (fraction 15) was found to contain the majority of the rat IgG_1 following chromatography on the Mono Q column. SDS–PAGE (reduced 5–18% gradient gel) analysis of the unseparated immune tissue culture fluid (TCF) revealed the antibody heavy and light chains, plus at least two other significant bands of protein. (Note that several other smaller bands were also observed that do not appear in the gel reproduction due to their low band density.) Fraction 15 was found to contain essentially pure antibody, which cleanly separated from the major albumin band of protein (fractions 17 and 18). The albumin component represents a carryover from the growth of the cells in serum-containing media. The immune TCF used in these studies was concentrated with an Amicon ultrafiltration chamber and a PM30 membrane (30K MW cutoff). Thus, the albumin was concentrated with the monoclonal antibody. How-

[7] J. A. Ledbetter and L. A. Herzenberg, *Immunol. Rev.* **47,** 63 (1979).

ever, other membranes or columns (such as the Amicon hollow-fiber system with the H1-P100 cartridge) can be used to concentrate the antibody while filtering the albumin.

EXAMPLE 3: ANALYSIS OF IMMUNOGLOBULINS BY ANION-EXCHANGE HPLC. Several commercially available polyclonal antibody preparations have been examined for their behavior on Mono Q HPLC columns, in comparison with monoclonal antibodies that we have produced, or that have been provided by collaborators.[4] All of the reagents tested were highly purified by anion exchange, and/or gel filtration liquid chromatography before the HPLC analysis was performed. Each of the antibody preparations eluted as a single peak from the Mono Q column. The method used to evaluate these preparations was as described in Examples 1 and 2. The results of these studies are shown in Table II.

Sheep IgG (Serono Laboratories) eluted from the Mono Q column 12.5 min after injection, whereas rabbit IgG (Miles Laboratories) and goat IgG (Cappel Laboratories) were obtained at 9.78 and 8.78 min, respectively. All of the mouse IgG monoclonal antibodies tested eluted during a similar time frame: 12.06–12.44 min for MOPC-21 (IgG$_1$), B6.2 (an IgG$_1$ anti-human mammary tumor-associated antigen), anti-CEA (IgG$_1$), anti-280K human melanoma-associated antigen (IgG$_{2a}$), and B1.1 (IgG$_{2a}$ anti-human mammary tumor-associated antigen).

Since anion-exchange liquid chromatography has been used for years in the purification and separation of antibody Fab fragments from Fc

TABLE II
CHROMATOGRAPHY OF MONOCLONAL AND POLYCLONAL
ANTIBODIES BY HPLC ANION EXCHANGE[a]

Antibody preparation	Elution time (min)[b]	
	IgG	F(ab')$_2$
Sheep IgG	12.5	9.83
Rabbit IgG	9.78	—
Goat IgG	8.78	—
Mouse IgG$_1$ (MOPC-21)	12.06	—
Mouse IgG$_1$ (B6.2)	12.44	—
Mouse IgG$_1$ (anti-CEA)	12.09	12.10
Mouse IgG$_{2a}$ (anti-280K MAA)	12.34	12.14
Mouse IgG$_{2a}$ (B1.1)	12.36	—

[a] Data from Burchiel et al.[4]; HPLC anion exchange performed with a Mono Q column (Pharmacia).
[b] See text for description of elution conditions.

TABLE III

COMMERCIAL CATION-EXCHANGE COLUMNS FOR THE SEPARATION OF PROTEINS[a]

	TSKgel SP-5PW	TSKgel CM-3SW	Mono S	SynChropak CM-300
Manufacturer	Toyo-Soda	Toyo-Soda	Pharmacia	SynChrome
Base material	Hydrophilic resin	Silica	Hydrophilic resin	Silica
Stable pH range	2–12	2–8	2–12	2–8
Pore size (exclusion limit for PEG)	1,000,000	30,000	500,000	150,000
Protein adsorption capacity	40 (mg hemoglobin/ml)	110 (mg hemoglobin/ml)	75 (mg IgG/ml)	?
Ionic group	$-CH_2CH_2CH_2SO_3^-$	$-CH_2COO^-$	$-CH_2SO_3^-$	$-CH_2COO^-$
pK_a	2.3	4.2	2.6	?
Ion-exchange capacity (meq/ml)	0.1	0.2	0.15	?
Particle size (μm)	10	10	10	10
Column size (mm i.d.)	75 × 7.5	75 × 7.5	50 × 5	?

[a] Data provided by Bio-Rad Laboratories, Inc.

portions of the antibody molecule following enzymatic digestion,[8] we examined the ability of Mono Q columns to distinguish between IgG and F(ab')$_2$ fragments (Table II). Our preliminary results indicate that some F(ab')$_2$ fragments (polyclonal sheep) elute at lower NaCl concentrations from the Mono Q column than an IgG fraction of the same preparation. However, we could not distinguish the F(ab')$_2$ fragments from the IgG fraction of two mouse monoclonal antibodies (anti-280K MAA IgG$_{2a}$ and anti-CEA IgG$_1$). Therefore, Mono Q HPLC may or may not be useful for the separation of IgG from F(ab')$_2$, Fab, or Fc depending upon the particular antibody reagent tested.

Cation-Exchange HPLC Chromatography

We have performed some preliminary studies on the use of cation-exchange HPLC for the purification and analysis of murine monoclonal IgG antibodies.[9] Several commercial cation-exchange HPLC columns are available from manufacturers. The properties of these columns are shown in Table III. In our studies, we used a Mono S HPLC column (Pharma-

[8] R. R. Porter, *Biochem. J.* **73**, 119 (1959).

[9] F. A. Liberatore, M. DuPuis, and S. Silvakoff, unpublished observations.

cia), and eluted the protein using a NaCl step gradient. A preferred method for the precipitation of monoclonal antibodies from ascites fluid is also described, since this method can be used to eliminate approximately half of the contaminating proteins and concentrate the monoclonal antibody. An example of the use of cation-exchange HPLC appears below.

EXAMPLE 4: PURIFICATION OF MOUSE MONOCLONAL IgG₁ BY MONO S CATION-EXCHANGE HPLC

Equipment and Reagents

Binary HPLC system. Note: an isocratic HPLC system can be alternatively used since a step gradient is used to elute samples, although this is most easily accomplished with a binary system.

500-μl sample injection loop

Mono S column with precolumn (Pharmacia) or other cation-exchange HPLC column

280-nm-wavelength absorbance monitor (8-μl flow cell)

Strip chart recorder

Sample buffer A: 10 mM sodium phosphate (pH 7.0)

buffer B: 1.0 M NaCl in 10 mM sodium phosphate (pH 7.0)

Ammonium sulfate precipitation reagents:

1 M Tris–HCl (pH 8.0)

100% saturated ammonium sulfate, $(NH_4)_2SO_4$

10 mM sodium phosphate (pH 7.5)

10 mM NaCl in 10 mM sodium phosphate (pH 7.5)

25 mM NaCl in 10 mM sodium phosphate (pH 7.5)

100 mM NaCl in 10 mM sodium phosphate (pH 7.5)

Immune ascites fluid

Method. A. Preferred Ammonium Sulfate Precipitation. (1) Add 0.1 volume of 1 M Tris–HCl (pH 8.0) to ascites fluid to buffer it during precipitation (i.e., add 2 ml Tris to 20 ml B6.2 or other immune ascites fluid). (2) Add 100% ammonium sulfate dropwise to ascites fluid at 4° until a 50% (v/v) concentration is reached (i.e., add 22 ml of 100% saturated ammonium sulfate to 22 ml of ascites). (3) Stir 1 hr at 4°. (4) Collect precipitate by centrifugation at 10,000 g at 4° for 10 min. (5) Dissolve pellet from 20 ml of ascites fluid in about 12 ml of 10 mM NaCl in 10 mM sodium phosphate (pH 7.5) at 4°. (6) Run a stepwise dialysis to remove the ammonium sulfate. Note: monoclonal antibodies may precipitate if they are desalted too quickly. (a) Dialyze at least 4 hr at 4° in 3 liters of 100 mM NaCl in 10 mM sodium phosphate (pH 7.5); (b) dialyze at least 4 hr at 4° in 3 liters of 25 mM NaCl in 10 mM sodium phosphate (pH 7.5); (c) dialyze at least 4 hr at 4° in 3 liters of 10 mM NaCl in 10 mM sodium phosphate (pH 7.5); (d) dialyze at least 4 hr at 4° in 3 liters of 10 mM sodium phosphate (pH 7.5). (7) Determine the protein concentration of the monoclonal antibody by measuring the 280 nm absorption, assuming that the absorption coefficient for monoclonal antibodies is in the range of 1.4 to 1.8 (this varies for different antibodies and proteins).

B. Purification of B6.2 Mouse IgG$_1$ Monoclonal Antibody Using Mono S Cation Exchange HPLC. (1) Filter buffers A (10 mM sodium phosphate, pH 7.5) and B (1.0 M NaCl in 10 mM sodium phosphate, pH 7.5) through 0.22-μm filters under vacuum. (2) Turn on the UV absorbance monitor (set at 280 nm), wait until a stable baseline is reached, and then zero the recorder. (3) Make a test run of the system with a blank (i.e., inject 500 μl of buffer A and then run the step gradient described below at a flow rate of 1 ml/min). Note: if there is an absorbance change during this run the column is either not clean, or it has not equilibrated with the buffers; do not proceed with a sample run until a stable baseline is reached. (4) While running 100% buffer A through the Mono S column at 1 ml/min, inject 500 μl of the B6.2 ascites fluid or ammonium sulfate-precipitated antibody. (5) After 4 min in buffer A, elute B6.2 antibody with 5% buffer B for 6 min at 1 ml/min. (6) Elute residual protein off of the column by running 100% B for 3 min at 1 ml/min. (7) Reequilibrate column in buffer A for 3 min at 1 ml/min. (8) Collect fractions in plastic (polypropylene) tubes or vials. Note: some antibodies show significant adsorption to glass and some plastic (polystyrene) tubes. Analyze by SDS–PAGE via the method of Laemmli.[5]

Results. The results of an experiment designed to purify the B6.2 monoclonal mouse IgG$_1$[9] antibody from an ammonium sulfate precipitate of ascites fluid using cation-exchange HPLC are shown in Fig. 4. Using the NaCl step gradient outlined above and a Mono S column, four main peaks of protein were eluted. The first peak appeared immediately after injection and proceeded for approximately 2 min. This represents protein (immunoglobulin, albumin, transferrin, and other proteins) that did not bind to the column. Low salt (50 mM NaCl) was used to obtain a second peak (fractions 8, 9) representing the B6.2 antibody, as determined using cell binding studies. A third peak (fraction 10), containing endogenous ascites antibody, was also obtained from the 50 mM NaCl elution. The final peak was eluted with high salt (1.0 M NaCl), and represents some residual antibody and other proteins present in the ammonium sulfate precipitate of the ascites fluid. It is important to note that in these studies the high isoelectric point of the B6.2 (pI = 7.3–7.4) resulted in a low salt elution for this protein at pH 7.5. This significantly contributed to the clean separation of the antibody from the other ascites fluid protein con-

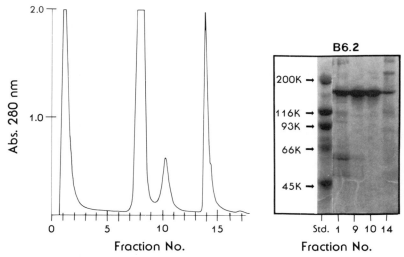

FIG. 4. Step-gradient elution of mouse monoclonal B6.2 from ammonium sulfate-precipi-tated ascites fluid using HPLC cation exchange (Pharmacia Mono S column). Fractions 1–3 were obtained following the injection of 500 μl of sample and washing with 10 mM sodium phosphate buffer (pH 7.5). Fractions 7–12 were obtained with 50 mM NaCl in sodium phosphate at pH 7.5, and the final fractions were eluted with 1.0 M NaCl in sodium phos-phate. While endogenous immunoglobulins were obtained in the initial elution buffer, frac-tions 8–9 were found to represent the B6.2 antibody (IgG$_1$), with additional endogenous IgG being seen in fraction 10. Other residual proteins were observed in fractions 14–15.

taminants, such as albumin (pI = 4.5–5.0) and transferrin (pI = 5.5–6.0), since these molecules are not protonated at pH 7.5 and do not bind to cation-exchange columns. Monoclonal antibodies with lower pI values would require a lower pH for buffer A and might require higher concen-trations of NaCl for elution. This point again illustrates the need to opti-mize HPLC separations individually for each specific monoclonal anti-body to be purified.

Gel Permeation HPLC

Molecular sieving has been a popular method for purifying many pro-teins, including various immunoglobulins.[10] As with classical liquid chro-matography, molecular sieving performed by HPLC is based upon the molecular size and conformation of the proteins to be separated, and is

[10] D. H. Cambell, J. S. Garvey, N. E. Cremer, and D. H. Sussdorf, *in* "Methods in Immu-nology," p. 198. Benjamin, New York, 1970.

dependent upon the particular effective pore size in the bead or particle matrix of the column. Proteins that are larger than the pores or channels in the bead matrix are excluded from the column (i.e., they do not pass through the beads to take a circuitous path of elution). These large molecules are excluded in the void volume (V_0) of the column. Small molecules and salts that completely penetrate the beads elute in the largest volume (V_t). Columns are chosen to separate molecules at some elution volume (V_e) intermediate to V_0 and V_t. Under ideal conditions proteins are eluted in accordance with their sieving properties (a function of size and conformation).

In practice, there are often several factors that influence the elution patterns of proteins from HPLC gel permeation (molecular sieving) columns, such as adsorption factors and ionic interactions. Ionic interactions can be minimized by using a moderate ionic strength buffer to chromatograph samples (i.e., greater than 50 mM concentration). Ionic interactions and adsorption appear to exert a more significant effect for the types of HPLC gel permeation columns that are currently available (Table IV), than for classical liquid chromatography gels such as Sephadex (Pharmacia), Ultra-Gel (LKB), or BioGel (Bio-Rad). Another factor that influences HPLC gel permeation separations is flow rate. These types of columns must be typically run at low flow rates (0.2 to 1.0 ml/min) in order to achieve good separations. Total protein concentration can also

TABLE IV
COMMERCIALLY AVAILABLE GEL PERMEATION COLUMNS USEFUL FOR PURIFYING
MONOCLONAL ANTIBODIES

	TSK-3000SW	TSK-5000PW	Zorbax GF-250
Manufacturer	Toyo-Soda	Toyo-Soda	Dupont
Base material	Polymerized diols on silica	Hydrophilic resin	Zirconia-stabilized silica with diols
Stable pH range	2–8	2–12	3–8.5
Pore size for protein exclusion	300,000	300,000–400,000	400,000
Protein capacity[a]	N/A	N/A	300 μg/250 μl
Particle size (μm)	10	10	4–5
Column size (mm i.d.)	300 × 7.5	300 × 7.5	250 × 9.4

[a] Defined as maximum amount of protein per given volume that can be separated without a 10% decrease in resolution of standard proteins that differ in size from each other by 2-fold and 4-fold; N/A, information not available from Toyo-Soda, but values should be similar as for the GF-250 column.

influence the separation of monoclonal antibodies from other proteins, and high protein concentrations can sometimes clog the column's pores. Gel permeation columns must be periodically cleaned using a variety of washing steps, such as excessive flushing with water followed by rinsing with isopropanol, to ensure continued satisfactory operation. One indication of a clogging column is an increase in pressure required to achieve a desired flow rate. In order to make sure that gel permeation columns are working properly, one should always run a known sample or standard set of proteins (sometimes provided with the column).

In summary, while HPLC gel permeation columns can be used effectively to purify and analyze monoclonal antibody preparations, one must proceed cautiously with careful monitoring of column performance. Special problems may be encountered when attempting to use elution volumes to estimate molecular size or conformation of proteins, including monoclonal antibodies and/or fragments.

EXAMPLE 5: ANALYSIS OF MOUSE IgG BY GEL PERMEATION HPLC

Equipment and Reagents

Isocratic HPLC system with UV absorbance monitor
Strip chart recorder
Zorbax Bio-Series GF-250 column with precolumn (Dupont)
100-μl injection loop
Sample buffer: 0.2 M sodium phosphate (pH 7.5)
Protein standards mixture
Antibody reagents to be analyzed

Method. (1) Equilibrate HPLC column in 0.2 M sodium phosphate (pH 7.5) at a flow rate of 1 ml/min until a stable baseline is reached on the absorbance monitor (280 nm). (2) Zero chart recorder. (3) Inject protein standards to determine column performance (see Fig. 5). (4) Inject sample (volume depends upon the protein concentration). (5) Elute samples from the column at a constant flow rate until all components have been recovered. (6) Collect protein fractions for further analysis.

Results. An HPLC gel permeation separation of protein standards is shown in Fig. 5. This experiment was performed using a Zorbax G-250 HPLC column (Dupont). The protein standards included thyroglobulin (MW 670K, peak 1), IgG (MW 160K, peak 2), bovine serum albumin (MW 68K, peak 3), ovalbumin (MW 45K, peak 4), myoglobin (MW 17.5K, peak 5), and a buffer component (sodium azide absorption, peak 6). While each of the protein components is clearly visualized, some overlap between the IgG and the bovine serum albumin (BSA) exists.

The chromatography of IgG and F(ab')$_2$ antibody fragments on the

PROTEIN TEST MIXTURE

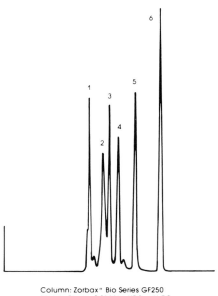

Column: Zorbax" Bio Series GF250
Mobile Phase: 0.2M Na₂HPO₄ pH 7.0
                        0.005% NaN₃

Flow Rate: 1 cm³/min
Temperature: Ambient
Detector: UV (280 nm)

PEAK IDENTITY
1. Thyroglobulin
2. IgG
3. BSA
4. Ovalbumin
5. Myoglobin
6. Sodium Azide

FIG. 5. Analysis of protein standards using gel permeation HPLC (Dupont Zorbax GF-250 column). A sample mixture was injected onto the column and samples were eluted at 1 ml/min in 0.2 M sodium phosphate buffer (pH 7.5). The identity of each of the sample standards is shown. (Zorbax GF-250 data were generously provided by E. I. du Pont de Nemours and Co.)

above column is shown in Fig. 6. The IgG (MW 160K, peak 2) and F(ab')₂ (MW 100K, peak 3) were clearly resolved by the column. Other investigators have also shown that antibody fragments can be separated from whole IgG molecules using HPLC gel permeation techniques.[11] In our

[11] P. Parham, M. J. Androlewicz, F. M. Brodsky, N. J. Holmes, and J. P. Ways, *J. Immunol. Methods* **53**, 133 (1982).

COINJECTION OF INTACT IgG
AND F(Ab')₂ OF IgG

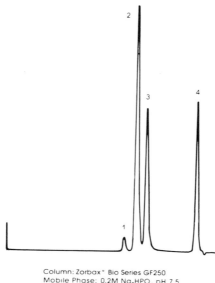

Column: Zorbax" Bio Series GF250
Mobile Phase: 0.2M Na₂HPO₄ pH 7.5
Flow Rate: 1 cm³/min
Temperature: Ambient
Detector: UV (280 nm)

PEAK IDENTITY:
1. Unknown
2. IgG
3. F(Ab')₂
4. Buffer Component

FIG. 6. Separation of F(ab')₂ from IgG using gel permeation HPLC (Dupont Zorbax GF-250 column). Conditions were as described in Fig. 5. (Zorbax GF-250 data were generously provided by E. I. du Pont de Nemours and Co.)

own experience, we have found that such separations are very much dependent upon flow rate, ionic strength of the buffer, and total protein concentration, as discussed previously.

Miscellaneous Methods for Purifying Monoclonal Antibodies by HPLC

As experience with HPLC methodology increases, new methods will be developed for the purification of proteins, including monoclonal antibodies. One such new HPLC method for the purification of monoclonal antibodies utilizes hydroxylapatite (BioGel-HPHT, Bio-Rad) chromatography, with antibodies being eluted with a phosphate gradient. Since this technique is discussed elsewhere in this volume, it will not be further described.

Other HPLC techniques that are likely to yield important analytical data on structural aspects of proteins and peptides may come out of more traditional HPLC columns designed for reverse-phase applications. Although some success has been achieved in the analysis of monoclonal antibodies via reverse phase, this approach is somewhat limited by the solvents needed for chromatography that generally denature antibodies. This approach may be more useful for the analysis of protein fragments and peptides. However, since the design of more "protein-friendly" HPLC reverse-phase columns appears to be a goal of some companies, such methodologies may not be too far in the future.

Acknowledgments

The author would like to thank Dr. Frederick A. Liberatore, Mary DuPuis, and Sheldon Sivakoff of the Immunopharmaceutical Research and Development Group at E. I. du Pont de Nemours and Co. for providing the unpublished data on the use of Mono S (Pharmacia) for antibody purification. The excellent technical assistance of Todd Thompson, Robert Fincher, and J. R. Billman is also appreciated.

This work was supported in part by Grant 1-RO1-ES03485-01 from the National Institutes of Health.

[58] Separation of IgG Idiotypes by High-Performance Hydroxylapatite Chromatography

By HECTOR JUAREZ-SALINAS, GARY S. OTT, JENG-CHYI CHEN, TIMOTHY L. BROOKS, and LARRY H. STANKER

Currently, several chromatographic techniques are available for immunoglobulin purification. These techniques include anion-exchange chromatography,[1] Cibacron Blue resins,[2] and affinity chromatography with protein A.[3] Although these techniques may produce immunoglobulin preparations of acceptable purity, they are not able to separate immunoglobulin molecules which differ solely in the idiotype. In this report we demonstrate the ability of high-performance hydroxylapatite (HPHT) chromatography to separate multiple idiotypes produced by certain hybri-

[1] S. Dissanayake and F. C. Hay, *Immunochemistry* **12,** 101 (1975).
[2] C. Bruck, D. Portetelle, C. Glineur, and A. Bollen, *J. Immunol. Methods* **53,** 313 (1982).
[3] J. J. Langone, *J. Immunol. Methods* **55,** 277 (1982).

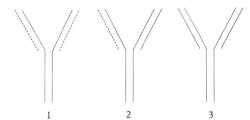

FIG. 1. Conceptual illustration of the proposed structures of H-1 idiotypes. Idiotype negative IgG has the myeloma-derived light chain (1); hybrid idiotype IgG has the B-cell-derived light chain in one arm and the myeloma-derived light chain in the other (2); idiotype positive has B-cell-derived light chain in both arms (3).

domas.[4,5] We also show that this separation can be performed at the analytical and preparative levels.

Generation of Hybridomas Which Produce Multiple IgG Idiotypes

The ideal system for the study of the chromatographic separation of idiotypes is provided by those hybridomas producing antibodies with multiple idiotypes. Hybridomas producing two or more idiotypes can be generated by utilizing a light and/or heavy chain producer myeloma for fusion. In this study we analyzed the IgG population produced by hybridoma H-1, which was generated by immunizing Biozzi mice with human hemoglobin and then fusing the spleen lymphocytes with a revertant SP2/0 myeloma which produces a light chain.[6] This myeloma was originated by spontaneous reversion of SP2/0 myeloma, which is originally a nonproducer.[7] The IgG produced by hybridoma H-1 was determined to belong to the IgG_1 κ subclass.

Since hybridoma H-1 was generated using a light chain producer for fusion, it should be synthesizing two different light chains: one derived from the B cell and the other from the myeloma. The IgG molecule containing the B-cell light chain in both antibody arms should be idiotype positive in both arms, while the hybrid IgG molecules, containing the B-cell light chain in one arm and the myeloma light chain in the other, should be idiotype positive only in one arm (hybrid idiotype). On the other hand, those IgG molecules containing only the myeloma light chain should be idiotype negative in both arms. Figure 1 shows the proposed structure of

[4] H. Juarez-Salinas, S. C. Engelhorn, W. L. Bigbee, M. A. Lowry, and L. H. Stanker, *Bio-Techniques* **2,** 164 (1984).
[5] L. H. Stanker, M. Vanderlaan, and H. Juarez-Salinas, *J. Immunol. Methods* **76,** 157 (1985).
[6] L. H. Stanker and M. Vanderlaan, unpublished results.
[7] M. Shulman, C. D. Wiede, and G. Köhler, *Nature (London)* **276,** 269 (1978).

each H-1 IgG species. As shown below, results obtained with HPHT chromatography of H-1 IgG strongly supports the existence of these species and, hence, demonstrates the usefulness of this technique for idiotype separation.

Prior to HPHT, H-1 IgG was purified and analyzed by sodium dodecyl sulfate–polyacrylamide gel electrophoresis (SDS–PAGE). Purification was achieved by protein A column chromatography. The SDS–PAGE of purified H-1 IgG is shown in Fig. 2. One heavy chain band and two, a slow and fast migrating, light chain bands were observed. The presence of two

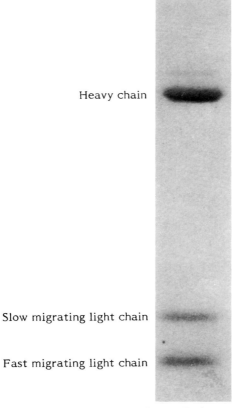

Heavy chain

Slow migrating light chain

Fast migrating light chain

FIG. 2. SDS–PAGE of protein A-purified H-1 IgG. Pure H-1 immunoglobulin, 20 μg, was loaded into 10% gels. Electrophoresis was performed following the procedure of Laemmli [V. Laemmli, *Nature* (*London*) **277**, 680 (1970)]. Proteins were stained with Coomassie Blue. H-1 IgG was separated in three bands. One band (50,000 MW) corresponded to the IgG heavy chain. The other two bands (25,000 MW) corresponded to the slow and fast migrating light chains.

light chain bands strongly suggested that hybridoma H-1 was indeed producing two light chains.

HPHT Separation of H-1 Idiotypes

The existence of multiple idiotypes in H-1 IgG was confirmed by
HPHT chromatography of the protein A-purified material and subsequent
SDS–PAGE analysis of the HPHT peaks, as indicated below.

Reagents and Instrumentation. Analytical HPHT chromatography
was performed in a Bio-Rad HPHT–MAPS HPLC system equipped with
a BioGel HPHT set consisting of a 7.8 × 100-mm HPHT analytical
column, with attached 4 × 50-mm guard column (Bio-Rad Laboratories,
Richmond, CA). Preparative HPHT chromatography was performed in a
Bio-Rad MAPS Preparative System 100 HPLC system equipped with a
preparative 21.5 × 50-mm BioGel HPHT column (Bio-Rad Laboratories,
Richmond, CA). Except when indicated, buffer A was 10 mM sodium
phosphate, 0.01 mM CaCl$_2$ (pH 6.8); buffer B was 300 mM sodium phosphate, 0.01 mM CaCl$_2$ (pH 6.8). HPHT chromatography was performed
using a 10–300 mM sodium phosphate linear gradient.

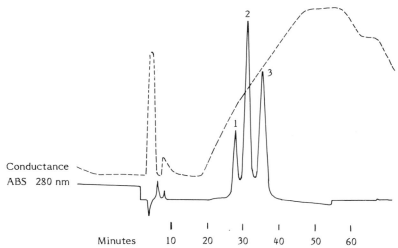

FIG. 3. HPHT chromatography of protein A-purified H-1 IgG. Protein A-purified IgG was
exhaustively dialyzed against 10 mM sodium phosphate, 0.01 mM CaCl$_2$ (pH 6.8) buffer.
Two milliliters of dialysate containing 2 mg of pure H-1 IgG was filtered through a 0.45-μm
filter prior to HPHT. After sample application column was washed with 20 ml of buffer A.
IgG was eluted with a 30-min gradient from 10 mM sodium phosphate, 0.01 mM CaCl$_2$ (pH
6.8) to 300 mM sodium phosphate, 0.01 mM CaCl$_2$ (pH 6.8). Flow rate was 1 ml/min.
Absorbance was monitored at 280 nm (——). Conductivity was monitored with a Bio-Rad
conductivity monitor (- - -).

Sample Preparation. Mouse ascites fluid was prepared for HPLC by filtration through a 0.45-μm filter. When indicated, IgG was precipitated with 50% ammonium sulfate and dialyzed exhaustively against HPHT buffer A prior to HPHT chromatography.

HPHT and SDS–PAGE of H-1 IgG. Figure 3 shows the HPHT chromatography of protein A-Purified H-1 IgG. Three clearly defined peaks (1, 2, and 3) were observed. The presence of three peaks supports the existence of three different H-1 IgG species, as suggested above. Since the SDS–PAGE profile of unfractionated IgG already indicated the presence of two light chains in H-1 ascites (Fig. 2), we analyzed the SDS–PAGE profile of HPHT peaks 1, 2, and 3 (Fig. 4). The distribution of light chains

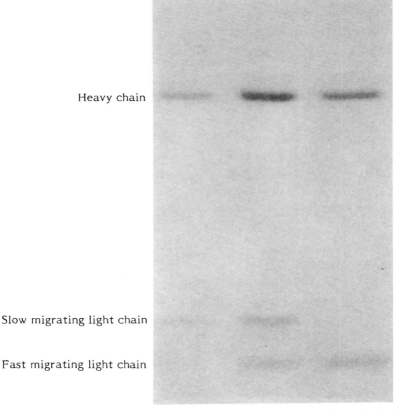

Fig. 4. SDS–PAGE of HPHT peaks. Peaks 1, 2, and 3 from the experiment depicted in Fig. 3 were collected and concentrated by ultrafiltration before SDS–PAGE. Approximately 10 μg from each peak was used for electrophoresis. Peak 1 contained slow migrating light chain (lane 1), peak 2 contained the slow and the fast migrating light chains (lane 2), and peak 3 contained the fast migrating light chain (lane 3).

among the HPHT peaks are in line with the proposal that H-1 IgG contains multiple idiotypes. Peak 1 contained only the slow migrating light chain, peak 2 was a hybrid containing the slower and fast migrating light chains, and peak 3 contained only the fast migrating light chain. Thus, HPHT chromatography seems to be capable of distinguishing between immunoglobulin molecules which differ in idiotype.

Preparative HPHT Chromatography. Currently, the need to purify large amounts of monoclonal antibodies for industrial and therapeutic use has become apparent. Therefore, it was of interest to test the ability of preparative HPHT to reproduce the separation obtained at the analytical level. Figure 5 shows the HPHT chromatogram obtained with 390 mg of ammonium sulfate-fractionated H-1 IgG. As observed in Fig. 5, H-1 IgG was separated in three peaks, yielding a profile very similar to that obtained with analytical HPHT. Thus, idiotype separations seem to be feasible at the analytical and preparative levels.

Activity Determination of Hydroxylapatite Peaks. The existence of three different idiotypes in H-1 IgG was further substantiated by analyzing the ability of hydroxylapatite peaks 1, 2, and 3 to recognize the anti-

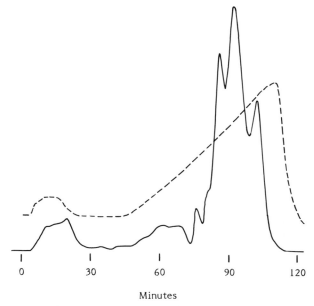

Minutes

FIG. 5. Preparative HPHT chromatography of ammonium sulfate-purified H-1 IgG. Ammonium sulfate-purified H-1 IgG, 390 mg, was chromatographed in a preparative HPHT column. IgG was eluted with a 60-min linear gradient from 50 mM sodium phosphate, 0.01 mM CaCl$_2$ (pH 6.8) to 240 mM sodium phosphate, 0.01 mM CaCl$_2$ (pH 6.8). Flow rate was 4 ml/min. A_{280} (——); conductivity (---).

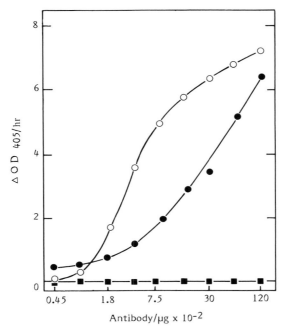

FIG. 6. Anti-human hemoglobin activity of hydroxylapatite peaks 1, 2, and 3. A sample corresponding to each HPHT peak was assayed for anti-hemoglobin activity using an enzyme-linked immunosorption assay (ELISA). Peak 1 (■), peak 2 (●), and peak 3 (○).

gen. Figure 6 shows the anti-human hemoglobin activity of hydroxylapatite peaks 1, 2, and 3. It can be observed that peak 3 was the most active (idiotype positive), while peak 2 was only partially active as expected for the hybrid idiotype, and peak 1 was inactive (idiotype negative). Peak fractions utilized in these experiments were obtained from a preliminary low-pressure hydroxylapatite separation of H-1 ascites, which yielded essentially the same separation as HPHT.

Concluding Remarks

Although situations as the one described above for hybridoma H-1 may arise frequently when generating hybridomas, the unavailability of chromatographic methods powerful enough to distinguish between different IgG species has precluded the adequate analysis of the immunoglobulin produced by such hybridomas. The results shown here demonstrate the usefulness of HPHT chromatography to separate IgG molecules on the basis of idiotype. This separation was achieved even when the IgG molecules belonged to the same IgG subclass (IgG, κ). Situations similar to the one described here should be suspected whenever the myeloma used for fusion is a producer of light and/or heavy chains or whenever double chain patterns are observed by SDS–PAGE or isoelectrofocusing. We have observed an identical situation to the one described here in hybridomas 10F7 (IgG$_1$, κ) and Cap-4 (IgM, κ) which were constructed using the same revertant SP2/0 myeloma used to generate H-1.[6] Other researchers, using another light chain producer myeloma (NS-1) for fusion, have observed similar HPHT patterns to the ones presented here for H-1.[8]

Recently, the construction of antibodies with hybrid idiotype has been done purposely, either for therapeutic[9,10] or diagnostic use.[11] The methodology presented here seems to be particularly well suited for the analytical and preparative purification of such hybrid molecules.

Acknowledgments

This work was performed under the auspices of the Chromatography Business Unit, Chemical Division, Bio-Rad Laboratories and the U.S. Department of Energy, by the Lawrence Livermore National Laboratory, under contract W-7405-ENG-48 with financial support of the Environmental Protection Agency, Grant R808642-01. We wish to thank Mrs. Pat Pierce-Hoffer for excellent help in typing the manuscript.

[8] R. M. Bartholomew and S. M. Hochschwender, personal communication.
[9] C. L. Reading, in "Hybridomas and Cellular Immortality" (B. H. Tom and J. D. Allyson, eds.), pp. 235–250. Plenum, New York, 1983.
[10] S. P. Cobbold and H. Waldmann, Nature (London) **308**, 460 (1984).
[11] C. Milstein and A. C. Cuello, Nature (London) **305**, 537 (1983).

[59] The Use of Rat Monoclonal Antibodies to Characterize, Quantify, and Purify Polyclonal or Monoclonal Mouse IgM

By Françoise Cormont, Patrick Manouvriez, Lieve De Clercq, and Hervé Bazin

The problems in determining the specificity and controlling the quality of polyclonal antisera make it difficult to establish universal antibody standards for routine applications. The use of monoclonal antibodies can circumvent these problems. This is true for all immunoglobulin isotypes and particularly for IgM. In this chapter, we describe a method to purify mouse IgM based on immunoaffinity chromatography and simple techniques to characterize this immunoglobulin by immunofluorescence tests, radioimmunoassays, or precipitation in agar.

Production and Purification of Rat Monoclonal Antibodies against Mouse IgM

A 3-month-old female LOU/C rat received, over a 2-week interval, two intraperitoneal injections of 250 μg monoclonal IgM (from BALB/c mice) and polyclonal IgM (from NMRI outbred mice) mixed with 0.2 ml of complete Freund's adjuvant (Difco). The booster inoculation (100 μg of BALB/c monoclonal IgM) was given intravenously after a rest period of 7 months, without adjuvant and 4 days before fusion. Spleen cells were fused with the nonsecreting LOU/C rat IR983F cell line[1] using a slightly modified version of the technique described by Köhler and Milstein.[2] Ten days after the fusion, supernatants were tested for anti-mouse IgM by radioimmunoassay and the positive hybridomas were cloned twice by limiting dilution. These rat hybridomas were used to inoculate subcutaneously female LOU/C. IgK-1b rats congeneic to the LOU/C strain.[3] The first passage on the LOU/C rat gave a solid tumor which was minced and injected ip into several LOU/C IgK-1b rats. Among various rat hybridomas which were all secreting anti-mouse IgM monoclonal antibodies, two were selected for their high production, LO-MM-8 (for LOU rat, anti-mouse IgM number 8) and LO-MM-9 (for LOU rat, anti-mouse IgM number 9). The *in vivo* production of monoclonal antibodies by the two rat hybridomas LO-MM-8 and LO-MM-9 is given in Table I. The second passage, and the first to give ascitic fluid, was named P2, the third passage P3, etc. The ascitic fluids and the serum contained rat monoclonal antibodies against mouse IgM, which were rapidly purified by affinity chromatography[3] on a column of MARK-3 monoclonal antibodies. LO-MM-8 and LO-MM-9 were determined to be, respectively, IgG$_1$ κ and IgG$_{2a}$ κ isotypes by use of monospecific antisera.[4]

Uses of Rat LO-MM-8 or LO-MM-9 Monoclonal Antibodies

Purification of Mouse IgM

In certain species, some IgM binds to protein A on *Staphylococcus aureus*.[5,6] However, in most cases, purification of IgM is rather difficult.

---

[1] H. Bazin, *in* "Protides of the Biological Fluids" (H. Peeters, ed.), Vol. 29, p. 615. Pergamon, Oxford, 1982.

[2] G. Köhler and C. Milstein, *Nature (London)* **256**, 495 (1975).

[3] H. Bazin, F. Cormont, and L. De Clercq, *J. Immunol. Methods* **71**, 9 (1984).

[4] H. Bazin, A. Beckers, and P. Querinjean, *Eur. J. Immunol.* **4**, 44 (1974).

[5] M. P. Chalon, R. W. Milne, and J. P. Vaerman, *Scand. J. Immunol.* **9**, 259 (1979).

[6] J. W. Goding, *J. Immunol. Methods* **20**, 241 (1978).

TABLE I
In Vivo PRODUCTION OF RAT MONOCLONAL ANTIBODIES IN ASCITES

Hybridoma	Transplantation number	Number of LOU/C rats	Quantity (ml)	Mean (ml/rat)
LO-MM-8	P2	5	175	35.0
	P3	30	1360	45.3
	Total	35	1535	43.8
LO-MM-9	P2	10	199	19.9
	P3	10	180	18.0
	P4	10	254	25.4
	P5	10	96	9.6
	P6	10	375	37.5
	P7	5	130	26.0
	Total	55	1234	22.4
	Grand total	90	2769	30.7

A method to purify mouse IgM by chromatography on Sephadex G-200 has been described.[7] IgM can also be prepared by precipitation with 40% saturated ammonium sulfate followed by gel filtration on Ultrogel AcA22, Sepharose 6B, or Sephacryl S-500.[8] These techniques usually require multiple steps and therefore provide low yields of purified IgM. They also rarely avoid contamination with α_2-macroglobulin. To circumvent these problems, we have used rat monoclonal antibodies against mouse IgM.

The immunoaffinity chromatography column was prepared as follows: 6.5 g of CNBr-activated Sepharose-4B (Pharmacia, Sweden) was suspended in 10^{-3} M HCl and washed for 15 min with 1400 ml of 10^{-3} M HCl on a sintered glass filter. Purified LO-MM-8 or LO-MM-9, 200 mg, was dissolved in 32.5 ml coupling buffer (NaH_2CO_3, 0.1 M, containing 0.5 M NaCl) and mixed with the gel in a stoppered vessel. The mixture was rotated for 1 hr at room temperature. Excess LO-MM-8 or LO-MM-9 was washed away with coupling buffer and excess active groups were blocked by incubation with Tris–HCl buffer (0.1 M, pH 8.0) for 1 hr. The gel was then washed successively with 0.1 M glycine–HCl (pH 2.8) and phosphate-buffered saline (pH 7). This two-buffer cycle was repeated twice. The gel was then packed in an Econocolumn (Bio-Rad). Its properties

[7] A. Gordon, B. Keil, K. Sebesta, O. Knesol, and F. Šorm, *Collect. Czech. Chem. Commun.* **15,** 1 (1950).

[8] J. W. Goding, "Monoclonal Antibodies: Principles and Practice," p. 115. Academic Press, New York, 1984.

TABLE II

QUANTITATION OF PURIFIED MOUSE IgM MAb FROM ASCITIC FLUID AND SUPERNATANT

Insolubilized rat MAb against mouse IgM	Mouse MAb[a]	Volume of ascitic fluid	Volume of supernatant (ml)	Purified IgM (mg)	Percentage of purified IgM recovered
LO-MM-8	PB1	30		19.6	>90
(190 mg)	MARTSH-1	10		10.1	>90
	MARTSH-3	6		8.1	>90
LO-MM-9	NMS	15		5.5	>90
(200 mg)	MARTSH-1	8		18.2	>90
	MARTSH-2	10		25.5	>90
	MARTSH-2		300	13.5	>50
	MARTSH-3	10		23.5	>90
	MARE-IR2	26		39	>90

[a] PB1, Mouse monoclonal IgM; MARTSH, mouse anti-rat TSH, thyroid stimulating hormone; NMS, normal mouse serum; MARE-IR2, mouse anti-idiotype of the IgE monoclonal rat Ig synthesized by the IR2 tumor.

remain unchanged for long periods at room temperature. The immunoaffinity column was stored at 4°.

A diagram of the method used to purify mouse IgM is given in Fig. 1. Normal mouse serum, ascitic fluid, or serum from mice carrying IgM-secreting hybridomas was centrifuged for 10 min at 12,000 g. The supernatants were filtered on an AP25 prefilter (Millipore), and then applied to the immunoaffinity column. The normal mouse serum proteins were not retained and passed through the column except for IgM, which was absorbed by the rat monoclonal anti-mouse IgM antibodies. The column was washed with 120 ml of PBS, then washed with 100 ml of PBS containing 2.5 M NaCl to elute aspecifically bound protein, and brought back to normal salinity with 100 ml of PBS. Adsorbed IgM was eluted with glycine–HCl buffer (0.1 M, NaCl 0.15 M, pH 2.8). As soon as the proteins were eluted, a neutral pH was restored in the column by washing it with PBS. The eluate was collected in 150-drop fractions in tubes containing 13 drops of 1 M Tris–HCl (pH 8).

The same technique can also be used with the supernatant produced by using a roller system[9] (Fig. 2). Quantities of purified IgM from ascitic fluid or supernatant using this method are given in Table II.

[9] M. Bodeus, G. Burtonboy, and H. Bazin, J. Immunol. Methods 79, 1 (1985).

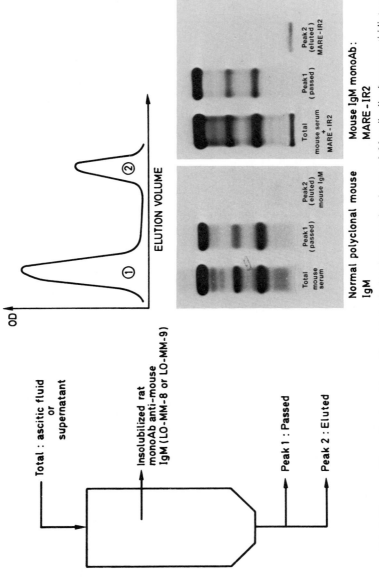

FIG. 1. Diagram of the method used to purify normal polyclonal or monoclonal mouse IgM antibodies [mouse anti-idiotype of the IgE rat monoclonal Ig (IR2 tumor): MARE-IR2].

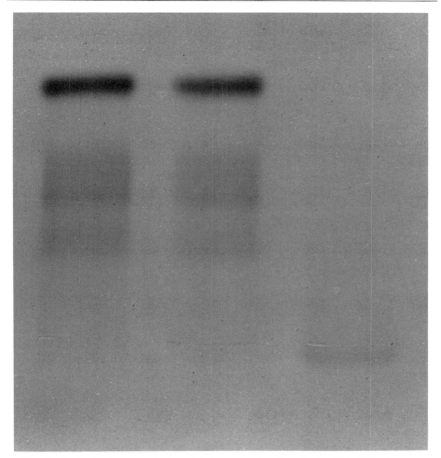

FIG. 2. Analysis of supernatant containing monoclonal antibody (MARTSH-2 = mouse anti-rat TSH) before and after purification on a column of LO-MM-9.

Precipitation in Agar

Both LO-MM-8 and LO-MM-9 rat monoclonal antibodies can precipi-tate mouse IgM in the double immunodiffusion Ouchterlony test (not shown). They can also precipitate mouse IgM in immunoelectrophoretic analysis. A gel made with 1.5% agarose (indubiose, IBF, France) in veronal buffer (pH 8.6) containing 2% sodium azide is poured hot onto a glass plate in order to obtain a 1.5-mm layer. Holes of the appropriate diameter (2.5 mm) are then punched, the distance between holes and the central trough being about 3.5 mm. The holes are filled with 7 μl of mouse

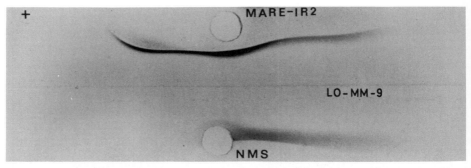

Fɪɢ. 3. Immunoelectrophoretic analysis of mouse ascitic fluid containing MARE-IR2 (mouse IgM monoclonal antibody against rat idiotype of the IR2 immunocytoma protein) (top well) and normal mouse serum (bottom well) developed by the LO-MM-9 rat monoclonal antibody against mouse IgM.

IgM (monoclonal or polyclonal). Electrophoresis is carried out at 100 V for 1.5 hr. After immunoelectrophoretic migration, the central trough is filled with about 140 μl diluted ascitic fluid of either rat monoclonal antibody LO-MM-8 or LO-MM-9 at a concentration of 1.5 mg/ml. A precipitation line is generally seen after 12 hr of diffusion at room temperature. LO-MM-9 can clearly precipitate mouse IgM in agar (Fig. 3). Experience in our laboratory shows that LO-MM-9 precipitates mouse IgM at a much lower concentration than LO-MM-8 and is preferred for this purpose.

Immunofluorescence Tests

LO-MM-8 and LO-MM-9 were conjugated to fluorescein isothiocyanate (FITC, Nordic, The Netherlands) following the method (slightly modified) of Cebra and Goldstein.[10] The purified monoclonal antibodies were dialyzed at a concentration of 10 mg/ml for 6 hr against 9% NaCl followed by 24 hr of dialysis against 0.1 M sodium carbonate–bicarbonate buffer (pH 9.5). The FITC was prepared dry at 1/1000 in Pevikon (Serva, Federal Republic of Germany) and was directly dissolved in the protein solution at a concentration of 5 mg of FITC–Pevikon/mg protein. The reaction mixture was agitated slowly in the dark for 1 hr at room temperature and then overnight at 4°. The solution was centrifuged and filtered on a 2 × 30-cm Sephadex G-25 (Pharmacia, Sweden) column equilibrated with PBS. Fluorescein-conjugated LO-MM-8 and LO-MM-9 were then used as follows.

[10] J. J. Cebra and G. Goldstein, *J. Immunol.* **95,** 230 (1965).

Normal mouse spleen cells were collected after injecting PBS plus 5% FCS and 0.2% azide with a syringe directly into the spleen (P. G. Holt, CIRU, Princess Margaret Hospital, Subiaco, Western Australia, personal communication). With this method the viability of the cells ranged from 95 to 100%. The cell suspension, 50 μl at a concentration of 10^6/ml, was incubated for 30 min at 4° with 50 μl of LO-MM-8 or LO-MM-9 labeled with FITC, supplemented with an excess of 300× normal rat immunoglobulins to avoid possible binding of LO-MM-8 or LO-MM-9 to Fc receptors. After two washes, cytocentrifuge slides were prepared with 50,000 cells in 100 μl of medium (500 rpm, 4 min) and mounted with buffered glycerol.[11] Thirty to forty percent of cells carrying IgM in normal mouse spleen can be recognized with this method.

Radioimmunoassays

The LO-MM-8 and LO-MM-9 monoclonal antibodies were labeled with ^{125}I following the method of De Meyts.[12] The following reagents were added to a cryotube in sequence: 5 μl of Na^{125}I at 7 μg/ml (100 mCi/ml), 5 μl of NaH$_2$PO$_4$ at 27.6 mg/ml, 300 μl of immunoglobulins (400 μg), and 50 μl of chloramine-T at 40 μg/ml. The reaction was allowed to proceed for 5 min. To determine iodine incorporation, one drop of iodine-containing solution was added to 500 μl PBS with 1% bovine serum albumin (PBS–BSA). Proteins were precipitated by addition of an equal volume of 20% trichloracetic acid. After centrifugation for 1 min at 19,000 g, the supernatant and precipitate were counted for radioactivity. If less than 45% of the iodine was incorporated, more chloramine-T was added to the iodination solution and the reaction continued for 5 min. If 45% of the radioactivity was incorporated, 50 μl of sodium metabisulfate (1.6 mg/ml) and 50 μl KI (1 mg/ml) were added and the mixture was applied to a G-25 column and eluted with PBS. The eluate was collected in 1- to 1.5-ml fractions. The first peak of radioactivity (the labeled protein) was stored at 4°. Before use, labeled proteins were diluted in PBS–BSA to give 1000 cpm/μl. Microtiter plates (Dynatech 1-220-24) were coated with 50 μl of LO-MM-8 or LO-MM-9 at a concentration of 50 μg/ml in PBS buffer diluted 1/10. After a first incubation of 2 hr at room temperature, plates were washed with 200 μl of PBS–BSA and incubated for 1 hr with 200 μl of PBS–BSA to ensure saturation of free sites. After the second incubation, plates were washed twice with 200 μl of PBS–BSA and once with 200 μl of PBS. The

---

[11] G. D. Johnson, R. S. Davidson, K. C. McNamel, G. Russell, D. Goodwin, and E. J. Holborow, *J. Immunol. Methods* **55**, 231 (1982).

[12] De Meyts, *in* "Methods in Receptor Research" (M. Blecher, ed.), Part I, p. 301. New York, 1980.

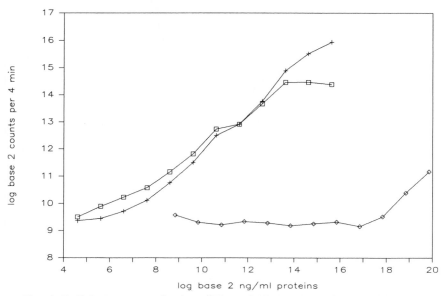

FIG. 4. Radioimmunoassay titration of mouse IgM or mouse IgG using iodinated LO-MM-8 on LO-MM-8 coated microtitration plates. (□) Monoclonal mouse IgM antibody, MARE-IR2; (+) polyclonal mouse IgM; (◇) monoclonal mouse IgG antibody, MARE-1.

dried plates could be stored at −20° for several weeks. Fifty microliters of monoclonal or polyclonal mouse IgM or IgG was added to the plates and incubated overnight at 4°. Plates were washed three times with 200 μl of PBS–BSA, incubated for 1 hr with 50 μl of LO-MM-8 or LO-MM-9 labeled with ^{125}I, and finally washed four times with 200 μl of PBS–BSA. Plates were dried before counting. The results given in Figs. 4 and 5 show that polyclonal and monoclonal mouse IgM bind to LO-MM-8 and LO-MM-9 but mouse IgG is not recognized by these two monoclonal antibodies.

Conclusions

Purified monoclonal antibodies against mouse IgM can be obtained in large quantities without any difficulty using simple methods. These antibodies can be used for the detection, quantification, or purification of mouse IgM and they bring a high level of reproductibility and a possible standardization of routine immunochemical techniques.

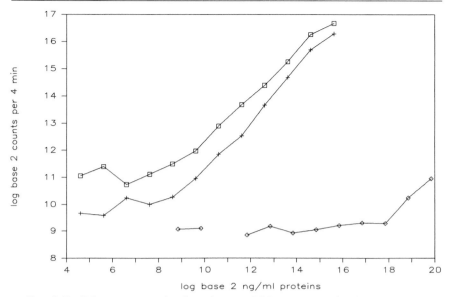

FIG. 5. Radioimmunoassay titration of mouse IgM or mouse IgG using iodinated LO-MM-9 on LO-MM-9 coated microtitration plates. (□) Monoclonal mouse IgM antibody, MARE-IR2; (+) polyclonal mouse IgM; (◇) monoclonal mouse IgG antibody, MARE-1.

Acknowledgments

This work was supported by the F.R.S.M. (Belgium) contract No. 3.4518.76 and by EURATOM contract BIO-C-358-81-B (Publication 2190). The authors appreciated the excellent technical assistance of C. Genart, F. Nisol, J. M. Malache, and J. P. Kints and thank F. Bolle for her help in preparing the manuscript. H. B. is a staff member of the Commission of the European Communities.

[60] Purification of IgG Monoclonal Antibodies from Ascitic Fluid Based on Rivanol Precipitation

By FRANTIŠEK FRANĚK

The procedure employing Rivanol[1] belongs to the spectrum of methods currently used for isolation of blood plasma immunoglobulin G (IgG)

---

[1] Rivanol, registered trademark of Farbwerke Hoechst AG: 2-ethoxy-6,9-diaminoacridine lactate.

with unimpaired antibody activity.[2-5] In contrast to precipitating agents that considerably alter the ionic strength or dielectric constant of the solvent, the cationic dye Rivanol acts through formation of insoluble complexes with negatively charged proteins.[6,7] Rivanol is therefore fully effective at concentrations lower than 1%, under conditions such that the ionic strength of the plasma is adequately reduced. The pH remains in the range of 7–8.2 throughout the purification and the dielectric constant is not altered, because no organic solvents are used. IgG preparations obtained by the Rivanol procedure have a very low dimer and oligomer content in comparison with IgG preparations obtained by methods that involve a shift of the pH to values below 5.

Rivanol acts as a bactericidal agent and as an efficient precipitating agent of viral particles and nucleic acids.[7] Human IgG preparations purified with the aid of Rivanol are free of viral antigen (Australia antigen).[8,9]

Mouse ascitic fluid contains proteins identical with those of blood plasma. However, their concentration and ratio are rather different and vary considerably in comparison with the composition of plasma. In addition, ascitic fluid often contains lipid particles and emulsified residues of hydrocarbons (Pristane, mineral oil) that have been injected into the peritoneal cavity as irritating agents. Ascitic fluid also contains subcellular particles liberated from dead cells; these particles do not sediment along with hybridoma and other cells upon centrifugation of the ascitic fluid. It should therefore be kept in mind that ascitic fluid represents a more complex body fluid than does blood plasma.

The major fraction of ascitic proteins is serum albumin. The presence of albumin is advantageous for the use of Rivanol, because albumin is effectively precipitated by this cationic agent. By analogy to precipitation of albumin in blood plasma, the voluminous albumin precipitate coprecipitates components such as lipid particles, lipoproteins, IgM, and aggregated proteins. Obviously viruses and nucleoproteins present in the fluid coprecipitate as well. Consequently, the Rivanol procedure is clearly a useful tool when the investigator requires a method yielding very pure IgG preparations from ascitic fluids.

[2] J. Hořejší, Cas. Lek. Cesk. 91, 704 (1952).
[3] J. Hořejší and R. Smetana, Acta Med. Scand. 155, 65 (1956).
[4] H. E. Schultze, H. Haupt, K. Heide, N. Heimberger, and H. G. Schwick, Immunochemistry 2, 273 (1965).
[5] E. Dietzel and H. Geiger, Behringwerk-Mitt. 43, 129 (1964).
[6] M. Šťastný and J. Hořejší, Clin. Chim. Acta 6, 782 (1961).
[7] A. R. Neurath and R. Brunner, Experientia 25, 668 (1969).
[8] D. D. Schroeder and M. M. Mozen, Science 168, 1462 (1970).
[9] J. Hořejší and J. Kořínek, Zentralbl. Bakteriol., Parasitenkd., Infektionskr. Hyg., Abt. 1: Orig., Reihe A 220, 513 (1972).

Purification Procedure

The novel, principal modification of the Rivanol procedure is designed with regard to the substantially different source and application of mouse monoclonal antibodies in comparison to the therapeutic application of human IgG, for which the original method was developed.

A volume of about 50 ml of ascitic fluid with a high concentration of monoclonal antibody may serve as a sufficient supply of monoclonal antibody for long-term laboratory work, or even for manufacturing a radioimmunoassay diagnostic kit on an industrial scale. Therefore, the new procedure is convenient for processing small volumes rather than liters of the fluid. With regard to the scarcity of the ascitic fluid, the new procedure is designed to minimize the number of steps and to avoid unnecessary dilution.

Before Rivanol is added, the ionic strength and the concentration of chloride ion in the fluid must be considerably reduced. In the original procedure this is accomplished by dilution with water. In the new procedure the ionic composition of the fluid is adjusted by dialysis, without increasing the volume. The number of steps is reduced by including gel chromatography in which IgG is separated from contaminating proteins simultaneously with efficient removal of Rivanol.

Solutions

Phosphate-buffered saline (PBS): 150 mM sodium chloride, 20 mM sodium dihydrogen phosphate, the pH adjusted to 7.4

Sodium acetate: 50 mM water solution

Rivanol: 3% (w/v) solution of 2-ethoxy-6,9-diaminoacridine lactate (pharmaceutical grade) in water; the pH adjusted to 8.2

Formic acid: 0.2% (v/v) water solution

Sodium azide: 10% (w/v) water solution

Equipment

Fraction collector

Micropump

Chromatographic column, 2-liter bed volume (6 × 71 cm), preferentially an all-glass column with fritted glass bottom because parts made of some plastic materials may be stained irreversibly by Rivanol. Suitable chromatographic columns are from Pharmacia (Uppsala, Sweden).

UV monitor, wavelength 280 nm or 254 nm

Dialysis. For a typical preparation a volume of 50 ml ascitic fluid is placed in dialysis tubing (Visking dialysis tubing 20/32) and dialyzed in the cold against three changes of 0.5–0.7 liter of the sodium acetate solution. This step takes 2 days without stirring, or 1 day with stirring. The ascitic fluid does not require any special treatment before dialysis. Neither high-speed centrifugation nor removal of oil droplets is necessary. A small fibrin clot, appearing frequently upon thawing the ascitic fluid that has been kept at subzero temperature, need not be removed. After dialysis, the fluid is poured into a glass beaker.

Precipitation by Rivanol. A volume of 9.0 ml of Rivanol solution is added slowly to 50 ml of dialyzed ascitic fluid, with continuous stirring with a glass rod at room temperature. A heavy yellow precipitate starts to form immediately. The mixture is left for 20 min, with occasional stirring. At the end of the period a major part of the precipitate appears as a paste that sticks to the bottom of the beaker and to the glass rod.

Filtration. The remaining precipitate suspended in the liquid phase is removed by filtration through a thick filter paper placed in a funnel. A clear yellow filtrate containing IgG and some other proteins is obtained.

Gel Chromatography. A chromatography column containing 2 liters of Sephadex G-100 (Pharmacia, Uppsala, Sweden) equilibrated in PBS is prepared in advance. The filtrate containing Rivanol must not come in contact with PBS, because chloride anion will precipitate Rivanol. There-fore, 30 ml of the sodium acetate solution is applied to the column before the filtrate. After soaking the filtrate in the Sephadex bed, another 30-ml portion of the sodium acetate solution is applied. The circuit of micro-pump–column–monitor–fraction collector is then connected, and the sample is eluted by pumping the formic acid solution onto the column at a flow rate of 50 to 60 ml/hr. Fractions are collected every 20 min, and the absorbance at 280 or 254 nm is recorded.

IgG moves through the column as the fastest component. Since it is colorless, its appearance in the effluent can only be detected by a UV monitor. The next zone is pink and, therefore, its position on the column can be observed. A typical elution profile is shown in Fig. 1. The relative heights of the first and the second peak depend on the concentration of the monoclonal immunoglobulin in a particular sample of ascitic fluid.

Rivanol moves as a yellow zone slightly slower than other salts, due to adsorption on the Sephadex matrix. It is washed out by the formic acid solution. After the elution of Rivanol, the Sephadex column may be reequilibrated in PBS and used for the next run.

Pooling of the Fractions. The elution profile (Fig. 1)[10] is formed by two

---

[10] Aliquots of fractions were mixed with pig anti-mouse IgG serum in the presence of polyethylene glycol 6000; after an incubation period 10 min at 37° the turbidity was measured at 500 nm.

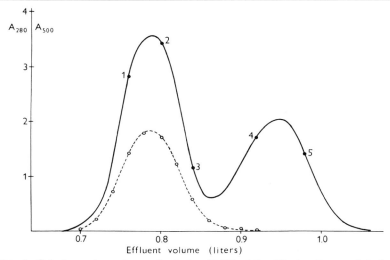

Fig. 1. Gel chromatography on Sephadex G-100 of the filtrate after precipitation by Rivanol. The column (6 × 71 cm) was equilibrated in PBS. Full line, concentration of protein monitored by absorbance at 280 nm. Dashed line, concentration of IgG determined by immunoprecipitate turbidity at 500 nm.[10] Aliquots were taken from several fractions (designated 1–5) and subjected to electrophoretic analysis (see Fig. 2).

overlapping peaks. As demonstrated by immunoprecipitation (turbidity curve in Fig. 1) and by electrophoresis (Fig. 2),[11–13] the first peak contains pure IgG, and the second consists of transferrin and remnants of serum albumin, accompanied by several trace proteins.

The recorded elution profile usually represents a satisfactory guide for deciding which fractions will be pooled. If quantification is particularly important, the absorbance at 280 nm may be measured in individual fractions. For obtaining a product of high purity, only the ascending part and the top of the first peak are collected; the overlapping part is rechromatographed. If purity is not the critical factor, the whole first peak including the overlapping part is pooled.

IgG is preserved by adding sodium azide to a final concentration of at least 0.05% and stored at 4°. The concentration of IgG in solutions obtained directly by pooling the fractions is usually in the range of 0.5–2 mg/ml, determined by measuring absorbance at 280 nm.

[11] U. K. Laemmli and M. Favre, *J. Mol. Biol.* **80,** 575 (1973).
[12] V. Hořejší, I. Hilgert, H. Krištofová, and O. Satayalai, *Immunol. Lett.* **8,** 279 (1984).
[13] J. Kovář and F. Franěk, this volume [23].

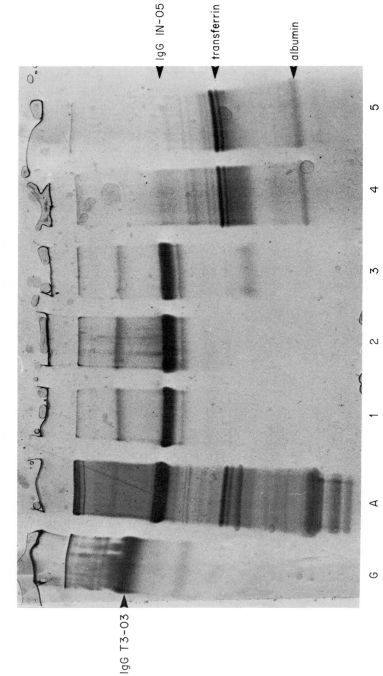

Fig. 2. Analysis of fractions obtained during IgG purification by polyacrylamide gel (6–25%) electrophoresis. The buffer system of Laemmli and Favre[11] was used with omission of sodium dodecyl sulfate. Purification of IgG₁ monoclonal antibody IN-05[12] is demonstrated. A, Original ascitic fluid; lanes 1–5, fractions indicated in Fig. 1; G, purified IgG₁ monoclonal antibody from hybridoma T3-03.[13]

Purity of IgG Preparations

The Rivanol procedure yields total IgG from mouse ascitic fluid. Thus the monoclonal antibody is not as pure as it would be by affinity purification using the corresponding immobilized antigen. The fraction of IgG represented by monoclonal antibody depends on the level secreted by the hybridoma growing in the peritoneal cavity. Since the level of polyclonal mouse IgG occurring in the ascitic fluid is generally very low (see the faint zones in IgG fractions in Fig. 2), most monoclonal IgG preparations obtained by the Rivanol procedure are suitable for direct use in quantitative microimmunoassays as well as for immobilization and use in affinity purification of antigens.

Alternative Techniques

The use of Sephadex G-100 for gel chromatography made the chromatography step somewhat lengthy. We tried Sephacryl S-200 (Pharmacia, Uppsala, Sweden) as an alternative chromatography support. This support made it possible to use flow rates several times faster. On the other hand, the Sephacryl matrix was found to display higher affinity for Rivanol and, consequently, elution of Rivanol from the Sephacryl column was more difficult.

The gel chromatography technique may not be convenient for large-scale purifications. In such cases, the filtrate containing IgG may be freed of Rivanol by adding sodium chloride to a final concentration of 5%. The precipitated chloride salt of Rivanol is removed by centrifugation, and the IgG further enriched by salting out. Precipitation with 50% saturated ammonium sulfate or 18 g sodium sulfate per 100 ml of solution may be used with equal success. Traces of Rivanol are removed from the IgG preparations by gel filtration on Sephadex G-25.

Concluding Remarks

The direct use of ascitic fluid as a source of monoclonal antibody is frequently undesirable. Ascitic fluids contain unstable lipid components that persist in the fluid upon centrifugation and cause turbidity interfering in certain immunochemical methods. The proteolytic activity due to enzymes of body fluids (plasmin) as well as the intracellular proteases (cathepsins) liberated from the necrotic part of the tumor may damage monoclonal antibodies during storage in the form of ascitic fluid.

The Rivanol procedure is one of the most efficient methods for the removal of all lipid material from the IgG preparations. Solutions of purified IgG are water-clear and colorless and are suitable for immunoassays in which a very low nonspecific background is required. In addition, nucleoproteins and viruses should be absent, by analogy with IgG preparations obtained from blood plasma.

The Rivanol procedure cannot be used for purification of IgM, because IgM coprecipitates with other unstable components of the ascitic fluid. The described procedure was successfully used with numerous monoclonal antibodies of the IgG_1, IgG_{2a}, and IgG_{2b} subclasses. One IgG_3 could not be purified by this method, because this monoclonal immunoglobulin precipitated during dialysis against 50 mM sodium acetate. Other examples of IgG_3 were not available to us; it is difficult to conclude whether low solubility at reduced ionic strength is a common property of all IgG_3 immunoglobulins.

In our laboratory purified monoclonal IgG antibodies are stored preferably in PBS solution at 4° preserved with sodium azide. Preparations of monoclonal antibodies were found to be active in radioimmunoassays or in immunohistochemical methods after storage for more than 2 years.

[61] Purification of Rat Monoclonal Antibodies

By Hervé Bazin, Françoise Cormont, and Lieve De Clercq

Introduction

Conventional procedures for purification of human, rabbit, or mouse immunoglobulins (Ig) can generally be applied to rat Ig. However, they are all based on the major properties of heterogeneous populations of Ig, which are not always found at a molecular level of a given monoclonal antibody. It is therefore important to specifically test some of these major characteristics: solubility, stability at acidic pH, electric charge, and molecular weight. The first task is to identify these properties as they are directly or loosely correlated with the class or subclass of the monoclonal antibody.

Identification of Isotype. The Ouchterlony test can be easily performed as follows. An appropriate volume of 1.5% agarose (indubiose, IBF, France) in a veronal buffer containing 2 parts per thousand of sodium azide at pH 8.6 is poured while warm onto a glass plate in order to obtain a 1.5-mm layer. Holes are usually punched in a circular pattern around a central hole, the distances between holes being 3–5 mm. The central hole (diameter 9 mm) is filled with 80 μl of *in vitro* culture supernatant and the peripheral holes (diameter 3 mm) with 5–10 μl of rabbit antisera against rat immunoglobulin classes or subclasses.[1] Antibody classes are difficult to determine in ascitic fluid, as the normal immunoglobulins from the host are also present. In such cases, the monoclonal antibody must be purified for testing of its isotype. Precipitation lines are generally seen after several hours of diffusion at room temperature. The isotype identification must be unambiguous. Radioimmunoassay or ELISA can also be used to increase the sensitivity of the tests. Antisera against rat Ig isotypes can be prepared as described in Bazin *et al.*,[1] or purchased commercially, but in the latter case, their specificity for one immunoglobulin isotype must be checked before use. Mouse monoclonal antibodies against rat Ig isotypes are commercially available (Byosis, France; Hybritech, USA; Serotec, Great Britain; Zymed, USA).

Various properties of rat Ig classes or subclasses are given in Table I.[1–9] Other properties such as solubility in distilled water or in salt solutions of increasing ionic strength, stability at room temperature or after lyophilization, and type of light chain must be determined for each individual monoclonal antibody.

Euglobulin Properties. A very simple test can be done by adding a small quantity of ascitic fluid drop by drop to Tris–HCl buffer (0.005 M, pH 7.0–8.0). Euglobulin monoclonal antibodies will precipitate as a white flocculate. A more accurate test can be done by extensive dialysis against a Tris–HCl buffer (0.005 M, pH 7.5) at 4°. If a precipitate occurs, it can be separated by centrifugation at 10,000 g for 30 min. The precipitate is then washed with the same buffer at 4°, centrifuged a second time, and redissolved in a Tris–HCl buffer (0.1 M, pH 8.0) or in phosphate-buffered saline (PBS). Some monoclonal antibodies will not redissolve and must be considered denatured.

Stability of the Monoclonal Antibody. Stability of a monoclonal antibody can be evaluated at 4°, at room temperature, or at 37°. It can be

[1] H. Bazin, A. Beckers, and P. Querinjean, *Eur. J. Immunol.* **4**, 44 (1974).
[2] P. Carter and H. Bazin, *in* "The Laboratory Rat" (H. J. Baker, J. R. Lindsey, and S. H. Weisbroth, eds.), Vol. 2, p. 182. Academic Press, New York, 1980.
[3] J. Rousseaux and H. Bazin, *Vet. Immunol. Immunopathol.* **1**, 61 (1979).
[4] H. Bazin, A. Beckers, G. Urbain-Vansanten, R. Pauwels, C. Bruyns, A. F. Tilkin, B. Platteau, and J. Urbain, *J. Immunol.* **121**, 2077 (1978).
[5] H. Bazin and A. Beckers, *in* "Molecular and Biological Aspects of the Acute Allergic Reaction" (S. G. O. Johansson, K. Stranberg, and B. Uvnas, eds.), Nobel Symp. No. 33, p. 125. Plenum, New York, 1976.
[6] J. A. Lebdetter and L. A. Herzenberg, *Immunol. Rev.* **47**, 63 (1979).
[7] J. Rousseaux, M. T. Picque, H. Bazin, and G. Biserte, *Mol. Immunol.* **18**, 639 (1981).
[8] G. A. Medgyesi, G. Füst, J. Gergely, and H. Bazin, *Immunochemistry* **15**, 125 (1978).
[9] R. Nilson, E. Myhre, and G. Kronvall, *Mol. Immunol.* **19**, 119 (1982).

TABLE I
SOME PROPERTIES OF RAT IMMUNOGLOBULINS[a]

	Refs.	IgM	IgD	IgA	IgE	IgG$_1$	IgG$_{2a}$	IgG$_{2b}$	IgG$_{2c}$
					Nomenclature[a]				
Molecular formula	2	(2H + 2L)5	(2H + 2L)	(2H + 2L)n	(2H + 2L)	(2H + 2L)	(2H + 2L)	(2H + 2L)	(2H + 2L)
Sedimentation coefficient	3	17–19 S	ND[b]	7 S (monomer)	7.6 S	6.7 S	6.4 S	6.5 S	6.7 S
Molecular weight[c]	3–5	900,000	140,000[d]	163,000 (monomer)	179,000 to 198,000	156,000	156,000	156,000	156,000
Molecular weight of the heavy chain[e]	3	72,000	60,000[d]	ND	72,000 to 75,000	55,000	50,000 to 52,000	55,000	50,000 to 52,000
Euglobulin properties	1	Often	No	No	No	No	No	No	Often
Binding to protein A	6–9	Occasional IgM MAb and 15–25% of polyclonal IgM	ND	Yes (at least partially)	No	Weak and variable binding at pH 8.0	Occasional MAb can bind	Very weak binding at pH 8.0	Binding at pH >7.0 elution at pH 4–5

[a] From Bazin et al.[1]
[b] Not determined.
[c] Determined by SDS–polyacrilamide gel electrophoresis (5, 7, or 12% acrylamide).
[d] See details in Ref. 4.
[e] Determined by SDS–polyacrilamide gel electrophoresis in reducing conditions (5–15% acrylamide).

studied after lyophilization or after a short period of time in an acidic buffer (glycine–HCl, 0.1 M, pH 2.8) followed by neutralization with a Tris–HCl buffer (0.1 M, pH 8.0) or glycine–NaOH buffer (0.1 M, pH 8.6). Various criteria of recovery can be studied after these tests, of which the most important are solubility in saline and antigen-binding activity.

Type of Light Chain. More than 95% of rat Ig carry κ light chains.[10] The supernatant of an *in vitro* hybridoma culture or purified monoclonal antibody can be tested by radioimmunoassay with a mouse monoclonal antibody against rat κ chain, such as the MARK-1[11] or by Ouchterlony analysis with the MARK-1 and the MARK-3.[12] (MARK-1 and MARK-3 BALB/c hybridomas are available upon request from Hervé Bazin), which mixed together precipitate κ light chain rat immunoglobulins of the IgK-1a allotype (as the LOU/C and LOU/M monoclonal antibodies are).

Various strategies for purification can then be adopted based on the physicochemical properties of the monoclonal antibody and the required degree of purity. Most rat monoclonal antibodies carry the κ light chain and are stable at acidic pH, at least for a short period of time (3–5 min). Such κ chain rat Ig can be purified by immunoaffinity chromatography on a column containing an insoluble matrix to which monoclonal antibodies against rat κ light chain are covalently linked. Table II[13] gives the various possible strategies for purifying rat monoclonal antibodies as a function of two major criteria: ascitic fluid or supernatant, and κ or λ type.

Immunoabsorbent Column of Insolubilized Monoclonal Antibodies against Rat κ Light Chain. The diagram of the technique is given in Fig. 1. Rat Ig can be purified by conventional procedures such as ammonium sulfate precipitation followed by DEAE–cellulose chromatography[2,3] or purchased from a commercial source. One hundred milligrams of rat Ig is coupled to 3–4 g of CNBr-activated Sepharose 4B (Pharmacia, Sweden), following the procedure given by the manufacturer. Monoclonal antibodies from the MARK-1 hybridoma (mouse anti-rat κ isotype-1) or MARK-3 hybridoma (mouse anti-rat κ IgK-1a allotype-3) can be used equally well.

MARK-1 or MARK-3 monoclonal antibody can be obtained in the ascitic fluid of BALB/c mice given 0.5 ml pristane (Aldrich Chemical Company, Milwaukee, WI) a few days prior to the injection of hybridoma cells, both by the intraperitoneal route.[14] Ascitic fluid is then centrifuged

[10] L. Hood, W. R. Gray, B. G. Sanders, and W. J. Dreyer, *Cold Spring Harbor Symp. Quant. Biol.* **32**, 133 (1967).

[11] H. Bazin, L. M. Xhurdebise, G. Burtonboy, A. M. Lebacq, L. De Clercq, and F. Cormont, *J. Immunol. Methods* **66**, 261 (1984).

[12] H. Bazin, F. Cormont, and L. De Clercq, *J. Immunol. Methods* **71**, 9 (1984).

[13] P. A. Underwood, J. F. Kelly, D. F. Haaman, and H. M. MacMillan, *J. Immunol. Methods* **60**, 33 (1983).

[14] N. Hoogenraad, T. Helman, and J. Hoogenraad, *J. Immunol. Methods* **61**, 317 (1983).

TABLE II

STRATEGIES TO PURIFY RAT MONOCLONAL ANTIBODIES

Techniques of purification	Refs.	Ascites	Supernatant	Degree of purity	Number of steps	Comments
Anti-κ type IAC[a]	11	x		MAb + polyclonal Ig of the κ type	1	Good recovery
Anti-κ type IAC	11		x	MAb of the κ type	1	Good recovery, good purity
Anti-κ allotype IAC	12	x		MAb of the same κ type	1	If produced in congeneic rat for the κ locus, good recovery, good purity
Anti-κ allotype IAC	11		x	MAb of the same κ allotype	1	Good recovery, good purity
Anti-Ig isotype IAC		x		MAb + polyclonal Ig of the same isotype	1	Must be used for λ type MAb, can be used for κ type MAb, good recovery
Anti-Ig isotype IAC			x	MAb	1	Must be used for λ type MAb, good recovery and purity
Protein A AC[b]	6–9	x		MAb + polyclonal Ig of the same isotype + trace of other Ig isotypes	1	IgG$_{2c}$ MAb and occasional IgG$_1$ and IgG$_{2a}$ can be purified
Protein A AC	13		x	MAb + calf or horse Ig	1	IgG$_{2c}$ MAb, occasional MAb of the IgG$_1$ or IgG$_{2a}$ isotypes; low recovery, except for IgG$_{2c}$ MAb
Conventional techniques	1–4	x		Correlated with the number of steps	Multiple steps	Percentage of recovery inversely correlated with the number of steps
Conventional techniques	1–4		x	Correlated with the number of steps	Multiple steps	Very low recovery

[a] IAC, Immunoaffinity column.

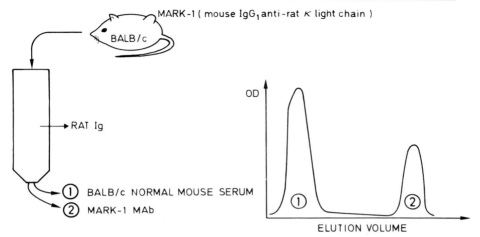

FIG. 1. Method used to purify mouse monoclonal antibodies (MARK-1 or MARK-3) to rat κ light chain. (Reproduced from Bazin *et al.*[11] with the permission of the editor of the *J. Immunol. Methods.*)

and can be directly applied to immobilized rat immunoglobulin. In general, we use about 15 ml of ascitic fluid at a concentration of 5–10 mg of antibody per milliliter for a column with about 150 mg of immobilized rat immunoglobulin. Under these conditions the first peak is devoid of monoclonal antibody. After washing the column with 20–30 ml of PBS and the same quantity of 5 M NaCl, an acidic buffer (glycine–HCl, pH 2.8, 0.1 M + 0.15 M NaCl) is used to elute bound protein. The elution of the first and second peaks can be monitored with a LKB (Uppsala, Sweden) Uvi-cord S during the complete cycle. After concentration by ultrafiltration (Immersible CX-30, Millipore), the two protein peaks are analyzed by agarose electrophoresis run in 1% agarose (indubiose, IBF, France) equilibrated with 63 mM sodium barbiturate, 15 mM barbital, 1.8 mM calcium lactate buffer adjusted to pH 8.6 with HCl. The results are shown in Fig. 2. From 150 to 200 mg of isolated MARK-1 or MARK-3 monoclonal antibodies are usually coupled to 7.5 g of CNBr-activated Sepharose 4B (Pharmacia, Sweden).

Purification of Rat Monoclonal Antibodies from *in Vitro* Supernatant
   Culture, Using a Column with Insolubilized κ Light Chain
   Monoclonal Antibody

The diagram of the technique is given in Fig. 3. The production of rat monoclonal antibodies can be achieved using small or large volume *in*

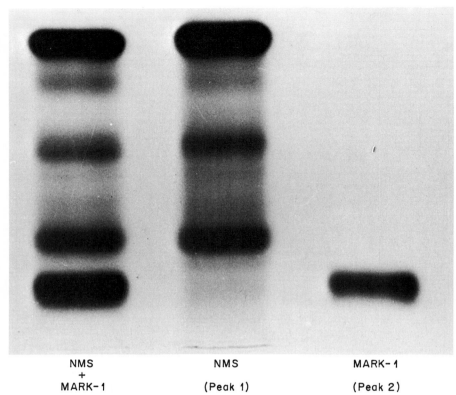

NMS	NMS	MARK-1
+		
MARK-1	(Peak 1)	(Peak 2)

FIG. 2. Agarose gel electrophoresis after purification of MARK-1 by immunoaffinity chromatography. From left to right, serum of a mouse carrying MARK-1; first peak, normal mouse serum; second peak, purified MARK-1. (Reproduced from Bazin *et al.*[11] with the permission of the editor of the *J. Immunol. Methods*.)

vitro culture. A very efficient and simple system is described in Bodeus *et al.*[15] which uses a roller system. Smaller quantities can be obtained in plastic flasks (Falcon).

As recommended by Goding,[16] it is advisable to "precycle" the immunoaffinity column before each run with the eluting buffer. *In vitro* culture supernatant, 50–500 ml, from a rat hybridoma line secreting immunoglobulins of the κ type is applied to a MARK (1 or 3) column at a rate of about

[15] M. Bodeus, G. Burtonboy, and H. Bazin, *J. Immunol. Methods* **79**, 1 (1985).
[16] J. Goding, "Monoclonal Antibodies: Principle and Practice," p. 276. Academic Press, New York, 1984.

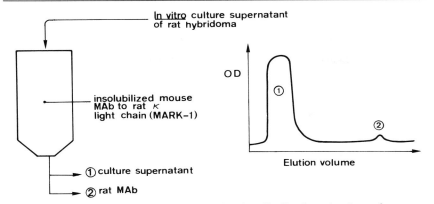

FIG. 3. Method used to purify rat monoclonal antibodies from *in vitro* culture super-natant.

2 ml/min, at room temperature. The column is then washed with PBS until the chart recorder reaches baseline, then washed again with 100 ml of PBS containing 5 M sodium chloride, and returned to normal salinity with PBS (100 ml). The pH of the column is decreased by running an acidic buffer (0.1 M glycine–HCl + 0.15 M NaCl, at pH 2.8). The pH of the eluate is returned to normal by adding drops of Tris 1 M in the collecting tubes or by neutralization with a glycine–NaOH (0.1 M, pH 8.6) buffer (Fig. 4).

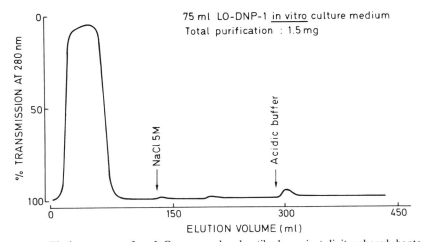

FIG. 4. Elution pattern of rat IgG₁ κ monoclonal antibody against dinitrophenyl hapten (LO-DNP-1) from a MARK-1 immunoabsorbent column with glycine–HCl buffer. (Reproduced from Bazin *et al.*[11] with the permission of the editor of the *J. Immunol. Methods.*)

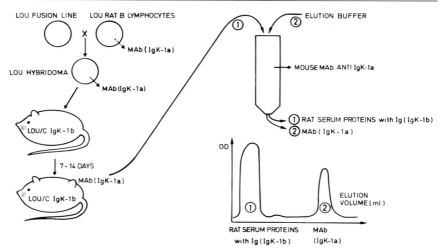

FIG. 5. Method used to purify the LOU monoclonal antibodies. (Reproduced from Bazin *et al.*[12] with the permission of the editor of the *J. Immunol. Methods.*)

Purification of Rat Monoclonal Antibodies from Ascitic Fluid or Serum by Immunoaffinity with a Mouse Monoclonal Antibody against Rat κ IgK-1a Allotype

The purification method is given in Fig. 5. In rats, a major immunoglobulin allotype is located on the constant part of the κ light chain.[17–19] Two alleles have been found, the IgK-1a being carried by the LOU/C strain and the IgK-1b allotype by the OKA strain.[18] Hybridomas made by fusing cells of the nonsecreting LOU/C IR983F cell line[20] with immune cells from LOU/C or LOU/M rats[21] are fully histocompatible with the LOU/C hybridoma into a LOU/C.IgK-1b(OKA) rat. They lead to the production of monoclonal antibodies of the IgK-1a allotype in addition to the normal polyclonal immunoglobulins of the IgK-1b allotype synthesized by the host. The LOU/C.IgK-1b(OKA) is a strain congeneic to the LOU/C strain, having the κ light chain locus from the OKA strain in the LOU/C background.[18] These rats will be referred to as LOU/C.IgK-1b.

[17] R. Wistar, Jr., *Immunology* **17**, 23 (1969).

[18] A. Beckers, P. Querinjean, and H. Bazin, *Immunochemistry* **11**, 605 (1974).

[19] G. A. Gutman, H. Bazin, O. V. Rochklin, and R. S. Nezlin, *Transplant. Proc.* **15**, 1685 (1983).

[20] H. Bazin, in "Protides of the Biological Fluids" (H. Peeters, ed.), Vol. 29, p. 615. Pergamon, Oxford, 1982.

[21] H. Bazin, A. Beckers, C. Deckers, and M. Moriame, *J. Natl. Cancer Inst. (U.S.)* **51**, 1359 (1973).

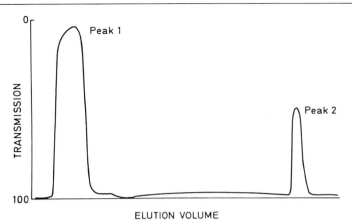

FIG. 6. Elution pattern on a MARK-3 column of rat LO-DNP-2 monoclonal antibody (IgG$_1$ κ antibody against DNP).

IgK-1a monoclonal antibodies can be separated from the normal host serum proteins including its own IgK-1b immunoglobulins by affinity chromatography with a mouse monoclonal antibody against rat κ IgK-1a allotype immobilized on a solid support.

Ten to 20 ml of serum or ascitic fluid from a LOU/C.IgK-1b rat carrying a LOU/C hybridoma is applied at a rate of 2 ml/min at room temperature to a column of 7.5 g of Sepharose 4B (Pharmacia, Sweden), onto which 200 mg of MARK-3 has been immobilized. The column is washed with 100–120 ml of PBS, then with 100 ml of PBS containing 5 M NaCl, and then again at normal salinity with 100 ml PBS. Antibody is eluted by decreasing the pH with glycine–HCl 0.1 M + 0.15 M NaCl buffer at pH 2.8. The eluate fractions are neutralized as rapidly as possible after the elution with Tris–HCl buffer (0.1 M, pH 8.0) or glycine–NaOH buffer (0.1 M, pH 8.6) (Figs. 6 and 7).

This method can be also used for rat–mouse hybridomas produced by fusing rat lymphocytes with mouse myeloma cells and grown in nude mice or nude rats.[22] In the case of hybridomas transplanted in nude mice, the mouse monoclonal antibodies used to purify the rat monoclonal antibody can be an anti-rat κ light chain such as the MARK-1 monoclonal antibody. Nude rats of the IgK-1b allotype must be used as host for hybridomas secreting IgK-1a monoclonal antibodies, and in this case, the MARK-3 monoclonal antibody can be used to purify the rat monoclonal antibody.

[22] S. A. Noeman, D. N. Misra, R. J. Yankes, H. W. Kunz, and T. J. Gill, III, *J. Immunol. Methods* **55**, 319 (1982).

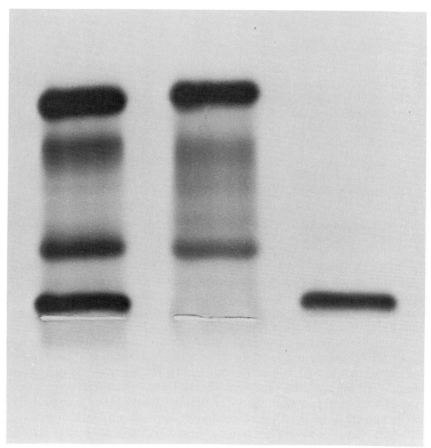

FIG. 7. Agarose gel electrophoresis of immunoaffinity-purified rat LO-HA-3 (IgG$_{2a}$ κ monoclonal antibody against human α chain which binds to IgA$_1$ and IgA$_2$, as kindly verified by J. P. Vaerman, University of Louvain, Brussels). From left to right, serum of a LOU/C.IgK-1b rat carrying LO-HA-3; peak 1, serum of the tumor host, including its own IgK-1b immunoglobulins; peak 2, purified LO-HA-3 monoclonal antibodies.

Limits of Immunoaffinity Chromatography as a Technique of Purification for Rat Monoclonal Antibodies

The major problem with immunoaffinity chromatography is linked to the stability of monoclonal antibodies at low pH, in that some rat monoclonal antibodies can be denatured. In order to avoid this problem mild elution conditions can be tested.[23–25] However, some monoclonal antibodies are exceptionally unstable and cannot be eluted without denaturation. They must be purified by conventional techniques.

Lambda-type monoclonal antibodies can be purified by immunoaffinity chromatography using an anti-rat λ monoclonal antibody (LeFèbvre and Bazin, unpublished results). They can also be purified by using monoclonal antibodies against rat immunoglobulin of the appropriate isotype, but in this case, the polyclonal immunoglobulin of the same isotype will contaminate the purified monoclonal antibody. By addition of the two immunoaffinity columns, a better degree of purity can be obtained.

Purification of Rat Monoclonal Antibodies by Using Anti-Isotype Immunoaffinity Column

Immunoaffinity chromatography has been proposed as a step in purifying human IgA or IgM from normal serum. This method uses a polyclonal immunoglobulin affinity column[26] and could be adapted to rat monoclonal antibodies using polyclonal antibodies prepared as described in Bazin *et al.*,[1] or those purchased commercially. However it is much easier to use mouse monoclonal antibodies against rat immunoglobulin isotypes such as those that we have developed or purchased. The technique is routinely used in our laboratory, at least for λ type monoclonal or polyclonal rat immunoglobulins.

Purification of Rat Monoclonal Antibodies by Using a Protein A Affinity Column

A protein A affinity column can be used in some cases but as a rule is not well adapted for the rat immunoglobulins. Details of procedures can be found in Refs. 6–9.

23 M. R. A. Morgan, P. J. Brown, M. J. Leyland, and P. D. G. Dean, *FEBS Lett.* **87,** 239 (1978).
24 K. K. Anderson, Y. Benyamin, P. Douzou, and C. Balny, *J. Immunol. Methods* **25,** 375 (1979).
25 D. Bureau and J. Daussant, *J. Immunol. Methods* **57,** 205 (1983).
26 A. W. Cripps, S. H. Neoh, and I. J. Smart, *J. Immunol. Methods* **57,** 197 (1983).

Purification of Rat Monoclonal Antibodies: Conventional Techniques

IgM

The various procedures that have been described[1,27–30] all depend on the euglobulin properties or molecular weight of IgM.

The ascitic fluid is diluted 2-fold with saline. Cooled, saturated ammonium sulfate adjusted to pH 7.4 is added dropwise and slowly stirred for 30 min at 4° at the appropriate final concentration. The final concentration required to precipitate a given monoclonal antibody must be determined by a preliminary test on small quantities of ascitic fluid. It will generally be between 30 and 50%. The precipitate is centrifuged at 10,000 g for 30 min at 4°, reprecipitated twice, redissolved in PBS, and then dialyzed against PBS at 4°.

For chromatography, the sample is dissolved in 2% (w/v) NaCl buffered with 0.02 M Tris–HCl (pH 8.0) and containing 0.1% (w/v) NaN$_3$, and dialyzed overnight against the same buffer at 4°. The sample is applied to an AcA34 or preferably an AcA22 column (LKB, Sweden) (diameter 2.5 cm, length 200 cm) and eluted with the same buffer. The first peak is the monoclonal IgM. IgM monoclonal antibodies are often euglobulins and contamination by α_2-macroglobulin can be reduced by precipitation as described, although the precipitation step can cause denaturation.

IgG$_1$

The serum or ascitic fluid is diluted 2-fold with saline and the protein fraction precipitated by 40% saturated ammonium sulfate. The precipitate is washed with 50% saturated ammonium sulfate and resuspended in saline, dialyzed against 0.05 M Tris–HCl buffer (pH 8.0), and applied to a DEAE–cellulose column (DE32, Whatman) equilibrated with the same buffer. Elution is carried out using a linear gradient of increasing concentrations of Tris and NaCl (final buffer: 0.1 M Tris–HCl + 0.5 M NaCl, pH 8.0).

A higher degree of purity can be obtained by filtration on an AcA34 column (LKB, Sweden). The first peak contains the monoclonal antibody. A final step of electrophoresis in Pevikon (Serva, Federal Republic

[27] R. Oriol, R. Binaghi, and E. Coltorti, *J. Immunol.* **104**, 932 (1971).
[28] N. E. Cremer, D. O. N. Taylor, E. H. Lennette, and S. J. Hagens, *J. Natl. Cancer Inst.* (*U.S.*) **51**, 905 (1973).
[29] J. R. McGhee, S. M. Michalek, and V. K. Ghanta, *Immunochemistry* **12**, 817 (1975).
[30] P. T. C. Van Breda Vriesman and J. D. Feldman, *Immunochemistry* **9**, 525 (1972).

of Germany) or agarose can give excellent results, although only limited amounts of the purified monoclonal antibody are recovered.

IgG_{2a} and IgG_{2b}

Various techniques have been described.[29,31] However as indicated in Rousseaux and Bazin,[3] the electrophoretic mobilities of these monoclonal antibodies range from γ_1 to γ_2. The former is isolated by a procedure similar to that described for IgG_1 monoclonal antibodies. For IgG_{2a} and IgG_{2b} monoclonal antibodies with γ_2 electrophoretic mobility the first steps are dilution 2-fold with saline and precipitation by ammonium sulfate at 40% saturation. The precipitate is washed with 50% saturated ammonium sulfate, resuspended in saline and equilibrated with 0.05 M Tris–HCl buffer (pH 8.0), and applied on a DEAE–cellulose column (DE34, Whatman) equilibrated with the same buffer. The monoclonal antibodies are eluted with a linear gradient (final buffer: 0.05 M Tris–HCl + 0.05 M NaCl, pH 8.0). The first peak contains the monoclonal antibody. A higher degree of purity can be achieved by including gel filtration on an AcA34 column (LKB, Sweden) or electrophoresis on Pevikon (Serva) or agarose.

IgG_{2c}

Monoclonal antibodies of this isotype possess strong euglobulin properties. They can be purified by euglobulin precipitation (as previously described), redissolving of the precipitate in an acetate buffer at pH 5.5, and filtration on an AcA34 column (LKB, Sweden). However, euglobulin precipitation is not always sufficient to eliminate other IgG subclasses and it is not always possible to redissolve the precipitate.

Another technique[3] can be used. The serum or the ascitic fluid is diluted 2-fold in saline, the globulins precipitated in 40% saturated ammonium sulfate, and then resuspended and dialyzed against 0.2 M sodium acetate, 0.1 M NaCl buffer (pH 4.2). The solution is applied to a CM–cellulose (CM-32, Whatman) column equilibrated with the same buffer. Elution is carried out with a linear gradient (final buffer 0.2 M sodium acetate, 0.2 M NaCl, pH 4.2).

Monoclonal antibodies of the IgA, IgD, or IgE isotypes are rarely obtained. Methods to purify them are described in Refs. 2, 3, 4, and 5.

[31] T. S. Bistany and T. B. Tomasi, *Fed. Proc., Fed. Am. Soc. Exp. Biol.* **28**, 280 (1969).

Acknowledgments

The authors wish to thank Bernadette Platteau, Françoise Nisol, Christine Genart, Jean-Pierre Kints, and Jean-Marie Malache for their excellent technical assistance and Françoise Bolle and Liliane De Greef for their help in preparing this chapter. This work was supported by the Fonds Cancérologique de la Caisse Générale d'Epargne et de Retraite (Belgium), contract 3.4518.16 from the F. R. S. M. (Belgium), and contract BIO-C-358-81-B of the European Communities (Publication 2191). H. B. is a staff member of the Commission of the European Communities.

[62] Preparation of F(ab')₂ Fragments from Mouse IgG of Various Subclasses

By Edmundo Lamoyi

Mouse monoclonal antibodies[1] (MAbs) of defined specificity and immunoglobulin subclass are being applied *in vitro* in a variety of immunochemical assays[2,3] and *in vivo* as diagnostic and therapeutic agents.[4,5] For some of these purposes it is often advantageous to use antibody fragments that are bivalent (i.e., retain both antigen-binding sites), but lack the Fc region of the IgG molecule. Such F(ab')₂ fragments are valuable in serological studies of membrane antigens of lymphoid and reticuloendothelial cells which can bind IgG "nonspecifically" through the Fc receptors in their surfaces.[6,7] In addition, for low-affinity antibodies, F(ab')₂ may be preferable to univalent Fab or Fab' fragments since bivalent binding to a single cell results in an increase of the association constant.

Limited proteolysis of IgG with the enzyme pepsin[8] has been widely used for the preparation of F(ab')₂ fragments. Peptic digestion has been

[1] G. Köhler and C. Milstein, *Nature (London)* **256,** 495 (1975).
[2] R. H. Kennett, T. J. McKearn, and K. B. Bechtol, "Monoclonal Antibodies." Plenum, New York, 1980.
[3] J. W. Goding, "Monoclonal Antibodies: Principles and Practice." Academic Press, New York, 1984.
[4] S. W. Burchiel and B. A. Rhodes, "Radioimmunoimaging and Radioimmunotherapy." Am. Elsevier, New York, 1983.
[5] R. A. Miller, D. G. Maloney, R. Warnke, and R. Levy, *N. Engl. J. Med.* **306,** 517 (1982).
[6] H. B. Dickler, *Adv. Immunol.* **24,** 167 (1976).
[7] This series, Vol. 93.
[8] A. Nisonoff, F. C. Wissler, L. N. Lipman, and D. L. Woernley, *Arch. Biochem. Biophys.* **89,** 230 (1960).

applied to the IgG of various species, including rabbit,[8,9] human,[10] and mouse.[11-14] In this chapter, procedures are described in detail for the preparation, assay, and purification of F(ab′)₂ from the various subclasses of mouse IgG.

Purification of Monoclonal IgG

Monoclonal mouse IgG antibodies can be purified by a variety of procedures. Affinity chromatography on antigen columns and elution with free hapten is the method of choice for purification of some anti-hapten antibodies such as anti-(4-hydroxy-3-nitrophenyl)acetyl,[15] anti-fluorescyl,[16] and anti-p-azophenylarsonate (anti-Ar).[17-19] The hapten is usually removed by gel filtration and/or exhaustive dialysis. Affinity-chromatography on protein A–Sepharose is commonly used for the rapid purification of small quantities of those immunoglobulins that bind to protein A.[20,21] However, elution from the column requires conditions (e.g., low pH, potassium thiocyanate) which may cause denaturation of the antibody. In addition, not all subclasses bind equally well, and nonspecific IgG, which may represent a large proportion of the total immunoglobulin in some ascites samples, will copurify with the MAb. Nevertheless, this method remains useful for fractionating the IgG from conventional mouse antisera into the different subclasses[22,23] and for the purification of MAb from hybridoma culture supernatants.[3]

In general, large quantities of sufficiently pure IgG monoclonal antibodies or myeloma proteins can be obtained by a combination of ammonium sulfate precipitation at 40–50% saturation, gel filtration on Sephadex G-200 at neutral pH, and/or ion-exchange chromatography on DEAE–

[9] A. Nisonoff, *Methods Med. Res.* **10**, 134 (1964).

[10] M. W. Turner, H. H. Bennich, and J. B. Natvig, *Clin. Exp. Immunol.* **7**, 603 (1970).

[11] G. Gorini, G. A. Medgyesi, and G. Doria, *J. Immunol.* **103**, 1132 (1969).

[12] F. B. Casey and S. Tokuda, *J. Immunol.* **105**, 1294 (1970).

[13] E. Lamoyi and A. Nisonoff, *J. Immunol. Methods* **56**, 235 (1983).

[14] P. Parham, *J. Immunol.* **131**, 2895 (1983).

[15] M. Reth, G. J. Hämmerling, and K. Rajewsky, *Eur. J. Immunol.* **8**, 393 (1978).

[16] D. M. Kranz and E. W. Voss, Jr., *Proc. Natl. Acad. Sci. U.S.A.* **78**, 5807 (1981).

[17] Y. Dohi and A. Nisonoff, *J. Exp. Med.* **150**, 909 (1979).

[18] E. Lamoyi, P. Estess, J. D. Capra, and A. Nisonoff, *J. Immunol.* **124**, 2834 (1980).

[19] E. Lamoyi, P. Estess, J. D. Capra, and A. Nisonoff, *J. Exp. Med.* **152**, 703 (1980).

[20] J. W. Goding, *J. Immunol. Methods* **20**, 241 (1978).

[21] J. J. Langone, *Adv. Immunol.* **32**, 157 (1982).

[22] P. L. Ey, S. J. Prowse, and C. R. Jenkin, *Immunochemistry* **15**, 429 (1978).

[23] I. Seppälä, H. Sarvas, F. Péterfy, and O. Mäkelä, *Scand. J. Immunol.* **14**, 335 (1981).

cellulose[24] or QAE–Sephadex A50 columns.[25] The IgG is usually eluted from the exchanger with a NaCl gradient. QAE–Sephadex is particularly useful to purify immunoglobulins which are not soluble at the low salt concentrations necessary for their binding to DEAE–cellulose. For small samples, zone electrophoresis in agarose blocks[26] can be substituted for ion-exchange chromatography with excellent results.

The purification stages of the MAbs are monitored by electrophoresis in agarose gels[27] or cellulose acetate membranes and by antigen-binding assays.

Peptic Digestion[9,13]

Materials

Pepsin, twice recrystallized (Worthington Biochemical Corp., Free-hold, NJ)
Sodium acetate, 0.1 M (pH 7.0)
Acetic acid, 2 M
Sodium acetate buffer, 0.1 M (pH 4.2 and pH 4.5)
Tris–HCl buffer, 2 M (pH 8.0)
Sodium hydroxide, 0.5 N.

Procedure. (1) Dialyze the purified immunoglobulin (2 to 10 mg/ml) against 0.1 M sodium acetate (pH 7.0) at 4° overnight. (2) Immediately before digestion, adjust the pH of the protein solution to 4.2 (for IgG$_1$, IgG$_{2a}$) or 4.5 (for IgG$_3$) by adding 2 M acetic acid dropwise with constant stirring, and warm the solution to 37°. (3) Prepare a 2 mg/ml solution of pepsin in 0.1 M acetate buffer (pH 4.2 or 4.5 as appropriate). (Pepsin is inactivated above pH 6.0.) (4) Add 1 mg of pepsin per 33 mg of antibody. Incubate the mixture at 37° for an optimal time period (see below). (5) To stop the digestion add 1/40 volume of 2 M Tris–HCl (pH 8.0) and raise the pH to 8.0 with 0.5 N NaOH.

Analytical Studies

Because there is variation among individual proteins of each subclass with respect to rate of digestion, the optimal pH and incubation period to obtain maximum yields of F(ab′)$_2$ fragments (and little intact IgG) from a particular mouse IgG are determined by preliminary studies. The course

---

[24] P. Parham, this series, Vol. 92, p. 110.
[25] J. C. Unkeless and H. N. Eisen, *J. Exp. Med.* **142,** 1520 (1975).
[26] J.-C. Jaton, D. CH. Brandt, and P. Vassalli, *in* "Immunological Methods" (I. Lefkovits and B. Pernis, eds.), p. 44. Academic Press, New York, 1979.
[27] B. G. Johansson, *Scand. J. Clin. Lab. Invest.* **29,** Suppl. 124, 7 (1972).

of digestion by pepsin is conveniently monitored by SDS–polyacrylamide gel electrophoresis (SDS–PAGE) and the amount of antibody activity associated with undegraded IgG and with F(ab')$_2$ fragments at different stages can be quantitated by radioimmunoassay (RIA).[13]

One to two milligrams of immunoglobulin in 1 ml of 0.1 M acetate buffer is digested with pepsin as described above. At the start of incubation and at intervals thereafter, 100-μl aliquots from the digest are removed and neutralized by adding approximately 22 μl of 1 M tris-base solution.

SDS–Polyacrylamide Gel Electrophoresis

For electrophoretic analysis a few microliters (5–40 μg of protein) from each aliquot are mixed with an equal volume of sample preparation buffer [120 mM Tris–HCl (pH 6.8), 4% SDS (w/v), 20% glycerol (v/v)] and heated for 3 min in a boiling water bath. The samples are then electrophoresed in 7.5% acrylamide gels prepared as described by Laemmli[28] (see also Blackshear[29]). Rabbit phosphorylase A (M_r 92,500), bovine serum albumin (M_r 66,000), and ovalbumin (M_r 47,000) are adequate molecular weight markers.

SDS–PAGE may be sufficient to determine the optimal conditions for preparation of F(ab')$_2$ fragments. However, this type of analysis does not necessarily reflect retention of antibody activity by the products.

Radioimmunoassay

Anti-Fab and Anti-Fc Reagents. The assay requires reagents to measure (1) the total antibody activity [F(ab')$_2$ plus intact IgG] of a sample and (2) the percentage of the activity contributed only by whole IgG. In the experiments reported here, rabbit antibodies to mouse Fab were used to quantitate total antibody activity. Undigested IgG was detected with goat anti-mouse Fc. The preparation of these reagents is described elsewhere.[13,30] In brief, antisera are raised by repeated immunization with purified mouse Fab and Fc fragments. Subsequently, the antisera are rendered specific for Fab and Fc determinants and then affinity purified on mouse IgG–Sepharose 4B immunoadsorbents. The antibodies are radiolabeled in solution with ^{125}I by the chloramine-T method.[31,32] Alterna-

[28] U. K. Laemmli, *Nature (London)* **227**, 680 (1970).

[29] P. J. Blackshear, this series, Vol. 104, p. 237.

[30] T. A. Springer, this series, Vol. 92, p. 147.

[31] W. M. Hunter and F. C. Greenwood, *Nature (London)* **194**, 495 (1962).

[32] W. M. Hunter, *in* "Handbook of Experimental Immunology" (D. M. Weir, ed.), p. 14.1. Blackwell, Oxford, 1978.

tively, if the antisera are not in ample supply, the antibodies can be radioiodinated while bound to the immunoadsorbent and subsequently eluted from the column.[33,34]

The availability of monoclonal antibodies specific for mouse κ[35,36] and $\lambda 1$[37] light chains or IgG heavy chains (cell lines available from ATCC) should make easier the preparation of reagents for the assay. As an alternative, ^{125}I-labeled protein A[38] could be used to detect Fc-bearing antibody, in particular IgG_2 or IgG_3.

Assay. The method is a modification of the solid-phase radioimmunoassay described by Klinman *et al.*[39] and reviewed in detail elsewhere[34,40] Briefly, the wells of poly(vinyl chloride) microtiter plates are coated with antigen (100 μl of 0.1–1 mg/ml). After 3 hr at room temperature the antigen is removed, and the plates are washed and saturated with an irrelevant protein mixture (5% horse serum or 1% FCS). After washing the plate, 50 μl of serial dilutions of the time point samples to be assayed are added to the plate in quadruplicate. Dilutions containing 20–600 ng/ml of the untreated IgG undergoing digestion should be included as controls. After standing at room temperature for additional 3 hr the plates are washed and the amount of antibody bound is determined by adding 100–200 ng of [125]-labeled anti-mouse Fc and ^{125}I-labeled anti-mouse Fab to identical sets of wells. The plates are incubated overnight at 4° and then washed and dried, and the wells removed with a hot wire cutter and counted. Thus, the total of the intact IgG remaining plus the amount of $F(ab')_2$ produced at every digestion stage is measured with the radiolabeled anti-Fab, whereas the undegraded IgG present in the sample is quantified with the anti-Fc reagent.

The time course of digestion of antibodies to membrane antigens can be evaluated in a similar assay using whole cells bound to the insoluble support.[34,41]

[33] L. E. M. Miles and C. N. Hales, *Biochem. J.* **108,** 611 (1968).
[34] T. T. Tsu and L. A. Herzenberg, *in* "Selected Methods in Cellular Immunology" (B. B. Mishell and S. M. Shiigi, eds.), p. 373. Freeman, San Francisco, California, 1980.
[35] D. E. Yelton, C. Desaymard, and M. D. Scharff, *Hybridoma* **1,** 5 (1981).
[36] C. F. Ware, J. L. Reade, and L. C. Der, *J. Immunol. Methods* **74,** 93 (1984).
[37] M. Reth, T. Imanishi-Kari, and K. Rajewsky, *Eur. J. Immunol.* **9,** 1004 (1979).
[38] J. J. Langone, this series, Vol. 70, p. 356.
[39] N. R. Klinman, A. R. Pickard, N. H. Sigal, P. J. Gearhart, E. S. Metcalf, and S. K. Pierce, *Ann. Immunol. (Paris)* **127C,** 489 (1976).
[40] A. S. Tung, this series, Vol. 92, p. 47.
[41] J. P. Brown, K. E. Hellström, and I. Hellström, this series, Vol. 92, p. 160.

Purification of F(ab')$_2$

Separation of F(ab')$_2$ fragments from small amounts of undegraded IgG, Fab', and low molecular weight peptides is readily accomplished by gel filtration in Sephadex G-150 at neutral pH. However, F(ab')$_2$ fragments purified this way may still contain traces of intact IgG when the digestion was rather incomplete. If necessary, further purification can be achieved by a second gel filtration on Sephadex G-200. Whole IgG can also be removed by chromatography on DE-52 columns equilibrated with 5 mM phosphate buffer (pH 8.0). Under this condition IgG is retained, but F(ab')$_2$ fragments pass through the column in most cases. Alternatively, for those subclasses that bind protein A, the undigested IgG can be removed by protein A–Sepharose chromatography.[20] (Note, however, that F(ab')$_2$ from two monoclonal antibodies have been reported to bind to protein A.[42]) The purity of the F(ab')$_2$ is determined by SDS–PAGE and RIA.

Results

Peptic Digestion of IgG$_1$

Two IgG$_1$ monoclonal anti-Ar antibodies (R16.7 and R49.20),[18,19] an IgG$_1$ fraction of specifically purified A/J serum anti-Ar, and the myeloma protein MOPC-21 were digested with pepsin at pH 4.2.

Figure 1 shows SDS–PAGE analyses of samples taken at 2, 4, 8 and 12 hr of digestion of MAb R16.7. Only a major product with a relative molecular weight (M_r) of 108,000, corresponding to that of F(ab')$_2$ fragments, was detected in each sample. The Fc fragment was completely degraded. After 12 hr there was a small amount of intact IgG remaining.

The quantitative data obtained by RIA are shown in Table I. Seventy percent of the original antibody activity was still present after 12 hr of peptic digestion; however, only 10% of the activity was associated with intact IgG molecules. Thus, the F(ab')$_2$ fragments produced are quite resistant to proteolysis by pepsin and maximum yields were obtained after 12 hr of digestion.

The rate of cleavage and yields of F(ab')$_2$ obtained with serum anti-Ar of the IgG$_1$ subclass and with the myeloma protein MOPC-21 were quite similar to those of MAb R16.7. In contrast, MAb R49.20 was rapidly

[42] W. W. Young, Jr., Y. Tamura, D. M. Wolock, and J. W. Fox, *J. Immunol.* **133**, 3163 (1984).

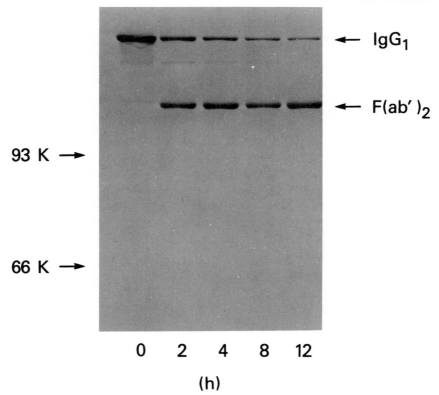

FIG. 1. SDS–PAGE analysis of peptic digestion of IgG_1 MAb R16.7. Digestion was carried out at pH 4.2 and 37°. Samples were removed at the times indicated, neutralized, and subjected to SDS–PAGE under nonreducing conditions in 7.5% gels. The position of molecular weight markers is shown. (From Lamoyi and Nisonoff.[13])

destroyed by pepsin under the same digestion conditions. The reason for this difference in sensitivity to pepsin is not known. It may be due to intrinsic variation among IgG_1 proteins or to a small degree of denaturation of R49.20.

Parham[14] studied the production of $F(ab')_2$ from BALB/c IgG_1 MAb as a function of pH in the range of 3.5–4.0. The digestions were performed at 37° in 0.1 M citrate buffers with IgG_1 at 1–2 mg/ml and pepsin at 25 μg/ml. The rate of digestion increased as the pH was decreased; at pH 4.0 the reaction required 48 hr for completion and at pH 3.5 cleavage was complete after 8 hr. At pH 3.5, $F(ab')_2$ fragments were obtained in 25–90% molar yield from the seven IgG_1 MAbs he tested.

TABLE I
Peptic Digestion of IgG₁ Anti-Ar MAb R16.7 [a,b]

Period of digestion (hr)	Percentage of original antibody activity remaining[c]	Percentage of original activity associated with IgG[d]
2	99	40
4	89	24
8	69	17
12	70	10

[a] From Lamoyi and Nisonoff.[13]
[b] Digestion was carried out at pH 4.2 and 37°.
[c] Determined by solid-phase RIA on BSA–Ar-coated trays using ¹²⁵I-labeled affinity-purified rabbit anti-mouse Fab as developing reagent.
[d] Determined by solid-phase RIA on BSA–Ar-coated trays using ¹²⁵I-labeled affinity-purified goat anti-mouse Fc as developing reagent.

Peptic Digestion of IgG₂ₐ

Two IgG₂ₐ monoclonal anti-Ar antibodies (R10.8 and R22.4) of A/J origin[18,19] and the BALB/c myeloma protein LPC-1 were studied.

The rates of digestion at pH 4.2 for these three proteins were very similar. However, the digestions proceeded more rapidly than those of IgG₁ proteins. The electrophoretic analyses of MAb R10.8 digestions are shown in Fig. 2. After 8 hr, only traces of intact IgG were detected. As with IgG₁ the major fragment produced had a M_r of 108,000–110,000. A smaller fragment ($M_r \sim 58,000$) with the characteristics of Fab' became apparent after 2 hr and increased in concentration with prolonged digestion. As determined by RIA (Table II) the best yield of F(ab')₂ fragments was obtained at 4 hr. The F(ab')₂ fragments of the IgG₂ₐ tested were less resistant to further degradation than those of IgG₁. Thus, after 8 hr of digestion only 29% of the original activity remained.

Peptic Digestion of IgG₂ᵦ

IgG₂ᵦ proteins were highly sensitive to digestion by pepsin. All four MAbs (R8.2, R9.3, R19.9, and R23.2) and the myeloma protein (MPC-11) studied were rapidly degraded without the formation of significant amounts of F(ab')₂ fragments. In 30 min of digestion at pH 4.2 the 4 MAbs were broken down almost completely to dialyzable peptides. A small

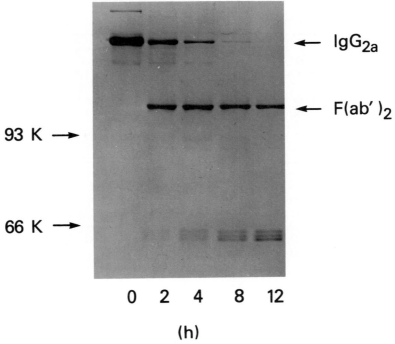

FIG. 2. SDS–PAGE analysis of peptic digestion of IgG$_{2a}$ MAb R10.8. Digestion was carried out at pH 4.2 and 37°. Samples were removed at the times indicated, neutralized, and subjected to SDS–PAGE under nonreducing conditions in 7.5% gels. The position of molecular weight markers is shown. (From Lamoyi and Nisonoff.[13])

TABLE II
PEPTIC DIGESTION OF IgG$_{2a}$ ANTI-Ar MAb R10.8[a,b]

Period of digestion (hr)	Percentage of original antibody activity remaining[c]	Percentage of original activity associated with IgG[d]
2	59	31
4	48	11
8	29	<2

[a] From Lamoyi and Nisonoff.[13]
[b] Digestions were carried out at pH 4.2 and 37°.
[c] See footnote c, Table I.
[d] See footnote d, Table I.

TABLE III
PEPTIC DIGESTION OF IgG₃ ANTI-Ar MAb R64.8 [a,b]

Period of digestion (min)	Percentage of original antibody activity remaining[c]	Percentage of original activity associated with IgG[d]
15	59	<1
30	45	0
45	34	0
60	29	0

[a] From Lamoyi and Nisonoff.[13]
[b] Digestion was carried out at pH 4.5 and 37°.
[c] See footnote c, Table I.
[d] See footnote d, Table I.

amount of fragments of M_r 50,000 was detectable in the digests of MPC-11.

Shorter periods of incubation or digestion at higher pH also failed to produce appreciable amounts of F(ab')₂ fragments. Thus, after digesting MAb R8.2 for 15 min at pH 4.5, a band with M_r similar to that of F(ab')₂ could be seen by SDS–PAGE. However, RIA of the samples showed that all of the antibody activity remaining was associated with molecules which possessed Fc segment. High sensitivity of IgG₂ᵦ proteins to peptic digestion was reported earlier by Gorini et al.[11] and has been recently observed by others.[14,43]

Peptic Digestion of IgG₃

The two IgG₃ proteins tested (J606 and MAb R64.8) were more sensitive to pepsin than those of the IgG₁ or IgG₂ₐ subclasses. Nevertheless, F(ab')₂ fragments were obtained in good yields from both proteins.

Anti-Ar MAb R64.8 was digested at pH 4.5 for 60 min. Samples were taken at 15-min intervals. No intact IgG was evident by SDS–PAGE (Fig. 3) or RIA (Table III) in any of the samples. In addition to F(ab')₂, two minor fragments of M_r ~96,000 and ~64,000 were produced. The nature of these two fragments is not known. The small fragment is probably related to Fab'. As can be seen in Fig. 3, the intensity of the F(ab')₂ band decreased with time and there was a concomitant increase of the

[43] J. Martínez-Quesada, T. Gallart, L. Borche, R. Vilella, J. Solé, and J. Vives, Immunología (Spain) 2, 125 (1983).

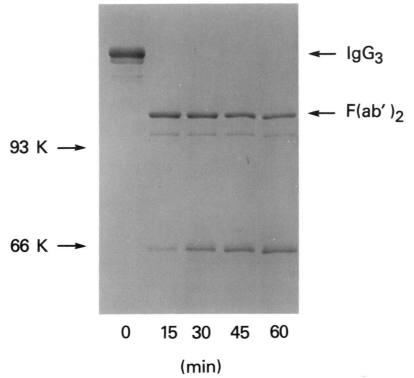

FIG. 3. SDS–PAGE analysis of peptic digestion of IgG₃ MAb R64.8. Digestion was carried out at pH 4.5 and 37°. Samples were removed at the times indicated, neutralized, and subjected to SDS–PAGE under nonreducing conditions in 7.5% gels. The position of molecular weight markers is shown. (From Lamoyi and Nisonoff.[13])

64,000-Da fragment. The F(ab')₂ fragments were not resistant to prolonged digestion. Thus, the antibody activity decreased from 59% of the original to 29% after 1 hr (Table III).

The fragmentation pattern obtained upon digestion at of the BALB/c myeloma protein J606 at pH 4.5 was very similar to that of MAb R64.8. The ~64,000-Da band was very faint. The F(ab')₂ was, however, more resistant to the effect of pepsin; its concentration did not change appreciably over an 8-hr period as assessed by SDS–PAGE.

Production of F(ab')₂ fragments by peptic digestion at pH 4.5 of two IgG₃ MAbs from AKR/J mice has been recently described.[44]

[44] J. Zikán, P. Dráber, and M. Vojtíšková, *Folia Biol.* (*Prague*) **28,** 377 (1982).

Summary and Comments

The effects of pepsin on the four subclasses of mouse IgG were investigated. It was possible to obtain $F(ab')_2$ fragments in good yield from IgG_1, IgG_{2a}, and IgG_3 proteins. The relative rates of digestion were $IgG_3 > IgG_{2a} > IgG_1$. Differences in the rates of digestion among individual proteins of the same subclass were noted. IgG_{2b} proteins were extremely sensitive to pepsin. All of five different IgG_{2b} proteins were degraded very rapidly without the detectable formation of antigen-binding $F(ab')_2$ fragments. One of the four IgG_1 proteins studied was also rapidly degraded; the other three IgG_1 gave good yields of $F(ab')_2$. The results demonstrate the need for preliminary studies on each IgG protein that is to undergo peptic digestion.

Mouse IgG subclasses also show differences in sensitivity to papain.[11,45,46] Therefore, it is recommended that kinetic studies also be performed for the preparation of mouse Fab and Fc fragments from monoclonal antibodies.

Acknowledgments

I wish to acknowledge the contribution of Dr. Alfred Nisonoff to these studies. I would also like to thank Drs. R. G. Mage and J. Miller for critically reading the manuscript and Ms. Shirley Starnes for editorial assistance.

[45] M. Potter, *Methods Cancer Res.* **2**, 105 (1967).
[46] E. Lamoyi and A. Nisonoff, unpublished results (1982).

[63] Optimal Conditions for the Preparation of Proteolytic Fragments from Monoclonal IgG of Different Rat IgG Subclasses

By J. ROUSSEAUX, R. ROUSSEAUX-PREVOST, and H. BAZIN

Enzymatic hydrolysis has been used for several years for the immunochemical analysis of immunoglobulins, especially for the characterization of IgG subclasses. The differential enzyme sensitivity and the differences in size of the fragments produced by enzymatic cleavage have constituted an alternative approach to the use of specific antisera in the IgG subclass characterization of myeloma proteins.[1] More recently, the development

[1] D. R. Stanworth and M. W. Turner, *in* "Handbook of Experimental Immunology" (D. M. Weir, ed.), Vol. 1, Chapter 6. Blackwell, Oxford, 1978.

of hybridoma technology and the use of monoclonal antibodies, in mouse as in rat, have enhanced interest in the detailed knowledge of enzyme sensitivity of IgG subclasses. Indeed, many monoclonal antibodies belong to one of the IgG subclasses, and in many cases preparation of Fab or F(ab')₂ from the antibodies is necessary for their use as immunological reagents, for example, when nonspecific binding to Fc receptors of various cells must be avoided. This chapter describes some procedures for the preparation of (1) monovalent fragments: Fab, Fab(t), or F(ab'), and (2) bivalent fragments: F(ab')₂ or F(ab)₂, from monoclonal rat IgG of each of the four IgG subclasses: IgG_1, IgG_{2a}, IgG_{2b}, and IgG_{2c}.

Preparation of Fab, Fab(t), or F(ab') Fragments

The cleavage of IgG to give Fab and Fc fragments is usually performed by papain digestion. However, proteins of the IgG_{2b} and IgG_{2c} subclasses may be digested with trypsin to give rise to Fab(t) and Fc(t) fragments. Incubation with pepsin of IgG_{2c} monoclonal proteins may give an F(ab') fragment.

Enzymatic Digestions

Digestion with Trypsin.[3] IgG, 10 mg/ml in 0.1 *M* Tris–HCl, 0.02 *M*-CaCl₂ buffer (pH 7.8), is incubated for 30 min at 37° before digestion with teine, at a final concentration of 10 mg/ml and incubated for 30 min at 37° before digestion with the enzyme. An aliquot of a suspension of mercuri-papain in 70% ethanol (Sigma Chemical Co.) is centrifuged, and the pellet dissolved in pH 7.0 buffer containing cysteine at a final concentration of 1 mg/ml. The solution of papain is added to the IgG solution (1 volume to 10 volumes of IgG, i.e., an enzyme : protein ratio of 1%, w/w). After incubation for 2–4 hr at 37°, the digestion is stopped with the addition of iodoacetamide (final concentration, 0.015 *M*).

Digestion with Trypsin.[3] IgG, 10 mg/ml in 0.1 *M* Tris–HCl, 0.02 *M*, CaCl₂ buffer (pH 7.8), is incubated for 30 min at 37° before digestion with trypsin. Trypsin, TPCK-treated (Worthington Biochemicals), is dissolved in the same buffer at a concentration of 2 mg/ml. The trypsin solution is added to the IgG solution (1 volume to 10 volumes, i.e., an enzyme to protein ratio of 2%, w/w). Incubation is performed for 4 hr at 37° and stopped with the addition of soybean trypsin inhibitor (Sigma Chemicals Co.) (2 volumes of a 2 mg/ml solution in digestion buffer are added to 10 volumes of protein solution).

[2] J. Rousseaux, G. Biserte, and H. Bazin, *Mol. Immunol.* **17,** 469 (1980).
[3] J. Rousseaux, R. Rousseaux-Prevost, H. Bazin, and G. Biserte, *Immunol. Lett.* **3,** 93 (1981).

Digestion with Pepsin.[2] IgG$_{2c}$, 10 mg/ml in 0.1 *M* sodium acetate buffer (pH 4.5), is incubated for 30 min at 37° before digestion. Pepsin (Sigma Chemical Co.) is dissolved in distilled water at a concentration of 1 mg/ml. The pepsin solution is added to the solution containing IgG$_{2c}$ (1 volume to 10 volumes, i.e., an enzyme : protein ratio of 1%, w/w). Incubation is performed for 18 hr at 37°, and stopped by raising the pH to 8 with 0.1 *M* NaOH (1.4 volume for 1 volume of IgG solution).

Controls of Enzymatic Digestion

Before preparation of Fab, Fab(t), or F(ab') fragments, an assay on a small amount of protein is advisable. Progress of the fragmentation can be followed by immunoelectrophoresis and polyacrylamide gel electrophoresis in SDS (PAGE–SDS). Immunoelectrophoresis with antisera to rat serum proteins (on one side) and to light chains (on the other side) is sufficient to show the effectiveness of fragmentation and the presence of Fab (or Fab-related) fragments. PAGE–SDS will show the presence of any undigested or partially digested material and of products of complete digestion: Fab and Fc, Fab(t) and Fc(t), F(ab'). The molecular weight of the fragments according to IgG subclass is given in Table I.

Optimal Conditions of Digestion According to IgG Subclass

Digestion with papain for 2 hr at 37° is usually sufficient to cleave IgG$_{2a}$ and IgG$_{2c}$ monoclonal immunoglobulins into Fab and Fc fragments. A time of 4 hr is better for an almost complete digestion of IgG$_1$ and IgG$_{2b}$ proteins. Cleavage with trypsin for 4 hr at 37° leads to an almost complete cleavage of IgG$_{2b}$ and IgG$_{2c}$ into Fab(t) and Fc(t) fragments. The yield of

TABLE I

MOLECULAR WEIGHTS IN PAGE–SDS OF THE Fab, Fc, Fab(t), Fc(t), AND F(ab') RELEASED BY ENZYMATIC DIGESTION OF RAT IgG SUBCLASSES

	Molecular weight × 10^{-3}				
	Fab	Fc	Fab(t)[a]	Fc(t)[a]	Fab'[a]
IgG$_1$	46–50	28	—	—	—
IgG$_{2a}$	46–50	27	—	—	—
IgG$_{2b}$	50	56	50	56	50
		27			
IgG$_{2c}$	50	50	50	50	46–52

[a] Fab(t) and Fc(t) are not released from trypsin digests of IgG$_1$ and IgG$_{2a}$. F(ab') is not obtained from pepsin digests of IgG$_1$ and IgG$_{2a}$.

TABLE II

OPTIMAL CONDITIONS FOR THE PREPARATION OF PROTEOLYTIC FRAGMENTS FROM MONOCLONAL
IgG OF DIFFERENT RAT IgG SUBCLASSES[a]

	IgG$_1$	IgG$_{2a}$	IgG$_{2b}$	IgG$_{2c}$
Fab and Fc	Papain, (1%, 4 hr)	Papain (1%, 2 hr)	Papain (1%, 4 hr)	Papain (1%, 2 hr)
Fab(t) and Fc(t)	—	—	Trypsin (2%, 4 hr)	Trypsin (2%, 4 hr)
F(ab')	—	—	Pepsin (5%, 18 hr)	Pepsin (5%, 18 hr)
F(ab')$_2$	Pepsin (1%, 4 hr) after acid pH incubation	Pepsin (1%, 4 hr) after acid pH incubation	Pepsin (5%, 18 hr)	Pepsin (1%, 4 hr)
F(ab)$_2$	—	—	S. aureus V8 proteinase (1/30, 4 hr)	—

[a] Percentages are enzyme : protein ratios (weight/weight). Enzymatic digestions are performed at 37°. Papain hydrolysis is performed with the addition of 0.1 M cysteine.

Fab(t) and Fc(t) obtained from IgG$_{2c}$ is better than the yield of Fab and Fc released by papain digestion. Fab(t) and Fc(t) are not obtained by trypsin digestion of IgG$_1$ and IgG$_{2a}$.[3] Digestion with pepsin of IgG$_{2c}$ under the experimental conditions indicated above gives large amounts of an F(ab') fragment with some F(ab')$_2$ still present. These optimal conditions are summarized in Table II.

Purification of the Fab, Fab(t), or (Fab') Fragments

Purification of the Fab or Fab(t) fragments is usually performed in our laboratory by gel filtration on Ultrogel AcA44 followed by DEAE–cellulose or DEAE–Trisacryl chromatography.[4] Alternatives to ion-exchange chromatography are affinity chromatography on protein A–Sepharose columns (for IgG$_{2c}$) or immunoaffinity chromatography on a column to which a monoclonal antibody to rat κ light chain is coupled.[5] The following procedures can be used:

IgG, 50 mg digested with papain or trypsin, is loaded on an Ultrogel AcA44 (IBF, France) column (2.6 × 90 cm). Undigested or partially digested IgG is eluted before Fc and Fab (see Fig. 1). Such a profile is obtained for IgG$_1$, IgG$_{2a}$, and IgG$_{2b}$ but not for IgG$_{2c}$, for which several peaks probably corresponding to aggregated Fc are obtained before elution of Fab. Fractions corresponding to Fab are pooled, concentrated,

[4] J. Rousseaux, R. Rousseaux-Prevost, and H. Bazin, *J. Immunol. Methods* **64,** 141 (1983).
[5] H. Bazin, F. Cormont, and L. DeClercq, *J. Immunol. Methods* **71,** 9 (1984).

A

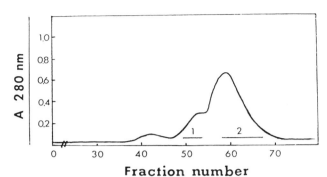

B

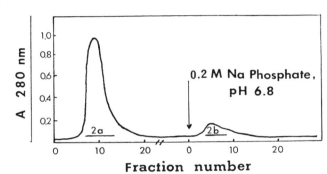

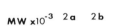

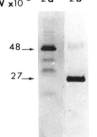

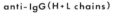

FIG. 1. Purification of Fab fragment released by papain digestion of monoclonal IgG$_{2a}$ (IR 530). (A) Gel filtration on Ultrogel AcA44 (column dimensions: 2.5 × 90 cm; flow rate 15 ml/ hr; 5-ml fractions; buffer: 0.01 M sodium phosphate, 0.15 M NaCl, pH 7.4) of 50 mg IgG$_{2a}$ IR 530 digested with papain for 2 hr at 37°. Peak 1, Fc fragment; peak 2, Fab fragment. (B) Purification of peak 2 (Fab fragment) by DEAE–cellulose chromatography (column dimensions: 2 × 15 cm; flow rate: 15 ml/hr; 5-ml fractions). Peak 2a, purified Fab; peak 2b, Fc (see controls by SDS–polyacrylamide gel electrophoresis and immunoelectrophoresis).

and equilibrated in 0.01 M sodium phosphate buffer (pH 7.8), either by dialysis or by gel filtration on a Trisacryl GF05 (IBF) column. Chromatography on a DEAE–cellulose (Whatman) or DEAE–Trisacryl (IBF) column (2 × 15 cm) is performed with the following buffers: 0.01 M sodium phosphate (pH 7.8); 0.01 M sodium phosphate (pH 6.8); 0.05 M sodium phosphate (pH 6.8), and 0.2 M sodium phosphate (pH 6.8). Fab or Fab(t) is usually eluted with the first or second buffer.

For monoclonal IgG_{2c} the Fab peak obtained by gel filtration on the AcA44 column can be purified by chromatography on a protein A–Sepharose column (1 × 3 cm) equilibrated in 0.14 M sodium phosphate buffer (pH 8). Fab is eluted at pH 8 and Fc eluted at pH 3.

The Fab peak from Ultrogel AcA44 is loaded on an immunoaffinity column (25 ml) containing a mouse monoclonal antibody (MARK-1) coupled to Sepharose 4B (about 200 mg for 25 ml of CNBr-activated Sepharose 4B). The column is washed with PBS (pH 7.4) containing 0.5 M NaCl (200 ml), and Fab is eluted with 0.1 M glycine–HCl, 0.15 M NaCl buffer, pH 2.8 (50 ml). The eluate is collected in a beaker containing 10 ml of 1 M Tris–HCl (pH 8.5).

Purification of the F(ab') fragment released by pepsin digestion of IgG_{2c} is performed by gel filtration on Ultrogel AcA44 as described above for Fab.

Preparation of F(ab')$_2$ or F(ab)$_2$ Fragments

Preparation of the F(ab')$_2$ fragment is performed by pepsin digestion. However, the optimal conditions will vary according to the IgG subclass. An alternative approach to obtain a bivalent fragment in the case of IgG_{2b} is to use *Staphylococcus aureus* V8 proteinase, which leads to the release of an F(ab)$_2$ fragment.

Digestion with Pepsin. Experimental conditions for pepsin digestion have been described above. However, two IgG subclasses, IgG_1 and IgG_{2a}, are resistant to pepsin under the classical conditions. This difficulty can be overcome if monoclonal IgG_1 or IgG_{2a} is incubated at acid pH before digestion with pepsin.[4] The following procedure can be used. IgG (15–20 mg/ml) in 0.01 M sodium phosphate, 0.15 M NaCl (pH 7.4) is dialyzed at 4° against 0.1 M sodium formate buffer (pH 2.8) (three changes of 100 volumes of buffer each, for 1 volume of IgG solution), then against 0.1 M sodium acetate buffer (pH 4.5) (same volumes as for sodium formate buffer). The concentration of the IgG solution is adjusted to 10 mg/ml, and digestion with pepsin is performed for 4 hr at 37° (enzyme : protein ratio, 1% w/w).

Digestion with S. aureus V8 Proteinase.[4,6] Monoclonal IgG$_{2b}$ is cleaved by this enzyme into F(ab)$_2$ and Fc-like fragments (with some additional F(ab)-like fragments). Digestion is performed as follows. IgG (10 mg/ml) in 0.1 M sodium phosphate, 0.002 M EDTA (pH 7.8) is incubated for 30 min at 37° before digestion. *Staphylococcus aureus* V8 proteinase (Miles Laboratories) is dissolved in the same buffer (1 mg in 0.3 ml buffer), and 1 volume of enzyme solution is added to 10 volume of IgG solution (enzyme : protein ratio, 1/30 w/w). After 4 hr at 37°, the digestion is stopped by rapidly freezing the solution. The material is stored at −20° until purification.

Control of the Digestion. Immunoelectrophoresis and PAGE–SDS will show the degree of fragmentation before purification of the products of digestion. The molecular weight of F(ab')$_2$ is about 95,000 to 105,000. The F(ab)$_2$-like fragments released from *S. aureus* V8 proteinase digests of IgG$_{2b}$ have an MW of 105,000 and the Fc-like fragment 27,000. A pFc' fragment is obtained from pepsin digests of IgG$_{2a}$, IgG$_{2b}$, and IgG$_{2c}$ monoclonal proteins (MW in PAGE–SDS, about 12,000).

Optimal Conditions. The optimal conditions for production of F(ab')$_2$ or F(ab)$_2$ according to IgG subclass are summarized in Table II.

Purification of F(ab')$_2$ or F(ab)$_2$ Fragments

Purification is achieved by gel filtration on AcA44 Ultrogel columns. Alternatively, when the digestion is complete and F(ab')$_2$ is the only product, ultrafiltration on an XM30 membrane (Amicon) is sufficient to remove small peptides. This procedure can be applied to IgG$_1$ and IgG$_{2a}$ digested with pepsin after incubation at acid pH.

Acknowledgments

The authors thank Elsevier Science Publishers for permission to reproduce previously published material.

[6] J. Rousseaux, R. Rousseaux-Prevost, H. Bazin, and G. Biserte, *Biochim. Biophys. Acta* **748**, 205 (1983).

[64] Tritium Radiolabeling of Antibodies to High Specific Activity with N-Succinimidyl [2,3-³H]Propionate: Use in Detecting and Analyzing Monoclonal Antibodies

By UDO KUMMER

For the preparation of any externally radiolabeled immunoglobulin the following principal requirements have to be satisfied. First, specific activities sufficient to work in highly sensitive radioimmunoassays or other kinds of analytical studies should be obtained. Second, the incorporated radioactive moiety should not lead to conformational perturbations affecting functional activity. Third, the labeling procedure should be both easy to perform and reproducible. Depending upon the chemical modification employed in the labeling procedure,[1,2] the radioisotope iodine-125 fulfills these above criteria and hence gains wide acceptance. However, this γ-emitting radionuclide with a half-life of 60 days is a recognized biohazard and its use is often considered an unacceptable risk.

This problem does not arise with β emitters such as tritium. Considering this important aspect we investigated whether tritium is a suitable alternative radioisotope for labeling immunoglobulins to specific activities comparable to those usually obtained using ¹²⁵I. This aim is achieved via an active ester reaction using N-succinimidyl [2,3-³H]propionate as the modifying reagent. Labeling by this reagent conjugates to primary amino groups of lysyl residues as its main (though by no means sole) target of attack, thereby introducing tritiated moieties into the protein. Since these residues are usually abundant, surface oriented, and highly reactive nucleophiles at the appropriate pH, acylation results in specific activities approaching that obtained with radioiodination and hence achieving acceptable sensitivity in the immunoassay system.

Procedure. All immunoglobulin samples to be ³H-labeled are dialyzed against 1000 volumes of 0.1 M borate/HCl buffer (pH 8.5) containing 0.5 M sodium chloride, dispensed into appropriate aliquots, and stored at −20° until used. The protein concentration should optimally be between 2.0 and 3.0 mg/ml, but lower or higher concentrations may also be radiolabeled satisfactorily. Prior to use, N-succinimidyl [2,3-³H]propionate ([³H]NSP; Amersham Buchler, West Germany) supplied as a toluene solution is transferred to a siliconized 0.8-ml glass vial with a ground-glass

---

[1] W. M. Hunter and F. C. Greenwood, *Nature (London)* **194**, 495 (1962).
[2] A. E. Bolton and W. M. Hunter, *Biochem. J.* **133**, 529 (1973).

stopper, and evaporated to dryness by directing a gentle stream of nitrogen gas onto the surface of the solution. This step is carried out in a well-ventilated hood, because the compound is slightly volatile as soon as all the solvent has been removed. The protein solution is then added into the vial by means of a pipet, and by drawing up and releasing several times the dry residue is dissolved. After mixing, the vial is stoppered and kept on ice with constant shaking.

The reaction is terminated after 45 min by applying the entire reaction mixture to a BioGel P-6DG column (Pharmacia Fine Chemicals, West Germany) equilibrated with phosphate-buffered saline, pH 7.4 (PBS) containing 0.1% sodium azide. The labeled proteins are separated from unincorporated reactants by passage through the column (20 × 1 cm) eluted with the equilibration buffer at a linear flow rate of 15 cm/hr. Fractions of 0.6 ml are collected in small test tubes containing 50 μl of 20% bovine serum albumin (BSA; fraction V Powder, Sigma Chemie, West Germany) in PBS with 0.1% sodium azide, and 10-μl aliquots drawn from each fraction are counted in an appropriate liquid scintillation cocktail, e.g., Scinti Gel (Carl Roth KG, West Germany). The protein peak contains more than 95% of bound radioactivity as judged by precipitation with 20% trichloroacetic acid, and from this, fractions comprising the major activity are pooled. When stored at 4° in a stabilizing medium (e.g., PBS with 2% BSA) with the addition of 0.1% sodium azide, the conjugates formed by this method are usable over long periods (up to 1 year) without significant loss of functional activity.

A suitable cross-linkage reaction should produce, in good yield, a stable conjugate with adequate labeling and with minimal impairment of functional activity. This method of linkage, which uses approximately a 1 : 7.5 molar ratio of protein : [^{3}H]NSP, routinely gives incorporation levels of an average number of 4 to 5 molecules [2,3-^{3}H]propionic acid groups per IgG molecule, i.e., between 60 and 70% of the [2,3-^{3}H]propionic acid moieties have been introduced into the protein with resultant specific activities of about 400 Ci/mmol (15 TBq/mmol) of tritium-labeled protein using N-succinimidyl [2,3-^{3}H]propionate at 105 Ci/mmol (3.89 TBq/mmol).

Figure 1 shows the result of a typical cross-linkage reaction after acylating 0.5 mg of a monoclonal rat IgG$_{2b}$ antibody with 2.5 mCi [^{3}H]NSP, followed by separation of the formed conjugate from the nonbound radioisotope on a BioGel P-6DG column with about 80–90% recovery of protein. From the binding features of this conjugate, tritium-labeled to a specific activity of about 400 Ci/mmol (15 TBq/mmol), it can be concluded this radiolabeled protein retains excellent functional properties (Fig. 3).

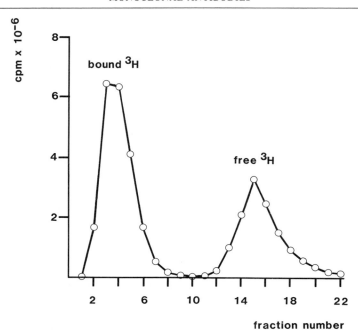

FIG. 1. Typical elution pattern after acylating 0.5 mg of a monoclonal rat IgG$_{2b}$ antibody with 2.5 mCi [^{3}H]NSP, followed by separation of the formed conjugate from the nonbound radioisotope on a BioGel P-6DG column. The counts per minute (cpm) are for 10-μl aliquots drawn from each fraction.

In contrast to reductive methylation,[3] acylation using [2,3-^{3}H]NSP as modifying agent introduces charged groups into the protein, thereby increasing the net charge of the molecule. The effect of these charges is overcome by the use of a relatively high salt concentration (0.5 M sodium chloride) in the coupling buffer solution. Without adversely affecting coupling efficiency, the high salt content minimizes protein–protein adsorption with resultant impairment of functional activity caused, first, by the polyelectrolyte nature of the protein itself and, second, by the chemical modification which introduces additional charged groups into the molecule. This protective effect on functional activity can be impressively demonstrated when a homogeneous population of large molecules such as monoclonal IgM antibodies are acylated to a high specific activity (800 Ci/mmol = 30 TBq/mmol). Whereas the degree of incorporation (an average number of 9–10 molecules [2,3-^{3}H]propionic acid groups per IgM molecule) as well as recovery of protein (about 70–80%) was nearly identical,

[3] B. F. Tack and R. L. Wilder, this series, Vol. 73, p. 138.

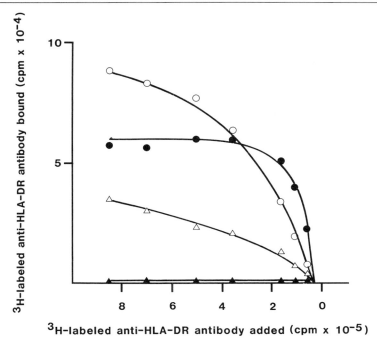

FIG. 2. The effect of salt concentration in the coupling buffer on functional activity. Increasing dilutions of MAb IFH Ia radiolabeled in coupling buffer with 0.5 M sodium chloride (closed symbols) and without sodium chloride (open symbols) were incubated with a constant number of target cells (● and ○, 2.5×10^5 Daudi cells as positive targets; ▲ and △, 2.5×10^5 Molt 4 cells as negative controls). Each data point represents the mean counts per minute (cpm) of two determinations.

Fig. 2 clearly shows that only that sample which was radiolabeled in coupling buffer solution containing 0.5 M sodium chloride retained excellent antigen-binding capacity with regard to dose-dependance, saturation, and specificity.

Although in our experience even extensive labeling of polyvalent antisera and monoclonal antibodies (including all Ig classes and subclasses of mouse and rat origin) did not detectably modify their functional activity, a few cautionary words may be in order. In contrast to conventional antisera, monoclonal antibodies have highly individual characteristics due to their homogeneous composition. They may be unusually sensitive to changes in pH or salt concentration.[4,5] Based on these properties, it may occasionally occur that certain monoclonal antibodies will be inactivated

[4] S. H. Herrmann and M. F. Mescher, *J. Biol. Chem.* **254,** 8713 (1979).
[5] D. W. Mason and A. F. Williams, *Biochem. J.* **187,** 1 (1980).

by conjugation. In this case, it may be convenient to use a trial of different conjugation ratios.

Specific examples of the application of this radiolabeling method to an indirect immunoassay for detection of antibody activity in hybridoma supernatants and to a binding assay using directly conjugated monoclonal antibodies will be presented in the following sections.

Application to Indirect Assay for Detection of Antibody Activity in Hybridoma Supernatants

In the course of producing hybridoma antibodies we became interested in screening assays capable of identifying hybridomas with a desired reactivity from among the majority making irrelevant immunoglobulins. Generally screening of antibody producing hybridomas requires testing of many hundreds of samples of culture supernatants. Even more tests are required during cloning and recloning of hybridomas. Any assay should therefore be designed for speed in addition to reproducibility and sensitivity. Numerous techniques have been described, such as radioimmunoassays, enzyme immunoassays, immunofluorescence assays, complement-dependent cytotoxicity assays, and hemolytic assays. The general all-purpose screening method we use for detecting monoclonal antibodies directed against cell-surface antigens is an indirect trace binding assay using specific antibody as a second-step reagent, purified from anti-immunoglobulin serum by immunoadsorption and tritium-labeled to high specific activity.

This double antibody assay has several attractive features as a method for screening hybridomas. First, the use of tritiated reagents eliminates many of the disadvantages of assays using radioiodinated reagents, such as high radiation hazard, requirement for frequent labeling owing to the short half-life of this isotope, and high background binding compared to tritiated reagents. Second, antibodies of any isotype can be detected by a single labeled anti-immunoglobulin antibody. Third, with the method adapted to microtiter plates, up to several hundred samples can be examined daily. In the following we present a method for screening hybridoma supernatants with tritiated anti-immunoglobulin which is a modification of a method by Dorval et al.,[6] who used radioiodinated protein A.

Procedure. The binding assay is carried out in 96-well plastic U-shaped microtiter plates. Appropriate viable cells in single-cell suspension are added to individual wells containing 50 μl of hybridoma tissue culture supernatant, ascitic fluid, or dilutions of these. The suspension is incubated for 45 min on ice with intermittent agitation. Following incuba-

[6] G. Dorval, K. Welsh, and H. Wigzell, *J. Immunol. Methods* **7,** 237 (1975).

tion the cells are pelleted (280 g, 5 min) and the supernatant removed by a quick shake after inverting the plate. In order to afford optimal resuspension of the pellet and hence avoid formation of cell clumps that detach during multiple washing and centrifugation steps, which possibly leads to false negative results, the plates are agitated for at least 1 min on a microtiter plate shaker (Flow Laboratories, West Germany) before addition of 100 μl of ice-cold washing buffer. All washing steps are performed with ice-cold PBS containing 0.2% BSA and 0.1% sodium azide. This washing step is repeated three times. To save time all additions to the wells are made with an eight-channel micropipet (Flow Laboratories).

Antibody bound to cell surface antigen is then quantitated by addition of 20 μl of tritiated anti-immunoglobulin antibody. After an additional 45-min incubation on ice, excess radiolabeled second antibody is removed by washing three times as before. The resuspended cells (in 100 μl PBS without carrier protein) are then transferred to glass fiber filters (Schleicher and Schuell, No. 6, West Germany) by means of a 12-channel cell harvester (O. Hiller Co, Madison, WI, USA) and washed extensively with ice-cold PBS. Finally the filters are dried and the resulting cell-bound radioactivity is determined by counting in a liquid scintillation spectrometer (Packard, Warrenville, IL, USA).

When dealing with cells, the number used per well is important. Depending on the homogeneity of a cell preparation used as source of targets and upon the density of a certain antigen expressed on the cell surface, we found that numbers ranging from 10^5 to 10^6 fresh cells give optimal results.

Normally, for screening purposes about 3×10^5 cpm of ^{3}H-labeled second-step reagent with a specific activity of about 400 Ci/mmol (15 TBq/mmol) is added to each individual well, yielding maximum signals of 15,000 to 20,000 cpm when first antibody is not limiting. Under those conditions background values are 200–400 cpm, depending on the target cell.

On the basis of this favorable signal-to-noise ratio in combination with a panel of cells giving a reaction pattern of real interest, a large spectrum of monoclonal antibodies has been identified. The assay is highly reproducible and easy to perform and appears to be comparable in terms of speed and sensitivity with similar assays using radioiodinated second antibody or protein A.

Application to Binding Assay Using Directly Conjugated
Monoclonal Antibody

As in any type of indirect binding assay accurate quantitation presents special problems. These problems may be ascribed to the use of anti-immunoglobulin antisera as second-stage amplifying antibodies, which contain a high proportion of antibodies directed to subclass-specific determinants on the Fc region. The proportion of binding thus depends on the subclass of the monoclonal antibody being tested. Furthermore, since the sensitivity of an assay depends to a large extent upon the background level of binding, an operational dilution of the labeled antibody is generally used at which the best signal-to-noise ratio is achieved. This dilution may often be below that amount needed to saturate all antigenic sites. The use of a directly radiolabeled monoclonal antibody in a cell binding assay bridges the gap between the simple yes/no readout obtained from the majority of indirect trace binding assays and the requirements for quantitative data, a prerequisite for analyzing binding characteristics of individual antibodies and for definitive determination of antigen density on a range of cell types.

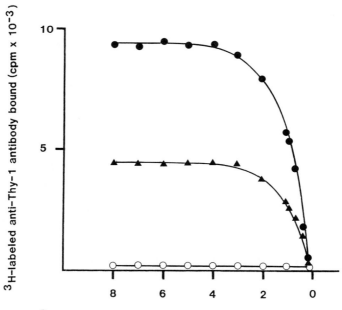

FIG. 3. Dose–response curves for binding of monomorphic monoclonal anti-Thy-1 antibody. A constant number of thymocytes ($\bullet$, 10^5 AKR/J thymocytes and $\blacktriangle$, 0.5×10^5 BALB/c thymocytes as positive target cells; $\bigcirc$, 10^5 Lewis thymocytes as negative control) was incubated with increasing dilutions of ^{3}H-labeled MAb anti-Thy-1 (specific activity, 400 Ci/mmol = 15 TBq/mmol). Each data point represents the mean counts per minute (cpm) of two determinations.

Procedure. The steps of the assay are discussed in detail in the above section. Briefly, appropriate target cells in convenient volumes (50–100 μl) are plated out in round-bottomed microtest wells. The cells are then incubated on ice for 45 min with suitable dilutions (10 μl) of tritium-labeled monoclonal antibody at 400 Ci/mmol (15 TBq/mmol). The resultant cell-bound radioactivity is determined following three successive washing and centrifugation steps.

An example of the binding results that are obtained from this assay, using a directly ^{3}H-labeled monoclonal reagent that recognizes a monomorphic determinant on the theta antigen of the mouse, is shown in Fig. 3. It is evident that the assay quantitatively discriminates the Thy-1 content of different amounts of homozygous thymocytes, when the dependence of ^{3}H]anti-Thy-1 binding as a function of ligand concentration was tested. The data of Fig. 3 also demonstrate that binding of radiolabeled monomorphic monoclonal anti-Thy-1 antibody is dose dependent, saturable, and specific, in that it does not bind to irrelevant cells (e.g., rat thymocytes).

The table shows an example of results obtained measuring HLA-DR antigens on human peripheral lymphocytes (PBL) and on Daudi cells, a B-cell line, in a side-by side comparison using the direct and indirect cellular binding assay. Although the monoclonal IgM antibody (with specificity for an antigenic determinant that is common to all HLA-DR gene prod-

COMPARISON OF INDIRECT VERSUS DIRECT
BINDING ASSAY FOR HLA-DR ANTIGENS

Cells[a]	Type of assay	
	Indirect[b]	Direct[c]
Human PBL	1,450[d]	750
Daudi	15,000	56,000
Molt 4	300	350

[a] 2.5×10^5 cells were added per well and subsequently assayed.
[b] 300,000 cpm of ^{3}H-labeled goat anti-mouse Ig (specific activity, 400 Ci/mmol = 15 TBq/mmol) was added to each individual well.
[c] 300,000 cpm of ^{3}H-labeled anti-HLA-DR antibody (specific activity, 800 Ci/mmol = 30 TBq/mmol) was added to each individual well.
[d] Values as means of two determinations.

ucts) is tritiated to a specific activity of about 800 Ci/mmol (30 TBq/ mmol), it is not surprising that the direct assay is less sensitive compared to the "sandwich" technique using second-stage enhancing antibody at about 400 Ci/mmol (15 TBq/mmol).

Competition binding assays as a modification of the direct binding assay can also be performed using directly tritiated monoclonal antibodies as indicator probes.[7] This type of assay is particularly useful for determining the specificity of monoclonal antibodies or helping to define regions of a target molecule that appear to have different biological roles.

Thus, directly tritiated immunoglobulins are very satisfactory in direct binding assays and modifications of these. Although less sensitive compared to the "sandwich" technique, the assays are highly reproducible and easy to perform, and produce excellent signal-to-noise ratios.

Conclusion

Acylation with N-succinimidyl [2,3-^{3}H]propionate is a highly specific method to radiolabel proteins under relatively mild conditions. This method of linkage produces conjugates with specific activities approaching those obtained with radioiodination. The labeled proteins retain excellent functional activity at the level of modification presented here. In addition, neither the labeling procedure nor conjugate purification requires special expertise.[8]

A variety of immunoglobulins, tritiated to high specific activity, have been used for direct and indirect immunoassay with favorable signal-to-noise ratios. For the reasons mentioned above, in addition to the long shelf-life and avoidance of γ-emitting radioisotopes, immunoassays using tritiated immunoglobulins are highly attractive.

[7] U. Kummer, S. Thierfelder, and S. Cobbold, in preparation.
[8] U. Kummer, E. Thiel, J. Doxiadis, M. Eulitz, S. Sladoljev, and S. Thierfelder, *J. Immunol. Methods* **42**, 367 (1981).

[65] Determination of the True Immunoreactive Fraction of Monoclonal Antibodies after Radiolabeling

By Tore Lindmo and Paul A. Bunn, Jr.

Radiolabeled monoclonal antibodies are extensively used in *in vitro* assays, and are increasingly used in *in vivo* external imaging of tumor tissue based on specific binding to tumor-associated antigens. Monoclonal antibodies have also shown potential value in experimental cancer therapy based on conjugation to radioisotopes of suitable radiation quality or to drugs and toxins. Common to all these applications is the fact that the conjugation procedure may destroy the immunoreactivity of the antibody, i.e., its ability to bind to the relevant antigen. There are at least two aspects to this problem: How much of the antibody is still able to bind to its antigen? What is the affinity of the remaining immunoreactive antibody?

The problem of unreactive radiolabel has been recognized in Scatchard analyses for determination of binding constants and binding capacities,[1-3] and appropriate corrections can be made if the immunoreactive fraction is known. But the use of antibody preparations of low immunoreactivity would be unacceptable for most *in vivo* applications since a significant nonreactive fraction would constitute a nonspecific background in radioimaging and a nonspecific dose in therapeutic applications.

There has been no generally accepted method for immunoreactivity testing of radiolabeled monoclonal antibodies. Intuitively, one would set up a binding assay under conditions of antigen excess so that all the antibody that is able to bind to antigen should be bound. The immunoreactive fraction would then be expressed as the amount of bound antibody relative to the total amount applied. A more accurate determination would be obtained if a series of increasing concentrations of antigen is used in the assay. One would then expect the relative amount of bound antibody to approach a plateau value which would thus define the immunoreactive fraction. In each instance the amount of nonspecific binding must be determined and subtracted from total binding, since nonspecific binding may increase as immunoreactivity decreases.

As will be seen in the following theoretical analysis, this conventional assay has several shortcomings. Based on the analysis, we propose a method in which the immunoreactive fraction is determined by extrapolation to conditions representing infinite antigen excess. The extrapolation is easily and accurately performed in a double-inverse linear plot which may be considered a modification of the Lineweaver–Burk plot. The principle of making the determination under conditions representing infinite antigen excess ensures that the true value of the immunoreactive fraction is obtained, as opposed to an apparent immunoreactive fraction found under conditions of limited antigen excess.

[1] S. E. Builder and I. H. Segel, *Anal. Biochem.* **85,** 413 (1978).
[2] E. M. Reimann and M. S. Soloff, *Biochim. Biophys. Acta* **533,** 130 (1978).
[3] D. Rodbard, *in* "Ligand Assay" (J. Langan and J. J. Clapp, eds.), p. 51. Masson, New York, 1981.

Theoretical Analysis

An analysis of the antibody–antigen binding reaction in terms of the law of mass action will identify the shortcomings of the conventional way of performing immunoreactivity tests, and at the same time will serve to illustrate the features of the present method.

Based on the simplifying assumption of monovalent binding, the equilibrium concentration of bound antibody–antigen complex [B] can be expressed as

$$[B] = K_a[Ab][Ag] \tag{1}$$

where K_a is the association constant and [Ab] and [Ag] are the concentrations of free antibody and antigen, respectively. Characteristic of the situation to be analyzed is that not all, but only a fraction r, of the antibody is immunoreactive. If [T] is the total concentration of antibody applied, then r[T] is the concentration of reactive antibody. Since the bound antibody necessarily must have come out of the reactive fraction, the concentration of remaining free, reactive antibody is r[T] − [B]. Since the mass equation only applies to the reactive antibody, the following expression is obtained:

$$[B] = K_a(r[T] - [B])[Ag] \tag{2}$$

In the conventional assay for immunoreactivity the relative binding [B]/[T] is plotted as a function of increasing antigen concentration. From Eq. (2) this relationship can be expressed as

$$[B]/[T] = r \frac{[Ag]}{[Ag] + 1/K_a} \tag{3}$$

This expression shows that [B]/[T] approximates the plateau value r if $[Ag] \gg 1/K_a$. For this method to give an accurate determination of r, it is required that the highest antigen concentration in the assay be much larger than the inverse of the association constant. Often this parameter is unknown for the antibody–antigen system in question, thus making it difficult to choose proper antigen concentrations. It may also be seen that for weakly binding antibodies ($K_a = 10^7$–10^8 M^{-1}), it will be difficult to achieve the necessary antigen concentration with cells having a realistic surface density of antigen. If $K_a = 10^8$ M^{-1}, a maximum cell concentration of 100 million cells/ml would be required to come within 5% of the true value for the immunoreactive fraction, even if it is assumed that there are as many as 10^6 binding sites/cell.

The double-inverse immunoreactivity plot is based on a different transformation of Eq. (2), which results in a linear relationship of [T]/[B] as a function of $1/[Ag]$:

$$[T]/[B] = 1/r + 1/rK_a[Ag] \qquad (4)$$

In a plot of $y = [T]/[B]$ as a function of $x = 1/[Ag]$, the origin of the abscissa will represent infinite antigen excess ($1/[Ag] = 0$). Moreover, extrapolation of the linear relationship to the intercept with the ordinate will determine the value $y_0 = 1/r$, which is the inverse of the immunoreactive fraction.

Implementation of the Immunoreactivity Assay

The procedure described below is suitable for simultaneous testing of several antibody preparations. By using incubation vials kept in 8×12 holders, applications, transfer, and sampling can be performed using multitip parallel pipets.

Reagents (per Antibody to Be Tested)

Bovine serum albumin (BSA; Sigma, St. Louis, MO) made up at 1% in phosphate-buffered saline (PBS) (1% BSA)

Cells (live or fixed) displaying relevant surface antigen (2 ml of cell suspension at 5×10^6 cells/ml)

Radiolabeled antibody to be tested ($16 \times 250 \mu l = 4$ ml at 40 ng/ml)

Same antibody unlabeled ($8 \times 50 \mu l = 0.4$ ml at 1 mg/ml)

Special Equipment

Incubation vials: 1-ml Micronic PPN Tubes with caps (Flow Laboratories, Gaithersburg, MD)

Incubation holder: Micronic 8×12 Tube Holder (Flow Laboratories)

Eight-channel pipetter: $50-250 \mu l$ Titertek (Flow Laboratories)

Filter-containing 8×12 harvesting plate: VP 107 Microfold (V&P Scientific, San Diego, CA)

Plate-sealing device, vacuum manifold, 8-channel washing dispenser (VP OK1 EIA Starter Kit from V&P Scientific)

Rotary mixer

Procedure (to Be Performed on Ice or at 4°). (1) Precoat incubation vials and harvesting plate with 1% BSA for at least 30 min. (2) Make up 2 ml of cell suspension at 5×10^6 cells/ml in 1% BSA. (3) Make two parallel serial 1:2 dilutions of cells directly in the incubation vials using 0.5 ml/tube and eight tubes for each series. The last two tubes in each series may serve as controls, one containing no cells, the other containing no antibody. (4) Add unlabeled antibody in excess (50 μg/vial) to one series. If the volume of antibody added is so large ($>50 \mu l$) that the cell suspension is significantly diluted, an equal volume of 1% BSA should be added to the vials of the other series. Incubate for 30 min with slow mixing on rotary mixer (4 rpm). (5) Add radiolabeled antibody (made up at 40 ng/ml in 1% BSA; use 250 μl/vial). Incubate for desired time with slow mixing. (6) Take replicate samples from each tube (e.g., 75 μl) using an 8-channel pipetter, and transfer either directly to gamma counting vials for counting of the total applied radioactivity, or to harvesting plate for collection of cellular fraction. (7) Apply vacuum to harvesting plate and wash eight times with 250 μl PBS per well, using an 8-channel washing dispenser. (8) Pick up individual filters with cells from harvesting plate using a thin needle, and transfer filters to gamma counting vials for counting of cell-bound radioactivity.

The reason for making up two parallel dilution series of cells (step 3 of procedure) is that one series is needed to determine the extent of nonspecific binding. This is achieved by presaturating the cells with unlabeled antibody prior to application of the radiolabeled antibody (step 4 of procedure).

The amount of radiolabeled antibody applied should be small in order to ensure antigen excess even at the dilute cell concentrations. We used antibody concentrations that were 100–400× lower than the concentration required to give saturation binding at the highest cell concentration. Volumes and concentrations mentioned in the above procedure are given as an example and general guideline, and can be changed without affecting the results of the procedure.

Incubation of cells with antibody directly in the wells of the filter-containing harvesting plate was tried initially, but was found to give much slower binding kinetics, presumably because of inadequate mixing. Incubation in separate vials in which the cells can be kept continuously well suspended was therefore found to be essential.

Example

The table shows the data obtained in an immunoreactivity test of the T101 monoclonal antibody.[4,5] This antibody recognizes a 65-kDa antigen on normal T cells and T-cell-derived malignancies as well as some B-cell malignancies. The antibody, which is of IgG_{2a} class, was labeled with ^{111}In by means of a diethylenetriamine-pentaacetic acid (DTPA) chelating kit

[4] I. Royston, J. A. Majda, S. M. Baird, B. L. Meserve, and J. C. Griffith, *J. Immunol.* **125**, 725 (1980).

[5] K. A. Foon, R. W. Schroff, P. A. Bunn, D. Mayer, P. G. Abrams, M. Fer, J. Ochs, G. C. Bottino, S. A. Scherwin, D. J. Carlo, R. B. Heberman, and R. K. Oldham, *Blood* **64**, 1085 (1984).

DATA FROM A BINDING ASSAY TO DETERMINE THE IMMUNOREACTIVE FRACTION OF ^{111}In-LABELED T101 MONOCLONAL ANTIBODY[a]

Cell concentration (million/ml)	Inverse cell concentration (ml/million)	No pretreatment		Presaturated cells		Calculated data[b]		
		Total[b] applied (cpm)	Total bound (cpm)	Total[b] applied (cpm)	Nonspecific binding (cpm)	Specific binding B (cpm)	B/T	T/B
3.2	0.3	10,927	9820 ± 78	11,227	144 ± 27	9676	0.87	1.14
1.6	0.6	11,254	8990 ± 56	11,091	145 ± 54	8845	0.80	1.25
0.8	1.2	10,807	7830 ± 190	11,175	164 ± 60	7666	0.69	1.44
0.4	2.4	10,923	6230 ± 86	10,896	174 ± 22	6056	0.55	1.83
0.2	4.8	11,193	4380 ± 61	11,066	165 ± 34	4155	0.38	2.66
0.1	9.6	11,060	2750 ± 28	11,157	147 ± 19	2603	0.24	4.25
No cells		No Ab	148 ± 17	No Ab	143 ± 18			

[a] Antibody (5 μCi/μg) at a final concentration of 13 ng/ml was incubated with live NCI-H516 cells for 1 hr at 4°. Replicate samples of 75 μl were taken for counting of total and cell-bound radioactivity (±SD).

[b] The mean value $T = 11,065 ± 245$ cpm was used for calculation of B/T and T/B.

provided by Hybritech (San Diego, CA) as part of a radioimaging trial of patients with T-cell malignancies at the National Cancer Institute.[6] The specific activity of the antibody was 5 μCi/μg, corresponding to an average of one ^{111}In atom per 60 antibody molecules.

The immunoreactivity was tested against NCI-H516 cells, a T-cell line established from malignant peripheral blood lymphocytes of a patient with adult T-cell lymphoma/leukemia. These cells are strongly positive for the T101 monoclonal antibody. The antigen is, however, destroyed by fixation, so live cells had to be used in the assay. This limits the incubation time since gradual cell disintegration will start to occur after a couple of hours.

The cells were prepared at 5 $\times$ 10^6 cells/ml and the assay was set up according to the above procedure. ^{111}In-labeled T101 to a final concentration of 13 ng/ml was added to the vials after presaturating the cells in one of the two dilution series with unlabeled T101. After 1 hr incubation at 4°, replicate samples of 75 μl were taken from each vial to determine the total radioactivity per sample (table, column 3 and 5) as well as the cell-bound radioactivity for the two dilution series (column 4 and 6). Specific binding B was expressed as the difference between total and nonspecific binding, and the mean value ($\pm$SD) of all samples counted for total radioactivity T (11065 $\pm$ 245 cpm) was used in calculation of the relative binding B/T and the inverse T/B.

In Fig. 1 the data from the table are plotted both in the conventional way of B/T as a function of increasing cell concentration (Fig. 1A) and as the double-inverse plot of T/B as a function of inverse cell concentrations (Fig. 1B). The data are plotted as a function of total cell concentration, which is proportional to the total rather than the free antigen concentration. Under conditions of antigen excess as required in this assay, however, these two concentrations will be nearly equal, and the approximation is assumed to be valid. The conventional plot of Fig. 1A approaches a plateau for increasing cell concentration, but the exact plateau value (i.e., the immunoreactive fraction) is difficult to determine, and the only conclusion that can be drawn is that $r \geq 0.87$. In the double-inverse immunoreactivity plot of Fig. 1B, the data can be well represented by a straight line, and extrapolation of this line to the intercept with the ordinate can be precisely performed to determine the immunoreactive fraction as the inverse of the intercept value. This value ($r = 1/1.07 = 0.93$) is determined under conditions corresponding to infinite antigen access, and thus represents the true immunoreactive fraction of the antibody tested.

[6] P. A. Bunn Jr., J. A. Carrasquillo, A. M. Keenan, R. W. Schroff, K. A. Foon, S. M. Hsu, A. F. Gazdar, J. C. Reynolds, P. Perentesis, and S. M. Larson, *Lancet* **2**, 1219 (1984).

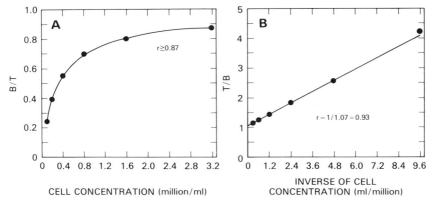

FIG. 1. Conventional (A) and double-inverse (B) immunoreactivity plot for ^{111}In-labeled T101 monoclonal antibody. The data underlying the figure are shown in the table. (Redrawn from Lindmo et al.[10])

Statistical considerations should be taken into account when determining the regression line of the immunoreactivity plot. If the nonspecific binding is low, it is reasonable to assume a constant relative error in the measured quantities T and B, i.e., a constant coefficient of variance.[7,8] Error analysis can then be used to show that the relative error of T/B will also be constant, given by the root mean square of the coefficients of variance for T and B, i.e., $CV_{T/B} = (CV_B^2 + CV_T^2)^{1/2}$. In a least-squares fitting of a straight line to the data it is therefore appropriate to apply constant percentage error weighting of the data.

Evaluation of the Method

The mass equation is based upon the assumption that the binding reaction has been allowed to reach equilibrium. In contrast to the T-cell antibody–antigen system used for the data in Fig. 1, the melanoma-associated antigen recognized by the 9.2.27 monoclonal antibody[9] was found suitable for studying incubation times long enough to ensure that equilibrium was reached.[10] This 250-kDa antigen is not destroyed by glutaraldehyde fixation (0.25%) and it is strongly expressed on most melanoma cell lines.

[7] P. J. Munson and D. Rodbard, *Anal. Biochem.* **107**, 220 (1980).
[8] D. Robard, R. H. Lenox, H. L. Wray, and D. Ramseth, *Clin. Chem.* (*Winston-Salem, N.C.*) **22**, 350 (1976).
[9] A. C. Morgan, D. R. Galloway, and R. A. Reisfeld, *Hybridoma* **1**, 17 (1981).
[10] T. Lindmo, E. Boven, F. Cuttitta, J. Fedorko, and P. A. Bunn Jr., *J. Immunol. Methods* **72**, 77 (1984).

The 9.2.27 IgG$_{2a}$ anti-melanoma antibody was radiolabeled with ^{125}I by the chloramine-T method[11] at a standard reaction time of 30 sec. The resulting specific radioactivity was 15 μCi/μg, corresponding to an average of one ^{125}I atom per antibody molecule.[10] The assay was set up with NCI-N892 melanoma cells at a maximum final concentration of 3.3×10^6 cells/ml and a final concentration of ^{125}I-labeled 9.2.27 antibody of 13 ng/ml. The cells were incubated at 4° with slow continuous mixing (4 rpm), and samples were taken at various times of incubation from 15 min to 21 hr. The results, corrected for nonspecific binding, are shown in Fig. 2A.

The shortest incubation time of 15 min resulted in an upward curvature of the plot, as would be predicted by a simple mathematical analysis. Assuming antigen excess and no reverse reaction, theoretical values can be estimated from $[B]/[T] = r[1 - \exp(-k[Ag]t)]$, leading to an upward curvature in a double-inverse plot. For the other incubation times, the data in Fig. 2A can be approximated by straight lines, even if complete equilibrium is reached only after 4 hr of incubation. The slope of the lines decreases with increasing incubation time due to gradually more complete binding in the more dilute cell suspensions. However, the value obtained by extrapolation to the intercept with the ordinate is the same for the various incubation times, indicating that the correct value for the immunoreactive fraction will be obtained even if the binding reaction has not reached complete equilibrium.

In Fig. 2B the same data are analyzed in more detail. Mean values ($\pm$SEM) for incubation times equal to or longer than 1 hr are shown for the four higher cell concentrations. The straight line has been determined by regression analysis of the data for the three higher cell concentrations. The value for the lowest cell concentration (2.4 ml/million) falls below the fitted line, indicating a systematic deviation.

The broken line in Fig. 2B shows the expected theoretical relationship between values of T/B and the inverse antigen concentration. This relationship was obtained from Eq. (4) after determining experimentally the remaining parameter values, i.e., the association constant K_a and the antibody-binding capacity per cell, which made it possible to convert cell concentrations into antigen concentrations. By Scatchard analysis the association constant for binding of 9.2.27 monoclonal antibody to fixed NCI-N892 cells was found to be 10^{10} M^{-1}, and the saturation binding capacity was found to be 5×10^5 molecules of 9.2.27 per cell.[10]

The theoretical data support our conclusion that the experimental value for dilute cell concentrations was too low, suggesting unexpectedly

[11] W. M. Hunter and F. C. Greenwood, *Nature (London)* **194**, 495 (1962).

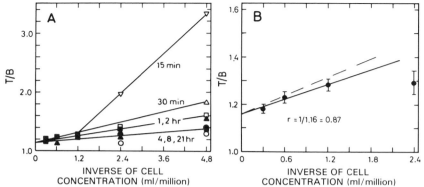

FIG. 2. Immunoreactivity plot for ^{125}I-labeled 9.2.27 (15 μCi/μg) monoclonal antibody tested against glutaraldehyde-fixed NCI-N892 melanoma cells. In (A) different symbols indicate mean values of duplicate samples taken after various times of incubation: ($\bigtriangledown$) 15 min; ($\bigtriangleup$) 30 min; ($\blacktriangle$) 1 hr; ($\square$) 2 hr; ($\blacksquare$) 4 hr; ($\bigcirc$) 8 hr; ($\bullet$) 21 hr. In (B) the mean values ($\pm$ SEM) for times equal to or longer than 1 hr are shown for the four higher cell concentrations in panel A. The fully drawn line is the regression line fitted to the data for the three highest cell concentrations. The broken line is the theoretical relationship calculated by inserting known values in Eq. (4). (Redrawn from Lindmo *et al.*[10])

high binding at low antigen concentration. In this range, the use of the total concentration instead of the free antigen concentration is no longer an accurate approximation. At the lowest cell concentration shown in Fig. 2B (2.4 ml/million cells) it can be calculated that about 17% of the binding sites were occupied.[10] Correcting the plot for this inaccuracy would, however, only move the data point further out on the abscissa, thus increasing the deviation from the theoretical relationship and from the straight line fitted to the data for the higher concentrations. These findings indicate that extrapolation should be based on the data for the higher cell concentrations if deviation from linearity is observed.

Figure 3A demonstrates that determination of the immunoreactive fraction at infinite antigen excess is insensitive to variation in the amount of antibody applied. The immunoreactive fraction of the 9.2.27 monoclonal antibody labeled with ^{131}I was tested against fixed melanoma cells. Use of a normal concentration of 16 ng/ml resulted in an immunoreactive fraction of 0.52. Applying a five times higher antibody concentration of 80 ng/ml resulted in a plot having a steeper slope, but nearly the same intercept value at the ordinate, with an immunoreactive fraction of 0.54.

Figure 3B shows that in cases in which the antigen withstands fixation, the value determined for the immunoreactive fraction is essentially the same whether live or fixed cells are used. In this case the antibody tested

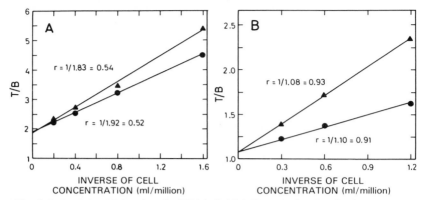

FIG. 3. Immunoreactivity plots for ^{131}I-labeled 9.2.27 monoclonal antibody (A) tested in a normal (●, 16 ng/ml) and five times higher concentration (▲, 80 ng/ml), and ^{125}I-labeled Zme 018 monoclonal antibody (B) tested against live (▲) and glutaraldehyde-fixed (●) melanoma cells.

was ^{125}I-labeled Zme 018.[12,13] This monoclonal antibody is directed against a different epitope on the same 250-kDa melanoma-associated antigen that is recognized by the 9.2.27 antibody.

Figure 4 shows two examples of the practical usefulness of the method. Figure 4A shows immunoreactivity plots for two differently ^{125}I-labeled preparations of the 9.2.27 monoclonal antibody. The lower curve shows the result for the antibody labeling according to the standard procedure, resulting in a specific radioactivity of 15 μCi/μg and an immunoreactive fraction of 0.87. The upper curve shows data for a more heavily labeled preparation obtained by increasing the duration of the chloramine-T reaction to 10 min.[10] This resulted in a specific radioactivity of 150 μCi/μg, corresponding to an average of 10 ^{125}I atoms per antibody molecule. This led to a decreased immunoreactive fraction of 0.58. The difference in slopes can largely be explained by the difference in immunoreactive fraction. This indicates that the association constant for the antibody–antigen interaction is about the same for the two antibody preparations.[10] Thus, destruction of the binding ability of the antibody by the prolonged chloramine-T reaction was probably for the individual antibody molecule an all-or-none phenomenon. For a gradual effect one would expect a lower immunoreactive fraction, but also a decreased association constant.

[12] B. S. Wilson, K. Imai, P. G. Natali, and S. Ferrone, *Int. J. Cancer* **28,** 293 (1981).
[13] P. G. Natali, R. Cavaliere, A. Bigotti, M. R. Nicotra, C. Russo, A. K. Ng, P. Giacomini, and S. Ferrone, *J. Immunol.* **130,** 1462 (1983).

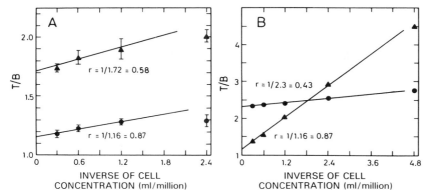

FIG. 4. (A) A comparison between immunoreactivity of 9.2.27 monoclonal antibody labeled to normal (●, 15 μCi/μg) and high (▲, 150 μCi/μg) specific radioactivity with [125]I. (B) A comparison between ^{125}I-labeled 9.2.27 (●) and Zme 018 (▲) monoclonal antibodies against different epitopes on the same melanoma-associated antigen on NCI-N892 cells.

Figure 4B shows immunoreactivity tests of the two ^{125}I-labeled antibodies 9.2.27 and Zme 018. In addition to the primary information about the immunoreactive fractions of 0.43 for the 9.2.27 and 0.87 for the Zme 018 antibody, the pronounced difference in slope of the plot may be of interest. Analytically, the slope is determined by $1/rK_an$, where n is the binding capacity per cell for the particular antibody. From the figure one can conclude that the value of $1/rK_an$ is about 7.5 times higher for the Zme 018 antibody than for 9.2.27. Taking the values of the immunoreactive fraction into account, this leads to the conclusion that K_an is about 15 times lower for Zme 018 than for 9.2.27.

Without further analysis it is not possible to conclude whether this is due to a lower binding capacity per cell or a lower association constant for the epitope recognized by the Zme 018 antibody. The fact that we observe the higher K_a or binding capacity for the antibody of lowest immunoreactive fraction (9.2.27) indicates that this is a biologically relevant observation and not only a consequence of the destructive effect of the radiolabeling on the binding properties of the antibody.

Concluding Remarks

In this presentation and evaluation of the immunoreactivity assay we have used data from different antibody–antigen systems and different radioisotopes and labeling procedures in order to illustrate the method. The results vary from more than 90% immunoreactive fraction for the

T101 antibody after ^{111}In labeling to less than 50% immunoreactivity in some cases after ^{125}I labeling of the 9.2.27 antibody. Our experience, as well as that of others, is that each antibody radiolabeling system shows individual but consistent patterns of decrease in immunoreactivity with radiolabeling.[14] Thus, of the two antibodies against 250-kDa melanoma-associated antigen, Zme 018 and 9.2.27, the former always had a high immunoreactive fraction after ^{125}I labeling with the chloramine-T or iodogen method, whereas 9.2.27 was quite sensitive to destruction by the iodination procedure. The T101 monoclonal antibody was also susceptible to destruction by iodination but consistently had high immunoreactive fraction after ^{111}In labeling.

The present method was routinely applied in a quality control procedure of ^{111}In-labeled T101 used in a clinical radioimaging trial of patients with lymphatic malignancies at the National Cancer Institute.[6] Each administration required freshly prepared, quality-tested radiolabeled antibody. In nine consecutive tests the mean immunoreactive fraction ($\pm SD$) was found to be 89 $\pm$ 8%.[15] Two cases had low values (78 and 73%); one of these represented a test performed on a week-old preparation, and in the other case free [^{111}In]DTPA caused the low value for the immunoreactive fraction. Excluding these two values would result in a mean immunoreactive fraction of 93 $\pm$ 4% for the other tests.[15]

There is an increasing interest in the use of radiolabeled monoclonal antibodies for specific localization of tumor tissue by means of external imaging and for potential applications in tumor therapy based on radiolabels of suitable radiation quality. Because most of these applications will require separate preparations of the radiolabeled antibody for each administration, there will be a need for quality control procedures.

The method given here addresses only part of that quality control problem, namely, how to determine the fraction of immunoreactive antibody after radiolabeling. However, knowledge of this parameter is important, since the presence of a significant nonreactive fraction will create a nonspecific background in radioimaging and a nonspecific dose in radiotherapy. The principle of determining the immunoreactive fraction under conditions representing infinite antigen excess ensures that the true value is obtained, as opposed to the value found under conditions of limited antigen excess. The procedure is easily set up and is quite robust in that the results are insensitive to variations in parameters of the assay, such as

[14] J. M. Ferens, K. A. Krohn, P. L. Beaumier, J. P. Brown, I. Hellström, J. A. Carrasquillo, and S. M. Larson, J. Nucl. Med. **25**, 367 (1984).
[15] J. C. Reynolds, personal communication (1984).

the exact amounts of antigen and antibody used, the incubation time, and the binding constant of the reaction.

This procedure should be supplemented with other methods. For example, unless an independent test is performed to determine the possible presence of free isotope, e.g., by trichloroacetic acid precipitation, one cannot conclude whether a low immunoreactive fraction is due to the presence of free isotope or nonreactive radiolabeled protein. Preferably, one should also verify that the binding constant of the radiolabeled antibody is the same as that of unlabeled antibody.

In comparative evaluations of different preparations of the same antibody, e.g., with different labels or Fab fragments versus complete immunoglobulin, the present method yields information about relative changes in the association constant that might have been caused by the preparation procedures. Under certain conditions this procedure can also be used to test the immunoreactivity of monoclonal antibodies conjugated to drugs or toxins. If the radiolabel is attached to the drug or the toxin part of the conjugate, the procedure can be directly applied. If this is not possible, the immunoreactive fraction of the conjugate can be determined in a two-step procedure based on radiolabeling of the antibody. By comparing the immunoreactive fraction of the radiolabeled antibody with that of the drug-conjugated radiolabeled antibody, a decreased immunoreactive fraction due to the conjugation procedure could be determined.

Acknowledgments

The authors are indebted to Drs. E. Boven, F. Cuttitta, and J. Fedorko for contributions during the development of this method. The monoclonal antibodies were kindly provided by Dr. R. M. Bartholomew, Hybritech, Inc. (T101 and Zme 018) and Dr. A. C. Morgan (9.2.27). This work was performed while the first author was a Fogarty International Fellow at the National Cancer Institute, Bethesda, MD.

Section III

Selected Applications of Monoclonal Antibodies

[66] Ultrasensitive Cooperative Immunoassays with Mixed Monoclonal Antibodies

By PAUL H. EHRLICH and WILLIAM R. MOYLE

Substitution of monoclonal antibodies in place of antisera has led to improved immunoassay technology since virtually unlimited quantities of a standardized reagent of known and frequently increased specificity can be obtained from hybridoma cell lines which have been selected for a given purpose. Unfortunately, the affinity for antigen of monoclonal antibodies is often less than that of antisera raised against the same antigen. This has led to loss of sensitivity, at least in the cases where the design of an assay could not be altered (i.e., by switching from a radioimmunoassay to a two-site immunoradiometric assay). For some antigens and monoclonal antibodies the loss in affinity can be partially offset and immunoassay sensitivity may be increased when mixtures of two or more monoclonal antibodies are used in the assay.[1-3] The resulting enhancement of sensitivity is due primarily to the formation of a circular complex consisting of one of each type of monoclonal antibody and two antigen molecules.[4] Immunoassays based on the formation of this complex have been termed a "cooperative immunoassay."[2] The sensitivity of a double-antibody radioimmunoassay with two monoclonal antibodies to human chorionic gonadotropin (hCG) has been increased 100- to 1000-fold over the sensitivity possible with the individual higher affinity monoclonal antibody. Other antigens and assay methods have also benefited from synergistic interactions. However, specificity of the immunoassay can also be greatly affected, with either increased or decreased specificity compared to the individual monoclonal antibodies. This effect cannot be predicted in advance by the characteristics of the individual antibodies. Therefore, mixing monoclonal antibodies can offer many opportunities for improving immunoassays, but the large number of variables that must be considered also greatly increases the complexity of standardizing and optimizing the assays. In this chapter, we describe some methods for devising and optimizing cooperative immunoassays and for avoiding the pitfalls that are possible with this system.

[1] P. H. Ehrlich, W. R. Moyle, Z. A. Moustafa, and R. E. Canfield, *J. Immunol.* **128**, 2709 (1982).
[2] P. H. Ehrlich and W. R. Moyle, *Science* **221**, 279 (1983).
[3] P. H. Ehrlich, W. R. Moyle, and R. E. Canfield, this series, Vol. 109, p. 638.
[4] W. R. Moyle, D. M. Anderson, and P. H. Ehrlich, *J. Immunol.* **131**, 1900 (1983).

Screening for Cooperative Monoclonal Antibodies

In order to perform cooperative immunoassays an appropriate pair of monoclonal antibodies must be isolated. At least at this time, analysis of the characteristics of individual monoclonal antibodies cannot be used to predict whether the antibodies will bind synergistically to the antigen. For example, antibodies that bind the different subunits of hCG are not necessarily cooperative even though it is known that they bind to different regions of the molecule. Thus, the first task is to find two antibodies that will bind antigen synergistically. Supernatants from hybridoma cultures can be screened in several assay systems directly to detect increased sensitivity for antigen with mixtures. However, this is usually tedious since it involves a careful comparison of each individual antibody with the mixture. We have devised a more convenient method for determining if two antibodies will cooperate in binding to antigen. It is based on the observation that the affinity of one antibody is usually a limiting factor in the amount of radiolabeled antigen that can be bound by that antibody. A synergistic antibody will increase the amount of radiolabel bound to the first antibody by forming a complex with the antigen and the first antibody, which increases the overall avidity of the first antibody for the antigen.

Example 1

One monoclonal antibody has already been cloned and 100 μg or more has been partially purified.

Reagents

A suitable buffer: for anti-hCG monoclonal antibodies, phosphate-buffered saline was used.
IgG-free horse serum
Purified monoclonal antibody against the antigen of interest
Radiolabeled antigen in 1% IgG-free horse serum or 1 mg bovine serum albumin/ml
Supernatant from hybridoma cultures to be analyzed

Procedure. Fifty microliters of the purified monoclonal antibody (about 70 μg/ml in phosphate-buffered saline) is incubated 18 hr or more at 4° or 1 hr at 37° in each well of a 96-well poly(vinyl chloride) microtiter plate. Note that although considerable latitude in the concentration of this solution is permitted, an excessive amount of antibody (i.e., larger than 5 μg/50 μl) can reduce the chances of finding useful antibodies because the surface concentration of antibodies becomes too high. After removing this solution and washing the plate with distilled water, the wells are incubated 2 hr with 10% IgG-free horse serum in phosphate-buffered saline to block the remaining adsorption sites on the plastic surface. This solution is removed, the wells are washed with distilled water, and each well is then incubated 18 hr at room temperature with 50 μl of a mixture of varying dilutions of cell supernatant (i.e., 1/2 to 1/1000) from a hybridoma colony to be examined and radiolabeled antigen (^{125}I-labeled hCG, approximately 20,000 cpm). The liquid is then aspirated, the plate is washed four times with distilled water, and radioactivity bound to each well is analyzed.

Control assays should include culture medium or supernatant from a hybridoma prepared against an unrelated antigen. If many supernatants are to be screened, it may be necessary to limit the number of assays, and, therefore, dilutions of supernatants. Frequently, one dilution of supernatant may be sufficient but this is subject to false negatives; i.e., some cooperative hybridomas will be missed since an antibody of too high titer in the liquid phase will cause no cooperativity to be detected, due to the fact that monovalent antibody–antigen interactions will be favored over the formation of the circular complex. False positives are not observed. However, we have observed that two antibodies may cooperate in one type of assay system, such as one solid-phase adsorbed antibody and one liquid-phase antibody, while not appearing to cooperate in a totally liquid-phase system. This has been shown to be the case for anti-hCG monoclonal antibodies B101 and B103.[5] From our experience with monoclonal antibodies directed against hCG, if one supernatant dilution must be chosen, a 1/50 to 1/100 dilution is a good starting point. Figure 1A shows some results of this method with solid-phase adsorbed anti-hCG monoclonal antibody B102. The antibodies that are synergistic are consistent with data obtained by other methods. B102 is synergistic in binding to hCG with antibodies A102, A103, and B101 but not with itself or antibody B103.

Example 2

No purified monoclonal antibody is available in large concentrated batches.

Reagents

Same as above for assays when one antibody is already purified
Anti-mouse immunoglobulin antiserum of high titer; goat anti-mouse F(ab) or affinity-purified anti-mouse immunoglobulin antibody

[5] P. H. Ehrlich, W. R. Moyle, and Z. A. Moustafa, *J. Immunol.* **131**, 1906 (1983).

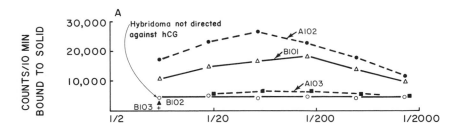

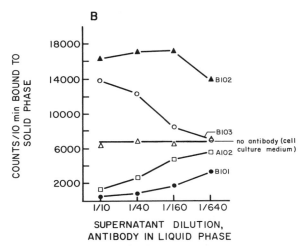

FIG. 1. Screening assay for the detection of synergistic pairs of monoclonal antibodies. (A) Effect of adding varying dilutions of different cell supernatants to ^{125}I-labeled hCG in the liquid phase above solid-bound B102. Microtiter wells were incubated with 75 μg B102/ml. (From Ehrlich *et al.*,[5] with permission.) (B) Effect of adding varying dilutions of different cell supernatants to ^{125}I-labeled hCG in the liquid phase above solid-bound B101. In this experiment, antibody B101 was from cell culture supernatant and was bound to the solid phase by goat anti-mouse F(ab) antiserum that had been adsorbed to the plastic. (From Ehrlich *et al.*,[3] with permission.)

Procedure. In this case the solid-phase monoclonal antibody cannot be adsorbed directly to the solid. For example, if only cell supernatant is available, the antibody is such a small fraction of the protein that random adsorption of protein to the plastic will result in very little antibody on the solid. Therefore, a more specific mechanism for attaching the antibody to the solid phase must be devised. We have used a goat anti-mouse F(ab) antiserum of high titer to achieve this goal. The high titer is necessary or, again, the antibodies of interest will be too small a fraction of the total protein.

An appropriate dilution of goat anti-mouse F(ab) antiserum must be determined. This can be done by performing the following procedure with only the first monoclonal antibody (i.e., not testing for synergy) and determining the dilution of the antiserum that results in a small but significant quantity of radiolabeled antigen being bound to the plastic. The goal is to optimize the chances of detecting a synergistic interaction. This will be prevented if too large an amount of antibody becomes adsorbed or if the concentration of radiolabeled antigen is too high. Typically, a cpm value 4-fold or greater above background should be acceptable when an antigen concentration which saturates less than half the antibody binding sites is used.

Fifty microliters of the appropriate dilution of goat anti-mouse F(ab) antiserum (for our antiserum a 100-fold dilution in phosphate-buffered saline was used) is incubated 18 hr or more at 4° in each well of a 96-well poly(vinyl chloride) microtiter plate. Alternatively, a solution of affinity-purified anti-mouse immunoglobulin antibody, approximately 50–100 μg/ml in phosphate-buffered saline, is used. The procedure is then the same as above with one purified monoclonal antibody (starting with the 10% IgG-free horse serum step). Figure 1B shows results with this procedure with solid-phase adsorbed antibody B101. The results are consistent with previously published data obtained by another method.

This procedure works well for the great majority of anti-hCG monoclonal antibodies that we have tested. However, for antibodies with very high affinities ($K > 10^{11} M^{-1}$), the method does not appear to work well because the affinity is so high that essentially all the antibody binding sites are already bound to antigen in the absence of a synergistic effect. Use of a radiolabeled antigen with a higher specific activity at lower concentrations is required for very high affinity antibodies. In addition, when the anti-mouse immunoglobulin antiserum is adsorbed to the microtiter plate, radiolabeled antigen must be used (and not radiolabeled hybridoma antibody), because the tracer amounts of radiolabeled antibody would bind to the solid directly through the anti-mouse F(ab) antiserum, either to unfilled sites or by exchange with bound first antibody. This is apparently not a problem with the radiolabeled antigen, because the majority of sites on the anti-mouse antibodies on the solid phase are saturated with the first hybridoma antibody and the few remaining sites do not affect the assay.

Methods for Performing Cooperative Immunoassays

Cooperative immunoassays are generally performed in similar ways to other immunoassays except that two monoclonal antibodies must be selected and the ratios and amounts used in the assays must be optimized. The circular complex is very stable and therefore changes in conditions, such as ionic strength of the buffers, are less critical in performing the assays. The selection process for synergistic monoclonal antibodies has been described above. The methods for determining the ratio and amounts of the monoclonal antibodies will now be summarized. In addition, another parameter, the amount of radiolabeled antigen (in immunoassays where the antigen is the tracer), must be carefully controlled.

There is some flexibility in the ratio of the concentrations of the two antibodies used in a cooperative immunoassay. However, if a certain dose response is desired, such as one which will result in the most sensitive assay or the largest range, the concentration ratios are restricted. Different ratios will result in different shapes of the antigen dose–response curves. A method for setting up a sensitive double-antibody liquid-phase radioimmunoassay is as follows. For a stock solution of each antibody determine the dilution that will bind half of the radiolabeled tracer, mix equal volumes of each of these dilutions, and then determine the dilution of the mixture that will bind 30–50% of the radiolabeled antigen. The dilution which gives this amount of binding should be used in the assay. For a pair of monoclonal antibodies that were strongly cooperative, anti-hCG monoclonal antibodies B101 and B102, the dilution of the mixture is about 10-fold.

The amount of radiolabel (or other indicator molecule) can also greatly affect the results of a cooperative immunoassay. In a double-antibody liquid-phase radioimmunoassay, the presence of high concentrations of radiolabel can mask the rise in antibody-bound radioactivity that occurs on addition of small amounts of unlabeled antigen. In this case, the results appear as a typical inhibition curve that is more sensitive than either of the two individual monoclonal antibodies. Therefore, if the most sensitive assay is desired, the radiolabeled antigen concentration must be lowered until a rise and then a fall in antibody-bound radioactivity is detected. With radiolabeled hCG and monoclonal antibodies with equilibrium binding constants of $10^8–10^9$ M^{-1}, this occurred with an antigen concentration in the picomolar range. In addition, this may result in very little total radioactivity in the assay and the specific activity of the antigen may have to be increased. We have found, however, that this can be avoided (with hCG at least) by just counting the assay tubes for longer times (10 min). At some antigen concentration, this solution is obviously not practicable.

Validation of the Specificity of Cooperative Immunoassays

The specificity of cooperative immunoassays can be increased or decreased compared to the specificity of the individual monoclonal antibodies. In addition, the change in specificity cannot be predicted from the properties of the individual monoclonal antibodies since the binding of antigen and a cross-reacting antigen depends on seven parameters. These include the equilibrium binding constant of each of the two antibodies for both antigen and cross-reacting antigen, and the probabilities of forming a circular complex from a two antibody–two antigen linear complex containing only antigen, only cross-reacting antigen, or one molecule each of antigen and cross-reacting antigen (the latter complex we have referred to as the hybrid circular complex). The formation of the different complexes can greatly affect specificity by favoring the binding of antigen or cross-reacting antigen to the antibody complex. For example, antibody A102 which binds hCG, human follitropin (hFSH), and human thyrotropin (hTSH) equally well, and antibody B103 which binds hFSH and hTSH with 7 and 12% cross-reactivity, have, in a cooperative immunoassay, no detectable binding to hFSH or hTSH while binding to hCG is very sensitive—a dramatic increase in specificity.[6] Conversely, a cooperative immunoassay composed of antibodies B101 and B103 causes the loss of some of the ability of these antibodies to distinguish between hCG and hCG β subunit.[6]

A complication in the determination of the specificity of cooperative immunoassays is the fact that the hybrid complex cannot form with pure standard solutions of antigen (or cross-reacting antigen). Therefore, using standard solutions to calibrate a cooperative immunoassay does not give an accurate picture of what is happening with unknown samples. In the case of the cooperative immunoassay involving monoclonal antibodies B103 and A102, hTSH can affect the amount of antibody-bound hCG at very low concentrations even though pure hTSH cannot itself be detected in this immunoradiometric assay.[6] Thus, mixtures of antigen and cross-reacting antigen should also be tested when calibrating a cooperative immunoassay. It is probable, however, that this effect becomes less important if the individual monoclonal antibodies have some specificity for

[6] P. H. Ehrlich and W. R. Moyle, *Clin. Chem.* (*Winston-Salem, N.C.*) **30,** 1523 (1984).

antigen over cross-reacting antibody (and, therefore, the specificity of the assay does not totally rely on the differences in the ability to form a circular complex).

In summary, the specificity of cooperative immunoassays must be rigorously tested before routine use. However, new opportunities are created by the cooperative immunoassay for assays of novel specificity. Even monoclonal antibodies with unpromising specificities may be combined to result in useful immunoassays. It is possible that this may also occur in antisera and is one mechanism by which the immune system achieves such high specificity.

[67] Use of Monoclonal Antibody to Increase the Sensitivity and Specificity of Precipitating Immunoassays and Cell Surface Binding Immunoassays

By ROBERT R. MONTGOMERY, THOMAS J. KUNICKI, and L. MICHAEL GLODE

Monoclonal antibodies represent powerful probes of protein and glycoprotein structure because they recognize single epitopes on complex molecules. Classical immunoassays that require antigen precipitation are not normally benefited by these nonprecipitating monoclonal antibodies, but by combining radiolabeled monoclonal antibodies with traditional precipitating antisera, the sensitivity and specificity of these assays are markedly increased. When a monoclonal antibody is used in an immunoassay, quantitation of single epitopes can be achieved. By combining monoclonal antibodies with polyclonal antibodies, the polyclonal antisera affect the precipitation of proteins bearing a large pool of epitopes while the radiolabeled monoclonal antibody directs the specificity of the radiolabel to this immunoprecipitate.

Monoclonal antibodies also provide us with the means to quantitate integral membrane proteins or surface-bound proteins on platelets or other cells. We have developed a whole-blood binding assay to diagnose hereditary deficiencies of specific platelet glycoproteins. A modification of this technique permitted us to study the cell surface binding of a single plasma protein in the presence of whole plasma. This latter technique uses the principle of the "neutral" antibody, antibody that is used to tag a special protein without inhibiting the function of that protein or the ability of that protein to bind to specific cell surface receptors. The binding of that protein can then be studied in the plasma milieu without the need to purify and radiolabel the protein directly.

Description of Antibodies

Production of Monoclonal Antibodies. Monoclonal antibodies used in this study were prepared against whole platelets or against purified proteins by methods described elsewhere.[1-4] All hybridomas were cloned and recloned by limiting cell dilution. Each monoclonal antibody was purified from mouse ascites fluid, using protein A affinity chromatography or caprylic acid precipitation.[4] The designation and specificity of each monoclonal antibody is as follows: AP1 (platelet membrane glycoprotein Ib), AP2 (glycoprotein IIb/IIIa), AP3 (platelet glycoprotein IIIa), E3A-R (cystathionase), AVW1, AVW2, and AVW3 (plasma von Willebrand factor, vWf).

Precipitating Polyspecific Antibodies. Polyspecific antisera were raised in rabbits against von Willebrand factor, cystathionase, or whole platelets.[3,5,6] The latter antisera recognized more than 15 different antigens from normal platelets when analyzed by crossed immunoelectrophoresis (CIE).[5]

Autoradiography of Radiolabeled Monoclonal Antibodies. All monoclonal antibodies were radiolabeled by the chloramine-T method.[7] Following electrophoresis, slides were washed, pressed, and dried. Autoradiography was performed using X-ray film (Kodak X-Omat RP film) with an intensifying screen at $-70°$ for 24–48 hr.

Use of Monoclonal Antibody in Precipitating Immunoassays

Although soluble plasma antigens may be quantitated with monoclonal antibodies by an enzyme-linked immunosorbent assay (ELISA), these assays are likely to detect a subset of epitopes that may or may not be

[1] R. R. Montgomery, T. J. Kunicki, C. Taves, D. Pidard, and M. Corcoran, *J. Clin. Invest.* **71**, 385 (1983).

[2] J. Schullek, J. Jordan, and R. R. Montgomery, *J. Clin. Invest.* **73**, 421 (1984).

[3] L. M. Glode, R. R. Montgomery, C. G. Smith, and D. R. Link, *J. Immunol. Methods* **48**, 13 (1982).

[4] P. J. Newman, R. W. Allen, R. A. Kahn, and T. J. Kunicki, *Blood* **65**, 227 (1985).

[5] T. J. Kunicki, D. Pidard, J.-P. Rosa, and A. T. Nurden, *Blood* **58**, 268 (1981).

[6] R. R. Montgomery and J. W. Johnson, *Blood* **60**, 930 (1982).

[7] P. J. McConahey and F. J. Dixon, *Int. Arch. Allergy Appl. Immunol.* **29**, 185 (1966).

distributed uniformly on the antigen molecules in question. In such circumstances, the monoclonal radiolabeled antibody can be used to detect the immunoprecipitate in a standard Laurell quantitative electroimmunoassay. Even a crude antiserum that recognizes multiple antigens can be made "monospecific" when used in combination with the labeled monoclonal antibody.

Quantitation of Cystathionase

We first used this technique to quantitate cystathionase.[3] A monoclonal antibody (E3A-R) was developed that inhibited the enzymatic activity of cystathionase. Although a precipitating polyspecific antibody was also developed, it recognized two antigens, only one of which was cystathionase. Thus this antiserum could not be used in a standard quantitative immunoassay. Combining the radiolabeled monoclonal antibody with this precipitating antibody, however, permitted the precise quantitation of cystathionase.

Method. Quantitative immunoelectrophoresis was performed in 0.9% agarose gels (SeaKem-ME Agarose, FMC Bioproducts, Rockland, ME). Agarose (0.9 g) was added to 100 ml of gel buffer (0.025 M veronal buffer, pH 8.6) and melted in a boiling water bath. The beaker containing the molten agarose was then placed in a 56° water bath. A 15-ml agarose aliquot containing 200 μl of a crude polyspecific antibody to cystathionase and 1 μg (10^6 cpm) of monoclonal antibody was poured onto a 3 × 4-in. piece of Gel-Bond (FMC Bioproducts, Rockland, ME). Sample wells were cut with a 3-mm well punch and 10 μl samples of serially diluted standard samples or test samples added to each well. The electrophoresis chamber buffer was 0.075 M veronal buffer (pH 8.6). Electrophoresis was performed overnight at 10 mA/slide. Slides were washed, dried, and autoradiographed.

Results. The coprecipitation of the radiolabeled monoclonal antibody permitted the specific visualization of the cystathionase "rocket" as shown in Fig. 1. The monoclonal antibody was bound to the antigen in the immunoprecipitate formed by the precipitating antibody. Although the intensity of the radioactivity is dependent on the number of epitopes recognized by the monoclonal antibody, the height of the precipitin peak is not affected by the monoclonal antibody. Levels of as little as 1.5 ng of cystathionase can be detected by this method.

Quantitation of Platelet Proteins Using a Polyspecific Anti-Platelet Antiserum and Specific Radiolabeled Monoclonal Antibodies

A more precise method for quantitation of platelet surface glycoproteins makes use of a polyspecific antiserum to whole platelets and the

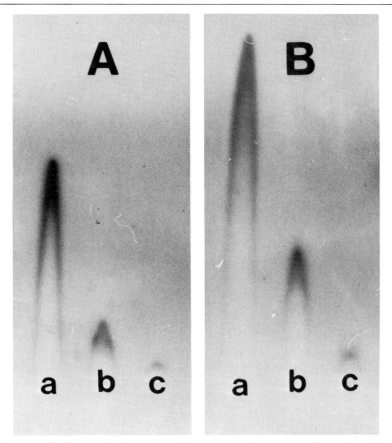

FIG. 1. Polyclonal antibody to cystathionase is made monospecific by the addition of radiolabeled monoclonal antibody directed against cystathionase. Wells contain 240 ng (a), 60 ng (b), and 15 ng (c) of cystathionase. (A) Contains 0.2% polyspecific antiserum to cystathionase and (B) contains 0.1% antiserum.

monoclonal antibodies, AP1 (GPIb) and AP2 (GPIIb/IIIa).[8] The radiolabeled monoclonal antibody causes the specific precipitin peak to be detectible by autoradiography.[1,8]

Methods. Platelets were washed in the presence of PGE-1, pelleted, and resuspended to a final concentration of 5×10^9/ml in buffer (200 μg leupeptin/ml, 0.038 M Tris, 0.1 M glycine, pH 8.7). Platelets were solubilized by the addition of one-tenth volume of 10% Triton X-100. The protein concentration was adjusted to 5–10 mg/ml. Agarose gels (15 ml, 1%

[8] S. M. Kristopeit and T. J. Kunicki, *Thromb. Res.* **36,** 133 (1984).

agarose, 0.5% Triton X-100 in Tris/glycine buffer without leupeptin) were mixed with 24 µg of IgG purified from antisera to whole platelets and 10^6 cpm of monoclonal antibody (AP1 or AP2). Five-microliter wells were punched and loaded with 5–10 µg of platelet lysate, and electrophoresis was performed for 4 hr at 10 V/cm. Slides were washed, dried, and autoradiographed.

Results. Figure 2 illustrates the simultaneous quantitation of GPIb and GPIIb/IIIa from the platelets of a patient with Glanzmann's thrombasthenia. The GPIb was normal and the GPIIb/IIIa was undetectible. This is a specific quantitative immunoassay regardless of the fact that the precipitating antibody produces greater than 15 precipitating peaks when analyzed on crossed immunoelectrophoresis.[5]

Rocket Inhibition Assay for Monoclonal Antibody Specificity

We developed the rocket inhibition assay in order to rapidly locate those fractions containing specific antibody when polyspecific precipitating antibody was eluted from an insolubilized antigen immunoaffinity column.[6] The eluted antibody, when mixed with specific antigen, inhibited precipitation of that antigen when it was subsequently assayed with crude antisera by quantitative electroimmunoassay. We adapted this technique for screening monoclonal antibodies to either intact antigens or specific proteolytic fragments of antigens. This adaptation enables the screening of monoclonal antibody with a crude, unpurified antigen—even plasma. The only requirement is that there be a polyspecific precipitating antibody to that antigen.

Method. Plasma vWf may be assayed by Laurell quantitative immunoassay using rabbit polyclonal antibody to vWf. In order to increase sensitivity, radiolabeled immunopurified polyclonal antibody may be added to the agarose. This labeled antibody is not necessary if the precipitin peak is easily stained with Coomassie blue.

Samples were initially mixed in a microtiter plate or microcentrifuge tubes and consist of 10 µl normal plasma mixed with 10 µl of hybridoma supernate. Following incubation for 15–30 min, 10 µl of polyspecific rabbit anti-mouse IgG was added and the samples reincubated for 30 min. Samples may or may not be centrifuged. A 10-µl sample was then added to each sample well on the Laurell plate and electrophoresis carried out in the standard manner. Note that the control must be normal plasma diluted 1 : 3. Where there is monoclonal antibody, the antigen rocket was inhibited.

Alternatively, proteolytically digested vWf (or other antigen) may be used as the test antigen to determine fragment specificity of the cloned monoclonal antibodies.

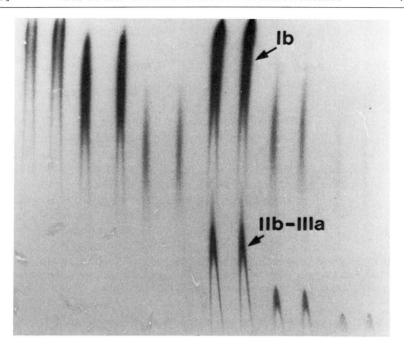

FIG. 2. Polyclonal polyspecific antibody to platelets is made monospecific to GPIb and GPIIb/IIIa by the addition of radiolabeled monoclonal antibodies AP1 and AP2 (see text). Normal platelet lysate has precipitin peaks to both GPIb and GPIIb/IIIa, while platelet lysate from Glanzmann's thrombasthenic platelets lacks the GPIIb/IIIa peak. Numbers denote the amount of total protein (μg) that was added to each well.

Results. Figure 3 illustrates the screening of hybridoma wells for antibody to vWf. When the hybridoma wells contained antibody to vWf, the antigen rocket was reduced or eliminated. Note that this screens for monoclonal antibody with only normal plasma used for the screening antigen. Large Laurell plates (8 × 3 in.) may be used to screen 50 samples at one time.

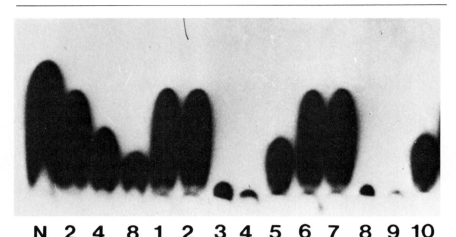

N 2 4 8 1 2 3 4 5 6 7 8 9 10

FIG. 3. Quantitative electroimmunoassay is carried out against polyclonal antibody to von Willebrand factor. Wells contain hybridoma supernate, normal plasma, and rabbit anti-mouse IgG. Wells 3, 4, 8, and 9 contain hybridoma antibody that inhibits the normal plasma vWf rocket (see text).

Screening for monoclonal antibody to specific fragments of an antigen is shown in Fig. 4. The antigen was purified plasma vWf that had been digested with trypsin into two immunologically distinct fragments. Our AVW1 monoclonal antibody recognizes the lowest rocket. This figure represents the screening of cloned hybridoma wells containing AVW1 monoclonal antibody. Where there is AVW1 from the microtiter well, the lower rocket is specifically eliminated.

Rocket Inhibition Assay for a von Willebrand Factor Fragment

We have identified a fragment of vWf that we have termed "vW frag" that demonstrates a partial immunologic identity with intact vWf (Fig. 5).[6] When assayed by Laurell rocket assay, this fragment is identified only when its concentration is greater than vWf. By virtue of its partial identity with vWf, the vW frag rocket fuses with the vWf rocket when lower concentrations are present. In order to quantitate its level in samples with lower concentrations of vW frag, we used an adaptation of the above method. The monoclonal antibody AVW1 recognizes an epitope that is absent on vW frag. Figure 5 shows the autoradiograph of a sample containing vW frag and vWf when analyzed by crossed immunoelectrophoresis with radiolabeled AVW1 (which identifies intact vWf and not vW frag)

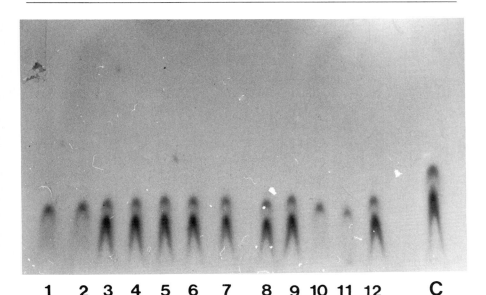

1   2 3   4   5   6   7   8   9 10 11 12   C

FIG. 4. Quantitative electroimmunoassay of purified vWf that has been proteolytically digested with trypsin to yield two fragments (see well C). Where monoclonal AVW1 is present in hybridoma supernates (1, 2, 10, 11), the lower vWF fragment is specifically inhibited. Other wells contain AVW2, a monoclonal antibody that recognizes an epitope cleaved by trypsin digestion.

or AVW2 (which identifies both vWf and vW frag) in the second dimension. AVW1 monoclonal antibody may be added to test samples and used along with antibody to mouse IgG to inhibit the vWf rockets, thereby permitting the vW frag rockets to be identified.

Method. Samples (10 μl) containing vWf with or without vW frag are mixed with AVW1 (10 μl) and incubated for 30 min. Rabbit anti-mouse IgG (10 μl, Zymed Laboratories, South San Francisco, CA) is added; the sample incubated for 30 min, and then centrifuged. This causes the intact vWf to be removed, leaving behind the vW frag. These samples may then be subjected to Laurell rocket assay into polyspecific radiolabeled antibody.

Results. Figure 6 illustrates the results of this assay. Since the vWf rockets were eliminated, the vW frag, if present, was easily identified and could be quantitated. If the rocket inhibition of vWf was not done, only the vWf rocket would be seen, and the separate vW frag would not

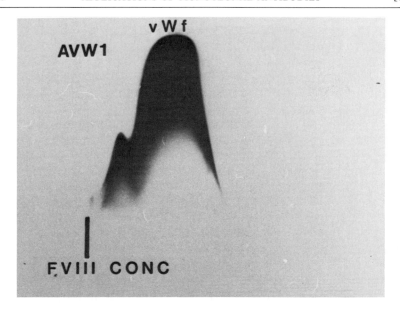

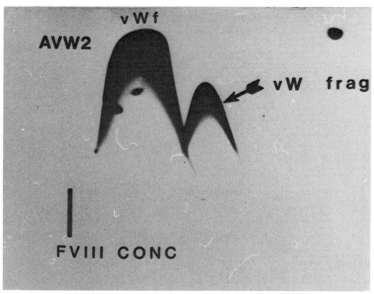

FIG. 5. AVW1 recognizes only intact vWf and not vW frag. AVW2 recognizes both vWf and vW frag. These are autoradiographs using the respective radiolabeled monoclonal antibodies.

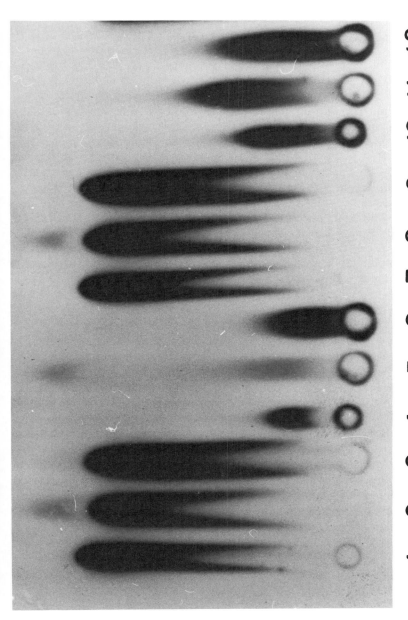

FIG. 6. Lanes 2, 5, 8, and 11 contain a plasma with both vWf and vW frag. The other lanes contain normal plasmas. Lanes 4–6 contain AVW1 and lanes 10–12 contain AVW2. All wells contain rabbit anti-mouse IgG. Rabbit anti-mouse IgG inhibits the vWf rockets but AVW1 only inhibits the vWf and leaves the vW frag peak uninhibited (lane 5).

unless each sample were subjected to crossed immunoelectrophoresis as in Fig. 5.

Indirect Immunoprecipitation in Agarose

The combination of nonprecipitating monoclonal antibody and precipitating rabbit anti-mouse IgG also permits the study of antigen specificity when polyspecific antibody to the putative antigen is not available. This method is similar to indirect immunoprecipitation in the fluid phase but it takes advantage of the greater purity of precipitated antigen resulting from electrophoresis in agarose gels, and is ideally suited to preparative applications.[8]

Method. The first dimension of the basic CIE technique[5] was used to separate platelet antigens in detergent lysates. First dimension gels were then excised and transferred to 8.3 × 10.2-cm sections of Gel-Bond (FMC Bioproducts, Rockland, ME). Intermediate gels (5.1 × 2.0 × 0.1 cm) were poured from a mixture of 1% agarose (SeaKem-ME, FMC Bioproducts), 0.5% Triton X-100, 0.038 M Tris, 0.1 M glycine, pH 8.7, and 2 μg murine monoclonal IgG/cm². Upper gels (10.2 × 4.8 × 0.1 cm) were poured from a mixture of affinity-purified rabbit anti-mouse IgG (Zymed Laboratories, South San Francisco, CA), 4 μg/cm², and the same agarose solution. Electrophoresis was performed at 2 V/cm for 18 hr at 15°. Following electrophoresis, gels were washed, dried, and stained as described.

Results. As shown in Fig. 7, this modification of the CIE method can be used for the indirect precipitation of antigens recognized by nonprecipitating murine monoclonal antibodies. In this figure, the results using AP1 (anti-GPIb), AP2 (anti-GPIIb/IIIa), AP3 (anti-GPIIIa), and AVW1 (anti-vWf)[1,2,4,9,10] are presented. In the case of the first three monoclonal antibodies, precipitin arcs were formed in positions (with respect to the first dimension) that are identical to those normally occupied by the respective antigens. Since they contain murine IgG, these precipitin arcs are coincident with the precipitin line produced by the interaction of rabbit anti-mouse IgG with the monoclonal antibodies alone. In the case of AVW1, only the precipitin line was detectable.

These results indicate that this method can be applied to the precipitation and preparative analysis of antigen by monoclonal antibodies. The failure to precipitate vWf was probably a result of two factors. First,

[9] J. R. Okita, D. Pidard, P. J. Newman, R. R. Montgomery, and T. J. Kunicki, *J. Cell Biol.* **100,** 317 (1985).
[10] D. Pidard, R. R. Montgomery, J. S. Bennett, and T. J. Kunicki, *J. Biol. Chem.* **258,** 12582 (1983).

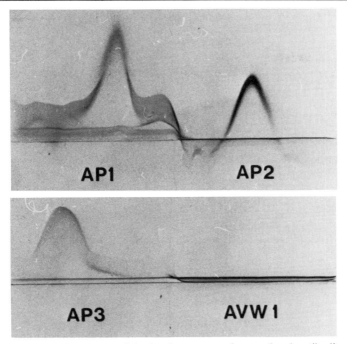

FIG. 7. Indirect immunoprecipitation in agarose of monoclonal antibodies to platelet proteins (see text).

significant cathodic migration of IgG due to electroendosmosis occurred in the agarose gels used in this CIE system. Indeed, the agarose used was initially chosen because of this property in order to increase the resolution of the standard CIE method.[5] Second, the mobility of vWf in the second dimension was significantly less anodic than that of the other antigens tested. Thus, the formation of the precipitin line by the rabbit anti-mouse antibody with the mouse IgG probably occurred prior to or in the absence of binding of vWf. In either case, a precipitin arc in the position of vWf would not be formed. Fibrinogen, another platelet antigen which has an extremely cathodic mobility in this system, also consistently failed to form a defined precipitin arc with a number of specific monoclonal antibodies (data not shown). It should be emphasized that this inadequacy of the method, as currently designed, can be corrected through manipulation of electrophoretic conditions and reagents.

The platelet lysate used to test AP3 was prepared in the presence of an amount of EDTA sufficient to dissociate the GPIIb/IIIa complex; thus, the mobility of GPIIIa in the first dimension of that gel was characteristic of free GPIIIa.[4] The platelet lysate used to test the remaining monoclonal antibodies, AP1, AP2, and AVW1, was prepared in the presence of excess calcium in order to maintain the integrity of the GPIIb/IIIa complex. The position of the AP2 precipitin arc is characteristic of that given by GPIIb/IIIa.[10] Note also that the positions of antigens precipitated by AP1 are characteristic of free GPIb (major peak to the left) and its proteolytic product, glycocalicin (minor peak to the right). This is the expected distribution of GPIb in a lysate prepared in the presence of calcium.[9]

Use of Monoclonal Antibody for Cell Surface Binding Immunoassays

Whole-Blood Binding Assay

We developed a specific and rapid whole-blood binding assay that makes use of monoclonal antibodies, such as AP1 (anti-GPIb) and AP2 (anti-GPIIb/IIIa), to diagnose hereditary platelet glycoprotein deficiencies, such as Glanzmann's thrombasthenia and the Bernard–Soulier syndrome.[1] The platelets need not be separated from plasma or even other cellular elements, and measurements can be performed on samples of whole blood. Bernard–Soulier syndrome platelets lack GPIb, while Glanzmann's thrombasthenic platelets lack the GPIIb/IIIa complex. When radiolabeled monoclonal antibodies to these glycoproteins are added to whole blood, they react only with platelets. When the cellular elements are centrifuged, radioactivity associated with the pellet represents specific binding to the platelet glycoproteins.

Methods. A 10-μl sample (10^6 cpm) of either radiolabeled AP1 or AP2 (10–50 μg/ml) was added to 200 μl of whole blood and incubated for 30 min. Aliquots (90 μl) were layered over 15% sucrose or a combination (9 : 1) of N-butyl phthalate and apiezon oil. Although our report initially used the latter method, 15% sucrose avoids the inversion problem that occasionally occurs with the oil and aqueous phases of the latter method. This method is intended to be semiquantitative but is more quantitative if performed in antibody excess.

Results. Figure 8 gives the results of whole-blood AP1 binding and AP2 binding for a group of normal individuals and patients with Bernard–Soulier syndrome or Glanzmann's thrombasthenia. The patients with Glanzmann's thrombasthenia do not bind AP2 because their platelets lack GPIIb/IIIa. The converse is identified when the Bernard–Soulier syndrome platelets are studied, because they lack GPIb and therefore do not bind AP1. Previously, the diagnosis of such patients could only be confirmed in a few laboratories after solubilizing the platelet membranes and analyzing these lysates on PAGE. This whole-blood assay may be performed in under 3 hr on as little as 200 μl of whole blood. More quantita-

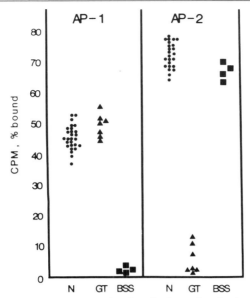

FIG. 8. Binding of radiolabeled monoclonal antibody to the platelets in whole blood of patients with hereditary platelet glycoprotein deficiencies (see text). N, Normal patients; GT, patients with Glanzmann's thrombasthenia; BSS, patients with Bernard–Soulier syndrome.

tive results are obtained if the monoclonal antibody is present in saturating amounts.

Ligand Binding to Platelets in the Plasma Milieu

We developed a cell binding assay to measure the binding of unpurified ligands to cell membrane receptors in the presence of normal plasma proteins.[2] For this purpose we select a monoclonal antibody that does not inhibit any physiological function of the protein to which it binds and have termed such an antibody a "neutral" antibody. Plasma von Willebrand factor is a complex glycoprotein composed of multimers that range in size from 400 kDa to 20 MDa.[6,11] Consequently, it is difficult to purify vWf and maintain the complex multimer distribution. Moreover, direct radiolabeling of vWf itself may result in an alteration of its multimeric composition. We have taken an alternative approach using the radiolabeled, "neutral" monoclonal antibody AVW1, which is specific for vWf. When added to normal plasma, AVW1 binds to all multimers of vWf. Following the addition of platelet agonists, the binding of vWf to platelets can be determined

[11] D. R. McCarroll, E. G. Levin, and R. R. Montgomery, *J. Clin. Invest.* **75**, 1089 (1985).

by counting the platelet-associated radioactivity following centrifugation. Such studies are therefore performed with unpurified antigen in the whole-plasma milieu. When purified vWf and washed platelets were previously studied, vWf bound either to GPIIb/IIIa, following thrombin or ADP/epinephrine stimulation, or to GPIb, following ristocetin stimulation. Our new method permitted us to study vWf binding in the presence of fibrinogen, a ligand known also to bind to GPIIb/IIIa following thrombin or ADP/epinephrine stimulation. Using this technique, we were able to demonstrate that fibrinogen inhibits the binding of vWf to GPIIb/IIIa when both ligands are present at concentrations normally found in the plasma milieu.[2]

Methods. Plasma vWf was labeled by the addition of 0.001–0.01 μg radiolabeled AVW1 (5 $\times$ 10^8 cpm/μg) to 1 ml of normal platelet-rich plasma, washed platelets in normal plasma, washed platelets in defibrinated plasma, or washed platelets in afibrinogenemic plasma. A 400-μl sample was mixed with 1 : 10 to 1 : 1000 volume of thrombin (5 U/ml), ADP/epinephrine (200 μM/200 μM), or ristocetin (15 mg/ml) and was incubated without agitation for up to 40 min. Samples were centrifuged directly or through 15% sucrose, and the bound radioactivity was determined.

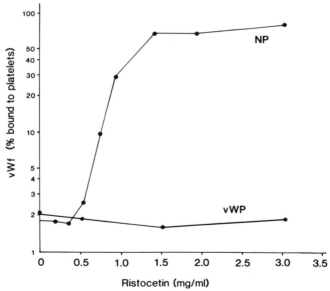

FIG. 9. Ristocetin-induced binding of plasma vWf to platelets using AVW1, a radiolabeled "neutral" antibody to vWf (see text). NP, Normal plasma; vWP, von Willebrand plasma.

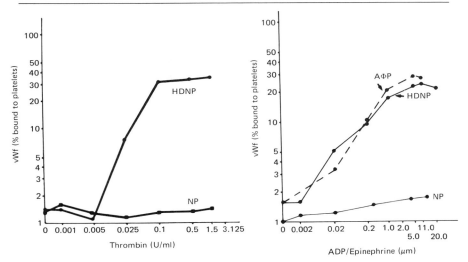

FIG. 10. Thrombin- and ADP/epinephrine-induced binding of plasma vWf to platelets and its inhibition by fibrinogen in the plasma milieu. NP, Normal plasma; HDNP, heat-defibrinated normal plasma; AφP, afibrinogenemic plasma. (Reproduced from Ref. 1 with permission from *J. Clin. Invest.*)

Results. Plasma vWf bound to GPIb when induced by ristocetin in the presence of normal plasma, as seen in Fig. 9. Binding of vWf to platelets induced by thrombin or ADP/epinephrine (Fig. 10) was inhibited when fibrinogen was present, but binding occurred to GPIIb/IIIa in the absence of fibrinogen (afibrinogenemic plasma or defibrinated plasma). Thus, binding of a plasma ligand to platelets was studied without purifying or radiolabeling the ligand directly. Only the monoclonal antibody was purified and labeled.

[68] Immunoaffinity Isolation of Membrane Antigens with Biotinylated Monoclonal Antibodies and Streptavidin–Agarose

By TIMOTHY V. UPDYKE and GARTH L. NICOLSON

The immunochemical analysis of radiolabeled, detergent-solubilized membrane antigens has been aided, in many cases, by the use of highly specific monoclonal antibodies (MAbs) and immunoadsorbants. Many

MAbs of murine and rat origin bind very weakly, if at all, to *Staphylococcus* protein A (SpA)–Sepharose, which is an efficient immunoaffinity isolation agent for human and rabbit antibodies and some MAbs of murine and rat origin.[1] Recently, an efficient immunoaffinity method for isolating membrane antigens with biotinylated MAbs (b-MAbs) and streptavidin–agarose has been compared with SpA–Sepharose and shown to be a superior method for isolating immune complexes formed with MAbs that have weak affinity for SpA.[2]

General requirements and detailed protocols for isolation of membrane antigens with b-MAbs and streptavidin–agarose will be described in this chapter. The detailed development and characterization of this method, as well as alternative streptavidin and avidin matrices, are discussed elsewhere.[2]

Immunoaffinity Isolation of Membrane Antigens with b-MAbs and Streptavidin–Agarose

The method described in this chapter takes advantage of the high (K_a $\sim 10^{15}$ M^{-1}) affinity of streptavidin for biotin. Streptavidin is a M_r $\sim 60,000$ protein secreted by *Streptomyces avidinii* that has four biotin-binding sites. Streptavidin is nonglycosylated and slightly anionic (pI 5.5–6.5).[3] When covalently linked to agarose, streptavidin has high binding capacity for b-MAbs and low nonspecific binding characteristics. Streptavidin–agarose can be used to efficiently bind immune complexes formed between b-MAbs and detergent-solubilized membrane antigens.[2] The following sections of this chapter present and discuss the essential elements and specific protocols of this immunoaffinity method.

Purification of MAbs

One of the most important requirements for the optimum performance of this method is that the primary MAb in the antigen isolation step be purified and properly biotinylated. There are several reasons for this. (1) In order to take full advantage of the high equilibrium constant of streptavidin for biotin, the primary b-MAb should bind directly to the affinity matrix. The efficiency of antigen isolation will then be limited essentially

[1] J. J. Langone, *J. Immunol. Methods* **55**, 277 (1982).
[2] T. V. Updyke and G. L. Nicolson, *J. Immunol. Methods* **73**, 83 (1984).
[3] L. Chaiet and F. J. Wolf, *Arch. Biochem. Biophys.* **106**, 1 (1964).

by the b-MAb affinity constant and size (e.g., IgG versus IgM), and the antigen size and epitope valency, all of which determine the size of the immune complex, its binding kinetics, and its accessibility to biotin-binding sites within the agarose matrix. (2) Impurities in the b-MAb preparation (including other immunoglobulins) will compete with the immune complexes for biotin-binding sites and may also contribute to increased nonspecific binding, as well as problems associated with the presence of proteases and nucleases. (3) The use of affinity-purified and biotinylated second antibody preparations to remove immune complexes formed with concentrated culture medium from hybridoma cells can result in much lower yields of isolated antigen (<10%, compared to that isolated with the same amount of purified b-MAb) and higher nonspecific binding (T. V. Updyke and G. L. Nicolson, unpublished observations). These effects are probably the result of several of the factors discussed in items 1 and 2, above.

There are several methods that can be used to purify MAbs, such as conventional chromatography, HPLC, and affinity chromatography (protein A, antibody, and antigen affinity). In all of these methods, except antigen affinity chromatography, the possibility of copurifying antibodies present in serum-containing culture medium or ascites fluid should be considered. Therefore, we routinely produce MAbs in serum-free medium. Details of serum-free MAb production and MAb purification are presented elsewhere.[2,4,5]

Biotinylation of MAbs

We have used two biotinylation procedures. The first uses N-hydroxysuccinimidobiotin (NHS-biotin, Calbiochem-Behring, La Jolla, CA), which is soluble only in polar organic solvents such as DMSO. The second procedure uses sulfosuccinimidobiotin (sulfo-NHS-biotin, Pierce Chemical Co., Rockford, IL), which is water soluble and more reactive with primary amino groups than NHS-biotin, thereby shortening the time required for biotinylation and eliminating exposure of MAbs to organic solvents. Thus far, differences in the reactivity or stability of a given b-MAb have not been detected after labeling with either of these two procedures.

[4] H. Murakami, H. Masui, G. H. Sato, N. Sueoka, T. P. Chow, and T. Kano-Sueoka, *Proc. Natl. Acad. Sci. U.S.A.* **79,** 1158 (1982).

[5] T. Oi and L. A. Herzenberg, *in* "Selected Methods in Cellular Immunology" (B. B. Mishell and S. M. Shiigi, eds.), p. 368. Freeman, San Francisco, California, 1980.

Another water-soluble biotinylating compound that we have recently begun to evaluate is sulfosuccinimidyl 6-(biotinamido)hexanoate (Pierce Chemical Co.). Its extended spacer arm may decrease steric hindrance and increase streptavidin–b-MAb conjugate stability compared with standard biotinyl conjugates.[6,7] However, we do not yet have comparative data on this latter compound.

Biotinylation of MAbs with NHS-Biotin (Detailed Procedure)

Stock Solutions

NHS-biotin, 2 mg/ml in anhydrous DMSO (room temperature). The stock solution may be stored at $-80°$ and used repeatedly.

0.1 M HEPES, pH 8.0, 0°

Purified MAb, 2–5 mg/ml in 0.1 M HEPES, pH 8.0, 0°

Protocol. (1) Add 1 mg of purified MAb to a polypropylene tube. (2) Add 0.1 M HEPES (pH 8.0) to a volume of 0.932 ml (vortex). (3) Add 68 μl NHS-biotin stock solution (vortex). (4) React at 0° for 4 hr. (5) Transfer to a Centricon 30 microconcentrator (Amicon, Danvers, MA) and wash five times with 2 ml 0.1 M HEPES (pH 8.0), 0.05% NaN$_3$, 4°. (6) Reconstitute b-MAb at 2–5 mg/ml with 0.1 M HEPES (pH 8.0), 0.05% NaN$_3$, and store aliquots at $-80°$ [biotinylated IgMs are reconstituted in 0.2 M HEPES (pH 7.5), 50% (v/v) glycerol, 0.05% NaN$_3$, and stored at $-20°$].

Biotinylation of MAbs with Sulfo-NHS-Biotin

Stock Solutions

2 mM sulfo-NHS-biotin, 0.887 mg/ml in 0.1 M HEPES (pH 8.0), prepared immediately before use.

0.1 M HEPES, pH 8.0, 25°

Purified MAb, 2–5 mg/ml in 0.1 M HEPES, pH 8.0, 25°

Protocol. (1) Add 1 mg of purified MAb to a polypropylene tube (this reaction may be performed in a Centricon 30 microconcentrator). (2) Add 0.1 M HEPES (pH 8.0) to a volume of 0.90 ml (vortex). (3) Add 100 μl of sulfo-NHS-biotin stock solution (vortex). (4) React at 25° for 30 min. (5) Transfer to a Centricon 30 and wash five times with 2 ml 0.1 M HEPES (pH 8.0), 0.05% NaN$_3$, 4°. (6) Reconstitute b-MAb at 2–5 mg/ml with 0.1 M HEPES (pH 8.0), 0.05% NaN$_3$, and store aliquots at $-80°$ (b-IgG) or $-20°$ [b-IgM in 0.2 M HEPES (pH 7.5), 50% (v/v) glycerol, 0.05% NaN$_3$].

The NHS-biotin procedure biotinylates MAbs to a greater extent due

[6] K. Hofmann, G. Titus, J. Montibeller, and F. M. Finn, *Biochemistry* **21,** 978 (1982).

[7] J. J. Leary, D. J. Brigati, and D. C. Ward, *Proc. Natl. Acad. Sci. U.S.A.* **80,** 4045 (1983).

to the higher molar ratio of NHS-biotin to protein (59:1 in the case of IgGs) than in the sulfo-NHS-biotin procedure (32:1 in the case of IgGs). There is no apparent advantage in using more highly biotinylated MAbs in the immunoaffinity isolation. However, we have not evaluated the effect of extent of biotinylation on other methods in which b-MAbs are employed, such as immunofluorescence or electron microscopy.

The use of Centricon 30 microconcentrators has several advantages. When small quantities of MAb are being desalted, the recovery of b-MAbs is much higher with these devices (compared to dialysis). For example, the percentage recovery of 1 mg b-MAb is 85–90% after the first use of the microconcentrator and essentially 100% thereafter. The microconcentrators may be stored and reused repeatedly with a given MAb or b-MAb, and several samples may be washed and concentrated simultaneously under controlled solute conditions with buffers that would not be economically feasible for dialysis.

The use of 0.1 M HEPES (pH 8.0) for buffering the NHS-biotin reaction may be obvious; however, its use as a reconstitution and storage buffer may not be. We have found that MAbs and b-MAbs are more stable in solution (and to repeated freezing and thawing) in 0.1–0.2 M HEPES buffer. Other zwitterionic buffers might have similar stabilizing and cryoprotectant properties as HEPES, but we have not investigated them.

Preparation of Streptavidin–Agarose

Streptavidin–agarose may be prepared by linking streptavidin (BRL, Bethesda Research Laboratories, Gaithersburg, MD) to Affi-Gel 15 (Bio-Rad Laboratories, Richmond, CA) as described below, or it may be purchased from BRL. Both products have similar amide linkage chemistry and chemical and physical stability. When compared at the same streptavidin–matrix linking ratio of ~1.5 mg streptavidin/ml gel, the BRL streptavidin–agarose was more efficient at removing b-MAb–antigen complexes than the streptavidin–Affi-Gel matrix (T. V. Updyke and G. L. Nicolson, unpublished observations). This difference may be due to the larger molecular exclusion limit of the BRL agarose matrix (M_r ~2 × 10^7 versus M_r ~5 × 10^6). All references to "streptavidin–agarose" apply to either product.

Detailed Procedure

Stock Solutions

0.1 M HEPES, pH 8.0, 0°
1 M ethanolamine–HCl, pH 8.0, 0°

HEPES-buffered saline (HBS): 10 mM HEPES, 150 mM NaCl, pH 7.5
(adjusted with KOH), 0.05% NaN$_3$, 0°
1 M NaCl, 5 mM HEPES, pH 7.5, 0°

Protocol. (1) Dissolve streptavidin at 2 mg/ml in 0.1 M HEPES, pH
8.0, 0°. (2) Wash 1 ml of Affi-Gel 15 with isopropanol (2 × 5 ml) followed
by cold H$_2$O (2 × 5 ml) on a fritted funnel. (3) Transfer washed gel to a
10 × 75-mm polypropylene tube (capped) and add 1 ml of streptavidin
solution. (4) Mix the components for 4 hr on a rotary wheel at 4°. (5)
Block remaining NHS groups on the gel by the addition of 0.1 ml of 1 M
ethanolamine–HCl (pH 8.0) for 1 hr. (6) Wash the gel with HBS two
times (15 volumes) with 1 M NaCl, 5 mM HEPES (pH 7.5) once, and
with HBS twice. (7) Store the streptavidin–agarose at 4°.

We use HEPES-buffered solutions and avoid Tris and phosphate
buffers, because in other procedures biotinyl ligands, such as lectins and
calmodulin, require the addition (and removal) of various divalent cations. Streptavidin–agarose is very stable to a number of denaturants (to
be discussed below), but prolonged storage in the presence of detergents
that are subject to autooxidation, such as the Triton, Tween, Brij, and
Lubrol series, should be avoided.

[^{14}C]Biotin Binding Assay

The biotin-binding activity of streptavidin–agarose is measured by
incubation of 1–10 μl of beads with 1 nmol of D-[*carbonyl*-^{14}C]biotin (51
mCi/mmol; Amersham, Arlington Heights, IL) in HBS (or test solution)
for 30 min in microfuge tubes with frequent vortexing. The samples are
then washed three times with 0.5 ml HBS (or test solution) by a 10-sec
centrifugation in a Beckman microfuge. The washed gel beads are transferred to scintillation vials with two 50-μl aliquots of H$_2$O, and radioactivity determined by liquid scintillation spectrometry. By assuming all four
biotin-binding sites are active and knowing the specific activity of
[^{14}C]biotin, the amount of streptavidin linked to the agarose matrix is
determined by calculating the nanomoles of streptavidin-binding sites
from the dpm of [^{14}C]biotin that is bound, and dividing by four times the
molecular weight of streptavidin. This results in a conservatively low
linking efficiency of ~80% (~90% by protein determination), or ~1.6 mg
of streptavidin/ml agarose under the conditions described in the previous
section.

Accurate pipetting of the streptavidin–agarose suspension is required.
We use disposable micropipets that have their bore diameter increased by
cutting 3–4 mm (single-edge razor) off the tip, preventing the agarose
particles from partially clogging the pipet tip, which can lead to variability
in the amounts delivered.

Stability of Streptavidin–Agarose

The stability of streptavidin–agarose after storage for 1 year under the conditions described above is >95%. The activity of streptavidin–agarose has been assayed in the presence of a number of detergents and denaturants and at various ionic strengths. Conditions under which 100% binding of [^{14}C]biotin have been obtained are listed in the table. To remove >95% of the [^{14}C]biotin that has bound to streptavidin–agarose, we have had to heat the beads at 100° for 30 min in 2% SDS, 150 mM DTT, 62 mM Tris–PO$_4$ (pH 6.8). The affinity matrix may not have the same stability characteristics when biotinylated macromolecule–streptavidin conjugates are formed.[6,7]

Radiolabeling and Solubilizing Membrane Antigens

There are several methods that can be used to radiolabel and solubilize membrane antigens. Their discussion is beyond the scope of this chapter. However, a few general comments can be made about conditions that may affect the outcome of the immunoaffinity isolation step with streptavidin–agarose. (1) If biosynthetic labeling with radiolabeled amino acids is performed, radiolabeled biotin-containing enzymes may have to be precleared from the reaction mixture prior to the addition of b-MAb. This avoids isolation of biotin-containing cell components along with the immune complexes. (2) The results of our streptavidin–agarose stability studies (section above) indicate that the affinity matrix can be used with virtually any solubilization condition that is compatible with the subunit structure of the antigen and the MAb-antigen binding reaction. Detailed discussion of various detergents that can be used and their properties is

SOLUTIONS ALLOWING OPTIMAL [^{14}C]BIOTIN BINDING
TO STREPTAVIDIN–AGAROSE

H$_2$O
5% NP-40
5% CHAPS or CHAPSO
5% Sulfobetaines 3-14 and 3-12 (SB$_{14}$ and SB$_{12}$)
2% SDS, 150 mM DTT, 62 mM Tris–PO$_4$, pH 6.8 (25°)
100 mM DTT, 200 mM EDTA, pH 7.2
1 M NaCl, or KCl
9 M Urea
4 M Tetramethylurea
4 M Guanidine–HCl, 0.1 M sodium acetate, pH 6.0

inappropriate here, and the reader should refer to other publications[8,9] and reviews.[10,11] (3) In most cases, we solubilize cells at a detergent : protein ratio of 5 : 1 to 10 : 1 (w/w) in the presence of 0.2 mM phenylmethylsulfonyl fluoride and store the centrifuged lysates (microfuge forces or greater) in liquid nitrogen or at $-80°$.

Immunoaffinity Isolation with b-MAbs and Streptavidin–Agarose

Once the various components have been assembled (purified b-MAbs, streptavidin–agarose, and radiolabeled, detergent-solubilized membrane antigens) the remaining procedure for isolation of membrane antigens is relatively simple.

Detailed Protocol. (1) Thaw detergent lysates (stored at $-80°$ or in liquid nitrogen). (2) Recentrifuge the lysates at 9000 g (or higher) for 5 min (or longer) at 4°. (3) Preclear biotinyl enzymes (depending on labeling procedure) with 1 μl streptavidin–agarose/100 μl of lysate [this is an excess amount for a 5 : 1 (v/v) detergent : cell pellet ratio or greater] with frequent vortexing for 30 min at 0°. (4) Centrifuge the lysates for 10 sec in the microfuge. (5) Place aliquots (50–100 μl) in new microfuge tubes. (6) Add 1–10 μg of each b-MAb to its appropriate tube (after centrifugation for 5 min in the microfuge to remove b-MAb aggregates). (7) Incubate for 1–3 hr at 0°.

(8) Add 10 μl of streptavidin–agarose [20 μl of a 50% suspension delivered with a modified (3 mm cut off the end) disposable pipet tip] to bind 10 μg b-MAb (or less) and vortex the suspension frequently (every 4–5 min) for 60 min at 0°. Repeat step 4 and carefully aspirate the supernatant solution. (9) Wash each gel four times with HBS + 0.1% NP-40, Triton X-100 or Tween 20 (see below). Repeat step 4, and carefully aspirate each supernatant wash. (10) Wash each gel pellet once with 0.5 ml 5 mM HEPES (pH 7.2) or H_2O (see below). (11) Add 25–50 μl SDS–polyacrylamide gel electrophoresis sample buffer or isoelectric focusing buffer (depending on the method of analysis) and process appropriately for electrophoresis, or store at $-80°$ (or $-20°$).

Recentrifugation of the lysates is required after a freezing and thawing step (no matter what the initial centrifugation force was) to remove aggregates, which would otherwise contribute to nonspecific binding. Higher forces and centrifugation times are better in this respect. The large size (60–150 μm) of streptavidin–agarose particles requires that they be fre-

[8] A. Helenius, D. R. McCaslin, E. Fries, and C. Tanford, this series, Vol. 56, p. 734.
[9] L. M. Hjelmeland, *Proc. Natl. Acad. Sci. U.S.A.* **77**, 6368 (1980).
[10] A. Helenius and K. Simons, *Biochim. Biophys. Acta* **415**, 29 (1975).
[11] C. Tanford and J. A. Reynolds, *Biochim. Biophys. Acta* **457**, 133 (1976).

quently agitated (vortexed), since they sediment quickly and decrease the interaction of streptavidin with the soluble b-MAb–antigen complexes. Although 10 μl of streptavidin–agarose will clear 10 μg b-MAb (IgG) in 30 min from 100 μl of HBS, the clearance of b-MAb–antigen complexes takes longer, with 60 min being optimal in most cases. Overnight incubations lead to higher nonspecific binding and should be avoided. Expensive detergents with relatively high critical micelle concentrations (i.e., 3-[(3-cholamidopropyl)-dimethylammonio]-1-propanesulfonate; CHAPS) can be used to solubilize membrane antigens. Once the binding of b-MAb–antigen (CHAPS micelle) to streptavidin–agarose has occurred, the washing buffers can contain an inexpensive detergent substitute, such as NP-40, Triton X-100, or Tween 20. In most cases, washing buffers at physiological pH and ionic strength are sufficient to effectively wash the isolated immune complexes on the streptavidin–agarose matrix. This is important, since many MAb–antigen interactions are sensitive to conditions of pH, ionic strength, and denaturants (chaotropes, strong detergents, etc.) that are required by some immunoprecipitation methods to reduce nonspecific binding. There is some minor nonspecific binding with this method (as well as SpA–agarose) resulting from the binding of membrane hydrophobic antigens to hydrophobic molecules in the detergent lysate. These problems can be minimized, if not eliminated, by using efficient detergents and carefully controlling detergent-to-protein ratios, as discussed in the previous section. Washing membrane antigen isolates with low ionic strength buffers (or H_2O) can reduce the amounts of actin and myosin, and can also reduce the salt content of the sample, improving electrophoretic separations.

Discussion

The method described in this chapter has been shown to be useful for isolating membrane antigens with MAbs that bind poorly to SpA.[2] The only disadvantage of this method compared with others is that it requires that the MAbs be purified and then modified by biotinylation. However, once these steps are taken, the same b-MAbs may be used in additional studies utilizing the streptavidin–biotin interaction, such as immunofluorescence, electron microscopy, ELISA, and immunoblotting. The development of new hydrophilic, colloidal, surface-linked streptavidin matrices should improve the speed and efficiency of isolating antigens, as well as other macromolecules, with b-MAbs and other biotinyl ligands.[2]

Acknowledgments

The authors wish to thank Eleanor Felonia for secretarial assistance. This work was supported by USPHS Grant R01-CA42346 and -CA29571 to G. L. Nicolson.

[69] An Indirect Rosette Technique for the Identification and Separation of Lymphocyte Populations by Monoclonal Antibodies

By KINGSTON MILLS

Monoclonal antibodies against cell surface antigens provide very convenient tools for the quantitative analysis and separation of lymphoid subpopulations. The detection and enumeration of cells labeled with the monoclonal antibody are usually performed by indirect immunofluorescence, either by microscopy or on the fluorescence-activated cell sorter (FACS), or less frequently by complement-mediated cytotoxicity or immunochemical staining. Separation of monoclonal antibody-labeled cells can be performed using the FACS, panning, or cytotoxicity techniques.

Rosetting provides a further method for the detection of monoclonal antibody-defined cell surface antigens, a method which has a number of advantages over alternative technologies. Rosetting allows the enumeration, direct morphological identification, and sterile separation of cells bearing the relevant surface structure, whereas no other method fulfills all these roles. Cytotoxicity only allows negative selection and requires complement-fixing antibody, and separation by means of panning, although very quick and simple, has the problem of nonspecific adherence to plastic surfaces. Enumeration by fluorescence microscopy is laborious and sometimes very subjective, and access to the sophisticated FACS equipment is not always readily available.

Rosetting techniques have previously been described for the detection of surface immunoglobulin (Ig)[1] and more recently for use with monoclonal antibodies.[2,3] In this chapter an indirect rosette technique is described in which the monoclonal antibody-labeled cells are detected by marker ox red blood cells (RBC) coated with anti-mouse Ig.

Indirect Rosette Technique

Coupling Procedure

The coupling procedure described here is an adaptation of the "aged" chromic chloride coupling technique first described by Gold and Fuden-

---

[1] N. R. Ling, S. Bishops, and R. Jefferies, *J. Immunol Methods* **15,** 279 (1977).
[2] J. Bernard, T. Ternynck, and D. Zagury, *Immunol. Lett.* **4,** 65 (1982).
[3] K. Mills, R. Armitage, and J. Cawley, *Immunol. Lett.* **6,** 241 (1983).

burg[4] and modified by Ling *et al.*[1] for the detection of surface Ig. Alternative technologies include the "fresh" chromic chloride[5] or benzoquinone[2] coupling techniques. However, the aged chromic chloride method is very simple and has proved particularly reliable.

Second Layer Antibody. Affinity-purified sheep or goat antibody to mouse Ig gives the best results. Rabbit antisera may be used but nonspecific Fc receptor binding can be a problem. Commercially available anti-mouse Ig (G, M, A, and light chains) raised in either sheep (Serotec) or goat (Nordic) has been used in this laboratory. Alternatively, immunospecific goat anti-mouse Ig can be prepared from hyperimmune serum by a method similar to that described by Good *et al.*[6] for rabbit antibody. The antiserum is passed over a column of mouse IgG coupled to Sepharose, and specific antibodies to mouse IgG are eluted with 0.1 M acetic acid in 0.15 M NaCl.

Exhaustive dialysis of the antibody preparation is carried out against several changes of 0.15 M saline over 2–3 days at 4°. The protein content of the dialysed material is estimated using the Lowry–Folin method, and aliquots containing 0.25 mg of protein (approximately 5 mg/ml) may be stored at $-20°$ for up to 1 year.

RBC. Ox or sheep RBC stored in Alsever's solution are washed four times with 0.15 M NaCl. Washed cells are used on the same day but cells stored in Alsever's solution for up to 3 weeks give satisfactory results.

Chromic Chloride. A 1 mg/ml solution of chromic chloride (CrCl$_3$ · 6H$_2$O) is prepared in 0.15 M NaCl, adjusted to pH 5.0 by the addition of a small volume of 0.1 M NaOH, and left at room temperature for at least 1 month with further weekly readjustments to pH 5.0 with NaOH. This aged solution of chromic chloride can be used for up to 1 year, but the pH should be checked occasionally and adjusted to pH 5.0 if necessary. An aliquot is diluted 1 : 10 with fresh 0.15 M saline just before use to give 0.1 mg chromic chloride/ml.

Coupling. Freshly washed packed ox RBC, 100 μl, are added to a glass tube with 25–50 μl of antibody (5 mg/ml). The suspension is rapidly agitated on a vortex mixer while 500 μl of chromic chloride, 0.1 mg/ml, is added dropwise. Approximately 1 ml of 0.15 M saline is carefully layered on top of the cells by running it down the side of the tube. The tubes are left overnight at 4°, and the RBC washed three times in phosphate-buf-

[4] E. R. Gold and H. H. Fudenberg, *J. Immunol.* **99**, 859 (1967).
[5] D. W. Dresser, *in* "Handbook of Experimental Immunology" (D. M. Weir, ed.), Vol. 2, p. 28.1. Blackwell, Oxford, 1978.
[6] A. H. Good, L. Wofsy, J. Kimura, and C. Henry, *in* "Selected Methods in Cellular Immunology" (B. B. Mishell and S. M. Shiigi, eds.), p. 278. Freeman, San Francisco, California, 1980.

fered saline and made up to 4 ml (5% solution) in RPMI medium supplemented with 10% fetal calf serum (FCS). Sensitized cells can be stored for up to 1 month at 4°, provided that they are prepared aseptically.

Comments. (1) All reagents and glassware used in the coupling procedure should be free of phosphate ions, which are known to inhibit the reaction. Filter-sterilized, rather than autoclaved, 0.15 M NaCl should be used in all cases. Glassware should be acid-washed before use. (2) Although anti-mouse Ig can be coupled to sheep RBC, agglutination of the RBC by the chromic chloride can be a problem. In addition, spontaneous rosetting of human T cells by unsensitized sheep RBC limits their use for indirect rosetting. Consequently, ox RBC are recommended as the most suitable marker. (3) Coupling of anti-mouse Ig to ox RBC in the presence of chromic chloride can be achieved after 15–30 min at room temperature; however, overnight incubation at 4° results in more effective coupling and whole Ig fractions can be used rather than affinity-purified antibody.

Preparation of Lymphoid Cells

Human Lymphocytes. Peripheral blood mononuclear cells (PBMC) are purified by centrifugation over Ficoll/Triosil (F/T) (density 1.077) for 30 min at 400 g. A tonsilar cell suspension is prepared by gently teasing a tonsil with a forceps in cold RPMI medium. Sheep erythrocyte positive (E^+) and negative (E^-) fractions are prepared by a rosetting technique that employs 2-aminoethylisothiouronium bromide (AET)-treated sheep RBC. PMBC or tonsilar lymphocytes are mixed with AET-treated sheep RBC (100 μl of 50% RBC to 1 × 10^7 lymphocytes), centrifuged at 200 g for 5 min, and incubated at 4° for 1 hr. The cell pellet is gently resuspended, layered over cold F/T, and centrifuged at 400 g for 30 min. The E^- cells (B cells, monocytes, and null lymphocytes) are found at the interface. Rosetted E^+ cells are recovered from the pellet by lysis of the sheep RBC with autologous plasma. Monocytes are removed from the E^- fraction by adherance to plastic for 1 hr at 37°.

Mouse Lymphocytes. A suspension of mouse spleen cells is prepared by teasing the organ through a stainless-steel sieve into RPMI medium containing 10% FCS. Cell aggregates are removed by passing the suspension through a fine gauze filter. The cell suspension is then centrifuged for 5 min at 300 g and resuspended in RPMI. Erythrocytes and dead cells are removed by centrifugation over 17% metrizamide (Nyegord & Co, Oslo, Norway; density 1.091; prepared by diluting a 35% stock solution in distilled water with RPMI) for 15 min at 800 g. T-cell-enriched preparations are obtained after monocyte depletion by adherance to plastic, and B-cells depletion by direct rosetting with ox RBC coupled with goat anti-mouse Ig as described below for the indirect technique.

Rosette Formation and Separation

For surface marker analysis 5–20 × 10⁴ lymphoid cells are incubated with 50 μl of appropriately diluted monoclonal antibody (0.1 μg purified antibody/ml or 1/100 dilution of tissue culture supernatant). After incubation for 30 min on ice, the cells are washed two to three times and one drop of anti-mouse Ig-coated ox RBC (2.5%) is added. The suspension is mixed, centrifuged at 200 g for 1 min, and placed on ice for 30 min before reading. The cells are resuspended after the addition of one to two drops of isotonic ethidium bromide and acridine orange solution (a differential stain for viable and nonviable cells). The percentage of viable cells (stained green) forming rosettes with the ox RBC are counted on a fluorescence microscope. Lymphocytes which bind four or more RBC are considered positive; however, in most cases the number of bound RBC is much greater (Fig. 1).

Cytological Examination of Rosetted Cells. Slide preparations of the rosetting cell suspension are made by centrifugation onto microscope slides on a Shandon–Elliott cytocentrifuge. The cell suspension, 100 μl diluted to 5 × 10⁴ lymphocytes/ml, is added to each sample chamber and centrifuged for 5 min at 500 rpm. Morphological details of the rosetted cells are examined by light microscopy after Romanowsky, nonspecific esterase, or acid phosphatase staining.[2,7]

Separation of Rosetting and Nonrosetting Cells. The lymphoid cell suspension is incubated for 30 min on ice with 100 μl monoclonal antibody (1 μg purified antibody/ml or undiluted tissue culture supernatant) per 10⁷ cells. After two washes in cold RPMI, the cells are adjusted to a concentration of 1 × 10⁷/ml and an equal volume of 2.5% anti-mouse Ig-coated ox RBC is added. The tubes are mixed, centrifuged at 200 g for 5 min, and then incubated on ice for a further 30 min. The cell pellet is gently resuspended by inversion, layered over F/T (human cells) or metrizamide (mouse cells), and centrifuged, respectively, at 400 g for 30 min or 800 g for 15 min at room temperature.

The nonrosetting cells are recovered from the interface and the rosetting cells from the pellet after ammonium chloride lysis of the RBC. The percentage of viable lymphocytes in each fraction is tested by ethidium bromide and acridine orange staining and is usually >95%.

Controls

The following control incubations are usually performed to confirm the specificity of the technique. Monoclonal antibody-labeled cells are

---

[7] R. J. Armitage, D. C. Linch, C. P. Worman, and J. C. Cawley, *Br. J. Haematol.* **51,** 605 (1982).

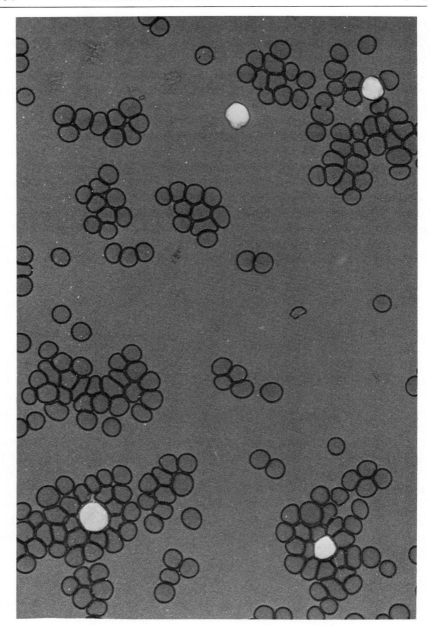

FIG. 1. Simultaneous UV and visible light microscopy of a cytocentrifuge slide preparation of rosettes formed with anti-Lyt-1-labeled mouse lymphocytes (B cell and monocyte
depleted). Brightly stained (acridine orange fluorescence) viable rosetting and nonrosetting
cells can readily be distinguished.

incubated with unsensitized ox RBC. Unsensitized lymphocytes or cells stained with irrelevant first-layer antibody of the same class as the test antibody are incubated with anti-mouse Ig-coated ox RBC. In all instances the percentage of positive cells in controls should be less than 1%, except in the case of mouse lymphoid suspensions in which sensitized ox RBC can bind to surface or extrinsic Ig present on contaminating B cells or monocytes.

Applications of the Rosette Technique

The indirect rosette technique has its widest application in the analysis and separation of human lymphoid subpopulations but can also be used with mouse lymphocytes. Here the problem of nonspecific binding of anti-Ig-coated ox RBC to mouse B cells and monocytes restricts its application to the study of T-cell subpopulations. Direct rosetting with the anti-Ig-coated ox RBC can readily be used to deplete B cells and monocytes (with extrinsic Ig) from heterogeneous mouse lymphoid preparations, thus allowing further analysis or separation on the basis of monoclonal antibody binding and indirect rosetting.

In this and other laboratories the indirect rosette technique has been used for (1) the phenotypic study of monoclonal antibody-defined lymphoid subsets in normal and malignant human peripheral blood and mouse spleen cell samples, (2) the phenotypic, cytochemical, or functional analysis of monoclonal antibody-labeled and rosette-separated human or mouse lymphoid cell suspensions, and (3) the purification of T-cell subpopulations from cultured mouse spleen cells for the establishment of long term T-cell lines.

The experiments described below serve to validate the technique as a sensitive and effective method for detecting and separating monoclonal antibody-labeled cells.

Analysis of Monoclonal Antibody-Labeled Cells

The rosette technique gave highly reproducible results in addition to being quick and simple to perform. Phenotypic analysis could be carried out on very small numbers of cells, with as little as 2×10^4 cells required per individual assay. As an analytical test, rosetting gave comparable results to indirect immunofluorescence[3] except in the case of low-density antigen expression, for which the rosette method appeared to be more sensitive (see below).

In E[+] lymphocytes from five normal individuals (Table I) the percentage of OKT4[+] plus OKT8[+] cells is approximately equal to the total number of T cells detected by the pan T-cell monoclonal antibody UCHT1 or

TABLE I
PHENOTYPIC ANALYSIS OF HUMAN AND
MOUSE LYMPHOID PREPARATIONS

Cell preparation	N	Surface marker[a]	Rosette-positive cells[b] (%)
E$^+$ PBMC	5	E	93 ± 3
		UCHT1	91 ± 5
		OKT4	63 ± 5
		OKT8	33 ± 6
Tonsil	10	E	34 ± 6
		UCHT1	33 ± 6
		SIg	64 ± 7
		BA1	64 ± 6
Mouse spleen	4	Thy-1	84 ± 2
(B cell and		Lyt-1	86 ± 5
monocyte depleted)		Lyt-2	25 ± 5
		L3T4	64 ± 3

[a] Human E$^+$ and SIg$^+$ cells were detected, respectively, by spontaneous rosetting with sheep RBC and by direct rosetting with ox RBC coupled with anti-human Ig. All other markers (monoclonal antibodies) were detected by indirect rosetting with anti-mouse Ig-coupled RBC.

[b] Second-layer-only controls were <1% for human lymphocyte samples and 3 ± 1% for the mouse spleen cell samples.

by E rosetting. OKT4 and OKT8 respectively stain reciprocal subpopulations of helper or MHC Class II-restricted and cytotoxic/suppressor or MHC Class I-restricted human T cells. The ratio of OKT4$^+$: OKT8$^+$ cells was 1.9, which is in close agreement with that reported by us and others[8] using immunofluorescence techniques.

The percentage of B cells in 10 tonsilar lymphocyte preparations assessed by the B-cell specific monoclonal antibody BA1 was identical to the number of surface Ig (SIg)-positive cells detected by direct rosetting with anti-human Ig-coupled ox RBC (Table I).

Anti-mouse Ig-coated ox RBC were also used to detect mouse monoclonal anti-Thy-1 and anti-L3T4 (GK1.5)[9] or rat monoclonal anti-Lyt-1 and anti-Lyt-2[10] antibodies bound to mouse lymphoid cells. Anti-L3T4

[8] G. Semenzato, F. Herrmann, and K. H. G. Mills, *Clin. Exp. Immunol.* **57,** 752 (1984).
[9] D. P. Dialynas, D. B. Wilde, P. Marrack, A. Pierres, K. A. Wall, W. Havran, G. Otten, M. R. Loken, M. Pierres, J. Kappler, and F. W. Fitch, *Immunol. Rev.* **74,** 29 (1983).
[10] J. A. Ledbetter and L. A. Herzenberg, *Immunol. Rev.* **47,** 63 (1979).

and anti-Lyt-2 label mutually exclusive subpopulations of Class II and Class I MHC-restricted mouse T cells, respectively.[9] Phenotypic analysis of B cell- and monocyte-depleted spleen cell preparations (4 samples) from normal CBA mice is shown in Table I. The sum of L3T4[+] and Lyt-2[+] cells closely approximates the total number of T cells detected by anti-Thy-1, while anti-Lyt-1 appears to label all T cells.

Sensitivity

The percentage of positive lymphocytes in human PBMC fractions labeled with increasing dilutions of monoclonal antibodies BA1 (E[-] preparation), OKT4, or OKT8 (E[+] preparations) is shown in Fig. 2. The minimum concentration of antibody required to detect 100% of positive cells was in the range 30–60 ng/ml. When compared with indirect immunofluorescence assessed by microscopy the minimum concentration was in the range of 125–250 ng/ml (data not shown).

The greater sensitivity of the rosette technique over complement-mediated lysis or immunofluorescence assessed by FACS analysis was demonstrated by the detection of IL-2 receptors with anti-Tac monoclonal

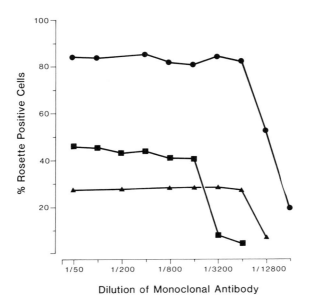

FIG. 2. Titration of monoclonal antibodies BA1 (●), OKT8 (▲), and OKT4 (■) against human lymphocyte preparations. Cells (1 × 10[5]) were labeled with 50 μl of serially diluted commercial stock reagents: OKT4 (50 μg/ml), OKT8 (100 μg/ml), or BA1 (400 μg/ml).

antibody on nonactivated normal human B cells.[11] In B-cell preparations from four normal individuals (83 ± 3% surface Ig[+], 2 ± 1% E[+] cells), 45 ± 13% of the cells were positive with anti-Tac detected by indirect rosetting, but negative with indirect immunofluorescence. Previous studies with anti-Tac using cytotoxicity[12] or FACS analysis[13] failed to detect IL-2 receptors on normal resting B cells, although the antigen was demonstrated by immunofluorescence on activated or leukemia B cells.[13,14] It is possible that the density of receptor expression is increased after activation and that very sensitive detection methods are required to demonstrate those found on resting B cells.

Phenotypic analysis of mouse lymphoid cell fractions using the indirect rosetting method demonstrate that the Lyt-1 surface antigen is probably expressed on all L3T4[+] or Lyt-2[+] splenic T cells. A Lyt-1[-], Lyt-2[+] positive population of T cells was previously demonstrated in the spleen[15]; however, with the use of more sensitive immunofluorescence technique this Lyt-1 antigen has recently been shown to be expressed on all mouse T cells but more weakly on a population of Lyt-2-positive cells.[16]

Separation of Human B-Cell or T-Cell Subpopulations

OKT4- and OKT8-positive subpopulations of human T cells were purified from E-enriched fractions by depletion of the rosetted cells after labeling the reciprocal subset with the monoclonal antibodies OKT8 and OKT4, respectively. The purity of the depleted fractions was approximately 80%, with less than 1% of contaminating T cells of the reciprocal subset (Table II). In some cases, positively enriched fractions were also prepared but the level of contamination was difficult to assess because of the failure of the bound antibody to cap after overnight incubation at 37°. Nevertheless, both positive and negatively enriched OKT4 "helper" cell fractions were shown to help pokeweed mitogen-stimulated B cells in the production of Ig, whereas OKT8[+] "suppressor" cells failed to do so.

Highly purified B-cell populations were prepared by negative or positive enrichment using the rosette technique. B cells prepared by positive

[11] R. J. Armitage and J. C. Cawley, *Clin. Exp. Immunol.* (in press).

[12] T. Uchiyama, S. Broder, and T. A. Waldmann, *J. Immunol.* **126,** 1393 (1981).

[13] L. K. L. Jung, T. Hara, and S. Man Fu, *J. Exp. Med.* **160,** 1597 (1984).

[14] T. A. Waldmann, C. K. Goldman, R. J. Robb, J. M. Depper, W. S. Leonard, S. O. Sharrow, K. F. Bongiovanni, S. J. Korsmeyer, and W. C. Greene, *J. Exp. Med.* **160,** 1450 (1984).

[15] H. Cantor and E. A. Boyse, *J. Exp. Med.* **141,** 1376 (1975).

[16] J. A. Ledbetter, R. L. Evans, M. Lipinski, C. Cunningham-Rundles, R. A. Good, and L. A. Herzenberg, *J. Exp. Med.* **153,** 310 (1981).

TABLE II

ANALYSIS OF HUMAN LYMPHOCYTE SUBPOPULATIONS SEPARATED BY ROSETTING MONOCLONAL ANTIBODY-STAINED CELLS

Original cell preparation	Cell fraction	No. samples tested	Recovery (%)	Positive cells (%)					
				UCHT1	OKT4	OKT8	E	BA1	SIg
E+ PBMC	OKT4-	5	16 ± 4	84 ± 7	0.6 ± 0.4	79 ± 5	87 ± 6	—	—
E+ PBMC	OKT8-	5	31 ± 5	86 ± 3	80 ± 6	0.5 ± 0.2	85 ± 3	—	—
E- tonsil	UCHT1-	2	75	<0.1	—	—	<0.1	98	100
E- PBMC	BA1+	1	33	0.2	—	—	<0.1	90	91

enrichment of BA1$^+$ rosettes from E-depleted PBMC preparations produced a fraction which had >90% B cells and 0.2% T cells. Alternatively, tonsilar B cells devoid of any detectable T cells were prepared by depleting UCHT1$^+$ rosettes from an E$^-$ fraction (Table II).

Separation of Mouse T-Cell Subpopulations

T-cell-enriched mouse spleen cells composed of 80–90% Thy-1$^+$ and <5% surface Ig$^+$ cells were further fractionated into L3T4$^+$ and Lyt-2$^+$ populations by rosette depletion of Lyt-2$^+$ and L3T4$^+$ cells, respectively. The purity of the depleted fractions was approximately 90%, with less than 2% contaminating T cells of the reciprocal subset (Table III).

Purification of L3T4$^+$ T cells (depleted of B cells and monocytes) from *in vitro* stimulated (secondary) immune spleen cells by enrichment of rosette positive cells gave a population which were 90% pure (Table III). These cells were capable of further responding to the immunizing antigen in the presence of irradiated antigen-presenting cells. Antigen-specific T-cell lines were established in this way.

Attempts to separate cultured cells on the FACS often resulted in low viability (10–60%) or poor recovery (10–50%) of positive cells. In comparison, rosette-enriched samples were 85–99% viable, and 50–80% of positively labeled cells were recovered.

Conclusions

The indirect rosette technique described here provides a simple and reproducible method for the enumeration, morphological identification, and separation of human lymphocyte populations labeled with mono-

TABLE III
MOUSE T-CELL SUBPOPULATIONS SEPARATED FROM B CELL- AND
MONOCYTE-DEPLETED SPLEEN CELL PREPARATIONS[a]

Cell fraction	Recovery (%)	Positive cells (%)			
		Lyt-1	Lyt-2	L3T4	Control[b]
L3T4$^-$	10	89	87	1	0
Lyt-2$^-$	38	83	1.5	82	1
L3T4^{+c}	32	88	5	91	5

[a] Results are means from two experiments.
[b] Rosetting with second layer only.
[c] Separated from cultured spleen cells; analysis carried out after overnight incubation of fractionated cells (at 37°).

clonal antibodies. Its application to the analysis or separation of mouse lymphoid cells is more limited since the ox RBC coated with anti-mouse Ig bind to Ig on the surface of the B cells or to Ig extrinsically bound to monocytes. However, it is possible to fractionate and subsequently phenotype T-cell subpopulations by first depleting the Ig-bearing cells by direct rosetting with anti-Ig-coupled ox RBC or simply by using negatively enriched fractions.

As a preparative technique, the rosette method gives purities and recoveries comparable with other methods of cell separation (cytotoxicity, panning, or FACS). A cell population can be positively or negatively enriched without loss of viability or function. However, negative selection proves to be more reliable and avoids the possibility of antigenic modulation or other changes associated with antibody binding. Rosetting is simpler and quicker than FACS sorting and more readily performed sterilely. In addition, its greater sensitivity allows detection of low-density antigenic expression and reduces the quantity of monoclonal antibody needed for cell staining.

In conclusion, the simple indirect rosette technique described here provides a widely applicable and in many ways more satisfactory alternative to the FACS or to other methods of analysis and separation of lymphocyte populations.

Acknowledgments

This work was supported in part by the Leukaemia Research Fund (United Kingdom). The original technique was developed with the collaboration of R. J. Armitage and C. P. Worman. I am grateful to J. C. Cawley for valuable discussions.

[70] Separation of T Cell Subpopulations by Monoclonal Antibodies and Affinity Chromatography

By RÜDIGER W. BRAUN and GUNTHER KÜMEL

Separation of B and T cells by immunoaffinity chromatography has been a useful tool in studying lymphocyte function for more than 10 years,[1–4] as recently reviewed by Basch et al.[5] As a method for lympho-

[1] H. Wigzell and B. Andersson, *J. Exp. Med.* **129**, 23 (1969).
[2] P. Truffa-Bachi and L. Wofsy, *Proc. Natl. Acad. Sci. U.S.A.* **66**, 585 (1970).
[3] L. Wofsy, J. Kimura, and P. Truffa-Bachi, *J. Immunol.* **107**, 725 (1971).
[4] L. Chess, R. P. MacDermott, and S. F. Schlossman, *J. Immunol.* **113**, 1113 (1974).
[5] R. S. Basch, J. W. Berman, and E. Lakow, *J. Immunol. Methods* **56**, 269 (1983).

cyte separation, affinity chromatography was first performed by Wigzell and Andersson[1] and later by Truffa-Bachi and Wofsy,[2] Wofsy and Kimura,[6] and Wofsy et al.[3] The availability of monoclonal antibodies (MAb) recognizing functionally distinct lymphocyte subsets has led to the use of affinity chromatographic techniques for the separation of MAb-labeled T cells.[7] Usually, for separation of T lymphocytes and their subsets an indirect modification of immunoaffinity chromatography is employed; i.e., MAb-labeled cells are purified by their adherence to a matrix-bound second antibody or staphylococcal protein A (SpA).[7–9]

A major advantage of affinity chromatography over other cell separation procedures is the possibility of simultaneous enrichment and depletion of a given cellular subset. Furthermore, if appropriate matrix material is used, immunoaffinity separation will not result in nonspecific stimulation or binding of lymphocyte subpopulations such as B cells or monocytes, problems that do occur in cell separation by panning.[10] Matrix materials used today, as will be described below, allow covalent binding of antibodies, which may help to reduce alterations in cell function resulting from membrane-bound antibody in positively selected populations. The use of MAb in affinity separation of cells has several advantages over the use of polyclonal antisera in that MAb consist of a homogeneous Ig subclass, exert an almost absolute epitope specificity, are available in large quantities, and are not subject to batch to batch variations. Furthermore, many MAb, in contrast to monospecific antisera, do not bind complement. This property may be advantageous for the use of positively selected T cells in cytotoxicity assays. The method is easy to perform, is applicable to large-scale separation of cells, and does not require expensive equipment.

Selection or adaptation of an immunoaffinity technique for the separation of a given cellular subset requires careful consideration of the relative advantages and possible pitfalls of the specific procedure, with particular respect to the elution profile, recovery of cells, purity of enriched and depleted subsets, and maintenance of the original bioactivity (e.g., mitogen or antigen responsiveness).

[6] L. Wofsy and J. Kimura, J. Immunol. 107, 725 (1971).

[7] R. Braun, H. Teute, H. Kirchner, and K. Munk, J. Immunol. Methods 54, 251 (1982).

[8] V. Ghete, G. Mota, and J. Sjöquist, J. Immunol. Methods 21, 133 (1978).

[9] P. S. Duffey, D. L. Drouillard, and C. P. Barbe, J. Immunol. Methods 45, 137 (1981).

[10] S. Fong, R. I. Fox, J. E. Rose, J. Liu, C. D. Tsonkas, D. A. Carson, and J. H. Vaughan, J. Immunol. Methods 46, 153 (1981).

Selection of a Separation Strategy

The wide spectrum of methods used to separate cell populations according to their immunoreactivity with a subset defining MAb can be divided into two categories. In the direct procedure the MAb is coupled to the matrix with or without a spacer molecule. Reactive cells are then chromatographed over the derivatized solid phase. Especially in this direct modification, however, effectiveness of the separation is highly dependent on the number and distribution of MAb reactive sites on the cell surface, the avidity of the MAb for the antigen, and the accessibility of binding sites for MAb. These characteristics are determined by the purity of the antibody preparation, loss of activity during the coupling procedure, whether the antibody is bound randomly or stereospecifically by the Fc part of the molecule, and also the nature and the number of bonds immobilizing the antibody molecule to the matrix. Multiple binding of the peptide chains to the solid phase is likely to result in conformational changes and reduction of binding capacity and specificity.

Strong and multiple binding of cells to immobilized antibodies, however, is not desirable since under these conditions cell binding is essentially irreversible, and may result in antigen stripping upon forced elution of tightly bound cells.[5,11] To circumvent these problems reversible mercury–sulfur bonds, reducible disulfide bonds, or degradable matrix materials have been used for detachment of matrix-bound cells (for review, see Ref. 12).

In an indirect modification, lymphocytes are first reacted with the respective MAb and then chromatographed over a matrix carrying a second antibody or SpA. In a further submodification the first antibody is labeled with fluorescein isothiocyanate (FITC),[13] arsonate,[14,15] biotin analogs,[5] or other ligands followed by chromatography of cells on a matrix offering binding sites for the respective hapten. These approaches avoid many of the problems of the direct procedure, and gentle elution of bound cells in most cases may be achieved with free ligands. These procedures thus combine the inherent specificity of the immune reaction with the versatility and practicability of affinity chromatography.

With respect to antibody–SpA and antibody–antibody interactions, however, not every monoclonal antibody is suited for use in indirect

[11] K. A. Ault and E. R. Unanue, *J. Exp. Med.* **139,** 110 (1974).
[12] H. Kiefer, *Eur. J. Immunol.* **5,** 624 (1975).
[13] D. W. Scott, *J. Exp. Med.* **144,** 69 (1976).
[14] S. Cammisuli and L. Wofsy, *J. Immunol.* **117,** 1765 (1976).
[15] L. Wofsy, C. Henry, and S. Cammisuli, *Contemp. Top. Mol. Immunol.* **7,** 215 (1978).

affinity chromatography. For example, matrix-bound SpA may not bind monoclonal IgA or IgM antibodies efficiently. Binding characteristics of protein A have recently been reviewed by Langone,[16] and the reader is referred to this chapter. Also, the affinity of anti-mouse IgG for different monoclonal antibodies will vary with the MAb IgG subclass according to the relative distribution and immunogenicity of IgG subclasses in the mouse serum used for immunization. Thus the use of monoclonal antibodies coupled to low molecular weight ligands as described above, in combination with the respective anti-hapten antibodies, can offer the advantage of more uniform results.[17-19] Furthermore, not every matrix-coupled ligand is suited for the separation of every cell type. For example, SpA may nonspecifically bind and stimulate B cells.

Choice of Matrix

The crucial factors in the selection of matrix material include stability, availability of a method for coupling ligands in biologically active form, high capacity, biological inertness, and ease of elution. In addition, the physical form of the matrix is important. Any material chosen can only be a compromise among these demands.

The separation characteristics of column chromatography generally require beaded matrices,[9] although application of column principles to immunoadsorbents in fiber form may offer advantages.[5] If bead structures are appropriately derivatized with a suitable antibody, the binding pattern of cells on a solid phase can be controlled to allow retardation of reactive cells in a reiterative process, in a multitude of differential events of weak but specific bond formation and detachment, while unbound cells can flow freely through the interspace between beads. This approach will lead to effective separation in high yields, retain viability and biospecific responsiveness, allow mild elution conditions, and minimize nonspecific binding or mechanical trapping of cells.

Due to the "stickiness" of the cell surface and its affinity for hydrophobic surfaces, a completely inert matrix material is not likely to be found. From the differential binding of lymphocytes to materials such as nylon or glass wool it is clear that the problem of nonspecific binding is an important consideration. Choice of matrix materials with a negative net

[16] J. J. Langone, this series, Vol. 70, p. 356.
[17] M. L. Jasiewicz, D. R. Schoenberg, and G. C. Mueller, *Exp. Cell Res.* **100,** 213 (1976).
[18] K. H. Singer, C. Johnston, D. B. Amos, and D. W. Scott, *Cell. Immunol.* **36,** 75 (1978).
[19] N. W. T. Clark, R. M. E. Parkhouse, and R. G. Simmonds, *J. Immunol. Methods* **51,** 167 (1982).

charge, such as carboxylic acid-derivatized polyacrylamide beads[20] and Sepharose 6MB modified by conjugation with CIBA blue dextran and albumination[9] is helpful in avoiding nonspecific binding. Bead size and exclusion limit of the porous structure also are important. Uniformly sized agarose beads of 200–300 μm provide the optimum compromise between good contact with cells, good flow characteristics, and low physical trapping of cells.[8] If smaller beads are chosen nonspecific steric retention of the cells may occur. In this case, batchwise procedures may be preferable.[21]

Of the large number of matrix materials described,[5] only beaded forms of cross-linked agarose, dextran, and polyacrylamide and albumin spheres polymerized by use of glutaraldehyde have been widely used in immunoaffinity chromatography of cells.

Preparation of the Columns

Coupling of Antibodies to the CNBr-Activated Matrix

Both the direct and indirect methods referred to above involve coupling of an antibody to the matrix. This can be achieved by directly coupling the antibody to a CNBr-activated agarose or dextran matrix, or by use of the heterobifunctional thiolation reagent SPDP[22] if thiolated beaded agarose is used. Alternatively, a spacer molecule or an extension arm can be introduced between matrix and antibody. Agarose beads derivatized by spacer molecules carrying carboxyl, amino, or other reactive groups in an activated form for direct coupling can be purchased from several manufacturers. The use of spacer groups, however, can lead to additional problems in T cell separation such as hydrophobic interaction with cell membranes or leakage of the ligand from the immunosorbent. The advantages of spacer molecules that can be degraded thermally, by enzymatic digestion, or by chemical cleavage have been discussed above.

A common variation of the spacer concept is the matrix immobilization of SpA to which the antibody to be coupled is subsequently bound by its Fc portion. This leads to the presentation of the immunoreactive antibody site, thus maximizing specificity and binding capacity of the immobilized antibody. The antibody can be cross-linked to immobilized SpA by carbodiimide, dimethyl suberimidate, or other bifunctional agents. Glu-

[20] M. M. Baran, D. M. Allen, S. R. Russell, M. E. Scheetz, II, and J. F. Monthony, *J. Immunol. Methods* **53**, 321 (1982).
[21] S. K. Sharma and P. P. Mahendroo, *J. Chromatogr.* **184**, 471 (1980).
[22] J. Carlsson, H. Drevin, and R. Axén, *Biochem. J.* **173**, 723 (1978).

taraldehyde was not found suitable for this purpose.[23] The use of SPDP as a coupling reagent may be advantageous, but has not been described for this purpose.

CNBr Activation of Agarose or Dextran

Though CNBr-activated agarose is commercially available in beaded form, albeit at about 10 times the price of agarose itself, a reliable and simple method that allows precise control of the degree of activation is still indispensable. The methods described for this purpose have continuously been improved over the years. Here an advanced technique is described that minimizes handling of the poisonous and volatile cyanogen bromide.[24] All procedures should be carried out in a well-ventilated fume hood.

Storage of CNBr. The reagent in the original flask is dissolved by addition of 0.5 ml of acetonitrile/g CNBr (concentration 1 g/ml), and stored in aliquots in glass tubes with metal caps or glass stoppers at $-20°C$.

Activation Reaction. Wet agarose or dextran slurry (for example, CL-Sepharose, Sepharose 4B, Sepharose 6MB, Sephadex), 20 g, is washed three times with distilled water in a filter funnel, sucked dry, and added to 30 ml of 3.3 M potassium phosphate buffer (pH 11.9 at 10-fold dilution) in a 250-ml glass beaker with a suspended magnetic stirrer that does not touch the bottom of the vessel. A 1-ml volume of the CNBr solution in acetronitrile (1 g/ml) is added, and the vessel is closed and stirred vigorously for 2 min to suspend the organic phase. The slurry is immediately transferred to a filter funnel with distilled water and washed rapidly with 300 ml of ice-cold 0.25 M phosphate buffer (pH 6), 500 ml distilled water at ambient temperature, and 200 ml of coupling buffer. The buffer is sucked off and the activated gel is immediately dispersed in a solution of the protein to be coupled.

Coupling of Antibody or SpA to CNBr-Activated Dextran or Agarose

The amount of protein coupled to the matrix should not be lower than 4 mg/g gel. If required, inert carrier protein such as bovine serum albumin can be added. The activated gel is carefully distributed in a solution of the protein (5 mg/ml) in coupling buffer (0.1 M NaHCO$_3$, 0.5 M NaCl, pH 8.5) and shaken gently at 4° for 24–48 hr. The binding efficiency is assessed by

[23] D. M. Gersten and S. S. Marchalonis, *J. Immunol. Methods* **24**, 305 (1978).
[24] G. Kümel, H. Daus, and H. Mauch, *J. Chromatogr.* **172**, 221 (1979).

measuring protein concentration in the supernatant. At least 90% of the protein should be bound. Unbound protein can be reused.

The immobilized antibody is washed three times with coupling buffer in a funnel, dispersed in 1 M ethanolamine–HCl (pH 9) for 2 hr at 4°, and washed three times with 150 ml of 0.5 M NaHCO$_3$. This is followed by two washes each with 100 ml of 0.1 M Na$_3$BO$_4$, 1 M NaCl (pH 8.5) and with 100 ml of 0.1 M CH$_3$COONa (pH 4.1), 1 M NaCl. This alternation between the latter two buffers is repeated twice. The gel is then equilibrated on the funnel with 0.01 M sodium phosphate, and can be stored at 4° as a wet slurry for several weeks if 0.02% NaN$_3$ is added to prevent microbial growth. After preparing the column (plastic or siliconized glass), a small volume of buffer to be used for elution of the cells should be used to equilibrate the gel.

Cross-Linking of Antibody to Immobilized SpA or Anti-Immunoglobulin

Lymphocyte-specific MAb of the IgG class can be bound to immobilized SpA while other Ig classes must be directly coupled to the membrane or to immobilized anti-immunoglobulin. The method described here is a variation of that described by Gersten.[23] Dry SpA–Sepharose 6MB, 250 mg, is swollen overnight at 4° in PBS to yield 1 ml gel slurry. Alternatively, 1 ml of settled gel carrying anti-immunoglobulin antibodies may be used. Monoclonal IgG antibody (100–500 μg) is incubated for 20 min with the gel at ambient temperature and with periodic agitation. The particles are washed five times with 5 ml PBS each, stored for 12–24 hr at 4°, and washed twice in 5 ml borate buffer (pH 8).

The centrifuged slurry is suspended in 5 ml of freshly prepared suberimidate hydrochloride in 0.1 M borate buffer (pH 8.0) for 30 min at room temperature, centrifuged, suspended in 5 ml 0.1 M borate buffer (pH 8.0) containing bovine serum albumin (BSA), 50 μg/ml, for 15 min, and washed three times in PBS (5 ml each). Before use, the column containing this adsorbent is washed with an equal volume of 0.15 M NaCl, 0.1 M CH$_3$COOH (pH 3) to elute remaining BSA and unreacted antibody and then equilibrated with elution buffer.

Siliconization of Glass and Plastic

To avoid cell adherence to the column wall, glass surfaces should be siliconized by a 10-min exposure to 1% dimethyldichlormethylsilane in benzene or trichlormethane at ambient temperature. This solution, if kept absolutely dry, can be reused many times. Excess reagent is washed off with distilled water. The glassware should then be kept at 80° for 1 hr, though this does not seem to be an absolute requirement. Plastic material can be siliconized with a 5% aqueous solution of Siliclad.

Monoclonal Antibody Labeling of Cells

For performance of indirect affinity chromatography, labeling of cells with the respective MAb preceding cell separation is necessary. This is usually performed as in indirect immunofluorescence; i.e., cells are washed and incubated in 0.1 M PBS (pH 7.2) containing 1% calf serum to cover Fc receptors and each aliquot of 10^7 cells/ml is further labeled at 4° for 45 min with approximately 1 μg of monoclonal antibody. Performance of the antibody labeling in the cold is an absolute requirement to avoid patching, capping, and shedding of membrane antigens. Addition of 0.01% NaN$_3$ also is recommended. The action of NaN$_3$ on the cell membrane is completely reversible if the agent is dialyzed or washed out when cell separation is completed.[25] This is achieved by incubation of separated cells for 30 min in excess medium with two or three changes.

After incubation, excess monoclonal antibody is removed from the cells by three washes in PBS deficient in Ca^{2+} and Mg^{2+} ions and containing 1% calf serum. The use of buffers containing divalent cations should be avoided in order to reduce nonspecific antibody binding.

Chromatography and Elution Procedure

In a widely applicable example of the direct immunoaffinity chromatography procedure, T cells are first incubated for 30 min at 4° in PBS (pH 7.2) containing 2% calf serum and 0.01% NaN$_3$ to cover Fc and other receptors (such as α, γ, or μ-receptors) and to avoid antigenic modulation during the later separation step. The cells to be separated are then allowed to flow into a column containing the MAb-coupled solid-phase support. Matrix material before application to the column should be carefully degassed to avoid inclusion of air bubbles, which may lead to a discontinuous buffer flow and to mechanical trapping of cells. A total bed volume of 5 ml is usually sufficient to separate up to 10^8 cells. After addition of cells, the column is incubated for 30 min at 4° to facilitate binding to the MAb. Subsequently, nonadherent cells are released by several washes with cold PBS (up to 50 ml). This cell population is considered to be depleted of the MAb-reactive subset.

Adherent cells may be released by competition with an excess of at least 5 μg MAb per 10^7 cells, which is added to the column followed by a

[25] A. D. Bershadsky, V. I. Gelfand, T. M. Svitkina, and I. S. Tint, *Exp. Cell Res.* **127**, 421 (1980).

further incubation period of 30 min at 4°. This approach, however, in our hands had led to only partial recovery of cells not exceeding 10–20%. Rubin obtained similar results for the elution of antigen-bound cells with free antigen or EDTA.[26] Thus, to obtain higher recovery, elution of attached cells by stirring or vortexing is preferable, although this may lead to a decrease in cell viability.[8] Dead cells may be removed from viable cells by Ficoll/metrizoate gradient centrifugation. Stripping of antigen by this procedure may occur, but was not observed by us. This might be due to the fact that only a small fraction of membrane antigens takes part in the interaction between lymphocytes and the immobilized MAb, leaving a major fraction free of antibody for subsequent reaction in indirect immunofluorescence.

In a typical example of the indirect modification of the procedure, the monoclonal antibody-labeled cells are separated over a column of polyacrylamide or agarose beads (e.g., Sepharose), to which SpA or an anti-mouse Ig antibody is covalently bound. The affinity constant of SpA ($\sim 10^8$) for IgG is high enough to allow effective binding of cells to the matrix.[8] Protein A, however, may also bind cells bearing surface immunoglobulins. Thus in general, we prefer anti-mouse IgG columns, which may help to reduce nonspecific attachment of cells. Before being transferred to columns the matrix should be carefully degassed. Subsequently, columns should be prewashed with 3% BSA in PBS to cover possible nonspecific binding sites.

A bed volume of at least 1 ml per each 10^7 cells should be used to achieve optimal separation. MAb-labeled lymphocytes are allowed to flow into the column and are incubated for 30 min at 4° in PBS or balanced salt solution including a minimum of 0.01% NaN_3 to avoid patching and capping. BSA at 1–3% may also be included to further reduce nonspecific binding. Incubation at room temperature or 37° is not recommended, since modulation of surface antigens may occur.

After incubation nonadherent cells are released by several washes with cold PBS. These cells are considered to be a population depleted of a given subset. Bound cells are preferentially released by competition with free affinity proteins. This is achieved by addition of first or second antibody to the column in at least 10-fold excess, sealing the outlet, and further incubation for 30 min to 1 hr in the cold. Released cells can now be eluted by a wash with cold buffer containing the respective competing antibody. A schematic outline of the method is given in Fig. 1.

As discussed above, mechanical removal of bound lymphocytes by vortexing, stirring, or resuspending is more rapid and efficient. This ap-

[26] B. Rubin, *J. Immunol.* **116**, 80 (1976).

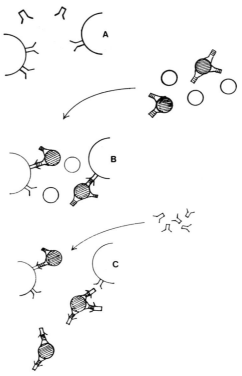

FIG. 1. Flow chart of cell separation by indirect immunoaffinity chromatography. (A) Coupling of antibody to the solid-phase support; (B) MAb labeling of cells and attachment of MAb-labeled cells to the matrix-bound second antibody; (C) detachment and elution of specifically bound cells by competition with second antibody.

proach, however, will result in a significant decrease of cell viability,[8] and may also influence cell function. Moreover, as already mentioned stripping of antigens may occur. The viability of specifically enriched lymphocyte populations obtained by affinity chromatography, as assessed by dye exclusion, varies between 85 and 98%, depending on the procedure used to release bound cells from the matrix.

The recovery of cells after affinity chromatography in general is between 80 and 98%, which is comparable to other affinity separation procedures. The purity of enriched subsets usually exceeds 90%, as determined by indirect immunofluorescence. Cell function, as assessed by mitogen responsiveness, and, for OKT4+ and OKT8+ cells, by helper and suppressor assays, in positively selected T cells is not altered.[7] We have observed, however, that e.g., OKT3-selected T cells show a high background of [3H]thymidine incorporation, which is probably due to the mitogenic activity of the OKT3 antibody.[27] Though affinity separated T4$^+$ and T8$^+$ cells did not show altered activities in helper and suppressor assays, it may be that other cell functions such as antigen recognition or mitogen responsiveness are changed by membrane-bound antibody[27–29] and subsequent antigen modulation. Such side effects may be partially overcome by brief incubation of cells in ice-cold 0.05 M acetate–NaCl buffer (pH 4) and subsequent washing,[30] by prolonged culture of cells, or by application of the direct modification of affinity chromatography. In the latter procedure the cell surface antigens will react exclusively with the MAb covalently bound to the matrix. Since the diameter of the beads by far exceeds the size of the lymphocyte, only a small fraction of the cell surface antigens will be accessible for antibody binding.

Alternative ways to release adherent cells from the matrix include digestion,[31,32] chemical cleavage, or melting[33] of matrix material and bridges introduced to bind the antibody to the solid-phase support.[34] With the former methods mechanically trapped cells also are released, and therefore the purity of the eluted subset is reduced.

Immunoaffinity chromatography is not only a method for positive selection but may also be used for simultaneous depletion of a given subset of cells. In general, contamination of depleted subsets does not exceed 3– 5%, and in our experiments we could reduce contamination to below 0.1%.[7] These results, however, as for positive selection, will depend on the relative affinity of the antibodies used for separation.

Regeneration of Matrix. Recycling of antibody-coupled beads and their multiple use is possible. Regeneration of antibody-binding sites is achieved by incubation of beads for at least 15 min in 0.1 M glycine–HCl buffer (pH 2.8–3.0) with subsequent washing in glycine–HCl and equilibration in PBS–azide (pH 7.2) including 1–3% BSA. Columns are repacked and stored at 4°.

For comparison of immunoaffinity chromatography to other positive selection methods the reader is referred to a recent review.[35] Results obtained by immunoaffinity separation of T lymphocytes with monoclonal

[27] J. P. van Wauwe, J. R. De Mey, and J. G. Goossens, *J. Immunol.* **124,** 2708 (1980).

[28] N. Hollander, *Immunol. Rev.* **68,** 43 (1982).

[29] F. A. Lemounier, D. Z. Birnbaum, P. C. Dubroil, and D. H. Caillol, *Scand. J. Immunol.* **16,** 233 (1982).

[30] K. Kumagai, T. Abo, T. Sekizawa, and M. Sasaki, *J. Immunol.* **115,** 982 (1975).

[31] S. F. Schlossman and L. Hudson, *J. Immunol.* **11,** 313 (1973).

[32] C. Webb, D. Teitelbaum, H. Rauch, A. Maoz, R. Arnon, and S. Fuchs, *J. Immunol.* **114,** 1469 (1975).

[33] E. F. Gold, R. Kleinman, and S. Bon-Efraim, *J. Immunol. Methods* **6,** 31 (1974).

[34] D. B. Thomas and B. Phillips, *Eur. J. Immunol.* **3,** 740 (1973).

[35] R. Braun, *in* "Handbook of Monoclonal Antibodies" (S. Ferrone and M. P. Dierich, eds.), p. 36. Noyes Publications, 1985.

antibodies are comparable to other positive selection procedures such as rosetting, panning, or fluorescence-activated cell sorting (FACS).

Conclusions

Affinity chromatographic separation of T cells by use of MAb at present is a valuable tool in studies of the function of T cells and their subsets. A broad array of procedures has been developed, of which an indirect modification using a matrix-bound second antibody appears to be the most practical and advantageous with respect to purity, functional activity, and viability of separated cells.

As in other positive separation techniques such as rosetting, panning, or FACS, the attachment of antibodies to the surface of enriched populations is still a problem. However, this difficulty may be overcome by using procedures to detach antibodies from the cell surface and by prolonged cultivation following cell separation. A major advantage of the method in comparison to rosetting or panning is that covalent binding of antibody to the matrix enhances specificity and allows regeneration and multiple use of the matrix.

The method is applicable to large-scale separation of cells and is rapid, inexpensive, and easy to perform. It is possible to obtain highly enriched or depleted cell populations which do not show obvious functional alterations. Immunoaffinity chromatography using MAb is at least comparable to panning, rosetting, or FACS.

[71] A Rapid Micromethod for the Enumeration of T Cell Subsets in Blood by Epifluorescence Microscopy

By Ian H. Frazer, Ian R. Mackay, and Frank Battye

Enumeration of lymphocyte subsets in blood using monoclonal antibodies (MAb) is necessary for optimal clinical assessment of immune deficiency. Enumeration of a given lymphocyte subset in the blood is usually done by exposing cells to a fluorochrome-labeled MAb and then counting stained cells using a flow cytometer or a microscope equipped for epifluorescence microscopy. Flow cytometry equipment is not always available, and it is inadvisable to send samples to a central laboratory for flow cytometry analysis because unreliable results may be obtained with stored blood when storage conditions are suboptimal.[1]

The acquired immune deficiency disease (AIDS) is a disease in which T cell subset analysis is particularly relevant. This disease is the result of infection with the HTLV-III virus,[2] which invades and damages T helper lymphocytes and thereby causes profound immunosuppression, with a characteristic fall in the ratio of helper (Th) to suppressor (Ts) T cells in the blood, by reason of a selective depletion of the helper T cell subset.[3] Assessment of the Th/Ts ratio is used as one of the screening tests for HTLV-III virus infection. There is therefore a need for a rapid micromethod for assessment of the Th/Ts ratio in blood, and of individual T cell subset numbers, that can be done on small samples using a microscope equipped for epifluorescence microscopy. This chapter describes such a rapid micromethod.

Methodological Principles

The rapid enumeration of T lymphocyte subsets in human blood by epifluorescence microscopy, using small-sample volumes, has been made possible by the elimination of the density flotation step normally required to obtain pure mononuclear cells from whole-blood samples. This can be achieved by one of two alternative techniques.

The first technique, which is applicable if only a ratio of Th/Ts cells is required, uses the new red-emitting fluorochrome phycoerythrin (PE)[4]; this dye, in contrast to the more commonly used red fluorochrome rhodamine, emits red light with enough intensity to allow enumeration of cells using direct, as opposed to indirect, immunofluorescence. Also this dye, in contrast to rhodamine, can be excited by the same wavelength as for excitation of the commonly employed green fluorochrome, fluorescein, so allowing simultaneous enumeration of two populations of stained cells by epifluorescence microscopy, even in unseparated blood.

The second technique, which is used if the absolute number of a particular lymphocyte subset in the blood needs to be determined, requires the use of propidium iodide (PI) as a nuclear stain.[5] PI emits orange fluorescence when intercalated into nuclear DNA and exposed to light,

[1] P. De Paoli, M. Reitano, S. Battistin, C. Castiglia, and G. Santini, *J. Immunol. Methods* **72**, 349 (1984).
[2] M. Popovic, M. G. Sarngadharan, E. Read, and R. C. Gallo, *Science* **224**, 497 (1984).
[3] J. L. Fahey, H. Prince, M. Waver, J. Groopman, B. Visscher, K. Schwartz, and R. Detels, *Am. J. Med.* **76**, 95 (1984).
[4] V. T. Oi, A. N. Glazer, and L. Stryer, *J. Cell Biol.* **93**, 981 (1982).
[5] C. G. Yeh, B. L. Hsi, and W. P. Faulk, *J. Immunol. Methods* **43**, 269 (1981).

and so provides for quick identification of nucleated cells among the red cells in unseparated blood. Cell membranes stained with MAb coupled to fluorescein, but not red fluorochromes, can be satisfactorily identified against the orange nuclear staining produced by PI.[6]

Justification of Methods

This section is presented in two parts. The first part describes the selection of optimal MAb and fluorochrome combinations for enumeration of T cells by epifluorescence microscopy, based on flow cytometry analysis of the intensity of staining of T cells by a range of MAbs and fluorochromes. The second part describes rapid micromethods for enumeration of T cell subsets by epifluorescence microscopy using these MAbs, and compares the results with enumeration by flow cytometry. Using micromethods, a screening procedure will allow rapid determination of the relative proportions of two T cell subsets in the blood using two-color epifluorescence microscopy, and an enumeration procedure will allow precise quantification of any selected subset.

Selection of Optimal Fluorochrome Combinations for Epifluorescence Microscopy

Monoclonal Antibodies and Fluorochromes. Optimal fluorochrome combinations for enumeration of T cells in blood by epifluorescence microscopy were determined by the studies outlined below. Monoclonal antibodies specific for all T cells (Leu4), the helper/inducer T cell subset (Leu3a), and the suppressor/cytotoxic T cell subset (Leu2a), and their biotin, fluorescein, and phycoerythrin conjugates, and the fluorescein and phycoerythrin conjugates of avidin, were purchased from Becton-Dickinson (La Jolla, CA). Affinity-purified fluorescein-conjugated sheep anti-mouse IgG from Silenus (Melbourne, Australia) was used at a dilution of 1 : 40.

Preparation of Stock Solutions. The following stock solutions were used.

Phosphate-buffered saline (PBS), pH 7.3: 2.85 g $Na_2HPO_4 \cdot 2H_2O$, 0.62 g $NaH_2PO_4 \cdot 2H_2O$, 7.00 g NaCl, and deionized distilled water (DDW) to 1 liter.

Eisen's balanced salt solution with fetal bovine serum (EBSS/FCS): 0.60 g Trizma base, 0.71 g Na_2HPO_4, 0.12 g $MgSO_4$, 7.00 g NaCl, 0.22 g $CaCl_2$, 0.45 g KCl, 0.02 g phenol red, DDW to 1 liter, and 20 ml fetal bovine serum (inactivated at 56° for 30 min).

---

[6] I. H. Frazer and I. R. Mackay, *J. Immunol. Methods* **57,** 137 (1983).

Cell fixative: 10 ml formalin (BDH Australia AnalaR grade), 25 g dextrose, 2 g sodium azide, and DDW to 1 liter.

Hemolytic Geys solution:

Stock A: 35 g NH_4Cl, 1.85 g KCl, 1.5 g $Na_2HPO_4 \cdot 12H_2O$, 0.12 g KH_2PO_4, 5 g glucose, 50 mg phenol red, and DDW to 1 liter.

Stock B: 0.42 g $MgCl_2 \cdot 6H_2O$, 0.14 g $MgSO_4 \cdot 7H_2O$, 0.34 g $CaCl_2$, and DDW to 100 ml.

Stock C: 2.25 g $NaHCO_3$, and DDW to 100 ml.

Working solution (prepared just prior to use): 20 parts A, 5 parts B, 5 parts C, and 70 parts DDW.

Preparation of Peripheral Blood Mononuclear Cells. Mononuclear cells (MNC) were prepared from venous blood diluted 1 : 1 with PBS containing 20 U/ml of preservative-free heparin (Weddel, United Kingdom), by density flotation on Isopaque/Ficoll of specific gravity 1.074 (Ficoll/Paque, Pharmacia, Sweden) at 400 *g* for 20 min at room temperature. Cells retained at the interface were washed three times with EBSS/ FCS for 5 min at 400 *g* at room temperature and adjusted to 20×10^6 cells/ ml. Air-dried smears of MNC prepared in this manner and stained with Giemsa stain (BDH) contained less than 2% of polymorphonuclear leukocytes.

Staining of T Cell Subsets and Enumeration by Flow Cytometry. Mononuclear cells prepared as above (1×10^6 cells in 50 μl EBSS/FCS) were exposed to MAb-conjugated to biotin or fluorochrome (5 μl) for 30 min at 4° in plastic microtiter trays (Linbro 76-042-05). Cells exposed to biotin-conjugated MAb were washed three times with 200 μl of EBSS/ FCS at 4° and 400 *g*, and then exposed to 20 μl of avidin-conjugated fluorochrome diluted 1 : 20 in EBSS/FCS for 30 min at 4°. All cells were then washed three times in PBS and resuspended in cell fixative. Flow cytometer analysis was performed using a FACS II cell sorter (Becton-Dickinson) with an argon ion laser (488 nm). Cells were analyzed for forward light scatter, and for red and green fluorescence with the fluorescence signals amplified using 3-decade log amplifiers. Intensity of fluorescence staining is expressed throughout this chapter on an arbitrary linear scale from 1 to 1000: this linearized figure for the fluorescence intensity (RFI) is derived from the 256-channel logarithmic scale using the formula $RFI = 10 \exp(\text{channel number}/83.33)$. Gating was employed to exclude from analysis cells and debris with small values for forward-angle light scatter.

Relative Intensity of Fluorescence Using Various Fluorochromes. Studies were made, using blood from 50 healthy subjects and patients with various illnesses, to compare the relative intensity of T cell staining produced by directly fluorescein-conjugated Leu2a, Leu3a, and Leu4 MAbs, by examining histograms of the distributions of fluorescence intensities of cells from peripheral blood stained with each of these MAbs. Cells stained with Leu2a were brightest, with a mean RFI of 84, and there was relatively little scatter about this mean, since 95% of the Leu2a+ve cells had an RFI between 57 and 128. Leu4+ve cells were generally less bright, with a mean RFI of 34 and there was a wider scatter about this mean, since 95% of cells had an RFI between 9 and 128. Cells stained with Leu3a were least bright, with a mean RFI of 14, and with a small scatter of brightness, since 95% of cells had an RFI between 9 and 25.

The minimum intensity of cell staining required to distinguish stained from unstained cells visually was established as follows. MNC labeled with fluorescein-conjugated Leu3a were examined by flow cytometry and by epifluorescence microscopy. Cells stained with Leu3a had, as cited above, a range of fluorescence intensities, and not all the cells scored as positive by flow cytometry were so identified visually; that is, the percentage of MNC scored as Leu3a+ve visually was always lower than the percentage scored as positive by flow cytometry analysis. In six experiments, comparison was made of the percentage of cells identified as positive by microscopy and the distribution histographs of RFI of the same cell population obtained with the flow cytometer, and it could be deduced that only cells with an RFI of greater than 11 could be scored as positive by eye. Hence fluorescein-conjugated Leu2a is suitable for quantification of Ts cells, using epifluorescence microscopy, whereas direct conjugates of Leu3a and Leu4 used in this way would give a spuriously low result for the Th and total T cell populations.

For Leu3a and Leu4, the most suitable combination of fluorochrome and procedures for use with an epifluorescence microscope was established as follows. The RFI of MNC stained with MAb by a two-layer indirect immunofluorescence technique was determined and compared with the direct technique. Considering first direct immunofluorescence with PE-conjugated MAb, results from four experiments (Table I) showed that Leu3a conjugated to PE stained all cells more brightly than did Leu3a conjugated to fluorescein, and all cells stained by the Leu3a-PE conjugate had an RFI greater than 14. Hence this direct conjugate is suitable for epifluorescence microscopy.

Two indirect immunofluorescence techniques were assessed; one used fluorescein or PE coupled to avidin and biotin-conjugted MAb, and the other used fluorescein coupled to a rabbit antibody to mouse IgG, and unconjugated MAb (Fig. 1). Either of the indirect immunofluorescence methods gave a considerably greater mean RFI, with each of the three MAbs tested, than did the direct method employing fluorescein-conjugated MAb, so allowing the identification of weakly fluorescent cells, in addition to the intensely labeled cells previously identified by the direct immunofluorescence technique (Fig. 1).

TABLE I

STAINING OF LYMPHOCYTES BY LEU2a, LEU3a, AND LEU4: COMPARISON OF DIRECT
AND INDIRECT IMMUNOFLUORESCENCE TECHNIQUES WITH PHYCOERYTHRIN
OR FLUORESCEIN

| | | Relative fluorescence intensity[a] | | | | |
| | | Direct IF | | Indirect IF[b] | | |
MAb		PE	FLU	PE–avidin	FLU–avidin	FLU–IgG
Leu2a	Mean	173	79	155	122	106
	95%	75–380	45–100	20–380	35–220	45–220
Leu3a	Mean	85	18	60	50	56
	95%	35–170	10–35	15–290	25–170	35–170
Leu4	Mean	N.D.	38	81	71	67
	95%		10–130	20–290	35–220	35–220

[a] For each MAb, values given represent the mean of the modal relative fluorescence intensity (RFI) from four experiments and the range of RFI within which 95% of the stained cells were found. IF, Immunofluorescence; PE, phycoerythrin; FLU, fluorescein.

[b] For procedures, see text.

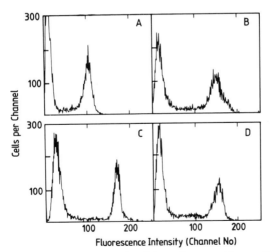

FIG. 1. Histographs of the intensity of staining of mononuclear cells from peripheral blood exposed to Leu3a, using various fluorochromes and a direct or indirect immunofluorescence (IF) technique: (A) Direct IF: fluorescein-conjugated Leu3a; (B) indirect IF: biotin-conjugated Leu3a + fluorescein-conjugated avidin; (C) direct IF: phycoerythrin-conjugated Leu3a; (D) indirect IF: Leu3a and fluorescein-conjugated anti-mouse IgG. The fluorescence intensity is shown on a log scale, with the brightest cells on the right, and 10,000 cells were counted for each histograph.

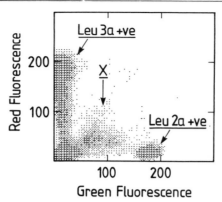

FIG. 2. A scatter plot of mononuclear cells double-labeled with PE-conjugated Leu3a and fluorescein-conjugated Leu2a. Cells not stained by either antibody are in the bottom left corner, cells labeled with Leu2a are in the bottom right, and cells labeled with Leu3a in the top left corner. No strongly double-labeled cells can be seen in the top right corner, but there is a population of weakly double-labeled cells (X), which are probably binding MAb by Fc receptors.

Results of experiments in which cells were exposed to PE-conjugated Leu2a and fluorescein-conjugated Leu3a simultaneously are illustrated in Fig. 2. These indicated that the cells which stained weakly with Leu2a or Leu3a using indirect immunofluorescence techniques stained with both Leu2a and Leu3a, thus representing separate cell population from the T cell subsets, which express exclusively one or the other of the subset markers; these weakly staining double-labeled cells are probably a mixture of B cells, macrophages, and K cells which bind the MAbs by the Fc receptor. Clearly, this cell population should not be counted among the cells specifically stained by a MAb when T cell subsets are being enumerated. For this reason, and because such double-labeled cells were less intensely stained using an indirect immunofluorescence technique which used the avidin–biotin combination (mean RFI 8) than one which used fluorescein-conjugated anti-IgG (mean RFI 12), the avidin–biotin system was selected for the rapid micromethod.

Rapid Micromethods for Enumeration of T Cell Subsets in Unseparated Blood

Exposure of Cells to MAb. Venous blood (200 µl) was anticoagulated with heparin 20 U/ml and cooled to 4° on ice, and exposed to 5 µl of fluorochrome or biotin-conjugated MAb for 15 min at 4° in 1.5-ml plastic "bullet" tubes (Eppendorf 3180, West Germany). For the screening procedure, cells were simultaneously exposed to PE-conjugated Leu2a and fluorescein-conjugated Leu3a, and for the enumeration procedure, a biotin-conjugated MAb was used. Cells were then washed three times with cold EBSS/FCS (1 ml) using a Beckman "Microfuge B" centrifuge for 15 sec at 4°. Supernatants were aspirated between washes, rather than poured off, and care was taken not to disturb the buffy coat during this procedure. Cells exposed to biotin-conjugated MAb were further exposed to fluorescein-conjugated avidin (1 : 20 in EBSS/FCS) on ice for 15 min, and washed three times as before.

Screening Procedure for Direct Determination of Th/Ts Ratio. Whole blood (20 μl) which had been simultaneously exposed to PE-conjugated Leu2a and fluorescein-conjugated Leu3a, as described above, was mixed with 20 μl of 90% (v/v) glycerol (BDH) in PBS and examined by epifluorescence microscopy. The ratio of red-staining to green-staining cells was calculated after counting 300 stained cells, using a Zeiss "Orthoplan" microscope equipped for epifluorescence microscopy and appropriate filter combinations for fluorescein (KP490, KP500, FT510, LP528). For 18 blood samples, the Th/Ts ratio determined by microscopy was compared with that determined by flow cytometer analysis of separated MNC, the latter being derived as the ratio of the absolute percentage of MNC stained by Leu3a and Leu2a. The correlation between the two methods ($r = 0.89$) was good (Fig. 3); the generally slightly higher ratio obtained with separated blood was attributed to the selective loss of Leu2a+ve cells by adherence to plastic and on the Ficoll/Isopaque gradient.[6]

For lymphopenic blood samples in which the total MNC was less than 1×10^6/ml, concentration of the MNC was necessary for more rapid counting, and was achieved by partial hemolysis of RBC beforehand with hemolytic Geys solution. Cells stained with MAb were resuspended, after the first wash in EBSS/FCS, in 200 μl hemolytic Geys solution, held for 2 min on ice, and washed twice in EBSS/FCS; there was approximately 80% lysis of RBC for most blood samples. If 100% lysis was obtained by longer exposure to Geys solution, resuspension of the white cell pellet was difficult.

Enumeration Procedure for Absolute Numbers of a T Cell Subset. The absolute count of a particular T cell subset in blood requires a total white cell count (WCC). Since the purpose here was to achieve methods which are rapid and use simple equipment, the WCC was obtained for the rapid micromethod using a hemocytometer and blood diluted 1 : 10 with 1.5% acetic acid with 0.2 g/liter of gentian violet in DDW, with the acceptance that this method has a greater coefficient of variation than a WCC derived from a Coulter counter.

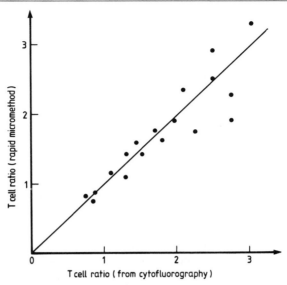

FIG. 3. A comparison of the Th/Ts ratios derived by two methods. The ratio derived by the micromethod, employing double-labeling with PE-conjugated Leu3a and fluorescein-conjugated Leu2a, is shown on the vertical axis, and the ratio derived by conventional flow cytometer analysis using fluorescein-conjugated MAb is shown on the horizontal axis. Results for 18 samples are shown.

Nuclear counterstaining with propidium iodide (PI) is required, and will occur if the plasma membrane is rendered permeable. This can be done quickly with a freezing mixture (liquid N_2 or dry ice/alcohol). Blood (200 μl) exposed to biotin-conjugated MAb and fluorescein-conjugated avidin as described above is resuspended after the third EBSS/FCS wash in 50% glycerol in PBS containing PI (Sigma), 10 μg/ml, a concentration found to give nuclear staining intense enough for identification of MNC and polymorphs, but not so intense as to prevent identification of membrane fluorescence produced by fluorescein. The sample, still in the original bullet tube, is then frozen by immersion in liquid nitrogen or dry ice/alcohol for 1 min, and thawed by rapid warming in a 37° water bath. The cells are examined by epifluorescence microscopy within 5 min of thawing, and those showing nuclear staining with PI can be scored according to their nuclear morphology as polymorphonuclear or mononuclear. Mononuclear cells can be further identified as having positive or negative membrane staining with the MAb. The absolute number of each T cell subset in blood is expressed per liter of blood, and is calculated as a product of the total WCC ($\times 10^{-9}$/liter) derived as described above, and the percentage of all nucleated (PI-staining) cells which had fluorescein-stained cytoplasmic membranes.

For 12 blood samples, and using the MAbs Leu2a, Leu3a, and Leu4, results obtained using the micromethod and flow cytometer analysis were compared (Table II). The absolute number (N) of each T cell subset in blood was determined using the flow cytometer, and was expressed per liter of blood. The calculation was based on (1) the total WCC ($\times 10^{-9}$/liter) derived by a Coulter counter, (2) the percentage of mononuclear white cells (% MNC) derived from a differential WCC performed on a Giemsa-stained air-dried blood smear, and (3) the percentage of MNC stained by the MAb with an RFI greater than 9 (Ab +ve MNC), according to the following formula:

$$N \ (\times 10^{-6}/\text{liter}) = (\% \text{ Ab +ve MNC} \times \% \text{ MNC} \times \text{WCC})/10$$

The micromethod and the flow cytometer produced similar results for the differential WCC, the absolute number of T cells, and the Th and Ts subsets (Table II). Repeated determination of the number of Leu2a+ve cells in one sample of blood gave slightly more consistent results with the flow cytometer with an interassay coefficient of variation of 3.2% as against 7.9% with the rapid micromethod, in keeping with the more accurate determination of the WCC by the Coulter counter when compared with manual methods, and the larger number of cells examined for membrane fluorescence (10,000) by the flow cytometer. Replicate samples of blood exposed to Leu2a or Leu3a, and stored at $-20°$ after freezing, were thawed at 4 hr, 24 hr, 4 days, and 2 weeks after freezing. The differential WCC and percentage of MAb-stained cells were unaltered in the 4-day

TABLE II

COMPARISON OF THE ANALYSIS OF T CELL SUBSETS BY THE RAPID MICROMETHOD WITH ANALYSIS USING THE FLOW CYTOMETER

Index	Units	Mean result[a]		Correlation coefficient (r)
		Micromethod	Flow cytometer	
WCC	$\times 10^{-9}$/liter	6.9 ± 1.3	6.2 ± 1.5	0.84
Differential WCC	% MNC	38 ± 12	36 ± 15	0.88
Leu4+ve cells	$\times 10^{-3}$/liter	1650 ± 230	1490 ± 270	0.78
Leu3a+ve cells	$\times 10^{-3}$/liter	1050 ± 220	980 ± 230	0.72
Leu2a+ve cells	$\times 10^{-3}$/liter	580 ± 170	490 ± 150	0.79

[a] Mean ± SD for 12 blood samples.

sample (data not shown) but samples thawed after 2 weeks of storage were unsatisfactory due to many disrupted cell nuclei.

An alternative method of rendering the cell membrane permeable without disrupting the cell was investigated. This consisted of fixing the cells after staining with MAb in hypotonic formalin. Stained cells were resuspended, after three washes in PBS, in 200 μl of 2.5% formalin (1% formaldehyde) in 1% glucose and were kept protected from light at 4° until examination. Just prior to examination 20 μl of PI (100 μg/ml) was added. This method required 24 hr to render all cell membranes permeable since, after 5 minutes, only 33 ± 4% of MNC had stained nuclei; however, by 24 hr 96 ± 3% were stained. The percentage of MNC stained by a MAb specific for T cells (Leu4) was unaltered by such fixation, the results being 69 ± 3% without fixation and 71% ± 4% after 24 hr fixation. Two weeks after fixation the nuclear morphology and the percentage of Leu4 positive cells, 68 ± 4%, were unaltered.

Selection of an Appropriate Micromethod

Determination merely of the ratio of Th to Ts cells in blood is most simply done by the screening procedure with two fluorochromes. Stained samples should be fixed in formalin as described, if storage is required, or if it is necessary to inactivate the HTLV-III virus.[7] The accuracy of this method is comparable with that achieved with flow cytometry.

Determination of absolute numbers of T cell subsets in blood, in addition to the ratio of Th to Ts cells, is preferable for a full assessment of immunocompetence[3]; hence, if a micromethod for enumerating a T cell subset is required, then the enumeration procedure using biotin-conjugated MAb and fluorescein-conjugated avidin in conjunction with nuclear counterstaining with PI is recommended as being almost as accurate as flow cytometry. If this method is to be used "in the field," with samples stored for later quantitation, then fixation of the stained cells with formalin is the preferred method for rendering the cells permeable. If rapid availability of results is important, then freeze-thawing of the cells is effective, although the samples cannot be stored indefinitely and must be examined quickly after thawing.

In conclusion, it is recognized that flow cytometer analysis has largely replaced epifluorescence microscopy for enumeration of T cell subsets in blood. However, a reliable micromethod using microscopy is applicable if a flow cytometer is not available, if small samples of blood must be analyzed, or if a rapid result is required.

[7] B. Spire, F. Barré-Sinoussi, L. Montagnier, and J. C. Chermann, *Lancet* **2,** 899 (1984).

[72] Cytotoxicity Assays Based on the Use of Antibody Secretion as a Measure of Hybridoma Viability

By J. Marbrook

Cytotoxic Lymphocyte Assays

The detection of cytotoxic cells has been achieved by a variety of techniques, the most widely used being the release of radioactive chromate from appropriate target cells.[1] In spite of a number of modifications which have added to the efficiency of the basic method, it was felt that the use of antibody secretion by target cells as an index of viability would be of great advantage, particularly if the antibody was of a class and specificity that would permit a simple and swift assay.

There are two main limitations to the ^{51}Cr release assay. First, there is a spontaneous release of [^{51}Cr]chromate from target cells, the magnitude of which depends on the target cell and the length of the killing step. Second, under standard conditions of isotope uptake, each target cell contains approximately 1–2 cpm of isotope so that approximately 5×10^3 target cells are needed to obtain a statistically significant estimate of the proportion of chromium released. Thus, any assay which allows a smaller number of targets to be used will increase the effector-to-target ratio and therefore the sensitivity of the assay.

With these considerations in mind, hybridoma cells were obvious candidates for target cells to measure cytotoxic cells so that the physiological function of antibody secretion could be used as an index of viability. Hybridoma cells which secrete antibody against heterologous erythrocytes were used so that target killing could be observed as a loss of hemolytic plaque-forming ability.[2] The methods adopted are outlined in relation to anti-sheep erythrocyte antibody. Similar approaches with anti-bovine erythrocytes and anti-horse erythrocytes have been followed.

Isolation of Anti-Erythrocyte Hybridoma Clones

The fusion and subsequent selection procedures are standard laboratory techniques (e.g., this series, Vol. [73]). Only the appropriate screening assays and the clonal selection procedures will be summarized here.

Screening Cultures for Specific Antibody. The hemolytic spot test is the simplest screening assay for hybridoma samples secreting anti-eryth-

---

[1] K. T. Brunner, J. Mauel, J.-C. Cerottini, and B. Chapuis, *Immunology* **14**, 181 (1968).
[2] M. A. Skinner and J. Marbrook, *J. Immunol. Methods* **42**, 171 (1981).

rocyte (RBC) antibody, and this may be carried out with sheep erythrocyte (SRBC) layers in 90-mm petri dishes. Prepare 0.7% agarose in standard phosphate-buffered saline and add washed RBC to a final concentration of 1%. Maintain the dissolved agarose at 45° before use. Pour 2 ml of RBC–agarose into each petri dish, distributing over the surface of the plate, and allow to solidify.

Place one drop (10–20 μl) of supernatant from cultures containing putative anti-RBC clones onto the surface of the agarose with a Pasteur pipet and allow to stand for 30 min. Wash any excess fluid from the plate with phosphate-buffered saline, add 1.5 ml of diluted (1 : 20) guinea pig serum on to the plate, and incubate at 37° for 60 min. Culture supernatants containing specific monoclonal antibody will yield spots of lysis and therefore fusion wells containing appropriate hybridomas can be identified. If a grid is drawn on the petri dish, up to 24 samples can be easily assayed on a single plate.

Should IgG-secreting hybridomas be sought, a solution of rabbit anti-mouse γ-globulin can be added to the plate before the guinea pig serum, to allow the detection of antibody which is inefficient at fixing complement. The optimum concentration of anti-mouse γ-globulin can be determined by carrying out dilution experiments with serum from immunized mice as a positive control. Mice taken 8–9 days after a SRBC challenge have a predominantly IgG serum titer.

The Selection of Hybridoma Clones. The usual step is to take cells from positive fusion cultures, clone the putative hybridoma cells, and select clones which secrete the required monoclonal antibody. With hybridoma cells secreting anti-RBC antibody, this can be achieved in a single step by setting up a hemolytic plaque assay under conditions in which plaque-forming cells (PFC) can proliferate. The procedure, therefore, is to allow hybridoma cells to settle on the base of a flat-bottomed well within a layer of SRBC in the presence of guinea pig serum. Clones of anti-RBC hybridoma can be picked from the center of hemolytic plaques directly with a fine Pasteur pipet under a dissecting microscope.

Materials

Cells from fusion cultures which are positive for antibody
Flat-bottomed 94-well plates
Culture medium (RPMI 1640) containing 10% fetal calf serum
4% suspension of SRBC in culture medium
Guinea pig serum (GPS) as a source of complement. The serum is usually absorbed with normal mouse spleen cells to remove cytotoxic material.

The assay mixture is made in the proportions of 0.3 ml GPS, 0.9 ml SRBC, and 3.2 ml culture medium. Cells from the fusion cultures are washed to remove secreted antibody from the culture medium. Appropriate dilutions of the hybridoma cells are added in 100 μl to the 96-well plate and 100 μl of the assay mixture is added to each well. The plates are incubated at 37° in a 5% CO_2 atmosphere. After 1–2 hr of incubation, hemolytic plaques are visible and the antibody-secreting cells proliferate so that clones may be removed from the plaque area after 48 hr (see Fig. 1).

This method may be used to isolate clones of hybridoma and as an assay for viable cells in subsequent experiments.

Use of Hybridomas as Target Cells to Measure Cytotoxicity

The hybridoma is usually derived from H-2^d parent fusion partners so that they are ideally suited to measure anti-H-2^d alloreactive cytotoxic T cells (CTL). The method for measuring such cytotoxic T cells is described here and modifications for measuring other cytotoxic cells are also mentioned. The plaque assay described follows the method using 96-well plates, but other plaque assays are applicable.[3]

Materials

A culture of cytotoxic T cells (CTL) (anti-H-2^d)
Hybridoma culture 4×10^3 cells/ml. Cells are washed in fresh medium to remove secreted antibody before use.
V-bottomed 96-well plate
Assay mix as outlined in previous section
Flat-bottomed 96-well plate

Graded numbers of CTL in 100 μl medium are placed in the 96-well plate, followed by 100 μl of hybridoma cells (400 cells per well). The plates are centrifuged at 100 g for 5 min at room temperature and incubated for 4 hr or overnight at 37° in a moist atmosphere of 5% CO_2 in air. After incubation, the culture supernatant is removed and the cells washed and resuspended in fresh medium. An appropriate dilution is added to a flat-bottomed 96-well plate with assay mixture such that viable hybridoma cells produce about 50 plaques in the assay plate. The number of hemolytic plaques can be counted after 2 hr or as long as 24 hr after the assay has been set up.

The cytotoxicity can be expressed as percentage plaque reduction[3] with the following formula:

$$\text{Cytotoxicity} = \frac{\text{PFC in control well} - \text{PFC in test wells}}{\text{PFC in control wells}} \times 100$$

[3] B. B. Mishell and S. M. Shiigi, eds., "Selected Methods in Cellular Immunology." Freeman, San Francisco, California, 1980.

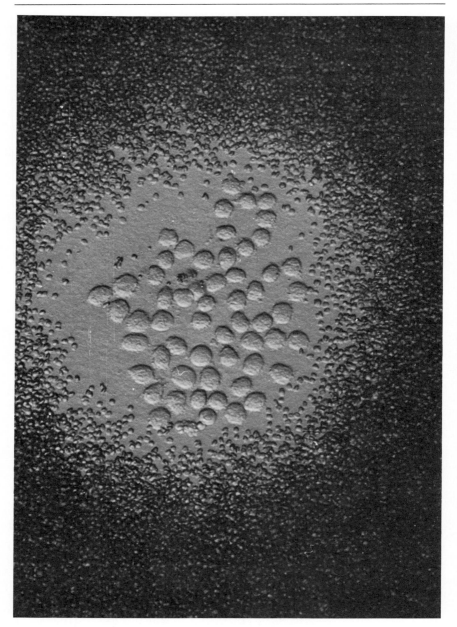

FIG. 1. A photograph of hybridoma cells proliferating in a hemolytic plaque. This illustrates the assay of viable hybridoma cells and the method for deriving clonal isolates.

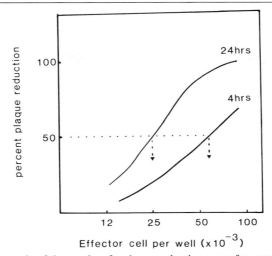

FIG. 2. An example of the results of a plaque reduction assay for cytotoxic T cells. The percentage plaque reduction is plotted against the number of cells containing cytotoxic T cells after 4 or 24 hr of incubation. The dotted lines indicate the arbitrary value of lytic units that would be the concentration required to cause 50% cytotoxicity.

An example of the results expressed graphically is presented in Fig. 2. As used in the ^{51}Cr release method, the amount of cytotoxicity can be expressed as arbitrary units, representing the concentration of the effector cell population which kill a proportion of the target cells in a given time.

Further Modifications to Measure Anti-Hapten Responses[4]. Hybridoma cells have been modified to measure anti-fluorescein and anti-trinitrophenol cytotoxic cells without any loss of viability of the cells. 2,4,6-Trinitrobenzene sulfuric acid (Sigma P5878) is dissolved in phosphate-buffered isotonic saline (pH 6.9) at a final concentration of 2 mM. Fluorescein isothiocyanate (Sigma F7250) is dissolved in isotonic bicarbonate-buffered saline (pH 9.0) at a final concentration of 500 μM. Cells to be coupled are washed once in balanced salt solution, and the cell pellet resuspended in 1 ml of hapten solution and incubated at 37° for 10 min. The cells are washed twice with an excess volume of culture medium before being used as target cells.

[4] T. Ezaki and J. Marbrook, *J. Immunol. Methods* **54**, 281 (1982).

Adaptation of the Plaque-Reduction Assay for Limiting
Dilution Cultures

Limiting dilution cultures have been extremely valuable in carrying out the clonal analysis of cytotoxic effector T cells.[5,6] This technique involves culturing lymphoid cells with appropriate stimulator cells under conditions in which CTL precursor cells (CTL-p) proliferate to form a clone of CTL. The concentration of responding cells is adjusted so that the cultures are limiting with respect to the presence of CTL-p, and therefore are either negative or positive with respect to their content of cytotoxic T cells. Under conditions in which there is a linear relationship between the number of responding cells and the proportion of negative cultures, the frequency of CTL precursors can be calculated.[7] Similarly, at responding cell concentrations, when there is a large percentage of negative cultures, there is a high probability that the cytotoxicity in a single culture is derived from a single CTL clone.

The measurement of individual cytotoxic clones requires an assay which is not only sensitive but also suitable for large numbers of samples so that limiting dilution cultures can be screened for cytotoxicity. The plaque reduction assay has been modified to meet these criteria and two variations have been used to measure cytotoxicity. The extent to which hybridoma cells are killed can be measured by assaying the amount of monoclonal antibody secreted over the 24-hr killing step. The amount of hemolytic monoclonal antibody can be assayed by observing the hemolysis of a standard amount of red cells, or by measuring the concentration of hemoglobin released by spectrophotometric methods. These methods allow the swift screening of 96-well plates and are summarized in Fig. 3.

The methods for setting up limiting dilution cultures will not be restated here. They have been summarized elsewhere,[5,8,9] and only the methods for detecting clones of cytotoxic cells will be presented.[10]

Materials

Limiting dilution cultures containing anti-*H-2^d* CTL (100 μl per well)
Hybridoma cells, 10^4 cells/ml, washed in fresh medium

[5] M. A. Skinner and J. Marbrook, *J. Exp. Med.* **143**, 1562 (1976).

[6] K. F. Lindahl and D. B. Wilson, *J. Exp. Med.* **145**, 508 (1977).

[7] S. Fazekas de St. Groth, *J. Immunol. Methods* **49**, 1211 (1982).

[8] N. Christensen, M. Skinner, and J. Marbrook, *Eur. J. Immunol.* **13**, 701 (1983).

[9] H. R. MacDonald, G.-C. Cerottini, J. E. Ryser, J. Maryanski, C. Taswell, M. B. Widmer, and K. T. Brunner, *Immunol. Rev.* **51**, 93 (1980).

[10] T. Ezaki, N. D. Christensen, M. A. Skinner, and J. Marbrook, *J. Immunol. Methods* **66**, 357 (1984).

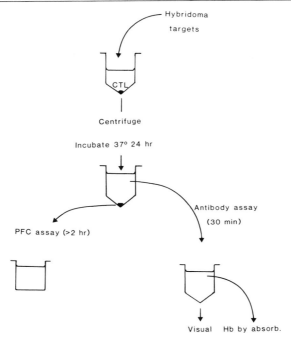

FIG. 3. A summary of the techniques used to measure cytotoxic cells. Each well in the diagram is from a 96-well microtiter plate. Details in text.

Assay mixture: 4% SRBC, guinea pig serum (1 : 15) in culture medium. Titertek eight-channel pipetter (Flow Laboratories, Finland) or equivalent

Hybridoma cells, 100 μl, are added to each well of the limiting dilution culture. The plate is centrifuged at 100 g for 5 min at room temperature and incubated for 24 hr at 37° in a humidified atmosphere of 5% CO_2 in air. After the killing stage, 50 μl of the supernatant is transferred to a new V-bottomed microtiter plate, together with 50 μl of the assay mixture containing sheep erythrocytes and guinea pig complement. The plates are incubated at 37° for 30 min, shaken gently to mix the released hemoglobulin (Hb), and then centrifuged at 200 g for 10 min to sediment the erythrocytes.

A qualitative estimation of the number of positive and negative cultures can be made by scoring visually for the presence or absence of red cell pellets.[10] A quantitative assay of the amount of monoclonal antibody may be measured spectrophotometrically using a scanner designed primarily for ELISA assays. Fifty microliters of the supernatant of the visual spot test assay contains sufficient hemoglobulin to be detected in a flat-bottomed microculture plate, using a wavelength of 404 nm in a multiscan spectrophometry analyzer (Model S.L.T. 210, Salzburger Electronic Industry, West Germany). In this case, the cytotoxicity is expressed as the percentage reduction of total antibody relative to that secreted by controls:

$$\text{Percentage cytotoxicity} = 100 - \text{percentage Hb released}$$

where

$$\text{Percentage Hb released} = \frac{\text{expt OD} - \text{background OD}}{\text{max OD} - \text{background OD}}$$

Max OD is the absorbance in the supernatant in the absence of CTL, background OD is the absorbance in the supernatant from wells without target cells, and expt OD is the absorbance in the test wells.

The experimental procedure outlined above was adjusted so that the amount of antibody secreted by 1000 hybridoma cells in 24 hr was sufficient to lyse the erythrocytes in the assay step. As a general method, it would be necessary to adjust the target cell number and/or the incubation time so that the visual scan and the hemoglobin estimation can be carried out as described, without the necessity for introducing additional dilution steps. In this way, the samples of cells and supernatants can be transferred directly to an assay well with a multichannel pipetter.

Use of Hybridoma Cells in Studying Tumor Cell Growth

With the sensitive methods for detecting cell-mediated responses against determinants on the surface of hybridoma cells, the cells are ideal candidates for studying the immune constraints on tumor growth. The standard tumor cell cloning procedures and somatic cell genetic techniques have provided evidence that the generation of tumor heterogeneity is a characteristic of tumor populations.[11,12] The selection of variants was pioneered by Fidler[13] and has now become a standard procedure in studying tumor progression.

Somatic cell hybridization has been used to study the genetic basis of tumorigenicity[14,15] and the availability of a combination of cell biology techniques has lead to the ambitious idea that tumor cells can be designed

[11] G. Poste and I. J. Fidler, *Nature (London)* **283,** 139 (1980).
[12] I. J. Fidler and M. L. Kripke, *Science* **197,** 893 (1977).
[13] I. J. Fidler, *Nature (London), New Biol.* **242,** 148 (1973).
[14] E. J. Stanbridge, C. J. Der, C. J. Doersen, R. Y. Nishimi, D. M. Reehl. B. E. Weissman, and J. E. Wilkinson, *Science* **215,** 252 (1982).
[15] O. M. Pereira-Smith and J. R. Smith, *Science* **221,** 964 (1983).

to have the appropriate characteristics that allow them to be used as models to study tumor progression and tumor immunity. The ease with which monoclonal antibody against heterologous antibody can be assayed and the quantal measurement of tumor cells as plaque-forming cells can be carried out endow hybridoma cells with some real advantages over other tumor cells.

The use of hybridoma cells secreting anti-bovine erythrocyte antibody has been described,[16] and variant populations have been isolated by successive passages through mice.

Methods

A hybridoma, designated Abo-1 and which secretes monoclonal antibody (IgG$_{2b}$) against bovine erythrocytes (BRBC), was maintained in culture as described previously.[10] The cells were passaged subcutaneously in newborn and athymic nude H-2^d mice. A strain of tumor cells was selected which would grow as an ascitic tumor after intraperitoneal injections. The ascitic cells were injected intravenously into (BALB/c × DBA/2)F$_1$ mice, and tumor colonies were found in the spleen after 17 days. After successive passages, a spleen-seeking variant was derived which grew predominantly as spleen colonies in normal adult F$_1$ mice.

The main advantage of this tumor model is the accuracy and sensitivity of measuring the tumor population. The growth can be followed as the increase in plaque-forming cells in the spleen, using the technique described above. Similarly, the tumor load can be followed by the noninvasive method of measuring the hemolytic antibody titer in serum samples (see Fig. 4). The growth of myeloma cells has been followed by measuring myeloma protein in the serum (see, for example, Ref. 17), but the ease of assaying hemolytic antibody may provide additional advantages.

It has been established that the original Abo-1 hybridoma strain, which will not grow in (BALB/c × DBA/2)F$_1$ mice, is immunogenic and will prime mice such that the subsequent growth of the spleen-seeking variant BSp is markedly suppressed. The suppression of growth is mediated by T cells.[16]

The following steps allow the study of variants in tumor progression. (1) The isolation of hybridoma clones by taking the cells growing in a hemolytic plaque. (2) The establishment of hybridoma *in vivo*. (3) An additional cloning step with a plaque assay (as above). (4) The isolation of sublines *in vivo* by passaging to impose appropriate selection pressures. In addition to the spleen-seeking variant described above, a variant which

[16] T. Ezaki and J. Marbrook, *Int. J. Cancer* **35**, 107 (1985).

[17] T. Hamaoka and H. Fujiwara, *Prog. Immunol., Int. Congr. Immunol., 5th, 1983* p. 1253 (1984).

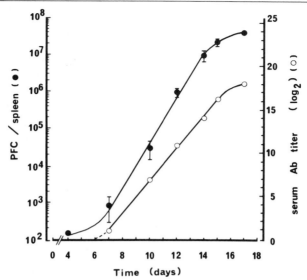

FIG. 4. The growth of anti-bovine erythrocyte hybridoma tumors in the spleen of (BALB/c × DBA/2)F₁ mice. The growth was followed by the number of PFC per spleen (●) and the serum hemolytic antibody titer (○). (From Ezaki and Marbrook.[16])

grows in the liver and tumor variants which grow on some $H\text{-}2^d$ mouse strains and not others have been derived. (5) Further *in vitro* cloning steps. (6) The cytotoxic assays outlined in the first section may be used to test the sensitivity of tumor cells to natural killers, or to test for cytotoxic cells of various specificities, as they are passaged.

Use of Hybridoma Cells in Screening Cytotoxic Drugs

The main advantage in using hybridoma cells as a model in studying cytotoxic effector cells is the sensitivity and precision with which the presence and viability of cells can be followed with antibody assays, particularly if they are as straightforward as hemolysin assays. These advantages also apply to screening assays for cytotoxic drugs. The sensitivity of a hybridoma cell to nitrogen mustard is described as an example of the potential of this technique.

Materials

Hybridoma secreting anti-sheep erythrocyte antibody (IgM)
RPMI tissue culture medium (Gibco, New Zealand) with 10% fetal calf serum

Sheep erythrocytes (SRBC) in assay mixture with guinea pig serum (see above)

Mechlorethanamine hydrochloride (kindly provided by Dr B. C. Baguley, Cancer Laboratories, School of Medicine, Auckland, New Zealand)

96-well flat-bottomed microtiter plate

Hybridoma cells are grown under standard tissue culture conditions. To cells growing in mid log phase (approximately 5×10^4 cells/ml), nitrogen mustard is added to a final concentration of 100–600 nM. After 45 min, the cells are taken and washed in fresh medium and a 100-μl sample added to the wells. SRBC and guinea pig serum (assay mixture) are then added to each well, and the plate incubated at 37° in a humidified atmosphere of 5% CO_2 in air. The number of hybridoma cells added to each well is adjusted so that approximately 50 hemolytic plaques are generated. After 20 and 40 hr, the total number of plaques are counted. In addition, the numbers of cells in each plaque are counted so that the proliferative potential of each antibody-secreting cell is measured. The results of an experiment are summarized in Figs. 5 and 6 to illustrate the parameters being measured in this procedure.

Experimental Example. The data summarized in Fig. 5 indicate the number of proliferating hybridoma cells in hemolytic plaques. The distribution of the number of cells per plaque was counted under a low-power microscope at 20 and 40 hr. The results from the control group and the cells exposed to drug concentrations of 100 and 200 nM are shown. It can

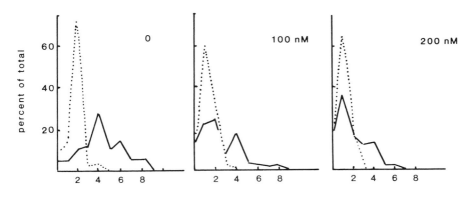

No. cells per plaque

FIG. 5. The proliferation of hybridoma cells in hemolytic plaques, following the exposure of cells to various concentrations of nitrogen mustard for 45 min. The distribution of plaques containing a given number of cells is expressed as a percentage of the total number of plaques. Cells per plaque were counted after 20 (dotted line) or 40 hr (solid line).

be seen that plaques may be derived from either proliferating clones, cells unable to proliferate, or cells which secrete antibody but are lysed subsequently as a delayed effect of drug toxicity. Survival curves are presented in Fig. 6. When the reduction of hemolytic plaques is used as an index of viability, the D_{50} is 800 nM where D_{50} is the concentration of drug reducing the measured parameter by 50%. However, when the number of hemolytic plaques which contain more than two cells after 40 hr in culture is assessed, the D_{50} is 100 nM, which thus indicates how a short-term clonogenic assay may be set up.

No attempt has been made to present a detailed analysis of cytotoxic drug assays which would require the use of the same technique to follow the kinetics of cell killing. Forty hours was selected as a period when the proliferating cells in plaques are easily counted. In experiments requiring a large clone size as the criterion for proliferation, the cells can be picked from the plaques with a fine Pasteur pipet and transferred to another assay well to facilitate the accurate estimation of clone size.

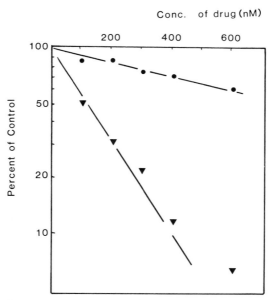

FIG. 6. Survival curves of hybridoma cells following 45 min treatment with nitrogen mustard. (●) The dose-dependent reduction of hemolytic plaque-forming cells. (▲) The reduction of plaques which contain more than two cells per plaque after 40 hr. Lines are drawn by inspection.

Summary and Future Developments

The ease with which the hybridoma cells may be detected make them ideal models for some investigations. If a series of hybridoma cells are employed, each secreting non-cross-reacting monoclonal antibody, the presence of individual tumor cells can be followed within a mixed population. This may lead to further developments of the methodology outlined above. The use of multiple targets to measure cytotoxicity, particularly in limiting dilution experiments, will allow the discriminatory ability of individual clones of cytotoxic T cells to be measured in a single assay. In the same way, the growth of one tumor cell *in vivo* can be followed in the presence of other tumor populations and make the interaction between tumor cells amenable to more quantitative study. The use of hybridoma cells in studying immune regulation[18] has not been reviewed, but the methods outlined above are clearly applicable to such studies.

Acknowledgments

These studies were supported by the Medical Research Council of New Zealand. I wish to thank Drs. Skinner and Ezaki and Eunice Hall for their invaluable help in the development of this work.

[18] T. F. Kresina, Y. Baine, and A. Nisonoff, *J. Immunol.* **130,** 1478 (1983).

[73] Use of Iron- or Selenium-Coupled Monoclonal Antibodies to Cell Surface Antigens as a Positive Selection System for Cells

By MARK BOTHWELL and TIMOTHY BLOCK

One of the basic experimental approaches of eukaryotic somatic cell genetics is the development of procedures which confer a selective growth advantage to cells possessing or lacking a particular biochemical characteristic. This allows one to isolate relatively rare mutant cells with a desired phenotype from a large population of cells which lack the phenotype. There are a variety of applications of this essential principle. For example, the ability to select for or against expression of particular biochemical markers is the basis of the methods used for isolation of somatic cell hybrids, such as the use of HAT selection for thymidine kinase expression in the generation of hybridomas. Another application is DNA-mediated gene transfer (transfection) in which new genetic information can be transferred into cultured cells, provided that a suitable selection or screening procedure is available to isolate the relatively rare genetic transformants.

Recently, a great deal of attention has been directed toward macromolecules at the cell surface, including receptors for hormones and growth factors, cell adhesion molecules, and differentiation antigens, because of their key role in mediating regulation of cell growth, adhesion, and cell–cell recognition and because of their involvement in oncogenesis. For genetic manipulation of such systems, we felt that it would be very useful to have a generally applicable method of selecting for expression of particular cell surface macromolecules. Several screening methods have been developed for this purpose. For example, the fluorescence-activated cell sorter applied to immunofluorescently labeled cells can be used to isolate rare cells expressing a particular antigen from among a population which does not.[1] Alternatively, discrete clones of cells may be screened for their ability to bind specific ligands or antibodies.[2] However, no direct selection method was available.

There are, however, methods for selection *against* expression of particular cell surface proteins. One of the most common involves using a specific ligand, such as a peptide hormone or a specific antibody, coupled to a potent toxin.[3,4] The toxicity of such conjugates results from the fact that many peptide hormones bound to cell surface receptors, and antibodies bound to cell surface antigens, are efficiently taken up by endocytotic mechanisms,[5-7] thus delivering the toxin into the cell. By analogy, we reasoned that conjugation of certain nutrients to antibodies against cell surface antigens might confer a selective growth advantage to cells bearing those antigens, in a suitably limiting growth medium.[8]

Three criteria were applied initially in choosing nutrients for this application. First, the nutrient must be one which is essential for growth of most or all cultured cell types. Second, it must be a nutrient which can conveniently be eliminated from the growth medium. Third, the nutrient

[1] R. Newman, D. Domingo, J. Trattor, and I. Trowbridge, *Nature (London)* **304,** 643 (1983).
[2] J. Strazdis, A. Lanahan, D. E. Johnson, R. Kucherlapati, and M. Bothwell, *Int. J. Neurosci.* **25,** 442 (1985).
[3] B. T.-M. Davis and J. F. Preston, *Science* **213,** 1385 (1981).
[4] H. E. Blythman, P. Casellas, O. Gras, P. Grob, F. K. Jansen, F. Paolucci, B. Pou, and H. Vidal, *Nature (London)* **290,** 145 (1981).
[5] T. F. Roth and K. R. Porter, *J. Cell Biol.* **20,** 313 (1984).
[6] R. Rodenwald, *J. Cell Biol.* **58,** 189 (1973).
[7] J. L. Goldstein, R. G. W. Anderson, and M. S. Brown, *Nature (London)* **279,** 679 (1979).
[8] T. Block and M. Bothwell, *Nature (London)* **301,** 342 (1983).

must be required by cells in exceedingly small amounts, so that the potentially inefficient endocytotic delivery mechanism will supply sufficient nutrient for cell growth. The nutrients we chose were based on our experience with culture of cells in fully defined (serum-free) medium. Many cell types can be cultured in fully defined media in which serum or other complex components are replaced by a limited number of hormones and other purified components.[9] Although the medium supplements required depend on the cell type being cultured, selenium and transferrin (for iron transport) are among the essential supplements for culture of most cell types. Thus, cells cultured in serum-free media can readily be made deficient in nutritionally available selenium and iron. We based our attempts to construct an antigen-dependent selection system on delivery of these two nutrients.

Antibody Delivery Systems for Iron and Selenium

As a convenient means to permit incorporation of nutritionally available iron into antibodies we chose ferritin. Ferritin is the iron-containing form of apoferritin, a protein which functions intracellularly as a transporter or sequesterer of iron.[10] Because ferritin has a physiological role in supplying iron, it seemed reasonable to hope that endocytotically delivered ferritin might provide nutritionally available iron. Additional advantages of ferritin for this purpose are that (1) a single ferritin molecule contains, and could deliver, many molecules of iron and (2) widespread use of ferritin–antibody conjugates as reagents for immunohistochemical electron microscopy has led to the development of excellent means for producing immunoreactive ferritin–antibody conjugates.

Selenium may be readily incorporated into antibodies by a very different method. Selenomethionine, a methionine analog containing selenium in the place of sulfur, is efficiently taken up by cells and incorporated translationally into protein in the place of methionine. Thus, culture of hybridomas in medium containing selenomethionine in place of methionine leads to synthesis and secretion of monoclonal antibodies containing selenium. It was not clear at the outset whether selenium in this form would become nutritionally available to the cell. However, since endocytotically internalized proteins are generally subject to extensive hydrolysis within lysozomes, there was reason to believe this approach might be successful, as indeed it is.

[9] D. Barnes and G. H. Sato, *Anal. Biochem.* **102,** 255 (1980).
[10] D. W. Fawcett, *J. Histochem. Cytochem.* **13,** 75 (1965).

An Experimental System for Evaluation of the Nutrient–Antibody Selection Approach

As an experimental system in which to examine whether we could achieve cell surface antigen-dependent cell growth using ferritin–antibody or selenium–antibody derivatives, we chose rat pheochromocytoma PC12 cells. This experimental system had the following desirable characteristics. (1) PC12 cells can be grown in a fully defined medium, in which the only supplements required (in addition to the base RPMI 1640 medium) are insulin, transferrin, and selenium.[11,12] (2) We have developed monoclonal antibodies against several prominent (and cell type-specific) PC12 cell surface antigens.[13] One of these antibodies in particular, C10-7, recognizes an antigen which is expressed only on PC12 cells and on closely related cell types of the sympathetic neuron/adrenal chromaffin cell lineage. (3) We have derived from PC12 cells a variant cell line (NR18A)[14] which lacks the C10-7 antigen, and which therefore serves as an important control for the specificity of the selection technique.

Preparation of Ferritin and Selenium Derivatives of C10-7 IgG

Transferrin is a common contaminant of mouse IgG preparations. In using ferritin–IgG to substitute for normal cellular transferrin requirements, obviously the IgG preparation used must be relatively free of transferrin. Mouse IgG subclasses 1, 2a, and 2b can be purified by chromatography on protein A–Sepharose.[15] For purification of C10-7 hybridoma IgG, mouse ascites fluid was precipitated with 50% saturated ammonium sulfate, and the precipitate was dialyzed against 10 mM sodium phosphate (pH 8.0). This material was absorbed onto protein A–Sepharose 4B (Pharmacia) equilibrated with the same buffer, and the C10-7 IgG was eluted with 0.1 M sodium citrate (pH 6.0).

To prepare the C10-7 IgG–ferritin conjugate, we employed glutaraldehyde as the coupling agent.[16] A 1200-fold molar excess of glutaraldehyde per apoferritin group was used. Horse ferritin, 10 mg in 1.14 ml 0.1 M sodium phosphate (pH 7.3), was mixed with 2 ml of 30% glutaraldehyde. After 30 min at room temperature, aggregates were removed by centrifugation in a Beckman microfuge for 4 min at 10,000 g. The supernatant was

[11] J. E. Bottenstein and G. H. Sato, *Proc. Natl. Acad. Sci. U.S.A.* **76**, 514 (1979).
[12] J. Strazdis and M. Bothwell, unpublished (1983).
[13] T. Block and M. Bothwell, *J. Neurochem.* **40**, 1654 (1983).
[14] M. Bothwell, A. L. Schechter, and K. M. Vaughn, *Cell* **21**, 857 (1980).
[15] P. L. Ey, S. J. Propuse, and C. R. Jenkins, *Immunochemistry* **15**, 429 (1978).
[16] Y. Kishida, B. R. Olsen, R. A. Berg, and D. J. Prockop, *J. Cell Biol.* **64**, 331 (1975).

then subjected to chromatography on Sephadex G-25 to separate activated ferritin from unreacted glutaraldehyde, as follows.

A column of Sephadex G-25, coarse (Pharmacia), 25-ml bed volume, was equilibrated with 0.1 M sodium phosphate (pH 7.3). The sample was applied and eluted at room temperature using the same buffer. Ferritin eluted at the void volume. Fractions containing ferritin were pooled on the basis of ferritin's easily visible brown-yellow color (which can be quantitatively monitored by absorbance at 435 nm). The activated ferritin was immediately reacted with C10-7 IgG, using a ferritin to IgG molar ratio of 4 : 1. To facilitate subsequent characterization of the product, a small amount of [^{35}S]methionine-labeled C10-7 IgG was included in this reaction. This is not essential, as immunochemical means could be used to follow the IgG during various fractionation steps. [^{35}S]Methionine-labeled C10-7 IgG was prepared by culturing C10-7 hybridoma cells for 2 days in the presence of 25 μCi [^{35}S]methionine/ml, in a serum-free medium consisting of RPMI 1640 supplemented with 35 μg transferrin/ml, 5 μg insulin/ml, 4 ng SeO$_2$/ml, and 20 μM ethanolamine.[17] The culture fluid was chromatographed on protein A–Sepharose, essentially as described above, to isolate the labeled IgG.

To be useful in nutrient selection, the ferritin–IgG must be isolated relatively free of unreacted ferritin and IgG. Ferritin–IgG was separated from IgG by chromatography on Sepharose 4B (Pharmacia). IgG-containing products were followed by scintillation counting of ^{35}S, while protein measurements, using the Coomassie G-250 dye binding method,[18] revealed the position of elution of the ferritin, which was in great weight excess. This chromatography step does not cleanly separate ferritin–IgG from ferritin, so a subsequent step of chromatography of the ferritin and IgG–ferritin mixture on protein A–Sepharose was employed. This was done essentially as described above.

Selenium-containing C10-7 IgG (IgG–Se) was prepared by culturing the C10-7 hybridoma in RPMI 1640 medium, containing 15 μg DL-selenomethionine/ml in place of methionine, and supplemented with 5 μg insulin/ml, 4 ng SeO$_2$/ml, 35 μg transferrin/ml, and 20 μM ethanolamine. Cells were cultured in the absence of serum so that hybridoma IgG could be isolated without contamination by serum IgG. In initial experiments, 25 μCi [^{75}Se]selenomethionine/ml was also included to assess the extent of incorporation of selenomethionine into IgG. These experiments demonstrated that selenomethionine-containing IgG is produced in yields comparable to those obtained with methionine. Medium from the cultured

[17] H. Murakami and H. Masui, *Proc. Natl. Acad. Sci. U.S.A.* **77,** 3464 (1980).
[18] M. Bradford, *Anal. Biochem.* **72,** 248 (1976).

hybridoma cells was collected after 2 days of culture, dialyzed against 10 mM sodium phosphate (pH 8.0), and purified by chromatography on protein A–Sepharose as described above.

For preparation of Se–IgM, IgM-secreting hybridoma cells were cultured in selenomethionine-containing medium as described. However, protein A–Sepharose chromatography cannot be used for purification of the modified immunoglobulin because IgM does not bind well to protein A. For our purposes, it has been sufficient merely to dialyze hybridoma culture medium to remove free SeO_2, before use in the selection protocol. Se–IgM prepared in this way is contaminated by small amounts of insulin and transferrin, which do not interfere in the selection scheme.

Examples of the Selection Technique

The ability of C10-7 IgG–ferritin to specifically promote proliferation of C10-7 antigen-bearing cells was assessed by comparing the growth of PC12 cells and NR18A cells in selective medium. PC12 cells and NR18A cells both grow well in serum-free medium consisting of RPMI 1640 supplemented with 5 μg insulin/ml, 4 ng SeO_2/ml, and 50 μg transferrin/ml. To promote good adhesion of the cells to the substratum in the absence of serum, cells were cultured on surfaces coated with rat tail collagen.[19] Cells were plated in collagen-coated 16-mm wells at a density of 2×10^4 cells per well, in 1 ml RPMI 1640 medium supplemented with 10% horse serum and 5% newborn calf serum. The next day, the medium was removed, attached cells were washed twice with RPMI 1640 medium without serum, and the medium was replaced by RPMI 1640 containing 5 μg insulin/ml and 4 ng SeO_2/ml, but with transferrin omitted. Cells typically continue to proliferate for several days after removal of transferrin, presumably due to utilization of internal pools of iron, and to recycling of bound transferrin. After 2 days in the absence of transferrin, growth medium was then additionally supplemented with either transferrin, free ferritin, C10-7 IgG, or C10-7 IgG–ferritin. Cells were cultured for 8 days with three changes of medium, and the extent of cell proliferation was assessed by counting cells.

The results for PC12 cells are shown in Fig. 1. C10-7 IgG–ferritin supported the growth of PC12 cells (to an extent comparable to transferrin) and did so at low concentrations. Free ferritin concentrations of 50 μg/ml or greater allowed limited cell proliferation, presumably due to nonspecific endocytotic internalization of ferritin. No cell growth was observed with C10-7 IgG alone. The effectiveness of C10-7 IgG–ferritin,

---

[19] M. B. Bornstein, *Lab. Invest.* **7,** 134 (1958).

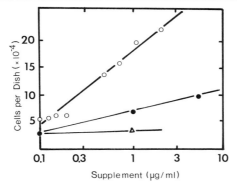

Supplement (μg/ml)

FIG. 1. Specific stimulation of PC12 cell growth by C10-7 IgG–ferritin. PC12 cells were cultured, as described in the text, for 2 days in RPMI 1640 supplemented with insulin (5 μg/ml) and SeO₂ (4 ng/ml), after which medium was additionally supplemented with various concentrations of ferritin (●), C10-7 IgG (△), or C10-7 IgG–ferritin (○). Cells were cultured for 6 additional days, after which cells were counted using a Coulter counter.

as compared to ferritin, apparently is due to specific binding to the C10-7 antigen, since NR18A cells, which lack the C10-7 antigen, show no specific stimulation of growth by C10-7 IgG–ferritin, as shown in Table I.

We tested in a model system the applicability of this specific growth stimulatory activity on PC12 cells as a selection technique. The model

TABLE I
PROLIFERATION OF PC12 AND NR18A CELLS WITH C10-7
IgG–FERRITIN[a]

Cell line	Iron source	Cell number[b] ($\times 10^{-4}$)
PC12	None	2.5
PC12	Transferrin (50 μg/ml)	20
PC12	C10-7 IgG–ferritin (0.5 μg/ml)	21
PC12	C10-7 IgG (0.5 μg/ml)	7.6
NR18A	None	8.0
NR18A	Transferrin (50 μg/ml)	26
NR18A	C10-7 IgG–ferritin (0.5 μg/ml)	7.5

[a] Cells were seeded in 16-mm collagen-coated wells at 20,000 cells per well in medium containing serum, and were cultured for 24 hr. Then cells were transferred to medium with serum omitted but supplemented with insulin and SeO₂, and cells were cultured for 2 days. Medium was then replaced with medium additionally supplemented with the iron source as noted above.

[b] Cells were removed and counted on day 10 using a hemacytometer.

system was produced by mixing small numbers of PC12 cells with larger numbers of NR18A cells. PC12 cells and NR18A cells are easily distinguished because PC12 cells have a more rounded morphology in culture. Mixtures of PC12 cells and NR18A cells were seeded in collagen-coated wells at various ratios. Cultures were cultured for 3 days in RPMI 1640 with insulin and SeO_2 to deplete iron supplies, and then medium was supplemented with 1 μg C10-7 IgG–ferritin/ml for the subsequent 3 weeks. At the end of the selection period, homogeneous populations of PC12 cells were present in all cultures, even in cultures which initially consisted of 1 : 10,000 ratios of PC12 to NR18A cells.

Similarly effective selection was obtained using the selenomethionine-containing antibodies on selenium-deprived cells. PC12 cells and NR18A cells were allowed to attach to collagen-coated wells as described previously, and were deprived of selenium for 2 days by growth in RPMI 1640 containing insulin and transferrin, but with SeO_2 omitted. On the third day this medium was supplemented with C10-7 IgG–Se. Figure 2 shows the results for PC12 cells after 8 days of culture. Methionine-containing C10-7

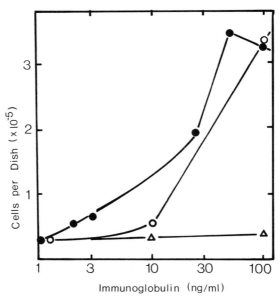

FIG. 2. Specific stimulation of PC12 cell growth by selenomethionine-containing antibodies. Cells were cultured, as described in the text, for 2 days in RPMI 1640 supplemented with insulin (5 μg/ml) and transferrin (50 μg/ml), after which medium was additionally supplemented with various concentrations of C10-7 IgG ($\triangle$), selenomethionine-containing C10-7 IgG ($\bullet$), or selenomethionine-containing 5A-7 IgM ($\bigcirc$) prepared as described in the text.

TABLE II
PROLIFERATION OF PC12 CELLS WITH NUTRITIONAL IRON AND SELENIUM
PROVIDED AS C10-7 IgG DERIVATIVES[a]

Iron source	Selenium source	Cell number[b] ($\times 10^{-4}$)
Transferrin (50 μg/ml)	C10-7 IgG–Se (100 ng/ml)	30
C10-7 IgG–ferritin (0.5 μg/ml)	SeO$_2$ (4 ng/ml)	32
C10-7 IgG–ferritin (0.5 μg/ml)	C10-7 IgG–Se (100 ng/ml)	32
None	None	4

[a] Cells were seeded in 16-mm collagen-coated wells at 20,000 cells per ml in medium containing serum, and were cultured 24 hr. Then cells were in serum-free medium supplemented with insulin for 2 days, and subsequently with the additions noted above.

[b] Cells were counted on day 10, using a hemacytometer.

IgG was ineffective in maintaining cell growth, while the seleno-methionine-containing C10-7 IgG maintained cell growth at concentrations of 100 ng/ml or less. Inhibition of growth was observed at IgG–Se concentrations greater than 100 ng/ml, possibly due to the toxicity of selenium in excessive amounts. Similar stimulation of cell growth was observed with the selenomethionine-containing IgM from a hybridoma (5A7) which is specific for an unrelated PC12 cell antigen. As might be expected, a more stringent selection can be applied by using specific antibody derivatives to fill simultaneously the iron and selenium requirements for cell growth, as shown in Table II.

We have tested the generality of the selection approach by applying it to a second antigen and cell type. We recently have developed monoclonal antibodies to the human nerve growth factor receptor.[20] Nerve growth factor receptors are present on many human melanoma cell lines, and A875 melanoma cells have particularly abundant nerve growth factor receptors.[21] Nerve growth factor receptor monoclonal antibody ME20.4 was isolated from ascites fluid as previously described[19] and was conjugated to ferritin as described above. As shown in Table III, the ferritin derivative of ME20.4 effectively supported the proliferation of A875 cells

[20] A. H. Ross, P. Grob, M. Bothwell, D. E. Elder, C. S. Ernst, N. Marano, B. F. D. Ghrist, C. C. Slemp, M. Herlym, B. Atkinson, and H. Koprowski, *Proc. Natl. Acad. Sci. U.S.A.* **81,** 6681 (1984).

[21] R. N. Fabricant, J. E. DeLarco, and G. J. Todaro, *Proc. Natl. Acad. Sci. U.S.A.* **74,** 565 (1977).

TABLE III
GROWTH OF A875 HUMAN MELANOMA CELLS WITH
ANTI-NERVE GROWTH FACTOR RECEPTOR IgG
CONJUGATED TO FERRITIN[a]

Iron source	Cell number[b] ($\times 10^{-4}$)
None	3
Transferrin (10 μg/ml)	40
ME20.4 IgG–ferritin (0.5 μg/ml)	36
C10-7 IgG–ferritin (0.5 μg/ml)	5

[a] A875 cells were seeded at 20,000 cells per 16-mm² well, in RPMI 1640 with 5 μg insulin, 4 ng SeO_2, and 10 μg ferritin per milliliter. After 24 hr, medium was replaced by medium containing insulin, SeO_2, and the iron sources noted above.
[b] Cells were removed at day 8 and counted using a hemacytometer.

in transferrin-deficient medium, while equivalent amounts of free ferritin, or the ferritin derivative of C10-7 IgG (whose antigen is absent from melanoma cells) were ineffective.

Applications of the Selection Technique

The primary application we propose for nutrient-antibody selection is for the isolation of genetically transformed cells expressing new cell surface antigens after DNA-mediated gene transfer. A number of cell types growing in tissue culture can be made to incorporate and stably express foreign DNA at a significant frequency. However, using the most common technique of exposing cells to DNA/calcium phosphate coprecipitates, the frequency of transformation is not high. Transfer of purified clonal plasmid DNA seldom occurs at a frequency greater than $1/10^3$,[22] and transfection with mammalian genomic DNA yields genetic transformation for any particular single copy gene at frequencies of $1/10^5$ or less. This dismal situation can be improved somewhat by exploiting the phenomenon of cotransformation. In populations of cells exposed to calcium phosphate-precipitated DNA, most cells do not stably incorporate DNA, while those few cells which do incorporate foreign DNA retain large quantities. Thus, cells which are transformed by a selectable marker DNA, and which are selected on that basis, frequently also stably express

[22] G. Scangos and F. Ruddle, *Gene* **14,** 7 (1981).

genes in the transfecting DNA which were not selected for. Selection for one phenotype enriches the population of cells for those which consumed other exogenous sequences at the time of transformation.[23-25]

Thus we have followed the following strategy. Thymidine kinase-deficient (TK⁻) cells are transfected with a mixture of plasmid TK DNA and cellular DNA. TK⁺ transformants are selected by growth of cells in HAT medium. This population of cells, enriched for those which incorporated foreign cellular DNA, is then subjected to nutrient-antibody selection to isolate clones expressing new antigens coded for by the transforming DNA. The advantage of using cotransformation with TK and HAT selection as an initial step is to reduce the necessary stringency required in the nutrient-antibody selection. It is possible that some cells, at a low frequency, may acquire the ability to survive in the nutrient-deficient medium by means other than through transformation. Reduction of the population of cells subjected to nutrient-antibody selection, by prior HAT selection, should reduce the likelihood of this occurring.

We have tested this approach by attempting to transfer the rat gene for the C10-7 antigen into TK⁻ mouse L cells, selecting transfected cells grown in transferrin-deficient medium with C10-7 IgG–ferritin. LTK⁻ (B82) cells were seeded at low density (16,000 cells/cm²) 1 day prior to transfection. Cells in 25-cm² flasks were transfected by the method of Wigler et al.[26] with a calcium phosphate precipitate of 1 μg plasmid TK and 40 μg PC12 cell high molecular weight genomic DNA per flask. For the purposes of transfection cells were cultured in DMEM (rather than RPMI 1640, whose higher phosphate concentration leads to excessive calcium phosphate formation) supplemented with 10% fetal calf serum. Two days after transfection, cells were washed twice with RPMI 1640 medium, and then cultured in RPMI 1640 supplemented with 5 μg insulin/ml, 4 ng SeO₂/ml, 15 ng leutinizing hormone/ml, 50 μg bovine serum albumin/ml, and HAT. After 2 days, the medium was replaced by medium additionally supplemented with 1 μg C10-7 IgG–ferritin/ml and cells were maintained in this medium for 3 weeks. With HAT selection alone (in medium supplemented with transferrin), colonies appeared at a frequency of about 1/10³, while selection with HAT and C10 IgG–ferritin without transferrin yielded colonies at a frequency of 1/10⁵ to 1/10⁶.

[23] M. Perucho and M. Wigler, Cold Spring Harbor Symp. Quant. Biol. **20,** 829 (1980).
[24] T. Block and R. G. Hughes, in "Cold Spring Harbor Workshop on Herpes Virus IV" (E. Keiff and P. Shaffer, eds.), p. 79. Cold Spring Harbor Lab., Cold Spring Harbor, New York, 1979.
[25] M. Wigler, R. Sweet, G.-K. Sim, B. Wold, A. Pellicer, E. Lacy, T. Maniatis, S. Silverstein, and R. Axel, Cell **16,** 777 (1979).
[26] M. Wigler, A. Pellicer, S. Silverstein, and R. Axel, Cell **14,** 725 (1978).

Healthy clones were isolated and grown up in quantity in doubly selective medium. Growth under these conditions was slow, so when stocks had been preserved in liquid nitrogen cells were propagated subsequently in serum-containing medium supplemented with HAT. Expression of transfected genes is sometimes relatively unstable, but selection for a selectable marker generally maintains the stability of expression of co-transfected DNA sequences.[22]

Transformants were examined for expression of C10-7 antigen using an ELISA assay. Two of eight putative transformant clones bound substantially more C10-7 antibody than did L cells (which do not normally express C10-7 antigen). The expression of C10-7 antigen on these cells was subsequently confirmed using indirect immunofluorescence microscopy.

We have not yet demonstrated by any direct means that expression of C10-7 antigen is the result of transformation by a rat gene. It is possible in principle that the selection procedure might have led to isolation of mutant L cells which have induced expression of the mouse C10-7 antigen homolog. Ambiguities of this type may be avoided when it is known that the monoclonal antibodies employed are species specific and do not cross-react with the native antigen of the host cell.

General Considerations and Prospects for Future Experimentation

For application of the nutrient–antibody approach to some cell lines, the lack of suitable serum-free growth media may be an impediment. The means by which such media are developed has been described[8]; however, it is frequently difficult to design an adequate serum-free medium. In such cases it may be possible to isolate variant cell lines which have gained the ability to grow in a medium which is inadequate for the parental cell line. For example, human hepatoma HepG2 cells do not grow well in any serum-free medium formulation we have tested. Exposure of a large population of HepG2 cells to RPMI 1640 supplemented with insulin, SeO_2, and transferrin led to massive cell death initially, but after continued maintenance of these cultures in the serum-free medium, clones appeared which proliferated rapidly in the serum-free medium.[27]

We have emphasized the application of this technique for gene transfer, but many other applications can be envisioned. For example, it seems likely that application of this selection technique to cells which already express the targeted antigen might lead to isolation of mutant cells which express increased quantities of the antigen. This would facilitate biochem-

[27] A. Lanahan and M. Bothwell, unpublished (1984).

ical characterization of a variety of cell surface antigens. It has recently become clear that overproduction of proteins in mammalian cells, as the result of intentional selection for overproduction, frequently occurs as a result of gene amplification.[28] Thus, it is probable that nutrient–antibody selection could be used as a means of generating cell populations which have amplified genes for particular cell surface antigens. This would facilitate obtaining molecular clones of these genes.

The selection technique we have described may serve as an alternative to screening techniques such as fluorescence-activated cell sorting. However, ideally, it could be used in conjunction with cell sorting techniques. Thus, preliminary enrichment of a cell population for cells bearing a particular antigen, using nutrient–antibody selection, followed by fluorescence-activated sorting of immunofluorescently labeled cells might allow isolation of antigen-bearing variants which occur at frequencies lower than can be dealt with by either approach singly.

Finally, it must be emphasized that these studies are preliminary. It may very well be possible to identify nutrients which are superior to iron or selenium for the purposes of nutrient–antibody selection. It is also possible to envision use of specific ligands other than antibodies, such as peptide hormones, as carriers of nutrients for such selection schemes. We have only begun to explore the generality of the potential of these approaches.

[28] R. T. Schimke, in "Gene Amplification" (R. T. Schimke, ed.), p. 9. Cold Spring Harbor Lab., Cold Spring Harbor, New York, 1982.

[74] Screening for Monoclonal Antibodies to Human Cellular and Soluble Antigens

By Daniel P. Eskinazi, William C. Eby, and Giuseppe A. Molinaro

Since the advent of hybridization of antibody-secreting cells with myeloma cells,[1] monoclonal antibodies have become a popular alternative to antisera. A critical step in monoclonal antibody production is the screening of a multitude of microcultures to identify the hybridomas that secrete the desired antibodies. Screening tests must provide quick and reliable information. A number of such techniques has been described.

[1] G. Köhler and C. Milstein, Nature (London) 256, 495 (1975).

The purpose of this chapter is to describe the techniques that we use for testing hybridoma supernatants for the presence of antibodies to soluble and cellular antigens. The first method is the ^{125}I-labeled staphylococcal protein A assay,[2] which has become popular because it is convenient and reliable, and can be applied to both soluble and cellular antigens. We also describe a modification of this assay designed to screen monoclonal antibodies against adherent cell lines in polyvinyl chloride plates (PVC). A second technique, the enzyme-linked immunoadsorbent assay (ELISA),[3] was originally designed for soluble antigens but has been adapted to detect antibodies to cellular structures. Finally, to screen hybridoma supernatants for antibodies to soluble antigens we describe a hemolytic assay based on the use of antigen-coated erythrocytes. In describing these techniques, we cite the original work and include a number of useful modifications either found scattered throughout the literature or designed for our own use but not yet reported.

Materials and Methods

Antigens and Antibodies. The soluble antigens used in this work were human immunoglobulin (Ig) molecules. Established cell lines derived from squamous cell carcinomas[4] were used for immunization and cell lines of various origin were used as target cells. The hybridomas were produced according to established methods.[1]

Fibronectin Isolation and Coating of Microtest Plates. To enhance cell monolayer formation, PVC microtest plates were precoated with fibronectin. Fibronectin was isolated from mouse or rabbit plasma as described by Engvall and Ruoslahti.[5] Briefly, plasma was passed over an adsorbent column of Sepharose 4B coupled to gelatin as described elsewhere.[6,7] After extensive washing with 1 M urea in 0.5 M Tris buffer (pH 7.5), fibronectin was eluted with 4.5 M urea in the same buffer. The eluate was successively dialyzed against 2 M urea, 1 M urea, and finally 0.05 M Tris buffer (pH 8.5). The purity of the final product was evaluated by sodium dodecyl sulfate–gel electrophoresis. In order to coat microtiter plates, 50 μl of fibronectin diluted to 10 μg/ml in PBS was added to each well and the plate was incubated for 2 hr at 37° according to preliminary

[2] J. P. Brown, J. M. Klitzman, and K. E. Hellström, *J. Immunol. Methods* **15,** 57 (1977).
[3] E. Engvall and P. Perlmann, *Immunochemistry* **8,** 871 (1971).
[4] T. E. Carey, K. A. Kimmel, D. R. Schwartz, D. E. Richter, S. R. Baker, and C. J. Krause, *Otolaryngol. Head Neck Surg.* **91,** 482 (1983).
[5] E. Engvall and E. Ruoslahti, *Int. J. Cancer* **20,** 1 (1977).
[6] R. Axén, J. Poráth, and S. Ernback, *Nature (London)* **214,** 1302 (1967).
[7] L. Wofsy and B. Burr, *J. Immunol.* **103,** 380 (1969).

titration experiments. After washing the wells six times with PBS, the microtest plates were placed 25–30 cm from a UV light source and irradiated in a sterile hood overnight.

Preparation of Cells for the Binding Assay. To detect cell surface antigens, target cells were used either live or dried. In the latter instance, medium was removed without disturbing the cells and the uncovered plates were placed in a drying oven set at 40° until all the overlying medium had evaporated. The time required to reach this point was, in general, 20–30 min.

To detect cytoplasmic in addition to surface antigens, cells were fixed with glutaraldehyde (GDA). In our hands, 0.1% GDA was sufficient to fix the cells and open up their membrane for antibody binding. For fixation, washed cells were incubated with 0.1% GDA in PBS for 5 min. After two washes, the cells were incubated for 5 more min with 0.2 M glycine in PBS to block unbound GDA-activated sites. The cells were then washed four times and the plates stored at 4°. We have found that storage up to 8 weeks did not decrease the binding of the antibodies. The effect of storage for longer periods of time was not tested. It might be noted that antigens which we evaluated, including β_2-microglobulin and HLA, did not appear to be significantly altered by this treatment.

Cells growing as monolayers could be used as living target cells by simply plating them in 250 μl of their usual growth medium. The number of cells plated depended on the cell size and their growth characteristics. For most cell lines, approximately 5×10^4 cells/well were required to reach confluency within 24–48 hr.

We used polystyrene plates for assays with dried or GDA-fixed cells and fibronectin-coated PVC plates for assays with live cells.

Protein A Iodination. Protein A was iodinated to a specific activity of approximately 2×10^7 cpm/μg by the chloramine-T method.[8] Protein A (Sigma Chem. Co., St. Louis, MO), 30 μg, was dissolved in 200 μl of a buffer containing 0.2 M borate, 0.15 M NaCl at pH 7.6. Na^{125}I, 1 mCi, was mixed with the protein A solution. Ten microliters of a 10 mg/ml solution of chloramine-T in distilled water was added to the mixture and allowed to react for 60 sec at room temperature. Then, 20 μl of a sodium metabisulfite solution, 20 mg/ml, was added to stop the reaction.

The unbound iodine was separated from the labeled protein essentially as described by Tuszynski *et al.*[9] Minicolumns were prepared by packing Sephadex G-25 fine into 1.5-ml polypropylene centrifuge tubes that had

[8] P. J. McConahey and F. J. Dixon, *Int. Arch. Allergy Appl. Immunol.* **29,** 185 (1966).
[9] G. P. Tuszynski, L. Knight, J. R. Piperno, and P. N. Walsh, *Anal. Biochem.* **106,** 118 (1980).

been pierced in the bottom with a 25-gauge needle. The minicolumn was fitted through a hole bored (with the sharp end of a pair of scissors) in the cap of a 15-ml Falcon centrifuge tube. The excess buffer was eliminated by centrifugation. The solution containing unbound iodine and labeled protein A was loaded on the minicolumn. The tube was then centrifuged at 200 g in a table-top clinical centrifuge for 30 sec. The unbound ^{125}I remained trapped in the Sephadex while approximately 250 μl of labeled material was recovered in the Falcon tube.

^{125}I-*Protein A Assay*. This assay was performed in fibronectin-coated PVC or in polystyrene 96-well microtiter plates. Prior to starting the assay, cells were washed six times with RPMI 1640 medium containing 1% bovine serum albumin and 0.1% sodium azide (wash medium) to lower nonspecific binding. All reagents were diluted so that each incubation was performed in a volume of 50 μl. Cells were then incubated for 1 hr on ice with the supernatant to be tested. To remove unbound material, the cells were washed six times with wash medium. A second incubation followed with rabbit antiserum against the primary antibody to detect non-protein A-binding primary antibodies and also to increase the sensitivity of the assay. The second incubation was performed with rabbit anti-mouse Ig for 1 hr on ice. Then the cells were washed six times with wash medium to remove any unbound rabbit immunoglobulin. Finally, a last incubation (1 hr on ice) was conducted with 10^5 cpm of ^{125}I-protein A per well. The cells were then washed six times with wash medium.

After the final wash, the procedure differed depending on the type of plate used in the assay. For PVC plates, the edges were cut off with a razor blade and the wells of the remainder of the plate were fitted into corresponding wells of a rigid polystyrene plate. In this process, the PVC plate can fit only partially into the polystyrene plate. A hot wire (or scalpel) could then be used to cut the PVC wells, with the polystyrene plate serving as a guide for the cutting instrument. Throughout the procedure, the PVC wells were left in their original position in the polystyrene plate and could then be transferred to appropriate tubes for counting in a gamma scintillation counter. For hard plates, 50 μl of 2 N NaOH was added to the wells at room temperature to dissolve the cell-bound labeled protein A, among other substances. This NaOH solution was transferred to individual test tubes and counted.

ELISA. The ELISA was performed according to the method described by Douillard et al.[10] with some modifications. Plates were incubated for 1 hr at room temperature with PBS containing 1% BSA and 0.05% Tween 20 to reduce subsequent nonspecific binding of the test reagents. Just

[10] J. Y. Douillard, T. Hoffman, and R. B. Herberman, *J. Immunol. Methods* **39,** 309 (1980).

prior to adding the hybridoma supernatants (or appropriate positive and negative controls), the PBS containing BSA and Tween 20 was flicked out of the wells and the plates were blotted dry on paper towels. Fifty microliters of supernatant was added to appropriate wells and allowed to incubate with the well contents for 1 hr at room temperature. The plates were washed four times and blotted dry on paper towels. The secondary reagent, i.e., peroxidase-labeled goat $F(ab')_2$ antibody to mouse Ig, was added and allowed to incubate for an additional hour at room temperature. Plates were washed three times with PBS–Tween 20 prior to adding a solution containing 0.1 mg o-phenylenediamine/ml (OPD) in 0.01% H_2O_2. The reaction was allowed to proceed for 15–30 min in the dark at room temperature and was stopped by the addition of 50 μl of 1 N H_2SO_4. Color development, reflecting antibody binding, was measured at 492 nm on a Dynatech microtiter reader.

Controls. Appropriate controls were included in each plate. To serve as negative controls, the primary antibody was replaced either by wash medium or by nonspecific Ig (i.e., pooled polyclonal IgG and/or IgM or individual monoclonal myeloma proteins of appropriate type). Nonspecific immunoglobulins were used at a concentration of 10 μg/ml, a concentration often not attained in hybridoma supernatants. In positive controls, the primary antibody was replaced by anti-human β_2-microglobulin or anti-HLA monoclonal antibodies (Becton-Dickinson, Oxnard, CA). All negative controls were found to yield similar results. Since anti-β_2 and anti-HLA antibodies were found to be interchangeable for our purpose, we included one positive (anti-β_2-microglobulin) and one negative (nonspecific Ig) control per plate. Every antibody tested for its binding to cell lines was also tested for its nonspecific binding to plastic.

Preparation of Antigen-Coated Erythrocytes. Human IgG isolated by DEAE chromatography from the serum of patients with multiple myeloma was bound to sheep erythrocytes by the chromium chloride method.[11] After the erythrocytes were washed five times with 0.15 M NaCl, one volume of the packed cells was mixed with one volume of IgG solution (1 mg/ml in 0.15 M NaCl) and one volume of $CrCl_3 \cdot 6H_2O$ solution (1 mg/ml in 0.15 M NaCl). The three reagents were allowed to react at room temperature for 5 min. Then, the coated erythrocytes were washed three times with 0.15 M NaCl and adjusted to a 10% suspension (v/v).

Preparation of Dishes for the Hemolytic Assay. SeaKem agarose (Marine Colloids, Rockland, MA) (0.9 g/dl) in 0.15 M NaCl was heated in a boiling water bath. Four milliliters was pipetted into 100 × 15-mm plastic petri dishes and allowed to solidify. Two milliliters was pipetted in 12 ×

---

[11] E. R. Gold and H. H. Fudenberg, *J. Immunol.* **99,** 859 (1967).

75-mm glass test tubes that had been prewarmed in a 45° water bath. Immediately after pipetting 0.2 ml of a 10% suspension of the antigen-coated erythrocytes, each tube was mixed and the contents were evenly spread on the surface of an agarose-coated petri dish by gentle swirling. After the erythrocyte-containing layer had solidified, the dishes were either used immediately or stored up to 1 week at 4° in a sealed container.

Hemolytic Assay. Three to five microliters of each supernatant was pipetted onto the surface of the hemolytic dish and incubated until absorbed. Two milliliters of an antiserum to the light and heavy chains of mouse Ig (Pel Freeze, Rogers, AR), absorbed with sheep erythrocytes and appropriately diluted in 0.15 M NaCl, was added to the dish and incubated at 37° for 1 hr. This Coomb's reagent was decanted and 2 ml of reconstituted guinea pig serum (GIBCO, Grand Island, NY) absorbed with sheep erythrocytes and diluted 1 : 10 in RPMI 1640 was added to the dish and incubated at 37° for 1 hr. The dish was then scored for the presence of lysis in the areas spotted with the supernatants. The positive controls were serial dilutions of the serum taken from the mouse at the time of the fusion or supernatants from already established hybridomas when available. The negative control was the spent supernatant of the parental myeloma cell line. A similar assay has been described by Bankert.[12]

Hemagglutination Assay. A 25-μl aliquot of each supernatant was pipetted into 96-well V-bottomed microtiter plates. Then 25 μl of a 1% suspension of the antigen-coated erythrocytes was added. The contents of the wells were mixed by gently tapping the plate. After 60 min at room temperature, 25 μl of a suitably diluted and absorbed rabbit antiserum to the light and heavy chains of mouse IgG was added to each well. The plates were scored for agglutination after 60 min at room temperature.

Results

Reliability of the ^{125}*I-Protein A Assay.* During the screening of monoclonal antibodies to adherent tumor cell lines, we observed that some cell lines would not grow in PVC plates but did grow in fibronectin-coated PVC plates. The cells assumed a similar morphology in polystyrene plates as in fibronectin-treated PVC plates (Fig. 1).[13] In this assay, the background counts of the negative controls (i.e., normal mouse serum, irrelevant monoclonal antibody, or myeloma protein of the same class as the antibody to be tested) were as low as 200 cpm out of 100,000 cpm of ^{125}I-

[12] R. B. Bankert, this series, Vol. 92, p. 182.
[13] D. P. Eskinazi, J. N. Hasson, and D. K. Kebo, *Immunol. Lett.* **5,** 161 (1982).

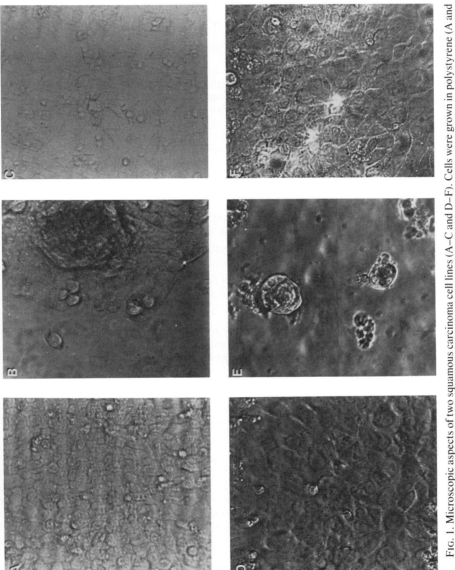

FIG. 1. Microscopic aspects of two squamous carcinoma cell lines (A–C and D–F). Cells were grown in polystyrene (A and D), uncoated PVC (B and E), and fibronectin-coated PVC (C and F) plates. (Reproduced from Eskinazi *et al.*,[13] with permission from Elsevier Biomedical Press.)

TABLE I

REPRODUCIBILITY AND BACKGROUND OF THE ^{125}I-PROTEIN A ASSAY

Primary reagent	Binding[a] of primary reagents to wells plated with											
	No cells			SCC-6			SCC-10A			SCC-19		
Normal mouse serum	431	311	256	741	637	648	589	577	669	471	451	557
Sp2/0-Ag14[b]	232	231	259	390	329	329	399	335	374	251	266	221
Anti-β_2	351	298	192	7896	8374	8171	4744	4025	3709	3931	4580	4255
Anti-HLA	188	169	158	7940	8155	8942	7490	5780	5491	9696	8223	6391

[a] Under each column, the three numbers represent triplicates. SCC-6, SCC-10A, and SCC-19 were cell lines derived from squamous cell carcinomas.[4]

[b] Sp2 was the myeloma cell line used as fusion partner in the preparation of the anti-β_2-microglobulin and anti-HLA monoclonal antibodies.

protein A added per well (Table I). We found that it was essential to evaluate each of the monoclonal antibodies for its nonspecific binding to empty wells. Indeed, some monoclonal antibodies bound nonspecifically to plastic surfaces as much as to the cells (Table II). Without these controls, much effort could be wasted in subcloning nonspecific hybridomas.

The mean coefficient of variation for the protein A assay was 4% ($\bar{x} \pm$ SD, 4% ± 3.8%) (Table II). Between assays, the results were quite repro-

TABLE II

NECESSITY OF A CONTROL FOR NONSPECIFIC BINDING OF MONOCLONAL ANTIBODIES TO MICROTEST PLATES

Primary reagent	Binding[a] of various monoclonal antibodies to wells plated with					
	No cells	SCC-6	SCC-8	SCC-10A	SCC-19	SH-1
Pooled mouse Ig[b]	159 ± 3	2260 ± 57	1564 ± 9	745 ± 77	2004 ± 38	401 ± 4
Anti-β_2	233 ± 49	8392 ± 242	5537 ± 164	1976 ± 66	6294 ± 152	1952 ± 103
H-7[c]	413 ± 42	7441 ± 947	6745 ± 905	4371 ± 136	6577 ± 253	6140 ± 63
MH-P25[d]	20874 ± 967	21942 ± 237	21921 ± 44	21858 ± 321	22492 ± 21	20578 ± 263

[a] Binding expressed as cpm ± SD (every experiment performed at least in triplicate). Cells were glutaraldehyde fixed. SCC-6, SCC-8, SCC-10A, and SCC-19 are cells lines derived from oral squamous cell carcinomas.[4] SH-1 is a cell line derived from a squamous cell carcinoma of the esophagus (gracious gift of Dr. Jane Galton, University of California at Los Angeles).

[b] 10 μg/ml.

[c] Monoclonal antibody reacting with cells.

[d] Monoclonal antibody reacting nonspecifically with polystyrene.

ducible, provided that the assays were performed on a consistent number of cells (e.g., confluent monolayers) and that protein A had a similar specific activity (Fig. 2). There was a slight but consistently higher sensitivity ($p < 0.01$) for the assay performed on fibronectin-coated PVC plates as compared to coated or uncoated polystyrene plates. Fibronectin-coating did not affect the sensitivity of the assay performed on polystyrene (Fig. 3, lower graph).

ELISA. Monoclonal antibodies were also tested by the ELISA for their binding to human adherent tumor cells. The ELISA method was sensitive and reliable. In essence, the results were very similar to what has been described for the radioimmunoassay. Nonspecific binding of both the enzyme-conjugated second antibody and standard IgG and IgM (negative controls) was low. Further negative controls suggested that the tumor cells contained no appreciable endogenous peroxidase (Fig. 4).

Cell Number. As expected, the number of cells plated per well bears directly on the results of the experiment. The optimal number of cells to be plated had to be evaluated for each cell line but was similar for protein A assay and ELISA. For the adherent squamous cell carcinoma cell lines tested, the optimal number was found to be 5×10^4 to 10^5 cells/well. With this number of cells, the monolayer was confluent within 24–48 hr. At

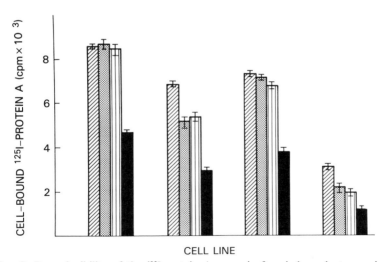

FIG. 2. Reproducibility of the ^{125}I-protein A assay in four independent experiments. Three of them were performed under similar experimental conditions. In the fourth one (■), ^{125}I-protein A had a specific activity one-half that of the protein A used in the previous experiments. Each group of bars represent binding of anti-β_2 antibody to a given cell line. Each experiment was performed in triplicate.

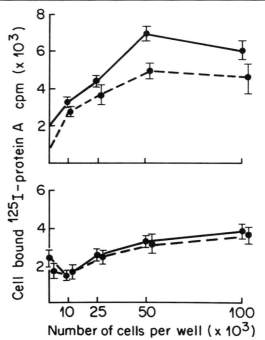

FIG. 3. Sensitivity of a radioimmunoassay using ^{125}I-labeled staphylococcal protein A to measure the binding of a monoclonal anti-β_2-microglobulin antibody to increasing numbers of human squamous cell carcinoma cells grown in uncoated (dashed line) and fibronectin-coated (solid line) plates. Upper graph: PVC; lower graph: polystyrene. (Reproduced from Eskinazi et al.,[13] with permission from Elsevier Biomedical Press.)

higher cell numbers, the number of cell-bound counts remained constant or slightly declined, possibly reflecting cell death or steric hindrance (Figs. 3 and 4).

Detection of Surface versus Cytoplasmic Antigens. Surface antigens are detected on live or dried cells while cytoplasmic antigens are detected on GDA-fixed cells. Dried cells are more convenient to handle than live cells. However, we have found an increased nonspecific binding and occasionally a decreased specific binding, suggesting a partial denaturation of the antigenic determinant by the drying process (Table III). Antibodies directed against surface antigen such as β_2-microglobulin, reacted with live cells as well as fixed cells (Table IV). Conversely, antibodies directed against cytoplasmic antigens reacted with fixed cells but not with live cells (Table IV). The same type of results was obtained with cells growing in suspension (data not shown).

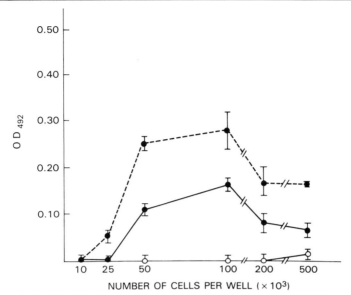

FIG. 4. Evaluation of optimal cell numbers in an ELISA assay. Binding of anti-β_2-microglobulin (●, solid line) and anti-HLA (●, dashed line) monoclonal antibodies to increasing numbers of human SCC cells; (○) negative control.

TABLE III
COMPARISON OF LIVE, DRIED, AND FIXED CELLS AS TARGET FOR THE
DETECTION OF SURFACE ANTIGENS

Primary reagent	Binding[a] of primary reagent to wells plated with			
	No cells	Live cells	Dried cells	Fixed cells
Pooled mouse Ig[b]	120 ± 15	790 ± 20	1800 ± 229	829 ± 68
Anti-β_2	575 ± 58	8991 ± 156	10030 ± 244	12260 ± 104
C6[c]	125 ± 22	5382 ± 209	3612 ± 168	4598 ± 251

[a] Binding expressed as cpm ± SD (every experiment performed at least in triplicate). Cells used were the SCC-10A cell line.[4]

[b] 10 μg/ml.

[c] Monoclonal antibody C6 reacts with SCC-10A and some other tumor cell lines.

TABLE IV
DETECTION OF SURFACE VERSUS
CYTOPLASMIC ANTIGENS

Monoclonal antibodies	Binding[a] of monoclonal antibodies to	
	Live cells	Fixed cells
Pooled mouse Ig[b]	398 ± 24	978 ± 54
Anti-β_2[c]	4483 ± 55	3355 ± 756
C6[c]	3660 ± 378	4962 ± 657
H-7[c]	487 ± 6	2444 ± 127

[a] Binding expressed as cpm ± SD (every experiment performed at least in triplicate).
[b] 10 μg/ml.
[c] Antibodies directed against surface antigens (e.g., anti-β_2 and C6) react with live as well as fixed cells. Antibodies directed to cytoplasmic antigens (e.g., H-7) react with fixed cells only.

Detection of Antibodies to Soluble Antigens. The ^{125}I-protein A assay and the ELISA described above can also be applied to the screening of antibodies to soluble antigens. In this instance, wells are coated with the relevant antigen instead of being seeded with the cells. These techniques have been extensively described and are essentially identical to the assays performed on cells.[2,3] However, we are not using these methods any longer because they are labor intensive and time-consuming. Instead we have been using a simpler, cheaper, and speedier strategy that combines a hemagglutination assay with a hemolytic assay. Thus, for the selection of hybridomas secreting antibodies to human Ig, the supernatants were first tested for hemagglutination of Ig-coated erythrocytes. The percentage of agglutinator supernatants varied with the fusions, and it was 3- to 5-fold greater with than without a Coomb's reagent. Then, the agglutinator supernatants were tested for ability to lyse the same indicator cells on agar gel, in the presence of a Coomb's reagent and complement. Fewer positives were found by this latter method. The degree of lysis varied from sample to sample (Fig. 5), but negative controls did not have any background. Therefore the identification of positives was clear cut.

Discussion

We have described three useful techniques to screen for binding of monoclonal antibodies to selected cellular and soluble antigens. These

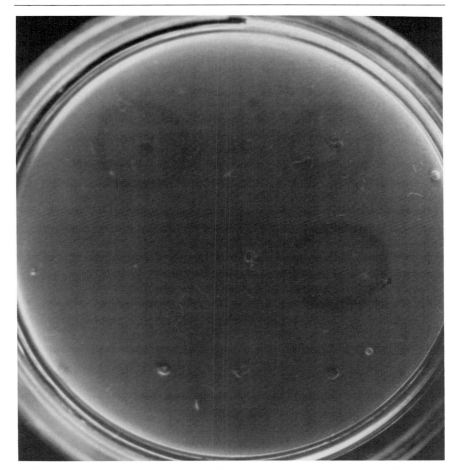

FIG. 5. Hemolytic assay on agar gel. Nine supernatants were tested for ability to lyse IgG-coated erythrocytes in a 35-mm dish. Four supernatants and the positive control were hemolytic. The other supernatants and the negative control gave no appreciable background lysis.

techniques and their variations have been repeatedly used and proved to be quite satisfactory for this purpose. The choice of a particular technique over another is often a matter of personal preference or convenience.

In our hands, the protein A binding assay was more sensitive and reliable than ELISA. Thus, we repeatedly found some supernatants were borderline and questionable by ELISA but reproducibly positive by the ^{125}I-protein A assay. In addition, the interassay variability was higher in the ELISA than in the protein A assay. We also found that fibronectin-coated PVC plates were as good as polystyrene plates for performing the protein A assay. The PVC plates had the advantage that cutting the PVC wells was faster than transferring the polystyrene well contents to counting tubes. Recently, we have facilitated the transfer of the well contents by using cotton swabs to absorb the NaOH used to dissolve the well contents. Yet, PVC plates may offer advantages over polystyrene plates for optical or electron microscopic observations.

Thus, we feel that ELISA and radioimmunoassay can each fulfill a purpose and complement each other. We tentatively suggest initial screening of hybridoma supernatants against cellular antigens by ELISA, since it appears that the variations observed in this assay will not be sufficient to miss worthwhile antibodies. Subsequent testing for finer data could employ the protein A assay, which seems to be more reliable and more quantitative.

Similarly, our current strategy for screening hybridoma supernatants for antibodies to soluble antigens makes use of two different techniques. In a first stage, supernatants are evaluated for their ability to agglutinate antigen-coated erythrocytes. This approach has some pitfalls but saves time and work. In less than 4 hr, one can readily and conveniently screen thousands of supernatants and identify the cultures presumptively secreting the antibody of interest. In a second stage, positive and borderline supernatants are retested for their ability to lyse antigen-coated erythrocytes by the hemolysis technique. This technique is more time-consuming but more reliable than hemagglutination.

In conclusion, our experience points to the advantage of selecting potentially useful hybridomas by using a pair of methods. In a first phase, we suggest using rapid screening to immediately eliminate obviously negative hybridomas. In a second phase, reactivity should be retested with a more reliable method to select the true positives to be subcloned.

Acknowledgments

The initial work on protein A assay was supported in part by the Research Grant CA 33014-01 from the National Cancer Institute and in part by the Concern Foundation of Los Angeles, Inc. We gratefully thank Dr. M. Jenkins for helpful criticism and Ms. C. A. Molinaro for editorial assistance.

[75] Epitope Ratio Analysis for the Simultaneous Study of Several Cell Surface Antigens[1]

By Bennett Kaufman and Richard Goldsby

Individual cell surface antigens are studied by any one of a number of techniques, including complement fixation/cytotoxicity,[1a] agglutination,[2] radioimmunoassay (RIA),[3] and fluorescence assays,[4] while two-color immunofluorescence[5] and a combination of radiolabeling and immunoenzymatic techniques[6] have been used to analyze two antigens at the same time. The technique of epitope ratio analysis (ERA)[7] can be used for the simultaneous analysis of three different antigens, and could be used in conjunction with fluorescence and enzymatic techniques to increase the number of determinants studied stimultaneously.

Monoclonal antibodies (MAb),[8] because of their specificity for single antigenic epitopes, homogeneity, ability to be biosynthetically labeled in culture, and potential to be obtained in quantity for long periods of time, represent ideal reagents for exploitation in ERA.

Principles of Epitope Ratio Analysis (ERA)

The energy spectrum of ^{125}I radiation overlaps the spectra of ^{3}H and ^{14}C, so the total counts/min (cpm) determined by liquid scintillation (LS) counting of a sample containing all three isotopes represents the sum of their individual cpm. The "float/flood" technique was developed to measure the different isotopes in each other's presence using LS counting. If a sample containing all three isotopes is placed in a glass vial surrounded by, but not containing, scintillation fluid, the β-radiation of the ^{3}H and ^{14}C

---

[1] The opinions or assertions contained herein are the private views of the authors and are not to be construed as official or as reflecting the views of the Department of the Army or the Department of Defense. Citation of trade names in this report does not constitute an official endorsement or approval of the use of such items.

[1a] T. Pearson, G. Galfré, A. Zeigler, and C. Milstein, *Eur. J. Immunol.* **7**, 684 (1977).

[2] C. A. Williams and M. M. Chase, *Methods Immunol. Immunochem.* **3**, 1 (1970).

[3] N. R. Klinman, *J. Exp. Med.* **136**, 241 (1972).

[4] J. J. Cebra and G. Goldstein, *J. Immunol.* **95**, 230 (1965).

[5] M. R. Loken, D. R. Parks, and L. A. Herzenberg, *J. Histochem. Cytochem.* **25**, 899 (1977).

[6] A. C. Cuello, J. V. Priestley, and C. Milstein, *Proc. Natl. Acad. Sci. U.S.A.* **79**, 665 (1982).

[7] B. M. Kaufman and R. A. Goldsby, *J. Immunol. Methods* **54**, 1 (1982).

[8] G. Köhler and C. Milstein, *Nature (London)* **256**, 495 (1975).

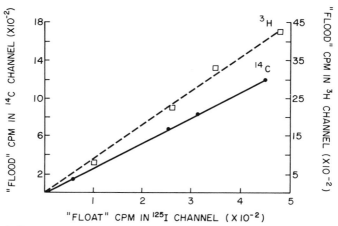

FIG. 1. Calibration curve of "float/flood" method for determination of ^{125}I cpm in ^{3}H and ^{14}C channels of LS counter. (□) ^{125}I counts in ^{3}H channel; (●) ^{125}I counts in ^{14}C channel.

isotopes cannot be detected; a portion of the ^{125}I γ-radiation will penetrate the vial into the scintillator and will be detected (the float mode). If the vial is now filled with scintillation fluid (the flood state), the radiation from the ^{3}H and ^{14}C isotopes can then be detected, along with the enhanced contribution from ^{125}I. By measuring standard ^{125}I-containing samples in both modes, the contribution of ^{125}I cpm in the ^{3}H and ^{14}C channels can be determined, and subsequently subtracted from the total cpm in the appropriate channels to yield the net cpm due to the other isotope(s). An example of a calibration curve derived from such an analysis is shown in Fig. 1; the relationship between cpm determined in both modes is linear over a wide range.

Any three-channel liquid scintillation spectrometer may be used for ERA; the "spillover" of cpm from any given isotope into the counting channels for the other isotope(s) used may be determined by the use of appropriate standards. An example of the spillover characteristics of the Beckman LS7500 system[9] using the factory-supplied ISOSETS for ^{125}I, ^{3}H, and ^{14}C is shown in the table.

There are a few requirements for the successful application of the ERA technique. (1) The isotopes used must be distinguishable. The γ-emitter ^{125}I is valuable because it can readily be detected separately from the β-emitters using the float/flood technique, and most antibodies can be labeled to high specific activity with ^{125}I without affecting antibody activ-

[9] Beckman Instruments, Irvine, California 92713.

PERCENTAGE COUNTS IN WINDOWS (SPILLOVER)[a]

Isotope standard	^{3}H window	^{125}I window	^{14}C window
^{3}H	97	2.7	—
^{125}I	63	37	—
^{14}C	17	54	30

[a] Isotope standards were individually counted, and percentage of total counts appearing in each ISOSET window was determined.

ity. Likewise, the different energy spectra of ^{3}H and ^{14}C allow them to be differentiated after appropriate spillover corrections (see above). (2) The antibodies must be labeled adequately to give detectable signals, even at low antibody concentration. Although this condition is readily obtained in chemically labeled purified antibodies, it may be more difficult to achieve by biosynthetic labeling. While dialyzed tissue culture supernatants have usually been adequate reagents, it may be necessary to concentrate some supernatants or purify the antibody somewhat (as by protein A chromatography) to obtain a usable reagent. (3) The experiments are carried out in antibody excess; thus, the amount of antibody bound is generally proportional to the number of antibody-binding sites present. Normally, this condition is also easily satisfied. (4) The binding of any one antibody in the ERA mixture must not interfere with the binding of any other antibody in the reagent, either sterically or competitively. The condition of independent binding is usually the case, but should be determined for each ERA mixture. Independent binding can be determined by comparing the binding of the specific antibody used alone with the binding of the antibody when used in the ERA mixture. An example of independent binding is shown in Fig. 2.

Methods

Preparation of ERA Reagent. Labeling of purified antibody or MAb with ^{125}I can be done using any of the commercially available kits or such published methods as the chloramine-T technique.[10] After iodination of the antibody, actively binding fractions can be obtained by eluting the antibody from a Sepharose–protein A column. Specific activities of such preparations are typically 2–6 × 10^6 cpm/μg.

[10] F. C. Greenwood, W. M. Hunter, and J. S. Glover, *Biochem. J.* **89,** 114 (1963).

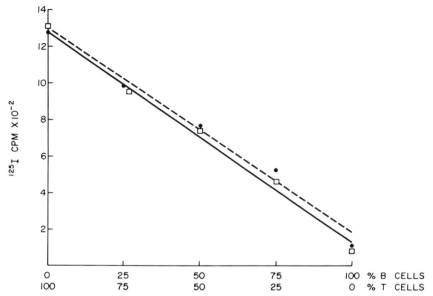

FIG. 2. Comparison of cpm of ^{125}I-labeled MAb binding to mixed cell suspension when MAb is used alone (□) or in an ERA mixture after subtraction of ^{3}H and ^{14}C cpm (●). The antibody in this example specifically binds to T-cell lines, and shows no binding to homologous B-cell lines. The ratio of the two cell types in the mixture was varied, while keeping the total cell number constant.

For biosynthetic labeling of MAb, antibody-producing hybridoma cells (2×10^7 total) are grown for 16 hr in commercially available minimum essential medium (MEM) lacking leucine, lysine, and tyrosine (GIBCO Select-Amine)[11] supplemented with 1% fetal bovine serum[11] and 0.10 mCi each of the above amino acids[12] labeled with ^{3}H or ^{14}C. The supernatant fluids are dialyzed against several changes of phosphate-buffered saline (PBS) plus 10% (v/v) MEM without serum, and made 0.01% in sodium azide before use. The specific activities of ^{3}H-labeled antibodies are usually 5–10×10^6 cpm/μg; those of ^{14}C-labeled antibodies, 5–10×10^5 cpm/μg.

A representative ERA reagent is a mixture of all three labeled MAbs in PBS containing 0.1% bovine serum albumin (BSA) and 0.01% sodium azide. For example, 50 μl of the mixture might contain 5×10^4 cpm of ^{3}H-labeled antibody, 2×10^4 cpm ^{14}C-labeled antibody, and 4×10^4 cpm of the ^{125}I-labeled antibody.

[11] GIBCO Laboratories, Grand Island, New York 14072.
[12] Amersham Corporation, Arlington Heights, Illinois 60005.

Use of ERA Reagent. (1) Harvest cells from culture fluid by gentle centrifugation, and resuspend in PBS + 0.1% BSA + 0.01% azide (WB) at a concentration of 1–6 × 10⁷ cells/ml. (2) Place 50 μl of cell suspension into each well of flexible poly(vinyl chloride) microtiter plates[13] (5 × 10⁵ to 3 × 10⁶ cells/well). (3) Add 50 μl of ERA reagent to each well, and incubate at room temperature for 1–2 hr, tapping plate occasionally to keep cells in suspension. (4) Wash plate by centrifugation at 1200–2000 rpm for 2–3 min (room temperature) and either aspirate fluid from wells or "flick" fluid out over sink. (CAUTION: fluids are radioactive, and must be handled and disposed of in accordance with radioactive waste-handling procedures.) (5) Add 100 μl of WB to each well, resuspend pellet using an orbital-type shaker, and recentrifuge as above. (6) Wash plate as above, for a total of three washes. (7) Add a drop of melted 2% agarose in saline to each well to prevent loss of cell pellet. This will not interfere with subsequent LS counting. (8) Cut wells from plate using a hot-wire cutter[14] and place resulting "cup" in a 35 × 12-mm (1/2 dram) glass shell vial.

(9) Carefully place each shell vial inside a 20-ml glass scintillation vial containing 10 ml scintillation fluid, and cap the vial. The shell vial will float in the fluid, but take care not to allow fluid inside the shell vial during handling (this is the float procedure). (10) Count samples in LS counter using appropriate counting windows. (11) Invert the scintillation vial to allow scintillation fluid inside the shell vial (the flood mode) and recount the samples using the same program. (12) By consulting the previously determined calibration curve (Fig. 1), determine what the ¹²⁵I cpm in the float mode are equivalent to in the flood mode in the ³H and ¹⁴C windows, and subtract those values from the total cpm in the windows to give the net cpm due to ³H and ¹⁴C alone. Likewise, corrections must also be made for spillover of ¹⁴C into the other counting windows (see table). (13) Comparison of cpm detected when using a single labeled MAb alone with net cpm obtained after extracting that MAb's cpm from the total cpm produced by an ERA mixture containing an equal amount of the same labeled MAb (applying the appropriate corrections due to spillover) demonstrates the validity of the method (see Fig. 2).

---

[13] Dynatech, Cooke Engineering, Alexandria, Virginia 22314.
[14] D. Lee, Inc., Sunnyvale, California 94087.

[76] Use of Monoclonal Antibodies as Radiopharmaceuticals for the Localization of Human Carcinoma Xenografts in Athymic Mice

By DAVID COLCHER, JOSE ESTEBAN, and FRANÇOISE MORNEX

Radiolabeled monoclonal antibodies reactive with the surface of human carcinoma cells may prove useful in the diagnosis and management of human cancer.[1,2] The detection of occult metastatic lesions at distal sites via gamma scanning could serve as an adjunct, for many types of cancer, in determining which patients should receive adjuvant therapy, while subsequent scanning could reveal which tumors are responding to therapy.

In order to test the efficacy of monoclonal antibodies as radiopharmaceutical agents it is necessary to develop appropriate model systems. The athymic mouse has been shown to be an excellent recipient for human tumor xenografts. Most studies have used either cells grown in culture or tumor pieces implanted subcutaneously in the athymic mouse. This method has proved very useful in examining the potential of monoclonal antibodies as radioimmunodetection agents. The study of the use of monoclonal antibodies as radiopharmaceuticals for the localization of human tumors necessitated the investigation of how to radiolabel a monoclonal antibody without loss of its immunoreactivity and to determine what form of the IgG molecule gives the best results. The intact IgG molecule is the easiest to use but because of its size and its ability to bind to Fc receptors, which may alter its biodistribution, it may not be the ideal radiopharmaceutical. Fragments of the IgG molecule lacking the Fc portion may be the most appropriate form to use to avoid this potential problem. The use of an antibody without the Fc portion may also reduce its immunogenicity in patients and thus minimize an immune response. The smaller fragments also clear from the body faster than does intact immunoglobulin and should result in a lower radiation dose to the host.

In order to determine which form of the antibody was best for radioimmunodetection and radioimmunotherapy, studies were undertaken to ra-

[1] J. Schlom and M. Weeks, in "Important Advances in Oncology" (V. T. deVita, S. Hellman, and S. A. Rosenberg, eds.), p. 172. Lippincott, Philadelphia, Pennsylvania, 1985.
[2] D. Colcher, P. Horan Hand, D. Wunderlich, M. Nuti, Y. A. Teramoto, D. Kufe, and J. Schlom, in "Immunodiagnostics" (R. Aloisi, ed.), p. 215. Alan R. Liss, Inc., New York, 1983.

diolabel IgG and fragments of monoclonal antibodies, reactive with human mammary and colon tumor-associated antigens, without significant loss of immunoreactivity, and to use them to localize human tumors in athymic mice. Studies were initiated with monoclonal antibodies B6.2 and B72.3, both of which bind to human breast and colon carcinomas.

Hybridoma Methodology

BALB/c mice were immunized with a membrane-enriched fraction of human breast tumor metastasis to the liver. The splenic lymphocytes were fused with the non-immunoglobulin-secreting myeloma cell line P3-NS1-Ag4.[3–5] The reactivities of the resulting monoclonal antibodies, including B6.2 and B72.3 (both IgG$_1$), have been described in detail elsewhere.[6,7] MAb B6.2 provided a good model for study because we had cell culture model systems to examine cell surface binding. MAb B6.2 binds to over 75% of the human breast carcinomas and 90% of human cell carcinomas, but it also binds to mature granulocytes. B6.2 thus provides a good model for study but its utility as an imaging agent in humans may limited to lymphoscintigraphy studies where granulocytes should not interfere. B72.3 binds to approximately 50% of human breast carcinomas and 80% of human colon carcinomas in immunohistochemistry studies, but very poorly to cell lines. B72.3 does not exhibit significant binding to any normal adult tissues. B72.3 has more potential as a radioimmunodetection and therapy agent but its model systems were difficult to establish.

Purification and Fragmentation of Monoclonal Antibodies

B6.2 and B72.3 IgG were purified from ascitic fluid obtained from BALB/c mice pristane-primed 10–14 days prior to being inoculated ip with 1×10^7 hybridoma cells. The resulting ascitic fluid was clarified by centrifugation at 10,000 g for 10 min. The supernatant was adjusted to 0.1 M Tris–HCl (pH 7.5) and the immunoglobulin precipitated by the addition of an equal volume of saturated ammonium sulfate. After 1 hr at 4° the immunoglobulin was pelleted by centrifugation at 10,000 g for 10 min,

[3] L. A. Herzenberg, L. A. Herzenberg, and C. Milstein, in "Handbook of Experimental Pathology" (D. M. Weir, ed.), p. 25.1. Blackwell, Oxford, 1978.

[4] G. Köhler and C. Milstein, Nature (London) 256, 494 (1975).

[5] G. Köhler and C. Milstein, Eur. J. Immunol. 6, 511 (1976).

[6] D. W. Kufe, L. Nadler, L. Sargent, H. Shapiro, P. Horan Hand, F. Austin, D. Colcher, and J. Schlom, Cancer Res. 43, 851 (1983).

[7] M. Nuti, D. Colcher, P. Horan Hand, F. Austin, and J. Schlom, in "Monoclonal Antibodies and Developments in Immunoassay" (A. Albertini and R. Elkins, eds.), p. 87. Elsevier/North-Holland Biomedical Press, Amsterdam, 1981.

dissolved in 5 ml of 5 mM sodium phosphate buffer (pH 7.5) for B6.2 (10 mM for B72.3), dialyzed against the same buffer, and applied to a 15-ml ion-exchange column (DE-52; Whatman). The column was washed with sodium phosphate buffer (pH 7.5) at the indicated concentration and the antibody was eluted with a salt gradient to 100 mM sodium phosphate (pH 7.5). Fractions (2 ml) were collected and the A_{280} was determined. Solid-phase RIAs using an extract of a human mammary tumor metastasis as antigen were used to localize fractions containing antibody. The appropriate fractions were pooled and dialyzed against PBS. The IgG was further purified by molecular sieving through Ultrogel AcA 44 in PBS. The protein concentration was determined by the method of Lowry *et al.*[8]

Control immunoglobulins were used to demonstrate the specificity of antibody binding. These include (1) MOPC-21, a myeloma IgG$_1$ which was purchased from Litton Bionetics, Inc. (Rockville, MD); and (2) normal murine immunoglobulin which was purified from sera of BALB/c mice. Methods for the purification of these immunoglobulins were as described above.

Fab′ fragments were generated for MAb B6.2 by the digestion of the purified IgG using pepsin. Ten milligrams of IgG was adjusted to 10 mM dithiothreitol in 150 mM Tris–HCl, 150 mM NaCl, 2 mM EDTA, pH 8.0, and incubated at room temperature for 1 hr. The thiol groups were blocked using 21 mM iodoacetamide (room temperature, 15 min). The immunoglobulin was then dialyzed against 100 mM sodium acetate (pH 4.5), and 100 μg of pepsin (Worthington) was then added. After incubation at 37° for 16 hr, the sample was adjusted to pH 8.0 with Tris base and concentrated to 1.5 ml. The Fab′ fragments were separated from the other digestion products by molecular sieving through Ultrogel AcA 44 in 100 mM Tris–HCl, 200 mM NaCl, 2 mM EDTA, pH 8.0. The column was monitored for A_{280} and for immunoreactivity in a solid-phase RIA. F(ab′)$_2$ fragments were prepared by pepsin digestion without any pretreatment with dithiothreitol or iodoacetamide. The fragments retained all their immunoreactivity when compared on a molar basis to the intact IgG. Methods for the preparation of fragments from control immunoglobulins and their purification were as described for B6.2.

Iodinations of Antibodies

The B6.2 IgG and fragments were labeled with Na^{125}I using Iodogen.[9] Iodogen (Pierce Chemical, Rockford, IL) was diluted in chloroform to 10

---

[8] O. H. Lowry, N. J. Rosebrough, A. L. Farr, and R. J. Randall, *J. Biol. Chem.* **193**, 265 (1951).

[9] D. Colcher, M. Zalutsky, W. Kaplan, D. Kufe, F. Austin, and J. Schlom, *Cancer Res.* **43**, 736 (1983).

mg/ml, and 200 μg was added to 12 × 75-mm glass test tubes. The chloroform was allowed to evaporate under a stream of nitrogen, and the test tubes were stoppered and stored at −20° until use. Twenty micrograms of B6.2 IgG was adjusted to 0.1 M sodium phosphate buffer (pH 7.2) and 1 mCi of Na^{125}I (New England Nuclear, Boston, MA) was added. After a 2-min incubation at room temperature the protein was removed from the insoluble Iodogen, and the unincorporated ^{125}I was separated from the antibody by gel filtration through Sephadex G-25 (Pharmacia Fine Chemicals) (10-ml column). The labeled antibody in the void was pooled and dialyzed against 10 mM sodium phosphate buffer (pH 7.2) containing 5 mM NaI. Specific activities of 15–50 μCi/μg of protein were easily obtained. Immunoreactivity of monoclonal antibody B6.2 and its fragments was determined by solid-phase RIA using cell extracts.[9] Five micrograms (in 50 μl) of the cell extracts was added to each well of 96-well microtiter polyvinyl plates and allowed to dry. To minimize nonspecific protein absorption, microtiter wells were treated with 100 μl of 5% bovine serum albumin (BSA) in PBS and incubated for 1 hr. This and all subsequent incubations were performed at 37°. The BSA was removed, and varying amounts of radiolabeled antibody (in 50 μl) were added. After a 1-hr incubation, the unbound immunoglobulin was removed by washing the plates with 1% BSA in PBS. The bound counts were detected by cutting the individual wells from the plate and measuring the radioactivity in a gamma counter. As can be seen in Fig. 1, the binding in solid-phase RIAs of the IgG (Fig. 1A), F(ab′)$_2$ (Fig. 1B), and Fab′ (Fig. 1C) is better to the extracts from a breast tumor metastasis to the liver than to extracts of the MCF-7 breast tumor cell line. No binding was observed, however, to extracts from normal human liver, normal human lymphoid cells, or rhabdomyosarcoma cells. The labeled antibody was also shown to bind to the surface of viable MCF-7 cells, thus retaining the same specificity as did the unlabeled antibody.[10] Greater than 70% of the antibody remained immunoreactive in sequential saturation solid-phase RIAs after labeling.

The iodinated antibodies were analyzed for purity by sodium dodecyl sulfate–polyacrylamide gel electrophoresis.[11,12] The labeled antibodies were analyzed with and without disruption by 2-mercaptoethanol to determine the size of the IgG and fragments after labeling and to examine the distribution of the ^{125}I in the heavy and light chains. After labeling, the IgG maintains its molecular weight of approximately 150,000. After disruption with 2-mercaptoethanol, the ^{125}I label migrates at M_r 50,000 and

[10] D. Colcher, P. Hand, M. Nuti, and J. Schlom, *Proc. Natl. Acad. Sci. U.S.A.* **78**, 3199 (1981).

[11] U. K. Laemmli, *Nature (London)* **227**, 680 (1970).

[12] W. F. Studier, *J. Mol. Biol.* **79**, 237 (1973).

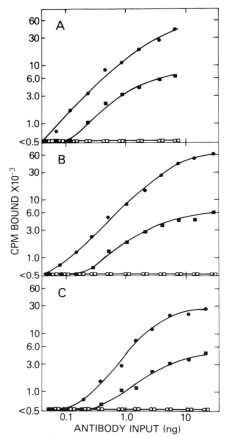

FIG. 1. Binding of radioactively labeled B6.2 to cell extracts. ^{125}I-labeled B6.2 IgG [53 μCi/μg, (A)], F(ab')$_2$ [19 μCi/μg, (B)], and Fab' [19 μCi/μg, (C)] were assayed for reactivity of cell extracts from a human breast tumor metastasis to the liver (●), the MCF-7 breast tumor cell line (■), normal human liver (○), and the A204 rhabdomyosarcoma cell line and the NC-37 human lymphoid cell line (□). The antibody input is adjusted for the different specific activities of the three forms of the iodinated antibody.

25,000 (Fig. 2), consistent with the size of the heavy and light chains of IgG. The F(ab')$_2$ changes from approximately M_r 100,000 to 2 polypeptides (M_r 25,000 and 27,000) when disrupted with 2-mercaptoethanol. The polypeptides of the labeled Fab' fragment migrate with molecular weights similar to those of the F(ab')$_2$ after disruption. Because the disulfide bonds are already disrupted and blocked with iodoacetamide, the Fab' fragment shows the same electrophoretic pattern without further disruption. Note that there is a 4-fold preferential labeling of the light chain (Fig.

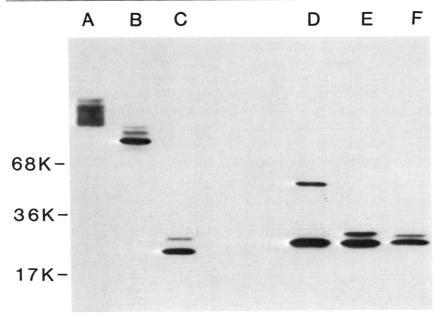

FIG. 2. Sodium dodecyl sulfate–polyacrylamide gel electrophoresis of ^{125}I-labeled B6.2 IgG and fragments. Iodinated IgG (lanes A and D), F(ab')$_2$ (lanes B and E), and Fab' (lanes C and F) were subjected to electrophoresis in a sodium dodecyl sulfate–polyacrylamide gel (5–20% gradient gel). The samples in lanes A–C were run without disruption, while the samples in lanes D–F were disrupted with 2-mercaptoethanol and heated to 100° for 2 min.

2), but this did not affect the immunological activity of the IgG and its fragments.

A great deal of information was obtained from the B6.2 system, but some major differences were observed with monoclonal antibody B72.3. B72.3 binds to an antigen, TAG-72, that has some properties of a mucin of greater than 10^6 D. When B72.3 IgG was iodinated using the Iodogen method established for B6.2 IgG, the antibody was labeled efficiently but the immunoreactivity was greatly reduced. Studies using a variety of other labeling techniques were undertaken using chloramine-T, lactoperoxidase, and Bolton–Hunter reagent.[13] The IgG was efficiently radiolabeled using all of these methods, but the immunoreactivity of the antibody was greatly reduced in all cases. The Iodogen method was therefore examined closely and after adjusting three major parameters, i.e.,

[13] P. E. Crowther and J. R. Harness, in "Handbook on Receptor Research" (S. M. Aloj and L. D. Kohn, eds.). Field Educational Publications Inc., San Francisco, California (in press).

ratios of immunoglobulin protein, iodine, and Iodogen, a protocol was obtained (40 μg of IgG, 0.5 mCi of Na ^{125}I, 20 μg of Iodogen) that yielded a labeled antibody that would bind over 80% of its radioactivity to tumor extracts as measured in sequential solid-phase RIAs. Assays were performed with the ^{125}I-labeled B72.3 IgG using overnight incubations at 4°. This yielded consistently higher levels of binding to extracts containing the TAG-72 antigen; this prolonged incubation was not needed for B6.2 IgG or fragments.

Tumor Distribution Studies with Monoclonal Antibody B6.2

We have shown that we can radiolabel B6.2 IgG and fragments and maintain their immunoreactivity. We therefore studied a variety of model systems in athymic mice, including human breast tumor xenografts established from cell lines and from transplantable breast tumors, to determine their utility as models to evaluate the antibody and fragments as radiopharmaceuticals.

Female athymic mice (nu/nu) on a BALB/c background were obtained from Charles River, Inc. at approximately 4 weeks of age. One week later, they were implanted sc with a 1- to 2-mm^3 pieces of the Clouser transplantable human breast carcinoma; this transplantable line was obtained from Dr. B. C. Giovanella (St. Joseph Hospital, Houston, TX), who established it in athymic mice directly from a biopsy. Mice were also inoculated sc with the human mammary tumor cell lines, MCF-7 and BT-20 (10^7 cells/animal), or with a human melanoma cell line, A375 (4×10^6 cells/animal). Cells were removed from culture flasks using 0.1% trypsin containing 0.5 mM EDTA, and washed twice in growth medium without serum. Approximately 10–20 days after athymic mice were implanted using trocars with pieces of a transplanted human mammary tumor (Clouser) the tumors grew to detectable nodules. While the growth rate of the tumors varied as did the final size obtained (0.5–2.5 cm in diameter), this model proved more useful than the other models we had studied.

Athymic mice bearing Clouser tumors 0.3–1.5 cm diameter were given iv injections of 0.1 μg (1.5 μCi) of B6.2 IgG or fragments. The mice were sacrificed at varying times by exsanguination, the tumor and selected tissues were excised and weighed, and radioactivity was measured in a gamma counter. The ratio of radioactivity per milligram in the tumor compared to that of various tissues rose over a 4-day period (Fig. 3, A–E) and then fell at 7 days. The tumor to tissue ratios were 10 : 1 or greater in the liver, spleen, and kidney at day 4. Ratios of activity per milligram in the tumor to that found in the brain and muscle were greater than 50 : 1 and as high as 110 : 1. Lower tumor to tissue ratios were obtained to blood

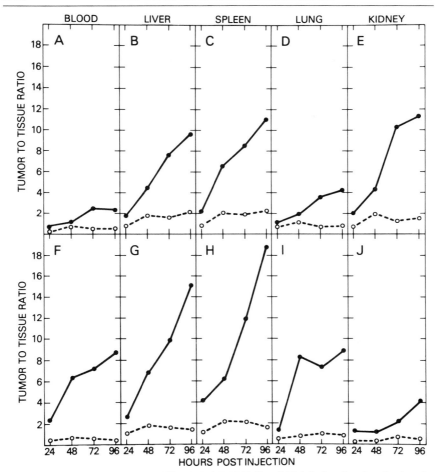

FIG. 3. Tissue distribution of ^{125}I-labeled B6.2 IgG and F(ab')₂ in athymic mice bearing human tumor transplants. Athymic mice bearing a transplantable human mammary tumor (Clouser) (●) or a human melanoma (A375) (○) were inoculated with ^{125}I-labeled B6.2. Approximately 1.5 μCi of IgG (A–E) or F(ab')₂ (F–J) was injected iv, and the mice were sacrificed at daily intervals. The radioactivity per milligram of tumor was determined and compared to that of various tissues; the averages of 2–20 mice per group are shown.

and the lungs (with its large blood pool). The absolute amount of ^{125}I-labeled IgG found in the tumor ranged from 2 to 15% of the injected dose, depending on tumor size.

When the Clouser mammary tumor-bearing mice were given injections of ^{125}I-labeled F(ab')₂ fragments of B6.2, higher tumor to tissue ratios were obtained (Fig. 3, F–J). The tumor to tissue ratios in the liver and spleen were 15 : 1 to 20 : 1 at 96 hr. The tumor to tissue ratios were somewhat lower with blood and lungs but were still higher than those obtained using IgG. This is probably due to the faster clearance of the $F(ab')_2$ fragments as compared to the IgG. The tumor to kidney ratios were relatively low and were probably a result of the more rapid clearance. The absolute amount of the ^{125}I-labeled $F(ab')_2$ fragments in the tumor ranged from 1 to 12% of the injected dose, depending on tumor size, with a decrease in radioactivity per milligram over the 4-day period.

Athymic mice bearing a human melanoma (A375), a tumor that shows no surface reactivity with B6.2 in live cell RIAs, were used as controls for nonspecific binding of the labeled antibody or antibody fragments to tumor tissue. No preferential localization of the monoclonal antibody was observed in the tumor; in fact, the activity per milligram in the tumor was lower than that found in many organs, resulting in ratios of <1 (Fig. 3, open symbols). Similarly, no localization was observed when either normal murine IgG or MOPC-21 IgG_1 (the same isotype as B6.2) from a murine myeloma, or their $F(ab')_2$ fragments, was inoculated into athymic mice bearing Clouser mammary tumors or melanomas.

Athymic mice bearing Clouser tumors were also given injections of ^{125}I-labeled B6.2 Fab'. The clearance rate of the Fab' fragment was considerably faster than that of the larger $F(ab')_2$ fragment and the intact IgG. Acceptable tumor to tissue ratios were obtained, but the fast clearance rate resulted in a large amount of the labeled Fab' being found in the kidney and bladder, resulting in low tumor to kidney ratios. These studies therefore indicate that $F(ab')_2$ fragments were superior to Fab' or intact IgG in the radioimmunolocalization studies with monoclonal antibody B6.2.

The blood clearance curves of ^{125}I activity following injection of ^{125}I-labeled B6.2 IgG, $F(ab')_2$, and Fab' into nude mice bearing Clouser tumors were studied. As expected, the smaller Fab' fragment cleared more rapidly than the $F(ab')_2$ fragment, which in turn cleared more rapidly than the intact IgG. While molecular size probably accounts for this behavior, it is also possible that the smaller fragments are dehalogenated more rapidly, which could also accelerate clearance of ^{125}I activity from the blood pool. The slow time components for the blood clearance of B6.2 IgG, $F(ab')_2$, and Fab' are 41, and 14, and 4 hr, respectively. Another way of expressing blood clearance data, perhaps more relevant to a potential imaging application, is the calculation of the time at which the activity in the blood pool has decreased to 10% of its initial value. For ^{125}I-labeled B6.2 IgG, $F(ab')_2$, and Fab', this occurs at 69, 32, and 4 hr, respectively.

Imaging of Human Tumors in Athymic Mice Using B6.2 IgG
  and Fragments

Studies were undertaken to determine whether the localization of the
^{125}I-labeled B6.2 and fragments in the tumors was sufficient to be detected
by gamma camera scanning. Athymic mice bearing the Clouser mammary
tumor or the A375 melanoma were given KI in drinking water, and received iv injections of approximately 30 μCi of ^{125}I-labeled B6.2 IgG. The
mice were imaged after intraperitoneal injection of 0.2 ml of 2,2,2-tribro-
moethanol (25 mg/ml, Pfaltz and Bauer) to ensure adequate anesthesia,
and then sacrificed at 24-hr intervals.

The Clouser tumors were easily detected at 24 hr (Fig. 4A) using
radiolabeled B6.2 IgG, with a small amount of activity detectable in the
blood pool. The tumor remained strongly positive over the 4-day period,
with the background activity decreasing to the point where it was barely
detectable at 96-hr (Fig. 4B). No tumor localization was observed using
radiolabeled B6.2 IgG in the mice bearing the control human melanomas
of similar size (Fig. 4C). Mice bearing Clouser mammary tumors or melanomas were also given injections of normal murine IgG radiolabeled with
^{125}I; the scanning data demonstrated no specific localization and were
consistent with the tissue distribution data given above.

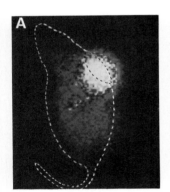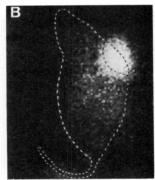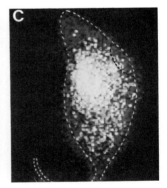

FIG. 4. Gamma camera scanning with B6.2 IgG of athymic mice bearing transplanted
human tumors. Athymic mice bearing a transplantable human mammary tumor [Clouser (A
and B)] or a human melanoma [A375 (C)] were inoculated with approximately 30 μCi of ^{125}I-
labeled B6.2 IgG (53 μCi/μg). The mice were scanned after various times [24 hr (A and C);
96 hr (B)] until an equal number of counts was detected in each field. The mammary tumors
and melanomas used in these scans were approximately 0.5 cm in diameter, and the approximate size is indicated in the figure by the dotted line. The raw data are presented without any
background subtraction.

Mice were also given injections of ^{125}I-labeled B6.2 F(ab')$_2$ fragments. The mice cleared the fragments faster than they cleared the intact IgG, and a significant amount of activity was observed in the kidneys and bladder at 24 hr (Fig. 5A), but tumors were clearly positive for localization of the ^{125}I-labeled B6.2 F(ab')$_2$ fragments. The activity was cleared from the kidneys and bladder by 48 hr, and the tumor to background ratio increased over the 4-day period of scanning, with little background, and good tumor localization was observed at 96 hr (Fig. 5B). No localization was observed with the radiolabeled B6.2 F(ab')$_2$ fragments in the athymic mice bearing the A375 melanoma (Fig. 5C), nor was any localization observed using normal murine F(ab')$_2$ in mammary tumor-bearing mice. While B6.2 F(ab')$_2$ fragments appeared to be best for radioimmunodetection, a smaller percentage of the injected dose was retained in the tumor as compared to the IgG. For therapy studies the intact IgG may be better because it will deliver a greater dose to the tumor.

Tumor Distribution Studies with Monoclonal Antibody 72.3

Radiolocalization studies were also performed with B72.3 using athymic mice bearing human colon carcinomas (LS-174T), in comparison with a human melanoma xenograft (A375) as a control for nonspecific uptake

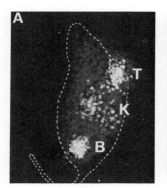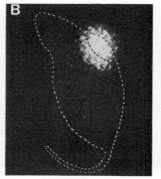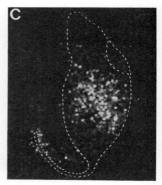

FIG. 5. Gamma camera scanning with B6.2 F(ab')$_2$ of athymic mice bearing transplanted human tumors. Athymic mice bearing a transplantable human mammary tumor [Clouser (A and B)] or a human melanoma [A375 (C)] were inoculated with approximately 30 μCi of ^{125}I-labeled B6.2 F(ab')$_2$ (19 μCi/μg). The mice were scanned after various times [24 hr (A); 96 hr (B and C)] until an equal number of counts was detected in each field. The mammary tumors and melanomas used in these scans were approximately 0.5 cm in diameter, and the approximate size is indicated in the figure by the dotted line. In A, the tumor, T, kidneys, K, and bladder, B, are indicated. The raw data are presented without any background subtraction.

of immunoglobulin. Athymic mice were given sc injections of 4×10^6 cells. Tumor growth was rapid with a doubling time of approximately 2–3 days for the LS-174T cells. After 7–10 days when the tumors were approximately 0.3–0.5 cm in diameter, the mice were given iv injections of approximately 1.5 μCi of ^{125}I-labeled B72.3 IgG or MOPC-21 IgG. The ratio of counts per milligram of tissue in the LS-174T tumor in comparison with that of various tissues was examined over a 7-day period. The tumor to tissue ratio rose over this period with tumor to liver, tumor to spleen, or tumor to kidney ratios of approximately 18 : 1 at day 7 (Fig. 6). Tumor to blood ratios also rose during this time, resulting in ratios of 5 : 1 at day 7. There was no specific uptake of ^{125}I-labeled B72.3 IgG in any of the normal organs examined. Approximately 10% of the injected dose per gram reached the tumor at day 2 postinoculation of the radiolabeled antibody.

A major difference between the B6.2 system and the B72.3 system is that the amount of the radiolabeled B72.3 at the tumor stayed essentially constant over a longer period of time; the activity on a per gram basis then

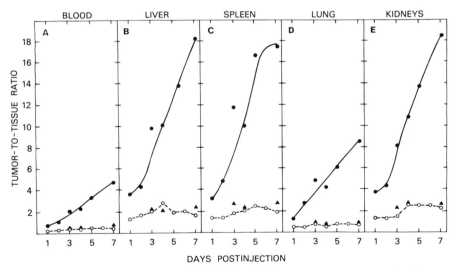

FIG. 6. Tissue distribution of ^{125}I-labeled B72.3 IgG in athymic mice bearing human tumors. Athymic mice bearing LS-174T colon carcinomas (●) or A375 melanomas (○) were inoculated with approximately 1.5 μCi of ^{125}I-labeled B72.3 IgG. The mice were sacrificed over a 7-day period, and radioactivity per milligram of tissue was determined. The ratio of the radioactivity per milligram in the tumor as compared to other organs was plotted. Mice bearing LS-174T colon carcinomas were also given injections of the control antibody MOPC-21 (▲).

began to drop as the tumor progressed in size. The increased tumor to tissue ratios result primarily from the clearance of labeled IgG from the blood pools. The absolute amount of radioactivity in the tumor rose over the first 2 days and then remained constant through day 7. Athymic mice bearing melanomas were used as controls; no specific uptake of ^{125}I-labeled B72.3 was observed in the tumors of these control animals. Similarly, no localization was observed in athymic mice bearing the colon carcinoma cell line when using ^{125}I-labeled MOPC-21 IgG as a control antibody.

Imaging of Human Xenografts in Athymic Mice with B72.3

Studies were then undertaken to determine whether localization of the ^{125}I-labeled B72.3 was sufficient to be detected by gamma camera scanning. Athymic mice bearing colon carcinomas or melanomas were given injections of approximately 70 μCi (approximately 5 μg) of ^{125}I-labeled B72.3 IgG; the higher dose was used to minimize imaging time. The mice bearing the human colon carcinomas demonstrated significant tumor uptake at early time points with most of the activity in the area of the tumor (Fig. 7A). The remaining activity in the mice was detected primarily in the area of the heart and lungs. No significant activity was seen in the liver, kidneys, bladder, or stomach. The lack of activity in these organs indicates that there is no significant breakdown of the radiolabeled antibody, nor is there a large amount of free iodine due to the dehalogenation of the antibody. At 48 hr (Fig. 7B), the activity was still seen predominantly in the tumor, with the activity in the area of the heart and lungs significantly decreased. A similar pattern was seen at 72 hr (Fig. 7C) with a continuing decrease in the activity in the vital organs. The proportion of the activity found in the tumor continued to increase. Several mice bearing the control tumor, the A375 melanoma, at the same site as the LS-174T tumors were imaged at similar time points. As seen in Fig. 7, D–F, no significant activity of the ^{125}I-labeled B72.3 was detected in the area of the melanomas. The activity was primarily seen in the area of the heart and lungs.

Even better images were obtained in the athymic mice bearing the colon carcinoma inoculated with ^{125}I-labeled B72.3 at later time points. The background activity cleared from the mice with a $T_{1/2}$ of approximately 7.5 days. The activity in the tumor stayed essentially constant over the 19-day period studied, while the activity in the rest of the body decreased significantly (table). No accumulation of activity was seen in any organ. The amount of ^{125}I-labeled B72.3 IgG in the colon carcinomas rose from 7% of the total activity in the mouse at day 1 to approximately 40% at day 19 (table).

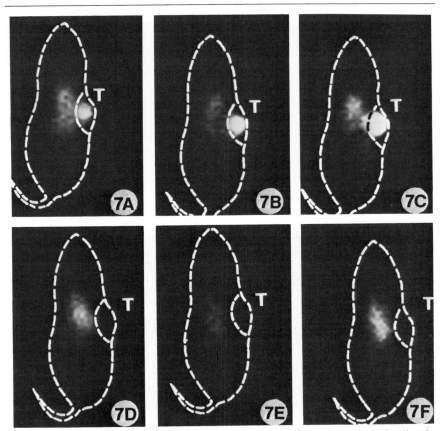

FIG. 7. Gamma camera scanning of athymic mice bearing human tumors. Athymic mice bearing LS-174T colon carcinomas (A–C) or A375 melanoma (D–F) were inoculated with approximately 70 μCi of ^{125}I-labeled B72.3 IgG. The mice were scanned after 1 (A, D), 2 (B, E), and 3 (C, F) days until 100,000 cpm were detected in the field. The images are displayed without blood pool corrections or contrast enhancement, and all are scaled to a common maximum value. T, Tumor.

This long retention of the radiolabeled B72.3 in the LS-174T tumor is highly desirable for clinical trials. In previous reports using monoclonal antibodies to other tumor-associated antigens, the interval from the time of the monoclonal antibody injection to optimal tumor localization was 3–7 days. The studies reported here demonstrate that specific B72.3 localization (i.e., percentage in tumor) is increasing at day 7 and indeed continues to rise through day 19. This is important because the increasing tumor to background ratios at late (post-day 7) time intervals make ra-

DISTRIBUTION OF ^{125}I-LABELED MONOCLONAL
ANTIBODY B72.3 IN AN ATHYMIC
MOUSE BEARING A HUMAN COLON
CARCINOMA XENOGRAFT[a]

Day	Activity in tumor (cpm)	Activity in total body (cpm)	Percentage in tumor
1	991	14,220	7.04
2	1,294	13,545	9.75
3	1,336	10,984	12.54
4	1,332	10,072	13.92
7	1,127	7,473	16.39
11	1,509	7,975	21.50
14	1,369	4,954	32.52
19	1,037	3,306	39.20

[a] Radioactivity was detected by the gamma camera in the region of interest. The counts are corrected for the nonuniformity of the pinhole and for the decay of the radionuclide. The percentage of radioactivity in the tumor is calculated after correction for the radioactivity of the normal tissue present in the region of the tumor.

diolabeled B72.3 an excellent candidate for therapeutic studies, since the time when the monoclonal antibody is bound to the tumor becomes an important factor in determining the total radiation dose received by tumor cells.

Conclusions

We have demonstrated the ability of ^{125}I-radiolabeled monoclonal antibodies to detect human mammary and colon carcinoma xenografts in athymic mice. The F(ab')$_2$ fragment of monoclonal B6.2 provided overall higher tumor to tissue ratios and a faster clearance when compared to the intact IgG, which makes them more suitable for radiolocalization studies. The intact IgG gave greater percentage and longer retention of the injected dose within the tumor. This points toward its potential as a superior radiopharmaceutical in therapy studies since the intact IgG will deliver a higher dose of radiation to the tumor.

The models described here provide excellent experimental systems for investigating the potential of radiolabeled monoclonal antibodies as radiopharmaceutical agents for tumor localization and therapy studies.

[77] Coating of Liposomes with Subunits of Monoclonal IgM Antibody and Targeting of the Liposomes

By Yoshiyuki Hashimoto, Minoru Sugawara, Toshio Kamiya, and Shinya Suzuki

Liposomes have attracted great interest because of their possible use in targeting drugs or bioactive substances to specific cells or tissues. Specific targeting of common liposomes, however, is limited to tissues containing mononuclear phagocytic cells which engulf liposomes in a non-selective fashion.[1,2] Therefore, in order to prepare liposomes capable of targeting selectively to cells or tissues, liposomes must be modified with a reagent that can selectively bind to a component characteristic of the appropriate target cells or tissues. Since different types of cells or tissues are found to express different types or amounts of markers such as antigenic molecules and receptors, antibodies to the antigens or ligands that bind to receptors can be used for the preparation of liposomes possessing selective affinity for the target cells or tissue. In this regard, the use of glycolipids having a terminal sugar residue reactive with a sugar binding substance present on the target cells is an elegant method.[3-6] Another method is the utilization of antibody specific or selective for the target cells or tissue. Thus, liposomes coated with an antibody can serve as an efficient carrier of drugs.[7-10]

[1] G. Poste, C. Bucana, A. Raz, P. Bugelski, R. Kirsh, and I. J. Fidler, *Cancer Res.* **42**, 1412 (1982).

[2] G. Poste, R. Kirsh, and T. Koestler, *in* "Liposome Technology" (G. Gregoriadis, ed.), Vol. III, p. 1. CRC Press, Boca Raton, Florida, 1984.

[3] M. S. Wu, J. C. Robbins, R. L. Bugianese, M. M. Ponpipom, and T. Y. Shen, *Biochim. Biophys. Acta* **674**, 19 (1981).

[4] M. R. Mauk, R. C. Camble, and J. D. Baldeschwieler, *Proc. Natl. Acad. Sci. U.S.A.* **77**, 4430 (1980).

[5] M. M. Ponpipom, T. Y. Shen, J. D. Baldeschwieler, and P-S. Wu, *in* "Liposome Technology" (G. Gregoriadis, ed.), Vol. III, p. 95. CRC Press, Boca Raton, Florida, 1984.

[6] B. K. Bachhawat, P. K. Das, and P. Ghosh, *in* "Liposome Technology" (G. Gregoriadis, ed.), Vol. III, p. 117. CRC Press, Boca Raton, Florida, 1984.

[7] A. Huang, L. Huang, and S. J. Kennel, *J. Biol. Chem.* **255**, 8015 (1980).

[8] A. Huang, Y. S. Tsao, S. J. Kennel, and L. Huang, *Biochim. Biophys. Acta* **716**, 140 (1982).

[9] L. D. Leserman, J. Barbet, F. M. Kourilsky, and J. N. Weinstein, *Nature (London)* **289**, 602 (1980).

[10] L. D. Leserman, P. Machy, and J. Barbet, *in* "Liposome Technology" (G. Gregoriadis, ed.), Vol. III, p. 29. CRC Press, Boca Raton, Florida, 1984.

This chapter describes a method for coupling monoclonal IgM antibody to liposomes and its application to cancer chemotherapy.

General Strategy for the Preparation of Antibody-Coated Liposomes

Selection of antibody and the coupling method is fundamentally important in the preparation of antibody-coated liposomes. The antibody to be used in coating liposomes should be specific for the antigen that is present on the cell surface of target cells in relatively large quantity and in cell-bound form. Such antibodies can be prepared by the monoclonal antibody technique developed by Köhler and Milstein,[11] because the monoclonal antibody raised against the target cells is reactive with only one antigenic determinant present on the target cells. Since antibody on liposomes may play a role in selective binding of the liposomes to target cells, any type or class of immunoglobulin can be used for the modification.

Covalent coupling of antibody to a liposome or its constituents has been performed by use of a cross-linking reagent. Amino or carboxyl groups present in immunoglobulin molecules generally serve as the reaction site in the coupling with a cross-linking reagent. However, since such functional groups are present in unrestricted sites of the immunoglobulin, attention must be paid to the inactivation of the antibody owing to blocking of its antigen reactive site (Fab) during the coupling reaction. Furthermore, by this type of coupling, the Fc portion of the antibody molecule will remain intact after the coupling with liposomes, and may result in binding to Fc receptor-bearing normal host cells. This binding may prevent migration of the liposome to the target cells. In order to avoid these undesirable side reactions during antibody modification, F(ab')₂ fragments bearing an SH group can, in principle, be used for the modification of liposomes, as reported by Martin and Papahadjupoulos[12] who used polyclonal rabbit immunoglobulins as the antibody source. However, application of this method to murine monoclonal antibodies appears to be impractical, because the yield of F(ab')₂ fragments of murine monoclonal antibodies is generally very low. As an alternative method for the utilization of SH groups in monoclonal antibodies for liposome modification, we used subunits of monoclonal IgM antibodies which carry SH groups at the terminal of the Fc part (Fig. 1). Coupling of these SH-bearing subunits of monoclonal IgM antibody with liposomes containing SH-reactive maleimide groups yields antibody-coated liposomes in which the Fc part of

[11] G. T. Köhler and C. Milstein, *Nature (London)* **277**, 680 (1975).
[12] F. J. Martin and D. Papahadjopoulos, *J. Biol. Chem.* **257**, 286 (1982).

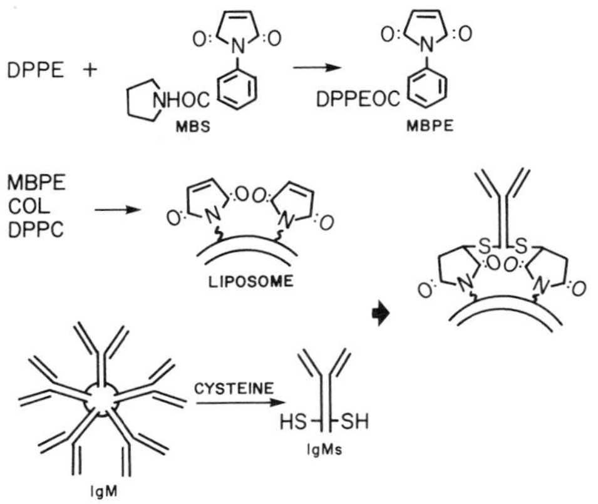

FIG. 1. Coating of liposomes with subunits of monoclonal IgM immunoglobulin. *m*-Maleimidobenzoyl(dipalmitoylphosphatidyl)ethanolamine (MBPE) was prepared from *m*-maleimidobenzoyl-*N*-hydroxysuccinimide ester (MBS) and dipalmitoylphosphatidylethanolamine (DPPE). A lipid film was prepared from a lipid mixture containing MBPE (2.5 μM), cholesterol (COL; 17.5 μM), and dipalmitoylphosphatidylcholine (DPPC; 25 μM) in chloroform. To prepare radiolabeled liposomes and actinomycin D-containing liposomes, cholesteryl[1-^{14}C]oleate and actinomycin D were added to the lipid mixture, respectively. After adding phosphate-buffered saline (PBS), the lipid film was vortexed and then sonicated. Subunits of monoclonal IgM immunoglobulin were coupled with the liposomes, and excess maleimide groups on the liposomes were blocked by adding cysteine.

the antibody is selectively used for the coupling, leading to inactivation in its binding with Fc receptor-bearing host cells.

Preparation and Purification of Monoclonal IgM Antibody

Antibodies can be obtained either from supernatants of hybridoma cultures or from ascites and sera of mice inoculated with hybridoma cells. The IgM fraction is easily separated from other components by gel filtration, but α_2-macroglobulin possessing a similar molecular weight (about 720,000) as IgM contaminates the fraction. The α_2-macroglobulin can be removed from IgM by preparative gel electrophoresis, affinity chromatography, or gel filtration using elution buffers of a specified ionic strength.

In general, we used hybridomas obtained by fusion between mouse myeloma and immune spleen cells: 2-11-G is a hybridoma clone prepared by fusion between NS-1 myeloma cells and spleen cells of a mouse immunized with MM46 C3H/He mouse mammary tumor cells and it secretes IgM antibody specific for a mammary tumor antigen of the mouse[13]; 3C6[14]

[13] M. Seto, T. Takahashi, M. Tanimoto, and Y. Nishizuka, *J. Immunol.* **128,** 201 (1982).
[14] K. Kikuchi, et al., unpublished data.

and HBA4[15] hybridoma clones were prepared by fusion between P3x63Ag8.653 mouse myeloma cells and spleen cells of mice immunized with B16 mouse melanoma cells and KU-1 human bladder cancer cells, respectively. They secrete IgM antibodies selective for immunizing tumor cells. Usually hybridoma cells (2×10^5/ml) were cultured for 5–7 days in RPMI 1640 medium supplemented with 10% heat-inactivated fetal calf serum (FCS). After collecting the supernatants, the remaining hybridoma cells (without washing) were further cultured in serum-free RPMI 1640 medium for 3 days and the supernatants collected. The supernatants of the FCS-added and FCS-free cultures were separately pooled and stored in a freezer at $-20°$ or $-80°$. Ascites fluids containing monoclonal antibody were obtained by injecting hybridoma cells (1×10^7/mouse) into the peritoneal cavity of syngeneic mice which had been treated with pristane (0.5 ml/mouse) 7 days before. The ascites fluids collected 8–10 days after inoculation with hybridoma cells were stored in a freezer at $-20°$ or $-80°$. The antibody concentration in the culture supernatants or ascites was determined by complement-dependent cytotoxicity or by enzyme-linked immunosorbent assay (ELISA).

Step 1. Ammonium Sulfate Precipitation. To culture supernatants is added $(NH_4)_2SO_4$ at 50% saturation. Ascites fluids are mixed with an equal volume of saturated $(NH_4)_2SO_4$ solution. The mixture is stirred for 4 hr at $4°$ and then centrifuged at 10,000 g for 10 min. The resultant precipitated material is dissolved in Tris–HCl buffer (50 mM Tris–HCl containing 1.7 M NaCl, pH 8.0) and dialyzed against the same buffer to obtain 30–50 times and 2–3 times concentrated crude IgM antibody from the culture supernatants and the ascites, respectively.

Step 2. Gel Filtration. Elution patterns can differ depending on the properties of each monoclonal IgM antibody. Therefore, individualized fractionation conditions must be selected.

For 3C6 IgM, the method described by Bouvet *et al.*[16] is adopted with a modification. An aliquot (100–150 mg protein in 10 ml Tris–HCl containing 1.7 M NaCl, pH 8.0) of the material obtained by step 1 is applied to a Sephacryl S-300 Superfine column (90×4.4 cm) equilibrated with 5 mM Tris–HCl (pH 8.0), and eluted by monitoring with a UV detector (280 nm) with the Tris–HCl buffer containing NaCl at a flow rate of 60 ml/hr. IgM antibody is eluted in the third peak and is separated from albumin, α-macroglobulin, and other protein components (Fig. 2). The IgM antibody can be recovered quantitatively.

[15] T. Masuko, H. Yagita, and Y. Hashimoto, *J. Natl. Cancer Inst.* **72**, 523 (1984).
[16] J-P. Bouvet, R. Pires, and J. Pillot, *J. Immunol. Methods* **66**, 299 (1984).

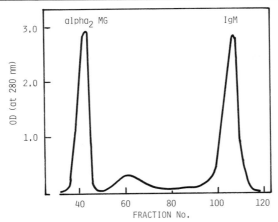

Fig. 2. Elution profile of $(NH_4)_2SO_4$-precipitated IgM on a Sephacryl S-300 column (90 × 4.4 cm) equilibrated with 5 mM Tris–HCl (pH 8.0), and eluted with the Tris–HCl buffer containing 1.7 M NaCl.

In the case of 2-11-G and HBA4 IgM antibodies, these monoclonal antibodies cannot be separated from α_2-macroglobulin by the method described above. The material obtained by $(NH_4)_2SO_4$ is dissolved in PBS and then dialyzed against 2 mM KH$_2$PO$_4$. Precipitated protein, collected by centrifugation, consists mainly of IgM antibody and is free of α_2-macroglobulin. This IgM fraction is purified by Sephacryl S-300 Superfine column chromatography using 0.2 M Tris–HCl (pH 8.6) for elution.

Preparation of Subunits of Monoclonal IgM Antibody

The method of Miller and Metzger[17] was adopted with a modification.[18] To 5 ml of 0.2% IgM solution in 0.2 M Tris–HCl buffer (pH 8.6) (peak fraction of IgM from gel fractionation) is added 0.05 M cysteine and the mixture is incubated with stirring at 27° for 10 min, cooled in an ice bath, and immediately applied to a Sephacryl S-300 column (75 × 2.4 cm) which has been equilibrated with pH 6.8 phosphate-buffered saline (PBS) containing 2 mM EDTA. Proteins are eluted with PBS containing 2 mM EDTA, and fractions containing the subunit of IgM (IgMs, MW 180,000) collected (Fig. 3). Since the SH groups in IgMs are very sensitive to oxidation, the IgM fractions are immediately used for coupling to liposomes. The yield of IgMs from IgM (2-11-G) is about 50%.

[17] F. Miller and H. Metzger, *J. Biol. Chem.* **240**, 3325 (1965).
[18] Y. Hashimoto, M. Sugawara, and H. Endoh, *J. Immunol. Methods* **62**, 155 (1983).

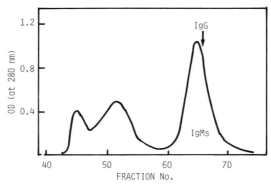

FIG. 3. Elution profile of cysteine-treated IgM immunoglobulin on a Sephacryl S-300 column (75 × 2.4 cm) equilibrated and eluted with PBS (pH 6.8) containing 2 mM EDTA.

Sodium dodecyl sulfate–polyacrylamide gel electrophoresis (SDS–PAGE) of cysteine-treated IgM reveals that IgM molecules are reduced to half-fragments (MW 90,000) of IgMs, but we confirmed that they associate to form IgMs with free SH groups after gel fractionation.

Although the method described above is useful for reduction of 2-11-G IgM antibody, the yield of IgMs from other monoclonal IgM antibodies (HBA4 against human bladder cancer and 3C6 against mouse melanoma-associated antigen) is lower. It is necessary to modify the concentration of IgM or cysteine in order to achieve a good yield of IgMs. For example, the optimum cysteine concentration for antibody 3C6 is 0.03 M and optimal IgM concentrations of 3C6 and HBA4 are 0.5 and 0.4%, respectively.

Preparation of Liposomes

m-Maleimidobenzoyl-N-hydroxysuccinimide ester (MBS) is used as the coupling reagent. In order to introduce the SH-reacting maleimide group into liposomes, the maleimide-bearing phospholipid is prepared based on the method of Martin and Papahadjopoulos[12] with a minor modification. MBS (25 μM) and dipalmitoylphosphatidylethanolamine (DPPE) (20 μM) are dissolved in 5 ml of chloroform–methanol (9 : 1). After addition of triethylamine (30 μM), the solution is kept at 25° with stirring under nitrogen. The yield of coupled product is checked by thin-layer chromatography (silica gel 60 F_{254}, Merck). A maximum yield of m-maleimidobenzoyl(dipalmitoylphosphatidyl)ethanolamine (MBPE) (R_f 0.62 in chloroform–methanol–water, 65 : 24 : 4) is obtained after 2 hr. To the reaction mixture is added 3.5 ml of methanol and then 2 ml of water. After shaking and standing, the chloroform layer is evaporated to dryness with the addition of a few drops of benzene. The resultant residue is dissolved in 2 ml of chloroform and purified by Unisil column chromatography. MBPE is identified as a ninhydrin-reaction-negative and phosphate-positive component.

To prepare liposomes, a lipid mixture containing dipalmitoylphosphatidylcholine (DPPC) (25 μmol), cholesterol (17.5 μmol), and MBPE (2.5 μmol) in chloroform is dried in a round-bottomed flask to form a thin lipid layer.[18] Radiolabeled liposomes and drug-containing liposomes are prepared by adding cholesteryl[1-^{14}C]oleate (3 μCi in our experiments) and a lipid-soluble drug (actinomycin D in our experiments[19]) to the lipid mixture, respectively. The lipid film is vortexed for 10 min with addition of 5 ml PBS (pH 6.8) and then sonicated in the cup horn of a Branson Model W-185 sonifier at power setting 7 for 1 hr. During sonication, a nitrogen gas atmosphere is maintained over the liposome suspension, which is kept on crushed ice to keep the suspension temperature under 25°. Aggregated and large size liposomes are removed by centrifugation at 10,000 g in a swinging bucket rotor for 30 min, and the upper 4 ml of the total 5 ml of liposome suspension is collected. The recovery of liposomes is 65–70% in terms of lipid.

The presence of maleimide residues on the liposomal surface can be determined by adding an SH-bearing compound (cysteine) to the liposome suspension, incubating, and analyzing the consumption of the added cysteine. It was confirmed that about 50% of liposome-integrated maleimide groups is present on the liposomal surface and the remaining present inside the vesicles.

Preparation and Purification of Antibody-Coated
Liposomes (Immunoliposomes)

The liposome suspension (4 ml) is mixed with IgMs solution (2 ml). The mixture is incubated for 1 hr at 37° and then treated with cysteine (0.83 mg/ml) for 30 min in order to block excess maleimide groups on the liposome surfaces. The purification of the immunoliposomes can be achieved by the following methods.

1. Density Gradient Centrifugation. A linear density gradient solution is made from the immunoliposome suspension (6 ml) and an equal volume of 20% dextran (Pharmacia Dextran 70) in PBS (pH 6.8). After centrifugation at 150,000 g for 16–20 hr, the gradient solution is divided into 10 fractions (each 1.2 ml) and the second fraction from the top collected.[18] More than 90% of the added liposomes can be recovered in this fraction.

[19] Y. Hashimoto, M. Sugawara, T. Masuko, and H. Hojo, *Cancer Res.* **43**, 5328 (1983).

2. Floating Method. The immunoliposome suspension (6 ml) is mixed with 6 ml of 20% dextran in PBS and then layered onto 4 ml of 8% dextran in PBS followed by 1 ml of PBS. The discontinuous dextran density-gradient solution is centrifuged with a swinging bucket rotor at 2000 g for 1 hr. Liposomes floating on the 8% dextran layer are collected. Recovery of liposomes is about 60%.

3. Gel Filtration. The immunoliposome suspension (2 ml) is applied to a Sepharose CL 4B column (4.7 × 1.5 cm) and eluted with 2.5% mannitol in PBS (pH 7.2) at a flow rate of 10 ml/hr. The immunoliposomes are obtained in the void volume fractions.

Size of Liposomes. The size of the liposomes can be measured by either freeze-fraction or freeze-substitution electron microscopy[20] or by analysis with a submicron particle size analyzer. The size distribution of the liposomal preparations prepared as above was analyzed with a Coulter N4 Submicron Particle Analyzer. The liposomes in the supernatant fraction of the sonicated liposomes showed a relatively homogeneous size distribution (58.5 ± 28.8 nm in diameter), whereas liposomes in the sedimented fraction were larger and more heterogeneous in size (176 ± 148 nm). Immunoliposomes purified by linear density gradient centrifugation contained liposomes 78.1 ± 38.7 nm in diameter.

Targeting of Immunoliposomes

[14]C-labeled immunoliposomes are examined for their binding capacity to target cells using ^{14}C-labeled unmodified liposomes, unrelated IgMs-coated liposomes, or bovine serum albumin (BSA)-coated liposomes as the controls.[18,19] Usually varying amounts (100 μl at maximum) of liposome suspension are added in triplicate to the target cell suspension containing 5 × 10⁴ cells in 1 ml of 10% FCS medium. After incubation for 1 hr at 37°, the cells are sedimented by centrifugation at 300 g for 10 min and then washed three times with PBS by centrifugation to remove unbound liposomes. The cell pellet is solubilized with Soluene (Packard), and radioactivity is measured by a standard scintillation technique using a toluene scintillation cocktail. An example of the results of the binding assay is shown in Fig. 4.

When glass (plastic) adherent target cells are used, they are treated with trypsin to obtain a single-cell suspension. In such cases, it is necessary to determine whether the antigen recognized by the monoclonal antibody is stable to the trypsin treatment. If it is unstable, the trypsinized

---

[20] G. Gregoriadis, ed., "Liposome Technology," Vol. I. CRC Press, Boca Raton, Florida, 1984.

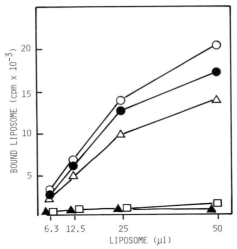

FIG. 4. Binding of 2-11-G IgMs-coated liposomes (immunoliposomes) to MM46 (antigen positive to 2-11-G) and MM48 (antigen negative mouse mammary tumor cells *in vitro*. Aliquots of radiolabeled liposomes were added to a tumor cell suspension (5×10^4 cells in 1 ml) and incubated for 60 min at 37°. Unbound liposomes were removed by centrifugation and washed with PBS, and the liposomes bound to tumor cells were counted based on radioactivity. (○) MM46 with immunoliposomes; (●) MM46 with chemoimmunoliposomes containing 0.3 μg of actinomycin D per 50 μl; (△) MM46 with chemoimmunoliposomes containing 1 μg of actinomycin D per 50 μl; (▲) MM46 with bovine serum albumin-coated liposomes; (□) MM 48 with immunoliposomes. (Reproduced from Hashimoto *et al.*[19])

cells are incubated with frequent agitation in culture medium for a few hours to allow reexpression of the antigen.

In order to determine whether liposomes are bound to the target cells via the antibody on the liposomes, the target cells are preincubated with the original IgM antibody, washed with PBS, and then incubated with the immunoliposomes. Reduction of liposome binding will indicate their antibody-specific binding to the target cells (table).

In Vitro Cytotoxicity of Drug-Containing Immunoliposomes (Chemoimmunoliposomes)

Common cytotoxicity assays such as visual cell counting by means of a dye exclusion method or isotope assays can be adopted. The following describes an example of the assay with [³H]thymidine.[19] Aliquots of a chemoimmunoliposome (containing actinomycin D in our experiments) suspension are added to a target cell suspension containing 5×10^4 cells in 1 ml of medium. After incubation for 60 min at 37°, the target cells are washed and then resuspended in 1 ml of culture medium. Aliquots (0.2 ml)

TARGETING OF 2-11-G IGMS-COATED ^{14}C-LABELED LIPOSOMES[a,b]

Target cells	MM antigen	Cell-bound liposomes (% of added), after preincubation with		
		PBS	BSA	2-11-G IgM
C57BL/6 mouse spleen	−	0.8	0.5	0.5
C3H/He mouse spleen	−	0.7	0.5	0.4
Meth A sarcoma	−	0.9	0.3	0.5
MM48	−	0.8	0.3	0.5
MM48-1B culture line	−	0.8	0.3	0.4
MM46	+	38.6	35.0	5.2
MM46-9E culture line	+	16.4	14.4	2.6

[a] Reproduced from Hashimoto et al.[18]

[b] Cells (50 × 10[3]) were pretreated with PBS or protein solution containing 75 μg of BSA or 2-11-G IgM. Aliquots of ^{14}C-labeled 2-11-G IgMs-coated liposomes (25 μl containing 0.28 μl phospholipid and 16.9 μg protein) were added to the cell suspensions and incubated for 60 min. The percentage of cell-bound liposomes was calculated as a ratio of radioactivity in target cells against radioactivity of added liposomes (22,990 cpm).

of the cell suspension are added in triplicate to wells of a Falcon No. 3034 microtest plate. After incubation for 12–24 hr at 37°, the target cells are pulsed with [³H]thymidine (0.5 μCi/well) for an additional 6 hr and harvested on a glass-fiber filter with a multiple cell harvester (Skatron, Norway). The radioactivity in the collected cells is measured. An example of the assay in a mouse mammary tumor system is illustrated in Fig. 5.

Integration of Cell-Bound Immunoliposomes into
    Target Cells (Endocytosis)

Encapsulated antimetabolites or drugs in liposomes must be internalized by the target cells for expression of drug activity. The integration of liposomes into target cells can be assayed by means of electron microscopy or by using liposomes containing a fluorescent label. Endocytosis of liposomes is also determined with radiolabeled liposomes by microautoradiography or protease treatment of the target cell-bound liposomes.

For microautoradiographic determination, target cells, treated with ^{14}C-labeled immuno- or chemoimmunoliposomes as described for the binding assay, are smeared on a slide glass and coated with an emulsion for microautography. After drying and being kept in the dark for 7–10 days at 4°, the cells on the slide are stained with Tetrachrome or Giemsa stain. Localization of liposomes is seen as clusters of silver grains.

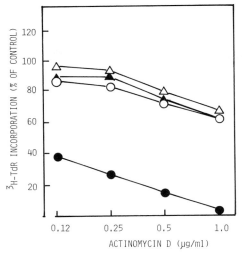

FIG. 5. *In vitro* cytotoxicity of chemoimmunoliposomes. MM46 or MM48 tumor cells were incubated with liposomes or free actinomycin D for 60 min. After washing, the tumor cells were further incubated for 12 hr and then pulsed with [³H]thymidine ([³H]TdR). (○) MM46 tumor cells with free actinomycin D; (●) MM46 tumor cells with chemoimmunolipo-somes containing 1 μg of actinomycin D per 50 μl; (△) MM48 tumor cells with free actino-mycin D; (▲) MM48 tumor cells with chemoimmunoliposomes containing 1 μg of actinomy-cin D per 50 μl. (Modified from Hashimoto *et al.*[19])

For protease treatment, target cells bound with immuno- or chemoim-munoliposomes are incubated in culture medium for several hours at 4° or 37° and then treated with either trypsin (0.5%) or pronase in Ca^{2+}- and Mg^{2+}-free PBS for 10 min at 37°. The cells are washed three times and the radioactivity retained on the cells is determined. The radioactivity lost or retained after protease treatment indicates the amount of liposomes re-maining on the cell surface and that of liposomes integrated into cells, respectively.

In Vivo Experiments

As an example of *in vivo* application of chemoimmunoliposomes, we describe a tumor therapy model with 2-11-G IgMs-coated liposomes con-taining actinomycin D in the membrane.[19]

Local Effect. MM46 mammary tumor cells (5×10^4 to 5×10^6/mouse) are injected ip into syngeneic C3H/He mice. After 1 day the mice are treated with a single ip injection of the chemoimmunoliposomes contain-ing 1 μg of actinomycin D (50 μl of the dextran density gradient-purified liposome suspension in 0.2 ml of PBS, pH 7.2). Smears of the ascites are made periodically and stained with Giemsa stain. Tumors in control mice or mice treated with 5 μg of free actinomycin D grow normally when observed 7 days after treatment. In contrast, several mice treated with the chemoimmunoliposomes were free of tumor and survived.

Systemic Effect. We further examined the systemic antitumor effect of the chemoimmunoliposomes. MM46 tumor cells (1×10^6) were injected sc into C3H/He mice. After 4 days, when the tumor grew to a palpable size (about 5 mm in diameter), the mice were treated with an iv injection of the chemoimmunoliposomes containing 1 μg of actinomycin D, BSA-coated liposomes containing 1 μg of actinomycin D, 3 μg of free actinomycin D, 100 μg (protein) of 2-11-G IgM, or PBS. To block phagocytosis of the injected liposomes, several groups of mice had been pretreated 1 hr before therapy with an iv injection of a suspension (6.7 μmol phospholipid in 0.2 ml of PBS) of unmodified multilamella liposomes prepared from dipalmitoylphosphatidylcholine (35 μmol), cholesterol (10 μmol), and dicetyl phosphate (5 μmol). Tumor sizes were periodically measured, and the mice were sacrificed 12 days after drug treatment. Tumor nodules were isolated from the mice and weighed.

A single iv injection of the chemoimmunoliposomes led to a slight inhibition of tumor growth as compared to that in PBS controls, but the difference was statistically insignificant. When pretreated with the multilamella liposomes, however, the tumor size in mice treated with the chemoimmunoliposomes tended to decrease for 4 days after the treatment and then began to increase. Tumor weights in these mice were significantly lower than those in either the PBS control mice (52 and 38% of controls in two experiments) or mice treated with multilamella liposomes plus BSA–liposomes containing actinomycin D. In contrast, the BSA–liposomes containing actinomycin D were not effective, but in the absence of multilamella liposome pretreatment, they enhanced the growth of tumor as compared to PBS controls. Free actinomycin D and 2-11-G IgM were also ineffective.

[78] Immunohistological Studies with Monoclonal Antibodies

By WAYNE W. HANCOCK and ROBERT C. ATKINS

The somatic cell hybridization technique,[1] resulting in stable hybridomas each secreting pure antibody of a single specificity and affinity, has produced a veritable flood of monoclonal antibodies directed against a

---

[1] G. Köhler and C. Milstein, *Nature (London)* **256**, 495 (1975).

large range of antigens. These antibodies have enormous potential for research, diagnostic, and therapeutic applications. However, particularly in the context of immunohistological labeling, monoclonal antibodies may also require certain special considerations due to their ultraspecificity. This chapter describes practical strategies and technical details for successful preparation and immunoperoxidase staining of cell smears and tissue sections with monoclonal antibodies, at the light microscope level. While the examples chosen include monoclonal antibodies to various human antigens, the methods described can, with minor alterations, be readily used for other species and tissue combinations.

Initial Considerations

Optimal and successful immunohistochemistry requires assessment of several factors so as to produce a standardized method for localization of a given antigen, or set of antigens, with reproducible and accurate results. Relevant technical aspects are considered in later sections. However, essentially every localization, whether for diagnostic or research purposes, involves a compromise between maintaining cell antigenicity and preserving morphological detail. The results of a particular combination of fixation, tissue processing, and immunohistological technique are still largely empirical. Although some broadly applicable combinations can be suggested, resolution can often be further improved by careful tinkering. However, poor technique and sloppiness are usually disastrous.

In theory, immunohistological labeling with polyclonal antibodies does present certain advantages over monoclonal antibodies. The multiple antibodies within an antiserum are usually directed against several determinants of a given antigen. Thus, when a tissue is fixed, embedded, sectioned, and stained, even if several determinants are totally destroyed, other determinants frequently remain at least partially intact and available for antibody binding. By contrast, since each monoclonal antibody is directed against a single determinant, if that determinant is at all significantly altered, often no antibody binding will occur. This all-or-none phenomenon in antigen preservation is a critical factor in the use of monoclonal antibodies, and frequently necessitates using cryostat sections with a resultant suboptimal preservation of morphology. Moreover, more sensitive techniques may be required to detect a given antigen using a monoclonal as compared to a similar polyclonal antibody, due to a need for greater amplification for adequate visualization of binding, especially if the determinant of interest is sparsely distributed.

Nevertheless, the advantages of using monoclonal antibodies, namely crisp, clean labeling of often previously unrecognized, biologically impor-

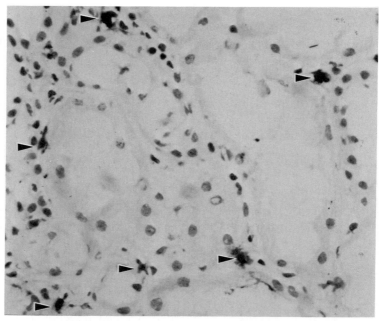

FIG. 1. Hybridoma technology has provided new tools for the definition and study of a variety of previously ill-defined cell types. Photomicrograph shows immunoperoxidase labeling of a PLP-fixed renal biopsy taken 3 days after the clinical onset of renal allograft rejection, using Leu-7, a monoclonal antibody to NK and K cells. Arrowheads indicate the Leu-7+ cells which are found in close proximity to intertubular capillaries and adjacent tubules. Such studies have implicated NK cells in the pathogenesis of kidney rejection. Four-layer PAP; cryostat section; hematoxylin; ×400. (From Hancock.[1a])

tant cell molecules (Fig. 1),[1a] with reproducible results, and minimal or no background staining, usually far outweigh these disadvantages. The principles of tissue processing, fixation, and immunohistological labeling are discussed in detail in standard texts, notably Sternberger's classic "Immunocytochemistry",[2] and "Techniques in Immunocytochemistry",[3] plus several recent review articles,[4–7] to which the reader is referred for

[1a] W. W. Hancock, *Immunol. Rev.* **77,** 61 (1984).

[2] L. A. Sternberger, "Immunocytochemistry." Wiley, New York, 1979.

[3] G. R. Bullock and P. Petrusz, eds., "Techniques in Immunocytochemistry," Vol. 1. Academic Press, New York, 1982.

[4] R. A. DeLellis, L. A. Sternberger, R. B. Mann, P. M. Banks, and P. K. Nakane, *Am. J. Clin. Pathol.* **71,** 483 (1979).

[5] E. Heyderman, *J. Clin. Pathol.* **32,** 971 (1979).

[6] A. G. Farr and P. K. Nakane, *J. Immunol. Methods* **47,** 129 (1981).

[7] B. Falini and C. R. Taylor, *Arch. Pathol. Lab. Med.* **107,** 105 (1983).

detailed discussion and references. The following sections deal only with those aspects which are directly relevant to the labeling of sections and cell smears with monoclonal antibodies using immunoperoxidase techniques. Alkaline phosphatase-based methods, which are of particular value for double-immunoenzymatic labeling, are outside the scope of this chapter and are fully discussed elsewhere.[8]

Tissue Handling

Tissues are best obtained as fresh as possible. Postmortem specimens may work, depending the time since death, the nature of the antigen in question, the site from which it is obtained, and the nature of any associated disease, with resultant potential for antigen breakdown or diffusion. Staining of postmortem tissues is often marred by significant background connective tissue staining. If storage is necessary, good results can still be obtained after storage at 4° for up to 24 hr in phosphate-buffered saline (PBS), pH 7.4, or in one of several commercially available transport media, particularly if specimens are sliced into small cubes (5 mm/side) beforehand.

Ideally in setting up a study of a particular antigen, some blocks are immediately "snap" frozen, and others are immersed in one of several fixatives of choice, such as neutral-buffered formalin, PLP[9] (see appendix for preparation), $HgCl_2$–formalin, and Bouin's solution. Fixed tissues are embedded by standard methods in polyester or paraffin waxes plus, if available, in methacrylate, Spurr's, and Lowacryl resins. Such an evaluation of multiple fixatives and embedding matrices is important if optimal morphological preservation is paramount (Fig. 2, a–c)[9a] and access to routinely prepared paraffin or resin material for retrospective studies is of interest (Fig. 2d).[9b] However, it should be recognized in advance that relatively few monoclonal antibodies are available which will work on routinely prepared paraffin sections, and that probably less than a dozen different antigens recognized by monoclonal antibodies have intact immunoreactivity in resin sections. In practice, unless previous information would suggest the likelihood of preservation of antigenicity in embedded tissues, the simplest approach would be to "snap" freeze some cubes, fix others with PLP (also to be eventually "snap" frozen), and formalin fix the rest.

[8] D. Y. Mason and R. E. Woolston, *in* "Techniques in Immunocytochemistry" (G. R. Bullock and P. Petrusz, eds.), Vol. 1, p. 135. Academic Press, New York, 1982.

[9] I. W. McLean and P. K. Nakane, *J. Histochem. Cytochem.* **22**, 1077 (1974).

[9a] W. W. Hancock and R. C. Atkins, *Nephron* **33**, 83 (1983).

[9b] W. W. Hancock and R. C. Atkins, *Am. J. Nephrol.* **4**, 177 (1984).

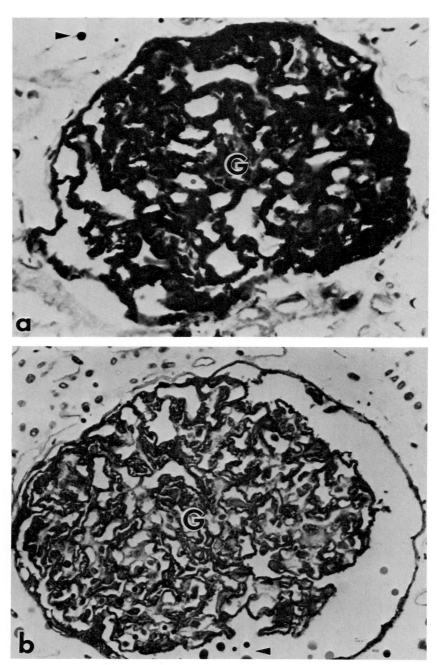

FIG. 2. Immunoperoxidase labeling of sections of human kidney using as monoclonal antibody (PHM5) to human glomerular epithelial cells (G).[9a] These sections illustrate the increased resolution achieved using fixed and embedded sections. (a) PHM5 appears to densely stain essentially all glomerular components in this 6-μm cryostat section. (b)

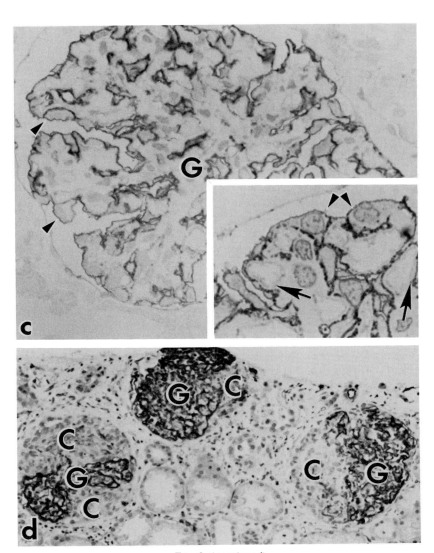

FIG. 2. (*continued*)

Greater discrimination of cell labeling is seen in this 3-μm paraffin section; PHM5 labeling is present on the outer part of the glomerulus and cells of Bowman's capsule. Arrowheads in (a) and (b) indicate residual endogenous peroxidase activity of red blood cells; other endogenous peroxidase activity was blocked using sodium azide. (c) Labeling of 1-μm Spurr's epoxy resin provides maximal resolution of PHM5 staining, which is essentially restricted to podocytes (arrowheads) and Bowman's capsule. Inset shows discrimination between labeled podocytes (arrowheads) and closely associated but unstained glomerular capillaries (arrows). (d) PHM5 staining of residual glomerular tuft cells but not crescent cells, C, in this 10-year-old routine biopsy from a patient with crescentic glomerulonephritis,[9b] illustrating the application of monoclonal cell markers for retrospective studies of routine pathology specimens. Four-layer PAP; PLP fixation except (d), which was formalin fixed; hematoxylin. (a, b, c) ×400; Inset, ×1000; (d) ×160.

Fixation

Based on the above comments, this section deals first with the question of fixation during the preparation and staining of cryostat sections, followed by a brief discussion of fixation in the preparation of embedded tissues.

Fixation before Freezing. This is done if optimally preserved cryostat sections are required, and especially if immunoelectron microscopy may also be performed on the same tissue specimen. The main disadvantage of fixation at this stage is the extra time involved, and the theoretical possibility that the particular fixative chosen (e.g., PLP) may alter certain antigens within the block, rendering it of no further use, though this has not been our experience at least with PLP.

Tissue cubes are fixed in fresh PLP (pH 7.2) for 2–4 hr at 4°, preferably on a rotating or shaking apparatus to provide more rapid penetration and fixation. Cubes are then washed for 24–48 hr in several changes of PBS containing 7% sucrose. The addition of sucrose has several purposes: sucrose is a hydrophilic molecule which, by binding molecules of water in the tissue, minimizes ice crystal formation during the rapid freezing process (cryoprotectant effect); it also improves membrane and cellular details (Fig. 1), makes it easier to cut fixed sections, and may also partially reverse the cross-linking effects of formaldehyde fixation, thereby maintaining antigenicity. Cubes are then oriented on pieces of cork, covered with OCT, and quick frozen in either isopentane chilled over dry ice or directly in liquid nitrogen, and stored at −80°. Sectioning is performed by covering a cryostat chuck with further OCT, placing the tissue block (with underlying cork) on the chuck, and freezing the specimen as before. The use of cork allows the correctly positioned specimen to be removed from the chuck after sectioning, stored, and recut in the same orientation at a later date. Cubes should be allowed to equilibrate in the cryostat to optimal cutting temperature (−10 to −20°), and sections are picked up onto gelatinized slides.

Fixation after Freezing and Sectioning. Sections may alternatively be fixed after cutting. This step is recommended to maintain morphology, stabilize tissue antigenicity, and aid in adhesion of the section to the glass slide during the labeling procedure. Acetone is the most simple and commonly used fixative. Since the benefit of PLP and similar paraformaldehyde-based fixatives is to maintain morphology during freezing and sectioning, postsectioning fixation with PLP usually offers little advantage when compared to the convenience of acetone. Nevertheless, if unsatisfactory results are obtained with acetone (especially inadequate staining intensity), PLP remains a useful alternative. Formol–acetone is the fixative of choice for cell smears (see section on "Cell Smears and Cultured Cells").

Acetone fixation: Air-dried sections are fixed for 10 min at room temperature, allowed to air-dry, and stained directly with monoclonal antibody.

PLP or 2% paraformaldehyde fixation: Air-dried sections are fixed for 10 min at 4°, washed for 5 min, and immunostained without further drying.

Fixation Prior to Embedding. A large range of fixatives have been successfully used in immunohistological studies; these are discussed in detail in Sternberger's "Immunocytochemistry"[2] and by Brandtzaeg.[10] Formaldehyde-based fixatives are the most commonly used fixatives for light microscopy. These include neutral-buffered formalin, formol–saline, various mercuric chloride-containing formaldehyde solutions (particularly good for preserving intracellular immunoglobulins), PLP, and formaldehyde-based combination fixatives such as Bouin's solution)formaldehyde/picric acid/ethanol/acetic acid). Less commonly used fixatives include methacarn (60% methanol/30% inhibisol/10% acetic acid), and 96% ethanol.[10] Glutaraldehyde-based fixatives are generally avoided; evidently the extensive cross-linking caused by this fixative, while resulting in excellent ultrastructural preservation, denatures most antigens, even when very low concentrations are used (<0.1%).

Immunohistological Staining

METHOD SELECTION AND SENSITIVITY. Which method to choose depends on several factors: a method should ideally provide sufficient sensitivity to detect the antigen(s) in question, in addition to high specificity, rapid operation, and low cost. In practice, sensitivity and specificity have become the main considerations. The sensitivity of various techniques may be evaluated by determining how far a particular antibody may be diluted before immunohistological staining is abolished, or by comparing the staining intensity at a given antibody dilution, or by testing the ability of different methods to detect a known antigen concentration when the antigen has been incorporated into an inert matrix.[10] However, although much is often written about the supposed superb sensitivity of a particular new immunohistological technique, surprisingly few studies have included direct comparisons. In this respect, indirect immunoperoxidase and indirect immunofluorescence techniques, while of comparable sensi-

---

[10] P. Brandtzaeg and T. O. Rognum, *Histochemistry* **81,** 213 (1984).

tivity to each other, are considered less sensitive than multilayer procedures.[2] Such differences have been minimized over recent years with the development and use of improved techniques for the production, affinity purification, and conjugation of polyclonal antibodies, partly in response to the challenge and demands of workers using monoclonal antibodies. Excellent peroxidase or fluorescently labeled, affinity-purified antimouse, antibodies are now available from several commercial sources, and produce good results with many monoclonal antibodies.

Nevertheless, the suggestion that triple- or more layer techniques provide greater sensitivity has been supported by some studies. Such studies[11-14] have compared the staining intensities or optimal working dilutions of primary monoclonal antibodies using the standard three-layer peroxidase–antiperoxidase (PAP) technique (using murine monoclonal or polyclonal PAP complexes), a four-layer modification of the PAP technique (using rabbit PAP), and various recently developed avidin–biotin methods, of which the avidin–biotin complex (or ABC) technique appears to be the more sensitive.[14] Indeed, the latter ABC technique was originally reported to be 40 times more sensitive than a three-layer PAP method, based on a comparison of the optimal primary antibody dilution. This result perhaps reflects the smaller size of the PAP complex formed using monoclonal antibodies to peroxidase. By contrast, the four-layer PAP method was shown to be more sensitive than either the three-layer PAP[11] or ABC techniques.[12] However, with the development of methods based on repetitive incubations[15-17] (see "Enhancing Sensitivity") allowing almost unlimited degrees of amplification, the question of relative method specificity has become essentially obsolete.

Since both the three-layer and indirect (two-layer) methods offer sufficient sensitivity for most applications, particularly with the use of affinity-purified conjugates, additional selection criteria such as time and cost have become increasingly important considerations. Indirect methods take about an hour to perform, which is at least 20 min less than three-layer PAP or ABC techniques, and 40 min less than four-layer PAP. The

[11] W. W. Hancock, G. J. Becker, and R. C. Atkins, *Am. J. Clin. Pathol.* **78**, 825 (1982).

[12] W. Y. Naritoku and C. R. Taylor, *J. Histochem. Cytochem.* **30**, 253 1982

[13] R. B. Nagle, V. A. Clark, K. M. McDaniel, and J. R. Davis, *J. Histochem. Cytochem.* **31**, 1010 (1983).

[14] S. M. Hsu, L. Raine, and H. Fanger, *J. Histochem. Cytochem.* **29**, 577 (1981).

[15] L. L. Vacca, *in* "Techniques in Immunocytochemistry" (G. R. Bullock and P. Petrusz, eds.), Vol. 1, p. 155. Academic Press, New York, 1982.

[16] P. Petrusz, P. Ordronneau, and J. C. W. Finley, *Histochem. J.* **12**, 333 (1980).

[17] P. M. Lansdorp, T. H. van de Kwast, M. de Boer, and W. P. Zeijlemaker, *J. Histochem. Cytochem.* **32**, 172 (1984).

current high cost of mouse PAP makes the three-layer PAP the most expensive method, followed by four-layer PAP, then ABC, with indirect methods being the least expensive.

GENERAL COMMENTS ON TECHNIQUE. Adding multiple sections to the same slide maximizes handling efficiency; handling six to eight sections per slide is very easy. The mixing of various primary antibodies is prevented by adding petroleum jelly or a similar nonwetable substance between the sections, just prior to staining, using an applicator stick. The jelly dissolves in xylene during mounting, though if solvent-soluble substrates (e.g., aminoethylcarbazole) are used, it has to be manually removed.

Monoclonal antibodies are applied at optimal dilutions, as determined by serial dilutions in preliminary experiments. Using monoclonal antibody-containing supernatants without further dilution is not a problem (albeit expensive), since the concentration of murine antibody is very low (typically 20–60 μg/ml) and this is immersed in a bath of 10% fetal calf serum (FCS) used in the culture of hybridoma cells. However, ascitic fluid or antibody purified from ascites typically contains 100–1000 times as much mouse immunoglobulin, of which only some 10% may be the specific monoclonal antibody of interest, with the rest consisting of extraneous immunoglobulins. Such ascitic fluid, unless appropriately diluted, may cause tremendous nonspecific binding because of the high immunoglobulin concentration, or even because of the presence of low-titer heterophile antibodies. Dilutions of monoclonal antibody are made in a carrier protein such as FCS or albumin, unless the antibody reacts with bovine serum components, when gelatin is a convenient alterative protein. Reagents are applied economically using a micropipet, with 25-μl aliquots for small sections and 50 μl for larger sections or cytospin smears. Incubations are performed for 15 min in a humidified environment, such as a covered box containing water below the level of the slides. Slides are vigorously washed for 5 min in slide racks atop a magnetic stirrer, using 300–400 ml of washing fluid (see appendix). At no stage once staining has begun are slides allowed to dry out.

CHROMAGEN SELECTION. In practice, there are three useful alternative chromagens for immunochemical labeling: diaminobenzidine (DAB), which produces an insoluble brown reaction product; aminoethylcarbazole (AEC), which produces a red product which is soluble in solvents; and 4-chloronaphthol (4CN), which results in a blue or slate-gray product also soluble in solvents (see appendix). DAB remains the standard and best chromagen due to its crisp, dense reaction product which is stable during standard dehydration, clearing, and mounting. DAB at one time was believed to be carcinogenic, leading many workers to switch to the alternative but inferior AEC chromagen. Although DAB is no longer thought to be carcinogenic, like all these chromagens it should be handled with care. AEC is of use mainly when DAB is contraindicated, such as when brown pigments are present. AEC-labeled sections are counterstained with Mayer's rather than Harris' hematoxylin, to avoid solubilization of AEC in the alcohol present within Harris' hematoxylin. The third chromagen, 4CN, generally produces only a disappointingly weak reaction product, even after prolonged incubations (>20 min). Thus, although the DAB/4CN combination is currently recommended for dual-color immunoperoxidase staining over DAB/AEC (red AEC contrasts only poorly with brown DAB deposits), this use of 4CN is likely to continue only until a suitable new chromagen is developed which produces an insoluble dense blue product. Comparison of other substrates producing similar colors (e.g., the dark brown Hanker–Yates reagent, or the blue substrate tetramethylbenzidine, TMB) have shown these to be less sensitive than DAB or AEC[18] for immunohistological purposes, though TMB is a valuable chromagen for studies of axonal transport. Once stained, slides are subject to gradual fading over many years, though is minimized by avoiding undue exposure to light.

INDIRECT IMMUNOPEROXIDASE. Sections or smears are incubated with monoclonal antibody, washed, and incubated with eproxidase-conjugated anti-mouse Ig, initially at a 1 : 40 dilution in PBS/1% FCS/1% serum of the species under investigation. Slides are then incubated with the substrate, washed, and mounted.

INDIRECT IMMUNOFLUORESCENCE. Slides are treated as for indirect immunoperoxidase, but a fluorescein- or rhodamine-conjugated anti-mouse antibody is used, again at 1 : 20–1 : 40 dilution in PBS/1% FCS/1% serum of the species under investigation. Following the second incubation and washing, slides are mounted (without counterstaining) in modified PVA (pH 8.2)[19] and stored in the dark at 4° until viewed under a fluorescent microscope. If PVA or a commercial substitute is unable, a mixture of PBS and glycerol (10% : 90%) when buffered to pH 8.2 is a suitable alternative mounting medium.

PAP TECHNIQUES. For three-layer PAP, slides are pretreated with 10% normal swine serum (NSS) for 5 min, followed by incubation with monoclonal antibody, a wash, anti-mouse Ig (1 : 40), a wash, and mouse PAP (1 : 50–1 : 100). Thereafter slides are treated with substrate and mounted. The four-layer PAP method is similarly performed except that

---

[18] J. Q. Trojanowski, M. A. Obrocka, and V. M. Y. Lee, *J. Histochem. Cytochem.* **31**, 1217 (1983).
[19] D. A. Lennette, *Am. J. Clin. Pathol.* **69**, 147 (1978).

the antibody incubation sequence is monoclonal antibody, rabbit anti-mouse Ig (1 : 400), swine anti-rabbit Ig (1 : 40), and rabbit PAP (1 : 50–1 : 100) (Fig. 1).

ABC TECHNIQUE. If initial experiments show the presence of significant amounts of endogenous biotin, this must be blocked before staining is begun by incubating with avidin and then excess biotin.[20] Thereafter slides are incubated with monoclonal antibody, anti-mouse Ig (1 : 200), and premixed avidin–biotinylated peroxidase complex, followed by substrate and mounting. To make the ABC complex, add 2 drops of avidin DH to 2 ml of Tris buffer, mix, add 2 drops of biotinylated peroxidase, mix again, and allow to stand for 15 min before use.

ENHANCING SENSITIVITY. While methods to boost sensitivity at the expense of specificity are of little value, certain technical modifications have been shown to improve sensitivity without compromising specificity. However, any anticipated benefits must usually be weighed against the extra processing time involved when using many of these modifications. A good way to improve staining intensity with minimal effort is to incubate the primary monoclonal antibody for an extended period, such as overnight in an appropriate humidified container placed at 4°. This may also prove more economical through greater dilution of often expensive or scarce antibodies. Other methods of proven value include multi-sandwich combinations, modifications of the DAB reaction, and post-DAB enhancement techniques.

Multiple sandwich methods, involving repetitions of various antibody incubations before the DAB reaction, have been developed particularly by Vacca,[15] Petrusz,[16] and others.[17] The optimal dilution of antibody layers is determined using the three-layer PAP method, and the same dilutions of link and PAP reagents are used in two or more applications, until the desired level of sensitivity is reached (Fig. 3). A further and special modification of this approach, the self-sandwich technique of Hsu and Ree,[21] requires the antigen under investigation to be characterized and available in a pure form. Layers of specific antibody, link anti-Ig, and specific antibody again, followed by purified antigen, are built up in sequential incubations, to achieve great sensitivity. Similar modifications of the ABC method can also be devised. In addition to the considerable increase in processing time using these methods, careful titration of all antisera must be performed. The use of antisera at high dilutions is required to avoid building up many layers of nonspecifically bound antibodies.

[20] G. S. Wood and R. Warnke, *J. Histochem. Cytochem.* **29**, 1196 (1981).
[21] S. M. Hsu and H. J. Ree, *Am. J. Clin. Pathol.* **74**, 32 (1980).

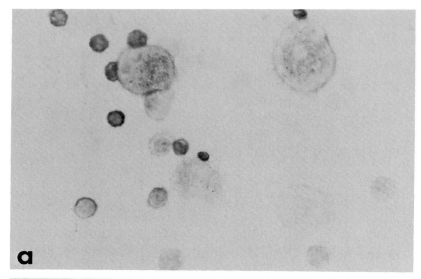

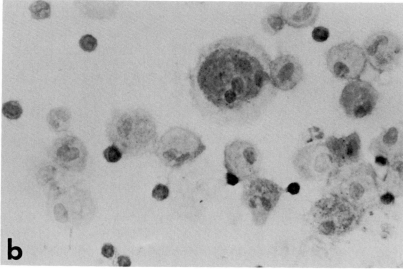

FIG. 3. Immunoperoxidase labeling (three-layer PAP) of alveolar lavage cells from a patient with pulmonary sarcoidosis, using OKT4, a monoclonal antibody to T helper cells. (a) OKT4 antibody labels the majority of small lymphocytes characteristically found in sarcoidosis. Adjacent large cells (alveolar macrophages) are also variably stained using OKT4. (b) By contrast with (a), a single repetition of bridging rabbit anti-mouse Ig and PAP complex incubations leads to markedly increased staining of alveolar macrophages (and lymphocytes). Such multiple sandwich methods are particularly useful for detecting low levels of a particular antigen (OKT4 has been independently shown to bind to macrophages as well as T helper cells, albeit at a significantly lesser density). PLP-fixed cytocentrifuge smear; ×450; hematoxylin.

Among the many modifications of the DAB reaction proposed to boost sensitivity, two warrant attention. The addition of 0.01 M imidazole to the DAB solution (using 0.1 M Tris–saline, pH 7.6, and incubating for 10 min at room temperature) significantly improves sensitivity.[18,22] Adding a source of metallic ions such as 0.5% $CuSO_4$ or 0.4% $NiCl_2$ to the DAB solution[23,24] also appears to improve staining intensity, though this is not a universal finding.[18] Nevertheless, metal ions do alter the color of the DAB product, allowing sequential double staining[23] and aiding photomicrography.

Two post-DAB enhancement methods have proved useful. Following the DAB reaction and washing, slides can be posttreated with osmium tetroxide (0.2% OsO_4 in water for 2 min); this step darkens the DAB product, but also the rest of the section or smear too if overdone. Finally, a somewhat lengthy but intriguing method for silver staining of DAB products was recently described by Gallyas et al.[25] Under controlled conditions this modified silver stain did not stain normal tissue components, and was reported to increase the sensitivity for detection of a test substrate by greater than two orders of magnitude.

BLOCKING ENDOGENOUS PEROXIDASE. Endogenous peroxidase is effectively blocked by incorporating sodium azide into the DAB solution[11] (0.3% azide is added during preparation of a Tris–saline bulk solution, and stored at 4°). This step blocks most endogenous peroxidases, but despite the warnings on many commercial packages of antibodies, does not affect the activity of horseradish peroxidase (HRP). Two important exceptions to this blocking effect of azide are the peroxidase-like activity of hemoglobin, and the peroxidase found in eosinophils, which interestingly is biochemically almost identical to HRP. There are two advantages of azide over the more commonly used blocking step of methanol/H_2O_2 (either 0.5% H_2O_2 for 15 min, or 0.3% H_2O_2 for 30 min). First, since there is no extra time devoted to a blocking step, there is a saving of 15–30 min depending on the concentration of H_2O_2 used. Second, the methanol/H_2O_2 mixture has a destructive effect on many cell surface and other antigens, particularly at the higher concentration. If the H_2O_2 block is used, and it is unknown whether the antigen(s) in question are labile in this solution (e.g., when screening a panel of new hybridoma supernatants), then the block should be performed later, i.e., after the monoclonal antibody for two-layer procedures or after the second antibody for three-

[22] W. Strauss, J. Histochem. Cytochem. **30**, 491 (1982).
[23] S. M. Hsu and E. Soban, J. Histochem. Cytochem. **30**, 1079 (1982).
[24] J. C. Adams, J. Histochem. Cytochem. **29**, 775 (1981).
[25] F. Gallyas, T. Gorcs, and I. Merchenthaler, J. Histochem. Cytochem. **30**, 183 (1982).

or four-layer methods. A third alternative is to block by incubating sections with phenylhydrazine (0.005 M in PBS) for 15–30 min, but like methanol/H_2O_2, this step can also diminish immunoreactivity.

PARAFFIN AND RESIN SECTIONS. If a monoclonal antibody is produced to a given antigen, and antibody binding detected even at very low levels, e.g., by radioimmunoassay, then in our experience binding can always be detected immunohistologically at least on cryostat sections. Unfortunately, as previously discussed, localization on cryostat sections may not give adequate resolution for a particular purpose. Moreover, most monoclonal antibodies derived to date do not react with routinely fixed and embedded tissues. If reactivity with standard sections is sought, but in practice proves to be weak or totally absent using the methods described, the following methods are worth trying.

Paraffin Sections and Enzyme Digestion. Proteolytic enzyme digestion of paraffin sections, through unknown mechanisms, can lead to successful staining even though undigested sections may be negative. Enzyme digestion is mainly of value for tissues treated with formaldehyde-based fixatives, notably neutral buffered formalin, formol–saline, $HgCl_2$–formalin, PLP, and various concentrations of paraformaldehyde. It has not been shown to work for tissues fixed in glutaraldehyde, Bouin's fixative, or precipitating fixatives such as ethanol, acetone, and methanol (see a single exception below). Enzyme digestion is a purely empirical technique involving one of several enzymes (trypsin, pronase, pepsin) each of which should be independently assessed (Fig. 4) using a range of enzyme concentrations and digestion times (see appendix). Underdigested sections may be only weakly stained, if at all. Overdigested sections usually lift off or, if they remain, show poor morphological preservation and artifactual staining patterns (e.g., nuclear staining). Sections to be digested should be mounted on ungelatinized slides, and stored at temperature or overnight at 37° to improve adhesion. Alternatively, sections may be mounted on slides treated with one of several commercial preparations designed for this purpose.

Recently a new combination of acetone fixation and digestion with hyaluronidase was used to localize for the first time a group of particularly labile T-cell antigens[26] within paraffin sections. This study showed that enzyme digestion may restore the immunoreactivity of non-formaldehyde-fixed tissues, and also demonstrated the sheer unpredictability of various new enzyme–fixative combinations for immunohistological studies.

[26] M. Tanaka, H. Tanaka, and E. Ishikawa, *J. Histochem. Cytochem.* **32,** 452 (1984).

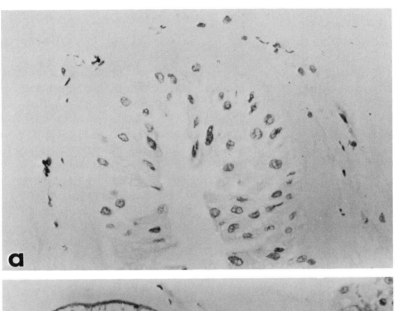

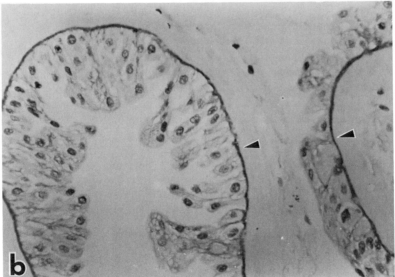

FIG. 4. Enzyme digestion of these routinely prepared formalin-fixed sections of human amnion yielded variable results depending upon the enzyme used. (a) Sections digested with pronase (using varying times and concentrations) were always unstained using a monoclonal antibody (PHM12) to human type IV collagen. Similar negative results were found following trypsin or no digestion at all. (b) However, digestion of sections with pepsin (1 mg/ml for 2 hr at 37°) restored immunoreactivity, allowing detection of type IV collagen in basement membranes (arrowheads). This result emphasizes the need to frequently evaluate several enzymes to achieve optimal staining of paraffin sections. Indirect immunoperoxidase; ×400; hematoxylin.

Modifications of Routine Paraffin Embedding. Over 30 years ago Sainte-Marie[27] showed that fixation, dehydration, and clearing of tissue specimens at 4° maintained antigenicity and permitted immunofluorescent studies of paraffin-embedded tissues. Sainte-Marie and subsequent investigators[10] using this approach have fixed specimens with 96% ethanol at 4° for 24–48 hr. We have found fixation with 96% ethanol or PLP at 4° results in preservation of many antigens otherwise destroyed in the routine embedding process, e.g., human class I and class II antigens,[28] and basement membrane proteins such as fibronectin and type IV collagen.[29] Just as for routine paraffin sections, PLP-fixed (but not ethanol-fixed) sections may require enzyme digestion. Once cut, sections should be dried onto slides at room temperature for up to 24 hr and then stained. Remaining tissue blocks retain immunoreactivity for over a year if stored at −20°.

Resin Sections. Epoxy- or methacrylate-embedded sections are nonreactive with most monoclonal (or polyclonal) antibodies. Moreover, enzyme digestion techniques such as those used to "unmask" antigens in formaldehyde-fixed paraffin sections are usually of no value. However, "etching," an analogous procedure to enzyme digestion, is used to enhance the immunoreactivity of resin-embedded sections (Fig. 1c). Etching solutions are described in the appendix. As with enzyme digestion, if one treatment does not work, the others should be tried.

CELL SMEARS AND CULTURED CELLS. Cell smears give best results when prepared using a cytocentrifuge. Cells are spun in a protein-containing solution (1% FCS or BSA) at 1000 rpm for 5 min. Smears are thoroughly air-dried by leaving them for several hours or overnight at room temperature, and stored in an air-tight box at −80°, or fixed and stained that day. Recommended fixatives are PLP, acetone, or formol–acetone (see appendix). Note that though formol–acetone gives superb morphology, because of its relatively harsh effect on many antigens, it is best used after the initial incubation; i.e., cells and monoclonal antibody are incubated in suspension, washed by centrifugation, cytospun, and then fixed with formol–acetone for 30 sec at room temperature. Smears are then washed in running tap water for 3 min before staining. Alternative fixation steps are PLP for 10 min at 4°, followed by washing, or acetone for 5 min at room temperature. As for section fixation, acetone-fixed smears are allowed to evaporate dry, and staining is begun by applying monoclonal antibody without prior rehydration.

---

[27] G. Sainte-Marie, *J. Histochem. Cytochem.* **10,** 250.
[28] W. Hancock, N. Kraft, and R. C. Atkins, *Pathology* **14,** 409 (1982).
[29] W. Hancock, N. Kraft, F. Clarke, and R. C. Atkins, *Pathology* **16,** 197 (1984).

Cultured cells intended for examination at the light microscope level are air-dried and stored unfixed at −80°, or fixed with either PLP or acetone (as above) and processed immediately thereafter. Note that if PLP or 2% paraformaldehyde in phosphate buffer are used as the sole fixatives, insufficient disruption of the cell membrane for adequate exposure of cytoplasmic antigens may occur. Labeling of cytoplasmic antigens requires cells to be "permeabilized" by treatment with Triton X-100, NP-40, or other nonionic detergent (0.5% for 5 min followed by washing), or by inclusion of the same concentration of detergent in the primary monoclonal antibody, or by treatment with acetone or methanol, e.g., 10 min at 4° (Fig. 5).

PHOTOMICROGRAPHY. Immunoenzymatically stained sections should be photographed using fine-grain low ASA-rating films. Ektachrome 50 and Agfa 50L are recommended for color reproduction, and Panatomic X or Copex Panrapid films are recommended for black and white photomicrography. Best results for black and white photography of DAB-stained sections are achieved using a blue rather than the green filter used for routine photomicrography. The most suitable widely available filter is a

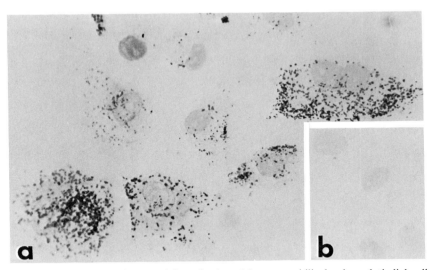

FIG. 5. Immunoperoxidase staining of cultured human umbilical vein endothelial cells with a monoclonal antibody to human factor VIII (a cytoplasmic antigen). Comparison of (a) Triton X-100-treated cells with (b) untreated cells illustrates the necessity of rendering cultured cells permeable if successful labeling of cytoplasmic antigens is to occur. PLP fixation; indirect immunoperoxidase; ×400; hematoxylin.

Wratten 80A blue filter, though even better results can be obtained using certain interference filter combinations.[30]

Troubleshooting Staining Problems

An enormous number of problems may potentially arise during immunoperoxidase staining, many of which, since they are the results of technical mishaps, are most simply remedied by repeating the run. Two common problems, each of which can consist of antigen-, antibody-, or method-related problems, are discussed here.

Weak or No Staining. Antigen: Inactivation or masking of the antigen during tissue preparation, e.g., wrong fixative, or need to enzyme digest embedded sections. Antibody: Overdilution of any of the antibody layers, or the use of incorrect antibody layers or sequences, or diluting any of the antibodies in a antigen-containing serum, thereby effectively absorbing the antibody's activity. Attention should also be paid to the expiry dates of any commercially prepared reagents, antibody storage conditions, and the avoidance of repeated freezing and thawing. Method: Forgetting to add H_2O_2 to the DAB or using old, inactive H_2O_2, or allowing the sections to dry out (keep moist at all times).

Strong Background Staining. Antigen: This may actually indicate a true pattern of labeling; e.g., antigen may in fact be diffusely distributed or there may be sharing of that particular determinant with other (e.g., connective tissue cells) cell types. Antibody: Inadequate dilution of the primary (if ascites) or subsequent antibodies, or failure to include at least 1% serum of the species from which the target tissue is derived in all nonprimary antibody dilutions. Method: Excessive times in the DAB solution, or failure to block endogenous peroxidase (assess by comparing the endogenous control slide with the medium control slide), overdigestion with proteolytic enzymes, or inadequate washing (use a magnetic stirrer and large volumes of washing fluid).

Appendix

Buffered 10% formalin (pH 7.0): Mix 100 ml of 40% formaldehyde and 900 ml tap water, and add 4 g of $NaH_2PO_4 \cdot H_2O$ and 6.5 g of Na_2HPO_4. Fix small cubes of tissue overnight and embed.

PLP preparation: Prepare stock A (0.1 M lysine in 0.05 M sodium phosphate buffer pH 7.4) by dissolving 1.83 g L-lysine–HCl in 50 ml distilled H_2O, adjust to pH 7.4 with 0.1 M Na_2HPO_4 (1.42 g/100 ml

---

[30] M. Moller, O. V. Glistrup, and W. Olsen, *J. Histochem. Cytochem.* **32,** 37 (1984).

H$_2$O), and make up to 100 ml with 0.1 M sodium phosphate buffer pH 7.4 (4:1 ratio of 0.1 M Na$_2$HPO$_4$ and 0.1 M NaHPO$_4$). Stock A is stable for a week at 4°. Prepare stock B by dissolving 8 g of paraformaldehyde in 100 ml of H$_2$O (requires heating to around 60° with stirring and adding a few drops of 4 M NaOH until clear). Stock B is then filtered and stored at 4° for up to 24 hr. The working solution of PLP consists of 3 parts stock A and 1 part stock B, plus 0.01 M sodium m-periodate (21.4 mg/10 ml), and adjusting the final pH from 6.2 to 7.4 with 4 M NaOH. Fix tissues for 2–4 hr at 4°, and smears for 10 min at 4°, followed by washing in buffer (see text).

Formol–acetone preparation: Mix 20 g Na$_2$HPO$_4$, 100 mg KH$_2$PO$_4$, 25 ml of 40% formaldehyde ("formalin"), 30 ml H$_2$O, and 45 ml of acetone. Fix smears for 30 sec at room temperature and wash in running water.

Gelatinized slides: Prepare 0.2% aqueous gelatin and filter. Clean glass slides by placing in a staining rack and immerse in running hot water for 10–15 min. Dip the cleaned glass into gelatin solution, drain, and air-dry at 56°.

Washing fluid: Dissolve 40 g NaCl, 5.75 g Na$_2$HPO$_4$, 1 g KCl, and 1 g KH$_2$PO$_4$ in 500 ml of distilled water. Dissolve 10 g of gelatin in 100 ml distilled water with heat and stirring. Add together and make up to 5 liters (pH ~7.4).

Tris–saline buffer: Dissolve 3.025 g Trizma-Base in 50–100 ml distilled water, bring pH to 7.6 with conc. HCl, add 4.25 NaCl, and make up to 500 ml with distilled water. Add 1.5 g sodium azide (i.e., 0.3%) as a blocking agent of endogenous peroxidases.

Chromagens

DAB: This should be made up just before use. Add 6 mg DAB to 10 ml 0.05 M Tris–saline (pH 7.6) (optionally containing 0.3% sodium azide to block endogenous peroxidases), plus 0.03% H$_2$O$_2$, filter if not clear, and incubate for 5–10 min at room temperature, depending upon antigen density and the method used. Stop reaction with running water.

AEC: Dissolve 2 mg AEC in 0.5 ml dimethyl formamide (using a glass container), stir, and add 9.5 ml 0.05 M sodium acetate buffer (pH 5.0) and 0.03% H$_2$O$_2$. Filter onto slide and incubate for 10–40 min at room temperature, rinse with acetate buffer, and check for suitable intensity of reddish labeling. When satisfactory staining is reached, slides are rinsed in running water, counterstained with Mayer's hematoxylin, and mounted within PBS/glycerol.

4CN: Dissolve 2 mg 4CN in 25 μl of absolute ethanol, stir, and add 4 ml 0.05 M Tris–saline (pH 7.6) and 0.03% H$_2$O$_2$. Remove the white precipitate by filtering onto slide, and look for the development of a blue-gray color in the section while incubating for 10–30 min at room temperature.

Enzyme digestion: The three most commonly used enzymes are trypsin, protease type VII ("pronase"), and pepsin. Trypsin: 0.01–0.1% trypsin (Sigma, T8128) in 0.1% $CaCl_2$ (pH 7.8 with 0.1 M NaOH) at 37° for 30–60 min. Pepsin: 0.1–0.4% pepsin (Sigma, P7012) in 0.1 M HCl (pH 2.0) at 37° for 30–120 min. Protease: 0.01–0.1% protease (Sigma P5255) in 0.05 M Tris–saline (pH 8.0) at 37° for 10 min. Remember not to use gelatinized slides, and prewarm solutions at 37° before commencing digestion. Digestion is stopped in cold running water.

Etching solutions: A dark brown saturated solution of NaOH in ethanol, termed sodium ethoxide, is prepared a few days in advance and stored at room temperature (under which conditions it is stable for months). Sections are immersed in this solution in a Coplin jar for 5–10 min, then rinsed well in absolute alcohol, and taken through graded alcohols to water, prior to immunoperoxidase staining. Alternative etching solutions are 5 or 10% H_2O_2 in methanol, saturated NaOH in methanol ("sodium methoxide"), 0.01% benzine/1% methanol in water, and 0.1% benzine/10% ethanol/90% methanol.

[79] Use of Alkaline Phosphatase-Conjugated Antibodies for Detection of Protein Antigens on Nitrocellulose Filters

By BRYAN M. TURNER

Enzyme-conjugated antibodies used in conjunction with histochemical staining techniques provide a sensitive and convenient approach to the detection of protein antigens on nitrocellulose filters. While this approach cannot always match the sensitivity of techniques employing radiolabeled antibody, it offers major advantages in terms of speed and simplicity. Alkaline phosphatase-conjugated antibodies are now available from several commercial suppliers and are extensively used for enzyme-linked immunoassay (ELISA). They have been less widely used for immunostaining techniques, which is surprising in view of the large number of methods available for localization of alkaline phosphatase activity.[1] Three alternative detection methods, all of which have given good results in the

[1] A. G. E. Pearse, "Histochemistry Theoretical and Applied." Churchill, London, 1968.

author's laboratory, are presented in detail below together with a brief description of procedures for protein binding, blocking, and application of antibody which we have found to be generally satisfactory.

Binding of Proteins to Nitrocellulose

Proteins can be applied to nitrocellulose filters either in solution, as in spot test procedures, or by transfer from acrylamide gels, the protein-blotting technique. For spot tests we have used a manifold (Bio-Rad Laboratories, Richmond, CA) which permits rapid application of antigen solutions to nitrocellulose filters as 3-mm diameter spots in an 8 × 12 configuration. Antibodies can be applied to the filter *in situ* but we have found it more convenient to remove the antigen-loaded filter from the apparatus and carry out subsequent incubations in sealed plastic bags (see below). Electrophoretic transfer of proteins from SDS–polyacrylamide gels is carried out essentially as described by Towbin *et al.*[2]

Blocking

Various reagents have been used for blocking protein binding sites on nitrocellulose prior to antibody application. These include diluted serum, solutions of purified proteins such as bovine serum albumin (BSA), ovalbumin or hemoglobin, and the nonionic detergent Tween-20. We have found that incubation for 1 hr in phosphate-buffered saline (PBS) containing 0.1% Tween-20 effectively prevents background staining of filters but does not prevent nonspecific binding of antibody to highly charged protein antigens, particularly the histones. Reduction of such binding requires the use of protein solutions. We have found a mixture containing 0.1% Tween-20 and 1% BSA in PBS to be generally satisfactory. It should be noted that Tween-20 will remove some proteins from nitrocellulose on prolonged exposure. It is therefore important to test for loss of antigen following exposure to Tween-20. Diluted serum is an effective blocking agent which we use routinely in combination with ^{125}I-labeled antibodies. However, we have noted some increase in background staining of filters blocked with serum and stained by the Fast Blue procedure (see below).

Application of Antibodies

Blocked filters are sealed into polythene bags containing sufficient antibody solution to coat the surface of the filter (about 0.2 ml/cm²). Bags

---

[2] H. Towbin, T. Staehelin, and J. Gordon, *Proc. Natl. Acad. Sci. U.S.A.* **76,** 4350 (1979).

of the appropriate size are prepared from polythene tubing (Express Polythene Co., Birmingham, United Kingdom) 2 or 4 in. wide using an electric bag sealer. Care should be taken to expel all air bubbles before sealing the bag. We have found the following incubation and washing procedures to be satisfactory.

(1) Incubate filters for 1 hr at 4° in first antibody suitably diluted in PBS/0.1% Tween. Tissue culture supernatants from hybridoma cell lines can usually be diluted at least 10-fold and ascitic fluid samples at least 1000-fold. To ensure uniform exposure of the filter to antibody the bags can be mounted on a rotary mixer or mixed occasionally by hand. (2) Wash by shaking in three changes of PBS/0.1% Tween, 5–10 min per change at room temperature. (3) Incubate for 1 hr at 4° in alkaline phosphatase-conjugated antibody to mouse immunoglobulins (or other species as appropriate) diluted in PBS/0.1% Tween. We currently use a 1 : 250 dilution of a conjugated IgG fraction of sheep antiserum to mouse IgG, IgA, and IgM obtained from Serotec Ltd. (Blackthorn, Bicester, Oxon, United Kingdom). If commercially available reagents are unsuitable, well-tried and relatively simple glutaraldehyde-mediated coupling procedures can be used to prepare conjugated antibodies at moderate cost.[3,4] (4) Wash the filters by shaking at room temperature in approximately 200-ml aliquots of PBS/0.1% Tween-20 (30 min), PBS/0.5 M NaCl (30 min), PBS (30 min), and distilled water (10 min).

Staining Procedures

β-Naphthyl Phosphate and Fast Blue

Principle. Alkaline phosphatase will hydrolyze the phosphate derivatives of a variety of substituted or unsubstituted naphthols. These include α- and β-naphthyl phosphates and the various naphthol AS phosphates.[1] The free phenol produced by cleavage of the phosphate moiety will react with a suitable diazotized amine to form an insoluble, intensely colored precipitate at the site of enzyme activity. There is therefore a wide choice of both substrate and diazo compounds for the coupling reaction. The high solubility of the α- and β-naphthyl phosphates compared with the substituted naphthol AS phosphates permits the use of higher substrate concentrations, and we have chosen to use these reagents (Fig. 1). The choice of diazotized amine depends on factors such as intensity of color development, stability at high pH, the nature of the precipitate, and inhi-

[3] S. Avrameas, *Immunochemistry* 6, 43 (1969).
[4] S. Avrameas and T. Ternynk, *Immunochemistry* 8, 1175 (1971).

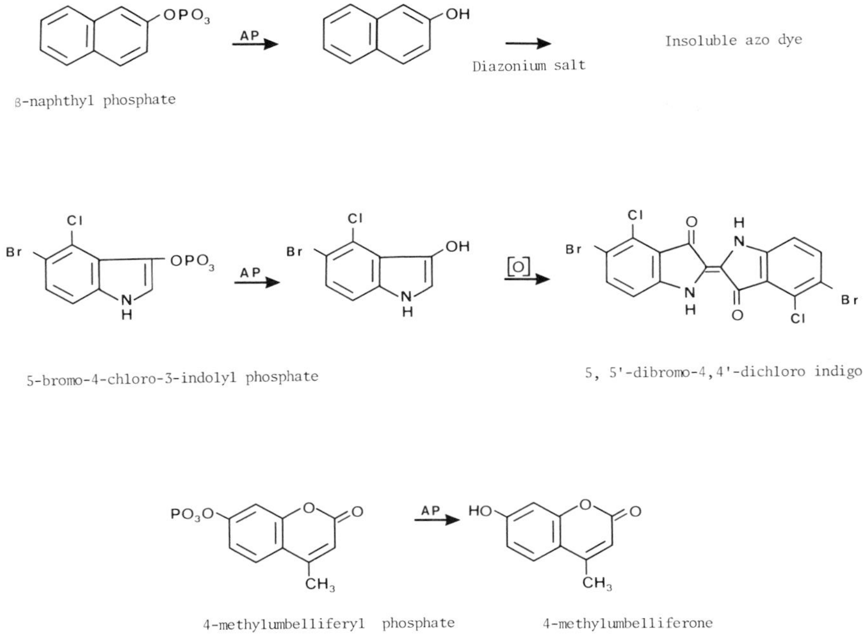

β-naphthyl phosphate

Diazonium salt → Insoluble azo dye

5-bromo-4-chloro-3-indolyl phosphate   5,5'-dibromo-4,4'-dichloro indigo

4-methylumbelliferyl phosphate   4-methylumbelliferone

FIG. 1. A summary of the three staining reactions for detection of alkaline phosphatase (AP) activity, which are described in detail in the text.

bition of enzyme activity. The latter is of particular significance as many diazonium salts cause a rapid reduction in alkaline phosphatase activity. On the basis of previous work (reviewed in Ref. 1) the two compounds which seem most suitable are Fast Blue B (*o*-dianisidine) and Fast Blue RR (4-benzoylamine-2,5-dimethoxyaniline). The use of this staining technique for detection of electrophoretically separated protein antigens has been described previously.[5]

Reagents

Fast Blue B or Fast Blue RR (BDH Chemicals Ltd, Poole, Dorset, United Kingdom)
β-Naphthyl phosphate sodium salt (Sigma Chemical Co.)
0.05 M boric acid, 0.05 M KCl to pH 9.2 with NaOH
0.1 M MgCl$_2$

Procedures. Dissolve 2–20 mg Fast Blue in 10 ml water just before use. Dissolve 10 mg β-naphthyl phosphate in 9.4 ml borate buffer and add

[5] B. M. Turner, *J. Immunol. Methods* **63,** 1 (1983).

0.6 ml 0.1 M MgCl$_2$. Combine the two solutions and apply immediately to the filter. Incubate at 37° for 5–30 min. A purple precipitate will form at the sites of enzyme activity. When color development has reached a suitable intensity the reaction can be stopped by briefly washing the filter in 70% ethanol and water. There appears to be some inhibition of enzyme activity during the staining reaction, presumably by the diazonium salt. High concentrations (1 mg/ml) give rapid and intense color development but the reaction stops within 5 min and there is no further increase in intensity of weakly stained regions. Lower concentrations cause some reduction in intensity but color development will continue for longer. On balance we find that lower concentrations give slightly higher sensitivity and that Fast Blue B gives a more intense color than Fast Blue RR. A brown precipitate forms in the staining mixture at higher concentrations of both Fast Blue B and RR. A pH of 9.2 is the lowest that can be used without a reduction in staining intensity. Variation in the Mg^{2+} concentration from 0.2 to 3 mM is without effect. Background staining of the filter is low and uniform if Tween-20 or BSA is used for blocking. Background staining can be more intense and patchy if the filter is exposed to high concentrations of serum during the blocking step.

5-Bromo-4-chloro-3-indolyl Phosphate

Principle. An alternative histochemical method for localization of alkaline phosphatase activity which avoids the use of azo dyes employs substituted indoxyl phosphates.[1] The substrate 5-bromo-4-chloro-3-indolyl phosphate (Fig. 1) has been used both for staining of tissue sections[6] and for detection of alkaline phosphatase-conjugated antibodies on cellulose acetate membranes.[7] Following removal of the phosphate group a progressive oxidation reaction results in the formation of blue, insoluble 5,5'-dibromo-4,4'-dichloroindigo. This reaction can be facilitated by the addition of oxidation catalysts such as nitro blue tetrazolium[6] or ferri- and ferrocyanide[8] though these are not essential at alkaline pH. The method described below is derived from that of Kohn *et al.*[7]

Reagents

5-Bromo-4-chloro-3-indolyl phosphate (Sigma Chemical Co.)
0.1 M CuSO$_4$

[6] S. Kirkeby and D. Moe, *Cell. Mol. Biol.* **28,** 261 (1982).
[7] J. Kohn, J. C. Raymond, M. Zimowski, and P. Riches, *Protides Biol. Fluids* **31,** 1083 (1984).
[8] Z. Lojda, *Histochemie* **37,** 375 (1973).

AMPD buffer (10.2 g 2-amino-2-methyl-1,3-propanediol; 10 mg $MgCl_2 \cdot 6H_2O$ in 1 liter distilled water adjusted to pH 10.4)

Procedure. Dissolve 5 mg of 5-bromo-4-chloro-3-indolyl phosphate in 20 ml AMPD buffer. Add 0.2 ml $CuSO_4$ solution. Apply to the filter strip and incubate at 37° for 30 min. A blue precipitate forms at the site of enzyme activity. The color continues to develop for at least 30 min. The reaction can be terminated by rinsing in 5% acetic acid or 70% ethanol followed by a distilled water rinse and drying of the filter.

Background staining of the filter is negligible. Faint bands can best be seen by placing the filter against a bright light source and viewing by transmitted light. Addition of copper sulfate as an oxidation catalyst results in a significant improvement in both the rate and intensity of color development. The tetrazolium salt MTT (Thiazolyl Blue, Sigma Chemical Co.) is also effective in this respect at a concentration of 0.1 mg/ml. A change in the color of the final reaction product in the presence of MTT suggests that a mixed precipitate is formed, presumably containing MTT formazan.

4-Methylumbelliferyl Phosphate

Principle. Derivatives of 4-methylumbelliferone (4-methyl-7-hydroxy-coumarin; Fig. 1) are widely used for the fluorimetric assay of hydrolytic enzymes. All these assays detect the enzyme-catalyzed conversion of the nonfluorescent derivative to fluorescent 4-methylumbelliferone. The latter emits visible light (at about 450 nm) when exposed to long-wave ultraviolet radiation. The substrate 4-methylumbelliferyl phosphate has been used to visualize both acid and alkaline phosphatase after electrophoresis in starch gels.[9] The method described below is based on this procedure.

Reagents

4-Methylumbelliferyl phosphate (Sigma Chemical Co.)
0.05 M boric acid, 0.05 M KCl to pH 10.0 with NaOH
0.1 M $MgCl_2$

Procedure. Dissolve 2 mg 4-methylumbelliferyl phosphate in 9.7 ml borate buffer plus 0.3 ml 0.1 M $MgCl_2$. The substrate dissolves readily and should be made up just before use. Cut a piece of filter paper slightly larger than the nitrocellulose filter to be stained (Whatman No. 1 is suitable) and soak it in the substrate solution. Lay the filter paper over the nitrocellulose strip, taking care to exclude all air bubbles. A piece of

---

[9] H. Harris and D. A. Hopkinson, "Handbook of Electrophoresis in Human Genetics." Elsevier/North-Holland, Amsterdam, 1976.

plastic wrap can be spread over the filter paper to minimize evaporation though this will be necessary only if enzyme activity is low and prolonged incubation is required. The progress of the reaction is monitored by exposing the filters to long-wave ultraviolet light (around 360 nm). We use two Sylvania F6T5/BLB tubes at a distance of about 10 cm. The fluorescent reaction product diffuses rapidly and is present on both the nitrocellulose and the overlaying filter paper. For maximum sensitivity the two should be kept together for examination under UV light. Excessive wetting of the filter paper will exacerbate the diffusion problem and cause a rapid loss of resolution of stained bands. When a satisfactory level of staining has been achieved, the filters can be frozen to slow the enzyme reaction and diffusion process or can be peeled apart and allowed to dry. The dried filters can be kept for several days and reexamined after careful wetting with alkaline buffer, although photography is recommended if a permanent record is required.

Relative Sensitivity

The sensitivity of the three staining methods described above was compared by a spot test procedure. Serial dilutions of mouse IgG were applied as 3-mm diameter spots and the filter incubated with alkaline phosphatase-conjugated antibody to mouse immunoglobulins diluted in PBS/0.1% Tween-20. Filter strips were stained in parallel by the three procedures described above. In this experiment the first two staining methods gave detectable staining at 50–100 ng per spot. However, the 4-methylumbelliferyl substrate gave easily detectable staining at 10 ng per spot, representing a 5- to 10-fold increase in sensitivity. Absolute sensitivity will depend on the antigen–antibody combinations employed (and can be considerably higher than that obtained in this experiment), but changes in these variables are unlikely to alter the relative sensitivity of the staining procedures. For some applications, the superior sensitivity of the 4-methylumbelliferyl substrate may be outweighed by loss of resolution due to diffusion of the reaction product. However, this problem can be minimized by careful application of the staining solution and by closely monitoring the progress of the reaction. We have found that, with care, the sharpness of protein bands detected by this procedure is comparable to that obtained with the Fast Blue or indolyl phosphate methods.

A novel approach to increasing the sensitivity of detection is to use polymerized enzyme conjugates. Leary et al.[10] have described procedures for the preparation of polymerized alkaline phosphatase using di-

[10] J. J. Leary, D. J. Brigati, and D. C. Ward, *Proc. Natl. Acad. Sci. U.S.A.* **80**, 4045 (1983).

succinimidyl suberate and for biotinylation of the resulting enzyme complex. The biotin-conjugated enzyme was used to detect biotinylated DNA probes by an avidin bridge technique. On nitrocellulose filters prepared by Southern blotting this procedure could detect bands containing as little as 3 pg of DNA.[10] The same approach could equally well be applied to detection of protein bands on nitrocellulose filters using biotin-conjugated antibodies.

β-Galactosidase Detection

As a wide variety of β-galactosidase-conjugated antibodies are now commercially available it is worth noting that the three staining methods described above can all be used for detection of β-galactosidase activity. β-Naphthyl-β-D-galactoside, 5-bromo-4-chloro-3-indolyl-β-D-galactoside, and 4-methylumbelliferyl-β-D-galactoside are all available (Sigma Chemical Co.; Aldrich Chemical Co.). The methods described should be modified by substitution of a less alkaline buffer, as recommended by the supplier of the conjugate. As the fluorescence of 4-methylumbelliferone (third method) is enhanced at alkaline pH, it may be advantageous to apply an alkaline buffer or ammonium hydroxide solution to the filter to stop the reaction.

Acknowledgments

I wish to thank my colleagues Suzanne Davies, Gill Fellows, and Will Whitfield for technical help and valuable discussions and Professor J. Kohn for providing details of staining procedures prior to publication. The financial support of the Medical Research Council, United Kingdom, and the Cancer Research Campaign is gratefully acknowledged.

[80] Stepwise Amplified Immunoenzyme Staining Techniques for the Detection of Monoclonal Antibodies and Antigens

By P. M. LANSDORP, A. W. WOGNUM, and W. P. ZEIJLEMAKER

Monoclonal antibodies are of increasing importance for the immunochemical detection of antigens in histological and cytological preparations and for the detection and quantitation of solid-phase antigens in general. The exquisite specificity and the absence of background staining of mono-

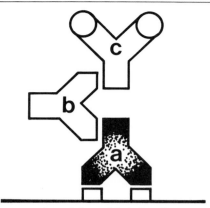

Fig. 1. Schematic presentation of the unlabeled antibody enzyme method.[1] Primary monoclonal antibody (a) bound to antigen is detected by subsequent incubation with (excess) anti-mouse Ig (b) and monoclonal anti-enzyme antibodies complexed with enzyme (c). In a final step the presence of enzyme is visualized with an appropriate enzyme substrate. Between each step the preparation is thoroughly washed to separate bound from unbound molecules.

clonal antibodies are, however, only fully exploited if optimal methods are used to detect their binding. In the unlabeled antibody enzyme method described by Sternberger,[1] antibodies bound to solid-phase antigens are detected by bridging of enzymes to the antigen via specific antibodies (Fig. 1). By this approach the problems inherent to the conjugation of antibodies are avoided. As a result the unlabeled antibody enzyme method is more sensitive and gives less nonspecific staining than conjugated antibody techniques.[1] The use of monoclonal antibodies against enzymes in the unlabeled antibody enzyme method, introduced in 1980,[2] has led to further improvements of the method. Complexes between enzymes and monoclonal anti-enzyme antibodies yield better immunochemical staining than polyclonal complexes,[3] are easily prepared in practically unlimited quantities, have a constant quality, and are stable upon storage. In our experience monoclonal peroxidase–anti-peroxidase (PAP) and alkaline phosphatase–anti-alkaline phosphatase (APAAP) complexes are very suitable for the screening of monoclonal antibodies against cell surface antigens[2] and for the detection of antigens on immunoblots. How-

[1] L. A. S. Sternberger, "Immunocytochemistry." Wiley, New York, 1979.
[2] P. M. Lansdorp, G. C. B. Astaldi, F. Oosterhof, M. C. Janssen, and W. P. Zeijlemaker, *J. Immunol. Methods* **39,** 393 (1980).
[3] D. Y. Mason, J. L. Cordell, Z. Abdulaziz, M. Naiem, and G. Bordenave, *J. Histochem. Cytochem.* **30,** 1114 (1982).

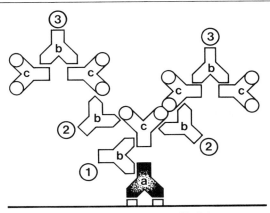

FIG. 2. Schematic presentation of stepwise amplified immunoenzyme staining techniques. Repetition of incubation steps (1, 2, and 3) with the anti-mouse Ig reagent (b) and monoclonal anti-enzyme antibodies complexed with enzyme (c) results in an increase in the number of enzyme molecules bound to a primary monoclonal antibody (a). Antigenic determinants on the monoclonal anti-enzyme antibodies serve as additional antigenic sites for amplification of the staining reaction.

ever, to obtain satisfactory staining of cells with monoclonal antibodies against antigens that are not abundantly expressed, the sensitivity of the unlabeled antibody enzyme method with monoclonal anti-enzyme antibodies is not sufficient. The sensitivity of the method can, however, be improved by repetition of the incubation steps with anti-mouse immunoglobulin (Ig) and enzyme–anti-enzyme complexes.[4] The principle of these procedures is illustrated in Fig. 2.

Quantitation of the effect of repetition of incubation cycles on background and specific staining revealed that the sensitivity of the technique could be increased up to 30-fold.[4] In Fig. 3 the effect is shown of stepwise amplification on the amount of alkaline phosphatase bound to blood platelets labeled with limiting quantities of a monoclonal anti-platelet antibody.[5] The result of stepwise amplified immunoperoxidase staining on the staining intensity of peripheral blood mononuclear cells incubated with two concentrations of a monoclonal antibody against a subpopulation of lymphocytes (leu 3a) is shown in Fig. 4. Repetition of the incubation steps resulted in enhanced contrast between stained and unstained cells and identification of the lymphocyte subpopulation at high dilutions

[4] P. M. Lansdorp, T. van der Kwast, M. de Boer, and W. P. Zeijlemaker, *J. Histochem. Cytochem.* **32,** 172 (1984).
[5] P. M. Lansdorp, F. Oosterhof, G. C. B. Astaldi, and W. P. Zeijlemaker, *Tissue Antigens* **19,** 11 (1982).

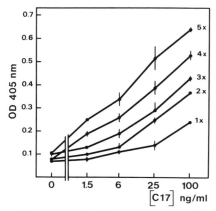

FIG. 3. Quantitation of the amount of alkaline phosphatase (the absorbance at 405 nm of the reaction product from the alkaline phosphatase substrate p-nitrophenyl phosphate on the ordinate) bound to blood platelets after different numbers of incubation cycles (1–5×). Cells in the wells of Terasaki microtest plates were incubated with limiting amounts of a monoclonal anti-platelet gp III[a] antibody (C17) prior to staining. Each point represents the mean of triplicate reactions; the standard deviations of the mean are represented by vertical bars. For details of similar experiments see Refs. 4 and 5.

of the antibody. Comparison of the sensitivity with indirect immunofluorescence using such experiments showed that lymphocyte subpopulations could be identified with stepwise amplified immunoperoxidase staining at antibody dilutions that yielded only background staining patterns in immunofluorescence (not shown). At present, stepwise amplified immunoenzyme staining techniques with either PAP or APAAP complexes are routinely applied in our laboratory with highly reproducible results for the detection of membrane and cytoplasmic antigens on cytospin preparations of various cell types.

In this chapter we provide details of the composition of the reagents and the procedures used for stepwise amplified immunoenzyme staining of cytological specimens, together with some of the observations that have formed the basis of our procedures.

Description of Reagents and Methods

Preparation of Cytological Samples. Cytospin preparations of cells or cell smears are thoroughly air-dried for 2–24 hr before fixation in buffered formol–acetone [BFA; 20 mg Na_2HPO_4, 100 mg KH_2PO_4, 45 ml of acetone, 25 ml of formaldehyde (37% v/v), 30 ml of H_2O] for 30 sec at room

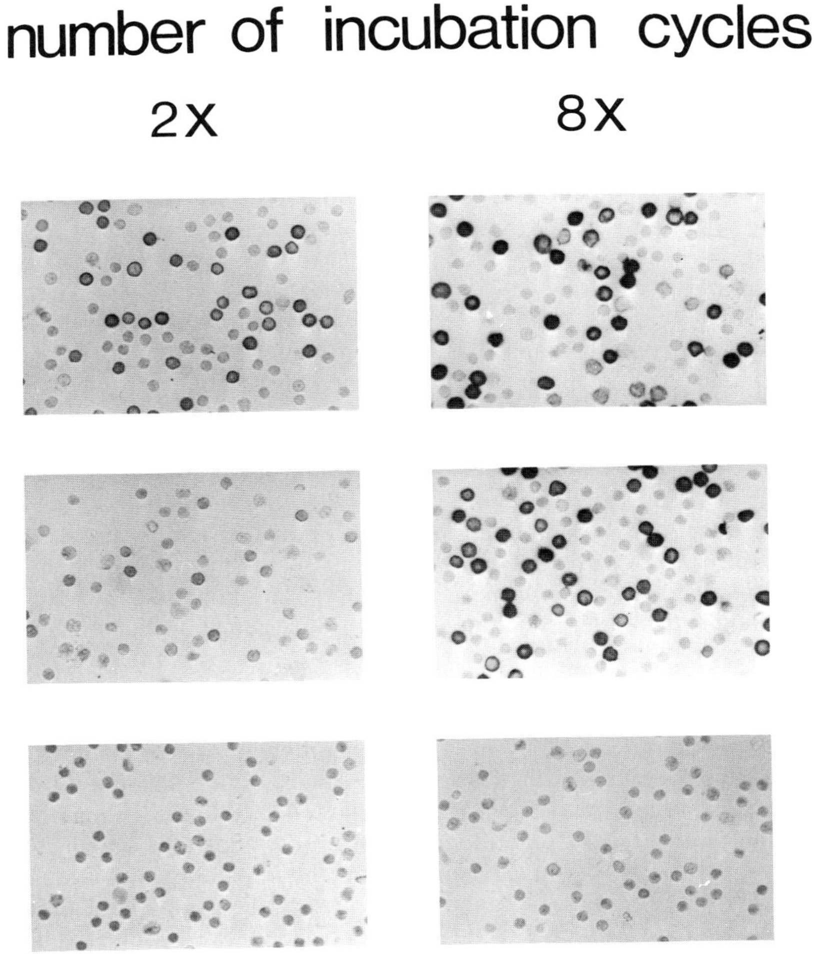

number of incubation cycles

2X   8X

Fig. 4. The effect of stepwise amplified immunoperoxidase staining on the staining intensity of human peripheral blood mononuclear cells labeled with monoclonal antibody leu 3a, specific for "helper lymphocytes" in saturating (top row, dilution 1 : 100) and limiting concentrations (middle row, dilution 1 : 2400). Unlabeled cells served as a control (bottom row).

temperature.[6] The fixative can be used repeatedly for periods up to 1 month, provided that evaporation is kept at a minimum. Other fixatives (e.g., acetone for 10 min at room temperature) can be used but may yield

[6] D. Y. Mason, C. Farrell, and C. R. Taylor, *Br. J. Haematol.* **31**, 361 (1975).

poorer preservation of cellular morphology. Fixation is required to avoid diffusion of cellular constituents and to attach the cells thoroughly to the slide. The latter procedure is important in view of the many incubation and wash steps involved in stepwise amplified immunoenzyme staining. After fixation, the slides are washed in Tris-buffered saline (TBS; 0.05 M Tris, 0.15 M NaCl; pH 7.5) by immersion of the slides into three subsequent jars for about 30 sec. All incubations and washing steps of the staining procedures, with the exception of the primary antibody incubation, are performed by immersion of the slides into jars with reagent or wash fluid.[4,7]

Primary Antibody Incubation. The slides are dried with paper tissue around the (fixed) cells and placed horizontally in a humidified, closed box. Primary monoclonal antibody is applied in the smallest volume (e.g., 50 μl for cytospin preparations) required to fully cover the cell preparation. A satisfactory solvent for antibodies is TBS with 5% nonimmune serum of the species in which the anti-mouse Ig antiserum was raised. The dilution of the primary antibody is selected to yield the highest specific and the lowest background staining using appropriate cytological specimens. Compared with less sensitive immunocytochemical procedures, the optimal dilutions of primary monoclonal antibodies are frequently higher and satisfactory staining can often be obtained at higher than the recommended dilutions, resulting in substantial savings in the use of primary antibody.

Although monoclonal antibodies of various Ig classes and subclasses can be detected with stepwise amplified immunoenzyme staining, the strongest staining is obtained when the primary antibodies and the anti-enzyme antibodies are of the same (sub)class. This effect was quantitated with dilutions of primary antibodies of the IgG_1 and IgG_{2a} subclass, respectively, and PAP complexes prepared with IgG_1 and IgG_{2a} monoclonal anti-peroxidase (the IgG_{2a} is in immunoglobulin subclass switch variant of the IgG_1 antibody prepared and kindly provided by J. Boot from our laboratory). The result is shown in Fig. 5. The most likely explanation for the observed differential staining efficiency is that Ig subclass-specific antibodies in the anti-mouse Ig contribute significantly in the bridging of primary and anti-enzyme antibodies (Fig. 1). For this reason satisfactory detection of monoclonal antibodies of subclasses that are not represented in the anti-enzyme complexes may require additional amplification steps (Fig. 2). In case the antigen under study is expressed at low levels, additional amplification may also be required.

[7] M. C. Sofroniew and U. Schnell, *J. Histochem. Cytochem.* **30,** 504 (1982).

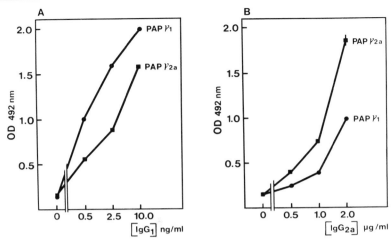

FIG. 5. Effect of subclass disparity between primary antibody and anti-peroxidase antibody on the efficiency of (single-bridge) PAP staining. The peroxidase activity is expressed as the absorbance at 492 nm of the reaction product of the peroxidase substrate o-phenylenediamine.[5] Abscissa: (A) concentration of IgG$_1$ primary monoclonal antibody C17 (anti-platelet gp III[a]) and (B) concentration of IgG$_{2a}$ monoclonal antibody W6/32 (anti-HLA-A, -B, and -C) used to label blood platelets fixed to the wells of Terasaki test plates. PAP complexes consisted of HRPO complexed to IgG$_1$ monoclonal anti-peroxidase (●) or to an IgG$_{2a}$ monoclonal heavy chain subclass switch variant of the same anti-peroxidase antibody (■).

Anti-Mouse Ig. For the bridging of primary monoclonal antibodies to PAP or APAAP complexes, any high-titered anti-mouse Ig antiserum is probably satisfactory. Polyclonal antiserum is prepared by conventional immunization procedures of animals (e.g., sheep or goats) with purified mouse IgM and IgG. In our hands, intramuscular immunization of sheep at monthly intervals at four sites with 100 μg of antigen dissolved in complete (first immunization) or incomplete (subsequent boosters) Freund's adjuvant, results in a suitable antiserum after a few months. Nonimmune serum is added to prevent nonspecific binding of anti-mouse Ig. Cross-reactivity of the anti-mouse Ig antiserum with (human) tissue constituents is prevented by adding normal human serum to the anti-mouse Ig reagent or by passage of the antiserum over a column of human immunoglobulins coupled to Sepharose. The composition of the anti-mouse Ig reagent as it is used in our laboratory is shown in the table.

Attempts have failed to use a (rat) monoclonal anti-mouse Ig for stepwise amplification of staining intensity. Although this reagent could be used to link monoclonal PAP complex to a primary monoclonal antibody, repetition of the incubation steps did not result in a measurable

COMPOSITION OF ANTI-MOUSE IG FOR PAP AND
APAAP STAINING

Constituent	Concentration (%, v/v)
Sheep anti-mouse Ig antiserum	2.5
Normal sheep serum	5
Normal human serum	5
Preservative (phenol)	0.5 (w/v)
Tris-buffered saline	87

increase in the amount of peroxidase bound. This observation suggests that effective amplification of the staining intensity requires antibodies against several antigenic determinants on mouse Ig.

Monoclonal Antibodies to Peroxidase and Alkaline Phosphatase. Monoclonal antibodies against horseradish peroxidase (HRPO) and alkaline phosphatase (AP), complexed with the respective enzymes are available from several commercial sources. In many instances it will be more convenient (and cheaper) to produce these antibodies in one's own laboratory. For this reason, information about the production and screening of monoclonal antibodies to HRPO and AP and the preparation of PAP and APAAP complexes is included in this chapter. Immunization of mice with purified HRPO (e.g., type I, Sigma, St. Louis, MO), or purified alkaline phosphatase from calf intestine (type VII, Sigma), and the fusion of spleen cells with myeloma cells are performed according to standard procedures.

In our experience, the efficiency of hybridoma production is greatly improved by fractionation of the mouse spleen cells before fusion[8] and by growth of the fusion products in medium supplemented with a source of growth factor for hybridomas, such as human endothelial culture supernatant.[9] Screening of hybridoma supernatants for anti-enzyme antibodies can be performed with an ELISA technique. For this purpose, the wells of microtiter ELISA plates are coated overnight at 4° with the immunoglobulin fraction (obtained by ion-exchange chromatography or salt fractionation) of a high-titered anti-mouse Ig antiserum diluted to approximately 10 μg/ml in a low-ionic-strength buffer of pH 7.4. In subsequent steps, diluted, for example in phosphate-buffered saline (PBS) containing 1%

[8] P. van Mourik, R. A. Rivero, T. van der Kwast, P. M. Lansdorp, and W. P. Zeijlemaker, *J. Immunol. Methods* **68,** 45 (1984).
[9] G. C. B. Astaldi, M. C. Janssen, P. M. Lansdorp, C. Willems, W. P. Zeijlemaker, and F. Oosterhof, *J. Immunol.* **125,** 1411 (1980).

(w/v) bovine serum albumin (BSA) (PBS–BSA) or undiluted hybridoma supernatant is added to the wells, followed by incubation with the appropriate enzyme, HRPO (grade II, Sigma) or alkaline phosphatase (type VII, Sigma), both at a concentration of approximately 10 μg/ml. Both enzymes can be diluted in PBS–BSA.

Incubations are carried out for 1–2 hr at 37°, and between each step the wells are thoroughly washed with PBS. Finally, the binding of the enzyme is detected by incubation of the wells with the appropriate enzyme substrate: 0.5 mg o-phenylenediamine (OPD; Eastman Kodak Co., cat. no. 678) in 100 mM phosphate buffer (pH 6.0) and 0.01% (w/v) H_2O_2 for peroxidase, or 1 mg/ml p-nitrophenyl phosphate (Sigma, St. Louis, MO, cat. no. 104-0) in 0.1 M carbonate buffer (pH 8.6) for alkaline phosphatase (AP). Positive reactions are easily identified by eye but can also be quantitated spectrophotometrically. Alternatively, hybridoma cell supernatants may be screened by testing their ability to form enzyme–antienzyme complexes. Such complexes are readily identified on monolayers of fixed cells (in the wells of Terasaki microtest plates) that have been incubated with monoclonal antibodies to cell surface antigens and antimouse Ig antibodies, as described by Lansdorp et al.[2,5] Quantitation of the enzyme activity bound to anti-enzyme antibodies allows selection of those antibodies that have the highest avidity for the enzyme. In our experience, monoclonal antibodies to alkaline phosphatase are easily prepared, in contrast to monoclonal antibodies to horseradish peroxidase. Apparently, the latter is a poor immunogen, which is in agreement with observations reported by others.[3]

Preparation of PAP and APAAP Complexes. Immune complexes between peroxidase and anti-peroxidase or between alkaline phosphatase and anti-alkaline phosphatase[10] are prepared simply by mixing the respective enzymes with their corresponding monoclonal antibodies. For PAP as well as APAAP complexes we observed that optimal results (i.e., high specific and low background staining) are obtained when the enzyme is mixed with anti-enzyme antibodies at an excess (molar ratio of about 10) and are allowed to interact overnight. It can be expected, however, that the optimal molar ratio will vary for each monoclonal antibody, depending on the affinity of the antibodies for the enzyme.

Optimal composition and also optimal dilution of the complexes are conveniently assayed by titration experiments with the complexes on monolayers of fixed cells that have been incubated with or without monoclonal antibodies and anti-mouse Ig antibodies.[2,5] For routine use of

---

[10] J. L. Cordell, B. Falini, W. N. Erber, A. K. Ghosh, Z. Abdulaziz, S. MacDonald, K. A. F. Pulford, H. Stein, and D. Y. Mason, *J. Histochem. Cytochem.* **32**, 219 (1984).

monoclonal PAP and APAAP complexes, it is not necessary to use purified antibodies or to know exactly the molar ratio of enzyme to antibody. Excellent immunocytochemical staining can be achieved by merely dissolving the lyophilized enzyme in undiluted hybridoma supernatant or by mixing culture supernatant 1 : 1 with a solution of enzyme in PBS–BSA. Peroxidase (grade II, Sigma) is added to a final concentration of 50 $\mu g/ml$; alkaline phosphatase is added at a concentration of 100–200 $\mu g/ml$ (type VII, Sigma) or 5 mg/ml (type I, Sigma). These mixtures are stored at 4° or −15°; they are used for staining without further purification, at dilutions ranging from 1 : 10 to 1 : 200 in PBS–BSA. Separation of enzyme–antienzyme complexes from unbound enzyme, e.g., by size exclusion chromatography, will result in partial dissociation of the complexes and thus in diminished performance. In our experience, the enzymatic activities of peroxidase and of alkaline phosphatase are not affected by complexing with the monoclonal antibodies used in the PAP and APAAP staining techniques.

For the preparation of PAP complexes it is often preferable to use impure preparations rather than pure enzyme preparations because some batches of purified peroxidase give unsatisfactory staining. Probably, extensive purification of peroxidase may result in loss of enzyme activity but not in loss of antigenic properties. On the other hand, some batches of nonpurified peroxidase may yield unacceptable background staining, possibly because of the presence of peroxidase-containing aggregates. These problems are not apparent for alkaline phosphatase. Economical considerations may favor the use of crude AP for the preparation of APAAP complexes, but some investigators prefer purer enzyme preparations because they have observed that proteolytic enzymes present in the crude AP preparations sometimes appear to damage cryosat tissue sections.[11]

Staining Procedure of Immunocytological Preparations with Stepwise Amplified Immunoenzyme Techniques. (1) After incubation with the primary monoclonal antibody, the slides are washed and placed in a microscope slide rack. Care should be taken to avoid unwanted staining with unbound monoclonal antibodies in the washing fluids. All further incubations and washing steps are performed by immersion of whole slides in staining jars (see below) at room temperature. (2) Endogenous peroxidase activity is blocked by incubation for 30 min with methanol containing 0.3% H_2O_2. Thereafter, the slides are washed by immersion in jars with TBS. This step is omitted in case endogenous peroxidase activity is ab-

---

[11] K. C. Galler, J. L. Cordell, B. Fallini, A. K. Ghosh, A. Heryet, J. R. G. Nash, K. A. Puflord, D. J. Moir, W. N. Erber, H. Stein, and D. Y. Mason, *J. Biol. Response Modif.* **2,** 369 (1983).

sent or, of course, when alkaline phosphatase is used as a tracer. (3) Nonspecific binding of anti-mouse Ig antibodies and thus nonspecific staining is inhibited by incubation with nonimmune serum (e.g., 5–10% normal sheep serum in TBS) for 20 min. (4) Incubate with anti-mouse Ig for 20 min, followed by washes in four subsequent jars with TBS for 15 sec each. Next, incubate with monoclonal PAP or APAAP complexes, and wash again. (5) Repeat step 4. The number of incubation cycles is dependent on the density of antigenic sites within the sample and the desired staining intensity. For most applications five or six complete incubation cycles will yield satisfactory results.

(6) Incubate with the appropriate enzyme substrate, counterstain, and mount the samples. (a) Substrate for peroxidase: the slides are incubated for 8 min with diaminobenzidine tetrahydrochloride (grade II, Sigma, cat. no. D5637) 0.5 mg/ml in TBS with 0.01% H_2O_2. (b) Substrate for alkaline phosphatase[12] is prepared by mixing 0.5 ml of a 5% (w/v) solution of new fuchsin (Chroma, Stuttgart, F.R.G., cat. no. 1b467) in 2 N HCl with 1.25 ml of a freshly prepared 4% (w/v) solution of sodium nitrite. This solution is added to 150 ml of 0.05 M Tris–HCl (pH 8.7) containing 100 mg levamisole (Sigma, cat. no. L9756), followed by the addition of 125 mg of naphthol AS-BI phosphoric acid (Sigma, cat. no. N2125) which has been freshly dissolved in a glass tube with dimethyl formamide (20 mg/ml). This substrate solution is filtered and used immediately for the staining of slides for 10–20 min.

After the substrate incubation, the slides are washed in running tap water, counterstained with Mayer's hematoxylin, dehydrated, and then mounted with malinol (Chroma, Stuttgart, West Germany) or DePex (BDH Chemicals Ltd., Poole, United Kingdom). An alternative substrate for alkaline phosphatase is Naphthol AS-MX-phosphate (Sigma, cat. no. N4875) with Fast Red TR (Sigma, cat. no. F1500) as a coupling agent. A solution of naphthol AS-MX-phosphate in dimethyl formamide (10 mg/ml) is freshly prepared in a glass tube and added to 0.1 M Tris–HCl buffer (pH 8.2) at a concentration of 2% (w/v). Fast Red TR salt is dissolved in this solution (1 mg/ml), and the solution is filtered. The slides are incubated in this solution for a period of up to 15 min followed by rinsing in running tap water and counterstaining. Because the reaction product of this substrate dissolves in organic solvents, the preparations are mounted in an aqueous mounting medium. Some fading of the counterstained structures and a somewhat lower optical quality of the preparations have to be taken into account. All substrate reagents are freshly prepared before each staining. *Note:* Since the substrates for peroxidase and alka-

---

[12] N. J. Malik and M. E. Daymon, *J. Clin. Pathol.* **35**, 1092 (1982).

line phosphatase are highly poisonous and possibly carcinogenic, these reagents should be handled with appropriate caution. The substrate reagents should be disposed after staining according to local regulations.

Immersion of Whole Slides and Reuse of Reagents. A disadvantage of the stepwise amplified immunoenzyme techniques is the amount of labor involved in the multiple incubations and washing steps. This limitation is, however, substantially reduced by immersion or whole slides into staining jars. Compared to conventional immunocytochemical staining procedures for cytological preparations, which use droplets of reagents, immersion of whole slides is more efficient and reproducible because all slides are handled in an identical manner and problems related to evaporation and dilution of the reagents are avoided. A similar approach to immunoperoxidase staining has been reported by Sofroniew and Schnell.[7]

A disadvantage of the use of staining jars is the requirement for large volumes of reagents. Most reagents can, however, be reused several times and stored for months without substantial decrease in antibody titer or enzyme activity, provided that microbial growth is prevented by addition of preservatives. For the preservation of PAP complexes the addition of NaN_3[7] is not recommended because the long-term stability of HRPO at low concentrations is affected by this preservative. The PAP reagent may be preserved by the addition of 0.5% (w/v) phenol. Phenol or NaN_3 (1 mg/ml) can be used for the other reagents, including APAAP complexes.

An automated programmable staining device, e.g., the Varistian 24-3 from Shandon (Shandon Southern Products Ltd., Runcorn, Cheshire, United Kingdom), for the repetitive incubations and washing steps can further reduce the amount of human labor and is especially suitable for the routine staining of large quantities of samples. In our laboratory, individual users bring their slides after primary (monoclonal) antibody incubation (up to a total of 60 slides). The slides are then stained semiautomatically (with the Shandon-Varistain 24-3) with five or six incubation cycles of stepwise amplified immunoenzyme staining. The substrate incubation, counterstaining, and dehydration are also performed with this device, which reduces the amount of labor to the preparation of reagents and washing fluids and mounting of the slides.

Applications

The sensitivity of immunocytochemical detection of monoclonal antibody binding, and not the specificity or binding of a monoclonal antibody as such, frequently determines the usefulness of a given monoclonal antibody. Most of the monoclonal antibodies that are used at present recognize determinants that are abundantly expressed or give good discrimination with conventional immunocytochemical procedures. With enzymes such as peroxidase or alkaline phosphatase, the critical factor seems to be the amount of enzyme required to give a visible signal. This implies that the only way to improve the sensitivity of antibody detection with these enzymes is to increase the number of enzyme molecules bound per monoclonal antibody bound. With the procedures described in this chapter, this is achieved in a stepwise fashion with relatively small molecules in contrast to procedures in which large enzyme-containing complexes are bound in a few steps. An example of the latter procedures are commercially available avidin–biotin peroxidase complexes.[13] In our experience both the sensitivity and the reproducibility of the latter approach are less than those of the stepwise amplified immunoenzyme staining techniques.[4] However, in view of the laboriousness of the stepwise procedures and because automated staining devices and necessary reagents are not available in every laboratory, it seems advantageous to apply these techniques only when high sensitivity is required. When the sensitivity of the detection method is not very important, the use of single-bridge PAP or APAAP techniques or even enzyme-labeled antibodies may be satisfactory. At present, the most important applications of stepwise amplified immunoenzyme techniques are the immunocytochemical detection of antigens on cytocentrifuge preparations (as described in this chapter) and the detection of antigens on cell smears and cryostat and paraffin tissue sections.[10,11]

Stepwise amplified immunoenzyme techniques can also be useful for amplification of the specific staining of antigens adsorbed to the wells of microtest plates and of antigens separated by gel electrophoresis and transferred to nitrocellulose filters (the immunoblotting technique). A major advantage of the immunoenzymatic detection of antigens on nitrocellulose blots as compared to the more conventional methods with isotope-labeled antibodies is the sharper resolution of the protein bands. The high sensitivity of stepwise amplified immunoenzyme techniques and the high resolution attainable in the immunoblotting technique suggest that these techniques may also be applied to a recently developed method for the cytochemical detection of specific nucleic acid sequences in microscopic (e.g., chromosome) preparations with hapten-modified DNA probes and anti-hapten antibodies.[14] However, it remains to be investigated whether the combination of this technique and stepwise amplified immunoenzyme staining will result in equal or better sensitivity as compared to the *in situ* hybridization methods in which isotope-labeled DNA probes are applied.

[13] S. M. Hsu, L. Raine, and H. Fauger, *J. Histochem. Cytochem.* **29,** 577 (1981).

[14] J. E. Landegent, N. Jansen in de Wal, R. A. Baan, J. H. J. Hoeijmakers, and M. van der Ploeg, *Exp. Cell Res.* **153,** 61 (1984).

Section IV

Summary

[81] Other Articles from Methods in Enzymology Related to Immunochemical Techniques

By HELEN VAN VUNAKIS and JOHN J. LANGONE

I. Production of Hybridomas

Vol. 58 [28]. Cell Fusion. R. H. Kennett.

Vol. 70 [1]. Basic Principles of Antigen–Antibody Reactions. E. A. Kabat.

Vol. 70 [2]. Proteins and Polypeptides as Antigens. P. H. Maurer and H. J. Callahan.

Vol. 70 [5]. Production of Reagent Antibodies. B. A. L. Hurn and M. Chantler.

Vol. 73 [1]. Preparation of Monoclonal Antibodies: Strategies and Procedures. G. Galfrè and C. Milstein.

Vol. 74 [29]. Production and Assay of Antibodies to Acetylcholine Receptors. J. Lindstrom, B. Einarson, and S. Tzartos.

Vol. 84 [1]. Radioimmunoassay of α-Fetoprotein with Polyclonal and Monoclonal Antibodies. E. Ruoslahti, M. Uotila, and E. Engvall.

Vol. 86 [34]. Monoclonal Antibodies against PGH Synthase: An Immunoradiometric Assay for Quantitating the Enzyme. D. L. DeWitt, J. S. Day, J. A. Gauger, and W. L. Smith.

Vol. 86 [35]. Monoclonal Antibodies against PGI_2 Synthase: An Immunoradiometric Assay for Quantitating the Enzyme. D. L. DeWitt and W. L. Smith.

Vol. 92 [1]. Human–Human Monoclonal Antibody-Producing Hybridomas: Technical Aspects. L. Olsson and H. S. Kaplan.

Vol. 92 [2]. Methods of Enhancing the Frequency of Antigen-Specific Hybridomas. R. P. Siraganian, P. C. Fox, and E. H. Berenstein.

Vol. 92 [3]. Spleen Cell Analysis and Optimal Immunization for High-Frequency Production of Specific Hybridomas. C. Stähli, Th. Staehelin, and V. Miggiano.

Vol. 92 [4]. Estimation of the Number of Monoclonal Hybridomas in a Cell-Fusion Experiment. A. L. De Blas, M. V. Ratnaparkhi, and J. E. Mosimann.

Vol. 92 [5]. Use of Human Endothelial Culture Supernatant (HECS) as a Growth Factor for Hybridomas. G. C. Astaldi.

Vol. 92 [6]. Production, Purification, and Characterization of Antigen-Specific Murine Monoclonal Antibodies of IgE Class. A. S. Tung.

Vol. 102 [9]. Production of Polyclonal and Monoclonal Antibodies to Calmodulin and Utilization of These Immunological Probes. J. G. Chafouleas, M. E. Riser, L. Lagace, and A. R. Means.

Vol. 103 [30]. Production of Monoclonal Antibodies Reacting with the Cytoplasm and Surface of Differentiated Cells. R. M. Scearce and G. S. Eisenbarth.

Vol. 108 [19]. Fluorescence-Activated Cell Sorting: Theory, Experimental Optimization, and Applications in Lymphoid Cell Biology. D. R. Parks and L. A. Herzenberg.

Vol. 108 [56]. Identification and Characterization of Human T Lymphocyte Antigens. P. L. Romain, O. Acuto, and S. F. Schlossman.

Vol. 108 [57]. Thy-1.1 and Thy-1.2 Alloantigens—An Overview. M. Letarte.

Vol. 109 [49]. Development of Monoclonal Antibodies against Parathyroid Hormone: Genetic Control of the Immune Response to Human PTH. S. R. Nussbaum, C. S. Lin, J. T. Potts, Jr., A. S. Rosenthal, and M. Rosenblatt.

METHODS IN ENZYMOLOGY, VOL. 121

II. Screening and Assessment of Monoclonal Antibodies

Vol. 92 [16]. Use of High-Resolution Two-Dimensional Gel Electrophoresis for Analysis of Monoclonal Antibodies and Their Specific Antigens. T. W. Pearson and N. L. Anderson.

Vol. 92 [17]. Screening of Monoclonal Immunoglobulins by Immunofixation on Cellulose Acetate. M. A. Pizzolato.

Vol. 92 [18]. A Solid-Phase Immunofluorescence Assay (SIFA) for Detection and Characterization of Monoclonal Antibodies against Soluble Antigens. B. Micheel, H. Fiebach, and U. Karsten.

Vol. 92 [19]. Identification and Characterization of Lymphocyte Hybridomas by Electrophoresis of Glucose-6-phosphate Isomerase Isozymes. T. J. Rogers and K. O'Day.

Vol. 98 [13]. Immunological Recognition of Modifications on Functionally Related Proteins. D. A. Knecht, R. C. Mirendorf, Jr., and R. L. Dimond.

Vol. 103 [30]. Production of Monoclonal Antibodies Reacting with the Cytoplasm and Surface of Differentiated Cells. R. M. Scearce and G. S. Eisenbarth.

Vol. 108 [19]. Fluorescence-Activated Cell Sorting: Theory, Experimental Optimization, and Application in Lymphoid Cell Biology. D. R. Parks and L. A. Herzenberg.

Vol. 108 [41]. Use of Fluorescent Antibodies in the Study of Lymphoid Cell Membrane Molecules. L. Forni and S. de Petris.

Vol. 108 [46]. Use of Monoclonal Antibodies in the Study of the Fine Specificity of Antigens Coded for by the Major Histocompatibility Complex in Mice. L. Flahertz and M. A. Lynes.

Vol. 108 [55]. HLA Antigens in Serum. M. A. Pellegrino, C. Russo, and J. P. Allison.

Vol. 108 [56]. Identification and Characterization of Human T Lymphocyte Antigens. P. L. Romain, O. Acuto, and S. F. Schlossman.

Vol. 108 [57]. Thy-1.1 and Thy-1.2 Alloantigens: An Overview. M. Letarte.

Vol. 109 [51]. Assay of Antibodies Directed against Cell Surface Receptors. S. I. Taylor, L. H. Underhill, and B. Marcus-Samuels.

Vol. 109 [52]. Characterization of Antisera to Prolactin Receptors. P. A. Kelly, M. Katoh, J. Djiane, L.-M. Houdebine, and I. Dusanter-Fourt.

Vol. 109 [53]. Assays of Thyroid-Stimulating Antibody. J. M. McKenzie and M. Zakarija.

Vol. 109 [63]. A Radioimmunoassay for Cyclic GMP with Femtomole Sensitivity Using Tritiated Label and Acetylated Ligands. P. R. M. Dobson and P. G. Strange.

Vol. 110 [40]. Isolation of Cytokinins by Immunoaffinity Chromatography and Analysis by High-Performance Liquid Chromatography Radioimmunoassay. E. M. S. MacDonald and R. O. Morris.

Vol. 118 [55]. ELISA Techniques. M. F. Clark, R. M. Lister, and M. Bar-Joseph.

Vol. 118 [56]. Serotyping Plant Viruses with Monoclonal Antibodies. E. L. Halk.

III. Selected Applications of Monoclonal Antibodies

Vol. 73 [28]. Methods for Binding Cells to Plastic: Application to Solid Phase Immunoassays for Cell-Surface Antigens. C. H. Heusser, J. W. Stocker, and R. H. Gisler.

Vol. 74 [29]. Production and Assay of Monoclonal Antibodies to Acetylcholine Receptors. J. Lindstrom, B. Einarson, and S. Tzartos.

Vol. 78 [72]. Purification of Recombinant Human Leukocyte Interferon (IFLrA) with Monoclonal Antibodies. T. Staehelin, D. S. Hobbs, H.-F. Kung, and S. Pestka.

Vol. 79 [76]. A Rapid Quantitative Assay of High Sensitivity for Human Leukocyte Interferon with Monoclonal Antibodies. T. Staehelin, C. Stähli, D. S. Hobbs, and S. Pestka.

Vol. 108 [49]. Isolation and Analysis of the Murine Ia Molecular Complex. S. E. Cullen.

Vol. 108 [50]. Immunochemical Purification and Analysis of Qa and TL Antigens. M. J. Soloski and E. S. Vitetta.

Vol. 108 [51]. Purification and Molecular Cloning of Rat Ia Antigens. W. R. McMaster.

Vol. 108 [52]. Purification of Human HLA-A and HLA-B Class I Histocompatibility Antigens. J. A. L. de Castro.

Vol. 108 [53]. Use of Monoclonal Antibody Immunoaffinity Columns to Purify Subsets of Human HLA-DR Antigens. D. W. Andrews, M. R. Bono, J. F. Kaufman, P. Knudsen, and J. L. Strominger.

Vol. 108 [54]. Use of HLA-DR Antigens Incorporated into Liposomes to Generate HLA-DR Specific Cytotoxic T Lymphocytes. J. C. Gorga, J. Foran, S. J. Burakoff, and J. L. Strominger.

Vol. 108 [55]. HLA Antigens in Serum. M. A. Pellegrino, C. Russo, and J. P. Allison.

Vol. 108 [56]. Identification and Characterization of Human T Lymphocyte Antigens. P. L. Romain, O. Acuto, and S. F. Schlossman.

Vol. 108 [57]. Thy-1.1 and Thy-1.2 Alloantigens: An Overview. M. Letarte.

Vol. 108 [59]. Lyt-1, Lyt-2, and Lyt-3 Antigens. P. D. Gottlieb, E. B. Reilly, P. J. Durda, and M. Niezgodka.

Vol. 108 [60]. Detection by Immunochemical Techniques of Cell Surface Markers on Epidermal Langerhans Cells. P. R. Bergstresser and D. V. Juarez.

Vol. 109 [49]. Development of Monoclonal Antibodies against Parathyroid Hormone: Genetic Control of the Immune Response to Human PTH. S. R. Nussbaum, C. S. Lin, J. T. Potts, Jr., A. S. Rosenthal, and M. Rosenblatt.

Vol. 109 [50]. Monoclonal Antibodies to Gonadotropin Subunits. P. H. Ehrlich, W. R. Moyle, and R. E. Canfield.

Vol. 109 [54]. A Monoclonal Antibody to Growth Hormone Receptors. J. S. A. Simpson and H. G. Friesen.

Vol. 112 [6]. Attachment of Monoclonal Antibodies to Microspheres. L. Illum and P. D. E. Jones.

Vol. 112 [14]. Poly(vinylpyridine) Microspheres. A. Schwartz and A. Rembaum.

Vol. 112 [16]. Preparation of Antibody-Toxin Conjugates. A. J. Cumber, J. A. Forrester, B. M. J. Foxwell, W. C. J. Ross, and P. E. Thorpe.

Vol. 112 [18]. Transferrin Receptor as a Target for Antibody-Drug Conjugates. D. L. Domingo and I. S. Trowbridge.

Vol. 116 [4]. Immunoglobulin E (IgE). K. Ishizaka.

Vol. 116 [9]. Antiallotypic Antibodies. S. Jackson and T. J. Kindt.

Vol. 116 [10]. Antiidiotypic Antibodies. D. E. Briles and J. F. Kearney.

Vol. 116 [22]. Antigen-Specific Suppressor Factors from Hybridoma Cell Lines. J. A. Kapp, C. M. Sorensen, and C. W. Pierce.

Vol. 116 [23]. Antigen-Specific Suppressor T Cells and Their Soluble Products. M. Taniguchi, M. Kanna, and T. Saito.

Vol. 116 [24]. GAT Antigen-Specific Suppressor Factors. K. Krupen, C. Turck, S. Stein, J. A. Kapp, and D. R. Webb.

Vol. 116 [25]. Antigen-Specific Helper Factor to Poly(Tyr,Glu)-poly(DLAla)-poly(Lys), TGAL. M. J. Taussig.

Vol. 116 [29]. Soluble Immune Response Suppressor. T. M. Aune, H. William Schnaper, and C. W. Pierce.

Vol. 116 [38]. Human Interleukin 2. R. J. Robb.

Vol. 119 [48]. Procedures for Binding an Antibody to Receptor-Bound Interferon. H. Arnheiter and K. C. Zoon.

Author Index

Numbers in parentheses are footnote reference numbers and indicate that an author's work is referred to although the name is not cited in the text.

Ciobaru, R., 28
Ciocca, D. R., 562, 569
Cindic, C. J. M., 872
Civin, C. I., 323, 325, 326(6), 327(6)
Claflin, J. L., 42
Clark, B. R., 463, 464, 468, 469(8), 470(8), 471(9)
Clark, C. A., 565, 578(20)
Clark, M. F., 873
Clark, M. P., 43
Clark, M. R., 307, 313, 314(11), 321(11), 548, 549, 553(9)
Clark, N. W. T., 740
Clark, V. A., 836
Clarke, F., 844
Clarke, G., 114, 121, 122(13), 126(13), 136(13)
Clarke, S. W., 234
Clavell, L. A., 166
Cleveland, P. H., 243, 525, 526, 527, 531(9, 10), 532(10), 538(4), 540(4, 7, 8)
Cleveland, W. L., 95, 96, 97, 101, 102(4, 13), 103, 105(22), 106(22), 107, 233
Click, R. E., 276
Cobbold, S. P., 226, 314, 321, 548, 549, 553(9), 622, 678
Cohen, E. P., 110
Cohen, R., 453
Cohen, S., 142(36), 143(36), 144, 146(36)
Cohn, M., 332, 335(3)
Colacino, J., 123, 129(35), 130(35)
Colcher, D., 802, 803, 804, 805, 876
Cole, B. C., 483, 484
Cole, M. D., 138
Cole, S. P. C., 132, 140, 145(6), 151(6), 154(6), 155, 156(66), 164, 165(6), 167(6)
Coleclough, C., 42
Coligan, J. E., 460
Coller, B. S., 412
Coller, H. A., 412
Collet-Cassart, D., 872
Collins, H. A., 166
Collins, J., 307, 320(1)
Colston, M. J., 406
Coltorti, E., 650
Colwell, D. E., 42(10, 11), 43, 45(11), 46(10, 11), 48
Connors, T. A., 389, 410(17)
Conrad, M. K., 167, 193, 194(5)
Conroy, J. M., 487

Conscience, J.-F., 70, 175, 307, 308, 309(17), 313(17), 317(17), 318(17), 321(17)
Conway de Macario, E., 509, 510, 512, 513, 514, 515, 516(3, 6), 517, 518, 519(2, 3, 6, 8, 9, 10), 520, 521(2, 9, 10), 522, 523(2, 10)
Coombs, R. R. A., 548, 549, 550, 551, 553(9), 549, 550(8)
Coon, H. G., 17
Cooney, M., 120, 169, 229
Cooper, M. D., 151
Copperman, R., 482, 483(4)
Corcoran, M., 703, 705(1), 712(1), 714(1)
Cordell, J. L., 567, 578, 856, 863, 864, 867(10, 11)
Cordonnier, M.-M., 307, 317(7)
Cormont, F., 235, 236, 238(8), 623, 641, 642(11, 12), 643(11), 644(11), 645(11), 646(12), 666
Cornish-Bowden, A., 206
Cossman, J., 138, 565, 576(25)
Cote, R. J., 113, 114
Cotman, C. W., 453
Cotton, R. G. H., 214, 322
Couderc, J., 332, 335(5)
Couillin, P., 337, 338(24)
Coutinho, A., 25, 229, 293, 341, 348(5), 557, 560(5)
Cowan, N. J., 211
Crainic, R., 337, 338(24)
Cranage, M. P., 548, 550(8), 551
Crawford, D. H., 139, 142, 143(23, 28), 144(23, 28)
Crawford, F. G., 460, 472
Creech, C., 122
Cremer, N. E., 599, 610, 650
Cremer, W. E., 461
Crichton, D., 480
Cripps, A. W., 649
Crissman, R. S., 183, 186(2), 187(2), 188(2), 191(2)
Croce, C. M., 5, 6, 7, 8, 110, 120, 122, 127, 128(23, 42), 129(50), 132, 140, 145(6), 149(4), 151(6), 154, 162, 164, 165(6, 81), 167(6), 168, 228, 229
Cross, P. A., 130
Crowther, P. E., 807
Crzych, J. M., 234, 236
Cuello, A. C., 210, 211(1, 2), 212(2), 214(1),

K

X

Y

Subject Index

A

growth control, 359–360
monoclonal antibody production, 352–360
  reactor design, 357–359
  results, 357
Agglutination assay, using protein A-sensitized erythrocytes, 556–561
  applications, 560
  characteristics, 559–560
  compared to reverse plaque-forming assay, 560–561
  detection limit, 559
  enhancing antibody, 558–559
  method, 557–559
  principle, 557
  residual antibody interference in, 560
Albumin, supplementation of serum-free medium, 279, 284
Alkaline phosphatase
  conjugation to antibody, 565
  enzyme label, for SIA, 519
  in enzyme-linked immunoassays, 498
  monoclonal antibody, in immunoenzyme staining, 862–863
  polymerized, in detection of protein bands on nitrocellulose filters, 854–855
  staining reactions for detection of, 850–854
Alkaline phosphatase-conjugated antibody
  for detection of protein antigens on nitrocellulose, 848–855
  immunoblotting with, 497–509
  preparation, 499–500
  uses, 848
Alkaline phosphatase–peroxidase, bispecific monoclonal antibody, 214
Alloantigens, antibodies, obtained from EBV-transformed cells, 143
Aminobenzyloxymethyl paper, 492
2-Aminoethanol. *See also* Ethanolamine
  supplementation of serum-free medium, 275, 276
3-Amino-9-ethylcarbazole, substrate for EIFSA, 530
Androctonus australis. See Scorpion
Anion-exchange chromatography, 615
Antibody
  anti-idiotypic, 95
    monoclonal, 127, 166
      screening assay, 428–431

auto-anti-idiotypic, 96
  generation
    fusion protocol, 98–99
    hybridoma cloning technique, 100–101
    hybridoma screening to identify anti-Id clones, 101–102
    hybridoma screening to identify anti-receptor clones, 102–105
    immunization protocol, 97
  immunogens for, 96–97
  hybrid idiotype, analysis, 622
  in vitro synthesis, hanging drop method, 331
  neutral, 715–716
  preserved in liquid nitrogen, 443–444
  serum autoantiidiotypic, detection, 425
  tritium-labeled, 442–444
Antibody–antigen binding, theoretical analysis, 680–681
Antibody dilution analysis, 474–478
  with labeled antigen, 476–478
Antibody-producing cells
  antibody secretion assay in culture supernatants, compared to culture-well RIA, 452
  culture-well assay system, 439–453
    threshold of detection, 448
  isotype-specific assays, 438
  measurement, 438
  secretion, kinetics of, in culture-well assay, 450–452
Antigen
  direct injection into target organ, 34
  presentation, in monoclonal antibody production, 41
  subcellular localization, 579
Antigen–antibody complex, for ascites induction, 391
  in nude rats, 400, 401
Antigen-capture enzyme immunoassay, 541, 543, 545–547. *See also* Enzyme immunofiltration assay
Antigen-coated culture wells, 444–447
Antigen-coated microtiter plates, preparation, 551–552
  fixed whole-cell preparations, 551–552
  simple antigen preparation, 551
Antigen hierarchy response, 18